Linear Equations and Slope

The slope, m, of a line between two distinct points (x_1, y_1) and (x_2, y_2):

$$m = \frac{y_2 - y_1}{x_2 - x_1}, \quad x_2 - x_1 \neq 0$$

Standard form: $ax + by = c$, a and b are not both zero

Horizontal line: $y = k$

Vertical line: $x = k$

Slope intercept form: $y = mx + b$

Point-slope formula: $y - y_1 = m(x - x_1)$

Midpoint Formula

Given two points (x_1, y_1) and (x_2, y_2), the midpoint is

$$\left(\frac{x_1 + x_2}{2}, \frac{y_1 + y_2}{2} \right)$$

Angles

Two angles are **complementary** if the sum of their measures is 90°.

Two angles are **supplementary** if the sum of their measures is 180°.

In the figure below, $\angle a$ and $\angle c$ are vertical angles and $\angle b$ and $\angle d$ are vertical angles. The measures of vertical angles are equal.

The sum of the measures of the angles of a triangle is 180°.

$$x° + y° + z° = 180°$$

Properties and Definitions of Exponents

Let a and b ($b \neq 0$) represent real numbers and m and n represent positive integers.

$$b^m b^n = b^{m+n}; \quad \frac{b^m}{b^n} = b^{m-n}; \quad (b^m)^n = b^{mn};$$

$$(ab)^m = a^m b^m; \quad \left(\frac{a}{b}\right)^m = \frac{a^m}{b^m}; \quad b^0 = 1; \quad b^{-n} = \left(\frac{1}{b}\right)^n$$

Difference of Squares:

$$a^2 - b^2 = (a + b)(a - b)$$

Difference of Cubes:

$$a^3 - b^3 = (a - b)(a^2 + ab + b^2)$$

Sum of Cubes:

$$a^3 + b^3 = (a + b)(a^2 - ab + b^2)$$

Perfect Square Trinomials:

$$a^2 + 2ab + b^2 = (a + b)^2$$
$$a^2 - 2ab + b^2 = (a - b)^2$$

The Quadratic Formula

The solutions to $ax^2 + bx + c = 0$ $(a \neq 0)$ are given by

$$x = \frac{-b \pm \sqrt{b^2 - 4ac}}{2a}$$

The Vertex Formula

For $f(x) = ax^2 + bx + c$ $(a \neq 0)$, the vertex is

$$\left(\frac{-b}{2a}, \frac{4ac - b^2}{4a} \right) \quad \text{or} \quad \left(\frac{-b}{2a}, f\left(\frac{-b}{2a}\right) \right)$$

The Distance Formula

The distance between two points (x_1, y_1) and (x_2, y_2) is

$$d = \sqrt{(x_2 - x_1)^2 + (y_2 - y_1)^2}$$

The Standard Form of a Circle

$(x - h)^2 + (y - k)^2 = r^2$ with center (h, k) and radius r

IMPORTANT:

HERE IS YOUR REGISTRATION CODE TO ACCESS
YOUR PREMIUM McGRAW-HILL ONLINE RESOURCES.

For key premium online resources you need THIS CODE to gain access. Once the code is entered, you will be able to use the Web resources for the length of your course.

If your course is using **WebCT** or **Blackboard**, you'll be able to use this code to access the McGraw-Hill content within your instructor's online course.

Access is provided if you have purchased a new book. If the registration code is missing from this book, the registration screen on our Website, and within your WebCT or Blackboard course, will tell you how to obtain your new code.

Registering for McGraw-Hill Online Resources

TO gain access to your MCGraw-Hill web resources simply follow the steps below:

1. USE YOUR WEB BROWSER TO GO TO: **www.mhhe.com/miller_oneill**
2. CLICK ON **FIRST TIME USER**.
3. ENTER THE REGISTRATION CODE* PRINTED ON THE TEAR-OFF BOOKMARK ON THE RIGHT.
4. AFTER YOU HAVE ENTERED YOUR REGISTRATION CODE, CLICK **REGISTER**.
5. FOLLOW THE INSTRUCTIONS TO SET-UP YOUR PERSONAL UserID AND PASSWORD.
6. WRITE YOUR UserID AND PASSWORD DOWN FOR FUTURE REFERENCE. KEEP IT IN A SAFE PLACE.

TO GAIN ACCESS to the McGraw-Hill content in your instructor's **WebCT** or **Blackboard** course simply log in to the course with the UserID and Password provided by your instructor. Enter the registration code exactly as it appears in the box to the right when prompted by the system. You will only need to use the code the first time you click on McGraw-Hill content.

Thank you, and welcome to your MCGraw-Hill online Resources!

* YOUR REGISTRATION CODE CAN BE USED ONLY ONCE TO ESTABLISH ACCESS. IT IS NOT TRANSFERABLE.

0-07-292173-0 T/A MILLER/O'NEILL: ALGEBRA FOR COLLEGE STUDENTS

MCGRAW-HILL

ONLINE RESOURCES

REGISTRATION CODE

ELNH-9132-MIET-2O7Q-ZXY2

ALGEBRA FOR COLLEGE STUDENTS

ALGEBRA FOR COLLEGE STUDENTS

JULIE MILLER
MOLLY O'NEILL
Daytona Beach Community College

 Higher Education

Boston   Burr Ridge, IL   Dubuque, IA   Madison, WI   New York   San Francisco   St. Louis
Bangkok   Bogotá   Caracas   Kuala Lumpur   Lisbon   London   Madrid   Mexico City
Milan   Montreal   New Delhi   Santiago   Seoul   Singapore   Sydney   Taipei   Toronto

Higher Education

ALGEBRA FOR COLLEGE STUDENTS

Published by McGraw-Hill, a business unit of The McGraw-Hill Companies, Inc., 1221 Avenue of the Americas, New York, NY 10020. Copyright © 2004 by The McGraw-Hill Companies, Inc. All rights reserved. No part of this publication may be reproduced or distributed in any form or by any means, or stored in a database or retrieval system, without the prior written consent of The McGraw-Hill Companies, Inc., including, but not limited to, in any network or other electronic storage or transmission, or broadcast for distance learning.

Some ancillaries, including electronic and print components, may not be available to customers outside the United States.

This book is printed on acid-free paper.

1 2 3 4 5 6 7 8 9 0 VNH/VNH 0 9 8 7 6 5 4 3
1 2 3 4 5 6 7 8 9 0 VNH/VNH 0 9 8 7 6 5 4 3

ISBN 0-07-288056-2
ISBN 0-07-288058-9 (Annotated Instructor's Edition)

Publisher: *William K. Barter*
Senior sponsoring editor: *David Dietz*
Developmental editor: *Erin Brown*
Executive marketing manager: *Marianne C. P. Rutter*
Senior marketing manager: *Mary K. Kittell*
Lead project manager: *Peggy J. Selle*
Production supervisor: *Sherry L. Kane*
Senior media project manager: *Tammy Juran*
Senior media technology producer: *Jeff Huettman*
Design manager: *K. Wayne Harms*
Cover/interior designer: *Rokusek Design*
Cover image: *Marty Honig/GettyImages*
Lead photo research coordinator: *Carrie K. Burger*
Supplement producer: *Brenda A. Ernzen*
Compositor: *The GTS Companies/York, PA Campus*
Typeface: *10/12 Times Ten*
Printer: *Von Hoffmann Corporation*

Photo Credits
Preface: Julie Miller photo by Marc Campbell; Molly O'Neill photo by Gail Beckwith. Chapter 1 Opener: © Vol. 43/PhotoDisc; p. 55: © PhotoDisc website; p. 61: © Corbis website, p. 74: © Corbis website; Chapter 2 Opener: © PhotoDisc website; p. 135: © PhotoDisc website; p. 136: © Vol. 107/Corbis; Chapter 3 Opener: Vol. 41/PhotoDisc; p. 182: © PhotoDisc website; p. 207: © Taxi/Getty; p. 235: © Vol. 68/PhotoDisc; p. 247: © Vol. 20/Corbis; p. 288: © Vol. 160/Corbis; p. 294: Courtesy of NOAA; p. 305: © Vol. 59/Corbis; Chapter 5 Opener: © Vol. 117/Corbis; p. 317: © NHPA, David E. Myers/Photo Researchers; p. 330: © Vol. 41/PhotoDisc; p. 333: © Corbis website; p. 366: © Tom McCarthy/Photo Edit; Chapter 6 Opener: © Vol. 44/Corbis; p. 415: © Tony Freeman/Photo Edit; p. 422: © Vol. 145/Corbis; p. 425: © Nathan Benn/Corbis; p. 445: © Vol. 56/Corbis; p. 490: © LouAnn Wilson; p. 504: © Corbis website, p. 515: © Vol. 102/Corbis; p. 516: © Corbis website; p. 532: © Stone/Getty; Chapter 8 Opener: © PhotoDisc website; p. 585: © Corbis website; p. 589: © Douglas Peebles/Corbis; p. 590: © Vol. 20/PhotoDisc; Chapter 9 Opener: © Vol. 67/PhotoDisc; p. 608: © Quest/SPL/Photo Researchers; p. 640: © The McGraw-Hill Higher Companies, Inc./John Thoeming, photographer; p. 659: © Corbis website; Chapter 10 Opener: © Gary Conner/Photo Edit; p. 679: © Corbis; p. 696: © PhotoDisc website; p. 740: © Jacana Scientific Control/Scott Berthoule/Photo Researchers, Inc.; p. 746: © Oliver Meckes/Photo Researchers, Inc.; Chapter 11 Opener: © PhotoDisc website; p. 767: © Mary Kate Denny/Photo Edit; Chapter 12 Opener: © Vol. 44/Corbis; p. 852: © PhotoDisc website; Chapter 13 Opener: © Corbis website; p. 926: © Corbis website.

Library of Congress Cataloging-in-Publication Data

Miller, Julie, 1962–.
  Algebra for college students / Julie Miller, Molly O'Neill.—1st ed.
    p. cm.
  Includes index.
  ISBN 0-07-288056-2 (acid-free paper)—ISBN 0-07-288058-9 (Annotated instructor's ed.)
  1. Algebra. I. O'Neill, Molly, 1953–. II. Title.

QA152.3.M54   2004
512—dc21   2003053961

www.mhhe.com

DEDICATION

To Nicolas, Erica, Max, and Jonas
—Julie Miller

To Nora, Michael, and Darcy
—Molly O'Neill

ABOUT THE AUTHORS

JULIE MILLER

Julie Miller has been on the faculty of the Mathematics Department at Daytona Beach Community College for 14 years, where she has taught developmental and upper level courses. Prior to her work at DBCC, she worked as a software engineer for General Electric in the area of flight and radar simulation. Julie earned a bachelor of science in applied mathematics from Union College in Schenectady, New York and a master of science in mathematics from the University of Florida. In addition to this textbook, she has authored several course supplements for college algebra, trigonometry, and precalculus, as well as several short works of fiction and nonfiction for young readers.

MOLLY O'NEILL

Molly O'Neill is also from Daytona Beach Community College, where she has taught for 16 years in the Mathematics Department. She has taught a variety of courses from developmental mathematics to calculus. Before she came to Florida, Molly taught as an adjunct instructor at the University of Michigan—Dearborn, Eastern Michigan University, Wayne State University, and Oakland Community College. Molly earned a bachelor of science in mathematics and a master of arts and teaching from Western Michigan University in Kalamazoo, Michigan. Besides this textbook, she has authored several course supplements for college algebra, trigonometry, and precalculus and has reviewed texts for developmental mathematics.

TABLE OF CONTENTS

chapter **1**

REVIEW OF BASIC ALGEBRAIC CONCEPTS   1

chapter **2**

LINEAR EQUATIONS IN TWO VARIABLES   87

chapter **6**

RADICALS AND COMPLEX NUMBERS   369

chapter **7**

FACTORING AND QUADRATIC FUNCTIONS   447

chapter **13**

SEQUENCES, SERIES, COUNTING, AND PROBABILITY   883

HELP YOURSELF

To succeed in mathematics, as in any subject, you must be willing to devote some of your time and attention to complete the homework assignments and prepare for exams. You must set aside time for yourself on a regular basis to put any classroom notes to use and work through homework exercises. As you study your notes and work on homework, you may find that some concepts are easier to understand than others. For this reason, you may need to have a concept explained more than once or in different ways. In addition to the explanations you may receive in the classroom or from tutors, this textbook and its accompanying products will provide you with additional explanations, worked examples, and exercise sets to help you master concepts and practice what you learn. If you use the resources available to you, with a little self-discipline and patience you should find that you achieve a passing grade in the course and build the groundwork necessary for further studies in mathematics.

SUPPLEMENTS

The following products were developed in conjunction with your textbook to offer you additional support in your course.

Student Edition—Online Learning Center

The Student Edition of the Online Learning Center (OLC), located at www.mhhe.com/miller_oneill, contains valuable resources that will help you improve your understanding of the topics presented in your course.

The Student Edition is passcode-protected. A passcode can be found at the front of your text and *is free when you purchase a new book*.

When you enter the Student Edition, you will find practice exercises and self-tests, video clips, animated lessons, access to NetTutor™, materials for a Student Portfolio, a downloadable formula card, and more!

NetTutor

NetTutor is a revolutionary system that enables you to interact with a live tutor over the World Wide Web by using NetTutor's Web-based, graphical chat capabilities. You can also submit questions and receive answers, browse previously answered questions, and view previous live chat sessions. Access to NetTutor can be made from home or school regardless of the type of Internet browser or computer you are using.

To learn more about NetTutor and to register, visit the Student Edition of the Online Learning Center.

Miller/O'Neill Tutorial SMART CD-ROM

The interactive SMART CD-ROM for use with *Algebra for College Students* is a self-paced tutorial specifically linked to the text. The CD reinforces topics through unlimited opportunities to review concepts and practice problem solving. It provides section-specific animated lessons with accompanying audio, practice exercises that enable you to work through problems with step-by-step guidance available, concept-matching problems that test vocabulary skills as well as identification of properties and rules, and more. This browser-based CD requires almost no computer training and will run on both Windows and Macintosh computers. Many of the features found on the SMART CD can also be accessed through the Student Edition of the Online Learning Center.

Miller/O'Neill Video Series (Videotapes or Video CDs)

The video series is based on problems taken directly from the Practice Exercises. The Practice Exercises contain icons that show which problems from the text appear in the video series. A mathematics instructor presents selected problems and works through them, following the solution methodology employed in the text. The video series is also available on video CDs.

Student's Solutions Manual

The *Student's Solutions Manual* provides comprehensive, worked-out solutions to odd-numbered exercises in the Practice Exercise sets, the Midchapter Reviews, the end-of-chapter Review Exercises, the Chapter Tests, and the Cumulative Review Exercises.

PUTTING IT ALL TOGETHER

This text and its accompanying supplements have been designed to offer you the kind of support that will help you succeed in your course. Here are a few suggestions for using the text and its accompanying materials.

To prepare for exams, rework assigned homework problems for practice. Also, work through the Chapter Tests and compare your answers with those in the back of the text. You can use the Student Portfolio, available on the Student Edition of the Online Learning Center, to keep your notes and other class-related papers such as quizzes and tests organized. If you save your tests, you can rework problems from the tests in preparation for other exams. You can also use the Vocabulary Worksheets from the Student Portfolio to review terms that might appear on your quizzes or exams.

If you are looking for extra help and are not able to get help in school due to conflicting schedules with your instructor or tutoring center, you can use NetTutor. The Student Edition of the Online Learning Center contains many other valuable elements such as "e-professors." The e-professors are tutorials based on topics selected from each section of the text. These tutorials present worked-out solutions to problems, similar to those found in your text. Another valuable source of help is the video series. If you cannot attend a class on a particular day or if you would just like more explanation, refer to the selected problems from the Practice Exercises of your text that have a video icon. Once you identify these problems, you can use the videotapes or videos on CD to watch an instructor present the solutions. If you would like a reminder or hint as to how various problems in the text are solved, refer to the solutions manual which offers worked-out solutions.

ACKNOWLEDGMENTS

Preparing a first edition mathematics text is an enormous undertaking that would never have been possible without the creative ideas and constructive feedback offered by many reviewers. We are especially thankful to the following instructors for their valuable feedback and careful review of the manuscript:

Karla Childs, *Pittsburg State University*
Julien Doucet, *Louisiana State University in Shreveport*
Michael Kirby, *Tidewater Community College*
Dr. Joanne Peeples, *El Paso Community College*
Jen Tyne, *University of Maine*

In addition, we would also like to thank the following reviewers of *Intermediate Algebra*. Their suggestions were also helpful in developing this manuscript:

Marwan Abu-Sawwa, *Florida Community College at Jacksonville*
Jannette Avery, *Monroe Community College*
Pam Baenziger, *Kirkwood Community College*
Jo Battaglia, *Pennsylvania State University*
Mary Kay Best, *Coastal Bend College*
Paul Blankenship, *Lexington Community College*
James C. Boyett, *Arkansas State University, Beebe*
Debra D. Bryant, *Tennessee Technological University*
Connie L. Buller, *Metropolitan Community College, Omaha*
Jimmy Chang, *St. Petersburg College*
Oiyin Pauline Chow, *Harrisburg Area Community College*
Julane Crabtree, *Johnson County Community College*
Katherine W. Creery, *University of Memphis*
Bettyann Daley, *University of Delaware*
Antonio David, *Del Mar College*
Dennis C. Ebersole, *Northampton Community College*
James M. Edmondson, *Santa Barbara City College*
Robert A. Farinelli, *Community College of Allegheny County, Boyce*
Toni Fountain, *Chattanooga State Technical Community College*
Chris J. Gardiner, *Eastern Michigan University*
Pamela Heard, *Langston University*
Celeste Hernandez, *Richland College*
Bruce Hoelter, *Raritan Valley Community College*
Glenn Hunt, *Riverside Community College*
Sarah Jackman, *Richland College*
Donald L. James, *Montgomery College*
Steven Kahn, *Anne Arundel Community College*
Richard Karwatka, *University of Wisconsin, Parkside*
William A. Kincaid, Sr., *Wilmington College*
Kathryn Kozak, *Coconino Community College*

Betty J. Larson, *South Dakota State University*

Deanna Li, *North Seattle Community College*

Timothy McKenna, *University of Michigan, Dearborn*

Ana M. Mantilla, *Pima Community College*

Mary Ann Misko, *Gadsden State Community College*

Jeffery Mock, *Diablo Valley College*

Stephen E. Mussack, *Moorpark College*

Cameron Neal, *Temple College*

Sue Nolen, *Mesa Community College*

Timothy Norfolk, *University of Akron*

Don Piele, *University of Wisconsin, Parkside*

Frances Rosamond, *National University*

Katalin Rozsa, *Mesa Community College*

Elizabeth Russell, *Glendale Community College*

Donna Sherrill, *Arkansas Technical University*

Bruce Sisko, *Belleville Area College (Southwestern Illinois College)*

Carolyn R. Smith, *Washington State University*

Sandra L. Spain, *Thomas Nelson Community College*

Daryl Stephens, *East Tennessee State University*

Elizabeth A. Swift, *Cerritos College*

Irving C. Tang, *Oklahoma State University, Oklahoma City*

Peggy Tibbs, *Arkansas Technical University*

Dr. Lee Topham, *Kingwood College*

John C. Wenger, *Harold Washington College*

Charles M. Wheeler, *Montgomery College*

Ethel R. Wheland, *University of Akron*

Denise A. Widup, *University of Wisconsin, Parkside*

Jeannine G. Vigerust, *New Mexico State University*

Special thanks go to Rosemary M. Karr, Ph.D. and Lesley Seale of Collin County Community College for preparing the *Instructor's Solutions Manual* and the *Student's Solutions Manual,* to Bryan Stewart of Tarrant County Junior College for his appearance in and work on the video series, and to Frank Purcell, Elka Block, and John Hunt for performing an accuracy check of the manuscript.

In addition to the assistance provided by the reviewers, we would also like to thank the many people behind the scenes at McGraw-Hill who have made this project possible. Our sincerest thanks to Erin Brown, David Dietz, and Bill Barter for being patient and kind editors, to Peggy Selle for keeping us on track during production, and to Mary Kittell and Marianne Rutter for their creative ideas promoting all of our efforts. We further appreciate the hard work of Wayne Harms, Carrie Burger, Tammy Juran, and Jeff Huettman.

Finally, we give special thanks to all the students and instructors who use *Algebra for College Students* in their classes.

Julie Miller and Molly O'Neill

KEY FEATURES

To get the most use out of your textbook, take a few minutes to familiarize yourself with its features.

Chapter Openers

Each chapter opens with an application relating to topics presented in the chapter. The Chapter Openers also contain website references for **Technology Connections**, Internet activities found in the Student Learning Site of the Online Learning Center, which further the scope of the application.

5

POLYNOMIALS

To plan a vacation overseas, an understanding of currency exchange rates is important. For example, if you visit Frankfurt, Germany, you will need to know how many Euros (the main unit of currency in Germany as well as 11 other European countries) may be exchanged for $1. If you visit Japan, you will need to know how many Yen may be exchanged for $1.

Because many countries outside the United States use the metric system, it is also helpful to know unit conversions for some common units of measurement. For example, 1 kilometer (km) is approximately 0.622 miles. Therefore, the distance of 305 km between Frankfurt, Germany, and Munich, Germany, is approximately 190 miles.

A linear function can be used to perform unit conversions. If x is a distance measured in kilometers, then the function defined by

$$m(x) = 0.622x$$

gives the corresponding distance in miles.

For more information about currency exchange and unit conversion, visit currencyex and unitconv at

www.mhhe.com/miller_oneill

---

28   **Chapter 1**   Review of Basic Algebraic Concepts

Concepts

1. Recognizing Terms, Factors, and Coefficients
2. Properties of Real Numbers
3. Distributive Property and Clearing Parentheses
4. Combining *Like* Terms
5. Simplifying Expressions

section

1.3   SIMPLIFYING EXPRESSIONS

1. Recognizing Terms, Factors, and Coefficients

An algebraic expression is the sum of one or more terms. A **term** is a constant or the product of a constant and one or more variables. For example, the expression

$$-6x^2 + 5xyz - 11 \quad \text{or} \quad -6x^2 + 5xyz + -11$$

consists of the terms $-6x^2$, $5xyz$, and -11.

The terms $-6x^2$ and $5xyz$ are **variable terms**, and the term -11 is called a **constant term**. It is important to distinguish between a term and the **factors** within a term. For example, the quantity $5xyz$ is one term, but the values 5, x, y, and z are factors within the term. The constant factor in a term is called the numerical coefficient (or simply **coefficient**) of the term. In the terms $-6x^2$, $5xyz$, and -11, the coefficients are -6, 5, and -11, respectively.

Terms are called *like* terms if they each have the same variables, and the corresponding variables are raised to the same powers. For example:

Like Terms			**Un***like* Terms			
$-6t$	and	$4t$	$-6t$	and	$4s$	(different variables)
$1.8ab$	and	$-3ab$	$1.8xy$	and	$-3x$	(different variables)
$\frac{1}{2}c^2d^3$	and	c^2d^3	$\frac{1}{2}c^2d^3$	and	c^2d	(different powers)
4	and	6	$4p$	and	6	(different variables)

example 1   Identifying Terms, Factors, Coefficients, and *Like* Terms

a. List the terms of the expression $-4x^2 - 7x + \frac{2}{3}$
b. Identify the coefficient of the term yz^3
c. Identify the pair of *like* terms: $16b$, $4b^2$ or $\frac{1}{2}c$, $-\frac{1}{6}c$

Solution:

a. The terms of the expression $-4x^2 - 7x + \frac{2}{3}$ are $-4x^2$, $-7x$, and $\frac{2}{3}$.
b. The term yz^3 can be written as $1yz^3$; therefore, the coefficient is 1.
c. $\frac{1}{2}c$, $-\frac{1}{6}c$ are *like* terms because they have the same variable raised to the same power.

2. Properties of Real Numbers

Simplifying algebraic expressions requires several important properties of real numbers that are stated in Table 1-3. Assume that a, b, and c represent real numbers or real-valued algebraic expressions:

Concepts

A list of important concepts is provided at the beginning of each section. Each concept corresponds to a heading within the section, making it easy to locate topics as you study or work through homework exercises.

$$m = \frac{y_2 - y_1}{x_2 - x_1} = \frac{2 - (-1)}{7 - 1} \qquad \text{Apply the slope formula.}$$

$$= \frac{3}{6}, \quad \text{or} \quad m = \frac{1}{2} \qquad \text{Simplify and reduce.}$$

The slope of the line can be verified from the graph (Figure 2-14).

Tip: The slope formula does not depend on which point is labeled (x_1, y_1) and which point is labeled (x_2, y_2). For example, reversing the order in which the points are labeled in Example 1 results in the same slope:

$(1, -1)$ and $(7, 2)$

(x_2, y_2) (x_1, y_1)

then $m = \dfrac{-1 - 2}{1 - 7} = \dfrac{-3}{-6} = \dfrac{1}{2}$

Figure 2-14

Special Elements

Tips
Tip boxes appear throughout the text and offer helpful hints and insight.

3. Positive, Negative, Zero, and Undefined Slopes

The value of the slope of a line may be positive, negative, zero, or undefined.

Lines that "increase," or "rise," from left to right have a **positive slope**.
Lines that "decrease," or "fall," from left to right have a **negative slope**.
Horizontal lines have a **zero slope**.
Vertical lines have an **undefined slope**.

Positive Slope   Negative Slope   Zero Slope   Undefined Slope

example 2   **Finding the Slope of a Line Between Two Points**

Find the slope of the line passing through the points $(3, -4)$ and $(-5, -1)$.

Solution:

$(3, -4)$ and $(-5, -1)$

(x_1, y_1) (x_2, y_2) Label points.

$m = \dfrac{y_2 - y_1}{x_2 - x_1} = \dfrac{-1 - (-4)}{-5 - 3}$ Apply the slope formula.

$= \dfrac{3}{-8} = -\dfrac{3}{8}$ Simplify.

Avoiding Mistakes
Through marginal notes labeled Avoiding Mistakes you are alerted to common errors and are shown methods to avoid them.

Solution:

a. $6\sqrt{11} + 2\sqrt{11}$

$= (6 + 2)\sqrt{11}$ Apply the distributive property.

$= 8\sqrt{11}$ Simplify.

b. $\sqrt{3} + \sqrt{3}$

$= 1\sqrt{3} + 1\sqrt{3}$ Note that $\sqrt{3} = 1\sqrt{3}$.

$= (1 + 1)\sqrt{3}$ Apply the distributive property.

$= 2\sqrt{3}$ Simplify.

c. $-2\sqrt[3]{ab} + 7\sqrt[3]{ab} - \sqrt[3]{ab}$

$= (-2 + 7 - 1)\sqrt[3]{ab}$ Apply the distributive property.

$= 4\sqrt[3]{ab}$ Simplify.

d. $\dfrac{1}{4}x\sqrt{3y} - \dfrac{3}{2}x\sqrt{3y}$

$= \left(\dfrac{1}{4} - \dfrac{3}{2}\right)x\sqrt{3y}$ Apply the distributive property.

$= \left(\dfrac{1}{4} - \dfrac{6}{4}\right)x\sqrt{3y}$ Get a common denominator.

$= -\dfrac{5}{4}x\sqrt{3y}$ Simplify.

Avoiding Mistakes

The process of adding *like* radicals with the distributive property is similar to adding *like* terms. The end result is that the numerical coefficients are added and the radical factor is unchanged.

$\sqrt{3} + \sqrt{3} = 1\sqrt{3} + 1\sqrt{3} = 2\sqrt{3}$
(correct)

Be careful: $\sqrt{3} + \sqrt{3} \neq \sqrt{10}$

In general: $\sqrt{x} + \sqrt{y} \neq \sqrt{x + y}$

Sometimes it is necessary to simplify radicals before adding or subtracting.

example 2   **Adding and Subtracting Radicals**

Simplify the radicals and add or subtract as indicated.

a. $3\sqrt{8} + \sqrt{2}$ b. $8\sqrt{x^3y^2} - 3y\sqrt{x^3}$

c. $\sqrt{50x^2y^3} - 13y\sqrt{2x^2y^3} + xy\sqrt{98y^3}$

Solution:

a. $3\sqrt{8} + \sqrt{2}$ The radicands are different. Try simplifying the radicals first.

$= 3 \cdot 2\sqrt{2} + \sqrt{2}$ Simplify: $\sqrt{8} = 2\sqrt{2}$

$= 6\sqrt{2} + \sqrt{2}$

$= (6 + 1)\sqrt{2}$ Apply the distributive property.

$= 7\sqrt{2}$ Simplify.

Graphing Calculator Boxes

Optional Graphing Calculator Boxes appear throughout the text. These boxes appear for your reference and may be included as part of your reading assignment, depending on the amount of emphasis your instructor places on the graphing calculator in your course. The boxes include screen captures and show how various techniques, such as analyzing and evaluating functions, can be performed.

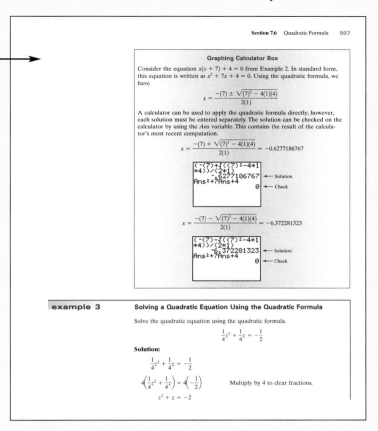

Section 7.6   Quadratic Formula   507

Graphing Calculator Box

Consider the equation $x(x + 7) + 4 = 0$ from Example 2. In standard form, this equation is written as $x^2 + 7x + 4 = 0$. Using the quadratic formula, we have

$$x = \frac{-(7) \pm \sqrt{(7)^2 - 4(1)(4)}}{2(1)}$$

A calculator can be used to apply the quadratic formula directly; however, each solution must be entered separately. The solution can be checked on the calculator by using the *Ans* variable. This contains the result of the calculator's most recent computation.

$$x = \frac{-(7) + \sqrt{(7)^2 - 4(1)(4)}}{2(1)} \approx -0.6277186767$$

$$x = \frac{-(7) - \sqrt{(7)^2 - 4(1)(4)}}{2(1)} \approx -6.372281323$$

example 3   **Solving a Quadratic Equation Using the Quadratic Formula**

Solve the quadratic equation using the quadratic formula.

$$\frac{1}{4}z^2 + \frac{1}{4}z = -\frac{1}{2}$$

Solution:

$$\frac{1}{4}z^2 + \frac{1}{4}z = -\frac{1}{2}$$

$$4\left(\frac{1}{4}z^2 + \frac{1}{4}z\right) = 4\left(-\frac{1}{2}\right) \qquad \text{Multiply by 4 to clear fractions.}$$

$$z^2 + z = -2$$

---

section 2.4   PRACTICE EXERCISES

1. True or false. If an answer is false, explain why.
   a. The graph of a linear equation always has an x-intercept.
   b. The graph of a linear equation always has a y-intercept.

2. True or false. If an answer is false, explain why.
   a. The x- and y-intercepts of a linear equation are always different points.
   b. Every graph of a line must have an x-intercept or a y-intercept or both.

3. $2x - 2y - 4 = 0$
4. $2x + 3y = -12$
5. $2x - 4 = 6$
6. $3 - 2y = -6$
7. Given the two points $(-3, -4)$ and $(3, -6)$:
   a. Find the slope of the line passing through the two points.
   b. Find an equation of the line passing through the two points. Write the answer in slope-intercept form and graph the line.
   c. Find an equation of any line parallel to the line found in part (b). (Answers may

■ **EXPANDING YOUR SKILLS**

37. Loraine is enrolled in an algebra class that meets 5 days per week. Her instructor gives a test every Friday. Loraine has a study plan and keeps a portfolio with notes, homework, test corrections, and vocabulary. She also records the amount of time per day that she studies and does homework. The following data represent the amount of time she studied per day and her weekly test grades.

Time Studied per Day (minutes) x	Weekly Test Grade (percent) y
60	69
70	74
80	79
90	84
100	89

Table for Exercise 37

   a. Graph the points on a rectangular coordinate system. Use appropriate scaling for the x- and y-axes. Do the data points appear to follow a linear trend?
   b. Find a linear equation that relates Loraine's

38. $(3, -4)(0, -5)(9, -2)$
39. $(4, 3)(-4, -1)(2, 2)$
40. $(0, 2)(-2, 12)(-1, 6)$
41. $(-2, -2)(0, -3)(-4, -1)$

▦ **GRAPHING CALCULATOR EXERCISES**

42. a. Graph the equation $y = 0.2x$ (*Hint*: Use a window defined by $0 \le x \le 25$ and $0 \le y \le 5$)
    b. Use an *Eval* or *Table* feature to confirm your answers to Exercise 15.

43. a. Graph the equation $y = 2.5x$ (*Hint*: Use a window defined by $0 \le x \le 12$ and $0 \le y \le 30$)
    b. Use an *Eval* or *Table* feature to confirm your answers to Exercise 16.

44. a. Graph the equation $y = 5.3x + 63.4$ (*Hint*: Use a window defined by $0 \le x \le 15$ and $0 \le y \le 150$)
    b. Use an *Eval* or *Table* feature to confirm your answers to Exercise 17.

45. a. Graph the equation $y = 142x + 9060$ (*Hint*: Use a window defined by $0 \le x \le 15$ and $0 \le y \le 15,000$)

Practice Exercises

The Practice Exercises contain a variety of problem types.

- **Applications** are based on real-world facts and figures. Working through these problems will help you improve your problem-solving skills.
- **Exercises keyed to video** 📼 are labeled with an icon to help you identify those exercises that appear in the video series that accompanies this text.
- **Calculator Exercises** 🖩 cover situations when a calculator can be used to help you perform calculations that might be overly time-consuming if done by hand. They are designed for use with either a scientific or a graphing calculator.
- **Expanding Your Skills**, found near the end of most Practice Exercise sets, are exercises that challenge your knowledge of the concepts presented.
- **Graphing Calculator Exercises**, also found at the end of appropriate exercise sets, offer you an opportunity to use a graphing calculator to explore concepts.

chapter 4   MIDCHAPTER REVIEW

For Exercises 1–6, list the domain and range of each relation. Then determine if the relation defines y as a function of x.

1.

State x	Percent Change in Population Since 1990 y
Colorado	16
Rhode Island	−1.3
Kentucky	5.3
Alabama	5.8

Midchapter Reviews

The Midchapter Reviews are provided to help you strengthen your understanding of concepts learned in the beginning of a chapter before you move on to new ideas presented later in the chapter.

End of Chapter Summary and Exercises

The **Summary**, found at the end of each chapter, outlines key concepts and terms for each section and illustrates concepts with examples. With this list, you can quickly identify important ideas and vocabulary to be reviewed before quizzes or exams. Following the Summary is a set of **Review Exercises** that are organized by section. A **Chapter Test** appears after each set of Review Exercises.

Chapters 2–13 also include a **Cumulative Review** that follows the Chapter Test. These end-of-chapter materials are useful resources that will help you prepare for quizzes or exams.

chapter 6   SUMMARY

SECTION 6.1—DEFINITION OF AN nth ROOT

KEY CONCEPTS:

b is an nth root of a if $b^n = a$.

The expression $\sqrt{a}$ represents the principal square root of a.

The expression $\sqrt[n]{a}$ represents the principal nth root of a.

$\sqrt[n]{a^n} = |a|$ if n is even.

$\sqrt[n]{a^n} = a$ if n is odd.

$\sqrt[n]{a}$ is not a real number if $a < 0$ and n is even.

$f(x) = \sqrt[n]{x}$ defines a radical function.

EXAMPLES:

2 is a square root of 4.

−2 is a square root of 4.

−3 is a cube root of −27.

$\sqrt{36} = 6$ $\sqrt[3]{-64} = -4$

$\sqrt[4]{(x+3)^4} = |x+3|$ $\sqrt[3]{(x+3)^3} = x+3$

$\sqrt[4]{-16}$ is not a real number.

For $g(x) = \sqrt{x}$ the domain is $[0, \infty)$.

For $h(x) = \sqrt[3]{x}$ the domain is $(-\infty, \infty)$.

chapter 6   REVIEW EXERCISES

For the exercises in this set, assume that all variables represent positive real numbers unless otherwise stated.

Section 6.1

1. True or false:
   a. The principal nth root of an even indexed root is always positive.
   b. The principal nth root of an odd indexed root is always positive.

2. Explain why $\sqrt{(-3)^2} = 3$ and $\sqrt{(-3)^2} \neq -3$.

3. Are the following statements true or false?
   a. $\sqrt{a^2 + b^2} = a + b$
   b. $\sqrt{(a+b)^2} = a + b$

For Exercises 4–6, simplify the radicals.

4. $\sqrt{\dfrac{50}{32}}$ 5. $\sqrt[4]{625}$ 6. $\sqrt{(-6)^2}$

chapter 6   TEST

1. a. What is the principal square root of 36?
   b. What is the negative square root of 36?

2. Which of the following are real numbers?
   a. $-\sqrt{100}$ b. $\sqrt{-100}$
   c. $-\sqrt[3]{1000}$ d. $\sqrt[3]{-1000}$

3. Simplify.
   a. $\sqrt[3]{y^3}$ b. $\sqrt[4]{y^4}$

For Exercises 4–11, simplify the radicals. Assume that all variables represent positive numbers.

4. $\sqrt[4]{81}$ 5. $\sqrt{\dfrac{16}{9}}$

6. $\sqrt[3]{32}$ 7. $\sqrt{a^4b^3c^5}$

8. $\sqrt{3x} \cdot \sqrt{6x^3}$ 9. $\sqrt{\dfrac{32w^6}{3w}}$

CUMULATIVE REVIEW EXERCISES, CHAPTERS 1–6

1. Simplify the expression:
   $6^2 - 2[5 - 8(3 - 1) + 4 \div 2]$

2. Simplify the expression:
   $3x - 3(-2x + 5) - 4y + 2(3x + 5) - y$

3. Solve the equation: $9(2y + 8) = 20 - (y + 5)$

4. Solve the inequality. Write the answer in interval notation. $2a - 4 < -14$

5. Write an equation of the line that is parallel to the line $2x + y = 9$ and passes through the point $(3, -1)$. Write the answer in slope-intercept form.

6. On the same coordinate system, graph the line $2x + y = 9$ and the line that you derived in Exercise 5. Verify that these two lines are indeed parallel.

APPLICATION INDEX

BUSINESS AND ECONOMICS

combinations of products possible, 916–918, 922

commissions, 48–49, 167–168

cost per unit produced, 585–586

currency exchange, 309

depreciation, 93–94

discounts, 49, 199

earnings from stock sale, 1

employment trends, 107

income distribution, 315–316

interest
  compound, 708–709, 736
  simple, 48–49, 79, 164–165, 386–387

investment growth, 50–51

job completion speed, 587–588

markup calculation, 50

minimum wage increase rate, 127–129

mortgage payment calculation, 535

national debt per capita, 314

profit calculation, 484–485

profit function, 763–765

salary plans, 100–101, 167–168, 675–676

sales tax calculation, 48–49

sales trends, 108

time optimization, 647–649

value *vs*. age calculation, 87

CONSUMER ISSUES

alarm code, possibility of guessing, 917–918

combinations of products possible, 916–918, 922

cost per item, 162–163

currency exchange, 309

discounts, 49, 199

earnings from stock sale, 1

fat content of ice cream, 594

gambling odds, 919

gasoline prices, 279

lottery odds, 883

mortgage payment calculation, 535

sales tax calculation, 48–49

unit conversions, 309

DISTANCE, RATE AND SPEED

airline flight, 165–166

bouncing ball
  distance traveled by, 902
  height attained by, 878–888

car, estimated from skid marks, 423

distance between two points, 634–635, 779–781

free-falling object
  distance fallen by, 498–499
  trajectory of, 747
  velocity of, 375

round trip, 53–54

speed of athlete per event, 586–587

speed of canoe *vs*. length, 292

trajectory of rocket, 486–487, 497–498, 762–763

wind speed, 165–166

EDUCATION

college enrollment trends, 149

degrees earned, male *vs*. female, 280–281, 330–331

financial aid recipients, 265–266

grade averages, 70–71

retention decay over time, 693–694

time optimization, 647–649

ENGINEERING

electrical resistance, 572

flight path, 321–322

road grade calculation, 105–106

rocket trajectory, 486–487, 497–498, 762–763

GEOMETRY

angles
  calculation of, 167, 180–181, 331
  complementary, finding, 58

area calculation
  of circle, 26–27
  of trapezoid, 24, 59–60
  of triangle, 214–215

boundary dimensions
  of rectangle, 57–58, 79, 331
  of square, 487
  of triangle, 378, 488, 508

distance between two points, 634–635, 779–781

feasible regions, 647–649

midpoint of a line, 133–134, 571

radius calculation, 61

volume calculation
  for pyramid, 422
  for rectangular box, 59, 342–343
  for sphere, 26–27

LAW ENFORCEMENT

gender ratios in, 585

license plates numbers, 923–924

speed of car, estimated from skid marks, 423

MEDICINE

AIDS perinatal cases per annum, 447

blood pressure, 13

body mass index (BMI), 601

disease risk calculation, 928

doctor's visit *vs*. age, 765

height *vs*. femur length in women, 238, 242–243

side effect risk, 935–936

smokers, female percentage of, 320–321

thyroid-stimulating hormone (TSH) levels, 606

wind chill factor, 369

NAVIGATION

distance between two points, 634–635, 779–781

distance calculation, 488, 508

midpoint calculation, 133–134, 571

relative location, 378–379

ALGEBRA FOR COLLEGE STUDENTS

REVIEW OF BASIC ALGEBRAIC CONCEPTS

As part of their monthly budget, many people save some of their earnings. Furthermore, financial advisors recommend that part of the savings be invested in long-term investments such as stocks and mutual funds. The price per share of such an investment fluctuates daily. To track the value of an investment, an individual may look up the value of a stock or mutual fund in the financial section of the newspaper or on the Internet.

For more information go to stockquote at

www.mhhe.com/miller_oneill

To determine the percent increase (or decrease) earned from the sale of a stock, we may use the formula:

$$\begin{matrix}\text{Percent} \\ \text{increase} \\ \text{(or decrease)}\end{matrix} = \left(\frac{\begin{matrix}\text{selling} \\ \text{price}\end{matrix} - \begin{matrix}\text{original} \\ \text{price}\end{matrix}}{\text{original price}} \right) \times 100\%$$

This and other applications of percentages are covered in Section 1.5.

section

1.1   SETS OF NUMBERS AND INTERVAL NOTATION

1. Introduction to Sets and Set-Builder Notation

Algebra is a powerful mathematical tool that is used to solve real-world problems in science, business, and many other fields. We begin our study of algebra with a review of basic definitions and notations used to express algebraic relationships.

In mathematics, a collection of elements is called a **set**, and the symbols { } are used to enclose the elements of the set. For example, the set {a, e, i, o, u} represents the vowels in the English alphabet. The set {1, 3, 5, 7} represents the first four positive odd numbers. Another method to express a set is to *describe* the elements of the set using **set-builder notation**. Consider the set {a, e, i, o, u} in set-builder notation.

Consider the set {1, 3, 5, 7} in set-builder notation.

2. Set of Real Numbers

Several sets of numbers are used extensively in algebra. The numbers you are familiar with in day-to-day calculations are elements of the set of **real numbers**, which can be represented graphically on a horizontal number line with a point labeled as 0. Positive real numbers are graphed to the right of 0 and negative real numbers are graphed to the left. Each point on the number line corresponds to exactly one real number, and for this reason, the line is called the **real number line** (Figure 1-1).

Figure 1-1

Several sets of numbers are **subsets** (or part) of the set of real numbers. These are

the set of natural numbers

the set of whole numbers

the set of integers
the set of rational numbers
the set of irrational numbers

Definition of the Natural Numbers, Whole Numbers, and Integers

The set of **natural numbers** is $\{1, 2, 3, \ldots\}$
The set of **whole numbers** is $\{0, 1, 2, 3, \ldots\}$
The set of **integers** is $\{\ldots -3, -2, -1, 0, 1, 2, 3, \ldots\}$

The set of rational numbers consists of all the numbers that can be defined as a ratio of two integers.

Definition of the Rational Numbers

The set of **rational numbers** is $\{\frac{p}{q} \mid p$ and q are integers and q does not equal zero$\}$

| example 1 | **Identifying Rational Numbers** |

Show that each number is a rational number by finding two integers whose ratio equals the given number.

a. $-\dfrac{4}{7}$ b. 8 c. $0.\overline{6}$ d. 0.87

Solution:

a. $-\frac{4}{7}$ is a rational number because it can be expressed as the ratio of the integers -4 and 7.
b. 8 is a rational number because it can be expressed as the ratio of the integers 8 and 1 ($8 = \frac{8}{1}$). In this example we see that *an integer is also a rational number.*
c. $0.\overline{6}$ represents the repeating decimal $0.6666666\ldots$ and can be expressed as the ratio of 2 and 3 ($0.\overline{6} = \frac{2}{3}$). In this example we see that *a repeating decimal is a rational number.*
d. 0.87 is the ratio of 87 and 100 ($0.87 = \frac{87}{100}$). In this example we see that *a terminating decimal is a rational number.*

Tip: Any rational number can be represented by a terminating decimal or by a repeating decimal.

Some real numbers such as the number π (pi) cannot be represented by the ratio of two integers. In decimal form, an irrational number is a nonterminating, nonrepeating decimal. The value of π, for example, can be approximated as $\pi \approx 3.1415926535897932$. However, the decimal digits continue indefinitely with no pattern. Other examples of irrational numbers are the square roots of nonperfect squares, such as $\sqrt{3}$ and $\sqrt{11}$.

Definition of the Irrational Numbers

The set of **irrational numbers** is $\{x \mid x$ is a real number that is not rational$\}$
Note: An irrational number cannot be written as a terminating decimal or as a repeating decimal.

The set of real numbers consists of both the rational numbers and the irrational numbers. The relationships among the sets of numbers discussed thus far are illustrated in Figure 1-2.

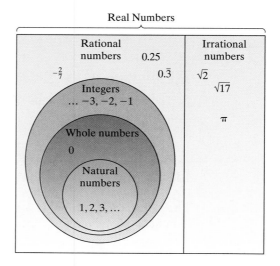

Figure 1-2

example 2

Classifying Numbers by Set

Check the set(s) to which each number belongs. The numbers may belong to more than one set.

	Natural Numbers	Whole Numbers	Integers	Rational Numbers	Irrational Numbers	Real Numbers
-6						
$\sqrt{23}$						
$-\frac{2}{7}$						
$\sqrt{9}$						
2.35						

Solution:

	Natural Numbers	Whole Numbers	Integers	Rational Numbers	Irrational Numbers	Real Numbers
-6			✓	✓		✓
$\sqrt{23}$					✓	✓
$-\frac{2}{7}$				✓		✓
$\sqrt{9} = 3$	✓	✓	✓	✓		✓
2.35				✓		✓

3. Inequalities

The relative size of two numbers can be compared using the real number line. We say that a is less than b (written mathematically as $a < b$) if a lies to the left of b on the number line.

$a < b$

We say that a is greater than b (written mathematically as $a > b$) if a lies to the right of b on the number line.

$a > b$

Table 1-1 summarizes the relational operators that compare two real numbers a and b.

Table 1-1		
Mathematical Expression	**Translation**	**Other Common Translations**
$a < b$	a is less than b	b exceeds a b is greater than a
$a > b$	a is greater than b	a exceeds b b is less than a
$a \leq b$	a is less than or equal to b	a is at most b a is no more than b
$a \geq b$	a is greater than or equal to b	a is no less than b a is at least b
$a = b$	a is equal to b	
$a \neq b$	a is not equal to b	
$a \approx b$	a is approximately equal to b	

The symbols $<$, $>$, $\leq$, $\geq$, and $\neq$ are called inequality signs, and the expressions $a < b$, $a > b$, $a \leq b$, $a \geq b$, and $a \neq b$ are called **inequalities**.

example 3

Ordering Real Numbers

Fill in the blank with the appropriate inequality symbol: $<$ or $>$

a. -2 _____ -5 b. $\dfrac{26}{7}$ _____ $\dfrac{23}{6}$ c. -1.3 _____ 2.8

Solution:

a. $-2 \underline{\quad > \quad} -5$

b. To compare $\frac{26}{7}$ and $\frac{23}{6}$, write the fractions as equivalent fractions with a common denominator.

$$\frac{26}{7} \cdot \frac{6}{6} = \frac{\mathbf{156}}{\mathbf{42}} = 3\frac{30}{42} \quad \text{and} \quad \frac{23}{6} \cdot \frac{7}{7} = \frac{\mathbf{161}}{\mathbf{42}} = 3\frac{35}{42}$$

Because $\dfrac{156}{42} < \dfrac{161}{42}$,   then $\dfrac{26}{7} \underline{\quad < \quad} \dfrac{23}{6}$

c. $-1.3 \underline{\quad < \quad} 2.8$

4.   Interval Notation

The set $\{x \mid x \geq 3\}$ represents all real numbers greater than or equal to 3. This set can be illustrated graphically on the number line.

By convention, a closed circle, $\bullet$, or a square bracket, [, is used to indicate that an "endpoint" ($x = 3$) *is included* in the set. This interval is a **closed interval** because its endpoint is included.

The set $\{x \mid x > 3\}$ represents all real numbers strictly greater than 3. This set can be illustrated graphically on the number line.

By convention, an open circle, $\bigcirc$, or a parenthesis, (, is used to indicate that an "endpoint" ($x = 3$) is *not* included in the set. This interval is an **open interval** because its endpoint is *not* included.

Notice that the sets $\{x \mid x \geq 3\}$ and $\{x \mid x > 3\}$ consist of an infinite number of elements that cannot all be listed. Another method to represent the elements of such sets is by using **interval notation**. To understand interval notation, first consider the real number line, which extends infinitely far to the left and right. The symbol, ∞, is used to represent infinity. The symbol, −∞, is used to represent negative infinity.

To express a set of real numbers in interval notation, sketch the graph first using the symbols (,), [, or]. Then use these symbols at the endpoints to define the interval.

example 4	**Expressing Sets Using Interval Notation**

Graph the sets on the number line and express the set in interval notation.

a. $\{x \mid x \geq 3\}$ b. $\{x \mid x > 3\}$ c. $\{x \mid x \leq -\frac{3}{2}\}$

Solution:

a.   **Set-Builder Notation**   **Graph**   **Interval Notation**

$\{x \mid x \geq 3\}$ $[3, \infty)$

The graph of the set $\{x \mid x \geq 3\}$ "begins" at 3 and extends infinitely far to the right. The corresponding interval notation "begins" at 3 and extends to ∞. Notice that a square bracket, [, is used at 3 for both the graph and the interval notation to include $x = 3$. *A parenthesis is always used at ∞ (and at −∞) because there is no endpoint.*

b.   **Set-Builder Notation**   **Graph**   **Interval Notation**

$\{x \mid x > 3\}$ $(3, \infty)$

c.   **Set-Builder Notation**   **Graph**   **Interval Notation**

$\{x \mid x \leq -\frac{3}{2}\}$ $(-\infty, -\frac{3}{2}]$

The graph of the set $\{x \mid x \leq -\frac{3}{2}\}$ extends infinitely far to the left. Interval notation is always written from left to right. Therefore, −∞ is written first followed by a comma and then followed by the right-hand endpoint $-\frac{3}{2}$.

Using Interval Notation

- The endpoints used in interval notation are always written from left to right. That is, the smaller number is written first, followed by a comma, followed by the larger number.
- Parentheses, (and), indicate that an endpoint is *excluded* from the set.
- Square brackets, [and], indicate that an endpoint is *included* in the set.
- Parentheses, (and), are always used with ∞ and $-\infty$.

Table 1-2 summarizes the solution sets for four general inequalities.

Table 1-2		
Set-Builder Notation	**Graph**	**Interval Notation**
$\{x \mid x > a\}$	 a	(a, ∞)
$\{x \mid x \geq a\}$	 a	$[a, \infty)$
$\{x \mid x < a\}$	 a	$(-\infty, a)$
$\{x \mid x \leq a\}$	 a	$(-\infty, a]$

5. Union and Intersection of Sets

Two or more sets can be combined by the operations of union and intersection.

A Union *B* and *A* Intersection *B*

The **union** of sets A and B, denoted $A \cup B$, is the set of elements that belong to set A or to set B or to both sets A and B.

The **intersection** of two sets A and B, denoted $A \cap B$, is the set of elements common to both A and B.

The concepts of the union and intersection of two sets are illustrated in Figure 1-3 and Figure 1-4:

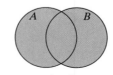

$A \cup B$
A union *B*
The elements in *A* or *B* or both

Figure 1-3

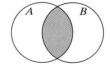

$A \cap B$
A intersection *B*
The elements in *A* and *B*

Figure 1-4

example 5

Finding the Union and Intersection of Sets

Given the sets: $A = \{a, b, c, d, e, f\}$ $B = \{a, c, e, g, i, k\}$ $C = \{g, h, i, j, k\}$

Find: a. $A \cup B$ b. $A \cap B$ c. $A \cap C$ d. $(A \cup B) \cap C$

Solution:

a. $A \cup B = \{a, b, c, d, e, f, g, i, k\}$ The union of A and B includes all the elements of A along with the elements of B. Notice that the elements a, c, and e are not listed twice.

b. $A \cap B = \{a, c, e\}$ The intersection of A and B includes only those elements that are common to both sets.

c. $A \cap C = \{\ \ \}$ (the **empty set**)   Because A and C share no common elements, the intersection of A and C is the empty, or null, set.

Tip: The empty set may be denoted by the symbol $\{\ \}$ or by the symbol $\varnothing$.

d. $(A \cup B) \cap C$
$= \{a, b, c, d, e, f, g, i, k\} \cap \{g, h, i, j, k\}$
$= \{g, i, k\}$

The set C is intersected with $A \cup B$. The elements g, i, and k are common to both sets.

Tip: To confirm the solution to Example 5, we can set up a diagram illustrating the relationship among the sets A, B, and C.

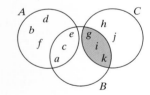

---

example 6

Finding the Union and Intersection of Sets

Given the sets: $A = \{x \mid x < 3\}$ $B = \{x \mid x \geq -2\}$ $C = \{x \mid x \geq 5\}$

Graph the following sets. Then express each set in interval notation.

a. $A \cap B$ b. $A \cup C$ c. $A \cup B$ d. $A \cap C$

Solution:
It is helpful to visualize the graphs of individual sets on the number line before taking the union or intersection.

a.   Graph of $A = \{x \mid x < 3\}$

Graph of $B = \{x \mid x \geq -2\}$

Graph of $A \cap B$ (the "overlap")

Interval Notation: $[-2, 3)$

Note that the set $A \cap B$ represents the real numbers greater than or equal to -2 *but* less than 3. This relationship can be written more concisely as a compound inequality: $-2 \le x < 3$. We can interpret this inequality as "x is between -2 and 3, including $x = -2$."

b.   Graph of $A = \{x \mid x < 3\}$

Graph of $C = \{x \mid x \ge 5\}$

Graph of $A \cup C$

Interval Notation: $(-\infty, 3) \cup [5, \infty)$ $A \cup C$ includes all elements from set A along with the elements from set C.

c.   Graph of $A = \{x \mid x < 3\}$

Graph of $B = \{x \mid x \ge -2\}$

Graph of $A \cup B$

Interval Notation: $(-\infty, \infty)$ $A \cup B$ includes all elements from set A along with the elements of set B. This encompasses all real numbers.

d.   Graph of $A = \{x \mid x < 3\}$

Graph of $C = \{x \mid x \ge 5\}$

Graph of $A \cap C$
(the sets do not "overlap")
$A \cap C$ is the empty set, $\{\ \}$.

6.   Translations Involving Inequalities

In Table 1-1, we learned that phrases such as "at least," "at most," "no more than," "no less than," and "between" can be translated into mathematical terms by using inequality signs.

example 7

Translating Inequalities

The intensity of a hurricane is often defined according to its maximum sustained winds, for which wind speed is measured to the nearest mile per hour. Translate the italicized phrases into mathematical inequalities.

a. A tropical storm is updated to hurricane status if the sustained wind speed, *w, is at least 74 miles per hour.*
b. Hurricanes are categorized according to intensity by the Saffir-Simpson scale. On a scale of 1 to 5, a category 5 hurricane is the most destructive. A category 5 hurricane has sustained winds, *w, exceeding 155 miles per hour.*
c. A category 4 hurricane has sustained winds, *w, of at least 131 miles per hour but no more than 155 miles per hour.*

Solution:

a. $w \geq 74$ mph
b. $w > 155$ mph
c. 131 mph $\leq w \leq 155$ mph

---

example 8   **Translating Inequalities**

The central pressure, *p*, (in millibars, mb) is often measured by reconnaissance aircraft that fly into tropical storms and hurricanes. Hurricane intensity may be rated according to the central pressure of a storm. Translate each inequality into an English phrase.

a. For a category 1 hurricane: $p \geq 980$ mb
b. For a category 2 hurricane: 965 mb $\leq p < 980$ mb
c. For a category 5 hurricane: $p < 920$ mb

Solution:

a. For a category 1 hurricane, the central pressure is at least 980 mb.
b. For a category 2 hurricane, the central pressure is greater than or equal to 965 mb but less than 980 mb.
c. For a category 5 hurricane, the central pressure is less than 920 mb.

---

section 1.1   PRACTICE EXERCISES

1. Simplify and graph the numbers on the number line.

$$\left\{ 1.7, \pi, \frac{8}{2}, -5, 4.\overline{2} \right\}$$

2. Simplify and graph the numbers on the number line.

$$\left\{ 1\tfrac{1}{2}, \frac{0}{4}, -\sqrt{9}, -\frac{1}{2}, \frac{6}{8} \right\}$$

3.   Check the sets to which each number belongs.

	Real Numbers	Irrational Numbers	Rational Numbers	Integers	Whole Numbers	Natural Numbers
5						
$-\sqrt{9}$						
-1.7						
$\dfrac{1}{2}$						
$\sqrt{7}$						
$\dfrac{0}{4}$						

4.   Check the sets to which each number belongs.

	Real Numbers	Irrational Numbers	Rational Numbers	Integers	Whole Numbers	Natural Numbers
$\dfrac{6}{8}$						
$1\frac{1}{2}$						
π						
$\dfrac{8}{2}$						
$4.\overline{2}$						

5.   a.   A person's average normal body temperature is 98.6°F. Write an inequality that describes the temperature for someone who has a fever. Let t represent temperature.

   b.   Graph the inequality from part a.

6.   a.   A movie theater charges $4.00 for tickets for senior citizens. This applies to people 60 and older. Write an inequality that describes the age of a senior citizen.

   b.   Graph the inequality from part a.

7.   a.   In many states the legal age for drinking is 21 years old. Write an inequality that describes the age for which it is *illegal* to drink.

   b.   Graph the inequality from part a and express the inequality in interval notation.

8.   a.   In many states it is illegal to drive under the age of 16. Write an inequality that describes the age for which it is illegal to drive.

   b.   Graph the inequality from part a and express the inequality in interval notation.

For Exercises 9–30, graph the sets and express each set in interval notation.

9.   All real numbers less than −3.

10.   All real numbers greater than 2.34.

11.   All real numbers greater than $\frac{5}{2}$.

12.   All real numbers less than $\frac{4}{7}$.

13.   All real numbers not less than 2.

14.   All real numbers not less than −3.

15.   All real numbers no more than −8.

16.   All real numbers no more than 5.

17.   All real numbers between −4 and 4.

18.   All real numbers between −7 and −1.

19.   All real numbers between −3 and 0, inclusive.

20.   All real numbers between −1 and 6, inclusive.

21. All real numbers at most 5.

22. All real numbers at most -2.

23. All real numbers at least 7.1.

24. All real numbers at least $\frac{1}{2}$.

25. $\{x \mid x > 8.6\}$

26. $\{x \mid x \leq -1\frac{1}{2}\}$

27. $\{x \mid -4 < x \leq 5\}$

28. $\{x \mid x \leq 4\} \cap \{x \mid x \geq -2\}$

29. $\{x \mid x < 5\} \cup \{x \mid x \geq 6.5\}$

30. $\{x \mid x < 3\} \cup \{x \mid x > 5\}$

For Exercises 31–38, write an expression in words that describes the set of numbers given by each interval. (Answers may vary.)

31. $(-\infty, -4)$ 32. $[2, \infty)$

33. $(-2, 7]$ 34. $(-3.9, 0)$

35. $[-180, 90]$ 36. $(-\infty, \infty)$

37. $(3.2, \infty)$ 38. $(-\infty, -1]$

39. Given: $M = \{-3, -1, 1, 3, 5\}$ and $N = \{-4, -3, -2, -1, 0\}$

List the elements of the following sets:

a. $M \cap N$ b. $M \cup N$

40. Given: $P = \{a, b, c, d, e, f, g, h, i\}$ and $Q = \{a, e, i, o, u\}$

List the elements of the following sets:

a. $P \cap Q$ b. $P \cup Q$

Let $A = \{x \mid x > -3\}$, $B = \{x \mid x \leq 0\}$, $C = \{x \mid -1 \leq x < 4\}$, and $D = \{x \mid 1 < x < 3\}$. For Exercises 41–48, graph the sets described here. Then express the answer in set-builder notation and in interval notation.

41. $A \cap B$ 42. $A \cup B$

43. $B \cup C$ 44. $B \cap C$

45. $C \cup D$ 46. $C \cap D$

47. $B \cap D$ 48. $A \cup D$

Blood pressure is defined as the pressure the blood exerts per unit area on a blood vessel wall. It is measured by taking two readings: the systolic pressure, which is pressure in the arteries at the peak of ventricular ejection, and the diastolic pressure, which is the pressure during ventricular relaxation. Blood pressure is reported in millimeters of mercury (mm Hg), with the systolic pressure appearing as the first number. For example, 120/80 is translated as "120 over 80" and represents a systolic pressure of 120 mm Hg and a diastolic pressure of 80 mm Hg. The following chart defines the ranges for normal blood pressure, high normal blood pressure, and high blood pressure (*hypertension*). (*Source:* American Heart Association)

Normal	systolic less than 130 mm Hg	diastolic less than 85 mm Hg
High normal	systolic 130–139 mm Hg	diastolic 85–89 mm Hg
Hypertension	systolic 140 mm Hg or greater	diastolic 90 mm Hg or greater

Table for Exercises 49–53

For Exercises 49–53, write an inequality using the variable p that represents each condition.

49. Normal systolic blood pressure

50. Diastolic pressure in hypertension

51. High normal range for systolic pressure

52. Systolic pressure in hypertension

53. Normal diastolic blood pressure

A pH scale determines whether a solution is acidic or alkaline. The pH scale runs from 0 to 14, with 0 being the most acidic and 14 being the most alkaline. A pH of 7 is neutral (distilled water has pH of 7).

For Exercises 54–58, write the pH ranges as inequalities and label the substances as acidic or alkaline.

54. Lemon juice: 2.2 through 2.4, inclusive

55. Eggs: 7.6 through 8.0, inclusive

56. Carbonated soft drinks: 3.0 through 3.5, inclusive

57. Milk: 6.6 through 6.9, inclusive

58. Milk of magnesia: 10.0 through 11.0, inclusive

Expanding Your Skills

For Exercises 59–66, identify the decimal as a rational number or an irrational number.

59. 0.777

60. 0.333

61. 0.3333 . . .

62. 1.1111 . . .

63. $2.71\overline{32}$

64. $8.15\overline{43}$

65. 0.101001000100001 . . .

66. 0.25225222522225 . . .

Concepts

1. **Opposite and Absolute Value**
2. **Addition and Subtraction of Real Numbers**
3. **Multiplication and Division of Real Numbers**
4. **Exponential Expressions**
5. **Square Roots**
6. **Order of Operations**
7. **Evaluating Expressions**

section

1.2   Operations on Real Numbers

1.   Opposite and Absolute Value

Several key definitions are associated with the set of real numbers and constitute the foundation of algebra. Two important definitions are the opposite of a real number and the absolute value of a real number.

Definition of the Opposite of a Real Number

Two numbers that are the same distance from 0 but on opposite sides of 0 on the number line are called **opposites** of each other.
Symbolically, we denote the opposite of a real number a as $-a$.

The numbers -4 and 4 are opposites of each other. Similarly, the numbers $\frac{3}{2}$ and $-\frac{3}{2}$ are opposites.

The Absolute Value of a Real Number

The **absolute value** of a real number a, denoted $|a|$, is the distance between a and 0 on the number line.
Note: The absolute value of any real number is *nonnegative*.

For example: $|5| = 5$ and $|-5| = 5$

example 1

Evaluating Absolute Value Expressions

Simplify the expressions: a. $|-2.5|$ b. $\left|\frac{5}{4}\right|$ c. $-|-4|$

Solution:

a. $|-2.5| = 2.5$

b. $\left|\frac{5}{4}\right| = \frac{5}{4}$

c. $-|-4| = -(4) = -4$

Graphing Calculator Box

Some calculators have an absolute value function.
For example,

```
abs(-2.5)
                   2.5
abs(5/4)▶Frac
                   5/4
-abs(-4)
                   -4
```

The absolute value of a number a is its distance from zero on the number line. The definition of $|a|$ may also be given symbolically depending on whether a is negative or nonnegative.

Definition of the Absolute Value of a Real Number

Let a be a real number. Then

1. If a is nonnegative (that is, $a \geq 0$) then $|a| = a$
2. If a is negative (that is, $a < 0$), then $|a| = -a$

This definition states that if a is a nonnegative number, then $|a|$ equals a itself. If a is a negative number, then $|a|$ equals the opposite of a. For example,

$|9| = 9$ Because 9 is positive, then $|9|$ equals the number 9 itself.

$|-7| = 7$ Because -7 is negative, then $|-7|$ equals the opposite of -7, which is 7.

2.   Addition and Subtraction of Real Numbers

The process of adding two real numbers is determined by the signs of the numbers.

Addition of Real Numbers

1. To add two numbers with the *same sign,* add their absolute values and apply the common sign to the sum.
2. To add two numbers with *different signs,* subtract the smaller absolute value from the larger absolute value. Then apply the sign of the number having the larger absolute value.

example 2   **Adding Real Numbers**

Perform the indicated operations:

a. $-2 + (-6)$ b. $-10.3 + 13.8$ c. $\frac{5}{6} + (-1\frac{1}{4})$

Solution:

a. $-2 + (-6)$

$$= -(|-2| + |-6|)$$
$$= -(2 + 6)$$
$$= -8$$

Because both numbers are negative, their sum will be negative.
Add the absolute values and apply the common sign.

b. $-10.3 + 13.8$

$$= (|13.8| - |-10.3|)$$
$$= 13.8 - 10.3$$
$$= 3.5$$

The numbers have *different* signs.
Subtract the smaller absolute value from the larger.
The sum will be positive because 13.8 has the larger absolute value.

c. $\dfrac{5}{6} + \left(-1\dfrac{1}{4}\right)$

$$= \frac{5}{6} + \left(-\frac{5}{4}\right)$$

Write the mixed number as a fraction.

$$= \frac{10}{12} + \left(-\frac{15}{12}\right)$$

Write the fractions with a common denominator.

The sum will be negative because $-\frac{15}{12}$ has the larger absolute value.

$$= -\left(\left|-\frac{15}{12}\right| - \left|\frac{10}{12}\right|\right)$$

Subtract the smaller absolute value from the larger.

$$= -\left(\frac{15}{12} - \frac{10}{12}\right)$$

Simplify the absolute values.

$$= -\left(\frac{5}{12}\right)$$

$$= -\frac{5}{12}$$

Subtraction of real numbers is defined in terms of the addition process. To subtract two real numbers, add the opposite of the second number to the first number.

Subtraction of Real Numbers

If a and b are real numbers, then $a - b = a + (-b)$

---

example 3

Subtracting Real Numbers

Perform the indicated operations:

a. $-13 - 5$ b. $2.7 - (-3.8)$ c. $\dfrac{5}{2} - 4\dfrac{2}{3}$

Solution:

a. $-13 - 5$

$\quad = -13 + (-5)$ Add the opposite of the second number to the first
$\quad = -18$ number.
                          Add.

b. $2.7 - (-3.8)$

$\quad = 2.7 + (3.8)$ Add the opposite of the second number to the first
$\quad = 6.5$ number.
                          Add.

c. $\dfrac{5}{2} - 4\dfrac{2}{3}$

$\quad = \dfrac{5}{2} + \left(-4\dfrac{2}{3}\right)$ Add the opposite of the second number to the first
                                                          number.

$\quad = \dfrac{5}{2} + \left(-\dfrac{14}{3}\right)$ Write the mixed number as a fraction.

$\quad = \dfrac{15}{6} + \left(-\dfrac{28}{6}\right)$ Get a common denominator and add.

$\quad = -\dfrac{13}{6}$ or $-2\dfrac{1}{6}$

---

3. Multiplication and Division of Real Numbers

The process of multiplying two real numbers is determined by the signs of the factors.

Multiplication of Real Numbers

1. The product of two real numbers with the *same* sign is *positive.*
2. The product of two real numbers with *different* signs is *negative.*
3. The product of any real number and zero is *zero.*

example 4   **Multiplying Real Numbers**

Multiply the real numbers:

a. $(2)(-5.1)$ b. $-\dfrac{2}{3} \cdot \dfrac{9}{8}$ c. $\left(-3\dfrac{1}{3}\right)\left(-\dfrac{3}{10}\right)$

Solution:

a. $(2)(-5.1)$

$= -10.2$ *Different* signs. The product is negative.

b. $-\dfrac{2}{3} \cdot \dfrac{9}{8}$

$= -\dfrac{18}{24}$ *Different* signs. The product is negative.

$= -\dfrac{3}{4}$ Reduce.

c. $\left(-3\dfrac{1}{3}\right)\left(-\dfrac{3}{10}\right)$

$= \left(-\dfrac{10}{3}\right)\left(-\dfrac{3}{10}\right)$ Write the mixed number as a fraction.

$= \dfrac{30}{30}$ *Same* signs. The product is positive.

$= 1$ Reduce.

Notice from Example 4c that $\left(-\frac{10}{3}\right)\left(-\frac{3}{10}\right) = 1$. If the product of two numbers is 1, then the numbers are said to be **reciprocals**. That is, the reciprocal of a real *number a* is $\frac{1}{a}$. Furthermore, $a \cdot \frac{1}{a} = 1$

> **Tip:** A number and its reciprocal have the same sign.
>
> $\left(-\dfrac{10}{3}\right)\left(-\dfrac{3}{10}\right) = 1$ $3 \cdot \dfrac{1}{3} = 1$

Recall that subtraction of real numbers was defined in terms of addition. In a similar way, division of real numbers can be defined in terms of multiplication. *To divide two real numbers, multiply the first number by the reciprocal of the second number.* For example:

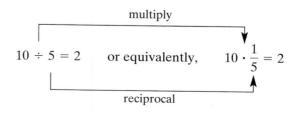

Because division of real numbers can be expressed in terms of multiplication, then the sign rules that apply to multiplication also apply to division.

$$10 \div 2 = 10 \cdot \frac{1}{2} = 5$$

$$-10 \div (-2) = -10 \cdot \left(-\frac{1}{2}\right) = 5$$

Dividing two numbers of the same sign produces a *positive* quotient.

$$10 \div (-2) = 10\left(-\frac{1}{2}\right) = -5$$

$$-10 \div 2 = -10 \cdot \frac{1}{2} = -5$$

Dividing two numbers of opposite signs produces a *negative* quotient.

Division of Real Numbers

Assume a and b are real numbers such that $b \neq 0$.

1. If a and b have the *same* signs, then the quotient $\frac{a}{b}$ is *positive*.
2. If a and b have *different* signs, then the quotient $\frac{a}{b}$ is *negative*.
3. $\frac{0}{b} = 0$
4. $\frac{b}{0}$ is undefined.

The relationship between multiplication and division can be used to investigate properties 3 and 4 in the preceding box. For example,

$$\frac{0}{6} = 0 \qquad \text{Because } 6 \times 0 = 0 \checkmark$$

$$\frac{6}{0} \text{ is undefined} \qquad \text{Because there is no number that when multiplied by 6 will equal 0}$$

Note: The quotient of 0 and 0 *cannot be determined.* Evaluating an expression of the form $\frac{0}{0} = ?$ is equivalent to asking "what number times zero will equal 0?" That is, $(0)(?) = 0$. Any real number will satisfy this requirement, however, expressions involving $\frac{0}{0}$ are usually discussed in advanced mathematics courses.

example 5   **Dividing Real Numbers**

Divide the real numbers:

a. $\dfrac{-42}{7}$ b. $\dfrac{-96}{-144}$ c. $\dfrac{-5}{-7}$ d. $3\dfrac{1}{10} \div \left(-\dfrac{2}{5}\right)$

Solution:

a. $\dfrac{-42}{7} = -6$ *Different* signs. The quotient is negative.

Tip: Recall that multiplication may be used to check a division problem. For example:

$$\frac{-42}{7} = -6 \Rightarrow (7) \cdot (-6) = -42 \checkmark$$

Tip: If the numerator and denominator are both negative, then the fraction is positive:

$$\frac{-5}{-7} = \frac{5}{7}$$

b. $\dfrac{-96}{-144} = \dfrac{2}{3}$ *Same* signs. The quotient is positive. Answer is reduced.

c. $\dfrac{-5}{-7} = \dfrac{5}{7}$ *Same* signs. The quotient is positive.

d. $3\dfrac{1}{10} \div \left(-\dfrac{2}{5}\right)$

$\quad = \dfrac{31}{10}\left(-\dfrac{5}{2}\right)$ Write the mixed number as an improper fraction, and multiply by the reciprocal of the second number.

$\quad = \dfrac{31}{\overset{}{\underset{2}{10}}}\left(-\dfrac{\overset{1}{5}}{2}\right)$

$\quad = -\dfrac{31}{4}$ *Different* signs. The quotient is negative.

Tip: If the numerator and denominator of a fraction have opposite signs, then the quotient will be negative. Therefore, a fraction has the same value whether the negative sign is written in the numerator, in the denominator, or in front of a fraction.

$$-\frac{31}{4} = \frac{-31}{4} = \frac{31}{-4}$$

4. Exponential Expressions

To simplify the process of repeated multiplication, exponential notation is often used. For example, the quantity $3 \cdot 3 \cdot 3 \cdot 3 \cdot 3$ can be written as 3^5 (three to the fifth power).

Definition of b^n

Let b represent any real number and n represent a positive integer. Then,

$$b^n = \underbrace{b \cdot b \cdot b \cdot b \cdot \cdots \cdot b}_{n\text{-factors of } b}$$

b^n is read as "b to the nth power."
b is called the **base** and n is called the **exponent**, or **power**.
b^2 is read as "b *squared*," and b^3 is read as "b *cubed*."

| example 6 | **Evaluating Exponential Expressions** |

Simplify the expression: a. 5^3 b. $(-2)^4$ c. -2^4 d. $\left(-\dfrac{1}{3}\right)^2$

Solution:

a. $5^3 = 5 \cdot 5 \cdot 5$ The base is 5, and the exponent is 3.
   $= 125$

b. $(-2)^4 = (-2)(-2)(-2)(-2)$ The base is -2, and the exponent is 4.
   $= 16$ The exponent, 4, applies to the entire contents of the parentheses.

c. $-2^4 = -[2 \cdot 2 \cdot 2 \cdot 2]$ The base is 2, and the exponent is 4.
   $= -[2 \cdot 2 \cdot 2 \cdot 2]$ Because no parentheses enclose the negative
   $= -16$ sign, the exponent applies only to 2.

> **Tip:** The quantity -2^4 can also be interpreted as $-1 \cdot 2^4$.
>
> $-2^4 = -1 \cdot 2^4 = -1 \cdot (2 \cdot 2 \cdot 2 \cdot 2) = -16$

d. $\left(-\dfrac{1}{3}\right)^2 = \left(-\dfrac{1}{3}\right)\left(-\dfrac{1}{3}\right)$ The base is $-\tfrac{1}{3}$, and the exponent is 2.
   $= \dfrac{1}{9}$

Graphing Calculator Box

On many calculators, the $\boxed{x^2}$ key is used to square a number. The $\boxed{\wedge}$ key is used to find the value of a base to any power.

```
5^3
              125
(-2)^4
               16
-2^4
              -16
```

---

5. Square Roots

The reverse operation to squaring a number is to find its square roots. For example, finding a square root of 9 is equivalent to asking "what number when squared equals 9?" One obvious answer is 3, because $(3)^2 = 9$. However, -3 is also a square root of 9 because $(-3)^2 = 9$. For now, we will focus on the **principal square root** which is always taken to be nonnegative.

The symbol, $\sqrt{}$, (called a **radical sign**) is used to denote the principal square root of a number. Therefore, the principal square root of 9 can be written as $\sqrt{9}$. The expression $\sqrt{64}$ represents the principal square root of 64.

example 7

Evaluating Square Roots

Evaluate the expressions, if possible: a. $\sqrt{81}$ b. $\sqrt{\dfrac{25}{64}}$ c. $\sqrt{-16}$

Solution:

a. $\sqrt{81} = 9$ because $(9)^2 = 81$

b. $\sqrt{\dfrac{25}{64}} = \dfrac{5}{8}$ because $\left(\dfrac{5}{8}\right)^2 = \dfrac{25}{64}$

c. $\sqrt{-16}$ is *not a real number* because no real number when squared will be negative.

Graphing Calculator Box

The $\boxed{\sqrt{}}$ key is used to find the square root of a positive real number.

Example 7c illustrates that the square root of a negative number is not a real number because no real number when squared will be negative.

The Square Root of a Negative Number

Let a be a negative real number. Then $\sqrt{a}$ is not a real number.

6.   Order of Operations

When algebraic expressions contain numerous operations, it is important to evaluate the operations in the proper order. Parentheses ( ), brackets [ ], and braces { } are used for grouping numbers and algebraic expressions. It is important to recognize that operations must be done within parentheses and other grouping symbols first. Other grouping symbols include absolute value bars, radical signs, and fraction bars.

Order of Operations

1.   First, simplify expressions within parentheses and other grouping symbols. These include absolute value bars, fraction bars, and radicals. If imbedded parentheses are present, start with the innermost parentheses.
2.   Evaluate expressions involving exponents and radicals.

3. Perform multiplication or division in the order in which they occur from left to right.
4. Perform addition or subtraction in the order in which they occur from left to right.

---

example 8   **Applying the Order of Operations**

Simplify the following expressions:

a. $10 - 5(2 - 5)^2 + 6 \div 3 + \sqrt{16 - 7}$ b. $\dfrac{|(-3)^3 + (5^2 - 3)|}{-15 \div (-3)(2)}$

Solution:

a. $10 - 5(2 - 5)^2 + 6 \div 3 + \sqrt{16 - 7}$

$= 10 - 5(-3)^2 + 6 \div 3 + \sqrt{9}$ Simplify inside the parentheses and radical.

$= 10 - 5(9) + 6 \div 3 + 3$ Simplify exponents and radicals.
$= 10 - 45 + 2 + 3$ Do multiplication and division from left to right.

$= -35 + 2 + 3$ Do addition and subtraction from left to right.

$= -33 + 3$
$= -30$

Tip: Don't try to do too many steps at once. Taking a shortcut may result in a careless error. For each step rewrite the entire expression changing only the operation being evaluated.

---

b. $\dfrac{|(-3)^3 + (5^2 - 3)|}{-15 \div (-3)(2)}$ Simplify numerator and denominator separately.

$= \dfrac{|(-3)^3 + (25 - 3)|}{5(2)}$ *Numerator:* Simplify inner parentheses.
Denominator: Do multiplication and division (left to right).

$= \dfrac{|(-3)^3 + (22)|}{10}$ *Numerator:* Simplify inner parentheses.
Denominator: Multiply.

$= \dfrac{|-27 + 22|}{10}$ Simplify exponents.

$= \dfrac{|-5|}{10}$ Add within the absolute value.

$= \dfrac{5}{10}$ or $\dfrac{1}{2}$ Evaluate the absolute value and reduce.

Graphing Calculator Box

To evaluate the expression

$$\frac{|(-3)^3 + (5^2 - 3)|}{-15 \div (-3)(2)}$$

on a graphing calculator, use parentheses to enclose the absolute value expression. Likewise, it is necessary to use parentheses to enclose the entire denominator.

7. Evaluating Expressions

The order of operations is followed when evaluating an algebraic expression or when evaluating a geometric formula. For a list of common geometry formulas, see the inside front cover of the text. It is important to note that some geometric formulas use Greek letters (such as π) and some formulas use variables with subscripts. A **subscript** is a number or letter written to the right of and slightly below a variable. Subscripts are used on variables to represent different quantities. For example, the area of a trapezoid is given by: $A = \frac{1}{2}(b_1 + b_2)h$. The values of b_1 and b_2 (read as "b sub 1" and "b sub 2") represent the two different bases of the trapezoid (Figure 1-5). This is illustrated in the next example.

Figure 1-5

example 9   **Evaluating an Algebraic Expression**

A home owner in North Carolina wants to buy protective film for a trapezoidal-shaped window. The film will adhere to shattered glass in the event that the glass breaks during a bad storm. Find the area of the window whose dimensions are given in Figure 1-6.

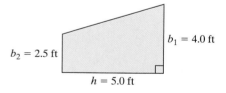

Figure 1-6

Solution:

$$A = \frac{1}{2}(b_1 + b_2)h$$

$$= \frac{1}{2}(4.0 \text{ ft} + 2.5 \text{ ft})(5.0 \text{ ft}) \qquad \text{Substitute } b_1 = 4.0 \text{ ft}, b_2 = 2.5 \text{ ft, and } h = 5.0 \text{ ft.}$$

$$= \frac{1}{2}(6.5 \text{ ft})(5.0 \text{ ft}) \qquad \text{Simplify inside parentheses.}$$

$$= 16.25 \text{ ft}^2 \qquad \text{Multiply from left to right.}$$

The area of the window is 16.25 ft^2.

Tip: Subscripts should not be confused with *superscripts*, which are written above a variable. Superscripts are used to denote powers.

$$b_2 \neq b^2$$

section 1.2   PRACTICE EXERCISES

For Exercises 1–4, describe the set:

1. {rational numbers} ∩ {integers}

2. {rational numbers} ∪ {irrational numbers}

3. {natural numbers} ∪ {0}

4. {integers} ∩ {whole numbers}

5. If the absolute value of a number can be thought of as its distance from zero, explain why an absolute value can never be negative.

6. If a number is negative, then its *opposite* will be: a. positive   b. negative.

7. If a number is negative, then its *reciprocal* will be: a. positive   b. negative.

8. If a number is negative, then its *absolute value* will be: a. positive   b. negative.

9. Complete the following table:

Number	Opposite	Reciprocal	Absolute Value
6			
	$-\dfrac{1}{11}$		
		$-\dfrac{1}{8}$	
	0.13		
1.1			
0			
		$-0.\overline{3}$	

10. Complete the following table:

Number	Opposite	Reciprocal	Absolute Value
−9			
	$\dfrac{2}{3}$		
		14	
	−2.5		
−1			
0			
		$2\dfrac{1}{9}$	

For Exercises 11–18, fill in the blank with the appropriate symbol (<, >, =).

11. $-|6|$ _____ $|-6|$ 12. $-(-5)$ _____ $-|-5|$

13. $|-4|$ _____ $|4|$ 14. $-|2|$ ____ (-2)

15. (-9) _____ $|-9|$ 16. $-(-8)$ _____ $-|8|$

17. $|2 + (-5)|$ _____ $|2| + |-5|$

18. $|4 + 3|$ _____ $|4| + |3|$

For Exercises 19–22, find the average of the set of data values by adding the values and dividing by the number of values.

19. Find the average high temperature for a week in April in Daytona Beach, Florida. (Round to the nearest tenth of a degree.)

Day	Mon.	Tues.	Wed.	Thur.	Fri.	Sat.	Sun.
High temperature	82°F	90°F	94°F	90°F	88°F	66°F	62°F

20. Find the average low temperature for a week in April in Daytona Beach, Florida. (Round to the nearest tenth of a degree.)

Day	Mon.	Tues.	Wed.	Thur.	Fri.	Sat.	Sun.
Low temperature	74°F	72°F	72°F	72°F	70°F	56°F	52°F

21. Find the average low temperature for a week in January in St. John's, Newfoundland. (Round to the nearest tenth of a degree.)

Day	Mon.	Tues.	Wed.	Thur.	Fri.	Sat.	Sun.
Low temperature	−18°C	−16°C	−20°C	−11°C	−4°C	−3°C	1°C

22. Find the average high temperature for a week in January in St. John's, Newfoundland. (Round to the nearest tenth of a degree.)

Day	Mon.	Tues.	Wed.	Thur.	Fri.	Sat.	Sun.
High temperature	$-2°C$	$-6°C$	$-7°C$	$0°C$	$1°C$	$8°C$	$10°C$

For Exercises 23–52, perform the indicated operations.

23. $-8 + 4$

24. $3 + (-7)$

25. $-12 + (-7)$

26. $-5 + (-11)$

27. $-7 - (-10)$

28. $-14 - (-2)$

29. $5 - (-9)$

30. $8 - (-4)$

31. $-6 - 15$

32. $-21 - 4$

33. $1.5 - 9.6$

34. $4.8 - 10$

35. $\dfrac{2}{3} + \left(-\dfrac{7}{3}\right)$

36. $-\dfrac{4}{7} + \left(\dfrac{11}{7}\right)$

37. $-\dfrac{5}{9} - \dfrac{14}{15}$

38. $-6 - \dfrac{2}{9}$

39. $4(-8)$

40. $-21(3)$

41. $\dfrac{2}{9} \cdot \dfrac{12}{7}$

42. $\left(-\dfrac{5}{9}\right) \cdot \left(-\dfrac{18}{11}\right)$

43. $-\dfrac{2}{3} \div \left(-\dfrac{6}{7}\right)$

44. $\dfrac{5}{8} \div (-5)$

45. $7 \div 0$

46. $\dfrac{1}{16} \div 0$

47. $0 \div (-3)$

48. $0 \div 11$

49. $(-1.2)(-3.1)$

50. $(4.6)(-2.25)$

51. $(5.418) \div (0.9)$

52. $(6.9) \div (7.5)$

For Exercises 53–70, simplify using the order of operations.

53. $6 + 10 \div 2 \cdot 3 - 4$

54. $12 \div 3 \cdot 4 - 18$

55. $4^2 - (5 - 2)^2 \cdot 3$

56. $5 - 3(8 \div 4)^2$

57. $2 - 5(9 - 4\sqrt{25})^2$

58. $5^2 - (\sqrt{9} + 4 \div 2)$

59. $\left(-\dfrac{3}{5}\right)^2 - \dfrac{3}{5} \cdot \dfrac{5}{9} + \dfrac{7}{10}$

60. $\dfrac{1}{2} - \left(\dfrac{2}{3} \div \dfrac{5}{9}\right) + \dfrac{5}{6}$

61. $1.75 \div 0.25 - (1.25)^2$

62. $5.4 - (0.3)^2 \div 0.09$

63. $\dfrac{\sqrt{10^2 - 8^2}}{3^2}$

64. $\dfrac{\sqrt{16 - 7} + 3^2}{\sqrt{16} - \sqrt{4}}$

65. $|-11| + |5| - (|7| + |-2|)$

66. $|-40| - (|-3| + |18|) - (-16)$

67. $\dfrac{8(-3) - 6}{-7 - (-2)}$

68. $\dfrac{6(-2) - 8}{-15 - (10)}$

69. $\left(\dfrac{1}{2}\right)^2 + \left(\dfrac{6 - 4}{5}\right)^2 + \left(\dfrac{5 + 2}{10}\right)^2$

70. $\left(\dfrac{2^3}{2^3 + 1}\right)^2 \div \left(\dfrac{8 - (-2)}{3^2}\right)^2$

71. The formula, $C = \frac{5}{9}(F - 32)$, converts temperatures in the Fahrenheit scale to the Celsius scale. Find the equivalent Celsius temperature for each Fahrenheit temperature:

   a. $77°F$ b. $212°F$ c. $32°F$ d. $-40°F$

72. The formula, $F = \frac{9}{5}C + 32$, converts Celsius temperatures to Fahrenheit temperatures. Find the equivalent Fahrenheit temperature for each Celsius temperature:

   a. $-5°C$ b. $0°C$ c. $37°C$ d. $-40°C$

73. The area of a circle is given by $A = \pi r^2$, where r is the radius of the circle. Find the area of a clock whose radius is $6\frac{1}{2}$ in. (Use the π key on your calculator and round the final answer to two decimal places.)

74. The volume of a sphere is given by $V = \frac{4}{3}\pi r^3$. Find the volume of a balloon whose radius is $15\frac{1}{2}$ cm (centimeters). (Use the π key on your calculator and round the final answer to two decimal places.)

Use the geometry formulas found in the inside front cover of the book to answer Exercises 75–84.

For Exercises 75–78, find the area.

75. Trapezoid

5¼ in.

2 in.

4½ in.

76. Parallelogram

8.5 m

6 m

77. Triangle

3.1 cm

5.2 cm

78. Rectangle

¾ yd

7⅙ yd

For Exercises 79–84, find the volume. (Use the π key on your calculator and round the final answer to one decimal place.)

79. Sphere

$r = 1.5$ ft

80. Right Circular Cone

$h = 12$ cm

$r = 5$ cm

81. Right Circular Cone

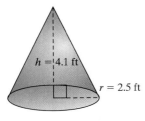

$h = 4.1$ ft

$r = 2.5$ ft

82. Sphere

$r = \frac{1}{2}$ yd

83. Cylinder

$h = 5$ in.

$r = 3$ in.

84. Cylinder

$h = 9.5$ m

$r = 4$ m

GRAPHING CALCULATOR EXERCISES

85. Which expression when entered into a graphing calculator will yield the correct value of $\frac{12}{6-2}$? Explain.

$$12/6 - 2 \quad \text{or} \quad 12/(6 - 2)$$

86. Which expression when entered into a graphing calculator will yield the correct value of $\frac{24-6}{3}$? Explain.

$$(24 - 6)/3 \quad \text{or} \quad 24 - 6/3$$

87. Which expression when entered into a graphing calculator will yield the correct value of $|-9 - 7|$? Explain.

$$\text{abs}(-9 - 7) \quad \text{or} \quad \text{abs} -9 - 7$$

88. Which expression when entered into a graphing calculator will yield the correct value of $\sqrt{25 - 9}$? Explain.

$$\sqrt{}\ 25 - 9 \quad \text{or} \quad \sqrt{}\ (25 - 9)$$

89. Verify your solution to Exercise 53 by entering the expression into a graphing calculator:

$$6 + 10/2 \times 3 - 4$$

90. Verify your solution to Exercise 54 by entering the expression into a graphing calculator:

$$12/3 \times 4 - 18$$

91. Verify your solution to Exercise 57 by entering the expression into a graphing calculator:

$$2 - 5 \times (9 - 4 \times \sqrt{}\ (25))^2$$

92. Verify your solution to Exercise 58 by entering the expression into a graphing calculator:

$$5^2 - (\sqrt{}\ (9) + 4/2)$$

93. Verify your solution to Exercise 63 by entering the expression into a graphing calculator:

$$(\sqrt{}\ (10^2 - 8^2))/3^2$$

94. Verify your solution to Exercise 64 by entering the expression into a graphing calculator:

$$(\sqrt{}\ (16 - 7) + 3^2)/(\sqrt{}\ (16) - \sqrt{}\ (4))$$

section
_____

1.3   SIMPLIFYING EXPRESSIONS

1. Recognizing Terms, Factors, and Coefficients

An algebraic expression is the sum of one or more terms. A **term** is a constant or the product of a constant and one or more variables. For example, the expression

$$-6x^2 + 5xyz - 11 \qquad \text{or} \qquad -6x^2 + 5xyz + -11$$
$$\text{consists of the terms } -6x^2, 5xyz, \text{ and } -11.$$

The terms $-6x^2$ and $5xyz$ are **variable terms**, and the term -11 is called a **constant term**. It is important to distinguish between a term and the **factors** within a term. For example, the quantity $5xyz$ is one term, but the values $5, x, y,$ and z are factors within the term. The constant factor in a term is called the numerical coefficient (or simply **coefficient**) of the term. In the terms $-6x^2, 5xyz,$ and $-11,$ the coefficients are $-6, 5,$ and $-11,$ respectively.

Terms are called *like* terms if they each have the same variables, and the corresponding variables are raised to the same powers. For example:

Like Terms			*Unlike* Terms			
$-6t$	and	$4t$	$-6t$	and	$4s$	(different variables)
$1.8ab$	and	$-3ab$	$1.8xy$	and	$-3x$	(different variables)
$\frac{1}{2}c^2d^3$	and	c^2d^3	$\frac{1}{2}c^2d^3$	and	c^2d	(different powers)
4	and	6	$4p$	and	6	(different variables)

---

example 1   **Identifying Terms, Factors, Coefficients, and *Like* Terms**

a. List the terms of the expression $-4x^2 - 7x + \frac{2}{3}$
b. Identify the coefficient of the term yz^3
c. Identify the pair of *like* terms: $16b, 4b^2$ or $\frac{1}{2}c, -\frac{1}{6}c$

Solution:

a. The terms of the expression $-4x^2 - 7x + \frac{2}{3}$ are $-4x^2, -7x,$ and $\frac{2}{3}.$
b. The term yz^3 can be written as $1yz^3$; therefore, the coefficient is 1.
c. $\frac{1}{2}c, -\frac{1}{6}c$ are *like* terms because they have the same variable raised to the same power.

---

2. Properties of Real Numbers

Simplifying algebraic expressions requires several important properties of real numbers that are stated in Table 1-3. Assume that $a, b,$ and c represent real numbers or real-valued algebraic expressions:

Table 1-3			
Property Name	**Algebraic Representation**	**Example**	**Description/Notes**
Commutative property of addition	$a + b = b + a$	$5 + 3 = 3 + 5$	The order in which two real numbers are added or multiplied does not affect the result.
Commutative property of multiplication	$a \cdot b = b \cdot a$	$(5)(3) = (3)(5)$	
Associative property of addition	$(a + b) + c = a + (b + c)$	$(2 + 3) + 7 = 2 + (3 + 7)$	The manner in which two real numbers are grouped under addition or multiplication does not affect the result.
Associative property of multiplication	$(a \cdot b)c = a(b \cdot c)$	$(2 \cdot 3)7 = 2(3 \cdot 7)$	
Distributive property of multiplication over addition	$a(b + c) = ab + ac$	$3(5 + 2) = 3 \cdot 5 + 3 \cdot 2$	A factor outside the parentheses is multiplied by each term inside the parentheses.
Identity property of addition	0 is the identity element for addition because $a + 0 = 0 + a = a$	$5 + 0 = 0 + 5 = 5$	Any number added to the identity element, 0, will remain unchanged.
Identity property of multiplication	1 is the identity element for multiplication because $a \cdot 1 = 1 \cdot a = a$	$5 \cdot 1 = 1 \cdot 5 = 5$	Any number multiplied by the identity element, 1, will remain unchanged.
Inverse property of addition	a and $(-a)$ are additive inverses because $a + (-a) = 0$ and $(-a) + a = 0$	$3 + (-3) = 0$	The sum of a number and its additive inverse (opposite) is the identity element, 0.
Inverse property of multiplication	a and $\frac{1}{a}$ are multiplicative inverses because $a \cdot \frac{1}{a} = 1$ and $\frac{1}{a} \cdot a = 1$ (provided $a \neq 0$)	$5 \cdot \frac{1}{5} = 1$	The product of a number and its multiplicative inverse (reciprocal) is the identity element, 1.

3.   Distributive Property and Clearing Parentheses

The properties of real numbers are used to multiply algebraic expressions. To multiply a term by an algebraic expression containing more than one term, we apply the **distributive property of multiplication over addition**.

example 2   **Applying the Distributive Property**

Apply the distributive property.

a. $4(2x + 5)$

b. $-(-3.4q + 5.7r)$

c. $-3(a + 2b - 5c)$

d. $-\dfrac{2}{3}\left(-9x + \dfrac{3}{8}y - 5\right)$

Solution:

a. $4(2x + 5)$

$= 4(2x) + 4(5)$ Apply the distributive property.

$= 8x + 20$ Simplify, using the associative property of multiplication.

b. $-(-3.4q + 5.7r)$ The negative sign preceding the parentheses can be interpreted as a factor of -1.

$= -1(-3.4q + 5.7r)$

$= -1(-3.4q) + (-1)(5.7r)$ Apply the distributive property.

$= 3.4q - 5.7r$

Tip: When applying the distributive property, a negative factor preceding the parentheses will change the signs of the terms within the parentheses.

$-3(a + 2b - 5c)$

$-3a - 6b + 15c$

c. $-3(a + 2b - 5c)$

$= -3(a) + (-3)(2b) + (-3)(-5c)$ Apply the distributive property.

$= -3a - 6b + 15c$ Simplify.

d. $-\dfrac{2}{3}\left(-9x + \dfrac{3}{8}y - 5\right)$

$= -\dfrac{2}{3}(-9x) + \left(-\dfrac{2}{3}\right)\left(\dfrac{3}{8}y\right) + \left(-\dfrac{2}{3}\right)(-5)$ Apply the distributive property.

$= \dfrac{18}{3}x - \dfrac{6}{24}y + \dfrac{10}{3}$ Simplify.

$= 6x - \dfrac{1}{4}y + \dfrac{10}{3}$ Reduce fractions.

Notice that the parentheses are removed after the distributive property is applied. Sometimes this is referred to as clearing parentheses.

4.   Combining *Like* Terms

Two terms can be added or subtracted only if they are *like* terms. To add or subtract *like* terms, we use the distributive property as shown in the next example.

example 3

Using the Distributive Property to Add and Subtract *Like* Terms

Add or subtract as indicated.

a. $-8x + 3x$

b. $4.75y^2 - 9.25y^2 + y^2$

Solution:

a. $-8x + 3x$

$\quad = x(-8 + 3)$ Apply the distributive property.

$\quad = x(-5)$ or $-5x$ Simplify.

b. $4.75y^2 - 9.25y^2 + y^2$

$\quad = 4.75y^2 - 9.25y^2 + 1y^2$ Notice that y^2 is interpreted as $1y^2$.

$\quad = y^2(4.75 - 9.25 + 1)$ Apply the distributive property.

$\quad = y^2(-3.5)$ Simplify.

$\quad = -3.5y^2$

Although the distributive property is used to add and subtract *like* terms, it is tedious to write each step. Observe that adding or subtracting *like* terms is a matter of combining the coefficients and leaving the variable factors unchanged. This can be shown in one step. This shortcut will be used throughout the text. For example,

$$4w + 7w = 11w \qquad 8ab^2 + 10ab^2 - 5ab^2 = 13ab^2$$

5. Simplifying Expressions

Clearing parentheses and combining *like* terms are important tools to simplifying algebraic expressions. This is demonstrated in the next example.

example 4

Clearing Parentheses and Combining *Like* Terms

Simplify by clearing parentheses and combining *like* terms.

a. $4 - 3(2x - 8) - 1$

b. $-(3s - 11t) - 5(2t + 8s) - 10s$

c. $2[1.5x + 4.7(x^2 - 5.2x) - 3x]$

d. $-\dfrac{1}{3}(3w - 6) - \left(\dfrac{1}{4}w + 4\right)$

Solution:

a. $4 - 3(2x - 8) - 1$

$\quad = 4 - 6x + 24 - 1$ Apply the distributive property.

$\quad = 4 + 24 - 1 - 6x$ Group *like* terms together.

$\quad = 27 - 6x$ Combine *like* terms.

$\quad = 27 - 6x$ or $-6x + 27$

Tip: The expression $27 - 6x$ is equal to $-6x + 27$. However, it is customary to write the variable term first.

b. $-(3s - 11t) - 5(2t + 8s) - 10s$

$= -3s + 11t - 10t - 40s - 10s$ Apply the distributive property.
$= -3s - 40s - 10s + 11t - 10t$ Group *like* terms together.
$= -53s + t$ Combine *like* terms.

c. $2[1.5x + 4.7(x^2 - 5.2x) - 3x]$

$= 2[1.5x + 4.7x^2 - 24.44x - 3x]$ Apply the distributive property to inner parentheses.
$= 2[1.5x - 24.44x - 3x + 4.7x^2]$ Group *like* terms together.
$= 2[-25.94x + 4.7x^2]$ Combine *like* terms.
$= -51.88x + 9.4x^2$ Apply the distributive property.
$= -51.88x + 9.4x^2$ or $9.4x^2 - 51.88x$

Tip: Using the commutative property of addition, the expression $-51.88x + 9.4x^2$ can also be written as $9.4x^2 + (-51.88x)$ or simply $9.4x^2 - 51.88x$. Although the expressions are all equal, it is customary to write the terms in descending order of the powers of the variable.

d. $-\dfrac{1}{3}(3w - 6) - \left(\dfrac{1}{4}w + 4\right)$

$= -\dfrac{3}{3}w + \dfrac{6}{3} - \dfrac{1}{4}w - 4$ Apply the distributive property.

$= -w + 2 - \dfrac{1}{4}w - 4$ Reduce fractions.

$= -\dfrac{4}{4}w - \dfrac{1}{4}w + 2 - 4$ Group *like* terms and find a common denominator.

$= -\dfrac{5}{4}w - 2$ Combine *like* terms.

---

section 1.3   PRACTICE EXERCISES

1. a. Classify the number -4 as a whole number, natural number, rational number, irrational number, integer, or real number. (Choose all that apply.)

    b. What is the reciprocal of -4?

    c. What is the opposite of -4?

    d. What is the absolute value of -4?

2. a. Classify the number $\frac{2}{3}$ as a whole number, natural number, rational number, irrational number, integer, or real number. (Choose all that apply.)

    b. What is the reciprocal of $\frac{2}{3}$?

    c. What is the opposite of $\frac{2}{3}$?

    d. What is the absolute value of $\frac{2}{3}$?

3. a. Classify the number 0 as a whole number, natural number, rational number, irrational number, integer, or real number. (Choose all that apply.)

    b. What is the reciprocal of 0 (if it exists)?

    c. What is the opposite of 0?

    d. What is the absolute value of 0?

4. a. Classify the number 1 as a whole number, natural number, rational number, irrational

number, integer, or real number. (Choose all that apply.)

b.   What is the reciprocal of 1?

c.   What is the opposite of 1?

d.   What is the absolute value of 1?

For Exercises 5–10, simplify and write the set in interval notation.

5. $\{x \mid x > |-3|\}$

6. $\left\{x \mid x \leq \left|-\dfrac{4}{3}\right|\right\}$

7. $\left\{p \mid p \leq -\left(-\dfrac{1}{3}\right)\right\}$

8. $\{p \mid p > -(-5)\}$

9. $\{q \mid q \geq \sqrt{25}\}$

10. $\{q \mid q < \sqrt{64}\}$

11.   Given the expression $2x^3 - 5xy + 6$

  a.   Determine the number of terms in the expression.

  b.   Identify the constant term.

  c.   List the coefficient of each term. Separate by commas.

12.   Given the expression $a^2 - 4ab - b^2 + 8$

  a.   Determine the number of terms in the expression.

  b.   Identify the constant term.

  c.   List the coefficient of each term. Separate by commas.

13.   Given the expression $pq - 7 + q^2 - 4q + p$

  a.   Determine the number of terms in the expression.

  b.   Identify the constant term.

  c.   List the coefficient of each term. Separate by commas.

14.   Given the expressions $7x - 1 + 3xy$

  a.   Determine the number of terms in the expression.

  b.   Identify the constant term.

  c.   List the coefficient of each term. Separate by commas.

For Exercises 15–18, simplify each expression two ways using (a) the order of operations (b) the distributive property.

15. $-3(5 + 7)$

16. $2(-8 + 1)$

17. $\dfrac{3}{2}\left(8 - \dfrac{1}{3}\right)$

18. $-\dfrac{1}{5}\left(-2 + \dfrac{1}{3}\right)$

For Exercises 19–42, clear parentheses and combine *like* terms.

19. $6b + 5 - 2b + 3$

20. $3x - 1 + x + 5$

21. $8y - 2 + y + 5y$

22. $-9a + a - 1 + 5a$

23. $4p^2 - 2p + 3p - 6 + 2p^2$

24. $6q - 9 + 3q^2 - q + 10$

25. $8(x - 3) + 1$

26. $-4(b + 2) - 3$

27. $-2(c + 3) - 2c$

28. $4(z - 4) - 3z$

29. $-(10w - 1) + 9 + w$

30. $-(2y + 7) - 4 + 3y$

31. $-9 - 4(2 - z) + 1$

32. $3 + 3(4 - w) - 11$

33. $4(2s - 7) - (s - 2)$

34. $2(t - 3) - (t - 7)$

35. $\dfrac{1}{2}(4 - 2c) + 5c$

36. $\dfrac{2}{3}(3d + 6) - 4d$

37. $3.1(2x + 2) - 4(1.2x - 1)$

38. $4.5(5 - y) + 3(1.9y + 1)$

39. $2\left[5\left(\dfrac{1}{2}a + 3\right) - (a^2 + a) + 4\right]$

40. $-3\left[3\left(b - \dfrac{2}{3}\right) - 2(b + 4) - 6b^2\right]$

41. $[(2y - 5) - 2(y - y^2)] - 3y$

42. $[-(x + 6) + 3(x^2 + 1)] + 2x$

For Exercises 43–50, identify as True or False.

43. $8 \cdot \dfrac{1}{8} = 8 \div 8$

44. $-2 \cdot 2 = 0$

45. $\dfrac{2}{7} \cdot 0 = \dfrac{2}{7}$

46. $-6 + 0 = -6$

47. $-2 + 2 = 0$

48. $6 \cdot \dfrac{1}{6} = 6 \div \dfrac{1}{6}$

49. $-6 + 0 = 6$

50. $\frac{1}{3} \cdot 1 = \frac{1}{3}$

66. What is another name for a multiplicative inverse?

67. What is another name for an additive inverse?

For Exercises 51–63, match each expression with the appropriate property.

68. Is the operation of subtraction commutative? Explain why or why not and give an example.

51. $3 + \frac{1}{2} = \frac{1}{2} + 3$

69. Is the operation of division commutative? Explain why or why not and give an example.

52. $7.2(4 - 1) = 7.2(4) - 7.2(1)$

53. $(6 + 8) + 2 = 6 + (8 + 2)$

54. $(4 + 19) + 7 = (19 + 4) + 7$

55. $9(4 \cdot 12) = (9 \cdot 4)12$

56. $\left(\frac{1}{4} + 2\right)20 = 5 + 40$

57. $(13 \cdot 41)6 = (41 \cdot 13)6$

58. $6(x + 3) = 6x + 18$

59. $3(y + 10) = 3(10 + y)$

60. $5(3 \cdot 7) = (5 \cdot 3)7$

61. $21(6 \cdot 8) = 21(8 \cdot 6)$

62. $\frac{2}{3} + \left(6 + \frac{1}{2}\right) = \left(\frac{2}{3} + 6\right) + \frac{1}{2}$

63. $(5p - 2)6 = 30p - 12$

a. Commutative property of addition

b. Associative property of multiplication

c. Distributive property of multiplication over addition

d. Commutative property of multiplication

e. Associative property of addition

64. What is the identity element for addition? Use it in an example.

65. What is the identity element for multiplication? Use it in an example.

■ EXPANDING YOUR SKILLS

70. Given the rectangular regions:

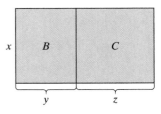

Figures for Exercise 70

a. Write an expression for the area of region A. (Do not simplify.)

b. Write an expression for the area of region B.

c. Write an expression for the area of region C.

d. Add the expressions for the area of regions B and C.

e. Show that the area of region A is equal to the sum of the areas of regions B and C. What property of real numbers does this illustrate?

section

1.4   LINEAR EQUATIONS IN ONE VARIABLE

1.   Definition of a Linear Equation in One Variable

A statement that equates two mathematical expressions is called an **equation**. There are many different types of equations. Here are some examples:

$$p + 3 = 11 \qquad \text{Linear equation}$$

$$w^2 = 9 \qquad \text{Quadratic equation}$$

$$-\frac{5}{x} + \frac{1}{3} = 0 \qquad \text{Rational equation}$$

A **solution to an equation** is a value of the variable that makes the equation a true statement. That is, a solution makes the right-hand side of the equation equal to the left-hand side of the equation.

Equation	Solution(s)	Check
$p + 3 = 11$	$p = 8$	$(8) + 3 \overset{?}{=} 11$
		$11 = 11 \checkmark$
$w^2 = 9$	$w = 3 \quad$ and $\quad w = -3$	$(3)^2 \overset{?}{=} 9 \qquad (-3)^2 \overset{?}{=} 9$
		$9 = 9 \checkmark \qquad\quad 9 = 9 \checkmark$
$-\dfrac{5}{x} + \dfrac{1}{3} = 0$	$x = 15$	$-\dfrac{5}{15} + \dfrac{1}{3} \overset{?}{=} 0$
		$-\dfrac{1}{3} + \dfrac{1}{3} \overset{?}{=} 0 \checkmark$

The set of all solutions to an equation is called the **solution set**. Hence the solution set for $p + 3 = 11$ is $\{8\}$, the solution set for $w^2 = 9$ is $\{-3, 3\}$, and the solution set for $-\frac{5}{x} + \frac{1}{3} = 0$ is $\{15\}$.

After studying the material in this text, you will be proficient at recognizing and solving a wide variety of algebraic equations. In this chapter we will focus on a specific type of equation called a linear equation in one variable.

Definition of a Linear Equation in One Variable

Let a and b be real numbers such that $a \neq 0$. A **linear equation in one variable** is an equation that can be written in the form:

$$ax + b = 0$$

2.   Solving Linear Equations

To solve a linear equation, the goal is to simplify the equation to isolate the variable. Each step used in simplifying an equation results in an equivalent equation. *Equivalent equations* have the same solution set. For example, the equations $2x + 3 = 7$ and $2x = 4$ are equivalent because $x = 2$ is the solution to both equations.

To simplify an equation, we may use the addition, subtraction, multiplication, and division properties of equality. These properties state that adding, subtracting, multiplying, or dividing the same quantity on each side of an equation results in an equivalent equation.

Addition and Subtraction Properties of Equality

Let a, b, and c represent real numbers.

Addition property of equality: If $a = b$, then $a + c = b + c$

Subtraction property of equality: If $a = b$, then $a - c = b - c$

Multiplication and Division Properties of Equality

Let a, b, and c represent real numbers.

Multiplication property of equality: If $a = b$, then $a \cdot c = b \cdot c$

Division property of equality: If $a = b$, then $\dfrac{a}{c} = \dfrac{b}{c}$ (provided $c \neq 0$)

---

example 1   **Solving Linear Equations**

Solve each equation.

a. $12 + x = 40$ b. $-\dfrac{1}{5}p = 2$ c. $4 = \dfrac{w}{2.2}$ d. $-x = 6$

Solution:

a. $12 + x = 40$

$12 - 12 + x = 40 - 12$ To isolate x, subtract 12 from both sides.

$x = 28$ Simplify.

Check: $12 + x = 40$ Check the solution in the original equation.

$12 + (28) \overset{?}{=} 40$

$40 = 40 \checkmark$ True statement

b. $-\dfrac{1}{5}p = 2$

$-5\left(-\dfrac{1}{5}p\right) = -5(2)$ To isolate p, multiply both sides by -5.

$p = -10$ Simplify.

Check: $-\dfrac{1}{5}p = 2$ Check the solution in the original equation.

$$-\dfrac{1}{5}(-10) \overset{?}{=} 2$$

$$2 = 2 \checkmark$$ True statement

c. $4 = \dfrac{w}{2.2}$

$$2.2(4) = \left(\dfrac{w}{2.2}\right) \cdot 2.2$$ To isolate w, multiply both sides by 2.2.

$$8.8 = w$$ Simplify.

Check: $4 = \dfrac{w}{2.2}$ Check the solution in the original equation.

$$4 \overset{?}{=} \dfrac{8.8}{2.2}$$

$$4 = 4 \checkmark$$ True statement

d. $-x = 6$

$$-1(-x) = -1(6)$$ To isolate x, multiply both sides by -1.

$$x = -6$$ Simplify.

Check: $-x = 6$ Check the solution in the original equation.

$$-(-6) \overset{?}{=} 6$$

$$6 = 6 \checkmark$$ True statement

For more complicated linear equations, several steps are required to isolate the variable. These steps are listed below:

Steps to Solve a Linear Equation in One Variable

1. Consider clearing fractions or decimals (if any are present) by multiplying both sides of the equation by a common denominator of all terms.
2. Simplify both sides of the equation by clearing parentheses and combining *like* terms.
3. Use the addition and subtraction properties of equality to collect the variable terms on one side of the equation.
4. Use the addition and subtraction properties of equality to collect the constant terms on the other side of the equation.
5. Use the multiplication and division properties of equality to make the coefficient of the variable term equal to 1.
6. Check your answer.

example 2   **Solving Linear Equations**

Solve the linear equations and check the answers.

a. $11z + 2 = 5(z - 2)$ b. $-3(x - 4) + 2 = 7 - (x + 1)$

c. $4[y - 3(y - 5)] = 2(6 - 5y)$

Solution:

a. $11z + 2 = 5(z - 2)$

           $11z + 2 = 5z - 10$ Clear parentheses.

      $11z - 5z + 2 = 5z - 5z - 10$ Subtract $5z$ from both sides.

           $6z + 2 = -10$ Combine *like* terms.

      $6z + 2 - 2 = -10 - 2$ Subtract 2 from both sides.

           $6z = -12$

           $\dfrac{6z}{6} = \dfrac{-12}{6}$ To isolate z, divide both sides of the equation by 6.

           $z = -2$ Simplify.

Check: $11z + 2 = 5(z - 2)$ Check the solution in the original equation.

           $11(-2) + 2 \overset{?}{=} 5(-2 - 2)$

           $-22 + 2 \overset{?}{=} 5(-4)$

           $-20 = -20$ ✓   True statement

b. $-3(x - 4) + 2 = 7 - (x + 1)$

      $-3x + 12 + 2 = 7 - x - 1$ Clear parentheses.

           $-3x + 14 = -x + 6$ Combine *like* terms.

      $-3x + x + 14 = -x + x + 6$ Add x to both sides of the equal sign.

           $-2x + 14 = 6$ Combine *like* terms.

      $-2x + 14 - 14 = 6 - 14$ Subtract 14 from both sides.

           $-2x = -8$

           $\dfrac{-2x}{-2} = \dfrac{-8}{-2}$ To isolate x, divide both sides by -2.

           $x = 4$ Simplify.

Check: $-3(x - 4) + 2 = 7 - (x + 1)$ Check the solution in the original equation.

           $-3(4 - 4) + 2 \overset{?}{=} 7 - (4 + 1)$

$$-3(0) + 2 \overset{?}{=} 7 - (5)$$

$$0 + 2 \overset{?}{=} 2$$

$$2 = 2 ✓ \qquad \text{True statement}$$

c. $\quad -4[y - 3(y - 5)] = 2(6 - 5y)$

$-4[y - 3y + 15] = 12 - 10y$	Clear parentheses and combine *like* terms.
$-4[-2y + 15] = 12 - 10y$	Combine *like* terms.
$8y - 60 = 12 - 10y$	Clear parentheses.
$8y + 10y - 60 = 12 - 10y + 10y$	Add $10y$ to both sides of the equal sign.
$18y - 60 = 12$	Combine *like* terms.
$18y - 60 + 60 = 12 + 60$	Add 60 to both sides of the equal sign.
$18y = 72$	
$\dfrac{18y}{18} = \dfrac{72}{18}$	To isolate y, divide both sides by 18.
$y = 4$	Simplify.

Check: $\quad -4[y - 3(y - 5)] = 2(6 - 5y)$

$$-4[4 - 3(4 - 5)] \overset{?}{=} 2(6 - 5(4))$$

$$-4[4 - 3(-1)] \overset{?}{=} 2(6 - 20)$$

$$-4[4 + 3] \overset{?}{=} 2(-14)$$

$$-4(7) \overset{?}{=} -28$$

$$-28 = -28 ✓ \qquad \text{True statement}$$

3. Clearing Fractions and Decimals

When an equation contains fractions or decimals, it is sometimes helpful to clear the fractions and decimals. This is accomplished by multiplying both sides of the equation by the least common denominator (LCD) of all terms within the equation. This is demonstrated in Example 3.

example 3

Solving Linear Equations by Clearing Fractions

Solve the equation:

$$\frac{1}{4}w + \frac{1}{3}w - 1 = \frac{1}{2}(w - 4)$$

Solution:

$$\frac{1}{4}w + \frac{1}{3}w - 1 = \frac{1}{2}(w - 4)$$

The LCD of all terms in the equation is 12.

$$12 \cdot \left(\frac{1}{4}w + \frac{1}{3}w - 1\right) = 12 \cdot \frac{1}{2}(w - 4)$$

Multiply both sides by 12 to clear fractions.

$$12 \cdot \frac{1}{4}w + 12 \cdot \frac{1}{3}w - 12 \cdot 1 = 6 \cdot (w - 4)$$

Apply the distributive property on the left.

On the right, simplify $12 \cdot \frac{1}{2} = 6$.

<table>
<tr><td></td></tr>
</table>

> ⬡ **Avoiding Mistakes**
>
> Notice that on the right-hand side of this equation, the product of 12 and $\frac{1}{2}$ is taken first, and then the result of 6 is distributed through the parentheses.

$$3w + 4w - 12 = 6w - 24$$

$$7w - 12 = 6w - 24$$

$$7w - 6w - 12 = 6w - 6w - 24$$

$$w - 12 = -24$$

$$w - 12 + 12 = -24 + 12$$

Add 12 to both sides.

$$w = -12$$

Check:

$$\frac{1}{4}w + \frac{1}{3}w - 1 = \frac{1}{2}(w - 4)$$

$$\frac{1}{4}(-12) + \frac{1}{3}(-12) - 1 \overset{?}{=} \frac{1}{2}(-12 - 4)$$

$$-3 - 4 - 1 \overset{?}{=} \frac{1}{2}(-16)$$

$$-8 = -8 \checkmark$$

True statement

Tip: The fractions in this equation can be eliminated by multiplying both sides of the equation by *any* common multiple of the denominators. For example, multiplying both sides of the equation by 24 produces the same solution.

$$24 \cdot \left(\frac{1}{4}w + \frac{1}{3}w - 1\right) = 24 \cdot \frac{1}{2}(w - 4)$$

$$6w + 8w - 24 = 12(w - 4)$$

$$14w - 24 = 12w - 48$$

$$2w = -24$$

$$w = -12$$

The same procedure used to clear fractions in an equation can be used to clear decimals.

example 4

Solving Linear Equations by Clearing Decimals

Solve the equation $0.05x - 0.1 = 2.05x$

Solution:
Recall that any terminating decimal can be written as a fraction. Therefore, the equation $0.05x - 0.1 = 2.05x$ is equivalent to

$$\frac{5}{100}x - \frac{1}{10} = \frac{205}{100}x$$

A convenient common denominator for all terms in this equation is 100. Multiplying both sides of the equation by 100 will have the effect of "moving" the decimal point two places to the right.

$$100(0.05x - 0.1) = 100(2.05x) \qquad \text{Multiply both sides by 100 to clear decimals.}$$

$$5x - 10 = 205x$$

$$5x - 5x - 10 = 205x - 5x \qquad \text{Subtract } 5x \text{ from both sides.}$$

$$-10 = 200x$$

$$\frac{-10}{200} = \frac{200x}{200} \qquad \text{To isolate } x, \text{ divide both sides by 200.}$$

$$-\frac{10}{200} = x$$

$$x = -\frac{1}{20} \qquad \text{or} \qquad x = -0.05$$

Check: $\qquad 0.05x - 0.1 = 2.05x$

$$0.05(-0.05) - 0.1 \overset{?}{=} 2.05(-0.05)$$

$$-0.0025 - 0.1 \overset{?}{=} -0.1025$$

$$-0.1025 = -0.1025 \checkmark \qquad \text{True statement}$$

4. Conditional Equations, Contradictions, and Identities

The solutions to a linear equation are the values of x that make the equation a true statement. A linear equation may have one unique solution, no solution, or an infinite number of solutions.

I. Conditional Equations

An equation that is true for some values of the variable but false for other values is called a **conditional equation**. The equation $x + 4 = 6$, is a conditional equation because it is true on the *condition* that $x = 2$. For other values of x, the statement $x + 4 = 6$ is false.

II. Contradictions

Some equations have no solution, such as $x + 1 = x + 2$. There is no value of x, that when increased by 1 will equal the same value increased by 2. If we tried to solve the equation by subtracting x from both sides, we get the contradiction $1 = 2$. This indicates that the equation has no solution. An equation that has no solution is called a **contradiction**.

$$x + 1 = x + 2$$
$$x - x + 1 = x - x + 2$$
$$1 = 2 \quad \text{(contradiction)} \qquad \text{No solution}$$

III. Identities

An equation that has all real numbers as its solution set is called an **identity**. For example, consider the equation, $x + 4 = x + 4$. Because the left- and right-hand sides are *identical*, any real number substituted for x will result in equal quantities on both sides. If we solve the equation, we get the identity $4 = 4$. In such a case, the solution is the set of all real numbers.

$$x + 4 = x + 4$$
$$x - x + 4 = x - x + 4$$
$$4 = 4 \quad \text{(identity)} \qquad \text{The solution is all real numbers.}$$

---

example 5   **Identifying Conditional Equations, Contradictions, and Identities**

Solve the equations. Identify each equation as a conditional equation, a contradiction, or an identity.

a. $3[x - (x + 1)] = -2$ b. $5(3 + c) + 2 = 2c + 3c + 17$

c. $4x - 3 = 17$

Solution:

a. $3[x - (x + 1)] = -2$

$\quad\quad 3[x - x - 1] = -2$ Clear parentheses.

$\quad\quad\quad\quad 3[-1] = -2$ Combine *like* terms.

$\quad\quad\quad\quad\quad -3 = -2$ Contradiction

This equation is a contradiction. There is no solution.

b. $5(3 + c) + 2 = 2c + 3c + 17$

$\quad 15 + 5c + 2 = 5c + 17$ Clear parentheses and combine *like* terms.

$\quad\quad 5c + 17 = 5c + 17$ Identity

$\quad\quad\quad\quad 0 = 0$

This equation is an identity. The solution is the set of all real numbers.

c. $4x - 3 = 17$

$4x - 3 + 3 = 17 + 3$ Add 3 to both sides.

$4x = 20$

$\dfrac{4x}{4} = \dfrac{20}{4}$ To isolate x, divide both sides by 4.

$x = 5$

This equation is a conditional equation. The solution is $x = 5$.

---

section 1.4   PRACTICE EXERCISES

For Exercises 1–4, simplify using the order of operations.

1. $-2 \div 2 \cdot 5(6 - 8)$ 2. $4^2 + 3(4 - 10) + 2^3$

3. $\dfrac{|5 - 6|}{3(5 - 7)}$ 4. $\dfrac{\sqrt{5^2 - 4^2}}{|2 - 5|}$

For Exercises 5–8, clear parentheses and combine *like* terms.

5. $8x - 3y + 2xy - 5x + 12xy$

6. $5ab + 5a - 13 - 2a + 17$

7. $2(3z - 4) - (z + 12)$

8. $-(6w - 5) + 3(4w - 5)$

For Exercises 9–14, label the equation as linear or nonlinear. If an equation is linear, write it in the form $ax + b = 0$.

9. $2x + 1 = 5$ 10. $10 = x + 6$

11. $x^2 + 7 = 9$ 12. $3 + x^3 - x = 4$

13. $\dfrac{1}{x} + 2 = 6$ 14. $5.2 - 7x = 0$

15. For the equation $2x - 1 = 5$, determine if any of the following are solutions.

    a. 2   b. 3   c. 0   d. -1

16. For the equation $2y - 3 = -2$, determine if any of the following are solutions.

    a. 1   b. $\dfrac{1}{2}$ c. 0   d. $-\dfrac{1}{2}$

For Exercises 17–36, solve the equations and check your solutions.

17. $x + 7 = 19$ 18. $-3 + y = -28$

19. $64x = -2$ 20. $\dfrac{t}{8} = -\dfrac{3}{4}$

21. $-\dfrac{7}{8} = -\dfrac{5}{6}z$ 22. $-\dfrac{12}{13} = 4b$

23. $a + \dfrac{2}{5} = 2$ 24. $-\dfrac{3}{8} + x = -\dfrac{7}{24}$

25. $2.53 = -2.3t$ 26. $-4.8 = 6.1 + y$

27. $p - 2.9 = 3.8$ 28. $-4.2a = 4.494$

29. $6q - 4 = 62$ 30. $2w - 15 = 15$

31. $4y - 17 = 35$ 32. $6z - 25 = 83$

33. $-5b + 9 = -71$ 34. $-3x + 18 = -66$

35. $16 = -10 + 13x$ 36. $15 = -12 + 9x$

For Exercises 37–38, solve the equations in two ways: (a) Use the distributive property first to clear the parentheses. (b) Clear the fractions first by multiplying each side of the equation by the least common denominator.

37. $\dfrac{1}{3}(3x + 6) = 7$ 38. $\dfrac{3}{4}(8 - 4x) = -3$

39. a. Simplify the expression $-2(y - 1) + 3(y + 2)$

    b. Solve the equation $-2(y - 1) + 3(y + 2) = 0$

    c. Explain the difference between simplifying an expression and solving an equation.

40. a. Simplify the expression $4w - 8(2 + w)$

    b. Solve the equation $4w - 8(2 + w) = 0$

    c. Explain the difference between simplifying an expression and solving an equation.

41. What is a conditional equation?

42. Explain the difference between a contradiction and an identity.

For Exercises 43–48, solve the following equations. Then label each as a conditional equation, a contradiction, or an identity.

43. $4x + 1 = 2(2x + 1) - 1$ 44. $3x + 6 = 3x$

45. $-11x + 4(x - 3) = -2x - 12$

46. $2x - 4 + 8x = 7x - 8 + 3x$

47. $5(x + 2) - 7 = 3$

48. $-7x + 8 + 4x = -3(x - 3) - 1$

For Exercises 49–70, solve the equations.

49. $10c + 3 = -3 + 12c$ 50. $2w + 21 = 6w - 7$

51. $12b - 15b - 8 + 6 = 4b + 6 - 1$

52. $4z + 2 - 3z + 5 = 3 + z + 4$

53. $5(x - 2) - 2x = 3x + 7$

54. $2x + 3(x - 5) = 15$

55. $\dfrac{c}{2} - \dfrac{c}{4} + \dfrac{3c}{8} = 1$ 56. $\dfrac{d}{5} - \dfrac{d}{10} + \dfrac{5d}{20} = \dfrac{7}{10}$

57. $0.75(8x - 4) = \dfrac{2}{3}(6x - 9)$

58. $-\dfrac{1}{2}(4z - 3) = -z$

59. $7(p + 2) - 4p = 3p + 14$

60. $6(z - 2) = 3z - 8 + 3z$

61. $4[3 + 5(3 - b) + 2b] = 6 - 2b$

62. $5x - (8 - x) = 2[-4 - (3 + 5x) - 13]$

63. $3 - \dfrac{3}{4}x = 9$ 64. $\dfrac{2}{3} - \dfrac{x + 2}{6} = \dfrac{5x - 2}{2}$

65. $\dfrac{2y - 9}{10} + \dfrac{3}{2} = y$ 66. $\dfrac{2}{3}x - \dfrac{5}{6}x - 3 = \dfrac{1}{2}x - 5$

67. $0.48x - 0.08x = 0.12(260 - x)$

68. $0.07w + 0.06(140 - w) = 90$

69. $0.5x + 0.25 = \dfrac{1}{3}x + \dfrac{5}{4}$

70. $0.2b + \dfrac{1}{3} = \dfrac{7}{15}$

EXPANDING YOUR SKILLS

For Exercises 71–74, solve the following equations.

71. $\dfrac{3x - 7}{2} + \dfrac{3 - 5x}{3} = \dfrac{3 - 6x}{5}$

72. $\dfrac{2y - 4}{5} = \dfrac{5y + 13}{4} + \dfrac{y}{2}$

73. $\dfrac{4}{3}(2q + 6) - \dfrac{5q - 6}{6} - \dfrac{q}{3} = 0$

74. $\dfrac{-3a + 9}{15} - \dfrac{2a - 5}{5} - \dfrac{a + 2}{10} = 0$

chapter 1   MIDCHAPTER REVIEW

1. Let $A = \left\{-7.1, -5\pi, -2, -\frac{1}{8}, 0, 0.\overline{3}, \sqrt{2}, \frac{7}{8}, 6, \frac{9}{2}\right\}$

   a. List all numbers from A that are rational numbers.

   b. List all numbers from A that are natural numbers.

   c. List all numbers from A that are real numbers.

   d. List all numbers from A that are irrational numbers.

   e. List all numbers from A that are whole numbers.

2. Match the following diagrams with the appropriate sets.

   a. $A \cup B$

   b. $A \cap B \cap C$

   c. $B \cup C$

   d. $C \cap B$

   e. $(A \cup B) \cap C$

   f. $A \cap B$

   i.

   ii.

   iii.

   iv.

   v.

   vi.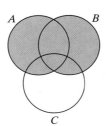

For Exercises 3–12, use the order of operations to simplify the expression.

3. $-\sqrt{4} + |-5| + \sqrt{25}$

4. $|-3| + 2^3 - (-2^2)$

5. $\left(-\frac{5}{3} - \frac{1}{3}\right) \div \frac{5}{3}$

6. $-\frac{5}{6} - \left(-\frac{4}{3} - \frac{2}{5}\right)$

7. $-6 - 5(-8) + (-5)^2$

8. $-7(-3) - (-2^3)$

9. $3(-5) + 7(-5) - 4(2)$

10. $(3^2 \cdot 2 - 8) \div 5$

11. $2\sqrt{100} - 10 \div 5$

12. $-8[4 + (-2^2 \cdot 3)]$

For Exercises 13–22, identify each exercise as an expression or an equation. Then simplify the expressions and solve the equations.

13. $13 + x = -21$

14. $0.29a + 4.495 - 0.12a$

15. $5x + 4 - 6x - 8$

16. $\frac{b}{4} + 21 = 38$

17. $7(2 + 4n) = 11 - 4n$

18. $\frac{1}{8}(2p - 8) = \frac{1}{4}(p - 4)$

19. $7 + 8b - 12 = 3b - 8 + 5b$

20. $0.09q + 0.10(5000 + 3q)$

21. $\frac{1}{2}c - \frac{2}{5} + \frac{1}{10}(c + 2)$

22. $2[3(3 - y) + 2] = 6 - 2y$

For Exercises 23–28, graph the sets and express each set in interval notation.

23. $\{x \mid x > -3\}$

24. $\{x \mid x \geq 6\}$

25. $\{x \mid x \leq 2\frac{1}{2}\}$

26. $\{x \mid x < 4.8\}$

27. $\{x \mid x < 0\} \cup \{x \mid x > 4\}$

28. $\{x \mid x \leq 13\} \cap \{x \mid x \geq 1\}$

section

1.5   APPLICATIONS OF LINEAR EQUATIONS IN ONE VARIABLE

1. Introduction to Problem Solving

One of the important applications of algebra is to develop mathematical models for understanding real-world phenomena. To solve an application problem, relevant information must be extracted from the wording of a problem and then translated into mathematical symbols. This is a skill that requires practice. The key is to stick with it and not to get discouraged.

Problem-Solving Flowchart for Word Problems

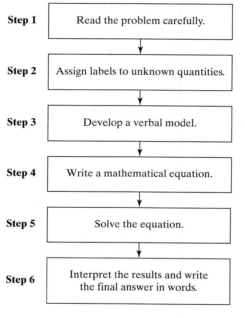

Step 1 | Read the problem carefully.
- Familiarize yourself with the problem. Identify the unknown, and if possible estimate the answer.

Step 2 | Assign labels to unknown quantities.
- Identify the unknown quantity or quantities. Let x represent one of the unknowns. Draw a picture and write down relevant formulas.

Step 3 | Develop a verbal model.
- Write an equation in *words*.

Step 4 | Write a mathematical equation.
- Replace the verbal model with a mathematical equation using x or other variable.

Step 5 | Solve the equation.
- Solve for the variable using the steps for solving linear equations.

Step 6 | Interpret the results and write the final answer in words.
- Once you've obtained a numerical value for the variable, recall what it represents in the context of the problem. Can this value be used to determine other unknowns in the problem? Write an answer to the word problem in *words*.

2. Translations Involving Linear Equations

---

example 1   **Translating and Solving a Linear Equation**

The sum of two numbers is 39. One number is 3 less than twice the other. What are the numbers?

Solution:

Step 1: Read the problem carefully.

Step 2: Let x represent one number.

Let $2x - 3$ represent the other number.

Step 3: (One number) + (Other number) = 39

Step 4: Replace the verbal model with a mathematical equation.

(One number) + (Other number) = 39

$$x \quad + \quad (2x - 3) \quad = 39$$

Step 5: Solve for x:

$$x + (2x - 3) = 39$$
$$3x - 3 = 39$$
$$3x = 42$$
$$\frac{3x}{3} = \frac{42}{3}$$
$$x = 14$$

Step 6: Interpret your results. Refer back to Step 2:

One number is x: $\longrightarrow$ 14

The other number is $2x - 3$:

$$2(14) - 3 \longrightarrow 25$$

Answer: The numbers are 14 and 25.

3. Applications Involving Consecutive Integers

example 2

Solving a Linear Equation Involving Consecutive Integers

The sum of two consecutive odd integers is -172. Find the integers.

Solution:

Step 1: Two consecutive odd integers differ by 2. For example, the pairs of numbers 1, 3 and -11, -9 are examples of consecutive odd integers.

Step 2: Label unknowns:

Let x represent the first integer.

Let $x + 2$ represent the next odd integer.

Step 3: Write an equation in words:

(First integer) + (Second integer) = -172

Step 4: Write a mathematical equation based on the verbal model:

(First integer) + (Second integer) = -172

$$x \quad + \quad (x + 2) \quad = -172$$

Step 5:   Solve for x:

$$x + (x + 2) = -172$$
$$2x + 2 = -172$$
$$2x = -174$$
$$x = -87$$

Step 6:   Interpret your results:

One number is x: ——————————————→ -87

The other integer is $x + 2$:

$$-87 + 2 \text{ ———————————→ } -85$$

Answer: The numbers are -87 and -85.

After completing a word problem, it is always a good idea to check that the answer is reasonable. Notice that -87 and -85 are consecutive odd integers, and the sum is equal to -172 as desired.

4.   Applications Involving Percentages and Rates

In many real-world applications, percentages are used to represent rates:

- In 1998, the sales tax rate in the state of Tennessee was 6%.
- An ice-cream machine is discounted 20%.
- A real estate sales broker receives a $4\frac{1}{2}$% commission on sales.
- A savings account earns 7% simple interest.

The following models are used to compute sales tax, commission, and simple interest. In each case the value is found by multiplying the base by the percentage.

Sales tax = (cost of merchandise)(tax rate)

Commission = (dollars in sales)(commission rate)

Simple interest = (principal)(annual interest rate)(time in years)
$$\text{└—→} I = Prt$$

example 3   **Solving a Percent Application**

A realtor made a 6% commission on a house that sold for \$112,000. How much was her commission?

Solution:

Let x represent the commission.   Label the variables.

(Commission) = (dollars in sales)(commission rate)   Verbal model

$x = (\$112{,}000)(0.06)$ Mathematical model

$x = \$6720$ Solve for x.

The realtor's commission is $6720.   Interpret the results.

---

example 4   **Solving a Percent Application**

A woman invests \$5000 in an account that earns $5\frac{1}{4}\%$ simple interest. If the money is invested for three years how much money is in the account at the end of the three-year period?

Solution:

Let x represent the total money in the account.   Label variables.

$P = \$5000$ (principal amount invested)

$r = 0.0525$ (interest rate)

$t = 3$ (time in years)

The total amount of money includes principal plus interest:

(Total money) = (principal) + (interest)   Verbal model

$x = P + Prt$ Mathematical model

$x = \$5000 + (\$5000)(0.0525)(3)$ Substitute for P, r, and t.

$x = \$5000 + \$787.50$

$x = \$5787.50$ Solve for x.

The total amount of money in the account is \$5787.50.   Interpret the results.

As consumers we often encounter situations in which merchandise has been marked up or marked down from its original cost. It is important to note that percent increase and percent decrease are based on the original cost. For example, suppose a microwave originally priced at \$305 is marked down 20%.

The discount is determined by 20% of the original price: $(0.20)(\$305) = \$61.00$. The new price is: $\$305.00 - \$61.00 = \$244.00$.

5. Applications Involving Percent Increase

example 5

Solving a Percent Increase Application

A college bookstore uses a standard markup of 22% on all books purchased wholesale from the publisher. If the bookstore sells a calculus book for $103.70, what was the original wholesale cost?

Solution:

Let x = original wholesale cost   Label the variables.

The selling price of the book is based on the original cost of the book, plus the bookstore's markup:

(Selling price) = (original price) + (markup)   Verbal model

(Selling price) = (original price) +
                (original price · markup rate)

$103.70 \quad = \quad x \quad + \quad (x)(0.22)$ Mathematical model

$103.70 = x + 0.22x$

$103.70 = 1.22x$ Combine *like* terms.

$\dfrac{103.70}{1.22} = x$

$x = \$85.00$ Simplify.

The original wholesale cost of the textbook was $85.00.   Interpret the results.

6. Applications Involving Principal and Interest

example 6

Solving an Investment Growth Application

Miguel had $10,000 to invest in two different mutual funds. One was a relatively safe bond fund that averaged 8% return on his investment at the end of one year. The other fund was a riskier stock fund that averaged 17% return in one year. If at the end of the year Miguel's portfolio grew to $11,475 ($1475 above his $10,000 investment), how much money did Miguel invest in each fund?

Solution:

This type of word problem is sometimes categorized as a mixture problem. Miguel is "mixing" his money between two different investments. We have to determine how the money was divided to earn $1475 in total growth.

    The information in this problem can be organized in a chart. (*Note:* There are two sources of money: the amount invested and the amount earned in growth.)

	8% Bond Fund	**17% Stock Fund**	**Total**
Amount invested ($)	x	$(10{,}000 - x)$	10,000
Amount earned in growth ($)	$0.08x$	$0.17(10{,}000 - x)$	1475

Because the amount of principal is unknown for both accounts, we can let x represent the amount invested in the bond fund. If Miguel spends x dollars in the bond fund, then he has $(10{,}000 - x)$ left over to spend in the stock fund. The return for each fund is found by multiplying the principal and the percentage growth rate.

To establish a mathematical model, we know that the total return ($1475) must equal the growth from the bond fund plus the growth from the stock fund:

(Growth from bond fund) + (growth from stock fund) = (total growth)

$$0.08x \qquad + \qquad 0.17(10{,}000 - x) \qquad = \qquad 1475$$

$0.08x + 0.17(10{,}000 - x) = 1475$	Mathematical model
$8x + 17(10{,}000 - x) = 147{,}500$	Multiply by 100 to clear decimals.
$8x + 170{,}000 - 17x = 147{,}500$	
$-9x + 170{,}000 = 147{,}500$	Combine *like* terms.
$-9x = -22{,}500$	Subtract 170,000 from both sides.
$\dfrac{-9x}{-9} = \dfrac{-22{,}500}{-9}$	
$x = 2500$	Solve for x and interpret the results.

The amount invested in the bond fund is $2500. The amount invested in the stock fund is $10{,}000 - x$ or $7500.

7. Applications Involving Mixtures

example 7

Solving a Mixture Application

How many liters of a 60% antifreeze solution must be added to 8 L of a 10% antifreeze solution to produce a 20% antifreeze solution?

Solution:

The given information is illustrated in Figure 1-7:

Figure 1-7

The information can be organized in a chart. Notice that an algebraic equation is derived from the second row of the table which relates the number of liters of pure antifreeze in each container.

	60% Antifreeze	**10% Antifreeze**	**Final Solution: 20% Antifreeze**
Number of liters of solution	x	8	$(8 + x)$
Number of liters of pure antifreeze	$0.60x$	$0.10(8)$	$0.20(8 + x)$

The amount of pure antifreeze in the final solution equals the sum of the amounts of antifreeze in the first two solutions.

$$\left(\begin{array}{c}\text{Pure antifreeze}\\\text{from solution 1}\end{array}\right) + \left(\begin{array}{c}\text{Pure antifreeze}\\\text{from solution 2}\end{array}\right) = \left(\begin{array}{c}\text{Pure antifreeze}\\\text{in the final solution}\end{array}\right)$$

$$0.60x \qquad + \qquad 0.10(8) \qquad = \qquad 0.20(8 + x)$$

$0.60x + 0.10(8) = 0.20(8 + x)$ Mathematical model

$0.6x + 0.8 = 1.6 + 0.2x$ Apply the distributive property.

$0.6x - 0.2x + 0.8 = 1.6 + 0.2x - 0.2x$ Subtract $0.2x$ from both sides.

$0.4x + 0.8 = 1.6$

$0.4x + 0.8 - 0.8 = 1.6 - 0.8$ Subtract 0.8 from both sides.

$0.4x = 0.8$

$\dfrac{0.4x}{0.4} = \dfrac{0.8}{0.4}$ Divide both sides by 0.4.

$x = 2$

Answer: 2 L of 60% antifreeze solution is necessary to make a final solution of 20% antifreeze.

■

8. Applications Involving Distance, Rate, and Time

The fundamental relationship among the variables distance, rate, and time is given by:

$$\textbf{Distance = (rate)(time)} \qquad \text{or} \qquad \textbf{d = rt}$$

For example, a motorist traveling 65 mph (miles per hour) for 3 h (hours) will travel a distance of:

$$d = (65 \text{ mph})(3 \text{ h}) = 195 \text{ miles}$$

---

example 8

Solving a Distance, Rate, Time Application

A hiker can hike $2\frac{1}{2}$ mph down a trail to visit Archuletta Lake. For the return trip back to her campsite (uphill), she is only able to go $1\frac{1}{2}$ mph. If the total time for the round trip is 4 h and 48 min (4.8 h), find:

a.   The time required to walk down to the lake
b.   The time required to return back to the campsite
c.   The total distance the hiker traveled

Solution:

The information given in the problem can be organized in a chart.

	Distance (miles)	Rate (mph)	Time (h)
Trip to the lake		2.5	t
Return trip		1.5	$(4.8 - t)$

Column 2: The rates of speed going to and from the lake are given in the statement of the problem.

Column 3: There are two unknown times. If we let t be the time required to go to the lake, then the time for the return trip must equal the total time minus t, $(4.8 - t)$

Column 1: To express the distance in terms of the time, t, we use the relationship $d = rt$. That is, multiply the quantities in the second and third columns.

	Distance (miles)	Rate (mph)	Time (h)
Trip to the lake	$2.5t$	2.5	t
Return trip	$1.5(4.8 - t)$	1.5	$(4.8 - t)$

To create a mathematical model, note that the distances to and from the lake are equal. Therefore:

$$\text{(Distance to lake)} = \text{(return distance)} \qquad \text{Verbal model}$$

$$2.5t = 1.5(4.8 - t) \qquad \text{Mathematical model}$$

$$2.5t = 7.2 - 1.5t \qquad \text{Apply the distributive property.}$$

$$2.5t + 1.5t = 7.2 - 1.5t + 1.5t \qquad \text{Add } 1.5t \text{ to both sides.}$$

$$4.0t = 7.2$$

$$\frac{4.0t}{4.0} = \frac{7.2}{4.0}$$

$$t = 1.8 \qquad \text{Solve for } t \text{ and interpret the results.}$$

Answers:

a. Because t represents the time required to go down to the lake, then 1.8 h is required for the trip to the lake.

b. The time required for the return trip is $(4.8 - t)$ or $(4.8 \text{ h} - 1.8 \text{ h}) = 3$ h. Therefore, the time required to return to camp is 3 h.

c. The total distance equals the distance to the lake and back. The distance to the lake is (2.5 mph)(1.8 h) = 4.5 miles. The distance back is (1.5 mph) (3.0 h) = 4.5 miles. Therefore, the total distance the hiker walked is 9.0 miles.

---

section 1.5   PRACTICE EXERCISES

For Exercises 1–10, solve the equations.

1. $7a - 2 = 11$

2. $2z + 6 = -15$

3. $4(x - 3) + 7 = 19$

4. $-3(y - 5) + 4 = 1$

5. $5(b + 4) - 3(2b + 8) = 3b$

6. $12c - 3c + 9 = 3(4 + 7c) - c$

7. $\dfrac{3}{8}p + \dfrac{3}{4} = p - \dfrac{3}{2}$

8. $\dfrac{1}{4} - 2x = 5$

9. $0.085(5)d - 0.075(4)d = 1250$

10. $0.50(1.5 - e) + 1.00e = 0.75(1.5)$

For the remaining exercises, follow the steps outlined in the Problem-Solving Flowchart found on page 46.

For Exercises 11–18, refer to Examples 1 and 2.

11. The larger of two numbers is 3 more than twice the smaller. The difference of the larger number and the smaller number is 8. Find the numbers.

12. One number is 3 less than another. Their sum is 15. Find the numbers.

13. The sum of 3 times a number and 2 is the same as the difference of the number and 4. Find the number.

14. Twice the sum of a number and 3 is the same as 1 subtracted from the number. Find the number.

15. The sum of three consecutive integers is −57. Find the integers.

16. Five times the smallest of three consecutive even integers is 10 more than twice the largest. Find the integers.

17. The sum of two integers is 30. Ten times one integer is 5 times the other integer. Find the integers. (*Hint:* If one number is x, then the other number is $30 - x$.)

18. The sum of two integers is 10. Three times one integer is 3 less than 8 times the other integer. Find the integers. (*Hint:* If one number is x, then the other number is $10 - x$.)

For Exercises 19–26, refer to Examples 3 and 4 to solve these problems involving percent.

19. If Ivory Soap is $99\frac{44}{100}$% pure, then what quantity of impurities will be found in a bar of Ivory Soap that weighs 4.5 oz (ounces)?

20. The following figure illustrates the number of votes received for Bill Clinton, Bob Dole, and Ross Perot in the 1996 presidential election. Compute the percentage of votes received by each candidate. (Round to the nearest tenth of a percent.)

Number of Votes by Candidate—1996 Presidential Election

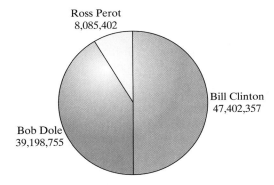

Figure for Exercise 20

21. To get a radio installed in a car, the installation and parts add up to $94.93. If the total bill is $100.63 including tax, what is the sales tax rate?

22. Wayne County has a sales tax rate of 7%. How much does Mike's Honda Civic cost before tax if the total cost of the car *plus tax* is $13,888.60?

23. An account executive earns $600 per month plus a 3% commission on sales. The executive's goal is to earn $2400 this month. How much must she sell to achieve this goal?

24. If a salesperson in a department store sells merchandise worth over $200 in one day, she receives a 12% commission on the sales over $200. If the sales total $424 on one particular day, how much commission did she earn?

25. Molly had the choice of taking out a 4-year car loan at 8.5% simple interest or a 5-year car loan at 7.75% simple interest. If she wishes to borrow $15,000, which option would demand less interest?

26. Robert can take out a 3-year loan at 8% simple interest or a 2-year loan at $8\frac{1}{2}$% simple interest. If he wishes to borrow $7000, which option would demand less interest?

For Exercises 27–30, refer to Example 5 to solve these percent increase or decrease problems. Round the answers to the nearest percent.

27. The price of a swimsuit increased from $34.99 to $39.49. What is the percent increase?

28. The price of a used text is $29.99 and the original price was $45.99. What is the percent decrease?

29. In 1996 the number of people that lived under the poverty level in the United States was 36,529,000. This number decreased to 35,574,000 in 1997. What is the percent decrease? (*Source: U.S. Bureau of the Census*)

30. The total number of physicians in the United States went from 720,325 in 1995 to 737,764 in 1996. What is the percent increase? (*Source: American Medical Association*)

For Exercises 31–42 refer to Examples 6 and 7 to solve these mixture problems.

31. For a car to survive a winter in Toronto, the radiator must contain at least 75% antifreeze solution. Jacques' truck has 6 L of 50% antifreeze mixture, some of which must be drained and replaced with pure antifreeze to bring the concentration to the 75% level. How much 50% solution should be drained and replaced by pure antifreeze to have 6 L of 75% antifreeze?

32. How many ounces of water must be added to 20 oz of an 8% salt solution to make a 2% salt solution?

33. Ronald has a 12% solution of the fertilizer Super Grow. How much pure Super Grow should he add to the mixture to get 32 oz of a 17.5% concentration?

34. How many liters of an 18% alcohol solution must be added to a 10% alcohol solution to get 20 L of a 15% alcohol solution?

35. For a performance of the play, *Company,* 375 tickets were sold. The price of the orchestra level seats was $25, and the balcony seats sold for $21. If the total revenue was $8875.00, how many of each type of ticket were sold?

36. Two different teas are mixed to make a blend that will be sold at a fair. Black tea sells for $2.20/lb (pound) and orange pekoe tea sells for $3.00/lb. How much of each should be used to obtain 4 lb of a blend selling for $2.50?

37. A nut mixture consists of almonds and cashews. Almonds are $4.98/lb and cashews are $6.98/lb. How many pounds of each type of nut should be mixed to produce 16 lb selling for $5.73/lb?

38. Two raffles are being held at a potluck dinner fund raiser. One raffle ticket costs $2.00 per ticket for a weekend vacation. The other costs $1.00 per ticket for free passes to a movie theater. If 208 tickets were sold and a total of $320 was received, how many of each type of ticket were sold?

39. Darrell has a total of $12,500 in two accounts. One account pays 8% simple interest per year and the other pays 12% simple interest. If he earned $1160 in the first year, how much did he invest in each account?

40. Lillian had $15,000 invested in two accounts, one paying 9% simple interest and one paying 10% simple interest. How much was invested in each account if the interest after one year is $1432?

41. Ms. Simmons deposited some money in an account paying 5% simple interest and twice that amount in an account paying 6% simple interest. If the total interest from the two accounts is $765 for one year, how much was deposited into each account?

42. Mr. Hall had some money in his bank earning 4.5% simple interest. He had $5000 more deposited in a credit union earning 6% simple interest. If his total interest for one year was $1140, how much did he have in each account?

For Exercises 43–48, refer to Example 8 to solve these problems involving distance, rate, and time.

43. Sarah planned a trip from Daytona Beach to Detroit to visit her family. She was told that the distance from Daytona Beach to Atlanta was approximately $\frac{2}{5}$ of the distance between Daytona and Detroit. If the distance from Daytona to Detroit is approximately 1140 miles, how far is it from Daytona to Atlanta?

44. In Exercise 43, if Sarah travels at an average rate of 50 mph, how long will it take her to reach Atlanta?

45. Two families live $131\frac{1}{4}$ miles apart and want to meet for a picnic. One family has a sports car and drives at an average rate of 60 mph. The other family has an old station wagon, lots of kids, and a dog, so they average only about 45 mph. If the families leave at the same time, how long will it take them to meet?

46. Maria and Shirley hike around a lake. They start from the same point but walk in opposite directions around the 14-mile shoreline. Maria walks 0.8 mph faster than Shirley. How fast does Shirley walk if they meet in $2\frac{1}{2}$ h?

47. Two cars leave from the same place at the same time and drive in opposite directions. One car travels an average of 10 mph faster than the other. After 2 hours, the cars are 280 miles apart. Find the speed of each car.

48. Two cars are 350 km (kilometer) apart and travel toward each other on the same road. One travels 110 kph (kilometers per hour) and the other travels 90 kph. How long will it take the two cars to meet?

section

1.6   LITERAL EQUATIONS AND APPLICATIONS TO GEOMETRY

1.   Applications Involving Perimeter

Some word problems involve the use of geometric formulas such as those listed in the inside front cover of this text.

---

example 1   Solving a Geometry Application

The length of a rectangular corral is 2 ft more than 3 times the width. The corral is situated such that one of its shorter sides is adjacent to a barn and does not require fencing. If the total amount of fencing is 774 ft, then

a.   Find the dimensions of the corral.
b.   Find the cost of fencing the corral if fencing costs $1.95/ft.

Solution:
Read the problem and draw a sketch (Figure 1-8).

Figure 1-8

Let x represent the width.   Label variables.

Let $3x + 2$ represent the length.

To create a verbal model, we might consider using the formula for the perimeter of a rectangle. However, the formula $P = 2L + 2W$ incorporates all four sides of the rectangle. The formula must be modified to include only one factor of the width.

$$\begin{pmatrix} \text{Distance around} \\ \text{three sides} \end{pmatrix} = \begin{pmatrix} \text{two times} \\ \text{the length} \end{pmatrix} + \begin{pmatrix} \text{one times} \\ \text{the width} \end{pmatrix} \quad \text{Verbal model}$$

$$774 \quad\quad = \quad 2(3x + 2) \quad + \quad\quad x \quad\quad \text{Mathematical model}$$

$774 = 2(3x + 2) + x$ Solve for x.

$774 = 6x + 4 + x$ Apply the distributive property.

$774 = 7x + 4$ Combine *like* terms.

$770 = 7x$ Subtract 4 from both sides.

$110 = x$ Divide by 7 on both sides.

$\quad x = 110$ ft

Because x represents the width, the width of the corral is 110 ft. The length is given by

$$3x + 2 \quad \text{or} \quad 3(110) + 2 = 332 \text{ ft} \qquad \text{Interpret the results.}$$

a. The width of the corral is 110 ft and the length is 332 ft. (To check the answer, verify that the three sides add up to 774 ft.)
b. To find the total cost of fencing the three sides, multiply the total amount of fencing times the cost per foot:

(Total cost) = (total feet of fencing)(cost per foot)

$$\text{Total cost} = (774 \text{ ft})(\$1.95/\text{ft})$$

$$= \$1509.30$$

The total cost to fence the three sides is $1509.30.

2. Applications Involving Complementary Angles

example 2

Figure 1-9

Solving a Geometry Application

Two angles are complementary. One angle is 10° less than 4 times the other angle. Find the measures of each angle. Figure 1-9.

Solution:

Let x represent one angle.

Let $4x - 10$ represent the other angle.

Recall that two angles are complementary if their sum is 90°. Therefore, a verbal model is:

(One angle) + (the complement of the angle) = 90° Verbal model

$x + (4x - 10) = 90$ Mathematical equation

$$5x - 10 = 90 \qquad\qquad \text{Solve for } x.$$

$$5x = 100$$

$$x = 20$$

If $x = 20$, then $4x - 10 = 4(20) - 10 = 70$. The two angles are 20° and 70°.

3. Literal Equations

Literal equations (or formulas) are equations that contain several variables. For instance, the formula for the perimeter of a rectangle, $P = 2L + 2W$, is an example of a literal equation. In this equation, P is expressed in terms of L and W. However, in science and other branches of applied mathematics, formulas may be more useful in alternative forms.

For example, the formula $P = 2L + 2W$ can be manipulated to solve for either L or W:

Solve for *L*

$P = 2L + 2W$

$P - 2W = 2L$ Subtract $2W$.

$\dfrac{P - 2W}{2} = L$ Divided by 2.

$L = \dfrac{P - 2W}{2}$

Solve for *W*

$P = 2L + 2W$

$P - 2L = 2W$ Subtract $2L$.

$\dfrac{P - 2L}{2} = W$ Divided by 2.

$W = \dfrac{P - 2L}{2}$

To solve a literal equation for a specified variable, use the addition, subtraction, multiplication, and division properties of equality.

---

example 3

Solving a Literal Equation

The formula for the volume of a rectangular box is $V = LWH$.

a.   Solve the formula $V = LWH$ for W.
b.   Find the value of W if $V = 200$ in.^{3}, $L = 20$ in., and $H = 5$ in. (Figure 1-10).

$V = 200$ in.^{3} $H = 5$ in. $W = ?$ $L = 20$ in.

Figure 1-10

Solution:

a. $V = LWH$ The goal is to isolate the variable W.

$\dfrac{V}{LH} = \dfrac{LWH}{LH}$ Divide both sides by LH.

$\dfrac{V}{LH} = W$ Simplify.

$W = \dfrac{V}{LH}$

b. $W = \dfrac{200 \text{ in.}^3}{(20 \text{ in.})(5 \text{ in.})}$ Substitute $V = 200$ in.^{3}, $L = 20$ in., and $H = 5$ in.

$W = 2$ in.   The width is 2 inches.

---

example 4

Solving a Literal Equation

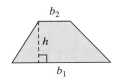

The formula to find the area of a trapezoid is given by: $A = \frac{1}{2}(b_1 + b_2)h$, where b_1 and b_2 are the lengths of the parallel sides and h is the height.
    Solve this formula for b_1.

Solution:

$$A = \tfrac{1}{2}(b_1 + b_2)h \qquad \text{The goal is to isolate } b_1.$$

$$2A = 2 \cdot \tfrac{1}{2}(b_1 + b_2)h \qquad \text{Multiply by 2 to clear fractions.}$$

$$2A = (b_1 + b_2)h \qquad \text{Apply the distributive property.}$$

$$2A = b_1h + b_2h$$

$$2A - b_2h = b_1h \qquad \text{Subtract } b_2h \text{ from both sides.}$$

$$\frac{2A - b_2h}{h} = \frac{b_1h}{h} \qquad \text{Divide by } h.$$

$$\frac{2A - b_2h}{h} = b_1$$

Tip: When solving a literal equation for a specified variable, there is sometimes more than one way to express your final answer. This flexibility often presents difficulty for students. Students may leave their answer in one form, but the answer given in the text looks different. Yet both forms may be correct. To know if your answer is equivalent to the form given in the text, you must try to manipulate it to look like the answer in the book, a process called "form-fitting."

The literal equation from Example 4 may be written in several different forms. The quantity $(2A - b_2h)/h$ can be split into two fractions and reduced. Any of the following forms is a valid representation of b_1:

$$b_1 = \frac{2A - b_2h}{h} = \frac{2A}{h} - \frac{b_2h}{h} = \frac{2A}{h} - b_2$$

example 5   **Solving a Linear Equation in Two Variables**

Given: $-2x + 3y = 5$, solve for y.

Solution:

$$-2x + 3y = 5$$

$$3y = 2x + 5 \qquad \text{Add } 2x \text{ to both sides.}$$

$$\frac{3y}{3} = \frac{2x + 5}{3} \qquad \text{Divide by 3 on both sides.}$$

$$y = \frac{2x + 5}{3} \quad \text{or} \quad y = \frac{2}{3}x + \frac{5}{3} \qquad \text{Simplify.}$$

4. Applications of Literal Equations

example 6

Applying a Literal Equation

Buckingham Fountain is one of Chicago's most familiar landmarks. With 133 jets spraying a total of 14,000 gal (gallons) of water per minute, Buckingham Fountain is one of the world's largest fountains. The circumference of the fountain is approximately 880 ft.

a. The circumference of a circle is given by $C = 2\pi r$. Solve the equation for r.
b. Use the equation from part a to find the radius and diameter of the fountain. (Use the π key on the calculator, and round the answers to one decimal place.)

Solution:

a. $C = 2\pi r$

$\dfrac{C}{2\pi} = \dfrac{2\pi r}{2\pi}$ To isolate r, divide both sides by 2π.

$\dfrac{C}{2\pi} = r$

$r = \dfrac{C}{2\pi}$

b. $r = \dfrac{880 \text{ ft}}{2\pi}$ Substitute $C = 880$ ft and use the π key on the calculator.

$r \approx 140.1 \text{ ft}$

The radius is approximately 140.1 ft. The diameter is twice the radius ($d = 2r$); therefore the diameter is approximately 280.2 ft.

---

section 1.6   PRACTICE EXERCISES

For Exercises 1–4, solve the equations.

1. $7 + 5x - (2x - 6) = 6(x + 1) + 21$

2. $\dfrac{3}{5}y - 3 + 2y = 5$

3. $3[z - (2 - 3z) - 4] = z - 7$

4. $2a - 4 + 8a = 7a - 8 + 3a$

5. The sum of 3 times a number and 1 is the same as the difference of the number and 3. Find the number.

6. The hand soap, Dove, is $\frac{1}{4}$ moisturizing cream. How much of a 4.5-oz bar is something other than moisturizing cream?

7. Jim received a raise of 20% of his old salary. He now makes $21,600 annually. What was his old salary?

8. Two hikers are 20 miles apart walking toward each other. One walks 1 mph faster than the other and they meet in 4 h. Determine how fast each hiker is walking.

9. Nicolas has a collection of 75 old stamps worth $23.40. Some are 34¢ stamps and some are 20¢ stamps. How many of each kind does he have?

10. The total surface area of the earth is approximately 510.072 million km² (square kilometers). Land area is 148.94 million km², and 361.132 million km² is water area.

   a. Find the percentage of earth's surface area that is land. (Round to the nearest tenth of a percent.)

   b. Find the percentage of earth's surface area that is water. (Round to the nearest tenth of a percent.)

For Exercises 11–28, use the geometry formulas listed in the inside front cover of the text.

11. The lengths of the sides of a triangle are given by three consecutive even integers. The perimeter is 24 m (meters). What is the length of each side?

12. A triangular garden has sides that can be represented by three consecutive integers. If the perimeter of the garden is 15 ft, what are the lengths of the sides?

13. Raoul would like to build a rectangular dog run in the rear of his backyard, away from the house. The width of the yard is $11\frac{1}{2}$ yd and Raoul wants an area of 92 yd² (square yards) for his dog.

   a. Find the dimensions of the dog run.

   b. How much fencing would Raoul need to enclose the dog run?

Figure for Exercise 13

14. George built a rectangular pen for his rabbit such that the length is 7 ft less than twice the width. If the perimeter is 40 ft, what are the dimensions of the pen?

15. Antoine wants to put edging in the form of a square around a tree in his front yard. He has enough money to buy 18 ft of edging. Find the dimensions of the square that will use all of the edging.

16. Julie wants to plant a flower garden in her backyard in the shape of a trapezoid adjacent to her house (see figure). She also wants a front yard garden in the same shape, but with sides half as long. What should the dimensions be for each garden if Julie only has a total of 60 ft of fencing?

Figure for Exercise 16

17. Two angles in a triangle are equal. The third angle is 2 times the sum of the equal angles. Find the measures of the three angles.

18. The smallest angle in a triangle is half the size of the largest. This middle angle is 25° less than the largest. Find the measures of the three angles.

19. Two angles are complementary. One angle is 5 times as large as the other angle. Find the measure of each angle.

20. Two angles are supplementary. One angle is 12° less than 3 times the other. Find the measure of each angle.

In Exercises 21–28, solve for x, and then find the measure of each angle.

21.

$(7x - 1)°$ $(2x + 1)°$

22.

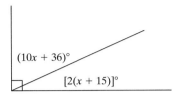

$(10x + 36)°$

$[2(x + 15)]°$

23.

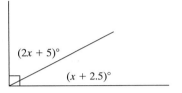

$(2x + 5)°$

$(x + 2.5)°$

24.

$(2x - 3)°$ $[3(x - 7)]°$

25.

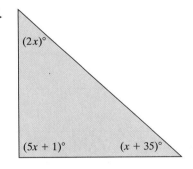

$(2x)°$

$(5x + 1)°$ $(x + 35)°$

26.

$(3x - 3)°$ $[3(5x + 1)]°$

27.

$[4(x - 6)]°$ $(2x - 2)°$

28.

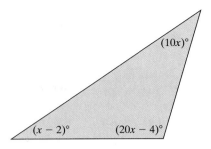

$(10x)°$

$(x - 2)°$ $(20x - 4)°$

29. Which of the expression(s) are equivalent to $-5/(x - 3)$?

a. $-\dfrac{5}{x - 3}$ b. $\dfrac{5}{3 - x}$ c. $\dfrac{5}{-x + 3}$

30. Which of the expression(s) are equivalent to $(z - 1)/-2$?

a. $\dfrac{1 - z}{2}$ b. $-\dfrac{z - 1}{2}$ c. $\dfrac{-z + 1}{2}$

31. Which of the expression(s) are equivalent to $(-x - 7)/y$?

a. $-\dfrac{x + 7}{y}$ b. $\dfrac{x + 7}{-y}$ c. $\dfrac{-x - 7}{-y}$

32. Which of the expression(s) are equivalent to $-3w/(-x - y)$?

a. $-\dfrac{3w}{-x - y}$ b. $\dfrac{3w}{x + y}$ c. $-\dfrac{-3w}{x + y}$

For Exercises 33–46, solve for the indicated variable.

33. $A = lw$ for l 34. $C_1 = \frac{5}{2}R$ for R

35. $I = Prt$ for P 36. $a + b + c = P$ for b

37. $W = K_2 - K_1$ for K_1

38. $y = mx + b$ for x

39. $F = \frac{9}{5}C + 32$ for C

40. $C = \frac{5}{9}(F - 32)$ for F

41. $K = \frac{1}{2}mv^2$ for v^2 42. $I = Prt$ for r

43. $v = v_0 + at$ for a 44. $a^2 + b^2 = c^2$ for b^2

45. $w = p(v_2 - v_1)$ for v_2

46. $A = lw$ for w

For Exercises 47–48, use the relationship between distance, rate, and time given by $d = rt$.

47. a. Solve $d = rt$ for rate, r.

  b. In 1998 Eddie Cheever won the Indianapolis 500 in 3 h, 26 min, 40 s (seconds) (3.444 h). Find his average rate of speed if the total distance is 500 miles. (Round to the nearest tenth of a mile per hour.)

48. a. Solve $d = rt$, for time, t.

  b. In 1998 Jeff Gordon won the Daytona 500 with an average speed of 161.551 mph. Find the time it took him to complete the race if the total distance is 500 miles. (Round to the nearest hundredth of an hour.)

For Exercises 49–50 use the fact that the force imparted by an object is equal to its mass times acceleration, $F = ma$.

49. a. Solve $F = ma$ for mass, m.

  b. The force on an object is 23 N (newtons, expressed as kilogram-meters per second squared) and the acceleration due to gravity is 9.8 m/s². Find the mass of the object. (The answer will be in kilograms. Round to the nearest hundredth of a kilogram.)

50. a. Solve $F = ma$ for acceleration, a.

  b. Approximate the acceleration of a 2000-kg mass influenced by a force of 15,000 N. (The answer will be in meters per second squared, m/s².)

In statistics the z-score formula, $z = (x - \mu)/\sigma$, is used in studying probability. Use this formula for Exercises 51–52.

51. a. Solve $z = (x - \mu)/\sigma$ for x.

  b. Find x when $z = 2.5$, $\mu = 100$, and $\sigma = 12$.

52. a. Solve $z = (x - \mu)/\sigma$ for σ.

  b. Find σ when $x = 150$, $z = 2.5$, and $\mu = 110$.

In Chapter 2 we will need to change equations from the form $ax + by = c$ to $y = mx + b$. To practice this skill, solve the equations for y in Exercises 53–64.

53. $3x + y = 6$

54. $x + y = -4$

55. $5x - 4y = 20$

56. $4x + 5y = 25$

57. $6x + 2y = 13$

58. $5x - 7y = 15$

59. $3x - 3y = 6$

60. $2x - 2y = 8$

61. $9x + \dfrac{4}{3}y = 5$

62. $4x - \dfrac{1}{3}y = 5$

63. $-x + \dfrac{2}{3}y = 0$

64. $x - \dfrac{1}{4}y = 0$

---

section

1.7 LINEAR INEQUALITIES IN ONE VARIABLE

1. Linear Inequalities in One Variable

In Sections 1.4–1.6, we learned how to solve linear equations and their applications. In this section, we will learn the process of solving linear *inequalities*. A **linear inequality** in one variable, x, is defined as any relationship of the form: $ax + b < 0$, $ax + b \leq 0$, $ax + b > 0$, or $ax + b \geq 0$, where $a \neq 0$.

The solution to the equation $x = 3$ can be graphed as a single point on the number line.

Now consider the *inequality* $x \le 3$. The solution set to an inequality is the set of real numbers that makes the inequality a true statement. In this case, the solution set is all real numbers less than or equal to 3. Because the solution set has an infinite number of values, the values cannot be listed. Instead, we can graph the solution set or represent the set in interval notation or in set-builder notation.

Graph   **Interval Notation**   **Set-Builder Notation**

$(-\infty, 3]$ $\{x \mid x \le 3\}$

The addition and subtraction properties of equality indicate that a value added to or subtracted from both sides of an equation results in an equivalent equation. The same is true for inequalities.

2. Addition and Subtraction Properties of Inequality

Addition and Subtraction Properties of Inequality

Let a, b, and c represent real numbers:

*Addition property of inequality:**   If $a < b$,

then $a + c < b + c$

*Subtraction property of inequality:**   If $a < b$

then $a - c < b - c$

*These properties may also be stated for $a \le b$, $a > b$, and $a \ge b$.

---

example 1   **Solving a Linear Inequality**

Solve the inequality. Graph the solution and write the solution set in interval notation.

$$3x - 7 > 2(x - 4) - 1$$

Solution:

$$3x - 7 > 2(x - 4) - 1$$
$$3x - 7 > 2x - 8 - 1 \qquad \text{Apply the distributive property.}$$
$$3x - 7 > 2x - 9$$
$$3x - 2x - 7 > 2x - 2x - 9 \qquad \text{Subtract } 2x \text{ from both sides.}$$
$$x - 7 > -9$$
$$x - 7 + 7 > -9 + 7 \qquad \text{Add 7 to both sides.}$$
$$x > -2$$

Graph   **Interval Notation**

$(-2, \infty)$

3. Multiplication and Division Properties of Inequality

Multiplying both sides of an equation by the same quantity results in an equivalent equation. However, the same is not always true for an inequality. If you multiply or divide an inequality by a *negative* quantity, the direction of the inequality symbol must be *reversed*.

For example, consider multiplying or dividing the inequality, $4 < 5$ by -1.

Multiply/Divide by -1: $4 < 5$

$-4 > -5$

$$-6\ -5\ -4\ -3\ -2\ -1\ \ 0\ \ 1\ \ 2\ \ 3\ \ 4\ \ 5\ \ 6$$

$-4 > -5$ $4 < 5$

The number 4 lies to the left of 5 on the number line. However, -4 lies to the right of -5. Changing the sign of two numbers changes their relative position on the number line. This is stated formally in the multiplication and division properties of inequality.

Multiplication and Division Properties of Inequality

Let a, b, and c represent real numbers, then,

*If c is *positive* and $a < b$, then $ac < bc$ and $\dfrac{a}{c} < \dfrac{b}{c}$

*If c is *negative* and $a < b$, then $ac > bc$ and $\dfrac{a}{c} > \dfrac{b}{c}$

The second statement indicates that if both sides of an inequality are multiplied or divided by a negative quantity, the inequality sign must be *reversed*.

*These properties may also be stated for $a \leq b$, $a > b$, and $a \geq b$.

---

4. Solving Linear Inequalities

example 2

Solving Linear Inequalities

Solve the inequalities. Graph the solution and write the solution set in interval notation.

a. $-2x - 5 < 2$ b. $-6(x - 3) \geq 2 - 2(x - 8)$

Solution:

a. $-2x - 5 < 2$

$-2x - 5 + 5 < 2 + 5$ Add 5 to both sides.

$-2x < 7$

$\dfrac{-2x}{-2} > \dfrac{7}{-2}$ Divide by -2 (*reverse* the inequality sign).

$x > -\dfrac{7}{2}$ or $x > -3.5$

Graph   **Interval Notation**

$-\frac{7}{2}$

$-5 \ -4 \ -3 \ -2 \ -1 \ \ 0 \ \ 1 \ \ 2 \ \ 3 \ \ 4 \ \ 5$

$\left(-\dfrac{7}{2}, \infty\right)$

Tip: The inequality $-2x - 5 < 2$ could have been solved by isolating x on the right-hand side of the inequality. This creates a positive coefficient on the x term and eliminates the need to divide by a negative number.

$-2x - 5 < 2$

$-5 < 2x + 2$ Add $2x$ to both sides.

$-7 < 2x$ Subtract 2 from both sides.

$\dfrac{-7}{2} < \dfrac{2x}{2}$ Divide by 2 (because 2 is positive, do *not* reverse the inequality sign).

$-\dfrac{7}{2} < x$ (Note that the inequality $-\frac{7}{2} < x$ is equivalent to $x > -\frac{7}{2}$.)

b. $-6(x - 3) \geq 2 - 2(x - 8)$

$-6x + 18 \geq 2 - 2x + 16$ Apply the distributive property.

$-6x + 18 \geq 18 - 2x$ Combine *like* terms.

$-6x + 2x + 18 \geq 18 - 2x + 2x$ Add $2x$ to both sides.

$-4x + 18 \geq 18$

$-4x + 18 - 18 \geq 18 - 18$ Subtract 18 from both sides.

$-4x \geq 0$

$\dfrac{-4x}{-4} \leq \dfrac{0}{-4}$ Divide by -4 (*reverse* the inequality sign).

$x \leq 0$

Graph   **Interval Notation**

$-5 \ -4 \ -3 \ -2 \ -1 \ \ 0 \ \ 1 \ \ 2 \ \ 3 \ \ 4 \ \ 5$

$(-\infty, 0]$

example 3

Solving a Linear Inequality

Solve the inequality $\dfrac{-5x + 2}{-3} > x + 2$. Graph the solution and write the solution set in interval notation.

Solution:

$$\frac{-5x + 2}{-3} > x + 2$$

$$-3\left(\frac{-5x + 2}{-3}\right) < -3(x + 2) \qquad \text{Multiply by } -3 \text{ to clear fractions (\textit{reverse} the inequality).}$$

$$-5x + 2 < -3x - 6$$

$$-5x + 3x + 2 < -3x + 3x - 6 \qquad \text{Add } 3x \text{ to both sides.}$$

$$-2x + 2 < -6$$

$$-2x + 2 - 2 < -6 - 2 \qquad \text{Subtract 2 from both sides.}$$

$$-2x < -8$$

$$\frac{-2x}{-2} > \frac{-8}{-2} \qquad \text{Divide by } -2 \text{ (the inequality sign is reversed \textit{again}).}$$

$$x > 4 \qquad \text{Simplify.}$$

Graph   **Interval Notation**

$$(4, \infty)$$

5. Checking Solutions of Inequalities with the Test Point Method

In Example 3, the inequality sign was reversed twice: once for multiplying the inequality by -3 and once for dividing by -5. If you are in doubt about whether you have the inequality sign in the correct direction, you can check your final answer by using the **test point method**. That is, pick a point in the proposed solution set and verify that it makes the original inequality true. Furthermore, any test point picked outside the solution set should make the original inequality false.

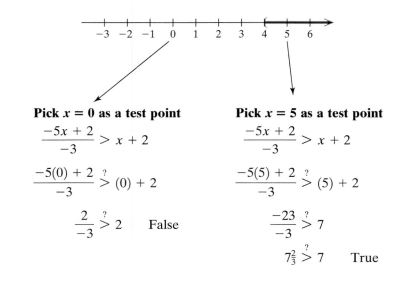

Pick $x = 0$ as a test point

$$\frac{-5x + 2}{-3} > x + 2$$

$$\frac{-5(0) + 2}{-3} \overset{?}{>} (0) + 2$$

$$\frac{2}{-3} \overset{?}{>} 2 \qquad \text{False}$$

Pick $x = 5$ as a test point

$$\frac{-5x + 2}{-3} > x + 2$$

$$\frac{-5(5) + 2}{-3} \overset{?}{>} (5) + 2$$

$$\frac{-23}{-3} \overset{?}{>} 7$$

$$7\tfrac{2}{3} \overset{?}{>} 7 \qquad \text{True}$$

Because a test point to the right of $x = 4$ makes the inequality true, we have shaded the correct part of the number line.

6.   Inequalities of the Form $a < x < b$

An inequality of the form $a < x < b$ is a type of **compound inequality**, one that defines two simultaneous conditions on the quantity x.

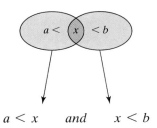

$$a < x \quad and \quad x < b$$

   The solution to the compound inequality $a < x < b$ is the *intersection* of the inequalities $a < x$ and $x < b$. To solve a compound inequality of this form, we can actually work with the inequality as a "three-part" inequality and isolate the variable, x.

---

example 4

Solving a Compound Inequality of the Form $a < x < b$

Solve the inequality: $-2 \le 3x + 1 < 5$. Graph the solution and express the solution set in interval notation.

Solution:
To solve the compound inequality $-2 \le 3x + 1 < 5$, isolate the variable x in the "middle." The operations performed on the middle portion of the inequality must also be performed on the left-hand side and right-hand side.

$$-2 \le 3x + 1 < 5$$

$$-2 - 1 \le 3x + 1 - 1 < 5 - 1 \qquad \text{Subtract 1 from all three parts of the inequality.}$$

$$-3 \le 3x < 4 \qquad \text{Simplify.}$$

$$\frac{-3}{3} \le \frac{3x}{3} < \frac{4}{3} \qquad \text{Divide by 3 in all three parts of the inequality.}$$

$$-1 \le x < \frac{4}{3} \qquad \text{Simplify.}$$

Graph   **Interval Notation**

$$\left[-1, \frac{4}{3} \right)$$

7.   Applications of Inequalities

example 5

Solving a Compound Inequality Application

Beth received grades of 87%, 82%, 96%, and 79% on her last four algebra tests. To graduate with honors, she needs at least a "B" in the course.

a.   What grade does she need to make on the fifth test to get a "B" in the course? Assume that the tests are weighted equally and that to earn a "B" the average of the test grades must be at least 80% but less than 90%.

b.   Is it possible for Beth to earn an "A" in the course if an "A" requires an average of 90% or more?

Solution:

a.   Let x represent the score on the fifth test.

The average of the five tests is given by: $\dfrac{87 + 82 + 96 + 79 + x}{5}$

To earn a "B," Beth requires:

$80 \leq$ (Average of test scores) < 90 Verbal model

$80 \leq \dfrac{87 + 82 + 96 + 79 + x}{5} < 90$ Mathematical model

$5(80) \leq 5\left(\dfrac{87 + 82 + 96 + 79 + x}{5}\right) < 5(90)$ Multiply by 5 to clear fractions.

$400 \leq 344 + x < 450$ Simplify.

$400 - 344 \leq 344 - 344 + x < 450 - 344$ Subtract 344 from all three parts.

$56 \leq x < 106$ Simplify.

To earn a "B" in the course, Beth must score at least 56% but less than 106% on the fifth exam. Realistically, she may score between 56% and 100% because a grade over 100% is not possible.

b.   To earn an "A," Beth's average would have to be greater than or equal to 90%.

(Average of test scores) ≥ 90 Verbal model

$\dfrac{87 + 82 + 96 + 79 + x}{5} \geq 90$ Mathematical equation

$5\left(\dfrac{87 + 82 + 96 + 79 + x}{5}\right) \geq 5(90)$ Clear fractions.

$344 + x \geq 450$ Simplify.

$x \geq 106$ Solve for x.

It would be impossible for Beth to earn an "A" in the course because she would have to earn at least a score of 106% on the fifth test. It is impossible to earn over 100%.

---

example 6

Solving a Linear Inequality Application

The number of registered passenger cars, N, in the United States has risen between 1960 and 1996 according to the equation $N = 2.5t + 64.4$, where t represents the number of years after 1960 ($t = 0$ corresponds to 1960, $t = 1$ corresponds to 1961, and so on). (Figure 1-11.)

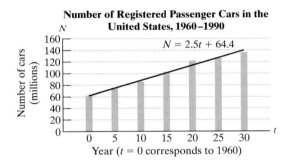

Figure 1-11

(*Source:* U.S. Department of Transportation)

a. For what years after 1960 was the number of registered passenger cars less than 89.4 million?
b. For what years was the number of registered passenger cars between 94.4 million and 101.9 million?
c. Predict the years that the number of passenger cars will exceed 154.4 million.

Solution:

a. We require $N < 89.4$ million.

$$N \qquad < 89.4$$

$$\overbrace{2.5t + 64.4} < 89.4 \qquad \text{Substitute the expression } 2.5t + 64.4 \text{ for } N.$$

$$2.5t + 64.4 - 64.4 < 89.4 - 64.4 \qquad \text{Subtract 64.4 from both sides.}$$

$$2.5t < 25$$

$$\frac{2.5t}{2.5} < \frac{25}{2.5} \qquad \text{Divide both sides by 2.5.}$$

$$t < 10 \qquad t = 10 \text{ corresponds to the year 1970.}$$

Before 1970 (but after 1960), the number of registered passenger cars was less than 89.4 million.

b.   We require $94.4 < N < 101.9$, hence:

$$94.4 < 2.5t + 64.4 < 101.9$$

Substitute the expression $2.5t + 64.4$ for N.

$$94.4 - 64.4 < 2.5t + 64.4 - 64.4 < 101.9 - 64.4$$

Subtract 64.4 from all three parts of the inequality.

$$30.0 < 2.5t < 37.5$$

$$\frac{30.0}{2.5} < \frac{2.5t}{2.5} < \frac{37.5}{2.5}$$

Divide by 2.5.

$$12 < t < 15$$

$t = 12$ corresponds to 1972 and $t = 15$ corresponds to 1975.

Between the years 1972 and 1975, the number of registered passenger cars was between 94.4 million and 101.9 million.

c.   We require $N > 154.4$

$$2.5t + 64.4 > 154.4$$ Substitute the expression $2.5t + 64.4$ for N.

$$2.5t > 90$$ Subtract 64.4 from both sides.

$$\frac{2.5t}{2.5} > \frac{90}{2.5}$$ Divide by 2.5.

$$t > 36$$ $t = 36$ corresponds to the year 1996.

After the year 1996, the number of registered passenger cars is predicted to exceed 154.4 million.

---

section 1.7   PRACTICE EXERCISES

1. Solve for v: $d = vt - 16t^2$

2. Solve for x: $4 + 5(4 - 2x) = -2(x - 1) - 4$

3. Five more than 3 times a number is 6 less than twice the number. Find the number.

4. Solve for y: $5x + 3y + 6 = 0$

5. A total of $900 is invested between two accounts: one paying 7% annual interest and one paying 8% annual interest. After one year the total interest is $67. How much was invested at each rate?

6. a.   The area of a triangle is given by $A = \frac{1}{2}bh$. Solve for h.

b.   If the area of a certain triangle is 10 cm^2 and the base is 3 cm, find the height.

7. Solve for t:

$$\frac{1}{5}t - \frac{1}{2} - \frac{1}{10}t + \frac{2}{5} = \frac{3}{10}t + \frac{1}{2}$$

8. Kesha walked to a store to pick up a bike that she had purchased and then rode the bike home. She averaged 14 mph on her bike and 3.5 mph walking. If the total time walking and biking took one hour, how far is the store from Kesha's home?

For Exercises 9–18, solve the inequalities. Graph the solution and write the solution set in interval notation.

9. $2x - 5 \geq 15$

10. $4z + 2 < 22$

11. $6z + 3 > 16$

12. $8w - 2 \leq 13$

13. $\dfrac{2}{3}t < -8$

14. $\dfrac{1}{5}p + 3 \geq -1$

15. $\dfrac{3}{4}(8y - 9) < 3$

16. $\dfrac{2}{5}(2x - 1) > 10$

17. $0.8a - 0.5 \leq 0.3a - 11$

18. $0.2w - 0.7 < 0.4 - 0.9w$

For Exercises 19–28, solve the inequalities. Recall that multiplication and division by a negative quantity changes the direction of the inequality sign. Graph the solution and write the solution set in interval notation. Check each answer using the test point method.

19. $-5x + 7 < 22$

20. $-3w - 6 > 9$

21. $-\dfrac{5}{6}x \leq -\dfrac{3}{4}$

22. $\dfrac{3k - 2}{-5} \leq 4$

23. $0.2t + 1 > 2.4 - 10$

24. $20 \leq 8 - \dfrac{1}{3}x$

25. $3 - 4(y + 2) \leq 6 + 4(2y + 1)$

26. $1 < 3 - 4(3b - 1)$

27. $7.2k - 51 \geq 5.7$

28. $6h - 2.92 \leq 16.58$

For Exercises 29–38, solve the compound inequalities. Graph the solution and write the solution set in interval notation.

29. $0 \leq 3a + 2 < 17$

30. $-8 < 4k - 7 < 11$

31. $5 < 4y - 3 < 21$

32. $7 \leq 3m - 5 < 10$

33. $1 \leq \dfrac{1}{5}x + 12 \leq 13$

34. $5 \leq \dfrac{1}{4}a + 1 < 9$

35. $6 \geq -2b - 3 > -6$

36. $4 > -3w - 7 \geq 2$

37. $8 > -w + 4 > -1$

38. $13 \geq -2h - 1 \geq 0$

39. Nolvia sells copy machines and her salary is $25,000 plus a 4% commission on sales. The equation $S = 25,000 + 0.04x$ represents her salary, S, in dollars in terms of her total sales in dollars, x.

a. How much money in sales does Nolvia need to earn a salary that exceeds $40,000?

b. How much money in sales does Nolvia need to earn a salary that exceeds $80,000?

c. Why is the money in sales required to earn a salary of $80,000 more than twice the money in sales required to earn a salary of $40,000?

40. The amount of money in a savings account, A, depends on the principal, P, the interest rate, r, and the time in years, t, that the money is invested. The equation $A = P + Prt$ shows the relationship among the variables for an account earning simple interest. If an investor deposits $5000 at $6\frac{1}{2}\%$ simple interest the account will grow according to the formula: $A = 5000 + 5000(0.065)t$

a. How many years will it take for the investment to exceed $10,000? (Round to the nearest tenth of a year.)

b. How many years will it take for the investment to exceed $15,000? (Round to the nearest tenth of a year.)

41. The revenue, R, for selling x fleece jackets is given by the equation $R = 49.95x$. The cost to produce x jackets is $C = 2300 + 18.50x$. Find the number of jackets that the company needs to sell to produce a profit. (*Hint:* A profit occurs when revenue exceeds cost.)

42. The revenue, R, for selling x mountain bikes is $R = 249.95x$. The cost to produce x bikes is $C = 56,000 + 140x$. Find the number of bikes that the company needs to sell to produce a profit.

43. The average high and low temperatures for Vancouver, British Columbia, in January are 5.6°C and 0°C, respectively. The formula relating Celsius temperatures to Fahrenheit temperatures is given by $C = \frac{5}{9}(F - 32)$. Convert the inequality $0.0° \leq C \leq 5.6°$ to an equivalent inequality using Fahrenheit temperatures.

44. On July 29, 2000, the temperatures for a major city in Texas ranged from 20°C to 29°C. The formula relating Celsius temperatures to Fahrenheit temperatures is given by $C = \frac{5}{9}(F - 32)$. Convert the inequality $20° \leq C \leq 29°$ to an equivalent inequality using Fahrenheit temperatures.

45. The poverty threshold, P, for four-person families between the years 1960 and 1995 can be approximated by the equation, $P = 1235 + 387t$. P is measured in dollars, and $t = 0$ corresponds to the year 1960, $t = 1$ corresponds to 1961, and so on. (*Source:* U.S. Bureau of the Census)

    a. For what years after 1960 was the poverty threshold under $7040.

    b. For what years after 1960 was the poverty threshold between $4331 and $10,136?

46. Between the years, 1960 and 1995, the average gas mileage (miles per gallon) for passenger cars has increased. The equation $N = 12.6 + 0.214t$ approximates the average gas mileage corresponding to the year, t, where $t = 0$ represents 1960, $t = 1$ represents 1961 and so on.

    a. For what years after 1960 was the average gas mileage less than 14.1 miles/gal? (Round to the nearest year.)

    b. For what years was the average gas mileage between 17.1 and 18.0 miles/gal? (Round to the nearest year.)

For Exercises 47–60, solve the inequalities. Graph the solution and write the solution set in interval notation. Check each answer using the test point method.

47. $-6p - 1 > 17$

48. $-4y + 1 \leq -11$

49. $\frac{3}{4}x - 8 \leq 1$

50. $-\frac{2}{5}a - 3 > 5$

51. $-1.2b - 0.4 \geq -0.4b$

52. $-0.4t + 1.2 < -2$

53. $1 < 3(2t - 4) \leq 12$

54. $4 \leq 2(5h - 3) < 14$

55. $-\frac{3}{4}c - \frac{5}{4} \geq 2c$

56. $-\frac{2}{3}q - \frac{1}{3} > \frac{1}{2}q$

57. $4 - 4(y - 2) < -5y + 6$

58. $6 - 6(k - 3) \geq -4k + 12$

59. $0 \leq 2q - 1 \leq 11$

60. $-10 < 7p - 1 < 1$

▮ EXPANDING YOUR SKILLS

For Exercises 61–65, assume $a > b$. Determine which inequality sign ($>$ or $<$) should be inserted to make a true statement. Assume $a \neq 0$ and $b \neq 0$.

61. $a + c$ _____ $b + c$, for $c > 0$

62. $a + c$ _____ $b + c$, for $c < 0$

63. ac _____ bc, for $c > 0$

64. ac _____ bc, for $c < 0$

65. $\frac{1}{a}$ _____ $\frac{1}{b}$

chapter 1   SUMMARY

SECTION 1.1—SETS OF NUMBERS AND INTERVAL NOTATION

KEY CONCEPTS:

Natural numbers: $\{1, 2, 3, \ldots\}$
Whole numbers: $\{0, 1, 2, 3, \ldots\}$
Integers: $\{\ldots -3, -2, -1, 0, 1, 2, 3, \ldots\}$

Rational numbers: $\left\{\dfrac{p}{q} \mid p \text{ and } q \text{ are integers and } q \text{ does not equal } 0\right\}$

Irrational numbers: $\{x \mid x \text{ is a real number that is not rational}\}$

Real numbers: $\{x \mid x \text{ is rational or } x \text{ is irrational}\}$

$a < b$ "a is less than b"
$a > b$ "a is greater than b"
$a \le b$ "a is less than or equal to b"
$a \ge b$ "a is greater than or equal to b"
$a < x < b$ "x is between a and b"

$A \cup B$ is the union of A and B and is the set of elements that belong to set A or set B or both sets A and B.
$A \cap B$ is the intersection of A and B and is the set of elements common to both A and B.

KEY TERMS:

closed interval
empty set
inequalities
integers
intersection
interval notation
irrational numbers
natural numbers
open interval

rational numbers
real number line
real numbers
set
set-builder notation
subsets
union
whole numbers

EXAMPLES:

Rational numbers:
$\frac{1}{7}, 0.5, 0.\overline{3}$

Irrational numbers:
$\sqrt{7}, \sqrt{2}, \pi$

Real number line:

Set-Builder Notation	Interval Notation	Graph
$\{x \mid x > a\}$	(a, ∞)	
$\{x \mid x \ge a\}$	$[a, \infty)$	
$\{x \mid x < a\}$	$(-\infty, a)$	
$\{x \mid x \le a\}$	$(-\infty, a]$	

$A \cup B$

$A \cap B$

SECTION 1.2—OPERATIONS ON REAL NUMBERS

KEY CONCEPTS:

The reciprocal of a number $a \neq 0$ is $\frac{1}{a}$.
The opposite of a number a is $-a$.
The absolute value of a, denoted $|a|$, is its distance from zero on the number line.

Addition of Real Numbers:

Same Signs: Add the absolute values of the numbers and apply the common sign to the sum.
Unlike Signs: Subtract the smaller absolute value from the larger absolute value. Then apply the sign of the number having the larger absolute value.

Subtraction of Real Numbers:

Add the opposite of the second number to the first number.

Multiplication and Division of Real Numbers:

Same Signs: Product or quotient is positive.
Opposite Signs: Product or quotient is negative.
The product of any real number and 0 is 0.
The quotient of 0 and a nonzero number is 0.
The quotient of a nonzero number and 0 is undefined.

Exponents and Radicals:

$b^4 = b \cdot b \cdot b \cdot b$ (b is the base, 4 is the exponent)
$\sqrt{b}$ is the principal square root of b (b is the radicand, $\sqrt{}$ is the radical sign).

Order of Operations:

1. Simplify expressions within parentheses and other grouping symbols first.
2. Evaluate expressions involving exponents and radicals.
3. Perform multiplication or division in order from left to right.
4. Perform addition or subtraction in order from left to right.

KEY TERMS:

absolute value	power
base	principal square root
exponent	radical sign
opposite	reciprocal
order of operations	subscript

EXAMPLES:

Given: -5
The reciprocal is $-\frac{1}{5}$. The opposite is 5.

The absolute value is 5.

Add:

$$-3 + (-4) = -7$$
$$-5 + 7 = 2$$

Subtract:

$$7 - (-5) = 7 + (5) = 12$$

Multiply or divide as indicated:

$$(-3)(-4) = 12; \qquad \frac{-15}{-3} = 5$$

$$(-2)(5) = -10; \qquad \frac{6}{-12} = -\frac{1}{2}$$

$$(-7)(0) = 0 \qquad\qquad 0 \div 9 = 0$$

$$-3 \div 0 \text{ is undefined}$$

Simplify the expressions:

$$6^3 = 6 \cdot 6 \cdot 6 = 216$$
$$\sqrt{100} = 10$$

Simplify:

$$10 - 5(3-1)^2 + \sqrt{16}$$
$$= 10 - 5(2)^2 + \sqrt{16}$$
$$= 10 - 5(4) + 4$$
$$= 10 - 20 + 4$$
$$= -10 + 4$$
$$= -6$$

SECTION 1.3—SIMPLIFYING EXPRESSIONS

KEY CONCEPTS:

A term is a constant or the product of a constant and one or more variables.

- A variable term contains at least one variable.
- A constant term has no variable.

The coefficient of a term is the numerical factor of the term.

Like terms have the same variables and the corresponding variables are raised to the same powers.

Distributive Property of Multiplication over Addition:

$a(b + c) = ab + ac$

Two terms can be added or subtracted if they are *like* terms. Sometimes it is necessary to clear parentheses before adding or subtracting *like* terms.

KEY TERMS:

associative property of addition
associative property of multiplication
coefficient
commutative property of addition
commutative property of multiplication
constant term
distributive property of multiplication over addition
factor
identity property of addition
identity property of multiplication
inverse property of addition
inverse property of multiplication
like terms
term
variable term

EXAMPLES:

Examples of terms:

$-2x$ Variable term has coefficient -2.

$x^2 y$ Variable term has coefficient 1.

6 Constant term has coefficient 6.

Like Terms:

$$3x \text{ and } -5x, 4ab^3 \text{ and } 2ab^3$$

Simplify using the distributive property:

$$2(x + 4y) = 2x + 8y$$
$$-(a + 6b - 5c) = -a - 6b + 5c$$

Simplify:

$$-4d + 12d + d$$
$$= 9d$$

Simplify:

$$-2[w - 4(w - 2)] + 3$$
$$= -2[w - 4w + 8] + 3$$
$$= -2[-3w + 8] + 3$$
$$= 6w - 16 + 3$$
$$= 6w - 13$$

SECTION 1.4—LINEAR EQUATIONS IN ONE VARIABLE

KEY CONCEPTS:

A linear equation in one variable can be written in the form $ax + b = 0\ (a \neq 0)$.

Steps to Solve a Linear Equation in One Variable:

1. Consider clearing fractions or decimals by multiplying both sides by a common denominator.
2. Simplify both sides of the equation by clearing parentheses and combining *like* terms.
3. Use the addition and subtraction properties of equality to collect the variable terms on one side of the equation.
4. Use the addition and subtraction properties of equality to collect the constant terms on the other side.
5. Use the multiplication and division properties of equality to make the coefficient on the variable term equal to 1.
6. Check your answer.

An equation that has no solution is called a contradiction.

An equation that has all real numbers as its solutions is called an identity.

KEY TERMS:

addition property of
   equality
conditional equation
contradiction
division property of
   equality
equation
identity

linear equation in one
   variable
multiplication property
   of equality
solution set
solution to an equation
subtraction property of
   equality

EXAMPLES:

Solve the equation:

$$\frac{1}{2}(x - 4) - \frac{3}{4}(x + 2) = \frac{1}{4}$$

$$4\left(\frac{1}{2}(x - 4) - \frac{3}{4}(x + 2)\right) = 4\left(\frac{1}{4}\right)$$

$$2(x - 4) - 3(x + 2) = 1$$

$$2x - 8 - 3x - 6 = 1$$

$$-x - 14 = 1$$

$$-x = 15$$

$$x = -15$$

Solve:

$$3x + 6 = 3(x - 5)$$

$$3x + 6 = 3x - 15$$

$$6 = -15 \qquad \text{Contradiction}$$

Solve:

$$-(5x + 12) - 3 = 5(-x - 3)$$

$$-5x - 12 - 3 = -5x - 15$$

$$-5x - 15 = -5x - 15$$

$$-15 = -15 \qquad \text{Identity}$$

SECTION 1.5—APPLICATIONS OF LINEAR EQUATIONS IN ONE VARIABLE

KEY CONCEPTS:

Problem-Solving Steps for Word Problems
1. Read the problem carefully.
2. Assign labels to unknown quantities.
3. Develop a verbal model.
4. Write a mathematical equation.
5. Solve the equation.
6. Interpret the results and write the final answer in words.

Sales Tax: (Cost of merchandise)(tax rate)
Commission: (Dollars in sales)(rate)
Simple Interest: $I = Prt$
Distance = (rate)(time) $d = rt$

KEY TERMS:

commission
$d = rt$
sales tax
simple interest

EXAMPLES:

1. Estella has $8500 to invest between two accounts: one bearing 6% simple interest, the other bearing 10% simple interest. At the end of one year, she has earned $750 in interest. Find the amount Estella has invested in each account.

2. Let x represent the amount at 6%. Then, $8500 - x$ is the amount at 10%

3. $\begin{pmatrix} \text{Interest from} \\ \text{6\% account} \end{pmatrix} + \begin{pmatrix} \text{interest from} \\ \text{10\% account} \end{pmatrix} = \begin{pmatrix} \text{total} \\ \text{interest} \end{pmatrix}$

4. $0.06x + 0.10(8500 - x) = 750$

5. $6x + 10(8500 - x) = 75{,}000$

$6x + 85{,}000 - 10x = 75{,}000$

$-4x = -10{,}000$

$x = 2500$

6. $x = 2500$,

$8500 - x = 6000$

$2500 was invested at 6% and $6000 was invested at 10%.

SECTION 1.6—LITERAL EQUATIONS AND APPLICATIONS TO GEOMETRY

KEY CONCEPTS:

Some useful formulas for word problems:

Perimeter:

Rectangle: $P = 2l + 2w$

Area:

Rectangle: $A = lw$

Square: $A = x^2$

Triangle: $A = \dfrac{1}{2}bh$

Trapezoid: $A = \dfrac{1}{2}(b_1 + b_2)h$

Angles:

Two angles whose measures total 90° are complementary angles.
Two angles whose measures total 180° are supplementary angles.

EXAMPLES:

A border of marigolds is to enclose a rectangular flower garden. If the length is twice the width and the perimeter is 25.5 ft, what are the dimensions of the garden?

$P = 2l + 2w$

$25.5 = 2(2x) + 2(x)$

$25.5 = 4x + 2x$

$25.5 = 6x$

$4.25 = x$

The width is 4.25 ft and the length is 2(4.25) ft or 8.5 ft.

Vertical angles are equal.

$a = c$

$b = d$

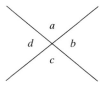

The sum of the angles of a triangle is 180°.

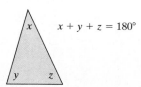

$x + y + z = 180°$

Literal equations are equations with several variables. To solve for a specific variable, follow the steps to solve a linear equation.

KEY TERMS:

literal equations

Solve for *y*:

$$4x - 5y = 20$$

$$-5y = -4x + 20$$

$$\frac{-5y}{-5} = \frac{-4x}{-5} + \frac{20}{-5}$$

$$y = \frac{4}{5}x - 4$$

SECTION 1.7—LINEAR INEQUALITIES IN ONE VARIABLE

KEY CONCEPTS:

A linear inequality in one variable can be written in the form:

$ax + b < 0$, $ax + b > 0$, $ax + b \leq 0$, or $ax + b \geq 0$.

Properties of Inequalities

1. If $a < b$, then $a + c < b + c$.
2. If $a < b$, then $a - c < b - c$.
3. If c is positive and $a < b$, then $ac < bc$ and $\frac{a}{c} < \frac{b}{c}$ $(c \neq 0)$.
4. If c is negative and $a < b$, then $ac > bc$ and $\frac{a}{c} > \frac{b}{c}$ $(c \neq 0)$.

The test point method can be used to check a linear inequality.
- Solve the related equation to find the boundary of the interval solution.
- Substitute test points from each region into the original inequality to see which interval makes the inequality true.

EXAMPLES:

Solve:

$$\frac{14 - x}{-2} < -3x$$

$$-2\left(\frac{14 - x}{-2}\right) > -2(-3x) \quad \text{(reverse the inequality sign)}$$

$$14 - x > 6x$$

$$-7x > -14$$

$$\frac{-7x}{-7} < \frac{-14}{-7} \quad \text{(reverse the inequality sign)}$$

$$x < 2$$

Interval notation: $(-\infty, 2)$

KEY TERMS:

addition property of
  inequality
compound inequality
division property of
  inequality
linear inequality

multiplication property
  of inequality
subtraction property of
  inequality
test point method

Check the inequality with the test point method.

test $x = 0$: $\dfrac{14 - (0)}{-2} \overset{?}{<} -3(0)$ True (shade)

test $x = 4$: $\dfrac{14 - (4)}{-2} < -3(4)$ False

Shade region I, but not region II.

---

chapter 1   REVIEW EXERCISES

Section 1.1

For Exercises 1–5, answers may vary.

1. List five natural numbers.

2. Find a number that is a whole number but not a natural number.

3. List three rational numbers that are not integers.

4. List three irrational numbers

5. List five integers, two of which are not whole numbers.

For Exercises 6–14, write an expression in words that describes the set of numbers given by each interval. (Answers may vary.)

6. $(7, 16)$ 7. $(0, 2.6]$ 8. $[-6, -3]$

9. $\left[\frac{3}{4}, 1\frac{1}{2}\right]$ 10. $(-\infty, -1)$ 11. $(8, \infty)$

12. $[-42, \infty)$ 13. $(-\infty, 13]$ 14. $(-\infty, \infty)$

15. Explain the difference between the union and intersection of two sets. You may use the sets C and D in the following diagram to provide an example.

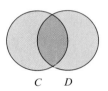

Figure for Exercise 15

Let $A = \{x \mid x < 2\}$, $B = \{x \mid x \geq -3\}$, $C = \{x \mid x \geq 0\}$, and $D = \{x \mid -1 < x < 5\}$. For Exercises 16–25, graph each set and write the set in interval notation.

16. A 17. B 18. C

19. D 20. $A \cap B$ 21. $A \cap C$

22. $B \cap D$ 23. $C \cap D$ 24. $A \cup C$

25. $C \cup D$

26. True or false: $x < 3$ is equivalent to $3 > x$

27. True or false: $-2 \leq x < 5$ is equivalent to $5 > x \geq -2$

Section 1.2

For Exercises 28–31, find the opposite, the reciprocal, and absolute value.

28. -8 29. -0.03 30. $\dfrac{4}{9}$ 31. 1

For Exercises 32–35, simplify the exponents and the roots.

32. $4^2, \sqrt{4}$ 33. $16^2, \sqrt{16}$ 34. $25^2, \sqrt{25}$

35. $9^2, \sqrt{9}$

For Exercises 36–53, perform the indicated operations.

36. $6 + (-8)$

37. $(-2) + (-5)$

38. $\dfrac{5}{8} - \left(-\dfrac{7}{12}\right)$

39. $-\dfrac{3}{8} - \dfrac{5}{12}$

40. $8(-2.7)$

41. $(-1.1)(7.41)$

42. $\dfrac{5}{8} \div \left(-\dfrac{13}{40}\right)$

43. $\left(-\dfrac{1}{4}\right) \div \left(-\dfrac{11}{16}\right)$

44. $2[(16 \div 8) - (-2)] + 4$

45. $5[(2 - 4) \cdot 3 - 2]$

46. $\dfrac{2 - 4(3 - 7)}{-4 - 5(1 - 3)}$

47. $\dfrac{12(2) - 8}{4(-3) + 2(5)}$

48. $3^2 + 2(|-10 + 5| \div 5)$

49. $|-18| - (|-3| \cdot 4^3 - 19 \cdot 10)$

50. $[7.82 - (-16.72606)] \div (2.31)^2$

51. $(6.96 + 3.27)^2 \div (-25.76 + 25.46)$

52. $105 - \sqrt{9}(6 + \sqrt{16})^2$

53. $-91 + \sqrt{4}(\sqrt{25} - 13)^2$

For Exercises 54–57, let x, y, and z be real numbers such that $x < 0$, $y < 0$, and $z < 0$. Determine the sign of each expression.

54. $\dfrac{xy}{x + y}$

55. $x + y + z$

56. $x^2 + y^2$

57. $\dfrac{x + y}{x + z}$

58. Given $h = \frac{1}{2}gt^2 + v_0 t + h_0$ find h if $g = -32$ ft/s^2, $v_0 = 64$ ft/s, $h_0 = 256$ ft, and $t = 4$ s.

59. Find the area of a parallelogram with base 42 in. and height 18 in.

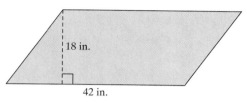

18 in.

42 in.

Figure for Exercise 59

60. Find the volume of a right circular cylinder whose height is 10.5 cm and radius is 2.2 cm. Use the π key on your calculator and round the final answer to the nearest tenth of a cubic centimeter.

2.2 cm

10.5 cm

Figure for Exercise 60

Section 1.3

For Exercises 61–66, answers may vary.

61. Write two *like* terms with coefficients 2 and -5.

62. Write two *like* terms with coefficients $\frac{4}{9}$ and -9.

63. Write two constant terms.

64. Write two variable terms.

65. Write two terms that are not *like* terms.

66. Must *like* terms have the same coefficient? Explain.

For Exercises 67–72, apply the distributive property and simplify.

67. $3(x + 5y)$

68. $-2(4a - b)$

69. $\frac{2}{3}(3a - 6b + 7)$

70. $\frac{1}{2}(x + 8y - 5)$

71. $-(-4x + 10y - z)$

72. $-(13a - b - 5c)$

For Exercises 73–78, clear parentheses and combine *like* terms.

73. $5 - 6q + 13q - 19$

74. $18p + 3 - 17p + 8p$

75. $7 - 3(y + 4) - 3y$

76. $10 - 2(2x + 3) - 5x$

77. $\frac{3}{5}(5x - 20) + \frac{2}{3}(3x + 9)$

78. $\frac{3}{4}(8x - 4) + \frac{1}{2}(6x + 4)$

For Exercises 79–84, answers may vary.

79. Write an example of the commutative property of addition.

80. Write an example of the associative property of addition.

81. Write an example of the associative property of multiplication.

82. Write an example of the commutative property of multiplication.

83. Write an example of the distributive property of multiplication over addition.

84. Write the identity elements for both addition and multiplication.

Section 1.4

85. Describe the solution set for a contradiction.

86. Describe the solution set for an identity.

For Exercises 87–102, solve the equations and identify each as a conditional equation, a contradiction, or an identity.

87. $x - 27 = -32$

88. $y + \frac{7}{8} = 1$

89. $5.8z = -3.886$

90. $-1.2 = 0.6 + 0.9x$

91. $-\frac{2}{3}w = -\frac{8}{27}$

92. $\frac{c}{4} + 8 = 16$

93. $7.23 + 0.6x = 0.2x$

94. $0.1y + 1.122 = 5.2y$

95. $-(4 + 3m) = 9(3 - m)$

96. $-2(5n - 6) = 3(-n - 3)$

97. $9k + 4 - 3k = 2(3k + 4) - 4$

98. $3(x + 3) - 2 = 3x + 2$

99. $\frac{10}{8}m + 18 - \frac{7}{8}m = \frac{3}{8}m + 25$

100. $\frac{2}{3}m + \frac{1}{3}(m - 1) = -\frac{1}{3}m + \frac{1}{3}(4m - 1)$

101. $[4 + 2(5 + y) - 2y] = 4y - 7$

102. $-[x - (4x + 2)] = 3(2x + 7)$

Section 1.5

103. Explain how you would label three consecutive integers.

104. Explain how you would label two consecutive odd integers.

105. Explain what the formula $d = rt$ means.

106. Explain what the formula $I = Prt$ means.

107. To do a rope trick, a magician needs to cut a piece of rope so that one piece is one-third the length of the other piece. If she begins with a $2\frac{2}{3}$-ft rope, what lengths will the two pieces of rope be?

108. Of three consecutive even integers, the sum of the smallest two integers is equal to 6 less than the largest. Find the integers.

109. Pat averages a rate of 11 mph on his bike. One day he rode for 45 min ($\frac{3}{4}$ h) and then got a flat tire and had to walk home. He walked the same path that he rode and it took him 2 h. What was his average rate walking?

110. A manager is offered a salary of $2000 a month or a commission of 4% of the gross sales. If the shop grosses an average of $49,187 per month, which method of payment should he choose?

111. How much 10% acid solution should be mixed with a 25% acid solution to produce 3 L of a solution that is 15% acid?

112. Sharyn invests $2000 more in an account that earns 9% simple interest than she invests in an account that earns 6% simple interest. How much did she invest in each account if her total interest is $405 after one year?

113. In 1993, approximately 6.5 million men were in college in the United States. This represents a 29% increase over the number of men in college in 1970. Approximate how many men were in college in 1970? (Round to the nearest tenth of a million.)

114. One number is 11 more than twice another. Their sum is 41. Find the numbers.

115. The number of deaths in the United States attributed to motor vehicles is shown by year in the following figure. (*Source:* National Safety Council)

   a. Compute the percent decrease in motor vehicle deaths between 1990 and 1992. (Round to the nearest whole percent.)

   b. Compute the percent increase in motor vehicle deaths between 1992 and 1994. (Round to the nearest whole percent.)

Number of Deaths in the United States Attributed to Motor Vehicles

Figure for Exercise 115

116. a. Cory made $30,403 in taxable income in 1996. If he pays 28% in federal income tax, determine the amount of tax he must pay.

   b. What is his net income (after taxes)?

Section 1.6

117. The lengths of the sides of a triangle are represented by three consecutive odd integers. If the perimeter of this triangle is 93 in., find the lengths of the three sides.

118. The length of a rectangle is 2 ft more than the width. Find the dimensions if the perimeter is 40 ft.

For Exercises 119–120, solve for x, and then find the measure of each angle.

119.

120.

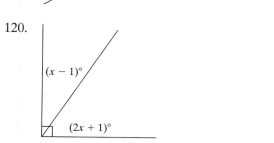

For Exercises 121–126, solve for the indicated variable.

121. $3x - 2y = 4$ for y

122. $8x - 2y = 12$ for x

123. $3x + 5y = 13$ for x

124. $-6x + y = 12$ for y

125. $S = 2\pi r + \pi r^2 h$ for h

126. $A = \dfrac{1}{2}bh$ for b

127. a. The circumference of a circle is given by $C = 2\pi r$. Solve this equation for π.

   b. Tom measures the radius of a circle to be 6 cm and the circumference to be 37.7 cm. Use these values to approximate π. (Round to two decimal places.)

Section 1.7

For Exercises 128–143, solve the inequalities. Graph the solution and write the solution set in interval notation.

128. $-6x - 2 > 6$

129. $-10x \leq 15$

130. $-2 \leq 3x - 9 \leq 15$

131. $0 < 8x + 1 < 11$

132. $11 \leq 6 - 3x$

133. $-2x - 12 \geq 13$

134. $5 - 7(x + 3) > 19x$

135. $4 - 3x \geq 10(-x + 5)$

136. $\dfrac{5 - 4x}{8} \geq 9$

137. $\dfrac{3 + 2x}{4} \leq 8$

138. $\dfrac{1}{2}t - \dfrac{3}{8} \leq \dfrac{13}{8}$

139. $\dfrac{7}{12} + \dfrac{1}{4}p \geq -\dfrac{2}{3}$

140. $3 > \dfrac{4 - q}{2} \geq -\dfrac{1}{2}$

141. $-11 < -5z - 2 \leq 0$

142. $0.11(29000) + 15r > 0.14(32000)$

143. $0.05x + 213 > 0.06(5200)$

144. One method to approximate your maximum heart rate is to subtract your age from 220. To maintain an aerobic workout, it is recommended that you sustain a heart rate of between 60% and 75% of your maximum heart rate.

    a. If the maximum heart rate, h, is given by the formula: $h = 220 - A$, where A is a person's age, find your own maximum heart rate. (Answers will vary.)

    b. Find the interval for your own heart rate that will sustain an aerobic workout. (Answers will vary.)

---

chapter 1   TEST

1. a. List the integers between -5 and 2, inclusive.

    b. List three rational numbers between 1 and 2. (Answers may vary.)

2. Explain the difference between the intervals $(-3, 4)$ and $[-3, 4]$.

3. Graph the sets and write each set in interval notation.

    a. All real numbers less than 6

    b. All real numbers at least -3

4. Given sets $A = \{x \mid x < -2\}$ and $B = \{x \mid x \geq -5\}$, graph $A \cap B$ and write the set in interval notation.

5. Write the opposite, reciprocal, and absolute value for each of the numbers:

    a. $-\dfrac{1}{2}$ b. 4 c. 0

6. Simplify: $|-8| - 4(2 - 3)^2 \div \sqrt{4}$

7. Given $z = (x - \mu)/(\sigma/\sqrt{n})$, find z when $n = 16$, $x = 18$, $\sigma = 1.8$, and $\mu = 17.5$. (Round the answer to one decimal place.)

8. True or False:

    a. $(x + y) + 2 = 2 + (x + y)$ is an example of the associative property of addition.

    b. $(2 \cdot 3) \cdot 5 = (3 \cdot 2) \cdot 5$ is an example of the commutative property of multiplication.

    c. $(x + 3)4 = 4x + 12$ is an example of the distributive property.

    d. $(10 + y) + z = 10 + (y + z)$ is an example of the associative property of addition.

9. Simplify the expressions:

    a. $5b + 2 - 7b + 6 - 14$

    b. $\dfrac{1}{2}(2x - 1) - \left(3x - \dfrac{3}{2}\right)$

For Exercises 10–13, solve the equations.

10. $\dfrac{x}{7} + 1 = 20$

11. $8 - 5(4 - 3z) = 2(4 - z) - 8z$

12. $0.12(x) + 0.08(60,000 - x) = 10,500$

13. $\dfrac{a - 2}{3} + \dfrac{a}{4} = \dfrac{1}{2}$

14. Label each equation as a conditional equation, an identity, or a contradiction.

    a. $(5x - 9) + 19 = 5(x + 2)$

    b. $2a - 2(1 + a) = 5$

    c. $(4w - 3) + 4 = 3(5 - w)$

15. The difference between two numbers is 72. If the larger is 5 times the smaller, find the two numbers.

16. Peggy is determined to get some exercise and walks to the store at a brisk rate of 4.5 mph. She meets Julie at the store and together they walk back at a slower rate of 3 mph. Peggy's total walking time was 1 h.

    a. How long did it take her to walk to the store?

    b. What is the distance to the store?

17. Shawnna banks at a credit union. Her money is distributed between two accounts: a certificate of deposit (CD) that earns 5% simple interest and a savings account that earns 3.5% simple interest. Shawnna has $100 less in her savings account than in the CD. If after one year her total interest is $81.50 how much did she invest in the CD?

18. A yield sign is in the shape of an equilateral triangle (all sides are equal). Its perimeter is 81 in. Find the length of the sides.

For Exercises 19–20, solve the equations for the indicated variable.

19. $4x + 2y = 6$ for y

20. $x = \mu + z\sigma$ for z

For Exercises 21–23, solve the inequalities. Graph the solution and write the solution set in interval notation.

21. $x + 8 > 42$

22. $-\dfrac{3}{2}x + 6 \geq x - 3$

23. $-2 < 3x - 1 \leq 5$

24. An elevator can accommodate a maximum weight of 2000 lb. If four passengers on the elevator have an average weight of 180 lb each, how many additional passengers of the same average weight can the elevator carry before the maximum weight capacity is exceeded?

LINEAR EQUATIONS IN TWO VARIABLES

The use of graphs in algebra can help us visualize relationships between variables. For example, if you have ever bought a used car or tried to sell one, you know that the *value* of the car depends in part on its *age*. For more information visit Kellybb at

www.mhhe.com/miller_oneill

Algebra can be used to create a mathematical model or equation that approximates the trend of the data. In this chapter, we will study a particular type of model called a linear equation in two variables.

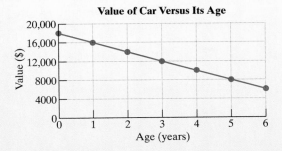

Value of Car Versus Its Age

section

2.1   LINEAR EQUATIONS IN TWO VARIABLES

1.   The Rectangular Coordinate System

One fundamental application of algebra is the graphical representation of numerical information (or data). For example, Table 2-1 shows the percentage of individuals who participate in leisure sports activities according to the age of the individual.

Table 2-1	
Age (years)	**Percentage of Individuals Participating in Leisure Sports Activities**
20	59
30	52
40	44
50	34
60	21
70	18

Source: U.S. National Endowment for the Arts.

Information in table form is difficult to picture and interpret. However, when the data are presented in a graph, there appears to be a downward trend in the participation in leisure sports activities for older age groups (Figure 2-1).

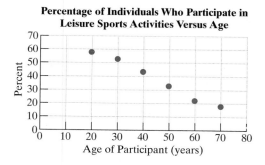

Percentage of Individuals Who Participate in Leisure Sports Activities Versus Age

Figure 2-1

In this example, two variables are related: age and the percentage of individuals who participate in leisure sports activities.

To picture two variables simultaneously, we use a graph with two number lines drawn at right angles to each other (Figure 2-2). This forms a **rectangular coordinate system**. The horizontal line is called the ***x*-axis**, and the vertical line is called the ***y*-axis**. The point where the lines intersect is called the **origin**. On the *x*-axis, the numbers to the right of the origin are positive and the numbers to the left are negative. On the *y*-axis, the numbers above the origin are positive and the numbers below are negative. The *x*- and *y*-axes divide the graphing area into four regions called **quadrants**.

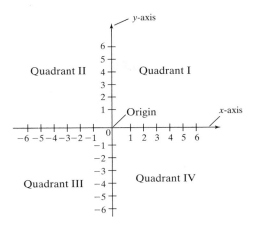

Figure 2-2

2. Plotting Points

Points graphed in a rectangular coordinate system are defined by two numbers as an **ordered pair**, (x, y). The first number (called the first coordinate or **abscissa**) is the horizontal position from the origin. The second number (called the second coordinate or **ordinate**) is the vertical position from the origin. The next example shows how points are plotted in a rectangular coordinate system.

---

example 1

Plotting Points

Plot the points.

a. $(4, 1)$ b. $(-3, 4)$ c. $(4, -3)$

d. $\left(-\frac{5}{2}, -2\right)$ e. $(0, 3)$ f. $(-4, 0)$

Tip: Notice that the points $(-3, 4)$ and $(4, -3)$ are in different quadrants. Changing the order of the coordinates changes the location of the point. That is why points are represented by *ordered* pairs (Figure 2-3).

Solution:

a. The point $(4, 1)$ is in Quadrant I.

b. The point $(-3, 4)$ is in Quadrant II.

c. The point $(4, -3)$ is in Quadrant IV.

d. The point $\left(-\frac{5}{2}, -2\right)$ can also be written as $(-2.5, -2)$. This point is in Quadrant III.

e. The point $(0, 3)$ is on the y-axis.

f. The point $(-4, 0)$ is located on the x-axis.

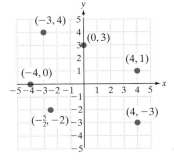

Figure 2-3

---

3. Graphing Linear Equations in Two Variables

The graph of the data points relating age and the percentage of individuals who participate in leisure sports seems to follow a straight line (Figure 2-1). For this reason, we say that there is a linear relationship between the two variables. In such a case, the variables can be defined by a linear equation in two variables.

A Linear Equation in Two Variables

Let a, b, and c be real numbers such that a and b are not both zero. Then, an equation that can be written in the form:

$$ax + by = c$$

is said to be a **linear equation in two variables**.

A *solution* to a linear equation in two variables is an ordered pair (x, y) that makes the equation a true statement. For example, the solutions to the equation $x + y = 3$ are ordered pairs whose x- and y-coordinates add up to 3. Several solutions appear in the following list.

Solution	Check
(x, y)	$x + y = 3$
$(1, 2)$	$(1) + (2) = 3$ ✔
$(0, 3)$	$(0) + (3) = 3$ ✔
$(3, 0)$	$(3) + (0) = 3$ ✔
$(-2, 5)$	$(-2) + (5) = 3$ ✔

By graphing these ordered pairs, we see that the solution points line up (see Figure 2-4). There are actually an infinite number of solutions to the equation $x + y = 3$. The graph of all solutions to the equation forms a line in the xy-plane. Conversely, each ordered pair on the line is a solution to the equation.

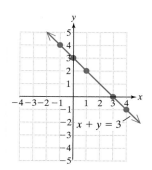

Figure 2-4

Graphing Calculator Box

Linear equations can be analyzed with a graphing calculator.

- For most calculators it is important to isolate the y-variable in the equation. Then enter the equation into the calculator. For example:

$$x + y = 3 \Rightarrow y = -x + 3$$

- A *Table* feature can be used to find many solutions to an equation. For example, several solutions to $y = -x + 3$ are shown:

- A *Graph* feature can be used to graph a line.

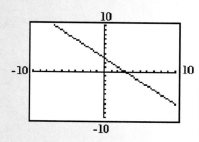

Because a linear equation is represented by a line, two points are sufficient to draw the graph. In practice, it is advisable to plot three points. If all three points lie on the same line, then you can be reasonably confident that the line was graphed correctly.

example 2

Graphing a Linear Equation

Graph the equation $3x + 5y = 15$.

Solution:
Because $3x + 5y = 15$ is a linear equation, at least two points are needed to graph the line. Substitute any value for x and solve the equation for y. Or substitute a value for y and solve for x. Three arbitrary values for x and y are shown in the table.

x	y
0	
	2
-1	

Substitute $x = 0$

$3x + 5y = 15$

$3(0) + 5y = 15$

$0 + 5y = 15$

$5y = 15$

$y = 3$

Substitute $y = 2$

$3x + 5y = 15$

$3x + 5(2) = 15$

$3x + 10 = 15$

$3x = 5$

$x = \dfrac{5}{3}$

Substitute $x = -1$

$3x + 5y = 15$

$3(-1) + 5y = 15$

$-3 + 5y = 15$

$5y = 18$

$y = \dfrac{18}{5}$

The completed table of ordered pairs is shown with the corresponding graph (Figure 2-5).

x	y
0	3
$\frac{5}{3}$	2
-1	$\frac{18}{5}$

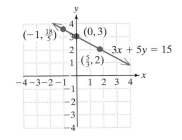

Figure 2-5

4. *x*-Intercepts and *y*-Intercepts

Any two points may be used to graph a line, however, sometimes it is convenient to find the points where the line intersects the *x*- and *y*-axes. These points are called the *x*- and *y*-intercepts.

Definition of *x*- and *y*-Intercepts

An **x-intercept** of an equation is a point $(a, 0)$ where the graph intersects the *x*-axis.
A **y-intercept** of an equation is a point $(0, b)$ where the graph intersects the *y*-axis.

In some applications, an *x*-intercept is defined as the *x-coordinate* of a point of intersection that a graph makes with the *x*-axis. For example, if an *x*-intercept is at the point (3, 0), it is sometimes stated simply as 3 (the *y*-coordinate is understood to be zero). Similarly, a *y*-intercept is sometimes defined as the *y-coordinate* of a point of intersection that a graph makes with the *y*-axis. For example, if a *y*-intercept is at the point (0, 7), it may be stated simply as 7 (the *x*-coordinate is understood to be zero).

To find the *x*- and *y*-intercepts from an equation in *x* and *y*, follow these steps:

Steps to Find the *x*- and *y*-Intercepts from an Equation

Given an equation in *x* and *y*,

1. Find the *x*-intercept(s) by substituting $y = 0$ into the equation and solving for *x*.
2. Find the *y*-intercept(s) by substituting $x = 0$ into the equation and solving for *y*.

---

example 3

Finding the *x*- and *y*-Intercepts of a Line

Find the *x*- and *y*-intercepts of the line $2x + 4y = 8$.

Solution:

To find the *x*-intercept, substitute $y = 0$

$$2x + 4y = 8$$
$$2x + 4(0) = 8$$
$$2x = 8$$
$$x = 4$$

The *x*-intercept is (4, 0).

To find the *y*-intercept, substitute $x = 0$

$$2x + 4y = 8$$
$$2(0) + 4y = 8$$
$$4y = 8$$
$$y = 2$$

The *y*-intercept is (0, 2).

In this case, the intercepts are two distinct points and may be used to graph the line. A third point can be found to verify that the points all fall on the same line (points that lie on the same line are said to be *collinear*). Choose a different value for either *x* or *y*, such as $y = 4$.

$$2x + 4(4) = 8 \qquad \text{Substitute } y = 4.$$
$$2x + 16 = 8 \qquad \text{Solve for } x.$$
$$2x = -8$$
$$x = -4 \qquad \text{The point } (-4, 4) \text{ lines up with the other two points}$$
$$\text{(Figure 2-6)}.$$

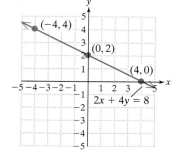

Figure 2-6

example 4

Finding the *x*- and *y*-Intercepts of a Line

Find the *x*- and *y*-intercepts of the line $y = \frac{1}{4}x$. Then graph the line.

Solution:

To find the *x*-intercept, substitute
$y = 0$

$$y = \frac{1}{4}x$$

$$(0) = \frac{1}{4}x$$

$$0 = x$$

The *x*-intercept is $(0, 0)$.

To find the *y*-intercept, substitute
$x = 0$

$$y = \frac{1}{4}x$$

$$y = \frac{1}{4}(0)$$

$$y = 0$$

The *y*-intercept is $(0, 0)$.

Notice the *x*- and *y*-intercepts are both located at the origin, $(0, 0)$. In this case, the intercepts do not yield two distinct points. Therefore, another point is necessary to draw the line. We may pick any value for either *x* or *y*. However, for this equation, it would be particularly convenient to pick a value for *x* that is a multiple of 4 such as $x = 4$.

$$y = \frac{1}{4}x$$

$$y = \frac{1}{4}(4) \qquad \text{Substitute } x = 4.$$

$$y = 1$$

The point $(4, 1)$ is a solution to the equation (Figure 2-7).

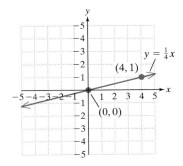

Figure 2-7

5. Applications of *x*- and *y*-Intercepts

example 5

Interpreting the *x*- and *y*-Intercepts of a Line

Companies and corporations are permitted to depreciate assets that have a known useful life span. This accounting practice is called *straight-line depreciation*. In this procedure the useful life span of the asset is determined and then the asset is depreciated by an equal amount each year until the taxable value of the asset is equal to zero.

The J. M. Gus trucking company purchases a new truck for $65,000. The truck will be depreciated at $13,000 per year. The equation that describes the depreciation line is:

$$y = 65,000 - 13,000x$$

where *y* represents the value of the truck in dollars and *x* is the age of the truck in years.

a. Find the x- and y-intercepts. Plot the intercepts on a rectangular coordinate system and draw the line that represents the straight-line depreciation.
b. What does the x-intercept represent in the context of this problem?
c. What does the y-intercept represent in the context of this problem?

Solution:

a. To find the x-intercept, substitute $y = 0$.

$$0 = 65{,}000 - 13{,}000x$$

$$13{,}000x = 65{,}000$$

$$x = 5$$

The x-intercept is $(5, 0)$.

To find the y-intercept, substitute $x = 0$.

$$y = 65{,}000 - 13{,}000(0)$$

$$y = 65{,}000$$

The y-intercept is $(0, 65{,}000)$.

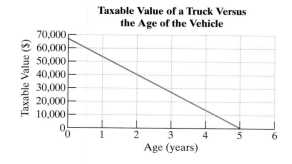

Taxable Value of a Truck Versus the Age of the Vehicle

b. The x-intercept, $(5, 0)$, indicates that when the truck is 5 years old the taxable value of the truck will be $0.
c. The y-intercept, $(0, 65{,}000)$, indicates that when the truck was new (0 years old), it was worth $65,000.

Graphing Calculator Box

The rectangular screen where a graph is displayed is called the *viewing window*. The default settings for the display on most calculators show both the x- and y-axes from -10 to 10. This is called the *standard viewing window*.

To graph the equation from Example 5 on a graphing calculator, the viewing window must be set to accommodate large values of y.

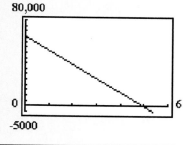

6. Horizontal and Vertical Lines

Recall that a linear equation can be written in the form $ax + by = c$, where a and b are not both zero. If either a or b is 0 then the resulting line is horizontal or vertical, respectively.

Definitions of Vertical and Horizontal Lines

1. A **vertical line** is a line that can be written in the form, $x = k$, where k is a constant.
2. A **horizontal line** is a line that can be written in the form, $y = k$, where k is a constant.

---

example 6

Graphing a Vertical Line

Graph the line $x = 6$.

Solution:
Because this equation is in the form $x = k$, the line is vertical and must cross the x-axis at $x = 6$ (Figure 2-8).

Alternative Solution:
Create a table of values for the equation $x = 6$. The choice for the x-coordinate must be 6, but y can be any real number.

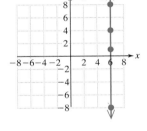

Figure 2-8

x	y
6	-8
6	1
6	4
6	8

---

example 7

Graphing a Horizontal Line

Graph the line $4y = -7$.

Solution:
The equation $4y = -7$ is equivalent to $y = -\frac{7}{4}$. Because the line is in the form $y = k$, the line must be horizontal and must pass through the y-axis at $y = -\frac{7}{4}$ (Figure 2-9).

Alternative Solution:
Create a table of values for the equation $4y = -7$. The choice for the y-coordinate must be $-\frac{7}{4}$, but x can be any real number.

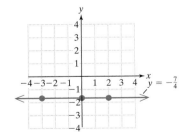

Figure 2-9

x	y
0	$-\frac{7}{4}$
-3	$-\frac{7}{4}$
2	$-\frac{7}{4}$

example 8

Finding an Equation of a Horizontal Line

The data in Table 2-2 represent the top batting averages in the American League from 1973 to 1992. A batting average represents the percentage of times a player gets on base as a result of a hit.

Table 2-2

Year (x)	Player	Average (y)	Year (x)	Player	Average (y)
1973	Rod Carew	0.350	1983	Wade Boggs	0.361
1974	Rod Carew	0.365	1984	Don Mattingly	0.343
1975	Rod Carew	0.359	1985	Wade Boggs	0.368
1976	George Brett	0.333	1986	Wade Boggs	0.357
1977	Rod Carew	0.388	1987	Wade Boggs	0.363
1978	Rod Carew	0.333	1988	Wade Boggs	0.366
1979	Fred Lynn	0.333	1989	Kirby Puckett	0.339
1980	George Brett	0.390	1990	George Brett	0.329
1981	Carney Lansford	0.336	1991	Julio Franco	0.341
1982	Willie Wilson	0.332	1992	Edgar Martinez	0.343

a.   Graph the data, letting the x-axis represent the year and the y-axis the batting average.
b.   Based on the graph of the data, do batting averages appear to be rising, falling, or remaining approximately constant?
c.   Write a linear equation that approximates the top batting averages for the American League from 1973 to 1992. Graph the equation.

Solution:

a.

Figure 2-10

b.   The top batting averages for the American League seem to fluctuate between 0.300 and 0.400 without an apparent upward or downward trend. The top batting averages are approximately *constant* for this time period (Figure 2-10).
c.   Because these values are relatively constant, an appropriate linear equation would be that of a horizontal line. Mathematically, a horizontal line is

represented by an equation of the form, $y = k$, where k is a constant. The mean, or "average," of the top 20 batting averages is 0.351. (*The mean is found by taking the sum of the 20 batting scores and dividing by 20.*) Hence the equation, $y = 0.351$, represents a constant linear equation for the top American League batting averages between 1973 and 1992 (Figure 2-11).

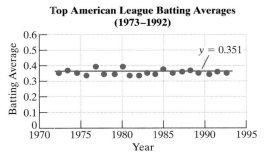

Figure 2-11

section 2.1   PRACTICE EXERCISES

1. Given the coordinates of a point, explain how to determine which quadrant the point is in.

2. What is meant by the word *ordered* in the term *ordered pair*?

3. Plot the points on a rectangular coordinate system.

   a. $(-2, 1)$ b. $(0, 4)$

   c. $(0, 0)$ d. $(-3, 0)$

   e. $\left(\dfrac{3}{2}, -\dfrac{7}{3}\right)$ f. $(-4.1, -2.7)$

4. Plot the points on a rectangular coordinate system.

   a. $(2.1, 0)$ b. $\left(0, \dfrac{2}{3}\right)$

   c. $(5, 3)$ d. $(-1.9, 4)$

   e. $(-2, -6)$ f. $\left(\dfrac{8}{5}, -\dfrac{9}{2}\right)$

5. Plot the points on a rectangular coordinate system.

   a. $(-2, 5)$ b. $\left(\dfrac{7}{2}, 0\right)$

   c. $(4, -3)$ d. $(0, -1.9)$

   e. $(2, 2)$ f. $(-3, -3)$

6. Plot the points on a rectangular coordinate system.

   a. $(-1, -3)$ b. $(0, 0)$

   c. $(0, 4)$ d. $\left(\dfrac{5}{2}, 1\right)$

   e. $(-1, 0)$ f. $(5, -2.5)$

7. The following chart gives the number of people (in millions) in the United States who reside in apartments.

Year (x)	Number of Households (in millions) Living in Apartments (y)
1970	8.5
1975	9.9
1980	10.8
1985	12.9
1990	14.2
1997	14.5

Source: U.S. Bureau of the Census.

Graph this information in the first quadrant of a rectangular coordinate system. Label the x-axis with the year and the y-axis with the number of households in millions.

8. The following chart gives the estimated advertising expenditures (in millions of dollars) in the United States.

Year (x)	Estimated Advertising Expenditures in the United States (in millions of dollars) (y)
1960	11,960
1970	19,550
1980	53,550
1990	129,590
1996	175,230
1997	187,529

Graph this information in the first quadrant of a rectangular coordinate system. Label the x-axis with the year and the y-axis with millions of dollars spent on advertising.

9. How can you tell if an equation is a linear equation in x and y?

10. For a linear equation in the form $ax + by = c$, explain why a and b cannot both be zero.

For Exercises 11–22, identify each equation as linear or nonlinear. If the equation is linear, write it in $ax + by = c$ form.

11. $5x - 3y - 11 = 0$

12. $-7x + y - 14 = 0$

13. $y = 3x + 7$

14. $x = \frac{2}{3}y + 5$

15. $2x^2 + 3y^2 = 7$

16. $11 + \frac{2x}{y} = 3$

17. $x + 2 = 5$

18. $y + 5 = 0$

19. $6xy + 2 = 0$

20. $2x^2 - y = 4$

21. $y = -3$

22. $x = -4$

23. Complete the following table to find the missing values of x or y that satisfy the equation $3x - 2y = 12$.

x	y
0	
	$-\frac{1}{2}$
-4	
	0
-5.1	

24. Complete the following table to find the missing values of x or y that satisfy the equation $4x + 3y = 18$.

x	y
	0
2.4	
	$\frac{7}{3}$
0	
	-1

25. Complete the following table to find the missing values of x or y that satisfy the equation $3x = 6$.

x	y
	5
2	
2	
	-1

26. Complete the following table to find the missing values of x or y that satisfy the equation $2y + 1 = -5$.

x	y
	−3
0	
−5	
	−3

In Exercises 27–38, graph the linear equation.

27. $x + y = 5$

28. $x + y = -8$

29. $3x - 4y = 12$

30. $5x + 3y = 15$

31. $y = -3x + 5$

32. $y = \dfrac{5}{3}x + 1$

33. $y = \dfrac{2}{5}x - 1$

34. $y = -2x + 2$

35. $x - 2 = 3$

36. $y + 2 = 1$

37. $2y + 3 = 0$

38. $x + 5 = 0$

39. What is meant by the terms *x-intercept* and *y-intercept*?

40. Given a linear equation, how do you find an *x*-intercept? How do you find a *y*-intercept?

For Exercises 41–50, (a) find the *x*-intercept (if it exists), (b) find the *y*-intercept (if it exists), and (c) graph the line.

41. $2x + 3y = 18$

42. $2x - 5y = 10$

43. $2x - 6 = 0$

44. $5y + 10 = 0$

45. $x - 2y = 4$

46. $5x + 3y = 0$

47. $5x - 3y = 0$

48. $x + y = 8$

49. $y = 6$

50. $x = 2$

51. In which of the Exercises, 41–50, are the *x*- and *y*-intercepts the same point? When the *x*- and *y*-intercepts are both at the origin, why do the intercepts not give you sufficient information to graph the line?

52. How can you tell from the equation of a line whether the line will pass through the origin?

53. In which of the equations in Exercises 41–50, does the line not have a *y*-intercept? Why?

54. In which of the equations in Exercises 41–50, did the line not have an *x*-intercept? Why?

55. A taxi company in Miami charges $2.00 for any distance up to the first mile and $1.10 for every mile thereafter. The cost of a cab ride can be modeled graphically as follows.

Figure for Exercise 55

a. Explain why the first part of the model is represented by a horizontal line.

b. What does the *y*-intercept mean in the context of this problem?

c. Explain why the line representing the cost of traveling more than 1 mile is not horizontal.

d. How much would it cost to take a cab $3\frac{1}{2}$ miles?

56. A salesperson makes a base salary of $10,000 a year plus a 5% commission on the total sales for the year. The yearly salary can be expressed as a linear equation as:

$$y = 10{,}000 + 0.05x$$

where *y* represents the yearly salary and *x* represents the total yearly sales.

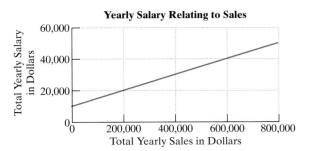

Figure for Exercise 56

a. What is the salesperson's salary for a year in which his sales total $500,000?

b. What is the salesperson's salary for a year in which his sales total $300,000?

c. What does the y-intercept mean in the context of this problem?

d. Why is it unreasonable to use negative values for x in this equation?

▪ EXPANDING YOUR SKILLS

57. Find the x- and y-intercepts for

$$\frac{x}{2} + \frac{y}{3} = 1$$

58. Find the x- and y-intercepts for

$$\frac{x}{7} + \frac{y}{4} = 1$$

59. Find the x- and y-intercepts for

$$\frac{x}{a} + \frac{y}{b} = 1$$

60. Write an equation of a line with intercepts $(6, 0)$ and $(0, 1)$.

▪ GRAPHING CALCULATOR EXERCISES

For Exercises 61–66, identify which equations are linear and which are nonlinear. Then use a graphing calculator to graph the equations on the standard viewing window to support your answer.

61. $y = 2x - 3$ 62. $y = |x|$ 63. $y = x^2 + 1$

64. $y = \dfrac{1}{x}$ 65. $y = 5$ 66. $y = x^3$

For Exercises 67–70, solve the equation for y. Use a graphing calculator to graph the equation on the standard viewing window.

67. $2x - 3y = 7$ 68. $4x + 2y = -2$

69. $3y = 9$ 70. $2y + 10 = 0$

71. Use a graphing calculator to graph the line given in Exercise 41. Approximate the values of the x- and y-intercepts to support your answer in Exercise 41.

72. Use a graphing calculator to graph the line given in Exercise 42. Approximate the values of the x- and y-intercepts to support your answer in Exercise 42.

73. Use a graphing calculator to graph the line given in Exercise 47. Approximate the values of the x- and y-intercepts to support your answer in Exercise 47.

74. Use a graphing calculator to graph the line given in Exercise 46. Approximate the values of the x- and y-intercepts to support your answer in Exercise 46.

Concepts

1. Introduction to the Slope of a Line

2. The Slope Formula

3. Positive, Negative, Zero, and Undefined Slopes

4. Parallel and Perpendicular Lines

5. Applications and Interpretation of Slope

section

2.2   SLOPE OF A LINE

1.   Introduction to the Slope of a Line

At a small company, two employees are hired with two different salary plans. Employee 1 was hired at $30,000 per year and receives a $500 annual raise. Employee 2 was hired at $22,000 per year, but receives a $1500 raise each year. The following graph represents the yearly salaries of each employee (Figure 2-12).

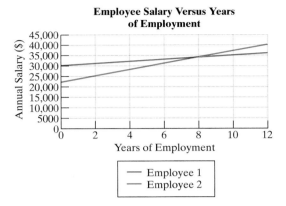

Figure 2-12

Employee 2 was not paid as much initially but receives a better raise each year. Hence, the line representing Employee 2's salary looks "steeper" because the salary is increasing at a faster rate. The *slope* of this line is therefore greater than the slope of the line representing the salary of Employee 1.

The **slope** of a line is measured by the ratio of the change in the vertical distance between two points to the change in the horizontal distance. The slope of a line can be written as the change in y over the change in x. As a memory device, we might think of the slope of a line as "*rise* over *run*."

$$\text{Slope} = \frac{\text{change in } y}{\text{change in } x} = \frac{\text{rise}}{\text{run}}$$

The slope of each line can be found by taking any two points on the line and finding the change in y and the change in x (Figure 2-13).

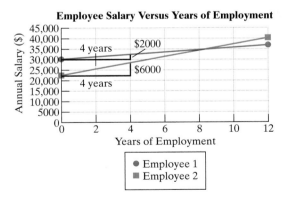

Figure 2-13

Employee 1

$$\text{Slope} = \frac{\text{change in } y}{\text{change in } x}$$

$$= \frac{\$2000}{4 \text{ years}} = \$500/\text{year}$$

Slope = \$500/year

Employee 2

$$\text{Slope} = \frac{\text{change in } y}{\text{change in } x}$$

$$= \frac{\$6000}{4 \text{ years}} = \$1500/\text{year}$$

Slope = \$1500/year

Notice that the slope of each line represents the rate of change in salary in dollars per year.

2.   The Slope Formula

The slope of a line may be found using *any* two points on the line—call these points (x_1, y_1) and (x_2, y_2). The change in y between the points can be found by taking the difference of the y-values: $y_2 - y_1$. The change in x can be found by taking the difference of the x-values in the same order: $x_2 - x_1$.

The slope of a line is often symbolized by the letter m and is given by the following formula.

Definition of the Slope of a Line

The **slope** of a line passing through the distinct points (x_1, y_1) and (x_2, y_2) is

$$m = \frac{y_2 - y_1}{x_2 - x_1} \quad \text{provided } x_2 - x_1 \neq 0$$

example 1

Finding the Slope of a Line Through Two Points

Find the slope of the line passing through the points $(1, -1)$ and $(7, 2)$.

Solution:

To use the slope formula, first label the coordinates of each point and then substitute their values into the slope formula.

$(1, -1)$ and $(7, 2)$

(x_1, y_1) (x_2, y_2) Label the points.

$$m = \frac{y_2 - y_1}{x_2 - x_1} = \frac{2 - (-1)}{7 - 1} \qquad \text{Apply the slope formula.}$$

$$= \frac{3}{6}, \qquad \text{or} \qquad m = \frac{1}{2} \qquad \text{Simplify and reduce.}$$

The slope of the line can be verified from the graph (Figure 2-14).

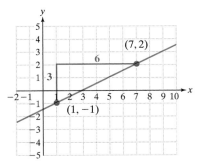

Figure 2-14

Tip: The slope formula does not depend on which point is labeled (x_1, y_1) and which point is labeled (x_2, y_2). For example, reversing the order in which the points are labeled in Example 1 results in the same slope:

$$\underset{(x_2, y_2)}{(1, -1)} \qquad \text{and} \qquad \underset{(x_1, y_1)}{(7, 2)}$$

then $m = \dfrac{-1 - 2}{1 - 7} = \dfrac{-3}{-6} = \dfrac{1}{2}$

3. Positive, Negative, Zero, and Undefined Slopes

The value of the slope of a line may be positive, negative, zero, or undefined.

Lines that "increase," or "rise," from left to right have a **positive slope**.
Lines that "decrease," or "fall," from left to right have a **negative slope**.
Horizontal lines have a **zero slope**.
Vertical lines have an **undefined slope**.

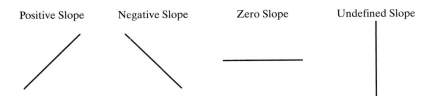

Positive Slope   Negative Slope   Zero Slope   Undefined Slope

---

example 2

Finding the Slope of a Line Between Two Points

Find the slope of the line passing through the points $(3, -4)$ and $(-5, -1)$.

Solution:

$$\underset{(x_1, y_1)}{(3, -4)} \qquad \text{and} \qquad \underset{(x_2, y_2)}{(-5, -1)} \qquad \text{Label points.}$$

$$m = \frac{y_2 - y_1}{x_2 - x_1} = \frac{-1 - (-4)}{-5 - 3} \qquad \text{Apply the slope formula.}$$

$$= \frac{3}{-8} = -\frac{3}{8} \qquad \text{Simplify.}$$

The two points can be graphed to verify that $-\frac{3}{8}$ is the correct slope (Figure 2-15).

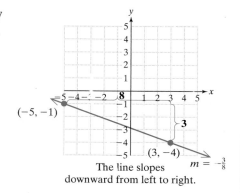

The line slopes downward from left to right.

Figure 2-15

example 3

Finding the Slope of a Line Between Two Points

Find the slope of the line passing through the points $(-3, 4)$ and $(-3, -2)$.

Solution:

$$
\begin{array}{ll}
(-3, 4) \qquad \text{and} \qquad (-3, -2) & \\
(x_1, y_1) \qquad\qquad\qquad (x_2, y_2) & \text{Label points.}
\end{array}
$$

$$m = \frac{y_2 - y_1}{x_2 - x_1} = \frac{-2 - 4}{-3 - (-3)} \qquad \text{Apply slope formula.}$$

$$= \frac{-6}{-3 + 3}$$

$$= \frac{-6}{0} \qquad \text{Undefined}$$

The slope is undefined. The points form a vertical line (Figure 2-16).

Figure 2-16

4.   Parallel and Perpendicular Lines

Lines that do not intersect are *parallel*. Nonvertical parallel lines have the same slope and different y-intercepts (Figure 2-17).

Lines that intersect at a right angle are *perpendicular*. If two lines are perpendicular then the slope of one line is the opposite of the reciprocal of the slope of the other (provided neither line is vertical) (Figure 2-18).

Slopes of Parallel Lines

If m_1 and m_2 represent the **slopes of two parallel** (nonvertical) **lines**, then

$$m_1 = m_2$$

Slopes of Perpendicular Lines

If $m_1 \neq 0$ and $m_2 \neq 0$ represent the **slopes of two perpendicular lines**, then

$$m_1 = -\frac{1}{m_2} \quad \text{or} \quad m_2 = -\frac{1}{m_1}$$

or equivalently, $m_1 \cdot m_2 = -1$

These two lines are parallel.

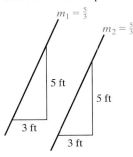

$m_1 = \frac{5}{3}$

$m_2 = \frac{5}{3}$

5 ft

5 ft

3 ft

3 ft

Figure 2-17

These lines are perpendicular.

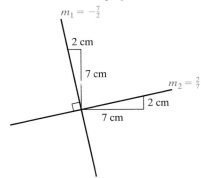

$m_1 = -\frac{7}{2}$

2 cm

7 cm

$m_2 = \frac{2}{7}$

2 cm

7 cm

Figure 2-18

---

example 4

Determining the Slope of Parallel and Perpendicular Lines

Suppose a given line has a slope of -5.

a. Find the slope of a line parallel to the given line.
b. Find the slope of a line perpendicular to the given line.

Solution:

a. The slope of a line parallel to the given line is $m = -5$ (same slope).
b. The slope of a line perpendicular to the given line is $m = \frac{1}{5}$ (the opposite of the reciprocal of -5).

---

5.   Applications and Interpretation of Slope

- If you've ever driven your car in the mountains, you may have seen road signs indicating the *percent grade*. Grade measures the slope of the road by the change in elevation per 100 ft horizontally. For example, a 4% grade means that there is a 4-ft rise in elevation for every 100 ft of horizontal distance.

4% Grade

$$m = \frac{4 \text{ ft}}{100 \text{ ft}} = 0.04 \qquad (4\% \text{ grade})$$

- When a person walks or runs on a treadmill during a stress test, the physician may change the grade of the treadmill. Increasing or decreasing the slope of the treadmill causes the patient's heart to work harder and the heart rate will increase or decrease accordingly.
- In northern states that have abundant snowfall during winter, the slope of the roof is very important. A flat roof in Michigan is dangerous because the weight of the snow in winter could cause the roof to collapse. On the other hand, a roof that is too steep may be difficult to work on.
- A *positive* slope of a line implies that as one variable increases, the other increases. For example, the rainfall-vegetation growth graph depicts the amount of rainfall on the *x*-axis and the height of a plant on the *y*-axis. We see a positive slope indicating that as rainfall increases, plants tend to grow more.
- A *negative* slope of a line implies that as one variable increases, the other decreases. For example, if the age of a used car is represented on the *x*-axis and its resale value is represented on the *y*-axis, the slope is negative. This is a decreasing trend because as a car increases in age, its resale value tends to decrease.

When two variables are related, the variable graphed on the horizontal axis is called the **independent variable**, and the variable graphed on the vertical axis is called the **dependent variable**. If a given value of *x* is independently chosen, the value of *y* is said to *depend on x*. For example, the height of a plant, *y*, *depends on* the amount of rainfall, *x*. The resale value of a car, *y*, *depends on* the age of the car, *x*.

---

example 5   **Predicting a Positive or Negative Slope Between Variables**

Assume that each of the following pairs of variables follows a linear trend. Would you expect a positive or negative slope?

	Dependent Variable, y		**Independent Variable, x**
a.	Gas mileage	versus	Speed of a car above 55 mph
b.	Test score	versus	Number of hours spent studying for a test
c.	Grade in a class	versus	Number of absences in the class
d.	Selling price of a house	versus	Number of square feet inside a house

Solution:

a. Negative: At speeds above 55 mph, the faster you drive, the lower the gas mileage.
b. Positive: In general, the more you study, the better your test score.
c. Negative: In general, the more absences you have, the lower your grade will be.
d. Positive: In general, the larger a house, the more expensive it is.

Mileage (mi/gal) — 55 — Speed (mph)

Test Score — Hours Studying

Grade — Number of Absences

Selling Price — Square Footage

example 6

Interpreting the Slope of a Line in an Application

The number of males 20 years old or older who were employed full time in the United States varied linearly from 1970 to 1998. Approximately 43.2 million males 20 years old or older were employed full time in 1970. By 1998, this number grew to 61.7 million (Figure 2-19).

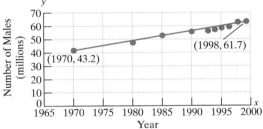

**Number of Males 20 Years Old or Older
Employed Full Time in the United States by Year**

(1998, 61.7)

(1970, 43.2)

Figure 2-19

Source: Current Population Survey.

a. Find the slope of the line using the points (1970, 43.2) and (1998, 61.7). Round the answer to two decimal places.

b. Interpret the meaning of the slope in the context of this problem.

Solution:

a. $(1970, 43.2)$ and $(1998, 61.7)$
   (x_1, y_1) (x_2, y_2) Label the points.

$$m = \frac{y_2 - y_1}{x_2 - x_1} = \frac{61.7 - 43.2}{1998 - 1970}$$ Apply the slope formula.

$$m = \frac{18.5}{28} \quad \text{or} \quad m \approx 0.66$$

b. The slope is approximately 0.66, meaning that the full-time work force of men has increased by approximately 0.66 million men (or 660,000 men) per year between 1970 and 1998.

example 7   **Finding the Slope of a Line in an Application**

Table 2-3 depicts the number of personal computers sold in the United States during the years 1990, 1994, and 1995. Data are rounded to the nearest thousand.

Table 2-3

Year	Number of Personal Computers Sold in the United States
1990	9,849,000
1994	18,605,000
1995	22,583,000

Source: U.S. Bureau of the Census.

a. Graph the data.
b. Find the average number of personal computers sold per year between 1990 and 1994 in the United States.
c. Find the average number of personal computers sold per year between 1994 and 1995 in the United States.
d. Which time interval shows the largest annual rate of increase in computer sales?

Solution:

a.

Number of Computers Sold in the United States

b. The slope of the line segment between 1990 and 1994 measures the average number of personal computers sold in the United States *per year* for that period.

(1990, 9,849,000)   and   (1994, 18,605,000)

(x_1, y_1) and (x_2, y_2)

$$m = \frac{18,605,000 - 9,849,000}{1994 - 1990} = \frac{8,756,000}{4} \approx 2,189,000 \text{ computers/year}$$

c. The slope of the line segment between 1994 and 1995 measures the average number of personal computers sold in the United States *per year* for that period.

(1994, 18,605,000)   and   (1995, 22,583,000)
(x_1, y_1) and (x_2, y_2)

$$m = \frac{22{,}583{,}000 - 18{,}605{,}000}{1995 - 1994} = \frac{3{,}978{,}800}{1} \approx 3{,}978{,}000 \text{ computers/year}$$

d. The average number of personal computers sold *per year* between 1990 and 1994 was slightly over 2 million (2,189,000 computers/year). However, between 1994 and 1995, computer sales were close to 4 million per year (3,978,000 computers/year). The yearly *rate* of computer sales was higher between 1994 and 1995.

section 2.2   PRACTICE EXERCISES

1. Find the missing coordinate so that the ordered pairs are solutions to the equation $2x - 3y = 6$.

    a. $(-1, \ )$ b. $(0, \ )$ c. $(\ , 0)$

2. Find the missing coordinate so that the ordered pairs are solutions to the equation $\frac{1}{2}x + y = 4$.

    a. $(0, \ )$ b. $(\ , 0)$ c. $(-4, \ )$

For Exercises 3–6, find the *x*- and *y*-intercepts (if possible) for each equation and sketch the graph.

3. $2x + 8 = 0$ 4. $4 - 2y = 0$

5. $2x - 2y - 6 = 0$ 6. $x + \dfrac{1}{3}y = 6$

7. In your own words, explain what the slope of a line represents.

8. Explain how to use the graph of a line to determine whether the slope of a line is positive, negative, zero, or undefined.

9. Can the slopes of two perpendicular lines both be positive? Explain your answer.

10. If the slope of a line is $\frac{4}{3}$, how many units of change in y will be produced by six units of change in x?

For Exercises 11–18, estimate the slope of the line from its graph.

11.

12.

13.

14.

15.

16.

17.

18.

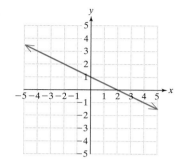

For Exercises 19–28, sketch a graph of the line through the two given points and find the slope.

19. $(6, 0)$ and $(0, -3)$ 20. $(-5, 0)$ and $(0, -4)$

21. $(-2, 3)$ and $(1, -2)$ 22. $(4, 5)$ and $(-1, 0)$

23. $(2, 3)$ and $(2, 7)$ 24. $(5, 2)$ and $(5, -3)$

25. $\left(\dfrac{3}{2}, \dfrac{4}{3}\right)$ and $\left(\dfrac{7}{2}, 1\right)$

26. $(-4.6, 4.1)$ and $(0, 6.4)$

27. $(1.1, 0.4)$ and $(-3.2, 0.4)$

28. $\left(-\dfrac{5}{3}, -1\right)$ and $\left(-\dfrac{3}{2}, -1\right)$

For Exercises 29–38, an equation of a line is given. Find: (a) two points on the line. (Answers may vary.) (b) the slope of the line. (c) the slope of any line perpendicular to the given line. (d) the slope of any line parallel to the given line.

29. $x - y = -4$ 30. $x - y = -6$

31. $y = 3x + 2$ 32. $y = -\dfrac{2}{3}x + 2$

33. $y - 3 = 0$ 34. $2x = 7$

35. $2x - y = 0$ 36. $5x + 4y = 0$

37. $x + 1 = -3$ 38. $2y = -5$

In Exercises 39–46, two points are given from each of two lines: L_1 and L_2. Without graphing the points, determine if the lines are perpendicular, parallel, or neither. In each case, explain your answer.

39. L_1: $(2, 5)$ and $(4, 9)$
     L_2: $(-1, 4)$ and $(3, 2)$

40. L_1: $(0, 0)$ and $(2, 3)$
     L_2: $(-2, 5)$ and $(0, -2)$

41. L_1: $(5, 3)$ and $(5, 9)$
     L_2: $(4, 2)$ and $(0, 2)$

42. L_1: $(3, 5)$ and $(2, 5)$
     L_2: $(2, 4)$ and $(0, 4)$

43. L_1: $(-3, -2)$ and $(2, 3)$
     L_2: $(-4, 1)$ and $(0, 5)$

44. L_1: $\left(\dfrac{1}{4}, \dfrac{2}{3}\right)$ and $\left(\dfrac{3}{4}, 1\right)$
     L_2: $\left(\dfrac{1}{2}, \dfrac{5}{4}\right)$ and $\left(\dfrac{5}{6}, \dfrac{3}{4}\right)$

45. L_1: $\left(-\dfrac{1}{5}, \dfrac{3}{2}\right)$ and $\left(\dfrac{3}{10}, -\dfrac{1}{2}\right)$
     L_2: $(3, -3)$ and $(1, 5)$

46. L_1: $(7, 1)$ and $(0, 0)$
     L_2: $(-10, -8)$ and $(4, -6)$

47. A 25-ft ladder is leaning against a house as shown in the diagram. Find the slope of the ladder.

24 ft

7 ft

Figure for Exercise 47

48. Find the pitch (slope) of the roof in the figure.

19 ft

15 ft

20 ft

Figure for Exercise 48

49. The following bar graph represents the per capita food consumption for beef, pork, chicken, turkey, and fish from the years 1970 to 1994.

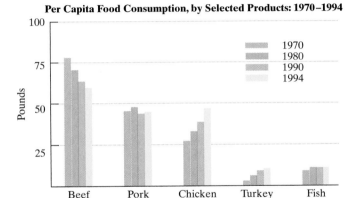

Per Capita Food Consumption, by Selected Products: 1970–1994

1970
1980
1990
1994

Pounds

100
75
50
25

Beef   Pork   Chicken   Turkey   Fish
Source: U.S. Bureau of the Census.

Figure for Exercise 49

a. Which one of the products shows a negative slope? What does a negative slope mean in the context of this graph?

b. Which products show a positive rate of increase? Which product shows the greatest rate of increase? Explain how this rate of increase relates to the slope of a line.

c. Which products show a slope of approximately zero? What does a slope of zero mean in the context of this graph?

50. The following graph shows the number of housing permits issued in Volusia and Flagler Counties in Florida from 1983 through 1995.

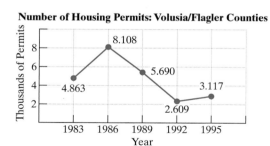

Number of Housing Permits: Volusia/Flagler Counties

Figure for Exercise 50

a. In which of the 3-year periods did the number of housing permits rise?

b. In what period did the number of housing permits decrease?

c. Compute the rate of change (slope) between each consecutive pair of data points. (Round to the nearest whole permit per year.)

51. The total enrollment in institutes of higher education (including 2-year and 4-year colleges, both public and private) in the United States has grown approximately linearly. In 1970, the number of male students who attended college was 5,044,000. That number increased to 6,524,000 by the year 1992. In 1970, the number of female students was 3,527,000 and grew to 7,963,000 by the year 1992. (*Source:* U. S. National Center for Education Statistics.)

a. Draw a graph such that the x-axis represents year and the y-axis represents college enrollment in *millions* of students. Let $x = 0$ represent the year 1970 and $x = 22$ represent the year 1992. Let y range from 0 to 8.

b. Plot the points $(0, 5.044)$ and $(22, 6.524)$. Draw a line between the points to represent the growth in enrollment of male college students between the years 1970 and 1992.

c. Plot the points $(0, 3.527)$ and $(22, 7.963)$. Draw a line between the points to represent the growth in enrollment of female college students between the years 1970 and 1992.

d. Compute the slope of each line. (Round to three decimal places.) Explain what each slope means in the context of this problem.

e. Which is larger, the rate of increase in the number of male college students or the rate of increase in the number of female college students?

f. In what year (approximately) did the number of female college students overtake the number of male college students?

52. The birthrate and death rate for selected countries for the year 1996 are given in the following table. The birthrate is computed from the number of births in 1996 per 1000 persons (based on midyear population). The death rate is computed from the number of deaths in 1996 per 1000 persons (based on midyear population).

Country	Crude Birthrate (number of births per 1000)	Crude Death Rate (number of deaths per 1000)
United States	14.8	8.8
Australia	14.0	6.9
Brazil	20.8	9.2
Bulgaria	8.3	13.6
China	17.0	6.9
Ethiopia	46.1	17.5
Italy	9.9	9.8
Saudi Arabia	38.3	37.2
Sweden	11.6	11.4
Ukraine	11.2	15.2

Source: U.S. Bureau of the Census.

a. Which country has the highest birthrate? Which country has the highest death rate?

b. Which country has the largest difference between the birthrate and death rate? What does this mean in terms of the population growth of that country?

c. Which countries have a larger death rate than birthrate? What does this mean in terms of the population growth (or decline) of these countries?

d. For which country is the birthrate approximately equal to the death rate? What does this mean in terms of the population growth of that country?

■ **EXPANDING YOUR SKILLS**

For Exercises 53–58, given a point, P, on a line and the slope, m, of the line, find a second point on the line (answers may vary). *Hint*: Graph the line to help you find the second point.

53. $P(0, 0)$ and $m = 2$

54. $P(-2, 1)$ and $m = -\dfrac{1}{3}$

55. $P(2, -3)$ and m is undefined

56. $P(-1, -4)$ and $m = \dfrac{4}{5}$

57. $P\left(0, \dfrac{4}{3}\right)$ and $m = -\dfrac{2}{3}$

58. $P(-2, 4)$ and $m = 0$

For Exercises 59–62, from the graphs provided, determine the intervals (in terms of x) of positive and negative slope.

59.

60.

61.

62.

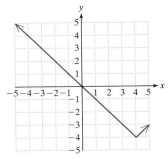

chapter 2   MIDCHAPTER REVIEW

1. Identify the *x*- and *y*-intercepts and find the slope of the line.

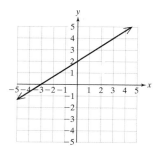

2. Identify the *x*- and *y*-intercepts and find the slope of the line.

For Exercises 3–6, graph the equation by plotting at least three points. Then identify the slope as positive, negative, zero, or undefined.

3. $3x - y = -6$

4. $2x - 4 = 0$

5. $-3y = 9$

6. $x + 4y = 10$

7. a. Find the slope of the line in the figure.

   b. Draw a line perpendicular to this line that goes through the point $(0, 2)$.

   c. What is the slope of the line drawn in part (b)?

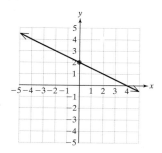

8. a. Find the slope of the line in the figure.

   b. Draw a line parallel to this line that goes through the point $(2, -1)$.

   c. What is the slope of the line drawn in part (b)?

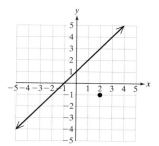

For Exercises 9–10, approximate the average slope from the figure.

9.

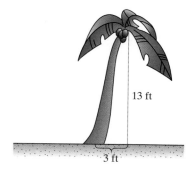

13 ft

3 ft

10.

Ski Slope

600 ft

156 ft

section

2.3 EQUATIONS OF A LINE

Concepts

1. Slope-Intercept Form

In Section 2.1, we learned that an equation of the form $ax + by = c$ (where a and b are not both zero) represents a line in a rectangular coordinate system. An equation of a line written in this way is said to be in **standard form**. In this section, we will learn a new form, called **slope-intercept form**, which is useful in determining the slope and y-intercept of a line.

Let $(0, b)$ represent the y-intercept of a line. Let (x, y) represent any other point on the line. Then the slope of the line through the two points is

$$m = \frac{(y_2 - y_1)}{(x_2 - x_1)} \quad \rightarrow \quad m = \frac{y - b}{x - 0} \qquad \text{Apply the slope formula.}$$

$$m = \frac{y - b}{x} \qquad \text{Simplify.}$$

$$m \cdot x = \left(\frac{y - b}{x}\right)x \qquad \text{Clear fractions.}$$

$$mx = y - b \qquad \text{Simplify.}$$

$$mx + b = y \quad \text{or} \quad y = mx + b \qquad \text{Solve for } y: \text{ slope-intercept form.}$$

Slope-Intercept Form of a Line

$y = mx + b$ is the slope-intercept form of a line.

m is the slope and the point $(0, b)$ is the y-intercept.

The equation, $y = -4x + 7$ is written in slope-intercept form. By inspection, we can see that the slope of the line is -4 and the y-intercept is $(0, 7)$.

2. Finding the Slope and y-Intercept of a Line

example 1   **Finding the Slope and y-Intercept of a Line**

Given the line $3x + 4y = 4$, find the slope and y-intercept.

Solution:
Write the equation in slope-intercept form, $y = mx + b$, by solving for y.

$$3x + 4y = 4$$

$$4y = -3x + 4$$

$$\frac{4y}{4} = \frac{-3x}{4} + \frac{4}{4}$$

$$y = -\frac{3}{4}x + 1 \qquad \text{The slope is } -\frac{3}{4} \text{ and the } y\text{-intercept is } (0, 1).$$

3.   Graphing a Line Using Slope-Intercept Form

The slope-intercept form is a useful tool to graph a line. The y-intercept is a known point on the line, and the slope indicates the "direction" of the line and can be used to find a second point. Using slope-intercept form to graph a line is demonstrated in the next example.

example 2

Graphing a Line by Using the Slope and y-Intercept

Graph the line $y = -\frac{3}{4}x + 1$ by using the slope and y-intercept.

Solution:
First plot the y-intercept $(0, 1)$.
The slope $m = -\frac{3}{4}$ can be written as

$$m = \frac{-3}{4}$$

the change in y is −3

the change in x is 4

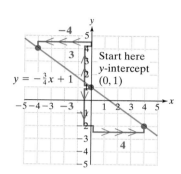

Figure 2-20

To find a second point on the line start at the y-intercept and move *down* 3 *units* and to the *right* 4 *units*. Then draw the line through the two points (Figure 2-20).
    Similarly, the slope can be written as:

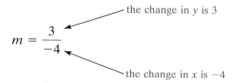

$$m = \frac{3}{-4}$$

the change in y is 3

the change in x is −4

To find a second point on the line start at the y-intercept and move *up* 3 *units* and to the *left* 4 *units*. Then draw the line through the two points (see Figure 2-20).

4.   Writing an Equation of a Line Using Slope-Intercept Form

The slope-intercept form of a line can also be used to write an equation of a line when the slope is known and a point on the line is known.

example 3

Writing an Equation of a Line Using Slope-Intercept Form

Write an equation of the line whose slope is $-\frac{1}{4}$ and whose y-intercept is $(0, -3)$.

Solution:

The slope is given as $m = -\frac{1}{4}$ and the y-intercept $(0, b)$ is given as $(0, -3)$. Substitute $m = -\frac{1}{4}$ and $b = -3$ into slope-intercept form.

$$y = mx + b$$

$$y = -\frac{1}{4}x - 3$$

In Example 3, both the slope and y-intercept were given in the problem, and the values of m and b could be substituted directly into slope-intercept form. What if the y-intercept is not known, but a different point is given instead? Example 4 illustrates this case.

example 4

Writing an Equation of a Line Using Slope-Intercept Form

Write an equation of the line having a slope of 2 and passing through the point $(-3, 1)$. Write the answer in slope-intercept form.

Solution:

To find an equation of a line using slope-intercept form, it is necessary to find the value of m and b. The slope is given in the problem as $m = 2$. Therefore, the slope-intercept form becomes

$$y = mx + b$$

$$= 2x + b$$

Because the point $(-3, 1)$ is on the line, it is a solution to the equation. Therefore, to find b, substitute the values of x and y from the ordered pair $(-3, 1)$ and solve the resulting equation.

$$y = 2x + b$$
$$1 = 2(-3) + b \qquad \text{Substitute } y = 1 \text{ and } x = -3.$$
$$1 = -6 + b \qquad \text{Simplify and solve for } b.$$
$$7 = b$$

Now with m and b known, the slope-intercept form is $y = 2x + 7$.

Tip: The equation from Example 4 can be checked by graphing the line $y = 2x + 7$. The slope $m = 2$ can be written as $m = \frac{2}{1}$. Therefore, to graph the line, start at the y-intercept $(0, 7)$ and move up 2 units and to the right 1 unit.

The graph verifies that the line passes through the point $(-3, 1)$ as it should.

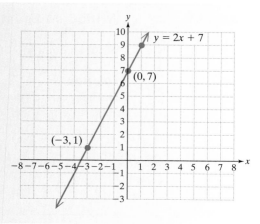

5.   The Point-Slope Formula

Another useful tool to study linear equations is the point-slope formula.

Suppose a line passes through a given point (x_1, y_1) and has slope m. If (x, y) is any other point on the line, then:

$$m = \frac{y - y_1}{x - x_1} \qquad \text{Slope formula}$$

$$m(x - x_1) = \frac{y - y_1}{x - x_1}(x - x_1) \qquad \text{Clear fractions.}$$

$$m(x - x_1) = y - y_1$$

or

$$y - y_1 = m(x - x_1) \qquad \text{Point-slope formula}$$

The Point-Slope Formula

The **point-slope formula** is given by

$$y - y_1 = m(x - x_1)$$

where m is the slope of the line and (x_1, y_1) is a known point on the line.

As its name indicates, the point-slope formula is used to find an equation of a line when a point on the line is known and the slope is known.

6.   Writing an Equation of a Line Using the Point-Slope Formula

example 5   **Using the Point-Slope Formula to Find an Equation of a Line**

Use the point-slope formula to find an equation of the line having a slope of $\frac{2}{3}$ and passing through the point $(-2, 1)$. Write the answer in slope-intercept form.

Solution:

$$m = \frac{2}{3} \quad \text{and} \quad (x_1, y_1) = (-2, 1)$$

$$y - y_1 = m(x - x_1)$$

$$y - 1 = \frac{2}{3}[x - (-2)] \qquad \text{Apply the point-slope formula.}$$

$$y - 1 = \frac{2}{3}(x + 2) \qquad \text{Simplify.}$$

To write the final answer in slope-intercept form, clear parentheses and solve for y.

$$y - 1 = \frac{2}{3}x + \frac{4}{3} \qquad \text{Clear parentheses.}$$

$$= \frac{2}{3}x + \frac{4}{3} + 1 \qquad \text{Solve for } y.$$

$$= \frac{2}{3}x + \frac{4}{3} + \frac{3}{3} \qquad \text{Find a common denominator.}$$

$$= \frac{2}{3}x + \frac{7}{3} \qquad \text{The final answer is written in slope-intercept form.}$$

Graphing Calculator Box

We can graph the line from Example 5 to determine whether it passes through the point $(-2, 1)$. We may use a *value* function (or *eval* function) on the calculator to find the value of y when x is -2.

A *trace* feature may be used to estimate points on a line. However, when tracing a graph, the calculator may not return the exact coordinates of points on the graph. This is a result of the choice of scaling and the limited pixel resolution on the calculator.

example 6

Finding an Equation of a Line Through Two Points

Find an equation of the line passing through the points $(5, -1)$ and $(3, 1)$. Write the final answer in slope-intercept form.

Solution:

The slope formula can be used to compute the slope of the line between two points. Once the slope is known, either the slope-intercept form or the point-slope formula can be used to find an equation of the line. We will use the point-slope formula in this example.

First find the slope.

$$m = \frac{y_2 - y_1}{x_2 - x_1} = \frac{1 - (-1)}{3 - 5} = \frac{2}{-2} = -1 \qquad \text{Hence, } m = -1.$$

Next, apply the point-slope formula.

$$y - y_1 = m(x - x_1)$$

$$y - 1 = -1(x - 3) \qquad \text{Substitute } m = -1 \text{ and use } \textit{either} \text{ point for } (x_1, y_1). \text{ We will use } (3, 1) \text{ for } (x_1, y_1).$$

$$y - 1 = -x + 3 \qquad \text{Clear parentheses.}$$

$$y = -x + 3 + 1 \qquad \text{Solve for } y.$$

$$y = -x + 4 \qquad \text{The final answer is in slope-intercept form.}$$

Tip: In Example 6, the point $(3, 1)$ was used for (x_1, y_1) in the point-slope formula. However, either point may have been used. Using the point $(5, -1)$ for (x_1, y_1) produces the same final equation:

$$y - (-1) = -1(x - 5)$$

$$y + 1 = -x + 5$$

$$y = -x + 4$$

example 7

Finding an Equation of a Line Perpendicular to Another Line

Find an equation of the line passing through the point $(4, 3)$ and perpendicular to the line $2x + 3y = 3$. Write the final answer in slope-intercept form.

Solution:

The slope of the given line can be found from its slope-intercept form.

$$2x + 3y = 3$$

$$3y = -2x + 3 \qquad \text{Solve for } y.$$

$$\frac{3y}{3} = \frac{-2x}{3} + \frac{3}{3}$$

$$y = -\frac{2}{3}x + 1 \qquad \text{The slope is } -\frac{2}{3}.$$

The slope of a line *perpendicular* to this line must be the opposite of the reciprocal of $-\frac{2}{3}$; hence, $m = \frac{3}{2}$. Using $m = \frac{3}{2}$ and the known point $(4, 3)$, we can apply slope-intercept form or the point-slope formula to find the equation of the line. In this example, we use the point-slope formula.

$$y - y_1 = m(x - x_1)$$ Apply the point-slope formula.

$$y - 3 = \frac{3}{2}(x - 4)$$ Substitute $m = \frac{3}{2}$ and $(4, 3)$ for (x_1, y_1).

$$y - 3 = \frac{3}{2}x - 6$$ Clear parentheses.

$$y = \frac{3}{2}x - 6 + 3$$ Solve for y.

$$y = \frac{3}{2}x - 3$$

Tip: In Example 7, we could have used slope-intercept form to find an equation of the line through the point $(4, 3)$, having slope $m = \frac{3}{2}$.

$$y = mx + b$$

$$3 = \frac{3}{2}(4) + b$$ Substitute $y = 3, x = 4, m = \frac{3}{2}$.

$$3 = 6 + b$$ Solve for b.

$$-3 = b$$

$$y = \frac{3}{2}x - 3$$ Slope-intercept form of the line

Graphing Calculator Box

From Example 7, the line $y = \frac{3}{2}x - 3$ should be perpendicular to the line $y = -\frac{2}{3}x + 1$ and should pass through the point $(4, 3)$.

 Note: In this example, we are using a square window option, which sets the scale to display distances on the x- and y-axes as equal units of measure.

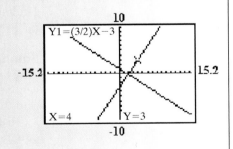

7. Different Forms of Linear Equations

A linear equation can be written in several different forms as summarized in Table 2-4.

Table 2-4

Form	Example	Comments
Standard Form $ax + by = c$	$2x + 3y = 6$	a and b must not *both* be zero.
Horizontal Line $y = k$ (k is constant)	$y = 3$	The slope is zero, and the y-intercept is $(0, k)$.
Vertical Line $x = k$ (k is constant)	$x = -2$	The slope is undefined and the x-intercept is $(k, 0)$.
Slope-Intercept Form $y = mx + b$ Slope is m y-Intercept is $(0, b)$	$y = -2x + 5$ slope $= -2$ y-intercept is $(0, 5)$	Solving a linear equation for y results in slope-intercept form. The coefficient of the x-term is the slope, and the constant defines the location of the y-intercept.
Point-Slope Formula $y - y_1 = m(x - x_1)$ Slope is m and (x_1, y_1) is a point on the line.	$m = -2$ $(x_1, y_1) = (3, 1)$ $y - 1 = -2(x - 3)$	This formula is typically used to build an equation of a line when a point on the line is known and the slope is known.

Although it is important to understand and apply slope-intercept form and the point-slope formula, they are not necessarily applicable to all problems. The following example illustrates how a little ingenuity may lead to a simple solution.

example 8

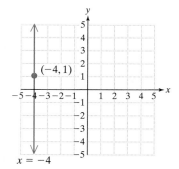

$x = -4$

Figure 2-21

Finding an Equation of a Line

Find an equation of the line passing through the point $(-4, 1)$ and perpendicular to the x-axis.

Solution:

Any line perpendicular to the x-axis must be *vertical*. Recall that all vertical lines can be written in the form $x = k$, where k is constant. A quick sketch can help find the value of the constant (Figure 2-21).

Because the line must pass through a point whose x-coordinate is -4, the equation of the line is $x = -4$.

Tip: Vertical lines cannot be written in slope-intercept form.

section 2.3 PRACTICE EXERCISES

1. Is the equation $2x - 3y - 4 = 0$ linear?

2. Is the equation $y = 5x + 2$ linear?

3. Given

$$\frac{x}{2} + \frac{y}{3} = \frac{1}{6}$$

a. Find the x-intercept.

b. Find the y-intercept.

c. Sketch the graph.

4. Given

$$2x - 5y = 7$$

a. Find the x-intercept.

b. Find the y-intercept.

c. Sketch the graph.

5. Using slopes, how do you determine whether two lines are parallel?

6. Using slopes of a line, how do you determine whether two lines are perpendicular?

7. Define the slope of a line.

8. Write the formula to find the slope of a line given two points, (x_1, y_1) and (x_2, y_2).

9. Given the two points $(-1, -2)$ and $(2, 4)$;

a. Find the slope of the line containing the two points.

b. Find the slope of a line parallel to the line containing the points.

c. Find the slope of a line perpendicular to the line containing the points.

10. Given the two points $(4, -3)$ and $(2, 3)$;

a. Find the slope of the line containing the two points.

b. Find the slope of a line parallel to the line containing the points.

c. Find the slope of a line perpendicular to the line containing the points.

 11. Graph the line that passes through the point $(2, 1)$ and has a slope of $-\frac{2}{3}$.

12. Graph the line that passes through the point $(-1, -4)$ and has a slope of $\frac{5}{3}$.

13. Graph the line that passes through the point $(0, 2)$ and has a slope of 3.

14. Graph the line that passes through the point $(0, 1)$ and has a slope of -4.

15. Graph the line that passes through the point $(-2, 6)$ and has a slope of 0.

16. Graph the line that passes through the point $(1, -7)$ and has a slope of 0.

In Exercises 17–22, match the equation with the correct graph.

17. $y = \frac{3}{2}x - 2$ a.

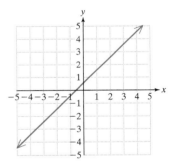

18. $y = -x + 3$ b.

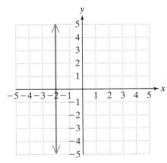

19. $y = \frac{13}{4}$ c.

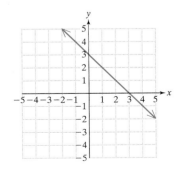

20. $y = x + \dfrac{1}{2}$ d.

21. $x = -2$ e.

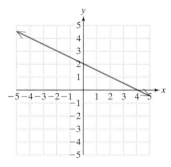

22. $y = -\dfrac{1}{2}x + 2$ f.

23. Is the equation $x = -2$ in slope-intercept form? Identify the slope and y-intercept.

24. Is the equation $x = 1$ in slope-intercept form? Identify the slope and y-intercept.

25. Is the equation $y = 3$ in slope-intercept form? Identify the slope and the y-intercept.

26. Is the equation $y = -5$ in slope-intercept form? Identify the slope and the y-intercept.

For Exercises 27–38, write the equations in slope-intercept form (if possible). Then graph each line using the slope and y-intercept.

27. $-4x + y = 2$
28. $3x + y = 5$
 29. $3x + 2y = 6$
30. $x - 2y = 8$

31. $5x - 3y = 6$
32. $x + 8y = 2$

33. $2 + \dfrac{1}{2}y = 1$
34. $2y - 4 = 0$

35. $3x - 1 = 5$
36. $2x + 1 = -5$

37. $2x - 5y = 0$
38. $3x - y = 0$

In Exercises 39–62, find an equation of the line satisfying the given conditions. Write your final answer in slope-intercept form.

39. The line passes through the point $(0, -2)$ and has a slope of 3.

40. The line passes through the point $(0, 5)$ and has a slope of $-\dfrac{1}{2}$.

41. The line passes through the point $(2, 7)$ and has a slope of 2.

42. The line passes through the point $(3, 10)$ and has a slope of -2.

43. The line passes through the point $(6, -3)$ and has a slope of $-\dfrac{4}{5}$.

 44. The line passes through the point $(7, -2)$ and has a slope of $\dfrac{7}{2}$.

45. The line passes through $(0, 4)$ and $(3, 0)$.

46. The line passes through $(1, 1)$ and $(3, 7)$.

47. The line passes through $(6, 12)$ and $(4, 10)$.

48. The line passes through $(-2, -1)$ and $(3, -4)$.

49. The line passes through the point $(2, -3)$ and has a zero slope.

50. The line contains the point $(3, 5)$ and has an undefined slope.

51. The line contains the point $\left(\dfrac{5}{2}, 0\right)$ and has an undefined slope.

52. The line contains the point $(3, 5)$ and has a zero slope.

53. The line contains the point $(3, 2)$ and is parallel to a line with slope $-\dfrac{3}{4}$.

54. The line contains the point $(3, 2)$ and is perpendicular to a line with slope $-\dfrac{3}{4}$.

55. The line contains the point $(2, 4)$ and is perpendicular to the line $y = -\frac{2}{3}x + 7$.

56. The line contains the point $(2, -5)$ and is parallel to $y = \frac{3}{4}x + \frac{7}{4}$.

57. The line contains the point $(4, -2)$ and is parallel to $3x - 4y = 8$.

58. The line contains the point $(-1, 6)$ and is perpendicular to the line $2x + 3y = 6$.

59. The line contains the point $(4, 5)$ and is parallel to the x-axis.

60. The line contains the point $(3, -2)$ and is perpendicular to the x-axis.

61. The line contains the point $(7, 11)$ and is perpendicular to the y-axis.

62. The line contains the point $(7, 11)$ and is parallel to the y-axis.

■ EXPANDING YOUR SKILLS

63. Create a "box" of four vertical and horizontal lines that encloses the point $(-3, 5)$. Write the equations of the lines. (Answers may vary.)

64. Create a "box" of four vertical and horizontal lines that enclose the point $(2, 7)$. Write the equations of the lines. (Answers may vary.)

65. Create a "box" of four non-vertical and non-horizontal lines that enclose the point $(0, 0)$. Write the equations of the lines. (Answers may vary.)

66. Create a "box" of four non-vertical and non-horizontal lines that enclose the point $(1, 1)$. Write the equations of the lines. (Answers may vary.)

■ GRAPHING CALCULATOR EXERCISES

67. Use a graphing calculator to graph the lines on the same viewing window. Then explain how the lines are related.

$$y_1 = \frac{1}{2}x + 4$$

$$y_2 = \frac{1}{2}x - 2$$

68. Use a graphing calculator to graph the lines on the same viewing window. Then explain how the lines are related.

$$y_1 = -\frac{1}{3}x + 5$$

$$y_2 = -\frac{1}{3}x - 3$$

69. Use a graphing calculator to graph the lines on the same viewing window. Then explain how the lines are related.

$$y_1 = x - 2$$
$$y_2 = 2x - 2$$
$$y_3 = 3x - 2$$

70. Use a graphing calculator to graph the lines on the same viewing window. Then explain how the lines are related.

$$y_1 = -2x + 1$$
$$y_2 = -3x + 1$$
$$y_3 = -4x + 1$$

71. Use a graphing calculator to graph the lines on a square viewing window. Then explain how the lines are related.

$$y_1 = 4x - 1$$
$$y_2 = -\frac{1}{4}x - 1$$

72. Use a graphing calculator to graph the lines on a square viewing window. Then explain how the lines are related.

$$y_1 = \frac{1}{2}x - 3$$
$$y_2 = -2x - 3$$

73. Use a graphing calculator to graph the equation from Exercise 45. Use an *Eval* feature to verify that the line passes through the points $(0, 4)$ and $(3, 0)$.

74. Use a graphing calculator to graph the equation from Exercise 46. Use an *Eval* feature to verify that the line passes through the points $(1, 1)$ and $(3, 7)$.

75. Use a graphing calculator to graph the equation you found from Exercise 55. Use an *Eval* feature to verify that the line passes through the point (2, 4) and is perpendicular to the line $y = -\frac{2}{3}x + 7$.

76. Use a graphing calculator to graph the equation you found from Exercise 56. Use an *Eval* feature to verify that the line passes through the point (2, −5) and is parallel to the line $y = \frac{3}{4}x + \frac{7}{4}$.

Concepts

1. **Writing a Linear Model**

2. **Interpreting a Linear Model**

3. **Finding a Linear Model from Observed Data Points**

4. **The Midpoint Formula**

5. **Applications of the Midpoint Formula**

section

2.4 APPLICATIONS OF LINEAR EQUATIONS AND GRAPHING

1. Writing a Linear Model

Algebra is a tool used to model events that occur in physical and biological sciences, sports, medicine, economics, business, and many other fields. The purpose of modeling is to represent a relationship between two or more variables with an algebraic equation.

For an equation written in slope-intercept form, $y = mx + b$, the term mx is the **variable term**, and the term b is the **constant term**. The value of the term mx changes with the value of x (this is why the slope is called a rate of change). However, the term b remains constant regardless of the value of x. With these ideas in mind, a linear equation can be created if the rate of change and the constant are known.

---

example 1

Finding a Linear Relationship

Buffalo, New York had 2 ft of snow (24 in.) on the ground before a snowstorm. During the storm, snow fell at an average rate of $\frac{5}{8}$ in./h.

a. Write a linear equation to compute the total snow depth, y, after x hours of the storm.
b. Graph the equation.
c. Use the equation to compute the depth of snow after 8 h.
d. If the snow depth is 31.5 in. at the end of the storm, determine how long the storm lasted.

Solution:

a. The constant or base amount of snow before the storm began is 24 in. The variable amount is given by $\frac{5}{8}$ in. of snow per hour. If m is replaced by $\frac{5}{8}$ and b is replaced by 24, we have the linear equation:

$$y = mx + b$$

$$y = \frac{5}{8}x + 24$$

b. The equation is in slope-intercept form and the corresponding graph is shown in Figure 2-22.

Figure 2-22

c. $y = \dfrac{5}{8}x + 24$

$y = \dfrac{5}{8}(8) + 24$ Substitute $x = 8$.

$y = 5 + 24$ Solve for y.

$y = 29$ in.

The snow depth is 29 in. after 8 h. The corresponding ordered pair is $(8, 29)$ and can be confirmed from the graph.

d. $y = \dfrac{5}{8}x + 24$

     $31.5 = \dfrac{5}{8}x + 24$ Substitute $y = 31.5$.

     $8(31.5) = 8\left(\dfrac{5}{8}x + 24\right)$ Multiply by 8 to clear fractions.

     $252 = 5x + 192$ Clear parentheses.

     $60 = 5x$ Solve for x.

     $12 = x$

The storm lasted for 12 h. The corresponding ordered pair is $(12, 31.5)$ and can be confirmed from the graph.

2. Interpreting a Linear Model

example 2   **Interpreting a Linear Model**

In 1938, President Franklin D. Roosevelt signed a bill enacting the Fair Labor Standards Act of 1938 (FLSA). In its final form, the act banned oppressive child labor and set the minimum hourly wage at 25 cents and the maximum workweek at 44 h. Over the years, the minimum hourly wage has been increased by the government to meet the rising cost of living.

The minimum hourly wage, y, (in dollars/hour) in the United States between 1960 and 1995 can be approximated by the equation:

$$y = 0.10x + 0.82 \quad x \geq 0$$

where x represents the number of years since 1960 ($x = 0$ corresponds to 1960, $x = 1$ corresponds to 1961, and so on) (Figure 2-23).

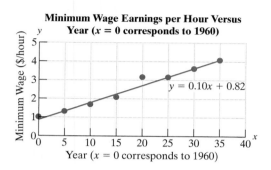

Minimum Wage Earnings per Hour Versus Year ($x = 0$ corresponds to 1960)

$y = 0.10x + 0.82$

Figure 2-23

a. Find the slope of the line and interpret the meaning of the slope in the context of this problem.
b. Find the y-intercept of the line and interpret the meaning of the y-intercept in the context of this problem.
c. Use the linear equation to approximate the minimum wage in 1985.
d. Use the linear equation to predict the minimum wage in the year 2010.

Solution:

a. The equation $y = 0.10x + 0.82$ is written in slope-intercept form. The slope is 0.10 and indicates that minimum hourly wage rose an average of $0.10 per year between 1960 and 1995.
b. The y-intercept is $(0, 0.82)$. The y-intercept indicates that the minimum wage in the year 1960 ($x = 0$) was approximately $0.82/h. (The actual value of minimum wage in 1960 was $1.00/h.)
c. The year 1985 is 25 years after the year 1960. Substitute $x = 25$ into the linear equation.

$$y = 0.10x + 0.82$$

$$y = 0.10(25) + 0.82 \qquad \text{Substitute } x = 25.$$

$$y = 2.50 + 0.82$$

$$y = 3.32$$

According to the linear model, the minimum wage in 1985 was approximately $3.32 per hour. (The actual minimum wage in 1985 was $3.35/h.)

d. The year 2010 is 50 years after the year 1960. Substitute $x = 50$ into the linear equation.

$$y = 0.10x + 0.82$$

$$y = 0.10(50) + 0.82 \qquad \text{Substitute } x = 50.$$

$$y = 5.82$$

According to the linear model, minimum wage in 2010 will be approximately $5.82/h provided the linear trend continues. (How does this compare with the current value for minimum wage?)

Graphing Calculator Box

A *Table* feature on a graphing calculator provides a means to evaluate the y-values of a linear equation for various values of *x*. For the equation $y = 0.10x + 0.82$ from Example 2, the table is set to begin at $x = 20$ and to increase *x* in increments of 5.

X	Y1
20	2.82
25	3.32
30	3.82
35	4.32
40	4.82
45	5.32
50	5.82

X=20

3. Finding a Linear Model from Observed Data Points

Graphing a set of data points offers a visual method to determine whether the points follow a linear pattern. If a linear trend exists, we say that there is a linear correlation between the two variables. The better the points "line up," the stronger the correlation.*

When two variables are correlated, it is often desirable to find a mathematical equation (or *model*) to describe the relationship between the variables.

example 3

Writing a Linear Model from Observed Data

Figure 2-24 represents the winning gold medal times for the women's 100-m freestyle swimming event for selected summer Olympics. Let *y* represent the winning time in seconds and let *x* represent the number of years since 1900 ($x = 0$ corresponds to 1900, $x = 1$ corresponds to 1901, and so on).

Women's 100-Meter Freestyle Winning Time for Selected Olympics Years

Figure 2-24

*The strength of a linear correlation can be measured mathematically using techniques often covered in statistics courses.

In 1924, the winning time was 72.4 s. This corresponds to the ordered pair (24, 72.4). In 1972, the winning time was 58.6 s, yielding the ordered pair (72, 58.6). Use these ordered pairs to find a linear equation to model the winning time versus the year.

Solution:

The slope formula can be used to compute the slope of the line between the two points. (Round the slope to two decimal places.)

$$(24, 72.4) \quad \text{and} \quad (72, 58.6)$$

$$(x_1, y_1) \quad \text{and} \quad (x_2, y_2)$$

$$m = \frac{y_2 - y_1}{x_2 - x_1} = \frac{58.6 - 72.4}{72 - 24} = -0.2875 \qquad \text{Hence, } m \approx -0.29.$$

$$y - y_1 = m(x - x_1) \qquad \qquad \text{Apply the point-slope formula using } m = -0.29 \text{ and the point } (24, 72.4).$$

$$y - 72.4 = -0.29(x - 24)$$

$$y - 72.4 = -0.29x + 6.96 \qquad \qquad \text{Clear parentheses.}$$

$$y = -0.29x + 6.96 + 72.4 \qquad \qquad \text{Solve for } y.$$

$$y = -0.29x + 79.36 \qquad \qquad \text{The answer is in slope-intercept form.}$$

Questions for Further Discussion

1. What is the slope of the line, and what does it mean in the context of the problem?

Solution:

The slope is -0.29 and indicates that the winning time in the women's 100-m Olympic freestyle event has *decreased* on the average by 0.29 s per year during this period.

2. Use the linear equation to approximate the winning time for the women's 100-m freestyle in the 1964 Olympics.

Solution:

The year 1964 is 64 years after the year 1900. Substitute $x = 64$ into the linear model.

$$y = -0.29x + 79.36$$

$$y = -0.29(64) + 79.36 \qquad \text{Substitute } x = 64.$$

$$y = -18.56 + 79.36$$

$$y = 60.8$$

According to the linear model, the winning time in 1964 was approximately 60.8 s. (The actual winning time in 1964 was set by Dawn Fraser from Australia in 59.5 s. The linear equation can only be used to *approximate* the winning time.)

3. Would it be practical to use the linear model to predict the winning time in the women's 100-m freestyle in the year 2050?

Solution:

It would not be practical to use the linear model $y = -0.29x + 79.36$ to predict the winning time in the year 2050. There is no guarantee that the linear trend will continue beyond the last observed data point in 1996. In fact, the linear trend cannot continue indefinitely, otherwise the swimmers' times would be negative by the year 2151. The potential for error increases for predictions made beyond the last observed data value.

---

example 4

Writing a Linear Model from Observed Data

Throughout his career, Shaquille O'Neal has been one of the highest scoring players in the NBA. As one would expect, the number of points Shaquille can make in a game is related to the number of minutes he plays. Table 2-5 displays the number of minutes Shaquille played and the corresponding number of points he made for selected games during his 1998–1999 season with the Los Angeles Lakers.

Table 2-5

Game	Minutes	Points
Feb 16, 1999 vs. Charlotte Hornets	26	20
March 10, 1999 vs. Los Angeles Clippers	36	31
March 14, 1999 vs. Sacramento Kings	39	33
April 6, 1999 vs. Utah Jazz	30	24
April 24, 1999 vs. San Antonio Spurs	34	26

a. Graph the data to determine whether a linear trend exists. Because the number of points scored *depends* on the number of minutes played, use the number of points as the dependent variable, y, and the number of minutes played as the independent variable, x.

b. Find an equation of the line through the ordered pairs $(26, 20)$ and $(34, 26)$.

Solution:

a.

Number of Points Scored by Shaquille O'Neal Versus the Number of Minutes Played

Figure 2-25

b. Figure 2-25 illustrates a linear pattern. We can use two points that seem to approximate the linear trend, for example, (26, 20) and (34, 26).

$$(26, 20) \quad \text{and} \quad (34, 26)$$

$$(x_1, y_1) \quad \text{and} \quad (x_2, y_2)$$

The slope of the line is

$$m = \frac{26 - 20}{34 - 26} = \frac{6}{8} = 0.75$$

$y - y_1 = m(x - x_1)$	Apply the point-slope formula.
$y - 20 = 0.75(x - 26)$	Substitute $m = 0.75$ and (26, 20) for (x_1, y_1).
$y - 20 = 0.75x - 19.5$	Clear parentheses.
$y = 0.75x + 0.5$	Solve for y.

Questions for Further Discussion

1. What does the equation $y = 0.75x + 0.5$ represent in the context of the observed data?

Solution:
This equation is a linear model that predicts the number of points Shaquille O'Neal will score versus the number of minutes he plays.

2. What is the slope of this line, and what does it represent in the context of this problem?

Solution:
The slope is 0.75. That is, for every minute played, Shaquille will expect to score an average of 0.75 points. Because 0.75 is equal to $\frac{3}{4}$, we can also say that Shaq will expect to score an average of 3 points for every 4 min he plays.

3. If Shaquille O'Neal plays for 38 min, predict the number of points he might score.

Solution:
Substitute $x = 38$ into the model.

$$y = 0.75x + 0.5$$

$$y = 0.75(38) + 0.5$$

$$y = 29$$

If Shaquille plays 38 min, he would be expected to score approximately 29 points.

4. If Shaquille scored only 17 points during a game, use the linear equation to approximate the number of minutes he played.

Solution:

$$y = 0.75x + 0.5$$

$$17 = 0.75x + 0.5 \qquad \text{Substitute } y = 17 \text{ into the equation.}$$

$$17 - 0.5 = 0.75x$$

$$16.5 = 0.75x$$

$$x = \frac{16.5}{0.75}$$

$$x = 22$$

If Shaquille scored 17 points, he may have played about 22 min.

4. The Midpoint Formula

Consider the line segment defined by the points (x_1, y_1) and (x_2, y_2). The midpoint of the line segment is given by the formula:

Midpoint formula: $\left(\dfrac{x_1 + x_2}{2}, \dfrac{y_1 + y_2}{2} \right)$

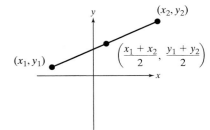

Tip: The midpoint of a line segment is found by taking the *average* of the x-coordinates and the *average* of the y-coordinates of the endpoints.

5. Applications of the Midpoint Formula

example 5

Applying the Midpoint Formula

A map of a national park is created so that the ranger station is at the origin of a rectangular grid. Two hikers are located at positions $(2, 3)$ and $(-5, -2)$ with respect to the ranger station where all units are in miles. The hikers would like to meet at a point halfway between them (Figure 2-26), but they are too far apart to communicate their positions to each other via radio. However, the hikers are both within radio range of the ranger station. If the ranger station relays each hiker's position to the other, at what point on the map should the hikers meet?

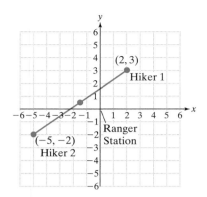

Figure 2-26

Solution:

To find the halfway point on the line segment between the two hikers, apply the midpoint formula:

$$(2, 3) \qquad \text{and} \qquad (-5, -2)$$

$$(x_1, y_1) \qquad \text{and} \qquad (x_2, y_2)$$

$$\left(\frac{x_1 + x_2}{2}, \frac{y_1 + y_2}{2}\right)$$

$$\left(\frac{2 + (-5)}{2}, \frac{3 + (-2)}{2}\right) \qquad \text{Apply the midpoint formula.}$$

$$\left(\frac{-3}{2}, \frac{1}{2}\right)$$

The halfway point between the hikers is located at $\left(-\frac{3}{2}, \frac{1}{2}\right)$ or $(-1.5, 0.5)$.

---

section 2.4   PRACTICE EXERCISES

1. True or false. If an answer is false, explain why.

   a. The graph of a linear equation always has an x-intercept.

   b. The graph of a linear equation always has a y-intercept.

2. True or false. If an answer is false, explain why.

   a. The x- and y-intercepts of a linear equation are always different points.

   b. Every graph of a line must have an x-intercept or a y-intercept or both.

For Exercises 3–6, write the equation in slope-intercept form (if possible) and graph the line.

3. $2x - 2y - 4 = 0$ 4. $2x + 3y = -12$

5. $2x - 4 = 6$ 6. $3 - 2y = -6$

7. Given the two points $(-3, -4)$ and $(3, -6)$:

   a. Find the slope of the line passing through the two points.

   b. Find an equation of the line passing through the two points. Write the answer in slope-intercept form and graph the line.

   c. Find an equation of any line parallel to the line found in part (b). (Answers may vary.)

   d. Find an equation of any line perpendicular to the line found in part (b). (Answers may vary.)

8. Given the two points $(-5, -1)$ and $(-2, -4)$:

    a. Find the slope of the line passing through the two points.

    b. Find an equation of the line passing through the two points. Write the answer in slope-intercept form and graph the line.

    c. Find an equation of any line parallel to the line found in part (b). (Answers may vary.)

    d. Find an equation of any line perpendicular to the line found in part (b). (Answers may vary.)

9. Find an equation of the line parallel to the y-axis and passing through the point $(-2, -3)$. Graph the line.

10. Find an equation of the line passing through the point $(-2, -3)$ and perpendicular to the y-axis. Write the answer in slope-intercept form and graph the line.

11. A car rental company charges a flat fee of $19.95 plus $0.20 per mile.

    a. Write an equation that expresses the cost, y, of renting a car if the car is driven for x miles.

    b. Graph the equation.

    c. What is the y-intercept and what does it mean in the context of this problem?

    d. Using the equation from part (a), find the cost of driving the rental car 50 miles, 100 miles, and 200 miles.

    e. Find the total cost of driving the rental car 100 miles if the sales tax is 6%.

    f. Is it reasonable to use negative values for x in the equation? Why or why not?

12. Alex is a sales representative and earns a base salary of $1000 per month plus a 4% commission on his sales for the month.

    a. Write a linear equation that expresses Alex's monthly salary, y, in terms of his sales, x.

    b. Graph the equation.

    c. What is the y-intercept and what does it represent in the context of this problem?

    d. What is the slope of the line and what does it represent in the context of this problem?

    e. How much will Alex make if his sales for a given month are $30,000?

13. Ava recently purchased a home in Crescent Beach, Florida. Her property taxes for the first year are $2742 per year. Ava estimates that her taxes will increase at a rate of $52 per year.

    a. Write an equation to compute Ava's yearly property taxes. Let y be the amount she pays in taxes, and let x be the time in years.

    b. Graph the line.

    c. What is the slope of this line? What does the slope of the line represent in the context of this problem?

    d. What is the y-intercept? What does the y-intercept represent in the context of this problem?

    e. What will Ava's yearly property tax be in 10 years? In 15 years?

14. Luigi Luna has started a chain of Italian restaurants called Luna Italiano. He has 19 restaurants in various locations in the northeast United States and Canada. He plans to open five new restaurants per year.

    a. Write a linear equation to express the number of stores Luigi opens, y, in terms of the time in years, x.

    b. How many stores will he have in 4 years?

    c. How many years will it take him to have 100 stores?

15. Sound travels at approximately one fifth of a mile per second. Therefore, for every 5 seconds difference between seeing lightning and hearing thunder, we can estimate that a storm is approximately 1 mile away. Let y represent the distance (in miles) that a storm is from an observer. Let x represent the difference in time between seeing

lightning and hearing thunder. Then the distance of the storm can be approximated by the equation $y = 0.2x$, where $x \geq 0$.

a. Use the linear model provided to determine how far away a storm is for the following differences in time between seeing lightning and hearing thunder:

11 s

4 s

15 s

b. If a storm is 4.2 miles away, how many seconds will pass between seeing lightning and hearing thunder?

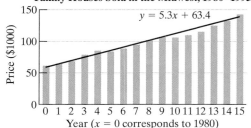 16. The force, y, (in pounds) required to stretch a particular spring x inches beyond its rest (or "equilibrium") position is given by the equation $y = 2.5x$, where $0 \leq x \leq 12$.

a. Use the equation to determine the amount of force necessary to stretch the spring 6 in. from its rest position. How much force is necessary to stretch the spring twice as far?

b. If 4 lb of force are exerted on the spring, how far will the spring be stretched?

17. The following figure represents the median cost of new privately owned one-family houses sold in the Midwest from 1980 to 1995.

Median Cost of New Privately Owned One-Family Houses Sold in the Midwest, 1980–1995

$y = 5.3x + 63.4$

Price ($1000)

Year ($x = 0$ corresponds to 1980)

Figure for Exercise 17

Source: U.S. Bureau of the Census and U.S. Department of Housing and Urban Development

Let y represent the median cost of a new privately owned one-family house sold in the Midwest. Let x represent the year, where $x = 0$ corresponds to the year 1980, $x = 1$ represents 1981, and so on. Then the median cost of new privately owned one-family houses sold in the Midwest can be approximated by the equation $y = 5.3x + 63.4$, where $0 \leq x \leq 15$.

a. Use the linear equation to approximate the median cost of new privately owned one-family houses sold in the Midwest in the year 1993.

b. Use the linear equation to approximate the median cost for the year 1988 and compare it with the actual median cost of $101,600.

c. What is the slope of the line and what does it mean in the context of this problem?

d. What is the y-intercept and what does it mean in the context of this problem?

 18. Let y represent the average number of miles driven per year for passenger cars in the United States between 1980 and 1995. Let x represent the year where $x = 0$ corresponds to 1980, $x = 1$ corresponds to 1981, and so on. The average yearly mileage for passenger cars can be approximated by the equation: $y = 142x + 9060$, where $0 \leq x \leq 15$.

Average Yearly Mileage for Passenger Cars, United States, 1980–1995

Number of Miles

$y = 142x + 9060$

Year ($x = 0$ corresponds to 1980)

Figure for Exercise 18

a. Use the linear equation to approximate the average yearly mileage for passenger cars in the United States in the year 1993.

b. Use the linear equation to approximate the average mileage for the year 1985 and compare it with the actual value of 9700 miles.

c. What is the slope of the line and what does it mean in the context of this problem?

d. What is the y-intercept and what does it mean in the context of this problem?

19. At a high school football game in Miami hot dogs were sold for $1.00 each. At the end of the night, it was determined that 650 hot dogs were sold. The following week, the price of hot dogs was raised to $1.50 and this resulted in fewer sales. Only 475 hot dogs were sold.

    a. Make a graph with the price of hot dogs on the x-axis and the corresponding sales on the y-axis. Graph the points $(1.00, 650)$ and $(1.50, 475)$ using suitable scaling on the x- and y-axes.

    b. Find an equation of the line through the given points. Write the equation in slope-intercept form.

    c. Use the equation from part (b) to predict the number of hot dogs that would sell if the price were changed to $1.70 per hot dog.

20. At a high school football game soft drinks were sold for $0.50 each. At the end of the night, it was determined that 1020 drinks were sold. The following week, the price of drinks was raised to $0.75 and this resulted in fewer sales. Only 820 drinks were sold.

    a. Make a graph with the price of drinks on the x-axis and the corresponding sales per night on the y-axis. Graph the points $(0.50, 1020)$ and $(0.75, 820)$ using suitable scaling on the x- and y-axes.

    b. Find an equation of the line through the given points. Write the equation in slope-intercept form.

    c. Use the equation from part (b) to predict the number of drinks that would sell if the price were changed to $0.85 per drink.

21. The following figure represents the winning heights for men's pole vault in selected Olympic games.

    Winning Pole Vault Height for Selected Olympic Games

    Year ($x = 0$ corresponds to 1900)

    Figure for Exercise 21

    a. Let y represent the winning height. Let x represent the year, where $x = 0$ corresponds to the year 1900, $x = 4$ represents 1904, and so on. Use the ordered pairs given in the graph $(0, 3.3)$ and $(96, 5.92)$ to find a linear equation to estimate the winning pole vault height versus the year. (Round the slope to three decimal places.)

    b. Use the linear equation from part (a) to approximate the winning vault for the 1920 Olympics.

    c. Use the linear equation to approximate the winning vault for 1976.

    d. The actual winning vault in 1920 was 4.09 m, and the actual winning vault in 1976 was 5.5 m. Are your answers from parts (b) and (c) different than these? Why?

    e. What is the slope of the line? What does the slope of the line mean in the context of this problem?

22. The following figure represents the winning time for the men's 100-m freestyle swimming event for selected Olympic games

    Winning Times for Men's 100-Meter Freestyle Swimming for Selected Olympic Games

    Year ($x = 0$ corresponds to 1948)

    Figure for Exercise 22

    a. Let y represent the winning time. Let x represent the number of years since 1948 (where $x = 0$ corresponds to the year 1948, $x = 4$ represents 1952, and so on). Use the ordered pairs given in the graph $(0, 57.3)$ and $(48, 48.7)$ to find a linear equation to estimate the winning time for the men's 100-m freestyle versus the year. (Round the slope to two decimal places.)

    b. Use the linear equation from part (a) to approximate the winning 100-m time for the year 1972 and compare it with the actual winning time of 51.2 s.

c.   Use the linear equation to approximate the winning time for the year 1988.

d.   What is the slope of the line and what does it mean in the context of this problem?

e.   Interpret the meaning of the *x*-intercept of this line in the context of this problem. Explain why the men's swimming times will never "reach" the *x*-intercept. Do you think this approximate linear trend will continue for the next 50 years, or will the men's swimming times begin to "level off" at some time in the future? Explain your answer.

For Exercises 23–26, find the midpoint of the line segment. Check your answers by plotting the midpoint on the graph.

23.

24.

25.

26.

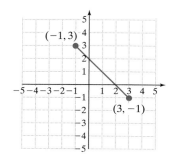

For Exercises 27–34, find the midpoint of the line segment between the two given points.

27. $(4, 0)$ and $(-6, 12)$ 28. $(-7, 2)$ and $(-3, -2)$

29. $(-3, 8)$ and $(3, -2)$ 30. $(0, 5)$ and $(4, -5)$

31. $(5, 2)$ and $(-6, 1)$ 32. $(-9, 3)$ and $(0, -4)$

33. $(-2.4, -3.1)$ and $(1.6, 1.1)$

34. $(0.8, 5.3)$ and $(-4.2, 7.1)$

35.   Two courier trucks leave their warehouse to make deliveries. One travels 20 miles north and 30 miles east. The other truck travels 5 miles south and 50 miles east. If the two drivers want to meet for lunch at a restaurant at a point halfway between them, where should they meet relative to the warehouse? (*Hint*: Label the warehouse as the origin and find the coordinates of the restaurant. See figure.)

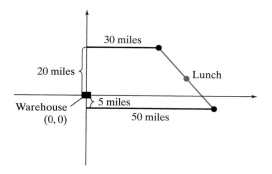

Figure for Exercise 35

36.   A map of a hiking area is drawn so that the visitors' center is at the origin of a rectangular grid. Two hikers are located at positions $(-1, 1)$ and $(-3, -2)$ with respect to the visitors' center where all units are in miles. A campground is

located exactly halfway between the hikers. What are the coordinates of the campground?

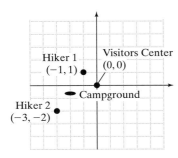

Figure for Exercise 36

EXPANDING YOUR SKILLS

37. Loraine is enrolled in an algebra class that meets 5 days per week. Her instructor gives a test every Friday. Loraine has a study plan and keeps a portfolio with notes, homework, test corrections, and vocabulary. She also records the amount of time per day that she studies and does homework. The following data represent the amount of time she studied per day and her weekly test grades.

Time Studied per Day (minutes) x	Weekly Test Grade (percent) y
60	69
70	74
80	79
90	84
100	89

Table for Exercise 37

a. Graph the points on a rectangular coordinate system. Use appropriate scaling for the x- and y-axes. Do the data points appear to follow a linear trend?

b. Find a linear equation that relates Loraine's weekly test score, y, to the amount of time she studied per day, x. (*Hint*: Pick two ordered pairs from the observed data and find an equation of the line through the points.)

c. How many minutes should Loraine study per day in order to score at least a 90% on her weekly examination? Would the equation used to determine the time Loraine needs to study to get a 90% work for other students? Why or why not?

d. If Loraine is only able to spend $\frac{1}{2}$ h per day studying her math, predict her test score for that week.

Points are *collinear* if they lie on the same line. For Exercises 38–41, use the slope formula to determine if the points are collinear.

38. $(3, -4)\, (0, -5)\, (9, -2)$

39. $(4, 3)\, (-4, -1)\, (2, 2)$

40. $(0, 2)\, (-2, 12)\, (-1, 6)$

41. $(-2, -2)\, (0, -3)\, (-4, -1)$

GRAPHING CALCULATOR EXERCISES

42. a. Graph the equation $y = 0.2x$ (*Hint*: Use a window defined by $0 \le x \le 25$ and $0 \le y \le 5$)

    b. Use an *Eval* or *Table* feature to confirm your answers to Exercise 15.

43. a. Graph the equation $y = 2.5x$ (*Hint*: Use a window defined by $0 \le x \le 12$ and $0 \le y \le 30$)

    b. Use an *Eval* or *Table* feature to confirm your answers to Exercise 16.

44. a. Graph the equation $y = 5.3x + 63.4$ (*Hint*: Use a window defined by $0 \le x \le 15$ and $0 \le y \le 150$)

    b. Use an *Eval* or *Table* feature to confirm your answers to Exercise 17.

45. a. Graph the equation $y = 142x + 9060$ (*Hint*: Use a window defined by $0 \le x \le 15$ and $0 \le y \le 15,000$)

    b. Use an *Eval* or *Table* feature to confirm your answers to Exercise 18.

chapter 2   SUMMARY

SECTION 2.1—LINEAR EQUATIONS IN TWO VARIABLES

KEY CONCEPTS:

A linear equation in two variables can be written in the form $ax + by = c$, where a, b, and c are real numbers and a and b are not both zero.

    The graph of a linear equation in two variables is a line and can be represented in the rectangular coordinate system.

An x-intercept of an equation is a point $(a, 0)$, where the graph intersects the x-axis.

A y-intercept of an equation is a point $(0, b)$, where the graph intersects the y-axis.

A vertical line can be written in the form $x = k$.
A horizontal line can be written in the form $y = k$.

KEY TERMS:

abscissa
horizontal line
linear equation in two
   variables
ordered pair
ordinate
origin
quadrant

rectangular coordinate
   system
vertical line
x-axis
x-intercept
y-axis
y-intercept

EXAMPLES:

Graph the equation:

$$3x - 4y = 12$$

Complete a table of ordered pairs.

x	y
0	-3
4	0
1	$-\dfrac{9}{4}$

Find the x- and y-intercepts:

$$2x + 3y = 8$$

x-intercept: $2x + 3(0) = 8$

$$2x = 8$$

$$x = 4 \qquad (4, 0)$$

y-intercept: $2(0) + 3y = 8$

$$3y = 8$$

$$y = \frac{8}{3} \qquad \left(0, \frac{8}{3}\right)$$

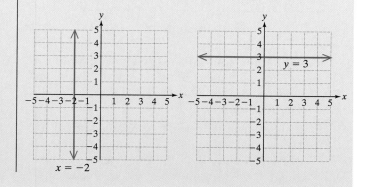

SECTION 2.2—SLOPE OF A LINE

KEY CONCEPTS:

The slope of a line, m, between two distinct points (x_1, y_1) and (x_2, y_2) is given by:

$$m = \frac{y_2 - y_1}{x_2 - x_1}, \quad x_2 - x_1 \neq 0$$

The slope of a line may be positive, negative, zero, or undefined.

Two parallel (nonvertical) lines have the same slope: $m_1 = m_2$.

Two lines are perpendicular if the slope of one line is the opposite of the reciprocal of the slope of the other line:

$$m_1 = \frac{-1}{m_2} \quad \text{or} \quad m_2 = \frac{-1}{m_1}$$

Or equivalently, $m_1 m_2 = -1$

KEY TERMS:

dependent variable
independent variable
negative slope
positive slope
slope
slopes of two parallel lines
slopes of two perpendicular lines
undefined slope
zero slope

EXAMPLES:

Find the slope of the line between (1, −3) and (−3, 7).

$$m = \frac{7 - (-3)}{-3 - 1} = \frac{10}{-4} = -\frac{5}{2}$$

Positive Slope

Negative Slope

Zero Slope

Undefined Slope

The slopes of two lines are given. Determine whether the lines are parallel, perpendicular, or neither.

a. $m_1 = -7$ and $m_2 = -7$: parallel

b. $m_1 = -\dfrac{1}{5}$ and $m_2 = 5$: perpendicular

c. $m_1 = -\dfrac{3}{2}$ and $m_2 = -\dfrac{2}{3}$: neither

SECTION 2.3—EQUATIONS OF A LINE

KEY CONCEPTS:

Standard Form: $ax + by = c$ (a and b are not both zero)

Horizontal Line: $y = k$

Vertical Line: $x = k$

Slope Intercept Form: $y = mx + b$

Point-Slope Formula: $y - y_1 = m(x - x_1)$

Slope-intercept form is used to identify the slope and y-intercept of a line when the equation is given. Slope-intercept form can also be used to graph a line.

The point-slope formula can be used to construct an equation of a line given a point and a slope.

KEY TERMS:

point-slope formula
slope-intercept form
standard form

EXAMPLES:

Find the slope and *y*-intercept:

$$7x - 2y = 4 \qquad \text{Solve for } y.$$

$$-2y = -7x + 4$$

$$y = \frac{7}{2}x - 2$$

The slope is $\frac{7}{2}$; the y-intercept is $(0, -2)$.

Find an equation of the line passing through the point (2, −3) and having slope *m* = −4.

Using the point-slope formula:

$$y - y_1 = m(x - x_1)$$

$$y - (-3) = -4(x - 2)$$

$$y + 3 = -4x + 8$$

$$y = -4x + 5$$

SECTION 2.4—APPLICATIONS OF LINEAR EQUATIONS AND GRAPHING

KEY CONCEPTS:

A linear model can be constructed to describe data for a given situation.

EXAMPLES:

The following graph shows the average net income for physicians for 1990–1995.

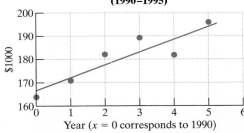

Average Net Income for U.S. Physicians (1990–1995)

Year ($x = 0$ corresponds to 1990)

The year 1990 corresponds to $x = 0$ and income is measured in \$1000s.

- Given two points from the data, use the point-slope formula to find an equation of the line.

Write an equation of the line using the points (1, 172) and (4, 188).

$$\text{Slope: } \frac{188 - 172}{4 - 1} = \frac{16}{3} \approx 5.3$$

$$y - 172 = 5.3(x - 1)$$

$$y - 172 = 5.3x - 5.3$$

$$y = 5.3x + 166.7$$

- Interpret the meaning of the slope and y-intercept in the context of the problem.

The slope, $m \approx 5.3$, indicates that the average income for physicians has increased by 5.3 thousand dollars (\$5300) per year.

The y-intercept, $(0, 166.7)$, means that the net income for physicians in 1990 ($x = 0$) was 166.7 thousand dollars (\$166,700).

- Use the equation to predict values.

Predict the average net income for physicians for 1996 ($x = 6$).

$$y = 5.3(6) + 166.7$$

$$= 198.5$$

The average net income was approximately 198.5 thousand dollars (\$198,500).

The midpoint between two points is found using the formula:

$$\left(\frac{x_1 + x_2}{2}, \frac{y_1 + y_2}{2} \right)$$

Find the midpoint between (−3, 1) and (5, 7)

$$\left(\frac{-3 + 5}{2}, \frac{1 + 7}{2} \right) = (1, 4)$$

KEY TERMS:

constant term
midpoint formula
variable term

---

chapter 2   REVIEW EXERCISES

Section 2.1

1. Label the following on the diagram:

    a. Origin

    b. x-Axis

    c. y-Axis

    d. Quadrant I

    e. Quadrant II

    f. Quadrant III

    g. Quadrant IV

2. The following table gives the percentages of eighth-grade students who used illicit drugs.

Year x	Percent y
1993	15.1
1994	18.5
1995	21.4
1996	23.6

Source: American Medical Association.

Table for Exercise 2

a. Identify the dependent and independent variables.

b. Plot these points on a graph.

c. Does this relationship appear to be linear?

For Exercises 3–5, complete the table.

3. $3x - 2y = -6$

x	y
0	
	0
1	
	−0.5
$\frac{2}{3}$	

4. $2y - 3 = 10$

x	y
0	
5	
$\frac{1}{4}$	
−6	

5. $6 - x = 2$

x	y
	0
	$\frac{1}{8}$
	1
	−2

For Exercises 6–9, graph the lines. In each case find at least three points and identify the x- and y-intercepts (if possible).

6. $2x = 3y - 6$

7. $5x - 2y = 0$

8. $2y = 6$

9. $-3x = 6$

Section 2.2

10. Find the slope of the lines:

    a.

b.

c.

11. Draw a line with slope 2 (answers may vary).

12. Draw a line with slope $-\frac{3}{4}$ (answers may vary).

For Exercises 13–16, find the slope of the line that passes through each pair of points.

13. $(2, 6)(-1, 0)$

14. $(7, 2)(-3, -5)$

15. $(8, 2)(3, 2)$

16. $\left(-4, \dfrac{1}{2}\right)(-4, 1)$

17. Ski resorts have a number of different slopes that are generally rated by difficulty. Using the mathematical definition of slope, explain the difference between the "bunny-slope" for beginners and a "double-diamond slope" for experts.

For Exercises 18–21, the slopes of two lines are given. Based on the slopes, are the lines parallel, perpendicular, or neither?

18. $\begin{cases} m_1 = -\dfrac{1}{3} \\ m_2 = 3 \end{cases}$

19. $\begin{cases} m_1 = \dfrac{5}{4} \\ m_2 = \dfrac{4}{5} \end{cases}$

20. $\begin{cases} m_1 = 7 \\ m_2 = 7 \end{cases}$

21. $\begin{cases} m_1 = \dfrac{3}{8} \\ m_2 = -\dfrac{3}{8} \end{cases}$

22. Approximate the slope of the stairway pictured here.

Figure for Exercise 22

Section 2.3

23. Write the following forms of lines from memory:

    a. Horizontal line

    b. Point-slope formula

    c. Standard form

    d. Vertical line

    e. Slope-intercept form

For Exercises 24–28, write your answer in slope-intercept form.

24. Write an equation of the line that has slope $\frac{1}{9}$ and y-intercept $(0, 6)$.

25. Write an equation of the line that has slope $-\frac{2}{3}$ and x-intercept $(3, 0)$.

26. Write an equation of the line that passes through the points $(-8, -1)$ and $(-5, 9)$.

27. Write an equation of the line that passes through the point $(6, -2)$ and is perpendicular to the line $y = -\frac{1}{3}x + 2$.

28. Write an equation of the line that passes through the point $(0, -3)$ and is parallel to the line $4x + 3y = -1$.

29. For each of the given conditions, find an equation of the line:

    a. Passing through the point $(-3, -2)$ and parallel to the x-axis.

b. Passing through the point $(-3, -2)$ and parallel to the y-axis.

c. Passing through the point $(-3, -2)$ and having an undefined slope.

d. Passing through the point $(-3, -2)$ and having a zero slope.

30. Are any of the lines in Exercise 29 the same?

Section 2.4

31. Molly Kay loves the beach and decides to spend the summer selling various ice cream products on the beach. From her accounting course, she knows that her total cost is calculated as:

Total cost = fixed cost + variable cost

She estimates that her fixed cost for the summer season is \$20/day. She also knows that each ice cream product costs her \$0.25 from her distributor.

a. Write a relationship for the daily cost, y, in terms of the number of ice cream products sold per day, x.

b. Graph the equation from part (a) by letting the horizontal axis represent the number of ice cream products sold per day and letting the vertical axis represent the daily cost.

c. What does the y-intercept represent in the context of this problem?

d. What is her cost if she sells 450 ice cream products?

e. What is the slope of the line?

f. What does the slope of the line represent in the context of this problem?

32. The following list of data shows the percent of public schools using CD-ROMs from 1992 to 1997. Let $x = 0$ represent the year 1992. Let y represent the percent of schools using CD-ROMs. Plot the data on a rectangular coordinate system.

Year	x	Percent
1992	0	7
1993	1	13
1994	2	29
1995	3	48
1996	4	54
1997	5	74

Source: Quality Education Data.

a. Use the points $(0, 7)$ and $(4, 54)$ to find an equation of the line. Write the line in slope-intercept form.

b. What is the slope of this line and what does it mean in the context of the problem?

c. What is the y-intercept and what does it mean in the context of the problem?

d. Use the equation to predict the percent of schools using CD-ROMs in 1999.

33. Find the midpoint of the line segment between the two points $(-13, 12)$ and $(4, -18)$.

34. Find the midpoint of the line segment between the two points $(1.2, -3.7)$ and $(-4.1, -8.3)$.

---

chapter 2   TEST

1. Given the equation $x - \frac{2}{3}y = 6$, complete the ordered pairs and graph the corresponding points. $(0, \quad) (\quad ,0) (\quad ,3)$

2. Determine whether the following statements are true or false and explain your answer.

a. The product of the x- and y-coordinates is positive only for points in Quadrant I.

b. The quotient of the x- and y-coordinates is negative only for points in Quadrant IV.

c. The point $(-2, -3)$ is in Quadrant III.

d. The point $(0, 0)$ lies on the x-axis.

3. Explain the process for finding the x- and y-intercepts.

For Exercises 4–7, identify the x- and y-intercepts (if possible) and graph the line.

4. $6x - 8y = 24$

5. $x = -4$

6. $3x = 5y$

7. $2y = -6$

8. Find the slope of the line given the following information:

    a. The line passes through the points $(7, -3)$ and $(-1, -8)$

    b. The line is given by $6x - 5y = 1$

9. Describe the relationship of the slopes of:

    a. Two parallel lines

    b. Two perpendicular lines

10. Write an equation that represents a line subject to the following conditions: (Answers may vary.)

    a. A line that does not pass through the origin and has a positive slope.

    b. A line with an undefined slope.

    c. A line perpendicular to the y-axis. What is the slope of such a line?

    d. A slanted line that passes through the origin and has a negative slope.

11. Write an equation of the line that passes through the point $(8, -\frac{1}{2})$ with slope -2. Write the answer in slope-intercept form.

12. Write an equation of the line that passes through the point $(-10, -3)$ and is perpendicular to $3x + y = 7$. Write the answer in slope-intercept form.

13. Jack sells used-cars. He is paid \$800/month plus \$300 commission for each automobile he sells.

    a. Write an equation that represents Jack's monthly earnings, y, in terms of the number of automobiles he sells, x.

    b. Graph the linear equation you found in part (a).

    c. What does the y-intercept mean in the context of this problem?

    d. How much will Jack earn in a month if he sells 17 automobiles?

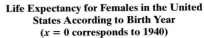 14. The following graph represents the life expectancy for females in the United States born from 1940 through 1990.

Life Expectancy for Females in the United States According to Birth Year
($x = 0$ corresponds to 1940)

Source: National Center for Health Statistics.

    a. Approximate the y-intercept from the graph. What does the y-intercept represent in the context of this problem?

    b. Using the two points $(0, 66)$ and $(30, 75)$ approximate the slope of the line. What does the slope of the line represent in the context of this problem?

    c. Use the y-intercept and the slope found in parts (a) and (b) to write an equation of the line by letting x represent the year of birth and y represent the corresponding life expectancy.

    d. Using the linear equation from part (c), approximate the life expectancy for women born in the United States in 1994. How does your answer compare with the reported life expectancy of 79 years?

15. Find the midpoint of the line segment between the two points $(21, -15)$ and $(5, 32)$.

CUMULATIVE REVIEW EXERCISES, CHAPTERS 1–2

1. Simplify the expression:

$$\frac{5 - 2^3 \div 4 + 7}{-1 - 3(4 - 1)}$$

2. Simplify the expression: $3 + \sqrt{25} - 8(\sqrt{9}) \div 6$

3. Solve the equation for z.

$$z - (3 + 2z) + 5 = -2z - 5$$

4. The formula for the volume of a right circular cylinder is $V = \pi r^2 h$.

   a. Solve for h.

   b. Find h if a soda can contains 355 cm^3 (which is approximately 12 oz) of soda, and the diameter is 6.6 cm. Round the answer to one decimal place.

5. Solve the inequalities. Write your answers in interval notation.

   a. $-5x - 4 \le -2(x - 1)$ b. $-x + 4 > 1$

For Exercises 6–7, (a) Find the x- and y-intercepts. (b) Find the slope. (c) Graph the line.

6. $3x - 5y = 10$

7. $2y + 4 = 10$

8. Find an equation of the line passing through $(1, -4)$ and parallel to $2x + y = 6$. Write the answer in slope-intercept form.

9. Find an equation of the line passing through $(1, -4)$ and perpendicular to $y = \frac{1}{4}x - 2$. Write the answer in slope-intercept form.

10. For $A = \{5, 10, 15, 20, 25, 30\}$ and $B = \{10, 20, 30, 40, 50\}$, list the elements in the following sets.

    a. $A \cup B$ b. $A \cap B$

11. Clear parentheses and combine *like* terms: $3a(2b + 3) - 7b + 5b(2 - a)$

12. Solve the equation for y. $2y - 2 + y = 3(y - 4)$

13. For each point, give the quadrant in which it lies.

    a. $(9, -1)$ b. $(-3, -12)$ c. $(-0.5, 3)$

14. Find an equation of a line passing through the points $(5, -2)$ and $(-3, 1)$. Write the answer in slope-intercept form.

Systems of Linear Equations and Matrices

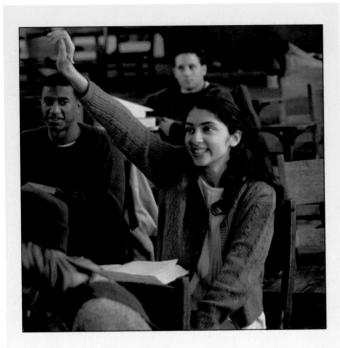

The enrollment for both men and women in U.S. colleges has shown a linear trend upward since 1970. Letting x represent the number of years after 1970, the attendance for women, y, (in thousands) can be modeled by the linear equation

$$y = 141.1x + 3606$$

Similarly, the attendance for men in college can be modeled by

$$y = 38.4x + 4540$$

Together, these equations form a system of linear equations in two variables. In this chapter we will learn techniques for solving systems of linear equations. Graphically, the solution to such a system represents the point of intersection of the two lines.

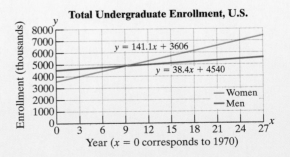

Total Undergraduate Enrollment, U.S.

From the graph, notice that the enrollment for women overtook the enrollment for men sometime around 1979. For more information about education statistics, visit edstat at

www.mhhe.com/miller_oneill

section

3.1   SYSTEMS OF LINEAR EQUATIONS IN TWO VARIABLES

1. Introduction to Systems of Linear Equations in Two Variables

In Chapter 1, we solved linear equations that contained a single variable; however, many application problems involve more than one unknown quantity. It is, therefore, often convenient to use two or more variables and to set up a system of equations.

---

example 1

Constructing a System of Linear Equations

Set up a system of equations to find two numbers whose sum is 16 and whose difference is 4.

Solution:

This problem describes two unknown numbers. Let x represent one number, and let y represent the other. The two conditions imposed on x and y can each be represented by a linear equation.

Find two numbers whose sum is 16: $x + y = 16$

Find two numbers whose difference is 4: $x - y = 4$

These two equations represent two independent relationships between x and y. Together they form a **system of linear equations in two variables**. A **solution to a system of equations in two variables**, x and y, is an ordered pair, (x, y), that satisfies each equation in the system. The solution set is the set of all such ordered pairs.

In this section, the following three methods will be presented to solve a system of equations in two variables: the graphing method, the addition method, and the substitution method.

---

2. The Graphing Method

Notice that the equations in Example 1 are both linear. That is, they can be written in the form: $ax + by = c$.

$$x + y = 16$$
$$x - y = 4$$

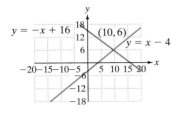

Figure 3-1

Using the **graphing method**, a solution to a system of two linear equations may be interpreted geometrically as a point of intersection between the two lines. Using slope-intercept form to graph the lines from Example 1, we have:

$$x + y = 16 \longrightarrow y = -x + 16$$
$$x - y = 4 \longrightarrow y = x - 4$$

The graphs of these equations intersect at the point $(10, 6)$ (Figure 3-1). Therefore, the ordered pair $(10, 6)$ satisfies both equations and must be a solution to the system.

To verify that $(10, 6)$ is a solution, substitute $x = 10$ and $y = 6$ into both equations:

$$x + y = 16 \longrightarrow (10) + (6) = 16 \checkmark$$
$$x - y = 4 \longrightarrow (10) - (6) = 4 \checkmark$$

3.   Consistent and Inconsistent Systems; Dependent and Independent Systems

The graphs of two linear equations may intersect in exactly *one point*, in *infinitely many points* (if the lines coincide), or at *no point* (if the lines are parallel). If a system of linear equations has one or more solutions, the system is said to be **consistent**. If a system of linear equations has no solution, it is said to be **inconsistent**.

If two linear equations represent the same line, then all points on the line are solutions to the system of equations. In such a case, the system is characterized as a **dependent system**. An **independent system** is one in which the two equations represent different lines. In summary, we have:

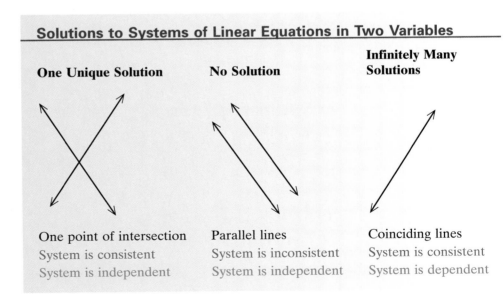

Solutions to Systems of Linear Equations in Two Variables

One Unique Solution	No Solution	Infinitely Many Solutions
One point of intersection	Parallel lines	Coinciding lines
System is consistent	System is inconsistent	System is consistent
System is independent	System is independent	System is dependent

4. The Substitution Method

Graphing a system of equations is one method to find the solution of the system. We will also present two algebraic methods to solve a system of equations. The first is called the **substitution method**. This technique is particularly important because it can be used to solve more advanced problems including nonlinear systems of equations.

The first step in the substitution process is to isolate one of the variables from one of the equations. Consider the system from Example 1:

$$x + y = 16$$
$$x - y = 4$$

Solving the first equation for x yields: $x = 16 - y$. Then, because x is equal to $16 - y$, the expression $16 - y$ may replace x in the second equation. This leaves the second equation in terms of y only.

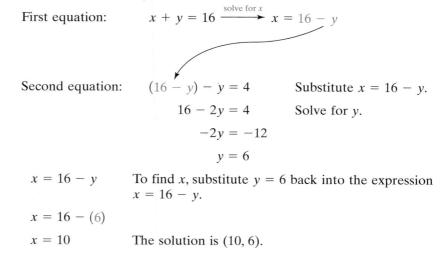

First equation: $x + y = 16 \xrightarrow{\text{solve for } x} x = 16 - y$

Second equation: $(16 - y) - y = 4$ Substitute $x = 16 - y$.

$16 - 2y = 4$ Solve for y.

$-2y = -12$

$y = 6$

$x = 16 - y$ To find x, substitute $y = 6$ back into the expression $x = 16 - y$.

$x = 16 - (6)$

$x = 10$ The solution is $(10, 6)$.

Solving a System of Equations by the Substitution Method

1. Isolate one of the variables from one equation.
2. Substitute the quantity found in step 1 into the *other* equation.
3. Solve the resulting equation.
4. Substitute the value found in step 3 back into the equation in step 1 to find the value of the remaining variable.
5. Check the solution in both equations and write the answer as an ordered pair.

---

example 2   **Using the Substitution Method to Solve a Linear System**

Solve the system using the substitution method:

$$3x - 2y = -7$$
$$6x + y = 6$$

Solution:

The y variable in the second equation is the easiest variable to isolate because its coefficient is 1.

$$3x - 2y = -7$$

$$6x + y = 6 \longrightarrow y = -6x + 6 \qquad \text{\textbf{Step 1:}} \quad \text{Solve the second equation for } y.$$

Avoiding Mistakes

Do not substitute $y = -6x + 6$ into the same equation from which it came. This mistake will result in an identity:

$$6x + y = 6$$
$$6x + (-6x + 6) = 6$$
$$6x - 6x + 6 = 6$$
$$6 = 6$$

$$3x - 2(-6x + 6) = -7 \qquad \text{\textbf{Step 2:}} \quad \text{Substitute the quantity } -6x + 6 \text{ for } y \text{ in the } \textit{other} \text{ equation.}$$
$$3x + 12x - 12 = -7$$
$$15x - 12 = -7$$

$$15x = 5 \qquad \text{\textbf{Step 3:}} \quad \text{Solve for } x.$$

$$\frac{15x}{15} = \frac{5}{15}$$

$$x = \frac{1}{3}$$

$$y = -6x + 6 \qquad \text{\textbf{Step 4:}} \quad \text{Substitute } x = \tfrac{1}{3} \text{ into the expression } y = -6x + 6.$$

$$y = -6\left(\frac{1}{3}\right) + 6$$

$$y = -2 + 6$$

$$y = 4$$

$$3x - 2y = -7 \qquad 6x + y = 6 \qquad \text{\textbf{Step 5:}} \quad \text{Check the ordered pair } (\tfrac{1}{3}, 4) \text{ in each original equation.}$$

$$3\left(\frac{1}{3}\right) - 2(4) \overset{?}{=} -7 \qquad 6\left(\frac{1}{3}\right) + 4 \overset{?}{=} 6$$

$$1 - 8 = -7 \checkmark \qquad 2 + 4 = 6 \checkmark$$

The solution is $(\tfrac{1}{3}, 4)$.

Graphing Calculator Box

A graphing calculator can be used to estimate the point of intersection of two graphs. One method is to use *Zoom* and *Trace* features. A second option provided by some calculators is to use an *Intersect* feature. Here, we check the solution to Example 2 by entering the equations in slope-intercept form and applying the *Intersect* function.

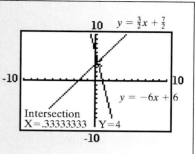

$$3x - 2y = -7 \longrightarrow y = \frac{3}{2}x + \frac{7}{2}$$

$$6x + y = 6 \longrightarrow y = -6x + 6$$

---

example 3

Using the Substitution Method to Solve a Linear System

Solve the system by using the substitution method.

$$x = 2y - 4$$

$$-2x + 4y = 6$$

Solution:

$$x = 2y - 4$$
$$-2x + 4y = 6$$

Step 1: The x variable is already isolated.

$$-2(2y - 4) + 4y = 6$$

Step 2: Substitute the quantity $x = 2y - 4$ into the *other* equation.

$$-4y + 8 + 4y = 6$$

Step 3: Solve for y.

$$8 = 6$$

The equation reduces to a contradiction, indicating that the system has no solution. Hence the lines never intersect and must be parallel. The system is *inconsistent*.

There is no solution.
The system is inconsistent.

Tip: The answer to Example 3 can be verified by writing each equation in slope-intercept form and graphing the equations.

Equation 1	**Equation 2**
$x = 2y - 4$	$-2x + 4y = 6$
$2y = x + 4$	$4y = 2x + 6$
$\dfrac{2y}{2} = \dfrac{x}{2} + \dfrac{4}{2}$	$\dfrac{4y}{4} = \dfrac{2x}{4} + \dfrac{6}{4}$
$y = \dfrac{1}{2}x + 2$	$y = \dfrac{1}{2}x + \dfrac{3}{2}$

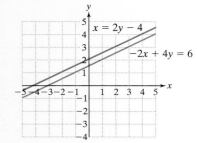

Notice that the equations have the same slope, but different y-intercepts; therefore, the lines must be parallel. There is no solution to this system of equations.

5. The Addition Method

In this section the last method we present to solve systems of linear equations is the **addition method** (sometimes called the elimination method). With the addition method, begin by writing both equations in standard form, $ax + by = c$. Then, multiply one or both equations by appropriate constants to create opposite coefficients on either the x- or y-variable. Then the equations may be added to eliminate the variable having opposite coefficients. This process is demonstrated in the next example.

example 4

Solving a System by the Addition Method

Solve the system by using the addition method.

$$3x - 4y = 2$$
$$4x + y = 9$$

Solution:

$$3x - 4y = 2 \qquad\qquad 3x - 4y = 2$$
$$4x + y = 9 \xrightarrow{\text{multiply by 4}} 16x + 4y = 36$$

Multiply the second equation by 4. This makes the coefficients of the y variables *opposite*.

$$3x - 4y = 2$$
$$\underline{16x + 4y = 36}$$
$$19x \qquad = 38$$
$$x \qquad = 2$$

Now if the equations are added, the y variable will be eliminated.

Solve for x.

Tip: Substituting $x = 2$ into the other equation, $4x + y = 9$, produces the same value for y.

$$4x + y = 9$$
$$4(2) + y = 9$$
$$8 + y = 9$$
$$y = 1$$

$$3x - 4y = 2$$
$$3(2) - 4y = 2$$
$$6 - 4y = 2$$
$$-4y = -4$$
$$y = 1$$

Substitute $x = 2$ back into one of the original equations and solve for y.

The solution is $(2, 1)$.

Check the solution $(2, 1)$ in each original equation:

$$3x - 4y = 2 \longrightarrow 3(2) - 4(1) \overset{?}{=} 2 \longrightarrow 6 - 4 = 2 \checkmark$$
$$4x + y = 9 \longrightarrow 4(2) + (1) \overset{?}{=} 9 \longrightarrow 8 + 1 = 9 \checkmark$$

The steps to solve a system of linear equations in two variables by the addition method is outlined in the following box.

Solving a System of Equations by the Addition Method

1. Write both equations in standard form: $ax + by = c$
2. Clear fractions or decimals (optional).
3. Multiply one or both equations by nonzero constants to create opposite coefficients for one of the variables.
4. Add the equations from step 3 to eliminate one variable.
5. Solve for the remaining variable.
6. Substitute the known value found in step 5 into one of the original equations to solve for the other variable.
7. Check the solution in *both* equations.

---

example 5   **Solving a System by the Addition Method**

Solve the system by using the addition method.

$$4x + 5y = 2$$
$$3x = 1 - 4y$$

Solution:

$$4x + 5y = 2 \longrightarrow 4x + 5y = 2$$
$$3x = 1 - 4y \longrightarrow 3x + 4y = 1$$

Step 1: Write both equations in standard form. There are no fractions or decimals.

We may choose to eliminate either variable. To eliminate x, change the coefficients to 12 and -12.

$$4x + 5y = 2 \xrightarrow{\text{multiply by 3}} 12x + 15y = 6$$ **Step 2:** Multiply the first equation by 3.

$$3x + 4y = 1 \xrightarrow{\text{multiply by }-4} -12x - 16y = -4$$ Multiply the second equation by -4.

$$12x + 15y = 6$$ **Step 3:** Add the
$$\underline{-12x - 16y = -4}$$ equations.

$$-y = 2$$ **Step 4:** Solve for y.
$$y = -2$$

$$4x + 5y = 2$$ **Step 5:** Substitute $y = -2$ back into one of the original equations and solve for x.
$$4x + 5(-2) = 2$$
$$4x - 10 = 2$$
$$4x = 12$$
$$x = 3$$

The solution is $(3, -2)$. **Step 6:** Check the solution $(3, -2)$ in each original equation:

$$4x + 5y = 2 \longrightarrow 4(3) + 5(-2) \overset{?}{=} 2 \longrightarrow 12 - 10 = 2 \checkmark$$
$$3x = 1 - 4y \longrightarrow 3(3) \overset{?}{=} 1 - 4(-2) \longrightarrow 9 = 1 + 8 \checkmark$$

Tip: To eliminate the x variable in Example 5, both equations were multiplied by appropriate constants to create $12x$ and $-12x$. We chose 12 because it is the *least common multiple* of 4 and 3.

We could have solved the system by eliminating the y-variable. To eliminate y we would multiply the top equation by 4 and the bottom equation by -5. This would make the coefficients of the y-variable 20 and -20, respectively.

$$4x + 5y = 2 \xrightarrow{\text{multiply by 4}} 16x + 20y = 8$$

$$3x + 4y = 1 \xrightarrow{\text{multiply by }-5} -15x - 20y = -5$$

example 6   Solving a System of Equations by the Addition Method

Solve the system by using the addition method.

$$x - 2y = 6 + y$$
$$0.05y = 0.02x - 0.10$$

Solution:

$$x - 2y = 6 + y \quad \longrightarrow \quad x - 3y = 6$$

$$0.05y = 0.02x - 0.10 \longrightarrow -0.02x + 0.05y = -0.10$$

Step 1: Write both equations in standard form.

$$x - 3y = 6$$

$$-0.02x + 0.05y = -0.10 \xrightarrow{\text{multiply by 100}} -2x + 5y = -10$$

Step 2: Clear decimals.

$$x - 3y = 6 \xrightarrow{\text{multiply by 2}} 2x - 6y = 12$$

$$-2x + 5y = -10 \quad \longrightarrow \quad \underline{-2x + 5y = -10}$$

$$-y = 2$$

Step 3: Create opposite coefficients.

Step 4: Add the equations.

$$y = -2$$

Step 5: Solve for y.

$$x - 2y = 6 + y$$

$$x - 2(-2) = 6 + (-2)$$

$$x + 4 = 4$$

$$x = 0$$

Step 6: To solve for x, substitute $y = -2$ into one of the original equations.

The solution is $(0, -2)$.

Step 7: Check the solution $(0, -2)$ in each original equation.

$$x - 2y = 6 + y \longrightarrow (0) - 2(-2) \overset{?}{=} 6 + (-2) \longrightarrow 4 = 4 \checkmark$$

$$0.05y = 0.02x - 0.10 \longrightarrow 0.05(-2) \overset{?}{=} 0.02(0) - 0.10 \longrightarrow -0.10 = -0.10 \checkmark$$

6. Solving a Dependent System

example 7

Solving a System of Equations by the Addition Method

Solve the system by using the addition method.

$$\frac{1}{5}x - \frac{1}{2}y = 1$$

$$-4x + 10y = -20$$

Solution:

$$\frac{1}{5}x - \frac{1}{2}y = 1$$

$$-4x + 10y = -20$$

Step 1:
Equations are in standard form.

$$10\left(\frac{1}{5}x - \frac{1}{2}y\right) = 10 \cdot 1 \longrightarrow 2x - 5y = 10$$

$$-4x + 10y = -20$$

Step 2:
Clear fractions.

$$2x - 5y = 10 \xrightarrow{\text{multiply by 2}} 4x - 10y = 20$$

$$-4x + 10y = -20 \longrightarrow \underline{-4x + 10y = -20}$$

$$0 = 0$$

Step 3:
Multiply the first equation by 2.

Step 4:
Add the equations.

Notice that both variables were eliminated. The system of equations is reduced to an identity, $0 = 0$. Therefore, the two original equations are equivalent and the system is dependent. The solution set consists of an infinite number of ordered pairs (x, y) that fall on the common line of intersection, $-4x + 10y = -20$, or equivalently $2x - 5y = 10$. The solution set can be written in set notation as:

$$\{(x, y) \mid 2x - 5y = 10\}$$

This is read as "the set of ordered pairs, (x, y), that satisfy the equation $2x - 5y = 10$."

The solution set $\{(x, y) \mid 2x - 5y = 10\}$ is called the **general solution to the dependent system** of equations. Essentially, this is a formula to generate all solutions to the system. By substituting arbitrary values of x, the corresponding y-values of the solution can be found (likewise, substituting an arbitrary value of y can generate the corresponding x-value). For example,

if $x = 0 \longrightarrow 2(0) - 5y = 10 \longrightarrow y = -2$ Solution point: $(0, -2)$

if $x = 1 \longrightarrow 2(1) - 5y = 10 \longrightarrow y = -\frac{8}{5}$ Solution point: $\left(1, -\frac{8}{5}\right)$

if $x = 2 \longrightarrow 2(2) - 5y = 10 \longrightarrow y = -\frac{6}{5}$ Solution point: $\left(2, -\frac{6}{5}\right)$

. . .

Notice in each case, the value of y *depends* on the choice of x and vice versa.

> **Tip:** By writing each equation from Example 7 in slope-intercept form, we can see that both original equations represent the same line. Each point on the line is a solution to the system of equations.
>
> **Equation 1**
>
> $\frac{1}{5}x - \frac{1}{2}y = 1$
>
> $2x - 5y = 10$
>
> $-5y = -2x + 10$
>
> $\frac{-5y}{-5} = \frac{-2x}{-5} + \frac{10}{-5}$
>
> $y = \frac{2}{5}x - 2$
>
> **Equation 2**
>
> $-4x + 10y = -20$
>
> $10y = 4x - 20$
>
> $\frac{10y}{10} = \frac{4x}{10} - \frac{20}{10}$
>
> $y = \frac{2}{5}x - 2$
>
>

---

section 3.1   PRACTICE EXERCISES

For each pair of equations in Exercises 1–6, (a) Write both equations in slope-intercept form. (b) Identify the slope of each line. (c) Identify the y-intercept of each line. (d) Label each pair of lines as parallel lines, coinciding lines, or intersecting lines.

1. $4x - y = 3$
     $-2x + y = 1$

2. $12x - 3y = -8$
     $4x - y = 0$

3. $x + 5y = 3$
     $2x + 10y = 6$

4. $-3x + y = -5$
     $x + 2y = 0$

5. $7x - 3y = 14$
     $14x - 6y = 22$

6. $3x - 2y = 5$
     $-6x + 4y = -10$

For Exercises 7–10, identify each statement as True or False.

7.   A consistent system is a system that always has a unique solution.

8.   A dependent system is a system that has no solution.

9.   If two lines coincide, they are dependent.

10. If two lines are parallel, they are independent.

11. Which of the following points are solutions to this system?

$$x - y = 6$$
$$4x + 3y = -4$$

$(4, -2)$ $(6, 0)$ $(2, -4)$ $(-1, 0)$

12. Which of the following points are solutions to this system?

$$x - 3y = 3$$
$$2x - 9y = 1$$

$(0, 1)$ $(4, 1)$ $\left(8, \frac{5}{3}\right)$ $\left(2, \frac{1}{3}\right)$

13. Describe the process of solving a system of linear equations using substitution.

14. Explain how to determine if a system of linear equations is dependent.

For Exercises 15–26, solve by using the substitution method. If the system is dependent, write the general solution as outlined in Example 7.

15. $4x + 12y = 4$
     $y = 5x + 11$

16. $y = -3x - 1$
     $2x - 3y = -8$

17. $x - 3y = -4$
    $2x + 3y = -5$

18. $x - y = 8$
    $3x + 2y = 9$

19. $5x - 2y = 10$
    $y = x - 1$

20. $2x - y = -1$
    $y = -2x$

21. $2x - 6y = -2$
    $x = 3y - 1$

22. $-2x + 4y = 22$
    $x = 2y - 11$

23. $y = \dfrac{1}{7}x + 3$
    $x - 7y = -4$

24. $x = -\dfrac{3}{2}y + \dfrac{1}{2}$
    $4x + 6y = 7$

25. $4x + 4y = 5$
    $x - 4y = -\dfrac{5}{2}$

26. $-2x + y = -6$
    $6x - 13y = -12$

27. Describe the process of solving a system of linear equations using the addition method.

28. Explain how to determine if a system of equations is inconsistent.

For Exercises 29–40, solve by using the addition method. If the system is dependent, write the general solution as outlined in Example 7.

29. $2x - 4y = 8$
    $-2x + y = 1$

30. $8x + 6y = -8$
    $x - 6y = -10$

31. $2x + 5y = 9$
    $4x - 7y = -16$

32. $x + 5y = 7$
    $2x + 7y = 8$

33. $5x - 2y = 27$
    $-3x + 5y = 18$

34. $6x - 3y = -3$
    $4x + 5y = -9$

35. $0.4x - 0.6y = 0.5$
    $0.2x - 0.3y = 0.7$

36. $0.3x + 0.6y = 0.7$
    $0.2x + 0.4y = 0.5$

37. $\dfrac{1}{4}x - \dfrac{1}{6}y = -2$
    $-\dfrac{1}{6}x + \dfrac{1}{5}y = 4$

38. $\dfrac{1}{3}x + \dfrac{1}{5}y = 7$
    $\dfrac{1}{6}x - \dfrac{2}{5}y = -4$

39. $3x - 2y = 1$
    $-6x + 4y = -2$

40. $3x - y = 4$
    $6x - 2y = 8$

41. Describe a situation in which you would prefer to use the substitution method over the addition method.

For Exercises 42–53, solve the systems using either the substitution method or the addition method. If a system does not have a unique solution, label the system as either dependent or inconsistent.

42. $x + y = 10$
    $2x - y = 8$

43. $x + y = 7$
    $x = y + 3$

44. $2x - y = 9$
    $y = -\dfrac{4}{3}x + 1$

45. $y = \dfrac{1}{2}x - 3$
    $x + 4y = 0$

46. $3x - 4y = 7$
    $6x + 2y = 9$

47. $x - 2y = 5$
    $-3x + 2y = -9$

48. $\dfrac{1}{3}x - \dfrac{1}{2}y = 0$
    $x - \dfrac{3}{2}y = 0$

49. $\dfrac{2}{5}x - \dfrac{2}{3}y = 0$
    $\dfrac{3}{5}x - y = 0$

50. $0.3x - 0.2y = 4$
    $0.2x + 0.3y = 0.5$

51. $-0.3x + 0.2y = 0.3$
    $0.9x - 0.8y = -0.3$

52. $y = 2x + 5$
    $-4x + 2y = -1$

53. $x = y + 4$
    $4x - 4y = 16$

EXPANDING YOUR SKILLS

For Exercises 54–57, solve the systems using either the substitution method or the addition method.

54. $\dfrac{1}{2}x + y = \dfrac{7}{6}$
    $x + 2y = 4.5$

55. $0.2x - 0.1y = -1.2$
    $x - \dfrac{1}{2}y = 3$

56. $3x - 2 = \dfrac{1}{3}(11 + 5y)$
    $x + \dfrac{2}{3}(2y - 3) = -2$

57. $2(2y + 3) - 2x = 1 - x$

$x + y = \dfrac{1}{5}(7 + y)$

GRAPHING CALCULATOR EXERCISES

58. Use a graphing calculator to graph the lines given in Exercise 15. Approximate the point of intersection from the graph to support your answer to Exercise 15.

59. Use a graphing calculator to graph the lines given in Exercise 16. Approximate the point of intersection from the graph to support your answer to Exercise 16.

60. Use a graphing calculator to graph the lines given in Exercise 17. Approximate the point of intersection from the graph to support your answer to Exercise 17.

61. Use a graphing calculator to graph the lines given in Exercise 18. Approximate the point of intersection from the graph to support your answer to Exercise 18.

62. Use a graphing calculator to graph the lines given in Exercise 44. Approximate the point of intersection from the graph to support your answer to Exercise 44.

63. Use a graphing calculator to graph the lines given in Exercise 43. Approximate the point of intersection from the graph to support your answer to Exercise 43.

Concepts

1. **Applications Involving Cost**
2. **Applications Involving Mixtures**
3. **Applications Involving Principal and Interest**
4. **Applications Involving Distance, Rate, and Time**
5. **Applications Involving Geometry**
6. **Applications Involving Business**

section

3.2 APPLICATIONS OF SYSTEMS OF LINEAR EQUATIONS IN TWO VARIABLES

1. Applications Involving Cost

example 1   **Solving a Mixture Application**

At an amusement park, five hot dogs and one drink costs $16. Two hot dogs and three drinks cost $9. Find the cost per hot dog and the cost per drink.

Solution:

Let x represent the cost per hot dog.   Label the variables.

Let y represent the cost per drink.

$\left(\begin{array}{c}\text{Cost of 5}\\\text{hot dogs}\end{array}\right) + \left(\begin{array}{c}\text{Cost of 1}\\\text{drink}\end{array}\right) = \$16 \longrightarrow 5x + y = 16$ Write two equations.

$\left(\begin{array}{c}\text{Cost of 2}\\\text{hot dogs}\end{array}\right) + \left(\begin{array}{c}\text{Cost of 3}\\\text{drinks}\end{array}\right) = \$9 \longrightarrow 2x + 3y = 9$

This system can be solved by either the substitution or the addition method. We will solve using the substitution method. The y-variable in the first equation is the easiest variable to isolate.

$$5x + y = 16 \longrightarrow y = -5x + 16$$

Solve for y in the first equation.

$$2x + 3y = 9$$

Substitute the quantity $-5x + 16$ for y in the *second* equation.

$$2x + 3(-5x + 16) = 9$$

$$2x - 15x + 48 = 9 \qquad \text{Clear parentheses.}$$

$$-13x + 48 = 9 \qquad \text{Solve for } x.$$

$$-13x = -39$$

$$x = 3$$

$$y = -5(3) + 16 \longrightarrow y = 1$$

Substitute $x = 3$ in the equation $y = -5x + 16$.

Because $x = 3$, the cost per hot dog is $3.00.

Because $y = 1$, the cost per drink is $1.00.

A word problem can be checked by verifying that the solution meets the conditions specified in the problem.

5 hot dogs + 1 drink $= 5(\$3.00) + 1(\$1.00) = \$16.00$ as expected

2 hot dogs + 3 drinks $= 2(\$3.00) + 3(\$1.00) = \$9.00$ as expected

2.   Applications Involving Mixtures

example 2

Solving an Application Involving Chemistry

One brand of cleaner used to etch concrete is 25% acid. A stronger industrial-strength cleaner is 50% acid. How many gallons of each cleaner should be mixed to produce 20 gal of a 40% acid solution?

Solution:

Let x represent the amount of 25% acid cleaner.

Let y represent the amount of 50% acid cleaner.

	25% Acid	50% Acid	40% Acid
Number of Gallons of Solution	x	y	20
Number of Gallons of Pure Acid	0.25x	0.50y	0.40(20), or 8

From the first row of the table, we have:

$$\begin{pmatrix} \text{Amount of} \\ \text{25\% solution} \end{pmatrix} + \begin{pmatrix} \text{Amount of} \\ \text{50\% solution} \end{pmatrix} = \begin{pmatrix} \text{Total amount} \\ \text{of solution} \end{pmatrix} \rightarrow x + y = 20$$

From the second row of the table we have:

$$\begin{pmatrix} \text{Amount of} \\ \text{pure acid in the} \\ 25\% \text{ solution} \end{pmatrix} + \begin{pmatrix} \text{Amount of} \\ \text{pure acid in the} \\ 50\% \text{ solution} \end{pmatrix} = \begin{pmatrix} \text{Amount of} \\ \text{pure acid in the} \\ \text{resulting solution} \end{pmatrix} \rightarrow 0.25x + 0.50y = 8$$

$$x + y = 20 \longrightarrow x + y = 20$$

$$0.25x + 0.50y = 8 \longrightarrow 25x + 50y = 800 \qquad \text{Multiply by 100 to clear fractions.}$$

$$x + y = 20 \xrightarrow{\text{multiply by } -25} -25x - 25y = -500 \qquad \text{Create opposite}$$
$$25x + 50y = 800 \longrightarrow \underline{\quad 25x + 50y = 800 \quad} \qquad \text{coefficients of } x.$$

$$25y = 300 \qquad \text{Add the equations to eliminate } x.$$

$$y = 12 \qquad \text{Solve for } y.$$

$$x + y = 20 \qquad \text{Substitute } y = 12$$
$$x + 12 = 20 \qquad \text{back into one of the original}$$
$$x = 8 \qquad \text{equations.}$$

Eight gal of 25% acid solution must be added to 12 gal of 50% acid solution to create 20 gal of a 40% acid solution.

■

3. Applications Involving Principal and Interest

example 3

Solving a Mixture Application Involving Finance

Serena invested money in two accounts: a savings account that yields 4.5% simple interest, and a certificate of deposit that yields 7% simple interest. The amount invested at 7% was twice the amount invested at 4.5%. How much did Serena invest in each account if the total interest at the end of one year was $1017.50?

Solution:

Let x represent the amount invested in the savings account (the 4.5% account)

Let y represent the amount invested in the certificate of deposit (the 7% account)

	4.5% Account	7% Account	Total
Principal	x	y	
Interest	$0.045x$	$0.07y$	1017.50

Because the amount invested at 7% was twice the amount invested at 4.5%, we have:

$$\begin{pmatrix} \text{Amount} \\ \text{invested} \\ \text{at } 7\% \end{pmatrix} = 2 \begin{pmatrix} \text{Amount} \\ \text{invested} \\ \text{at } 4.5\% \end{pmatrix} \rightarrow y = 2x$$

From the second row of the table, we have:

$$\begin{pmatrix} \text{Interest} \\ \text{earned from} \\ 4.5\% \text{ account} \end{pmatrix} + \begin{pmatrix} \text{Interest} \\ \text{earned from} \\ 7\% \text{ account} \end{pmatrix} = \begin{pmatrix} \text{Total} \\ \text{interest} \end{pmatrix} \rightarrow 0.045x + 0.07y = 1017.50$$

$$y = 2x$$

$45x + 70y = 1{,}017{,}500$	Multiply by 1000 to clear decimals.
	Because the y-variable in the first equation is isolated, we will use the substitution method.
$45x + 70(2x) = 1{,}017{,}500$	Substitute the quantity, $2x$, into the second equation.
$45x + 140x = 1{,}017{,}500$	Solve for x.
$185x = 1{,}017{,}500$	
$x = \dfrac{1{,}017{,}500}{185}$	
$x = 5500$	
$y = 2x$	
$y = 2(5500)$	Substitute $x = 5500$ into the equation $y = 2x$ to solve for y.
$y = 11{,}000$	

Because $x = 5500$, then the amount invested in the savings account is $5500.

Because $y = 11{,}000$, then the amount invested in the certificate of deposit is $11,000.

Check: $11,000 is twice $5500. Furthermore,

$$\begin{pmatrix} \text{Interest} \\ \text{earned from} \\ 4.5\% \text{ account} \end{pmatrix} + \begin{pmatrix} \text{Interest} \\ \text{earned from} \\ 7\% \text{ account} \end{pmatrix} = \$5500(0.045) + \$11{,}000(0.07) = 1017.50 \checkmark$$

4. Applications Involving Distance, Rate, and Time

example 4

Solving a Distance, Rate, and Time Application

A plane flies 660 miles from Atlanta to Miami in 1.2 h when traveling with a tail-wind. The return flight against the same wind takes 1.5 h. Find the speed of the plane in still air and the speed of the wind.

Solution:

Let x represent the speed of the plane in still air.

Let y represent the speed of the wind.

The speed of the plane *with* the wind: (Plane's still air speed) + (wind speed): $x + y$

The speed of the plane *against* the wind: (Plane's still air speed) − (wind speed): $x - y$

Set up a chart to organize the given information:

	Distance	Rate	Time
With a Tailwind	660	$x + y$	1.2
Against a Head Wind	660	$x - y$	1.5

Two equations can be found by using the relationship $d = rt$ (distance = rate · time)

$$\left(\begin{array}{c}\text{Distance}\\\text{with the}\\\text{wind}\end{array}\right) = \left(\begin{array}{c}\text{speed}\\\text{with the}\\\text{wind}\end{array}\right)\left(\begin{array}{c}\text{time}\\\text{with the}\\\text{wind}\end{array}\right) \longrightarrow 660 = (x + y)(1.2)$$

$$\left(\begin{array}{c}\text{Distance}\\\text{against}\\\text{wind}\end{array}\right) = \left(\begin{array}{c}\text{speed}\\\text{against}\\\text{the wind}\end{array}\right)\left(\begin{array}{c}\text{time}\\\text{against}\\\text{the wind}\end{array}\right) \longrightarrow 660 = (x - y)(1.5)$$

$660 = (x + y)(1.2)$ Notice that the first equation may be *divided* by

$660 = (x - y)(1.5)$ 1.2 and still leave integer coefficients. Similarly, the second equation may be simplified by dividing by 1.5.

$$660 = (x + y)(1.2) \xrightarrow{\text{divide by 1.2}} \frac{660}{1.2} = \frac{(x + y)\cancel{1.2}}{\cancel{1.2}} \longrightarrow 550 = x + y$$

$$660 = (x - y)(1.5) \xrightarrow{\text{divide by 1.5}} \frac{660}{1.5} = \frac{(x - y)\cancel{1.5}}{\cancel{1.5}} \longrightarrow 400 = x - y$$

$550 = x + y$

$\underline{440 = x - y}$

$990 = 2x$ Add the equations.

$\dfrac{990}{2} = x$ Solve for x.

$x = 495$

$550 = (495) + y$ Substitute $x = 495$ into the equation $550 = x + y$.

$55 = y$ Solve for y.

The speed of the plane in still air is 495 mph and the speed of the wind is 55 mph.

5. Applications Involving Geometry

example 5

Solving a Geometry Application

The sum of the two acute angles in a right triangle is 90°. One angle is 6° less than 2 times the measure of the other angle. Find the measure of each angle.

Solution:

Let x represent one angle.

Let y represent the other angle.

The sum of the two acute angles is 90°: $x + y = 90$

One angle is 6° less than 2 times the other angle: $x = 2y - 6$

$$x + y = 90$$
$$x = 2y - 6$$

Because one variable is already isolated, we will use the substitution method.

$$(2y - 6) + y = 90$$
$$3y - 6 = 90$$

Substitute $x = 2y - 6$ into the first equation.

$$3y = 96$$
$$y = 32$$

$$x = 2y - 6$$
$$x = 2(32) - 6$$

To find x, substitute $y = 32$ into the equation $x = 2y - 6$.

$$x = 64 - 6$$
$$x = 58$$

The two acute angles in the triangle are 32° and 58°.

6. Applications Involving Business

example 6

Solving a Business Application

Jake must decide between two sales jobs. One job will pay a base salary of $20,000/year, plus 5% commission on sales. A second job pays a base salary of $25,000/year, plus 4% commission on sales.

a. Write a linear equation representing the total salary (commission plus base salary) for the first job. (Let y_1 represent total salary and x represent sales in dollars.)

b. Write a linear equation representing the total salary (commission plus base salary) for the second job. (Let y_2 represent total salary and x represent sales in dollars.)

c. Graph the equations from parts (a) and (b).

d. If Jake's total sales are $200,000 for a given year, what would his total salary be in the first job? In the second job?

e. If Jake's total sales are $900,000, which job would yield the higher total salary?

f. How many dollars in sales would result in equal pay in both jobs?

Solution:

a. The total salary for job 1: $y_1 = 0.05x + 20,000$

b. The total salary for job 2: $y_2 = 0.04x + 25,000$

c.

d. For $x = \$200,000$: $\quad y_1 = 0.05(200,000) + 20,000 \quad\longrightarrow\quad y_1 = \$30,000$

For $x = \$200,000$: $\quad y_2 = 0.04(200,000) + 25,000 \quad\longrightarrow\quad y_2 = \$33,000$

If Jake has $200,000 in sales, job 2 would yield a better salary.

e. For $x = \$900,000$: $\quad y_1 = 0.05(900,000) + 20,000 \quad\longrightarrow\quad y_1 = \$65,000$

For $x = \$900,000$: $\quad y_2 = 0.04(900,000) + 25,000 \quad\longrightarrow\quad y_2 = \$61,000$

If Jake has $900,000 in sales, job 1 would yield a better salary.

f. For the two jobs to result in equal pay, y_1 must equal y_2.

$$y_1 = y_2$$

$$0.05x + 20,000 = 0.04x + 25,000$$

$0.01x + 20,000 = 25,000$ Subtract $0.04x$ from both sides.

$0.01x = 5000$ Subtract 20,000 from both sides.

$$x = \frac{5000}{0.01} \quad \text{or} \quad x = \$500,000 \text{ in sales}$$

Based on the results of Example 6, job 2 would pay more for sales less than $500,000. For sales above $500,000, job 1 pays more. If exactly $500,000 in sales is made, then both jobs would pay the same amount. Notice that $x = \$500,000$ corresponds to the point of intersection between the two graphs.

section 3.2   PRACTICE EXERCISES

1. How do you determine if a system of equations is dependent?

2. How do you determine if a system of equations is inconsistent?

3. Given the system: $y = 9 - 2x$

$$3x - y = 16$$

   a. Which method would you prefer to solve this system? Choose from the addition method, the substitution method, or the graphing method.

   b. Solve the system.

4. Given the system: $7x - y = -25$

$$2x + 5y = 14$$

   a. Which method would you prefer to solve this system? Choose from the addition method, the substitution method, or the graphing method.

   b. Solve the system.

5. Solve this system using any method:

   $5x + 2y = 6$

   $-2x - y = 3$

6. Solve this system using any method:

   $x = 5y - 2$

   $-3x + 7y = 14$

For Exercises 7–10, determine if the two linear equations represent parallel, intersecting, or coinciding lines by comparing their slopes and y-intercepts.

7. $y = 3x + 2$

   $y = 3x - 5$

8. $y = 4x + 6$

   $y = 4x - 11$

9. $y = -5x - 3$

   $y = 5x - 3$

10. $x = 6$

    $y = -2$

For Exercises 11–26, solve the mixture applications.

11. Sam has a pocket full of change consisting of dimes and quarters. The total value is $3.15. There are seven more quarters than dimes. How many of each coin are there?

12. Crystal has several dimes and quarters in her purse, totaling $2.70. There is one less dime than there are quarters. How many of each coin are there?

13. A coin collection consists of 50¢ pieces and $1 coins. If there are a total of 21 coins worth $15.50, how many 50¢ pieces and $1 coins are there?

14. Suzy has a piggy bank consisting of nickels and dimes. If there are 30 coins worth $1.90, how many nickels and dimes are in the bank?

15. The local community college theater put on a production of *A Funny Thing Happened on the Way to the Forum*. There were 186 tickets sold, some for $16 (nonstudent price) and some for $12 (student price). If the receipts for one performance totaled $2640, how many of each type of ticket were sold?

16. Jack and Diane bought school supplies. Jack spent $8.00 on four notebooks and five pencils. Diane spent $5.91 on three notebooks and three pencils. What is the cost of one notebook and what is the cost of one pencil?

17. Jacob bought lunch for his fellow office workers on Monday. He spent $7.35 on three hamburgers and two fish sandwiches. Ralph bought lunch on Tuesday and spent $7.15 for four hamburgers and one fish sandwich. What is the price of a hamburger and what is the price of a fish sandwich?

18. A group of four golfers pays $77 to play a round of golf. Of these four, one is a member of the club and three are nonmembers. Another group of golfers consists of two members and one nonmember and pays a total of $29. What is the cost for a member to play a round of golf and what is the cost for a nonmember?

19. Alex invested $27,000 in two accounts: one that pays 10% simple interest and one that pays 12% simple interest. At the end of the first year, his total return was $2990. How much was invested in each account?

20. Sonia invested a total of $12,000 into two accounts paying 7.5% and 6% simple interest, respectively. If her total return at the end of the first year was $840, how much did she invest in each account?

21. A credit union offers 5.5% simple interest on a certificate of deposit (CD) and 3.5% simple interest on a savings account. If Mr. Roderick invested $200 more in the CD than in the savings account and the total interest after the first year was $245, how much was invested in each account?

22. Ms. Kioki divided $20,000 into two accounts paying 10% and 12% simple interest. At the end of the first year, the total interest from both accounts was $2250. Find the amount invested in each account.

23. A chemistry student wants to mix an 18% acid solution with a 45% acid solution to get 16 L of a 36% acid solution. How many liters of the 18% solution and how many liters of the 45% solution should be mixed?

24. A jar of face cream contains 18% moisturizer, and another is 24% moisturizer. How many ounces of each should be combined to get 12 oz of a cream that is 22% moisturizer?

25. How much pure bleach must be combined with a solution that is 4% bleach to make 12 oz of a 12% bleach solution?

26. A fruit punch that contains 25% fruit juice is combined with a fruit drink that contains 10% fruit juice. How many ounces of each should be used to make 48 oz of a mixture that is 15% fruit juice?

For Exercises 27–30, solve the applications involving distance, rate, and time.

27. A small plane requires 40 min ($\frac{2}{3}$ h) to fly between Vancouver, British Columbia, and Seattle, Washington. A train requires 1 h and 20 min ($1\frac{1}{3}$ h) to complete the same trip. The plane travels 90 mph faster than the train.

    a. Find the average speed of the plane and the average speed of the train.

    b. How far is it between the two cities?

28. The Gulf Stream is a warm ocean current that extends from the eastern side of the Gulf of Mexico up through the Florida Straits and along the southeastern coast of the United States to Cape Hatteras, North Carolina. A boat travels with the current 100 miles from Miami, Florida, to Freeport, Bahamas, in 2.5 h. The return trip against the same current takes $3\frac{1}{3}$ h. Find the average speed of the boat in still water and the average speed of the current.

29. Jeannie and Juan rollerblade in opposite directions. Juan averages 2 mph faster than Jeannie. If they began at the same place and ended up 20 miles apart after 2 h, how fast did each of them travel?

30. A plane flew 720 miles in 3 h with the wind. It would take 4 h to travel the same distance against the wind. What is the rate of the plane in still air and the rate of wind?

For Exercises 31–36, solve the applications involving geometry. If necessary, refer to the geometry formulas listed in the inside front cover of the text.

31. In a right triangle, one acute angle is 6° more than 3 times the other. If the sum of the two acute angles must equal 90°, find the measures of the acute angles.

32. An isosceles triangle has two angles of the same measure (see figure). If the angle represented by y is 3° less than the angle x, find the measure of all angles of the triangle. (Recall that the sum of the measures of the angles of a triangle is 180°.)

Figure for Exercise 32

33. Two angles are supplementary. One angle is 2° less than 3 times the other. What are the measures of the two angles?

34. One angle is 5 times another. If the two angles are supplementary, find the measures of the angles.

35. One angle is 3° more than twice another. If the two angles are complementary, find the measures of the angles.

36. Two angles are complementary. One angle is 15° more than 2 times the other. What are the measures of the two angles?

For Exercises 37–40, solve the business applications.

37. A rental car company rents a compact car for $20 a day, plus $0.25 per mile. A midsize car rents for $30 a day, plus $0.20 per mile.

    The cost, y_c, to rent a compact car for one day is given by the equation:

    $y_c = 20 + 0.25x$ where x is the number of miles driven

    The cost, y_m, to rent a midsize car for one day is given by the equation:

    $y_m = 30 + 0.20x$ where x is the number of miles driven

    Find the number of miles at which the cost to rent either car would be the same and confirm your answer with the graph.

Cost to Rent a Car Versus Mileage

$y_c = 0.25x + 20$

$y_m = 0.2x + 30$

● Compact
■ Midsize

Figure for Exercise 37

38. One phone company charges $0.15/min for long distance calls. A second company, charges only $0.10/min for long distance calls, but adds a monthly fee of $4.95.

    The total bill for one month, y_1, for company 1 is given by the equation:

    $y_1 = 0.15x$ where x is the number of minutes of long distance

    The total bill for one month y_2, for company 2 is given by the equation:

    $y_2 = 0.10x + 4.95$ where x is the number of minutes of long distance

    Find the number of minutes of long distance for which the total bill from either company would be the same, and confirm your answer with the graph.

Monthly Phone Cost Versus Number of Long Distance Minutes

$y_1 = 0.15x$

$y_2 = 0.1x + 4.95$

Number of Minutes Long Distance

● Company 1
■ Company 2

Figure for Exercise 38

39. The *demand* for a certain printer cartridge is related to the price. In general, the higher the price, x, the lower the demand, y. The *supply* for the printer cartridges is also related to price. The higher the price, the greater the incentive for the supplier to stock the item. The supply and demand for the printer cartridges depends on the price according to the equations:

$y_d = -10x + 500$ where x is the price per cartridge in dollars, and y_d is the demand measured in 1000s of cartridges.

$y_s = \dfrac{20}{3}x$ where x is the price per cartridge in dollars, and y_s is the supply measured in 1000s of cartridges.

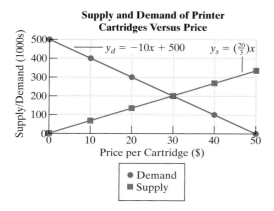

Supply and Demand of Printer Cartridges Versus Price

$y_d = -10x + 500$ $y_s = \left(\frac{20}{3}\right)x$

● Demand
■ Supply

Figure for Exercise 39

Find the price at which the supply and demand are in equilibrium (supply = demand), and confirm your answer with the graph.

40. The supply and demand for a pack of note cards depends on the price according to the equations:

$y_d = -130x + 660$ where x is the price per pack in dollars and y_d is the demand in 1000s of note cards.

$y_s = 90x$ where x is the price per pack in dollars and y_s is the supply measured in 1000s of note cards.

Supply and Demand of Note Cards Versus Price

$y_d = -130x + 660$

$y_s = 90x$

● Demand
■ Supply

Figure for Exercise 40

Find the price at which the supply and demand are in equilibrium (supply = demand), and confirm your answer with the graph.

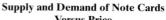 **GRAPHING CALCULATOR EXERCISES**

41. Refer to Exercise 37. Graph the equations on a viewing window defined by $0 \le x \le 500$ and $0 \le y \le 150$. Use an *Intersect* feature to approximate the point of intersection.

42. Refer to Exercise 38. Graph the equations on a viewing window defined by $0 \le x \le 200$ and $0 \le y \le 25$. Use an *Intersect* feature to approximate the point of intersection.

43. Refer to Exercise 39. Graph the equations on a viewing window defined by $0 \le x \le 60$ and $0 \le y \le 600$. Use an *Intersect* feature to approximate the point of intersection.

44. Refer to Exercise 40. Graph the equations on a viewing window defined by $0 \le x \le 5$ and $0 \le y \le 400$. Use an *Intersect* feature to approximate the point of intersection.

section

3.3   SYSTEMS OF LINEAR EQUATIONS IN THREE VARIABLES

Concepts

1.   Introduction to Linear Equations in Three Variables

In Section 3.1, we solved systems of linear equations in two variables. In this section, we will expand the discussion to solving systems involving three variables.

A **linear equation in three variables** can be written in the form $ax + by + cz = d$, where a, b, and c are not all zero. For example, the equation $2x + 3y + z = 6$ is a linear equation in three variables. Solutions to this equation are **ordered triples** of the form (x, y, z) that satisfy the equation. Some solutions to the equation $2x + 3y + z = 6$ are:

Solution: Check:

$(1, 1, 1) \longrightarrow 2(1) + 3(1) + (1) = 6$ ✓

$(2, 0, 2) \longrightarrow 2(2) + 3(0) + (2) = 6$ ✓

$(0, 1, 3) \longrightarrow 2(0) + 3(1) + (3) = 6$ ✓

Infinitely many ordered triples serve as solutions to the equation $2x + 3y + z = 6$. These solutions can be graphed in a three-dimensional coordinate system such as the one shown in Figure 3-2.

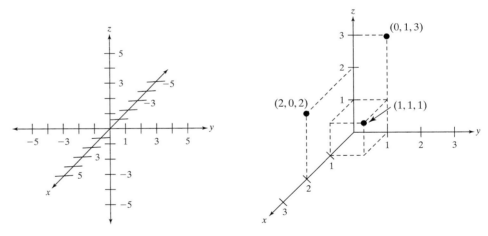

Figure 3-2   **Figure 3-3**

The coordinate axes divide three-dimensional space into eight parts called *octants*.

The solution points $(1, 1, 1)$, $(2, 0, 2)$ and $(0, 1, 3)$ are shown in Figure 3-3. Graphing points in three dimensions usually requires the aid of a computer.

The set of ordered triples that are solutions to a linear equation in three variables may be represented graphically by a plane in space. Figure 3-4 shows a portion of the plane $2x + 3y + x = 6$ in the first octant.

Figure 3-4

2. Solutions to Systems of Linear Equations in Three Variables

A **solution to a system of linear equations in three variables** is an ordered triple that satisfies *each* equation. Geometrically, a solution is a point of intersection of the planes represented by the equations in the system.

System of Linear Equations

$$2x + y - 3z = -7$$
$$3x - 2y + z = 11$$
$$-2x - 3y - 2z = 3$$

A solution is an intersection point among the planes.

A system of linear equations in three variables may have *one unique solution, infinitely many solutions,* or *no solution.* Figures 3-5, 3-6, and 3-7 summarize each situation.

- One unique solution (planes intersect at one point; see Figure 3-5).
- The system is consistent.
- The system is independent.

Figure 3-5

Figure 3-6

- No solution (the three planes do not all intersect; see Figure 3-6).
- The system is inconsistent.
- The system is independent.

Figure 3-7

- Infinitely many solutions (planes intersect at infinitely many points; see Figure 3-7).
- The system is consistent.
- The system is dependent.

3.   Solving Systems of Linear Equations in Three Variables

To solve a system involving three variables, the goal is to eliminate one variable. This reduces the system to two equations in two variables. One strategy for eliminating a variable is to pair up the original equations two at a time.

Solving a System of Three Linear Equations and Three Variables

1. Write each equation in standard form, $ax + by + cz = d$.
2. Choose a pair of equations to eliminate one of the variables using the addition method.
3. Choose a different pair of equations and eliminate the *same* variable.
4. Once steps 2 and 3 are complete, you should have two equations in two variables. Solve this system using the methods from Section 3.1.
5. Substitute the values of the variables found in step 4 into any of the three original equations that contain the third variable. Solve for the third variable.
6. Check the solution in each of the original equations.

---

example 1   **Solving a System of Linear Equations in Three Variables**

Solve the system:
$$2x + y - 3z = -7$$
$$3x - 2y + z = 11$$
$$-2x - 3y - 2z = 3$$

Solution:

$\boxed{A}$ $2x + y - 3z = -7$
$\boxed{B}$ $3x - 2y + z = 11$
$\boxed{C}$ $-2x - 3y - 2z = 3$

Step 1:   The equations are already in standard form.

- It is often helpful to label the equations.
- The y-variable can be easily eliminated from equations $\boxed{A}$ and $\boxed{B}$ and from equations $\boxed{A}$ and $\boxed{C}$. This is accomplished by creating opposite coefficients for the y terms and then adding the equations.

$\boxed{A}$ $2x + y - 3z = -7$ $\xrightarrow{\text{multiply by 2}}$ $4x + 2y - 6z = -14$

$\boxed{B}$ $3x - 2y + z = 11$ $\xrightarrow{\hspace{1cm}}$ $\underline{3x - 2y + z = 11}$

$\hspace{6cm} 7x \hspace{1.5cm} - 5z = -3$ $\boxed{D}$

Step 2: Eliminate the y-variable from equations $\boxed{A}$ and $\boxed{B}$.

Tip: It is important to note that in steps 2 and 3, the *same* variable is eliminated.

$\boxed{A}$ $2x + y - 3z = -7$ $\xrightarrow{\text{multiply by 3}}$ $6x + 3y - 9z = -21$

$\boxed{C}$ $-2x - 3y - 2z = 3$ $\xrightarrow{\hspace{1cm}}$ $\underline{-2x - 3y - 2z = 3}$

$\hspace{6cm} 4x \hspace{1.5cm} - 11z = -18$ $\boxed{E}$

Step 3: Eliminate the y-variable again, this time from equations $\boxed{A}$ and $\boxed{C}$.

$\boxed{D}$ $7x - 5z = -3$ $\xrightarrow{\text{multiply by } -4}$ $-28x + 20z = 12$

$\boxed{E}$ $4x - 11z = -18$ $\xrightarrow{\text{multiply by 7}}$ $\underline{28x - 77z = -126}$

$\hspace{6cm} -57z = -114$

$\hspace{6cm} \dfrac{-57z}{-57} = \dfrac{-114}{-57}$

$\hspace{6cm} z = 2$

Step 4: Now equations $\boxed{D}$ and $\boxed{E}$ can be paired up to form a linear system in two variables. Solve this system.

Once one variable has been found, substitute this value into either equation in the two-variable system, that is, either equation $\boxed{D}$ or $\boxed{E}$.

$\boxed{D}$ $7x - 5z = -3$

$\hspace{0.5cm} 7x - 5(2) = -3$ $\hspace{1cm}$ Substitute $z = 2$ into equation $\boxed{D}$.

$\hspace{0.5cm} 7x - 10 = -3$

$\hspace{1.5cm} 7x = 7$

$\hspace{1.5cm} x = 1$

$\boxed{A}$ $2x + y - 3z = -7$

$\hspace{0.3cm} 2(1) + y - 3(2) = -7$

$\hspace{1cm} 2 + y - 6 = -7$

$\hspace{1.5cm} y - 4 = -7$

$\hspace{1.8cm} y = -3$

Step 5: Now that two variables are known, substitute these values (x and z) into any of the original three equations to find the remaining variable, y. Substitute $x = 1$ and $z = 2$ into equation $\boxed{A}$.

The solution is $(1, -3, 2)$. **Step 6:** Check the ordered triple in the three original equations.

$$\text{Check:}\quad \begin{aligned} 2x + y - 3z &= -7 \rightarrow 2(1) + (-3) - 3(2) = -7 \checkmark \\ 3x - 2y + z &= 11 \rightarrow 3(1) - 2(-3) + (2) = 11 \checkmark \\ -2x - 3y - 2z &= 3 \rightarrow -2(1) - 3(-3) - 2(2) = 3 \checkmark \end{aligned}$$

---

example 2

Solving a System of Linear Equations in Three Variables

Solve the system:

$$\boxed{A}\quad 2x \qquad + z = -1$$
$$\boxed{B}\qquad 2y + 4z = 0$$
$$\boxed{C}\quad x + y - z = 3$$

Solution:

Equations $\boxed{A}$ and $\boxed{B}$ both have missing variables. This actually simplifies the process of eliminating variables. Notice that equation $\boxed{B}$ is missing the x-variable. Therefore, we can eliminate x again by pairing up equations $\boxed{A}$ and $\boxed{C}$:

Step 1:
The equations are already in standard form.

$$\boxed{A}\ 2x \quad\ + z = -1 \xrightarrow{} 2x \qquad + z = -1$$
$$\boxed{C}\ x + y - z = \ \ 3 \xrightarrow{\text{multiply by }-2} -2x - 2y + 2z = -6$$
$$\underline{}$$
$$-2y + 3z = -7 \quad \boxed{D}$$

Step 2:
Eliminate one of the variables.

Step 3:
The same variable is missing from equation $\boxed{B}$.

$$\boxed{B}\quad 2y + 4z = \ \ 0$$
$$\boxed{D}\ \underline{-2y + 3z = -7}$$
$$7z = -7$$
$$z = -1$$

Step 4:
The pair of equations $\boxed{B}$ and $\boxed{D}$ form a system of linear equations in two variables. Solve this system by the methods of Section 3.1.

$\boxed{B}$ $2y + \quad 4z = 0$

$\qquad 2y + 4(-1) = 0$

$\qquad\quad 2y - 4 = 0$

$\qquad\qquad 2y = 4$

$\qquad\qquad y = 2$

Substitute $z = -1$ into either equation $\boxed{B}$ or $\boxed{D}$ to solve for y.

$\boxed{C}$ $x + \quad y - \quad z = 3$

$\qquad x + (2) - (-1) = 3$

$\qquad\qquad x + 3 = 3$

$\qquad\qquad\quad x = 0$

Step 5: Substitute $z = -1$ and $y = 2$ into one of the three original equations to solve for x. However, because x is not present in equation $\boxed{B}$, use either equation $\boxed{A}$ or $\boxed{C}$ to solve for x.

The solution is $(0, 2, -1)$.

Step 6: Check the solution in each original equation.

$\boxed{A}$ $2x \qquad + \; z = -1 \longrightarrow 2(0) \qquad + \; (-1) \overset{?}{=} -1$ ✓

$\boxed{B}$ $\qquad 2y + 4z = \quad 0 \longrightarrow \qquad 2(2) + 4(-1) \overset{?}{=} \quad 0$ ✓

$\boxed{C}$ $x + \; y - \; z = \quad 3 \longrightarrow (0) + \; (2) - \; (-1) \overset{?}{=} \quad 3$ ✓

4. Solving a Dependent System of Linear Equations in Three Variables

example 3

Solving a System of Linear Equations in Three Variables

Solve the system.

$\boxed{A}$ $3x + \; y - \; z = 8$

$\boxed{B}$ $2x - \; y + 2z = 3$

$\boxed{C}$ $x + 2y - 3z = 5$

Solution:

The first step is to make a decision regarding the variable to eliminate. The y-variable is particularly easy to eliminate because the coefficients of y in equations $\boxed{A}$ and $\boxed{B}$ are already opposite. The y-variable can be eliminated from equations $\boxed{B}$ and $\boxed{C}$ by multiplying equation $\boxed{B}$ by 2.

$\boxed{A}$ $3x + y - \; z = 8$

$\boxed{B}$ $\underline{2x - y + 2z = 3}$

$\qquad 5x \qquad + \; z = 11 \;\; \boxed{D}$

Pair up equations $\boxed{A}$ and $\boxed{B}$ to eliminate y.

$\boxed{B}$ $2x - \; y + 2z = 3 \xrightarrow{\text{multiply by 2}} 4x - 2y + 4z = \quad 6$

$\boxed{C}$ $x + 2y - 3z = 5 \longrightarrow \underline{\quad x + 2y - 3z = \quad 5}$

$\qquad\qquad\qquad\qquad\qquad\qquad 5x \qquad + \; z = 11 \;\; \boxed{E}$

Pair up equations $\boxed{B}$ and $\boxed{C}$ to eliminate y.

$$\boxed{D} \quad 5x + z = 11 \xrightarrow{\text{multiply by } -1} -5x - z = -11$$

$$\boxed{E} \quad 5x + z = 11 \xrightarrow{\phantom{\text{multiply by } -1}} \underline{5x + z = 11}$$

$$0 = 0$$

Because equations $\boxed{D}$ and $\boxed{E}$ are equivalent equations, it appears that this is a dependent system. By eliminating variables we obtain the identity, $0 = 0$.

The system is dependent, indicating that there are infinitely many solutions. To find a general solution we need to express an ordered triple that represents the dependency among the variables. Notice that z can easily be expressed in terms of x from equation $\boxed{E}$: $z = 11 - 5x$. Therefore, if x is taken as an arbitrary real number, then z is dependent on x. In a similar way, y can be expressed in terms of x by substituting $z = 11 - 5x$ in equation $\boxed{C}$:

$$\boxed{C} \quad x + 2y - 3z = 5 \longrightarrow x + 2y - 3(11 - 5x) = 5$$

$$x + 2y - 33 + 15x = 5$$

$$2y + 16x - 33 = 5$$

$$2y = 38 - 16x$$

$$\frac{2y}{2} = \frac{38}{2} - \frac{16x}{2}$$

$$y = 19 - 8x$$

If x is taken as an arbitrary real number, then y and z both *depend* on x. This dependency can be used to express a general solution for this system of equations:

$$\{(x, y, z) \mid x \text{ is any real number}, y = 19 - 8x, z = 11 - 5x\}$$

This general solution yields an infinite number of solutions. To find some specific solutions, choose arbitrary values for x and calculate the corresponding values for y and z:

if $x = 0$,   then $y = 19 - 8(0) = 19$ and $z = 11 - 5(0) = 11$ $\rightarrow (0, 19, 11)$

if $x = 1$,   then $y = 19 - 8(1) = 11$ and $z = 11 - 5(1) = 6$ $\rightarrow (1, 11, 6)$

if $x = -2$, then $y = 19 - 8(-2) = 35$ and $z = 11 - 5(-2) = 21 \rightarrow (-2, 35, 21)$

· · ·

Note: The general solution defines y and z in terms of arbitrary values of x. In a similar way, a general solution can be found where x and z are defined in terms of arbitrary values of y. Likewise, a general solution can be found where x and y are defined in terms of arbitrary values of z.

$$\left\{ (x, y, z) \,\middle|\, x = \frac{19 - y}{8}, \ y \text{ is any real number}, \ z = \frac{5y - 7}{8} \right\}$$

$$\left\{ (x, y, z) \,\middle|\, x = \frac{11 - z}{5}, \ y = \frac{7 + 8z}{5}, \ z \text{ is any real number} \right\}$$

5. Applications of Linear Equations in Three Variables

example 4

Applying Systems of Linear Equations in Three Variables

In a triangle, the smallest angle is $10°$ more than half the largest angle. The middle angle is $12°$ more than the smallest angle. Find the measures of each angle.

Solution:

Let x represent the measure of the smallest angle.

Let y represent the measure of the middle angle.

Let z represent the measure of the largest angle.

To solve for three variables, we need to establish three independent relationships among x, y, and z.

$\boxed{A}$ $\ x = \dfrac{z}{2} + 10$	The smallest angle is $10°$ more than half the largest angle.
$\boxed{B}$ $\ y = x + 12$	The middle angle is $12°$ more than the smallest angle.
$\boxed{C}$ $\ x + y + z = 180$	The sum of the angles inscribed in a triangle is $180°$.

Clear fractions and write each equation in standard form.

Standard Form

$\boxed{A}$ $\ x \qquad = \dfrac{z}{2} + 10 \xrightarrow{\text{multiply by 2}} 2x = z + 20 \longrightarrow 2x \qquad - z = 20$

$\boxed{B}$ $\qquad y \ = x + 12 \longrightarrow \qquad\qquad\qquad -x + y \qquad = 12$

$\boxed{C}$ $\ x + y + z = \quad 180 \longrightarrow \qquad\qquad\qquad x + y + z = 180$

Notice equation $\boxed{B}$ is missing the z-variable. Therefore, we can eliminate z again by pairing up equations $\boxed{A}$ and $\boxed{C}$.

$\boxed{A}$ $\ 2x \qquad - z = \ \ 20$

$\boxed{C}$ $\ \underline{x + y + z = 180}$

$\qquad 3x + y \qquad = 200 \quad \boxed{D}$

$$\boxed{B} \quad -x + y = 12 \xrightarrow{\text{multiply by } -1} x - y = -12$$

Pair up equations $\boxed{B}$ and $\boxed{D}$ to form a system of two variables.

$$\boxed{D} \quad 3x + y = 200 \xrightarrow{} 3x + y = 200$$

$$4x \qquad = 188$$

$$\frac{4x}{4} = \frac{188}{4} \quad \text{Solve for } x.$$

$$x = 47°$$

From equation $\boxed{B}$ we have: $-x + y = 12 \rightarrow -47 + y = 12 \rightarrow y = 59$

From equation $\boxed{C}$ we have: $x + y + z = 180 \rightarrow 47 + 59 + z = 180 \rightarrow z = 74$

The smallest angle is 47°, the middle angle is 59°, and the largest angle is 74°.

---

section 3.3 PRACTICE EXERCISES

For Exercises 1–4, solve the systems using two methods: (a) the substitution method and (b) the addition method.

1. $3x + y = 4$

   $4x + y = 5$

2. $2x - 5y = 3$

   $-4x + 10y = 3$

3. $\frac{1}{2}x - \frac{1}{3}y = 1$

   $x - \frac{2}{3}y = 2$

4. $\frac{1}{2}x + \frac{1}{3}y = 13$

   $\frac{2}{5}x + \frac{1}{4}y = 10$

5. Two cars leave Kansas City at the same time. One travels east and one travels west. After 3 h the cars are 369 miles apart. If one car travels 7 mph slower than the other, find the speed of each car.

6. How many solutions are possible when solving a system of three equations with three variables?

7. Which of the following points are solutions to the system?

   $(2, 1, 7) \qquad (3, -10, -6) \qquad (4, 0, 2)$

   $2x - y + z = 10$

   $4x + 2y - 3z = 10$

   $x - 3y + 2z = 8$

8. Which of the following points are solutions to the system?

   $(1, 1, 3) \qquad (0, 0, 4) \qquad (4, 2, 1)$

   $-3x - 3y - 6z = -24$

   $-9x - 6y + 3z = -45$

   $9x + 3y - 9z = 33$

9. Which of the following points are solutions to the system?

   $(0, 4, 3) \qquad (3, 6, 10) \qquad (3, 3, 1)$

   $x + 2y - z = 5$

   $x - 3y + z = -5$

   $-2x + y - z = -4$

10. Which of the following points are solutions to the system?

    $(12, 2, -2) \qquad (4, 2, 1) \qquad (1, 1, 1)$

    $-x - y - 4z = -6$

    $x - 3y + z = -1$

    $4x + y - z = 4$

For Exercises 11–20, solve the system of equations.

11. $x + y + z = 6$

$-x + y - z = -2$

$2x + 3y + z = 11$

12. $x - y - z = -11$

$x + y - z = 15$

$2x - y + z = -9$

13. $-3x + y - z = 8$

$-4x + 2y + 3z = -3$

$2x + 3y - 2z = -1$

14. $2x + 3y + 3z = 15$

$3x - 6y - 6z = -23$

$-9x - 3y + 6z = 8$

15. $2x - y + z = -1$

$-3x + 2y - 2z = 1$

$5x + 3y + 3z = 16$

16. $4x - 3y + 2z = 12$

$-3x + 2y - 3z = -5$

$2x - y + 7z = -8$

17. $2x - 3y + 2z = -1$

$x + 2y = -4$

$x + z = 1$

18. $x + y + z = 2$

$2x - z = 5$

$3y + z = 2$

19. $4x + 9y = 8$

$8x + 6z = -1$

$6y + 6z = -1$

20. $3x + 2z = 11$

$y - 7z = 4$

$x - 6y = 1$

21. A triangle has one angle that is 5° more than twice the smallest angle and the largest angle is

11° less than 3 times the smallest angle. Find the measures of the three angles.

22. The largest angle of a triangle is 4° less than 5 times the smallest angle. The middle angle is twice the smallest. Find the measures of the three angles.

23. The perimeter of a triangle is 54 cm. The longest side is equal to the sum of the other two sides. The smallest side is half as long as the middle side. Find the lengths of the three sides.

24. The perimeter of a triangle is 5 ft. The smallest side is 4 in. less than the middle side and the middle side is half the length of the largest side. What are the measures of the three sides in *inches*?

25. A movie theater charges $7 for adults, $5 for children under 17, and $4 for seniors over 60. For one showing of *Titanic* the theater sold 222 tickets and took in $1383. If twice as many adult tickets were sold as the total of children and senior tickets, how many tickets of each kind were sold?

26. Goofie Golf has 18 holes that are par 3, par 4, or par 5. Most of the holes are par 4. In fact, there are 3 times as many par 4s as par 3s. There are 3 more par 5s than par 3s. How many of each type are there?

27. Combining peanuts, pecans, and cashews makes a party mixture of nuts. If the amount of peanuts equals the amount of pecans and cashews combined, and there are twice as many cashews as pecans, how many ounces of each nut is used to make 48 oz of party mixture?

28. Souvenir hats, T-shirts, and jackets are sold at a rock concert. Three hats, two T-shirts, and one jacket cost $140. Two hats, two T-shirts, and two jackets cost $170. One hat, three T-shirts, and

two jackets cost $180. Find the prices of the individual items.

For Exercises 29–38, solve the system. If there is not a unique solution, label the system as either dependent or inconsistent.

29. $2x + y + 3z = 2$

   $x - y + 2z = -4$

   $x + 3y - z = 1$

30. $x + y - z = 0$

   $3x - 2y + 6z = 1$

   $7x + 3y + z = 4$

31. $6x - 2y + 2z = 2$

   $4x + 8y - 2z = 5$

   $-2x - 4y + z = -2$

32. $3x + 2y + z = 3$

   $x - 3y + z = 4$

   $-6x - 4y - 2z = 1$

33. $\frac{1}{2}x + \frac{2}{3}y \quad = \frac{5}{2}$

   $\frac{1}{5}x \quad - \frac{1}{2}z = -\frac{3}{10}$

   $\frac{1}{3}y - \frac{1}{4}z = \frac{3}{4}$

34. $\frac{1}{2}x + \frac{1}{4}y + z = 3$

   $\frac{1}{8}x + \frac{1}{4}y + \frac{1}{4}z = \frac{9}{8}$

   $x - y - \frac{2}{3}z = \frac{1}{3}$

35. $2x + y - 3z = -3$

   $3x - 2y + 4z = 1$

   $4x + 2y - 6z = -6$

36. $2x + y \quad = -3$

   $2y + 16z = -10$

   $-7x - 3y + 4z = 8$

37. $\quad -0.1y + 0.2z = 0.2$

   $0.1x + 0.1y + 0.1z = 0.2$

   $-0.1x \quad + 0.3z = 0.2$

38. $0.1x - 0.2y \quad = 0$

   $0.3y + 0.1z = -0.1$

   $0.4x \quad - 0.1z = 1.2$

The systems in Exercises 39–44 are called homogeneous systems because each system has (0, 0, 0) as a solution. However if a system is dependent it will have infinitely many more solutions. For each system determine whether (0, 0, 0) is the only solution, or if the system is dependent.

39. $2x - 4y + 8z = 0$

   $-x - 3y + z = 0$

   $x - 2y + 5z = 0$

40. $2x - 4y + z = 0$

   $x - 3y - z = 0$

   $3x - y + 2z = 0$

41. $4x - 2y - 3z = 0$

   $-8x - y + z = 0$

   $2x - y - \frac{3}{2}z = 0$

42. $x + \frac{1}{2}y + z = 0$

   $\frac{2}{3}x - \frac{1}{3}y + z = 0$

   $\frac{3}{5}x - y + \frac{4}{5}z = 0$

43. $5x + y \quad = 0$

   $4y - z = 0$

   $-6x \quad + 2z = 0$

44. $-x \quad - z = 0$

   $6y + 3z = 0$

   $5x + y \quad = 0$

For Exercises 45–48, solve the dependent system by finding a general solution. See Example 3.

45. $-3x + 4y - z = -4$

$x + 2y + z = 4$

$-12x + 16y - 4z = -16$

46. $2x - y - 3z = 1$

$x + 2y + 4z = 3$

$4x - 2y - 6z = 2$

47. $2x + y \qquad = -3$

$2y + 16z = -18$

$-7x - 3y + 4z = 6$

48. $5x + y \qquad = 3$

$2x \qquad + z = -1$

$3x + y - z = 4$

---

chapter 3   MIDCHAPTER REVIEW

For Exercises 1–3, solve the system using the graphing method.

1. $y = 2x - 2$

$y = -3x + 3$

2. $2x - y = -4$

$-2x + y = -1$

3. $y = 3x + 1$

$-6x + 2y = 2$

For Exercises 4–6, solve the system using the substitution method.

4. $x + y = 1$

$y = x - 3$

5. $y = 2x - 8$

$x - \dfrac{1}{2}y = 4$

6. $4x - 8y = 9$

$x = 2y + 3$

For Exercises 7–9, solve the system using the addition method.

7. $-x + 5y = -12$

$2x - 10y = 24$

8. $x - y = 5$

$2x - 5y = 1$

9. $7x + y = 2$

$x + \dfrac{1}{7}y = 1$

For Exercises 10–12, solve the system of three equations.

10. $x - 2y + 3z = 9$

$2x - 5y + 5z = 17$

$-x + 3y \qquad = -4$

11. $2x - y \qquad = -8$

$x \qquad - z = -8$

$y + 3z = 22$

12. $4x - 2y - 2z = 5$

$2x - y - z = 7$

$-2x + y + z = 3$

13. Darcy bought coffee and doughnuts for her office for two mornings. The first morning she bought three cups of coffee and six doughnuts and spent $9.30. The next morning she bought two cups of coffee and five doughnuts and spent $7.00. What is the price of a doughnut and what is the price of cup of coffee?

14. The measure of one angle of a triangle is $72°$ less than the largest angle. The third angle is one-tenth the measure of the largest angle. What is the measure of each angle?

---

section

3.4   SOLVING SYSTEMS OF LINEAR EQUATIONS USING MATRICES

1.   Introduction to Matrices

In Sections 3.1 and 3.3, we solved systems of linear equations using the substitution method and the addition method. We now present a third method called the Gauss-Jordan method that uses matrices to solve a linear system.

A **matrix** is a rectangular array of numbers (the plural of matrix is matrices). The rows of a matrix are read horizontally and the columns of a matrix are read vertically. Every number or entry within a matrix is called an element of the matrix.

The **order of a matrix** is determined by the number of rows and number of columns. A matrix with m rows and n columns is an $m \times n$ (read as "m by n") matrix. Notice that with the order of a matrix, the number of rows is given first, followed by the number of columns.

2.   The Order of a Matrix

---

example 1

Determining the Order of a Matrix

Determine the order of each matrix.

a. $\begin{bmatrix} 2 & -4 & 1 \\ 5 & \pi & \sqrt{7} \end{bmatrix}$ b. $\begin{bmatrix} 1.9 \\ 0 \\ 7.2 \\ -6.1 \end{bmatrix}$ c. $\begin{bmatrix} 1 & 0 & 0 \\ 0 & 1 & 0 \\ 0 & 0 & 1 \end{bmatrix}$ d. $\begin{bmatrix} a & b & c \end{bmatrix}$

Solution:

a. This matrix has two rows and three columns. Therefore, it is a 2×3 matrix.
b. This matrix has four rows and one column. Therefore, it is a 4×1 matrix. A matrix with one column is called a **column matrix**.
c. This matrix has three rows and three columns. Therefore, it is a 3×3 matrix. A matrix with the same number rows and columns is called a **square matrix**.
d. This matrix has one row and three columns. Therefore, it is a 1×3 matrix. A matrix with one row is called a **row matrix**.

3. Augmented Matrices

A matrix can be used to represent a system of linear equations written in standard form. To do so, we extract the coefficients of the variable terms and the constants within the equation. For example, consider the system:

$$2x - y = 5$$
$$x + 2y = -5$$

The matrix **A** is called the **coefficient matrix**.

$$\mathbf{A} = \begin{bmatrix} 2 & -1 \\ 1 & 2 \end{bmatrix}$$

If we extract both the coefficients and the constants from the equations, we can construct the **augmented matrix** of the system:

$$\left[\begin{array}{cc|c} 2 & -1 & 5 \\ 1 & 2 & -5 \end{array}\right]$$

A vertical bar is inserted into an augmented matrix to designate the position of the equal signs.

---

example 2

Writing the Augmented Matrix of a System of Linear Equations

Write the augmented matrix for each linear system.

a. $-3x - 4y = 3$
    $2x + 4y = 2$

b. $2x \quad\quad - 3z = 14$
    $\quad 2y + z = 2$
    $\quad x + y \quad\quad = 4$

Tip: Notice that zeros are inserted to denote the coefficient of each missing term.

Solution:

a. $\left[\begin{array}{cc|c} -3 & -4 & 3 \\ 2 & 4 & 2 \end{array}\right]$

b. $\left[\begin{array}{ccc|c} 2 & 0 & -3 & 14 \\ 0 & 2 & 1 & 2 \\ 1 & 1 & 0 & 4 \end{array}\right]$

---

example 3

Writing a Linear System from an Augmented Matrix

Write a system of linear equations represented by each augmented matrix.

a. $\left[\begin{array}{cc|c} 2 & -5 & -8 \\ 4 & 1 & 6 \end{array}\right]$

b. $\left[\begin{array}{ccc|c} 2 & -1 & 3 & 14 \\ 1 & 1 & -2 & -5 \\ 3 & 1 & -1 & 2 \end{array}\right]$

c. $\left[\begin{array}{ccc|c} 1 & 0 & 0 & 4 \\ 0 & 1 & 0 & -1 \\ 0 & 0 & 1 & 0 \end{array}\right]$

Solution:

a. $\quad 2x - 5y = -8$ $\qquad\qquad$ b. $\quad 2x - y + 3z = 14$

$\qquad 4x + \quad y = 6$ $\qquad\qquad\qquad\quad x + y - 2z = -5$

$\qquad\qquad\qquad\qquad\qquad\qquad\qquad\quad 3x + y - \quad z = 2$

c. $\quad x + 0y + 0z = 4 \qquad x = 4$

$\quad 0x + \quad y + 0z = -1 \quad$ or $\quad y = -1$

$\quad 0x + 0y + \quad z = 0 \qquad z = 0$

4. The Gauss-Jordan Method

We know that interchanging two equations results in an equivalent system of linear equations. Interchanging two rows in an augmented matrix results in an equivalent augmented matrix. Similarly, because each row in an augmented matrix represents a linear equation, we can perform the following elementary row operations that result in an equivalent augmented matrix.

Elementary Row Operations

The following **elementary row operations** performed on an augmented matrix produce an equivalent augmented matrix:

1. Interchange two rows.
2. Multiply every element in a row by a nonzero real number.
3. Add a multiple of one row to another row.

5. Solving Systems of Linear Equations Using the Gauss-Jordan Method

When solving a system of linear equations by any method, the goal is to write a series of simpler but equivalent systems of equations until the solution is obvious. The **Gauss-Jordan method** uses a series of elementary row operations performed on the augmented matrix to produce a simpler augmented matrix. In particular, we want to produce an augmented matrix that has 1's along the diagonal of the matrix of coefficients and 0's for the remaining entries in the matrix of coefficients. A matrix written in this way is said to be written in **reduced row echelon form**. For example, the augmented matrix from Example 3(c) is written in reduced row echelon form.

$$\left[\begin{array}{ccc|c} 1 & 0 & 0 & 4 \\ 0 & 1 & 0 & -1 \\ 0 & 0 & 1 & 0 \end{array}\right]$$

The solution to the corresponding system of equations is easily recognized as $x = 4$, $y = -1$, and $z = 0$.

Similarly, the matrix **B** represents a solution of $x = a$ and $y = b$.

$$\mathbf{B} = \left[\begin{array}{cc|c} 1 & 0 & a \\ 0 & 1 & b \end{array}\right]$$

example 4

Solving a System of Linear Equations Using the Gauss-Jordan Method

Use the Gauss-Jordan method to solve the system:

$$2x - y = 5$$
$$x + 2y = -5$$

Solution:

$$\begin{bmatrix} 2 & -1 & | & 5 \\ 1 & 2 & | & -5 \end{bmatrix}$$

$$\xrightarrow{R_1 \Leftrightarrow R_2} \begin{bmatrix} 1 & 2 & | & -5 \\ 2 & -1 & | & 5 \end{bmatrix}$$ Switch rows 1 and 2 to get a 1 in the upper left position.

$$\xrightarrow{-2R_1 + R_2 \Rightarrow R_2} \begin{bmatrix} 1 & 2 & | & -5 \\ 0 & -5 & | & 15 \end{bmatrix}$$ Multiply row 1 by -2 and add the result to row 2. This produces an entry of 0 below the upper left position.

$$\xrightarrow{-\frac{1}{5}R_2 \Rightarrow R_2} \begin{bmatrix} 1 & 2 & | & -5 \\ 0 & 1 & | & -3 \end{bmatrix}$$ Multiply row 2 by $-\frac{1}{5}$ to produce a 1 along the diagonal in the second row.

$$\xrightarrow{-2R_2 + R_1 \Rightarrow R_1} \begin{bmatrix} 1 & 0 & | & 1 \\ 0 & 1 & | & -3 \end{bmatrix}$$ Multiply row 2 by -2 and add the result to row 1. This produces a 0 in the first row, second column.

The matrix **C** is in reduced row echelon form. From the augmented matrix, we have, $x = 1$ and $y = -3$. The solution to the system is $(1, -3)$.

$$\mathbf{C} = \begin{bmatrix} 1 & 0 & | & 1 \\ 0 & 1 & | & -3 \end{bmatrix}$$

example 5

Solving a System of Linear Equations Using the Gauss-Jordan Method

Use the Gauss-Jordan method to solve the system:

$$x = -y + 5$$
$$-2x + 2z = y - 10$$
$$3x + 6y + 7z = 14$$

Solution:

First write each equation in the system in standard form.

$$x = -y + 5 \longrightarrow x + y = 5$$
$$-2x + 2z = y - 10 \longrightarrow -2x - y + 2z = -10$$
$$3x + 6y + 7z = 14 \longrightarrow 3x + 6y + 7z = 14$$

$$\begin{bmatrix} 1 & 1 & 0 & | & 5 \\ -2 & -1 & 2 & | & -10 \\ 3 & 6 & 7 & | & 14 \end{bmatrix}$$ Set up the augmented matrix.

$2R_1 + R_2 \Rightarrow R_2$ ⟶
$-3R_1 + R_3 \Rightarrow R_3$ ⟶
$$\begin{bmatrix} 1 & 1 & 0 & | & 5 \\ 0 & 1 & 2 & | & 0 \\ 0 & 3 & 7 & | & -1 \end{bmatrix}$$ Multiply row 1 by 2 and add the result to row 2. Multiply row 1 by -3 and add the result to row 3.

$-1R_2 + R_1 \Rightarrow R_1$ ⟶
$-3R_2 + R_3 \Rightarrow R_3$ ⟶
$$\begin{bmatrix} 1 & 0 & -2 & | & 5 \\ 0 & 1 & 2 & | & 0 \\ 0 & 0 & 1 & | & -1 \end{bmatrix}$$ Multiply row 2 by -1 and add the result to row 1. Multiply row 2 by -3 and add the result to row 3.

$2R_3 + R_1 \Rightarrow R_1$ ⟶
$-2R_3 + R_2 \Rightarrow R_2$ ⟶
$$\begin{bmatrix} 1 & 0 & 0 & | & 3 \\ 0 & 1 & 0 & | & 2 \\ 0 & 0 & 1 & | & -1 \end{bmatrix}$$ Multiply row 3 by 2 and add the result to row 1. Multiply row 3 by -2 and add the result to row 2.

From the reduced row echelon form of the matrix, we have $x = 3$, $y = 2$, and $z = -1$. The solution to the system is $(3, 2, -1)$.

■

6. Inconsistent and Dependent Systems of Equations

It is particularly easy to recognize a dependent or inconsistent system of equations from the reduced row echelon form of an augmented matrix. This is demonstrated in the next two examples.

example 6 **Solving a Dependent System of Equations Using the Gauss-Jordan Method**

Use Gaussian elimination to solve the system:

$$x - 3y = 4$$

$$\frac{1}{2}x - \frac{3}{2}y = 2$$

Solution:

$$\begin{bmatrix} 1 & -3 & | & 4 \\ \frac{1}{2} & -\frac{3}{2} & | & 2 \end{bmatrix}$$ Set up the augmented matrix.

$-\frac{1}{2}R_1 + R_2 \Rightarrow R_2$ ⟶
$$\begin{bmatrix} 1 & -3 & | & 4 \\ 0 & 0 & | & 0 \end{bmatrix}$$ Multiply row 1 by $-\frac{1}{2}$ and add the result to row 2.

The second row of the augmented matrix represents the equation $0 = 0$; hence, the system is dependent. The solution is the set of all ordered pairs, (x, y) such that $x - 3y = 4$.

---

example 7

Solving an Inconsistent System of Equations Using the Gauss-Jordan Method

Use the Gauss-Jordan method to solve the system:

$$2x - 5y = 10$$

$$\frac{2}{5}x - y = 7$$

Solution:

$$\begin{bmatrix} 2 & -5 & | & 10 \\ \frac{2}{5} & -1 & | & 7 \end{bmatrix}$$ Set up the augmented matrix.

$$\xrightarrow{-\frac{1}{5}R_1 + R_2 \Rightarrow R_2} \begin{bmatrix} 2 & -5 & | & 10 \\ 0 & 0 & | & 5 \end{bmatrix}$$ Multiply row 1 by $-\frac{1}{5}$ and add the result to row 2.

The second row of the augmented matrix represents the contradiction $0 = 5$; hence, the system is inconsistent. There is no solution.

Graphing Calculator Box

Many graphing calculators have a matrix editor in which the user defines the order of the matrix and then enters the elements of the matrix. For example, the 2×3 matrix:

$$\mathbf{D} = \begin{bmatrix} 2 & -3 & | & -13 \\ 3 & 1 & | & 8 \end{bmatrix}$$

is entered as shown in the following two figures.

    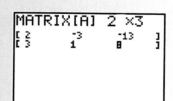

Once an augmented matrix has been entered into a graphing calculator a *rref* function can be used to transform the matrix into reduced row echelon form (see figure).

section 3.4 PRACTICE EXERCISES

For Exercises 1–4, solve the system using any method.

1. $5x + y = 6$
   $-3x + 2y = -1$

2. $x - 6y = 9$
   $x + 2y = 13$

3. $x + y - z = 8$
   $x - 2y + z = 3$
   $x + 3y + 2z = 7$

4. $2x - y + z = -4$
   $-x + y + 3z = -7$
   $x + 3y - 4z = 22$

5. What is an augmented matrix?

6. What is a coefficient matrix?

7. How do you determine the order of a matrix?

8. What is a square matrix?

For Exercises 9–16, (a) Determine the order of each matrix. (b) Determine if the matrix is a row matrix, a column matrix, a square matrix, or none of these.

9. $\begin{bmatrix} 4 \\ 5 \\ -3 \\ 0 \end{bmatrix}$

10. $\begin{bmatrix} 5 \\ -1 \\ 2 \end{bmatrix}$

11. $\begin{bmatrix} -9 & 4 & 3 \\ -1 & -8 & 4 \\ 5 & 8 & 7 \end{bmatrix}$

12. $\begin{bmatrix} 3 & -9 \\ -1 & -3 \end{bmatrix}$

13. $\begin{bmatrix} 4 & -7 \end{bmatrix}$

14. $\begin{bmatrix} 0 & -8 & 11 & 5 \end{bmatrix}$

15. $\begin{bmatrix} 5 & -8.1 & 4.2 & 0 \\ 4.3 & -9 & 18 & 3 \end{bmatrix}$

16. $\begin{bmatrix} \frac{1}{3} & \frac{3}{4} & 6 \\ -2 & 1 & -\frac{7}{8} \end{bmatrix}$

For Exercises 17–24, set up the augmented matrix.

17. $x - 2y = -1$
    $2x + y = -7$

18. $x - 3y = 3$
    $2x - 5y = 4$

19. $-9x + 13y = -5$
    $7x + 5y = 19$

20. $3x - 2y = 6$
    $4x - 10y = -3$

21. $x + y + z = 6$
    $x - y + z = 2$
    $x + y - z = 0$

22. $2x - 3y + z = 8$
    $x + 3y + 8z = 1$
    $3x - y + 2z = -1$

23. $x - 2y = 5 - z$
    $2x + 6y + 3z = -2$
    $3x - y - 2z = 1$

24. $5x + 2z = 17$
    $8x - y + 6z = 26$
    $8x + 3y - 12z = 24$

25. Given the matrix **E**:
    $$\mathbf{E} = \begin{bmatrix} 3 & -2 & 8 \\ 9 & -1 & 7 \end{bmatrix}$$
    a. What is the element in the second row and third column?
    b. What is the element in the first row and second column?

26. Given the matrix **F**:
    $$\mathbf{F} = \begin{bmatrix} 1 & 8 & 0 \\ 12 & -13 & -2 \end{bmatrix}$$
    a. What is the element in the second row and second column?
    b. What is the element in the first row and third column?

27. Given the matrix **G**:
    $$\mathbf{G} = \begin{bmatrix} 0.5 & 1.6 & 0 \\ 4 & -2.9 & -6 \end{bmatrix}$$
    a. What is the element in the first row and third column?
    b. What is the element in the second row and first column?

28. Given the matrix **H**:

$$\mathbf{H} = \left[\begin{array}{cc|c} \frac{1}{2} & -2 & 9 \\ 8 & \frac{3}{4} & 0 \end{array}\right]$$

a. What is the element in the first row and first column?

b. What is the element in the second row and second column?

29. Given the matrix **Z**:

$$\mathbf{Z} = \left[\begin{array}{cc|c} 2 & 1 & 11 \\ 2 & -1 & 1 \end{array}\right]$$

write the matrix obtained by multiplying the elements in the first row by $\frac{1}{2}$.

30. Given the matrix **J**:

$$\mathbf{J} = \left[\begin{array}{cc|c} 1 & 1 & 7 \\ 0 & 3 & -6 \end{array}\right]$$

write the matrix obtained by multiplying the elements in the second row by $\frac{1}{3}$.

31. Given the matrix **K**:

$$\mathbf{K} = \left[\begin{array}{cc|c} 5 & 2 & 1 \\ 1 & -4 & 3 \end{array}\right]$$

write the matrix obtained by interchanging rows 1 and 2.

32. Given the matrix **L**:

$$\mathbf{L} = \left[\begin{array}{cc|c} 9 & 6 & 13 \\ -7 & 2 & 19 \end{array}\right]$$

write the matrix obtained by interchanging rows 1 and 2.

33. Given the matrix **M**:

$$\mathbf{M} = \left[\begin{array}{cc|c} 1 & 5 & 2 \\ -3 & -4 & -1 \end{array}\right]$$

write the matrix obtained by multiplying the first row by 3 and adding the result to row 2.

34. Given the matrix **N**:

$$\mathbf{N} = \left[\begin{array}{cc|c} 1 & 3 & -5 \\ -2 & 2 & 12 \end{array}\right]$$

write the matrix obtained by multiplying the first row by 2 and adding the result to row 2.

35. Given the matrix **P**:

$$\mathbf{P} = \left[\begin{array}{cc|c} 1 & 6 & -4 \\ 0 & 1 & 3 \end{array}\right]$$

write the matrix obtained by multiplying the second row by -6 and adding the result to row 1.

36. Given the matrix **Q**:

$$\mathbf{Q} = \left[\begin{array}{cc|c} 1 & 4 & 8 \\ 0 & 1 & 4 \end{array}\right]$$

write the matrix obtained by multiplying the second row by -4 and adding the result to row 1.

37. Given the matrix **R**:

$$\mathbf{R} = \left[\begin{array}{ccc|c} 1 & 3 & 0 & -1 \\ 4 & 1 & -5 & 6 \\ -2 & 0 & -3 & 10 \end{array}\right]$$

a. Write the matrix obtained by multiplying the first row by -4 and adding the result to row 2.

b. Using the matrix obtained from part (a), write the matrix obtained by multiplying the first row by 2 and adding the result to row 3.

38. Given the matrix **S**:

$$\mathbf{S} = \left[\begin{array}{ccc|c} 1 & 2 & 0 & 10 \\ 5 & 1 & -4 & 3 \\ -3 & 4 & 5 & 2 \end{array}\right]$$

a. Write the matrix obtained by multiplying the first row by -5 and adding the result to row 2.

b. Using the matrix obtained from part (a), write the matrix obtained by multiplying the first row by 3 and adding the result to row 3.

39. Given the matrix **T**:

$$\mathbf{T} = \left[\begin{array}{ccc|c} 1 & -3 & 4 & 5 \\ 0 & 1 & 3 & -3 \\ 0 & 5 & 9 & 8 \end{array}\right]$$

a. Write the matrix obtained by multiplying the second row by 3 and adding the result to row 1.

b. Using the matrix obtained from part (a), write the matrix obtained by multiplying the second row by -5 and adding the result to row 3.

40. Given the matrix **U**:

$$\mathbf{U} = \left[\begin{array}{ccc|c} 1 & 2 & 9 & 10 \\ 0 & 1 & 4 & 12 \\ 0 & -4 & -2 & -20 \end{array}\right]$$

   a. Write the matrix obtained by multiplying the second row by -2 and adding the result to row 1.

   b. Using the matrix obtained from part (a), write the matrix obtained by multiplying the second row by 4 and adding the result to row 3.

41. Given the matrix **V**:

$$\mathbf{V} = \left[\begin{array}{ccc|c} 1 & 0 & 3 & 7 \\ 0 & 1 & -8 & -11 \\ 0 & 0 & 1 & 4 \end{array}\right]$$

   a. Write the matrix obtained by multiplying the third row by -3 and adding the result to row 1.

   b. Using the matrix obtained from part (a), write the matrix obtained by multiplying the third row by 8 and adding the result to row 2.

42. Given the matrix **W**:

$$\mathbf{W} = \left[\begin{array}{ccc|c} 1 & 0 & 5 & 2 \\ 0 & 1 & 6 & -6 \\ 0 & 0 & 1 & 10 \end{array}\right]$$

   a. Write the matrix obtained by multiplying the third row by -5 and adding the result to row 1.

   b. Using the matrix obtained from part (a), write the matrix obtained by multiplying the third row by -6 and adding the result to row 2.

For Exercises 43–46, use the augmented matrices **A**, **B**, and **C** to answer true or false.

$$\mathbf{A} = \left[\begin{array}{cc|c} 6 & -4 & 2 \\ 5 & -2 & 7 \end{array}\right] \quad \mathbf{B} = \left[\begin{array}{cc|c} 5 & -2 & 7 \\ 6 & -4 & 2 \end{array}\right]$$

$$\mathbf{C} = \left[\begin{array}{cc|c} 1 & -\frac{2}{3} & \frac{1}{3} \\ 5 & 2 & 7 \end{array}\right]$$

43. The matrix **A** is a 3×2 matrix.

44. Matrix **B** is equivalent to matrix **A**.

45. Matrix **A** is equivalent to matrix **C**.

46. Matrix **B** is equivalent to matrix **C**.

For Exercises 47–50, write a corresponding system of equations from the augmented matrix.

47. $\left[\begin{array}{cc|c} 1 & 0 & -1 \\ 0 & 1 & -7 \end{array}\right]$

48. $\left[\begin{array}{cc|c} 1 & 0 & 0 \\ 0 & 1 & 5 \end{array}\right]$

49. $\left[\begin{array}{ccc|c} 1 & 0 & 0 & 8 \\ 0 & 1 & 0 & 0 \\ 0 & 0 & 1 & -1 \end{array}\right]$

50. $\left[\begin{array}{ccc|c} 1 & 0 & 0 & 2.7 \\ 0 & 1 & 0 & \pi \\ 0 & 0 & 1 & -1.1 \end{array}\right]$

51. What does the notation $R_2 \Leftrightarrow R_1$ mean when performing the Gauss-Jordan method?

52. What does the notation $2R_3 \Rightarrow R_3$ mean when performing the Gauss-Jordan method?

53. What does the notation $-3R_1 + R_2 \Rightarrow R_2$ mean when performing the Gauss-Jordan method?

54. What does the notation $4R_2 + R_3 \Rightarrow R_3$ mean when performing the Gauss-Jordan method?

For Exercises 55–74, solve the systems using the Gauss-Jordan method.

55. $\begin{aligned} x - 2y &= -1 \\ 2x + y &= -7 \end{aligned}$

56. $\begin{aligned} x - 3y &= 3 \\ 2x - 5y &= 4 \end{aligned}$

57. $\begin{aligned} x + 3y &= 6 \\ -4x - 9y &= 3 \end{aligned}$

58. $\begin{aligned} 2x - 3y &= -2 \\ x + 2y &= 13 \end{aligned}$

59. $\begin{aligned} x + 3y &= 3 \\ 4x + 12y &= 12 \end{aligned}$

60. $\begin{aligned} 2x + 5y &= 1 \\ -4x - 10y &= -2 \end{aligned}$

61. $\begin{aligned} x - y &= 4 \\ 2x + y &= 5 \end{aligned}$

62. $\begin{aligned} 2x - y &= 0 \\ x + y &= 3 \end{aligned}$

63. $\begin{aligned} x + 3y &= -1 \\ -3x - 6y &= 12 \end{aligned}$

64. $\begin{aligned} x + y &= 4 \\ 2x - 4y &= -4 \end{aligned}$

65. $\begin{aligned} 3x + y &= -4 \\ -6x - 2y &= 3 \end{aligned}$

66. $\begin{aligned} 2x + y &= 4 \\ 6x + 3y &= -1 \end{aligned}$

67. $\begin{aligned} x + y + z &= 6 \\ x - y + z &= 2 \\ x + y - z &= 0 \end{aligned}$

68. $2x - 3y - 2z = 11$

    $x + 3y + 8z = 1$

    $3x - y + 14z = -2$

69. $x - 2y \quad\;\; = 5 - z$

    $2x + 6y + 3z = -10$

    $3x - y - 2z = 5$

70. $5x \quad\;\; - 10z = 15$

    $x - y + 6z = 23$

    $x + 3y - 12z = 13$

71. $x + y - z = 2$

    $2x - y + z = 1$

    $-x + y + z = 2$

72. $x + y + z = 6$

    $x - y - z = -4$

    $-x + y - z = -2$

73. $-x + 2y - z = -6$

    $x - 2y + z = -5$

    $3x + y + 2z = 4$

74. $4x + 8y + 4z = 9$

    $5x + 10y + 5z = 12$

    $x + 3y + 4z = 10$

GRAPHING CALCULATOR EXERCISES

For Exercises 75–86, use the matrix features on a graphing calculator to express each augmented matrix in reduced row echelon form. Compare your results to the solution you obtained in the indicated exercise.

75. $\begin{bmatrix} 1 & -2 & | & -1 \\ 2 & 1 & | & -7 \end{bmatrix}$

    Compare with Exercise 55.

76. $\begin{bmatrix} 1 & -3 & | & 3 \\ 2 & -5 & | & 4 \end{bmatrix}$

    Compare with Exercise 56.

77. $\begin{bmatrix} 1 & 3 & | & 6 \\ -4 & -9 & | & 3 \end{bmatrix}$

    Compare with Exercise 57.

78. $\begin{bmatrix} 2 & -3 & | & -2 \\ 1 & 2 & | & 13 \end{bmatrix}$

    Compare with Exercise 58.

79. $\begin{bmatrix} 1 & 3 & | & 3 \\ 4 & 12 & | & 12 \end{bmatrix}$

    Compare with Exercise 59.

80. $\begin{bmatrix} 2 & 5 & | & 1 \\ -4 & -10 & | & -2 \end{bmatrix}$

    Compare with Exercise 60.

81. $\begin{bmatrix} 1 & 1 & 1 & | & 6 \\ 1 & -1 & 1 & | & 2 \\ 1 & 1 & -1 & | & 0 \end{bmatrix}$

    Compare with Exercise 67.

82. $\begin{bmatrix} 2 & -3 & -2 & | & 11 \\ 1 & 3 & 8 & | & 1 \\ 3 & -1 & 14 & | & -2 \end{bmatrix}$

    Compare with Exercise 68.

83. $\begin{bmatrix} 1 & -2 & 1 & | & 5 \\ 2 & 6 & 3 & | & -10 \\ 3 & -1 & -2 & | & 5 \end{bmatrix}$

    Compare with Exercise 69.

84. $\begin{bmatrix} 5 & 0 & -10 & | & 15 \\ 1 & -1 & 6 & | & 23 \\ 1 & 3 & -12 & | & 13 \end{bmatrix}$

    Compare with Exercise 70.

85. $\begin{bmatrix} 1 & 1 & -1 & | & 2 \\ 2 & -1 & 1 & | & 1 \\ -1 & 1 & 1 & | & 2 \end{bmatrix}$

    Compare with Exercise 71.

86. $\begin{bmatrix} 4 & 8 & 4 & | & 9 \\ 5 & 10 & 5 & | & 12 \\ 1 & 3 & 4 & | & 10 \end{bmatrix}$

    Compare with Exercise 74.

section

3.5   ALGEBRA OF MATRICES

1.   Equality of Matrices

In Section 3.4, we learned that matrices provide a useful tool to solve a system of linear equations. In addition, matrices have other powerful applications in business and science. To understand and apply matrices effectively, we must first develop algebraic operations on matrices. Recall that a matrix is a rectangular array of numbers. The rows of a matrix are read horizontally and the columns of a matrix are read vertically. Every number or entry within a matrix is called an element of the matrix.

The **order of a matrix** is determined by the number of rows and number of columns. A matrix with m rows and n columns is an $m \times n$ (read as "m by n") matrix. Notice that with the order of a matrix, the number of rows is given first, followed by the number of columns.

In this section we will denote a matrix by a capital letter or by a lowercase letter written within matrix brackets. For example, a matrix may be denoted as $\mathbf{A}$ or $[a_{ij}]$. The notation $[a_{ij}]$ denotes the matrix, and a_{ij} denotes the element in the ith row and jth column. For example, consider the matrix,

$$[a_{ij}] = \begin{bmatrix} 2 & 3 & -1 \\ 5 & 4 & 7 \end{bmatrix}$$

the element a_{12} represents the element in the first row, second column. Therefore, $a_{12} = 3$. Similarly, a_{23} represents the element in the second row, third column. Hence $a_{23} = 7$.

Two matrices are equal if the corresponding elements are equal.

Equality of Two Matrices

Given two matrices of the same order, $\mathbf{A} = [a_{ij}]$, and $\mathbf{B} = [b_{ij}]$, then $\mathbf{A} = \mathbf{B}$ if and only if $a_{ij} = b_{ij}$ for every i and j.

example 1   **Finding Elements of Equal Matrices**

Given $\mathbf{A} = \begin{bmatrix} 2 & 4 \\ 1 & x \\ 5 & 7 \end{bmatrix}$ and $\mathbf{B} = \begin{bmatrix} 2 & 4 \\ 1 & -3 \\ y & 7 \end{bmatrix}$.

Find x and y such that $\mathbf{A} = \mathbf{B}$.

Solution:

If $\mathbf{A} = \mathbf{B}$, we require $x = -3$ and $y = 5$.

2. Addition of Matrices

To add two matrices it is necessary that the matrices have the same order. In such a case, we add the matrices by adding the individual elements.

Addition of Matrices

If $\mathbf{A} = [a_{ij}]$ and $\mathbf{B} = [b_{ij}]$ are matrices of order $m \times n$, then the sum of the matrices is the $m \times n$ matrix defined by

$$\mathbf{A} + \mathbf{B} = [a_{ij} + b_{ij}] \quad \text{for all } i \text{ and } j$$

example 2   **Adding Matrices**

Given, $\mathbf{A} = \begin{bmatrix} 3 & \frac{7}{3} & -1 \\ 4 & 2 & -5 \\ 0 & 6 & \frac{1}{2} \end{bmatrix}$, $\quad \mathbf{B} = \begin{bmatrix} 5 & 2 & 1 \\ -6 & 0 & 4 \end{bmatrix}$, $\quad$ and

$$\mathbf{C} = \begin{bmatrix} -1 & \frac{2}{3} & 5 \\ 0 & 1 & 0 \\ 0 & -6 & \frac{3}{2} \end{bmatrix}$$

Add the matrices (if possible).   a. $\mathbf{A} + \mathbf{C}$ b. $\mathbf{B} + \mathbf{C}$

Solution:

a. $\mathbf{A} + \mathbf{C} = \begin{bmatrix} 3 & \frac{7}{3} & -1 \\ 4 & 2 & -5 \\ 0 & 6 & \frac{1}{2} \end{bmatrix} + \begin{bmatrix} -1 & \frac{2}{3} & 5 \\ 0 & 1 & 0 \\ 0 & -6 & \frac{3}{2} \end{bmatrix}$

$$= \begin{bmatrix} 3 + (-1) & \frac{7}{3} + \frac{2}{3} & -1 + 5 \\ 4 + 0 & 2 + 1 & -5 + 0 \\ 0 + 0 & 6 + (-6) & \frac{1}{2} + \frac{3}{2} \end{bmatrix}$$

$$= \begin{bmatrix} 2 & \frac{9}{3} & 4 \\ 4 & 3 & -5 \\ 0 & 0 & \frac{4}{2} \end{bmatrix}$$

$$= \begin{bmatrix} 2 & 3 & 4 \\ 4 & 3 & -5 \\ 0 & 0 & 2 \end{bmatrix}$$

b. $\mathbf{B} + \mathbf{C}$ is undefined because $\mathbf{B}$ is a 2×3 matrix, whereas $\mathbf{C}$ is a 3×3 matrix. The matrices have different orders.

3. Additive Inverse of a Matrix

For a real number a, the opposite (or additive inverse) of a is $-a$. Similarly, for a matrix $\mathbf{A} = [a_{ij}]$, the **additive inverse of A** is $-\mathbf{A} = [-a_{ij}]$.

example 3

Finding the Additive Inverse of a Matrix

Given, $\mathbf{A} = \begin{bmatrix} 4 & -2 & 1 & 6 \\ \frac{1}{2} & -2 & -\pi & 4.3 \end{bmatrix}$

a. Find $-\mathbf{A}$

b. Find $\mathbf{A} + (-\mathbf{A})$

Solution:

a. $-\mathbf{A} = \begin{bmatrix} -4 & 2 & -1 & -6 \\ -\frac{1}{2} & 2 & \pi & -4.3 \end{bmatrix}$

b. $\mathbf{A} + (-\mathbf{A}) = \begin{bmatrix} 4 & -2 & 1 & 6 \\ \frac{1}{2} & -2 & -\pi & 4.3 \end{bmatrix} + \begin{bmatrix} -4 & 2 & -1 & -6 \\ -\frac{1}{2} & 2 & \pi & -4.3 \end{bmatrix}$

$= \begin{bmatrix} 4 + (-4) & -2 + 2 & 1 + (-1) & 6 + (-6) \\ \frac{1}{2} + (-\frac{1}{2}) & -2 + 2 & -\pi + \pi & 4.3 + (-4.3) \end{bmatrix}$

$= \begin{bmatrix} 0 & 0 & 0 & 0 \\ 0 & 0 & 0 & 0 \end{bmatrix}$

In Example 3, the result of the sum $\mathbf{A} + (-\mathbf{A})$ is a 2×4 matrix whose elements are all zero. Any matrix that consists of all zeros is called a **zero matrix** and is denoted by $\mathbf{0}$.

4. Subtraction of Matrices

Subtraction of Matrices

Given two matrices of the same order, $\mathbf{A} - \mathbf{B}$ is defined as

$$\mathbf{A} - \mathbf{B} = \mathbf{A} + (-\mathbf{B})$$

example 4

Subtracting Matrices

Given, $\mathbf{M} = \begin{bmatrix} -1 & 5 \\ 7 & 4 \end{bmatrix}$, $\mathbf{N} = \begin{bmatrix} 30 & -40 \\ -100 & 20 \end{bmatrix}$, and $\mathbf{P} = \begin{bmatrix} 14 & -22 \\ -1 & 0 \end{bmatrix}$

a. Find $\mathbf{M} - \mathbf{P}$

b. Find $\mathbf{M} - \mathbf{N} + \mathbf{P}$

Solution:

a. $\mathbf{M} - \mathbf{P} = \begin{bmatrix} -1 & 5 \\ 7 & 4 \end{bmatrix} - \begin{bmatrix} 14 & -22 \\ -1 & 0 \end{bmatrix}$

$= \begin{bmatrix} -1 & 5 \\ 7 & 4 \end{bmatrix} + \begin{bmatrix} -14 & 22 \\ 1 & 0 \end{bmatrix}$

$= \begin{bmatrix} -15 & 27 \\ 8 & 4 \end{bmatrix}$

b. $\mathbf{M} - \mathbf{N} + \mathbf{P} = \begin{bmatrix} -1 & 5 \\ 7 & 4 \end{bmatrix} - \begin{bmatrix} 30 & -40 \\ -100 & 20 \end{bmatrix} + \begin{bmatrix} 14 & -22 \\ -1 & 0 \end{bmatrix}$

$= \begin{bmatrix} -1 & 5 \\ 7 & 4 \end{bmatrix} + \begin{bmatrix} -30 & 40 \\ 100 & -20 \end{bmatrix} + \begin{bmatrix} 14 & -22 \\ -1 & 0 \end{bmatrix}$

$= \begin{bmatrix} -17 & 23 \\ 106 & -16 \end{bmatrix}$

5. Properties of Matrix Addition

The following properties of matrix addition are similar to the addition properties of real numbers.

Properties of Matrix Addition

Given the matrices $\mathbf{A}$, $\mathbf{B}$, and $\mathbf{C}$, and the zero matrix, $\mathbf{0}$, each of order $m \times n$, then the following properties hold:

$$\mathbf{A} + \mathbf{B} = \mathbf{B} + \mathbf{A}$$

$$(\mathbf{A} + \mathbf{B}) + \mathbf{C} = \mathbf{A} + (\mathbf{B} + \mathbf{C})$$

$$\mathbf{A} + (-\mathbf{A}) = -\mathbf{A} + \mathbf{A} = \mathbf{0}$$

$$\mathbf{A} + \mathbf{0} = \mathbf{0} + \mathbf{A} = \mathbf{A}$$

6. Multiplication of a Real Number and a Matrix

Two types of multiplication will be considered involving a matrix. The first is the product of a matrix and a real number. The second is the product of a matrix and another matrix.

The Product of a Real Number and a Matrix

Let k be a real number and $\mathbf{A} = [a_{ij}]$ be an $m \times n$ matrix. Then

$$k\mathbf{A} = [ka_{ij}]$$

Using this definition we see that to find the product of a real number k, called a scalar, and a matrix, we multiply each individual element of the matrix by k. This type of multiplication of a real number and a matrix is called **scalar multiplication**.

example 5

Multiplying a Real Number and a Matrix

A contractor builds two types of model homes (model A and model B) with an option to purchase an upgrade to the deluxe package. The deluxe package allows the buyer to select tile floors, window treatments, and a pool. Matrix A represents the cost for each option.

$$
\begin{array}{cc}
\text{Model A} & \text{Model B}
\end{array}
$$

$$
\mathbf{A} = \begin{bmatrix} \$10,000 & \$8,000 \\ \$7,500 & \$6,000 \\ \$22,000 & \$22,000 \end{bmatrix}
\begin{array}{l} \text{Tile floors} \\ \text{Window treatments} \\ \text{Pool} \end{array}
$$

a. The contractor offers a 15% discount for the deluxe package. Find the matrix $\mathbf{D}$, defined by $\mathbf{D} = 0.15\mathbf{A}$

b. If matrix $\mathbf{D}$ defines the discount for the deluxe package, find a matrix $\mathbf{N}$ that defines the new costs for the deluxe package.

Solution:

a. $\mathbf{D} = 0.15\mathbf{A} = 0.15 \begin{bmatrix} \$10,000 & \$8,000 \\ \$7,500 & \$6,000 \\ \$22,000 & \$22,000 \end{bmatrix}$

$$
= \begin{bmatrix} 0.15(\$10,000) & 0.15(\$8,000) \\ 0.15(\$7,500) & 0.15(\$6,000) \\ 0.15(\$22,000) & 0.15(\$22,000) \end{bmatrix}
$$

$$
= \begin{bmatrix} \$1,500 & \$1,200 \\ \$1,125 & \$900 \\ \$3,300 & \$3,300 \end{bmatrix}
$$

b. The new cost is equal to the original cost minus the discount. Therefore,

$$
\mathbf{N} = \mathbf{A} - \mathbf{D} = \begin{bmatrix} \$10,000 & \$8,000 \\ \$7,500 & \$6,000 \\ \$22,000 & \$22,000 \end{bmatrix} - \begin{bmatrix} \$1,500 & \$1,200 \\ \$1,125 & \$900 \\ \$3,300 & \$3,300 \end{bmatrix}
$$

$$
= \begin{bmatrix} \$8,500 & \$6,800 \\ \$6,375 & \$5,100 \\ \$18,700 & \$18,700 \end{bmatrix}
$$

The definition of scalar multiplication leads to the following properties.

> ## Properties of Scalar Multiplication
>
> Let s and t be real numbers and $\mathbf{A}$ and $\mathbf{B}$ be $m \times n$ matrices. Then,
>
> $$(s + t)\mathbf{A} = s\mathbf{A} + t\mathbf{A}$$
>
> $$s(\mathbf{A} + \mathbf{B}) = s\mathbf{A} + s\mathbf{B}$$
>
> $$s(t\mathbf{A}) = (st)\mathbf{A}$$

7. Multiplication of Matrices

Finding the product of two matrices is somewhat more complicated than finding the product of a scalar and a matrix. We will demonstrate the following process and then offer a formal definition of matrix multiplication.

$$\text{Given, } \mathbf{A} = \begin{bmatrix} 2 & -3 & 1 \\ -4 & 7 & 0 \end{bmatrix} \quad \text{and} \quad \mathbf{B} = \begin{bmatrix} 9 & -6 \\ 10 & 5 \\ -4 & 8 \end{bmatrix}$$

Find the product $\mathbf{AB}$.

First we will multiply the elements of the first row of matrix $\mathbf{A}$ (highlighted in red) by the corresponding elements in the first column of matrix $\mathbf{B}$ (highlighted in blue). The sum of these products becomes the element in the first row, first column of $\mathbf{AB}$.

$$\begin{bmatrix} 2 & -3 & 1 \\ -4 & 7 & 0 \end{bmatrix} \cdot \begin{bmatrix} 9 & -6 \\ 10 & 5 \\ -4 & 8 \end{bmatrix}$$

$$2(9) + (-3)(10) + 1(-4) = -16 \quad \text{(element in the first row, first column of } \mathbf{AB}\text{)}$$

We repeat this process multiplying the elements in the first row of $\mathbf{A}$ by the elements in the second column of $\mathbf{B}$. The sum of these products becomes the element in the first row, second column of $\mathbf{AB}$.

$$\begin{bmatrix} 2 & -3 & 1 \\ -4 & 7 & 0 \end{bmatrix} \cdot \begin{bmatrix} 9 & -6 \\ 10 & 5 \\ -4 & 8 \end{bmatrix}$$

$$2(-6) + (-3)(5) + 1(8) = -19 \quad \text{(element in the first row, second column of } \mathbf{AB}\text{)}$$

This process continues with the elements of each row of matrix $\mathbf{A}$ multiplied by the elements of each column of matrix $\mathbf{B}$.

$$\begin{bmatrix} 2 & -3 & 1 \\ -4 & 7 & 0 \end{bmatrix} \cdot \begin{bmatrix} 9 & -6 \\ 10 & 5 \\ -4 & 8 \end{bmatrix}$$

$$(-4)(9) + 7(10) + 0(-4) = 34 \quad \text{(element in the second row, first column of } \mathbf{AB}\text{)}$$

$$\begin{bmatrix} 2 & -3 & 1 \\ -4 & 7 & 0 \end{bmatrix} \cdot \begin{bmatrix} 9 & -6 \\ 10 & 5 \\ -4 & 8 \end{bmatrix}$$

$(-4)(-6) + 7(5) + 0(8) = 59$ (element in the second row, second column of **AB**)

The product **AB** is

$$\mathbf{AB} = \begin{bmatrix} -16 & -19 \\ 34 & 59 \end{bmatrix}$$

Inherent in the process of multiplying matrices is the assumption that the number of columns in matrix **A** is equal to the number of rows in matrix **B** so that the corresponding elements "match up." That is, if **A** is an $m \times p$ matrix, then matrix **B** must have p rows for the product **AB** to be defined. Furthermore, if **A** is an $m \times p$ matrix and **B** is a $p \times n$ matrix, then the product **AB** will be an $m \times n$ matrix. That is, the product matrix will have the number of rows of **A** and the number of columns of **B**. For example,

A   B

$$\begin{bmatrix} 2 & -3 & 1 \\ -4 & 7 & 0 \end{bmatrix} \cdot \begin{bmatrix} 9 & -6 \\ 10 & 5 \\ -4 & 8 \end{bmatrix}$$

2 × 3   3 × 2

these must be equal

the product **AB** will be a 2 × 2 matrix

The product **MN** shown next is undefined because the number of columns of **M** is two, whereas the number of rows of **N** is three.

M   ·   N

$$\begin{bmatrix} -2 & 6 \\ 1 & 4 \\ 0 & 5 \\ -3 & 7 \end{bmatrix} \cdot \begin{bmatrix} 4 & 6 & -2 \\ 1 & 5 & 9 \\ -7 & 1 & 4 \end{bmatrix}$$

4 × 2   3 × 3

not equal

We now give the formal definition of the product of two matrices.

Matrix Multiplication

If A is an $m \times p$ matrix and B is a $p \times n$ matrix, then the product AB is an $m \times n$ matrix. For the matrix AB, the element in the ith row and jth column is the sum of the products of the corresponding elements in the ith row of A and the jth column of B.

Formally, if

$$A = \begin{bmatrix} a_{11} & a_{12} & \cdots & a_{1p} \\ a_{21} & a_{22} & \cdots & a_{2p} \\ \cdots & \cdots & \cdots & \cdots \\ a_{m1} & a_{m2} & \cdots & a_{mp} \end{bmatrix} \quad \text{and} \quad B = \begin{bmatrix} b_{11} & b_{12} & \cdots & b_{1n} \\ b_{21} & b_{22} & \cdots & b_{2n} \\ \cdots & \cdots & \cdots & \cdots \\ b_{p1} & b_{p2} & \cdots & b_{pn} \end{bmatrix},$$

then the elements in the matrix $C = AB$ are given by:

$$c_{ij} = a_{i1} \cdot b_{1j} + a_{i2} \cdot b_{2j} + \cdots + a_{ip} \cdot b_{pj}$$

Note: If the number of columns in A does not equal the number of rows in B, then the product AB is not defined.

example 6

Finding the Product of Two Matrices

Given, $A = \begin{bmatrix} 1 & 3 & 1 \\ 2 & 4 & 6 \\ -4 & -1 & 7 \end{bmatrix}$, $B = \begin{bmatrix} 3 & -2 & 1 \end{bmatrix}$, and $C = \begin{bmatrix} 2 & -1 & 0 \\ 5 & -6 & 2 \\ 1 & -10 & 0 \end{bmatrix}$

a. Find AC (if possible)

b. Find CA (if possible)

c. Find AB (if possible)

d. Find BC (if possible)

Solution:

a. First we must determine whether the product AC is defined. A is a 3×3 matrix and C is a 3×3 matrix. The number of columns in A and the number of rows of C are equal. The product is a 3×3 matrix.

The product AC will be a 3×3 matrix.

$$\mathbf{AC} = \begin{bmatrix} 1 & 3 & 1 \\ 2 & 4 & 6 \\ -4 & -1 & 7 \end{bmatrix} \cdot \begin{bmatrix} 2 & -1 & 0 \\ 5 & -6 & 2 \\ 1 & -10 & 0 \end{bmatrix}$$

$$= \begin{bmatrix} (1)(2) + (3)(5) + (1)(1) & (1)(-1) + (3)(-6) + (1)(-10) & (1)(0) + (3)(2) + (1)(0) \\ (2)(2) + (4)(5) + (6)(1) & (2)(-1) + (4)(-6) + (6)(-10) & (2)(0) + (4)(2) + (6)(0) \\ (-4)(2) + (-1)(5) + (7)(1) & (-4)(-1) + (-1)(-6) + (7)(-10) & (-4)(0) + (-1)(2) + (7)(0) \end{bmatrix}$$

$$= \begin{bmatrix} 18 & -29 & 6 \\ 30 & -86 & 8 \\ -6 & -60 & -2 \end{bmatrix}$$

b. $$\mathbf{CA} = \begin{bmatrix} 2 & -1 & 0 \\ 5 & -6 & 2 \\ 1 & -10 & 0 \end{bmatrix} \cdot \begin{bmatrix} 1 & 3 & 1 \\ 2 & 4 & 6 \\ -4 & -1 & 7 \end{bmatrix}$$

$$= \begin{bmatrix} (2)(1) + (-1)(2) + (0)(-4) & (2)(3) + (-1)(4) + (0)(-1) & (2)(1) + (-1)(6) + (0)(7) \\ (5)(1) + (-6)(2) + (2)(-4) & (5)(3) + (-6)(4) + (2)(-1) & (5)(1) + (-6)(6) + (2)(7) \\ (1)(1) + (-10)(2) + (0)(-4) & (1)(3) + (-10)(4) + (0)(-1) & (1)(1) + (-10)(6) + (0)(7) \end{bmatrix}$$

$$= \begin{bmatrix} 0 & 2 & -4 \\ -15 & -11 & -17 \\ -19 & -37 & -59 \end{bmatrix}$$

Tip: From Examples 6(a) and 6(b), we see that in general matrix multiplication is not commutative because $\mathbf{AC} \neq \mathbf{CA}$.

c.   Matrix **A** is a 3×3 matrix and matrix **B** is a 1×3 matrix. The number of columns in **A** and the number of rows of **B** are not equal; therefore, **AB** is not defined.

$$\begin{array}{cc} \mathbf{A} & \mathbf{B} \\ 3 \times 3 & 1 \times 3 \end{array}$$

not equal

d.   First we must determine whether the product **BC** is defined. **B** is a 1×3 matrix and **C** is a 3×3 matrix. The number of columns in **B** and the number of rows of **C** are equal. The product is a 1×3 matrix.

$$\begin{array}{cc} \mathbf{B} & \mathbf{C} \\ 1 \times 3 & 3 \times 3 \end{array}$$

equal

The product **BC** will be a 1×3 matrix.

$$\mathbf{BC} = \begin{bmatrix} 3 & -2 & 1 \end{bmatrix} \cdot \begin{bmatrix} 2 & -1 & 0 \\ 5 & -6 & 2 \\ 1 & -10 & 0 \end{bmatrix}$$

$$= \begin{bmatrix} (3)(2) + (-2)(5) + (1)(1) & 3(-1) + (-2)(-6) + (1)(-10) & (3)(0) + (-2)(2) + (1)(0) \end{bmatrix}$$

$$= \begin{bmatrix} -3 & -1 & -4 \end{bmatrix}$$

Graphing Calculator Box

A graphing calculator can be used to perform operations on matrices. To do so, first use the matrix editor to define the order of a matrix and the elements of the matrix.

Although matrix multiplication is not a commutative operation, the following properties are true, provided the constituent sums and products are well defined.

Properties of Matrix Multiplication

If **A**, **B**, and **C** are matrices, then

$$(\mathbf{AB})\mathbf{C} = \mathbf{A}(\mathbf{BC})$$

$$\mathbf{A}(\mathbf{B} + \mathbf{C}) = \mathbf{AB} + \mathbf{AC}$$

$$(\mathbf{B} + \mathbf{C})\mathbf{A} = \mathbf{BA} + \mathbf{CA}$$

provided all sums and products are well defined.

example 7

Multiplying Matrices

Find the product: $\begin{bmatrix} 1 & 0 \\ 0 & 1 \end{bmatrix} \cdot \begin{bmatrix} -3 & 2 \\ -1 & 5 \end{bmatrix}$

Solution:

$$\begin{bmatrix} 1 & 0 \\ 0 & 1 \end{bmatrix} \cdot \begin{bmatrix} -3 & 2 \\ -1 & 5 \end{bmatrix} = \begin{bmatrix} (1)(-3) + (0)(-1) & (1)(2) + (0)(5) \\ (0)(-3) + (1)(-1) & (0)(2) + (1)(5) \end{bmatrix}$$

$$= \begin{bmatrix} -3 & 2 \\ -1 & 5 \end{bmatrix}$$

An $n \times n$ matrix with 1's along the main diagonal (the diagonal from upper left to lower right) and 0's everywhere else is called an **identity matrix**, and is denoted by $\mathbf{I}_n$. The number 1 is the identity element for multiplication of real numbers, and the matrix $\mathbf{I}_n$ is the identity element for matrix multiplication. Therefore, given an $n \times n$ identity matrix, $\mathbf{I}_n$, and an $n \times n$ matrix, $\mathbf{A}$, we have

$$\mathbf{I}_n \cdot \mathbf{A} = \mathbf{A} \cdot \mathbf{I}_n = \mathbf{A}$$

section 3.5   PRACTICE EXERCISES

For Exercises 1–9, identify the a_{ij} element in matrix **A**.

$$\mathbf{A} = \begin{bmatrix} 4 & -2 & 5 \\ 0 & 6 & 7 \\ -1 & 3 & 8 \end{bmatrix}$$

1. a_{23}

2. a_{32}

3. a_{13}

4. a_{22}

5. a_{33}

6. a_{11}

7. a_{21}

8. a_{31}

9. a_{12}

10. Explain the difference between $[a_{ij}]$ and a_{ij}.

11. Explain how to determine if two matrices are equal.

For Exercises 12–15, given that the matrices are equal, solve for the variables.

12. $\begin{bmatrix} 3 & 5 & 2 \\ -1 & 2 & 5 \end{bmatrix} = \begin{bmatrix} 3 & 5 & x \\ -1 & 2 & y \end{bmatrix}$

13. $\begin{bmatrix} 0 & 4 \\ -6 & 1 \end{bmatrix} = \begin{bmatrix} x & 4 \\ y & 1 \end{bmatrix}$

14. $\begin{bmatrix} x & 10 & 3 \\ -2 & 13 & 0 \\ 1 & 9 & -3 \end{bmatrix} = \begin{bmatrix} 8 & 10 & 3 \\ -2 & y & 0 \\ 1 & 9 & z \end{bmatrix}$

15. $\begin{bmatrix} 7 & -1 \\ \frac{2}{3} & x \\ y & 0 \end{bmatrix} = \begin{bmatrix} 7 & z \\ \frac{2}{3} & 5 \\ \frac{3}{4} & 0 \end{bmatrix}$

16. Explain why two matrices must be of the same order to be added.

For Exercises 17–20, add the matrices.

17. $\begin{bmatrix} 4 & 6 \\ -1 & 3 \end{bmatrix} + \begin{bmatrix} 0 & 3 \\ 9 & -2 \end{bmatrix}$

18. $\begin{bmatrix} 1 & 1 \\ -3 & 2 \end{bmatrix} + \begin{bmatrix} -1 & 4 \\ 0 & 8 \end{bmatrix}$

19. $\begin{bmatrix} 10 & 3 & -2 \\ 9 & 2 & -3 \end{bmatrix} + \begin{bmatrix} -5 & 9 & 12 \\ 8 & 1 & 0 \end{bmatrix}$

20. $\begin{bmatrix} 14 & 3 \\ 7 & 0 \\ -6 & 2 \end{bmatrix} + \begin{bmatrix} 4 & -3 \\ 11 & -2 \\ -4 & 6 \end{bmatrix}$

21. For the matrix **B**, find its additive inverse, $-\mathbf{B}$.

$$\mathbf{B} = \begin{bmatrix} -4 & 5 & 9 \\ 8 & -2 & 6 \\ -\frac{3}{8} & 3 & 0 \end{bmatrix}$$

22. For the matrix **C**, find its additive inverse, $-\mathbf{C}$.

$$\mathbf{C} = \begin{bmatrix} 7 & 1 \\ -4 & 2 \end{bmatrix}$$

For Exercises 23–26, subtract the matrices.

23. $\begin{bmatrix} 4 & 5 \\ 1 & -2 \end{bmatrix} - \begin{bmatrix} 0 & -4 \\ 6 & 8 \end{bmatrix}$

24. $\begin{bmatrix} -7 & 1 & 4 \\ 3 & 6 & 10 \\ 9 & 12 & -1 \end{bmatrix} - \begin{bmatrix} -7 & 3 & 9 \\ 11 & 4 & -2 \\ 0 & 1 & -2 \end{bmatrix}$

25. $\begin{bmatrix} -2 & 0 \\ 3 & -9 \\ 11 & 8 \\ 8 & 3 \end{bmatrix} - \begin{bmatrix} 13 & -1 \\ 0 & -6 \\ 2 & 5 \\ 2 & -4 \end{bmatrix}$

26. $\begin{bmatrix} -1 & 5 & 9 \\ 0 & 10 & -2 \end{bmatrix} - \begin{bmatrix} 0 & -7 & -2 \\ 11 & -2 & 1 \end{bmatrix}$

For Exercises 27–30, multiply by the scalar.

27. $8 \cdot \begin{bmatrix} 3 & -2 \\ 4 & -1 \end{bmatrix}$

28. $-3 \cdot \begin{bmatrix} 2 & -1 \\ 0 & -3 \\ 3 & 9 \end{bmatrix}$

29. $-4 \cdot \begin{bmatrix} 0 & 3 & -5 \\ 3 & -2 & 10 \end{bmatrix}$

30. $6 \cdot \begin{bmatrix} 2 & 3 & 0 \\ -1 & 4 & 4 \\ 0 & 2 & 7 \end{bmatrix}$

The definition of scalar multiplication can be used to factor out a constant from a matrix. For example

$$\begin{bmatrix} 12 & 6 \\ 4 & -8 \\ 2 & 1 \end{bmatrix} = \begin{bmatrix} 2 \cdot 6 & 2 \cdot 3 \\ 2 \cdot 2 & 2 \cdot (-4) \\ 2 \cdot 1 & 2 \cdot \frac{1}{2} \end{bmatrix} = 2 \begin{bmatrix} 6 & 3 \\ 2 & -4 \\ 1 & \frac{1}{2} \end{bmatrix}$$

For Exercises 31–34, factor out the given constant from each matrix.

31. $\begin{bmatrix} 30 & 40 \\ -10 & 100 \end{bmatrix}; 10$

32. $\begin{bmatrix} 15 & 20 & 5 \\ 0 & 25 & -10 \end{bmatrix}; -5$

33. $\begin{bmatrix} 12 & 28 \\ -4 & 16 \\ 8 & 20 \end{bmatrix}; -4$

34. $\begin{bmatrix} -28 & 14 \\ 0 & -7 \end{bmatrix}; 7$

35. The manager of Pizza City needs to make a schedule for his drivers for next weekend. The hours of four drivers are given in the following matrices.

First Weekend

	Fri.	Sat.	Sun.
Driver 1	8	6	5
Driver 2	6	5	10
Driver 3	8	8	6
Driver 4	9	4	6

$= \mathbf{D}$

Second Weekend

	Fri.	Sat.	Sun.
Driver 1	7	6	8
Driver 2	5	5	6
Driver 3	8	4	7
Driver 4	6	5	8

$= \mathbf{E}$

To make the schedule for next weekend, the manager will use the average number of hours of the two previous weekends. Find $\frac{1}{2} \cdot (\mathbf{D} + \mathbf{E})$.

36. A company has to increase its printing rates for two of its most popular copiers. The following matrix displays the current rates.

	Price per 100 black/white copies	Price per 100 color copies
Deluxe copier	\$2.00	\$3.00
Super copier	\$2.00	\$4.00

$= \mathbf{F}$

To calculate a 15% increase in rates, find $\mathbf{F} + (0.15)\mathbf{F}$.

For Exercises 37–48, perform the indicated operations, if possible.

$$M = \begin{bmatrix} 4 & -1 & 5 \\ -2 & 6 & 0 \end{bmatrix} \quad N = \begin{bmatrix} 5 & -4 & 0 \\ 6 & -8 & 1 \end{bmatrix}$$

$$P = \begin{bmatrix} 7 & 10 \\ 3 & -6 \end{bmatrix} \quad Q = \begin{bmatrix} -2 & 6 & -5 \\ 2 & 8 & 12 \end{bmatrix}$$

37. $M + N$

38. $M + P$

39. $N + P$

40. $N + Q$

41. $M - Q$

42. $Q - N$

43. $M + 2N$

44. $3N - M$

45. $M + N - P$

46. $N - P + Q$

47. $-3N + Q - M$

48. $Q - 4M + N$

49. Kwan is planning a barbecue for the office. He is in charge of purchasing the meat, including hamburger, chicken, and pork chops. The matrices given represent the amount and price of each type of meat.

Weight (lb)

Hamburger	Chicken	Pork	
[8	12	6]	= R

$$S = \begin{bmatrix} 1.99 \\ 2.79 \\ 1.29 \end{bmatrix} \begin{array}{l} \$ \text{ per pound for hamburger} \\ \$ \text{ per pound for chicken} \\ \$ \text{ per pound for pork} \end{array}$$

To find the total cost, multiply $R \cdot S$.

50. Dave goes to the office supply store to pick up supplies for the office. Multiply $U \cdot V$ to determine how much money he needs to take from petty cash.

Pens	Felt-tip markers	Staplers	Tape dispensers	
[20	12	4	6]	= U

$$V = \begin{bmatrix} 1.09 \\ 1.29 \\ 5.49 \\ 4.99 \end{bmatrix} \begin{array}{l} \$ \text{ per pen} \\ \$ \text{ per marker} \\ \$ \text{ per stapler} \\ \$ \text{ per dispenser} \end{array}$$

For Exercises 51–60, multiply, if possible.

$$W = \begin{bmatrix} 9 & 3 \\ 0 & -1 \\ 2 & -2 \end{bmatrix} \quad X = \begin{bmatrix} 5 & -2 \\ -1 & 4 \end{bmatrix}$$

$$Y = \begin{bmatrix} 0 & -4 & 2 \\ 8 & 2 & 6 \\ -1 & 7 & 1 \end{bmatrix} \quad Z = \begin{bmatrix} -4 & 2 & 5 \\ 1 & 8 & -6 \end{bmatrix}$$

51. $X \cdot Z$

52. $Z \cdot Y$

53. $W \cdot X$

54. $W \cdot Z$

55. $W \cdot Y$

56. $Y \cdot Z$

57. X^2 (*Hint:* $X^2 = X \cdot X$)

58. Y^2

59. W^2

60. Z^2

61. The total unit sales at a concession stand for soft drinks and hot dogs for three softball games are given in matrix X. Matrix Y represents the cost per unit for soft drinks and hot dogs. Matrix Z represents the selling price per unit for soft drinks and hot dogs.

	Soft drinks	Hot dogs	
$X =$	100	52	Game 1
	70	38	Game 2
	86	44	Game 3

$$Y = \begin{bmatrix} 0.40 \\ 0.75 \end{bmatrix} \begin{array}{l} \text{Soft drinks} \\ \text{Hot dogs} \end{array} \quad \text{Cost (\$)}$$

Selling price ($)

$$\mathbf{Z} = \begin{bmatrix} 1.00 \\ 2.50 \end{bmatrix} \begin{matrix} \text{Soft drinks} \\ \text{Hot dogs} \end{matrix}$$

a. Find $\mathbf{C} = \mathbf{XY}$ and interpret the matrix $\mathbf{C}$.

b. Find $\mathbf{R} = \mathbf{XZ}$ and interpret the matrix $\mathbf{R}$.

c. Find $\mathbf{P} = \mathbf{R} - \mathbf{C}$ and interpret the matrix $\mathbf{P}$.

62. The total unit sales for shoes, jerseys, and hats for an athletic store are given in matrix $\mathbf{X}$. The price matrix for each item is given by matrix $\mathbf{Y}$.

$$\mathbf{X} = \begin{matrix} \text{Shoes} & \text{Jerseys} & \text{Hats} \\ \begin{bmatrix} 60 & 50 & 75 \\ 40 & 20 & 65 \\ 100 & 90 & 120 \end{bmatrix} \end{matrix} \begin{matrix} \text{Store A} \\ \text{Store B} \\ \text{Store C} \end{matrix} \qquad \mathbf{Y} = \begin{matrix} \text{Price (\$)} \\ \begin{bmatrix} 79 \\ 49 \\ 16 \end{bmatrix} \end{matrix} \begin{matrix} \text{Shoes} \\ \text{Jerseys} \\ \text{Hats} \end{matrix}$$

a. Find $\mathbf{R} = \mathbf{XY}$ and interpret the matrix $\mathbf{R}$.

b. Determine the total revenue for store A.

c. Determine the total revenue for store B.

d. Determine the total revenue for store C.

For Exercises 63–66, write the system of equations that is equivalent to the given matrix equation.

63. $\begin{bmatrix} 6 & 5 \\ 1 & -3 \end{bmatrix} \cdot \begin{bmatrix} x \\ y \end{bmatrix} = \begin{bmatrix} 1 \\ 4 \end{bmatrix}$

64. $\begin{bmatrix} -3 & 7 \\ 2 & -1 \end{bmatrix} \cdot \begin{bmatrix} x \\ y \end{bmatrix} = \begin{bmatrix} 14 \\ -13 \end{bmatrix}$

65. $\begin{bmatrix} 1 & -2 & 1 \\ 2 & 1 & -1 \\ 3 & 2 & -2 \end{bmatrix} \cdot \begin{bmatrix} x \\ y \\ z \end{bmatrix} = \begin{bmatrix} 7 \\ 0 \\ -2 \end{bmatrix}$

66. $\begin{bmatrix} 2 & -1 & 1 \\ 0 & 2 & -3 \\ 0 & 3 & 2 \end{bmatrix} \cdot \begin{bmatrix} x \\ y \\ z \end{bmatrix} = \begin{bmatrix} 8 \\ -11 \\ 3 \end{bmatrix}$

EXPANDING YOUR SKILLS

In a two-dimensional graph, matrix multiplication can be used to change the scale of a figure by multiplying each coordinate of the figure by a scaling factor. The scaling factor for the x-coordinate may be different from the scaling factor for the y-coordinate. If the scaling

factors are denoted by s and t, then a point (x_1, y_1) is changed to a point (x_2, y_2) according to the equations

$$x_2 = s \cdot x_1 \qquad \text{and} \qquad y_2 = t \cdot y_1$$

Notice that the following matrix equation produces the same set of equations.

$$\begin{bmatrix} s & 0 \\ 0 & t \end{bmatrix} \cdot \begin{bmatrix} x_1 \\ y_1 \end{bmatrix} = \begin{bmatrix} x_2 \\ y_2 \end{bmatrix}$$

Now consider the rectangle defined by the points $A(-2, 1)$, $B(-2, -1)$, $C(2, 1)$, and $D(2, -1)$ (see figure). The coordinates of these points can be represented in matrix $\mathbf{M}$. The rows and columns have been labeled accordingly.

$$\mathbf{M} = \begin{matrix} & A & B & C & D \\ x & \\ y \end{matrix} \begin{bmatrix} -2 & -2 & 2 & 2 \\ 1 & -1 & 1 & -1 \end{bmatrix}$$

To change the size of the rectangle, to a rectangle with half the original length (in the x-direction) and three times the height (in the y-direction), we have the matrix, $\mathbf{N}$.

$$\mathbf{N} = \begin{bmatrix} \frac{1}{2} & 0 \\ 0 & 3 \end{bmatrix} \cdot \begin{bmatrix} -2 & -2 & 2 & 2 \\ 1 & -1 & 1 & -1 \end{bmatrix} = \begin{bmatrix} -1 & -1 & 1 & 1 \\ 3 & -3 & 3 & -3 \end{bmatrix}$$

The coordinates of the "new" points are given by matrix $\mathbf{N}$: $A(-1, 3)$, $B(-1, -3)$, $C(1, 3)$, and $D(1, -3)$ (see figure).

Use this process to complete Exercises 67–70.

67. a. Graph the rectangle defined by the points $(-4, 2), (-4, -2), (4, 2),$ and $(4, -2).$

    b. Multiply the matrices.
    $$\mathbf{N} = \begin{bmatrix} \frac{1}{4} & 0 \\ 0 & 3 \end{bmatrix} \cdot \begin{bmatrix} -4 & -4 & 4 & 4 \\ 2 & -2 & 2 & -2 \end{bmatrix}$$

    c. Graph the rectangle defined by the points in matrix **N**.

    d. Explain the effect that the product of matrices had on the size of the original rectangle.

68. a. Graph the rectangle defined by the points $(-1, 6), (-1, -6), (1, 6),$ and $(1, -6).$

    b. Multiply the matrices.
    $$\mathbf{N} = \begin{bmatrix} 6 & 0 \\ 0 & \frac{1}{6} \end{bmatrix} \cdot \begin{bmatrix} -1 & -1 & 1 & 1 \\ 6 & -6 & 6 & -6 \end{bmatrix}$$

    c. Graph the rectangle defined by the points in matrix **N**.

    d. Explain the effect that the product of matrices had on the size of the original rectangle.

69. a. Given the square defined by the points $(-1, 1),$ $(-1, -1), (1, 1)$ and $(1, -1),$ write a product of matrices that will create a new square whose sides are four times the length of the original.

    b. Sketch the original points and the points defining the new square.

70. a. Given the square defined by the points $(-3, 3),$ $(-3, -3), (3, 3)$ and $(3, -3),$ write a product of matrices that will create a new square whose sides are $\frac{1}{3}$ the length of the original.

    b. Sketch the original points and the points defining the new square.

---

section

3.6 DETERMINANTS

1. Introduction to Determinants

Associated with every square matrix is a real number called the **determinant** of the matrix. A determinant of a square matrix **A**, denoted det**A**, is written by enclosing the elements of the matrix within two vertical bars. For example,

$$\text{if } \mathbf{A} = \begin{bmatrix} 2 & -1 \\ 6 & 0 \end{bmatrix}, \quad \text{then det}\mathbf{A} = \begin{vmatrix} 2 & -1 \\ 6 & 0 \end{vmatrix}$$

$$\text{if } \mathbf{B} = \begin{bmatrix} 0 & -5 & 1 \\ 4 & 0 & \frac{1}{2} \\ -2 & 10 & 1 \end{bmatrix}, \quad \text{then det}\mathbf{B} = \begin{vmatrix} 0 & -5 & 1 \\ 4 & 0 & \frac{1}{2} \\ -2 & 10 & 1 \end{vmatrix}$$

Determinants have many applications in mathematics, including solving systems of linear equations, finding the area of a triangle, determining whether three points are collinear, and finding an equation of a line between two points.

2.   Determinant of a 2 × 2 Matrix

The determinant of a 2 × 2 matrix is defined as follows:

Determinant of a 2 × 2 Matrix

$$\begin{vmatrix} a & b \\ c & d \end{vmatrix} = ad - bc$$

example 1

Evaluating a 2 × 2 Determinant

Evaluate the determinants.

a. $\begin{vmatrix} 6 & -2 \\ 5 & \frac{1}{3} \end{vmatrix}$

b. $\begin{vmatrix} 2 & -11 \\ 0 & 0 \end{vmatrix}$

Solution:

a. $\begin{vmatrix} 6 & -2 \\ 5 & \frac{1}{3} \end{vmatrix}$ For this determinant, $a = 6, b = -2, c = 5,$ and $d = \frac{1}{3}$

$$ad - bc = (6)\left(\frac{1}{3}\right) - (-2)(5)$$

$$= 2 + 10$$

$$= 12$$

b. $\begin{vmatrix} 2 & -11 \\ 0 & 0 \end{vmatrix}$ For this determinant, $a = 2, b = -11, c = 0, d = 0$

$$ad - bc = (2)(0) - (-11)(0)$$

$$= 0 - 0$$

$$= 0$$

3.   Minor of an Element in a 3 × 3 Matrix

To find the determinant of a 3 × 3 matrix, we first need to define the **minor** of an element of the matrix. For any element of a 3 × 3 matrix, the minor of that element is the determinant of the 2 × 2 matrix obtained by deleting the row and column in which the element resides. For example, consider the matrix

$$\begin{bmatrix} 5 & -1 & 6 \\ 0 & -7 & 1 \\ 4 & 2 & 6 \end{bmatrix}$$

The minor of the element 5 is found by deleting the first row and first column and then evaluating the determinant of the remaining 2 × 2 matrix:

$$\begin{bmatrix} 5 & -1 & 6 \\ 0 & -7 & 1 \\ 4 & 2 & 6 \end{bmatrix}$$ Now evaluate the determinant: $\begin{vmatrix} -7 & 1 \\ 2 & 6 \end{vmatrix} = (-7)(6) - (1)(2)$

$$= -44.$$

For this matrix, the minor for the element 5 is −44.

To find the minor of the element −7, delete the second row and second column, and then evaluate the determinant of the remaining 2 × 2 matrix.

$$\begin{bmatrix} 5 & -1 & 6 \\ 0 & -7 & 1 \\ 4 & 2 & 6 \end{bmatrix}$$ Now evaluate the determinant: $\begin{vmatrix} 5 & 6 \\ 4 & 6 \end{vmatrix} = (5)(6) - (6)(4) = 6.$

For this matrix, the minor for the element −7 is 6.

---

example 2 **Determining the Minor for Elements in a 3 × 3 matrix**

Find the minor for each element in the first column of the matrix.

$$\begin{bmatrix} 3 & 4 & -1 \\ 2 & -4 & 5 \\ 0 & 1 & -6 \end{bmatrix}$$

Solution:

For 3: $\begin{bmatrix} 3 & 4 & -1 \\ 2 & -4 & 5 \\ 0 & 1 & -6 \end{bmatrix}$ The minor is: $\begin{vmatrix} -4 & 5 \\ 1 & -6 \end{vmatrix} = (-4)(-6) - (5)(1) = 19$

For 2: $\begin{bmatrix} 3 & 4 & -1 \\ 2 & -4 & 5 \\ 0 & 1 & -6 \end{bmatrix}$ The minor is: $\begin{vmatrix} 4 & -1 \\ 1 & -6 \end{vmatrix} = (4)(-6) - (-1)(1) = -23$

For 0: $\begin{bmatrix} 3 & 4 & -1 \\ 2 & -4 & 5 \\ 0 & 1 & -6 \end{bmatrix}$ The minor is: $\begin{vmatrix} 4 & -1 \\ -4 & 5 \end{vmatrix} = (4)(5) - (-1)(-4) = 16$

4. Determinant of a 3 × 3 Matrix

The determinant of a 3 × 3 matrix is defined as follows.

Definition of a 3 × 3 Determinant

$$\begin{vmatrix} a_1 & b_1 & c_1 \\ a_2 & b_2 & c_2 \\ a_3 & b_3 & c_3 \end{vmatrix} = a_1 \cdot \begin{vmatrix} b_2 & c_2 \\ b_3 & c_3 \end{vmatrix} - a_2 \cdot \begin{vmatrix} b_1 & c_1 \\ b_3 & c_3 \end{vmatrix} + a_3 \cdot \begin{vmatrix} b_1 & c_1 \\ b_2 & c_2 \end{vmatrix}$$

From this definition, we see that the determinant of a 3 × 3 matrix can be written as

$$a_1 \cdot (\text{minor of } a_1) - a_2 \cdot (\text{minor of } a_2) + a_3 \cdot (\text{minor of } a_3)$$

Evaluating determinants in this way is called expanding minors.

example 3

Evaluating a 3 × 3 Determinant

Evaluate the determinant: $\begin{vmatrix} 2 & 4 & 2 \\ 1 & -3 & 0 \\ -5 & 5 & -1 \end{vmatrix}$

Solution:

$$\begin{vmatrix} 2 & 4 & 2 \\ 1 & -3 & 0 \\ -5 & 5 & -1 \end{vmatrix} = 2 \cdot \begin{vmatrix} -3 & 0 \\ 5 & -1 \end{vmatrix} - (1) \cdot \begin{vmatrix} 4 & 2 \\ 5 & -1 \end{vmatrix} + (-5) \cdot \begin{vmatrix} 4 & 2 \\ -3 & 0 \end{vmatrix}$$

$$= 2[(-3)(-1) - (0)(5)] - 1[(4)(-1) - (2)(5)] - 5[(4)(0) - (2)(-3)]$$

$$= 2(3) - 1(-14) - 5(6)$$

$$= 6 + 14 - 30$$

$$= -10$$

Tip: There is another method to determine the signs for each term of the expansion. For the a_{ij} element, multiply the term by $(-1)^{i+j}$.

Although we defined the determinant of a matrix by expanding the minors of the elements in the first column, *any row or column may be used*. However, we must choose the correct sign for each term in the expansion. The following array of signs is helpful.

$$\begin{array}{ccc} + & - & + \\ - & + & - \\ + & - & + \end{array}$$

The signs alternate for each row and column, beginning with + in the first row, first column.

example 4

Evaluating a 3 × 3 Determinant

Evaluate the determinant

$$\begin{vmatrix} 2 & 4 & 2 \\ 1 & -3 & 0 \\ -5 & 5 & -1 \end{vmatrix}$$

by expanding minors about the elements in the second row.

Solution:

signs obtained from the array of signs

$$\begin{vmatrix} 2 & 4 & 2 \\ 1 & -3 & 0 \\ -5 & 5 & -1 \end{vmatrix} = -(1)\cdot\begin{vmatrix} 4 & 2 \\ 5 & -1 \end{vmatrix} + (-3)\cdot\begin{vmatrix} 2 & 2 \\ -5 & -1 \end{vmatrix} - (0)\cdot\begin{vmatrix} 2 & 4 \\ -5 & 5 \end{vmatrix}$$

$$= -1[(4)(-1) - (2)(5)] - 3[(2)(-1) - (2)(-5)] - 0$$

$$= -1(-14) - 3(8)$$

$$= 14 - 24$$

$$= -10$$

Notice that the value of the determinant obtained in Examples 3 and 4 is the same.

Graphing Calculator Box

The determinant of a matrix can be evaluated on a graphing calculator. First use the matrix editor to enter the elements of the matrix. Then use a *Det* function to evaluate the determinant. The determinant from Examples 3 and 4 is evaluated below.

In Example 4, the third term in the expansion of minors was zero because the element 0 when multiplied by its minor is zero. To simplify the arithmetic in evaluating a determinant of a 3 × 3 matrix, choose the row or column that has the most 0 elements.

example 5

Evaluating a 3 × 3 Determinant

Evaluate the determinant: $\begin{vmatrix} \frac{1}{2} & 0 & 4 \\ -6 & 0 & 2 \\ 5 & 0 & -8 \end{vmatrix}$

Solution:

We will expand about the elements in the second column.

$$\begin{vmatrix} \frac{1}{2} & 0 & 4 \\ -6 & 0 & 2 \\ 5 & 0 & -8 \end{vmatrix} = -(0) \cdot \begin{vmatrix} -6 & 2 \\ 5 & -8 \end{vmatrix} + (0) \cdot \begin{vmatrix} \frac{1}{2} & 4 \\ 5 & -8 \end{vmatrix} - (0) \cdot \begin{vmatrix} \frac{1}{2} & 4 \\ -6 & 2 \end{vmatrix}$$

$$= 0 + 0 - 0$$

$$= 0$$

Example 5 illustrates that the value of a determinant having one column of all zeros is 0. Similarly, the value of a determinant having one row of all zeros is 0 [see Example 1(b)].

5.   Geometry and Applications of Determinants

Determinants have numerous applications in a variety of branches of mathematics. One application to geometry is in finding the area of a triangle whose vertices are (x_1, y_1), (x_2, y_2), and (x_3, y_3).

Finding the Area of a Triangle Using Determinants

The area of a triangle with vertices (x_1, y_1), (x_2, y_2), and (x_3, y_3) is given by

the absolute value of $\dfrac{1}{2} \cdot \begin{vmatrix} x_1 & y_1 & 1 \\ x_2 & y_2 & 1 \\ x_3 & y_3 & 1 \end{vmatrix}$

example 6

Finding the Area of a Triangle Using Determinants

Find the area of the triangle whose vertices are $(-4, 2)$, $(3, 2)$ and $(-4, 5)$ (see Figure 3-8).

Solution:

(x_1, y_1)	(x_2, y_2)	(x_3, y_3)	Label the points
$(-4, 2)$	$(3, 2)$	$(-4, 5)$	

Figure 3-8

First evaluate the determinant $\begin{vmatrix} x_1 & y_1 & 1 \\ x_2 & y_2 & 1 \\ x_3 & y_3 & 1 \end{vmatrix} = \begin{vmatrix} -4 & 2 & 1 \\ 3 & 2 & 1 \\ -4 & 5 & 1 \end{vmatrix}$

We will expand about the first column.

$$\begin{vmatrix} -4 & 2 & 1 \\ 3 & 2 & 1 \\ -4 & 5 & 1 \end{vmatrix} = -4 \cdot \begin{vmatrix} 2 & 1 \\ 5 & 1 \end{vmatrix} - (3) \cdot \begin{vmatrix} 2 & 1 \\ 5 & 1 \end{vmatrix} + (-4) \cdot \begin{vmatrix} 2 & 1 \\ 2 & 1 \end{vmatrix}$$

$$= -4(-3) - 3(-3) - 4(0)$$

$$= 12 + 9 - 0$$

$$= 21$$

The area of the triangle is

$$\left| \frac{1}{2} \cdot 21 \right| = \frac{21}{2} \quad \text{(measured in square units)}$$

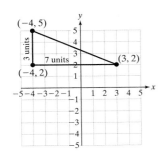

Figure 3-9

From Figure 3-9, we see that the triangle in Example 6 is a right triangle. Therefore, we can confirm that the area is $\frac{21}{2}$ by applying the familiar formula, $A = \frac{1}{2} bh$.

$$A = \frac{1}{2}(7)(3)$$

$$= \frac{21}{2} \quad \text{as desired.}$$

---

section 3.6   PRACTICE EXERCISES

For Exercises 1–10, evaluate the determinant of the 2×2 matrix.

1. $\begin{vmatrix} -3 & 1 \\ 5 & 2 \end{vmatrix}$

2. $\begin{vmatrix} 5 & 6 \\ 4 & 8 \end{vmatrix}$

3. $\begin{vmatrix} -2 & 2 \\ -3 & -5 \end{vmatrix}$

4. $\begin{vmatrix} 5 & -1 \\ 1 & 0 \end{vmatrix}$

5. $\begin{vmatrix} \frac{1}{2} & 3 \\ -2 & 4 \end{vmatrix}$

6. $\begin{vmatrix} -3 & \frac{1}{4} \\ 8 & -2 \end{vmatrix}$

7. $\begin{vmatrix} 0 & 9 \\ 0 & -7 \end{vmatrix}$

8. $\begin{vmatrix} 0 & 0 \\ -1 & 8 \end{vmatrix}$

9. $\begin{vmatrix} \frac{1}{6} & \frac{7}{3} \\ \frac{3}{4} & -\frac{5}{2} \end{vmatrix}$

10. $\begin{vmatrix} \frac{2}{3} & \frac{1}{3} \\ \frac{6}{7} & \frac{5}{7} \end{vmatrix}$

For Exercises 11–19, evaluate the minor corresponding to the given element from matrix **A**.

$$\mathbf{A} = \begin{bmatrix} 4 & -1 & 8 \\ 2 & 6 & 0 \\ -7 & 5 & 3 \end{bmatrix}$$

11. 4

12. −1

13. 8

14. 2

15. 6

16. 0

17. −7

18. 5

19. 3

20. Construct the sign array for a 3×3 matrix.

21. What is the purpose of the sign array that you constructed in Exercise 20?

22. Evaluate the determinant of matrix **B** using expansion by minors.

$$\mathbf{B} = \begin{bmatrix} 0 & 1 & 2 \\ 3 & -1 & 2 \\ 3 & 2 & -2 \end{bmatrix}$$

   a. About the first column

   b. About the second row

23. Evaluate the determinant of matrix **C** using expansion by minors.

$$\mathbf{C} = \begin{bmatrix} 4 & 1 & 3 \\ 2 & -2 & 1 \\ 3 & 1 & 2 \end{bmatrix}$$

   a. About the first row

   b. About the second column

24. Evaluate the determinant of matrix **D** using expansion by minors.

$$\mathbf{D} = \begin{bmatrix} 2 & 3 & 0 \\ 6 & 4 & 1 \\ 1 & 2 & 0 \end{bmatrix}$$

   a. About the first row

   b. About the third column

25. Evaluate the determinant of matrix **E** using expansion by minors.

$$\mathbf{E} = \begin{bmatrix} 2 & 1 & 1 \\ 0 & 0 & 5 \\ 5 & 0 & 4 \end{bmatrix}$$

   a. About the first row

   b. About the second column

26. When evaluating the determinant of a 3×3 matrix, explain the advantage of being able to choose any row or column about which to expand minors.

For Exercises 27–36, evaluate the determinant of the 3×3 matrix.

27. $\begin{vmatrix} 8 & 2 & -4 \\ 4 & 0 & 2 \\ 3 & 0 & -1 \end{vmatrix}$

28. $\begin{vmatrix} 5 & 2 & 1 \\ 3 & -6 & 0 \\ -2 & 8 & 0 \end{vmatrix}$

29. $\begin{vmatrix} -2 & 1 & 3 \\ 1 & 4 & 4 \\ 1 & 0 & 2 \end{vmatrix}$

30. $\begin{vmatrix} 3 & 2 & 1 \\ 1 & -1 & 2 \\ 1 & 0 & 4 \end{vmatrix}$

31. $\begin{vmatrix} -1 & 4 & 2 \\ 2 & 1 & 1 \\ -2 & 1 & 3 \end{vmatrix}$

32. $\begin{vmatrix} -3 & -2 & -1 \\ 1 & 2 & 3 \\ 2 & -1 & 1 \end{vmatrix}$

33. $\begin{vmatrix} -5 & 4 & 2 \\ 0 & 0 & 0 \\ 3 & -1 & 5 \end{vmatrix}$

34. $\begin{vmatrix} 0 & 5 & -8 \\ 0 & -4 & 1 \\ 0 & 3 & 6 \end{vmatrix}$

35. $\begin{vmatrix} -1 & 0 & \frac{1}{2} \\ -3 & 2 & -5 \\ 4 & -2 & 6 \end{vmatrix}$

36. $\begin{vmatrix} \frac{2}{3} & 1 & 0 \\ 6 & 4 & 1 \\ 1 & 2 & 0 \end{vmatrix}$

For Exercises 37–46, evaluate the determinants of the matrices.

37. $\begin{vmatrix} x & 3 \\ y & -2 \end{vmatrix}$

38. $\begin{vmatrix} a & 2 \\ b & 8 \end{vmatrix}$

39. $\begin{vmatrix} m & 1 \\ n & 0 \end{vmatrix}$

40. $\begin{vmatrix} u & 0 \\ v & -1 \end{vmatrix}$

41. $\begin{vmatrix} a & 5 & -1 \\ b & -3 & 0 \\ c & 3 & 4 \end{vmatrix}$

42. $\begin{vmatrix} x & 0 & 3 \\ y & -2 & 6 \\ z & -1 & 1 \end{vmatrix}$

43. $\begin{vmatrix} p & 0 & q \\ r & 0 & s \\ t & 0 & u \end{vmatrix}$

44. $\begin{vmatrix} f & e & 0 \\ d & c & 0 \\ b & a & 0 \end{vmatrix}$

45. $\begin{vmatrix} x & y & 1 \\ 4 & -2 & 1 \\ -1 & 5 & 1 \end{vmatrix}$

46. $\begin{vmatrix} x & y & 1 \\ 4 & -5 & 1 \\ 2 & 2 & 1 \end{vmatrix}$

For Exercises 47–52, find the area the triangle given its vertices. (See Example 6)

47. $(3, -1), (1, 6), (-2, 1)$

48. $(4, 0), (-3, -2), (-3, 2)$

49. $(5, 3), (4, 5), (0, 4)$

50. $(1, 2), (-3, -1), (2, -2)$

51. $(2, 4), (4, \frac{1}{2}), (6, -2)$

52. $(\frac{2}{3}, 1), (-2, 3), (0, 6)$

Three distinct points (x_1, y_1), (x_2, y_2), and (x_3, y_3) are collinear (fall on the same line) if

$$\begin{vmatrix} x_1 & y_1 & 1 \\ x_2 & y_2 & 1 \\ x_3 & y_3 & 1 \end{vmatrix} = 0$$

For Exercises 53–60, determine if the points are collinear.

53. $(1, 4), (0, 1), (-1, -2)$

54. $(-2, -4), (0, -5), (4, -7)$

55. $(-6, 3), (8, 3), (-1, 3)$

56. $(5, -1), (5, 9), (5, -5)$

57. $(1, \frac{7}{3}), (3, 3), (-1, \frac{5}{3})$

58. $(-1, -\frac{3}{4}), (-4, 0), (1, -\frac{5}{4})$

59. $(2, 1), (0, -5), (1, 2)$

60. $(1, -9), (-2, -6), (3, 1)$

Given two distinct points (x_1, y_1) and (x_2, y_2), an equation of the line passing through the points is given by

$$\begin{vmatrix} x & y & 1 \\ x_1 & y_1 & 1 \\ x_2 & y_2 & 1 \end{vmatrix} = 0$$

For Exercises 61–68, write an equation of the line passing through the two given points.

61. $(1, 1), (0, -4)$

62. $(3, 4), (5, 0)$

63. $(3, -4), (-2, 2)$

64. $(4, -2), (1, 3)$

65. $(-3, 5), (1, 5)$

66. $(7, -2), (4, -2)$

67. $(4, -1), (4, 10)$

68. $(3, 6), (3, -1)$

EXPANDING YOUR SKILLS

For Exercises 69–72, write an algebraic expression by evaluating the determinant of the matrix.

69. $\begin{vmatrix} 4x & 8 \\ 2 & x \end{vmatrix}$

70. $\begin{vmatrix} 2y & 6 \\ 3 & y \end{vmatrix}$

71. $\begin{vmatrix} 3t + 1 & 4 \\ 2t & 5 \end{vmatrix}$

72. $\begin{vmatrix} 4p & 3 \\ p - 6 & 2 \end{vmatrix}$

For Exercises 73–76, solve the equation.

73. $\begin{vmatrix} 6 & x \\ 2 & -4 \end{vmatrix} = 14$

74. $\begin{vmatrix} y & -2 \\ 8 & 7 \end{vmatrix} = 30$

75. $\begin{vmatrix} 3 & 1 & 0 \\ 0 & 4 & -2 \\ 1 & 0 & w \end{vmatrix} = 10$

76. $\begin{vmatrix} -1 & 0 & 2 \\ 4 & t & 0 \\ 0 & -5 & 3 \end{vmatrix} = -4$

For Exercises 77–78, evaluate the determinant of the 4×4 matrix using expansion by minors about the first column.

77. $\begin{vmatrix} 1 & 0 & 3 & 0 \\ 0 & 1 & 2 & 4 \\ -2 & 0 & 0 & 1 \\ 4 & -1 & -2 & 0 \end{vmatrix}$

78. $\begin{vmatrix} 5 & 2 & 0 & 0 \\ 0 & 4 & -1 & 1 \\ -1 & 0 & 3 & 0 \\ 0 & -2 & 1 & 0 \end{vmatrix}$

section

3.7   CRAMER'S RULE

1.   Cramer's Rule for a 2 × 2 System of Linear Equations

In Sections 3.1 and 3.4, we learned three methods to solve a system of linear equations: the substitution method, the addition method, and the method of Gaussian elimination. In this section, we will learn another method called Cramer's rule to solve a system of linear equations.

Cramer's Rule for a 2 × 2 System of Linear Equations

The solution to the system

$$a_1 x + b_1 y = c_1$$
$$a_2 x + b_2 y = c_2$$

is given by: $x = \dfrac{\mathbf{D}_x}{\mathbf{D}}$ and $y = \dfrac{\mathbf{D}_y}{\mathbf{D}}$

where $\mathbf{D} = \begin{vmatrix} a_1 & b_1 \\ a_2 & b_2 \end{vmatrix}$ (and $\mathbf{D} \neq 0$), $\mathbf{D}_x = \begin{vmatrix} c_1 & b_1 \\ c_2 & b_2 \end{vmatrix}$, $\mathbf{D}_y = \begin{vmatrix} a_1 & c_1 \\ a_2 & c_2 \end{vmatrix}$

---

example 1

Using Cramer's Rule to Solve a 2 × 2 System of Linear Equations

Solve the system using Cramer's rule.

$$3x - 5y = 11$$
$$-x + 3y = -5$$

Solution:

For this system: $a_1 = 3, \quad b_1 = -5, c_1 = 11$

$$a_2 = -1, b_2 = 3, \quad c_2 = -5$$

$$\mathbf{D} = \begin{vmatrix} 3 & -5 \\ -1 & 3 \end{vmatrix} = (3)(3) - (-5)(-1) = 9 - 5 = 4$$

$$\mathbf{D}_x = \begin{vmatrix} 11 & -5 \\ -5 & 3 \end{vmatrix} = (11)(3) - (-5)(-5) = 33 - 25 = 8$$

$$\mathbf{D}_y = \begin{vmatrix} 3 & 11 \\ -1 & -5 \end{vmatrix} = (3)(-5) - (11)(-1) = -15 + 11 = -4$$

Therefore,

$$x = \frac{\mathbf{D}_x}{\mathbf{D}} = \frac{8}{4} = 2 \qquad y = \frac{\mathbf{D}_y}{\mathbf{D}} = \frac{-4}{4} = -1$$

The solution is $(2, -1)$. <u>Check</u>: $3x - 5y = 11 \longrightarrow 3(2) - 5(-1) \overset{?}{=} 11$ ✓

$$-x + 3y = -5 \longrightarrow -(2) + 3(-1) \overset{?}{=} -5$$ ✓

Tip: Here are some memory tips to remember Cramer's rule.

Coefficients of
x-terms   y-terms

1. The determinant **D** is the determinant of the coefficients of x and y.

$$\mathbf{D} = \begin{vmatrix} a_1 & b_1 \\ a_2 & b_2 \end{vmatrix}$$

x-coefficients
replaced by c_1 and c_2

2. The determinant $\mathbf{D}_x$ has the column of x-term coefficients replaced by c_1 and c_2.

$$\mathbf{D}_x = \begin{vmatrix} c_1 & b_1 \\ c_2 & b_2 \end{vmatrix}$$

y-coefficients
replaced by c_1 and c_2

3. The determinant $\mathbf{D}_y$ has the column of y-term coefficients replaced by c_1 and c_2.

$$\mathbf{D}_y = \begin{vmatrix} a_1 & c_1 \\ a_2 & c_2 \end{vmatrix}$$

It is important to note that the linear equations must be written in standard form to apply Cramer's rule.

example 2

Using Cramer's Rule to Solve a 2 × 2 System of Linear Equations

Solve the system using Cramer's rule:

$$-16y = -40x - 7$$
$$40y = 24x + 27$$

Solution:

$$-16y = -40x - 7 \longrightarrow 40x - 16y = -7 \qquad \text{Rewrite each equation in standard form.}$$

$$40y = 24x + 27 \longrightarrow -24x + 40y = 27$$

$$\mathbf{D} = \begin{vmatrix} 40 & -16 \\ -24 & 40 \end{vmatrix} = (40)(40) - (-16)(-24) = 1216$$

$$\mathbf{D}_x = \begin{vmatrix} -7 & -16 \\ 27 & 40 \end{vmatrix} = (-7)(40) - (-16)(27) = 152$$

$$\mathbf{D}_y = \begin{vmatrix} 40 & -7 \\ -24 & 27 \end{vmatrix} = (40)(27) - (-7)(-24) = 912$$

Therefore,

$$x = \frac{\mathbf{D}_x}{\mathbf{D}} = \frac{152}{1216} = \frac{1}{8} \qquad y = \frac{\mathbf{D}_y}{\mathbf{D}} = \frac{912}{1216} = \frac{3}{4}$$

The solution $\left(\frac{1}{8}, \frac{3}{4}\right)$ checks in the original equations.

2. Cramer's Rule for a 3 × 3 System of Linear Equations

Cramer's rule can be used to solve a 3 × 3 system of linear equations using a similar pattern of determinants.

Cramer's Rule for a 3 × 3 System of Linear Equations

The solution to the system

$$a_1x + b_1y + c_1z = d_1$$

$$a_2x + b_2y + c_2z = d_2$$

$$a_3x + b_3y + c_3z = d_3$$

is given by:

$$x = \frac{D_x}{D}, \qquad y = \frac{D_y}{D}, \qquad \text{and} \qquad z = \frac{D_z}{D}$$

where $D = \begin{vmatrix} a_1 & b_1 & c_1 \\ a_2 & b_2 & c_2 \\ a_3 & b_3 & c_3 \end{vmatrix}$ (and $D \neq 0$), $\quad D_x = \begin{vmatrix} d_1 & b_1 & c_1 \\ d_2 & b_2 & c_2 \\ d_3 & b_3 & c_3 \end{vmatrix},$

$$D_y = \begin{vmatrix} a_1 & d_1 & c_1 \\ a_2 & d_2 & c_2 \\ a_3 & d_3 & c_3 \end{vmatrix}, \qquad\qquad D_z = \begin{vmatrix} a_1 & b_1 & d_1 \\ a_2 & b_2 & d_2 \\ a_3 & b_3 & d_3 \end{vmatrix}$$

---

example 3

Using Cramer's Rule to Solve a 3 × 3 System of Linear Equations

Solve the system using Cramer's rule:

$$x - 2y + 4z = 3$$

$$x - 4y + 3z = -5$$

$$x + 3y - 2z = 6$$

Solution:

$$D = \begin{vmatrix} 1 & -2 & 4 \\ 1 & -4 & 3 \\ 1 & 3 & -2 \end{vmatrix} = 1 \cdot \begin{vmatrix} -4 & 3 \\ 3 & -2 \end{vmatrix} - 1 \cdot \begin{vmatrix} -2 & 4 \\ 3 & -2 \end{vmatrix} + 1 \cdot \begin{vmatrix} -2 & 4 \\ -4 & 3 \end{vmatrix}$$

$$= 1(-1) - 1(-8) + 1(10)$$

$$= 17$$

$$D_x = \begin{vmatrix} 3 & -2 & 4 \\ -5 & -4 & 3 \\ 6 & 3 & -2 \end{vmatrix} = 3 \cdot \begin{vmatrix} -4 & 3 \\ 3 & -2 \end{vmatrix} - (-5) \cdot \begin{vmatrix} -2 & 4 \\ 3 & -2 \end{vmatrix} + 6 \cdot \begin{vmatrix} -2 & 4 \\ -4 & 3 \end{vmatrix}$$

$$= 3(-1) + 5(-8) + 6(10)$$

$$= 17$$

$$\mathbf{D}_y = \begin{vmatrix} 1 & 3 & 4 \\ 1 & -5 & 3 \\ 1 & 6 & -2 \end{vmatrix} = 1 \cdot \begin{vmatrix} -5 & 3 \\ 6 & -2 \end{vmatrix} - 1 \cdot \begin{vmatrix} 3 & 4 \\ 6 & -2 \end{vmatrix} + 1 \cdot \begin{vmatrix} 3 & 4 \\ -5 & 3 \end{vmatrix}$$

$$= 1(-8) - 1(-30) + 1(29)$$

$$= 51$$

$$\mathbf{D}_z = \begin{vmatrix} 1 & -2 & 3 \\ 1 & -4 & -5 \\ 1 & 3 & 6 \end{vmatrix} = 1 \cdot \begin{vmatrix} -4 & -5 \\ 3 & 6 \end{vmatrix} - 1 \cdot \begin{vmatrix} -2 & 3 \\ 3 & 6 \end{vmatrix} + 1 \cdot \begin{vmatrix} -2 & 3 \\ -4 & -5 \end{vmatrix}$$

$$= 1(-9) - 1(-21) + 1(22)$$

$$= 34$$

Hence

$$x = \frac{\mathbf{D}_x}{\mathbf{D}} = \frac{17}{17} = 1 \qquad y = \frac{\mathbf{D}_y}{\mathbf{D}} = \frac{51}{17} = 3 \qquad \text{and} \qquad z = \frac{\mathbf{D}_z}{\mathbf{D}} = \frac{34}{17} = 2$$

The solution is $(1, 3, 2)$.

$$\begin{aligned} \underline{\text{Check:}} \quad x - 2y + 4z &= 3 & (1) - 2(3) + 4(2) &\overset{?}{=} 3 \quad \checkmark \\ x - 4y + 3z &= -5 & (1) - 4(3) + 3(2) &\overset{?}{=} -5 \checkmark \\ x + 3y - 2z &= 6 & (1) + 3(3) - 2(2) &\overset{?}{=} 6 \quad \checkmark \end{aligned}$$

Cramer's rule may seem cumbersome for solving a 3×3 system of linear equations. However, it provides convenient formulas that can be programmed into a computer or calculator to solve for x, y, and z. Cramer's rule can also be extended to solve a 4×4 system of linear equations, a 5×5 system of linear equations and in general, an $n \times n$ system of linear equations.

3. Inconsistent and Dependent Systems

It is important to remember that Cramer's rule does not apply if $\mathbf{D} = 0$. In such a case, the system of equations is either dependent or inconsistent, and another method must be used to analyze the system.

example 4

Analyzing a Dependent System of Equations

Solve the system using Cramer's rule (if possible).

$$2x - 3y = 6$$

$$-6x + 9y = -18$$

Solution:

$$\mathbf{D} = \begin{vmatrix} 2 & -3 \\ -6 & 9 \end{vmatrix} = (2)(9) - (-3)(-6) = 18 - 18 = 0$$

Because $D = 0$, Cramer's rule does not apply. Using the addition method to solve the system, we have

$$2x - 3y = 6 \quad \xrightarrow{\text{multiply by 3}} \quad 6x - 9y = 18$$

$$-6x + 9y = -18 \quad \longrightarrow \quad \underline{-6x + 9y = -18}$$

$$0 = 0 \qquad \text{The system is dependent.}$$

The solution is: $\{(x, y) \mid 2x - 3y = 6\}$

---

example 5

Analyzing an Inconsistent System of Equations

Solve the system using Cramer's rule (if possible).

$$x + y - 3z = -4 \qquad (1)$$
$$2x + 2y - 6z = 5 \qquad (2)$$
$$3x - y + z = 2 \qquad (3)$$

Solution:

$$D = \begin{vmatrix} 1 & 1 & -3 \\ 2 & 2 & -6 \\ 3 & -1 & 1 \end{vmatrix} = 1 \cdot \begin{vmatrix} 2 & -6 \\ -1 & 1 \end{vmatrix} - (2) \cdot \begin{vmatrix} 1 & -3 \\ -1 & 1 \end{vmatrix} + 3 \cdot \begin{vmatrix} 1 & -3 \\ 2 & -6 \end{vmatrix}$$

$$= 1(-4) - 2(-2) + 3(0)$$

$$= -4 + 4 + 0$$

$$= 0$$

Because $D = 0$, Cramer's rule does not apply. Eliminating the x-variable in equations (1) and (2), we reach a contradiction.

$$x + y - 3z = -4 \quad \xrightarrow{\text{multiply by } -2} \quad -2x - 2y + 6z = 8$$

$$2x + 2y - 6z = 5 \quad \longrightarrow \quad \underline{2x + 2y - 6z = 5}$$

$$0 = 13 \qquad \text{Contradiction}$$

The system has no solution.

section 3.7   PRACTICE EXERCISES

For Exercises 1–6, evaluate the determinants represented by $\mathbf{D}$, $\mathbf{D}_x$, and $\mathbf{D}_y$.

1. $4x + 6y = 9$
    $-2x + y = 12$

2. $-3x + 8y = -10$
    $5x + 5y = -13$

3. $\dfrac{1}{3}x - y = 7$
    $4x - 8y = -21$

4. $6x - \dfrac{1}{2}y = 11$

    $\dfrac{2}{3}x + y = 1$

5. $y = 5x - 9$
    $y = x - 10$

6. $y = -4x + 12$
    $y = 3x - 8$

For Exercises 7–14, solve the system using Cramer's rule.

7. $2x + y = 3$
    $x - 4y = 6$

8. $2x - y = -1$
    $3x + y = 6$

9. $x - 4y = 8$
    $3x + 7y = 5$

10. $7x + 3y = 4$
    $5x - 4y = 9$

11. $4x - 3y = 5$
    $2x + 5y = 7$

12. $2x + 3y = 4$
    $6x - 12y = -5$

13. $2x + 2y = 0$
    $6x = -12y$

14. $y = x$
    $12x - 3y = 0$

15. When does Cramer's rule not apply in solving a system of equations?

16. How can a system be solved if Cramer's rule does not apply?

For Exercises 17–22, solve the system of equations using Cramer's rule if possible. If not possible, use another method.

17. $4x - 2y = 3$
    $-2x + y = 1$

18. $6x - 6y = 5$
    $x - y = 8$

19. $4x + y = 0$
    $x - 7y = 0$

20. $-3x - 2y = 0$
    $-x + 5y = 0$

21. $x + 5y = 3$
    $2x + 10y = 6$

22. $-2x - 10y = -4$
    $x + 5y = 2$

For Exercises 23–24, set up a system of equations with two variables and solve using Cramer's rule.

23. Katia has several dimes and quarters in her wallet, totaling $2.05. There are three fewer quarters than there are dimes. How many of each coin are there?

24. Wallace has a pocket full of change consisting of dimes and nickels. The total value is $1.15. There is one more dime than there are nickels. How many of each coin are there?

For Exercises 25–32, solve for the indicated variable using Cramer's rule.

25. $2x - y + 3z = 9$
    $x + 4y + 4z = 5$ for x
    $3x + 2y + 2z = 5$

26. $x + 2y + 3z = 8$
    $2x - 3y + z = 5$ for y
    $3x - 4y + 2z = 9$

27. $3x - 2y + 2z = 5$
$6x + 3y - 4z = -1$ for z
$3x - y + 2z = 4$

28. $4x + 4y - 3z = 3$
$8x + 2y + 3y = 0$ for x
$4x - 4y + 6z = -3$

29. $3x + y - 2z = 1$
$-2x - 3y + z = 4$ for x
$x + y - 4z = -6$

30. $-x + 9y - z = -1$
$4x - 3y + z = 3$ for z
$2x + 8y - 2z = 4$

31. $5x + 6z = 5$
$-2x + y = -6$ for y
$3y - z = 3$

32. $8x + y = 1$
$7y + z = 0$ for y
$x - 3z = -2$

For Exercises 33–38, solve the system using Cramer's rule, if possible.

33. $x = 3$
$-x + 3y = 3$
$y + 2z = 4$

34. $4x + z = 7$
$y = 2$
$x + z = 4$

35. $x + y + 8z = 3$
$2x + y + 11z = 4$
$x + 3z = 0$

36. $-8x + y + z = 6$
$2x - y + z = 3$
$3x - z = 0$

37. $2x + y - 2z = 3$
$x - 3y + 2z = 1$
$3x - 9y + 6z = -3$

38. $4x - 2y + 6z = 1$
$2x - y + 3z = 2$
$3x + 4y + 2z = 1$

For Exercises 39–40, set up a system of equations with three variables and solve using Cramer's rule.

39. The smallest angle in a triangle is 30° less than the middle angle. The largest angle is 3° more than five times the smallest angle. Find the measures of the three angles. (Recall: The sum of the measures of the angles in a triangle is 180°.)

40. The largest angle of a triangle is five times the smallest angle. The middle angle is 18° less than the largest angle. Find the measures of the three angles.

▓ EXPANDING YOUR SKILLS

For Exercises 41–42, refer to the following system of four variables.

$$x + y + z + w = 0$$
$$2x - z + w = 5$$
$$2x + y - w = 0$$
$$y + z = -1$$

41. a. Evaluate the determinant, $\mathbf{D}$

   b. Evaluate the determinant, $\mathbf{D}_x$.

   c. Solve for x by computing $\dfrac{\mathbf{D}_x}{\mathbf{D}}$

42. a. Evaluate the determinant, $\mathbf{D}_y$.

   b. Solve for y by computing $\dfrac{\mathbf{D}_y}{\mathbf{D}}$

---

chapter 3   SUMMARY

SECTION 3.1—SYSTEMS OF LINEAR EQUATIONS IN TWO VARIABLES

KEY CONCEPTS:

A system of two linear equations can be solved by the graphing method, the substitution method, or the addition method.

A solution to a system of linear equations is an ordered pair that satisfies each equation in the system. Graphically, this represents a point of intersection of the lines.

There may be one solution, infinitely many solutions, or no solution.

One solution   Many solutions   No solution
Consistent   Consistent   Inconsistent
Independent   Dependent   Independent

A system is consistent if there is at least one solution. A system is inconsistent if there is no solution. An inconsistent system is detected by a contradiction (such as $0 = 5$).

A system is independent if the two equations represent different lines. A system is dependent if the two equations represent the same line. This produces infinitely many solutions. A dependent system is detected by an identity (such as $0 = 0$).

KEY TERMS:

addition method
consistent system
dependent system
general solution to a
    dependent system
graphing method
inconsistent system
independent system

solution to a system of
    equations in two
    variables
substitution method
system of linear
    equations in two
    variables

EXAMPLES:

Solve the system by graphing:

$2x + y = 5$

$2y = -6x + 14$

The point of intersection is $(2, 1)$.

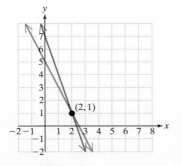

Solve the system by substitution:

$$2x + y = 5 \rightarrow y = -2x + 5$$

$$2y = -6x + 14 \rightarrow 2(-2x + 5) = -6x + 14$$

$$-4x + 10 = -6x + 14$$

$$2x = 4$$

$$x = 2$$

$$y = -2(2) + 5 \rightarrow y = 1$$

Solve the system by the addition method:

$$2x + y = 5 \rightarrow -4x - 2y = -10$$

$$2y = -6x + 14 \rightarrow \underline{6x + 2y = 14}$$

$$2x = 4$$

$$x = 2$$

$$y = 1$$

The system is inconsistent:

$$2x + y = 3 \rightarrow 4x + 2y = 6$$

$$-4x - 2y = 1 \rightarrow \underline{-4x - 2y = 1}$$

$$0 = 7 \qquad \text{Contradiction}$$

The system is dependent:

$$x + 3y = 1 \rightarrow -2x - 6y = -2$$

$$2x + 6y = 2 \rightarrow \underline{2x + 6y = 2}$$

$$0 = 0 \qquad \text{Identity}$$

Section 3.2—Applications of Systems of Linear Equations in Two Variables

Key Concepts:

Solve applications of systems of linear equations in two variables.

- Mixture applications
- Applications involving distance, rate, and time
- Geometry applications
- Business applications

Steps to solve applications:

1. Label two variables.
2. Construct a verbal model.
3. Write two equations.
4. Solve the system.
5. Write the answer.

Examples:

Mercedes invested $1500 more in a certificate of deposit that pays 6.5% simple interest than she did in a savings account that pays 4% simple interest. If her total interest at the end of one year is $622.50, find the amount she invested in the 6.5% account.

Let x represent the amount of money invested at 6.5%. Let y represent the amount of money invested at 4%.

$$\begin{pmatrix} \text{Amount invested} \\ \text{at } 6.5\% \end{pmatrix} = \$1500 + \begin{pmatrix} \text{Amount invested} \\ \text{at } 4\% \end{pmatrix}$$

$$\begin{pmatrix} \text{Interest earned} \\ \text{from } 6.5\% \\ \text{account} \end{pmatrix} + \begin{pmatrix} \text{Interest earned} \\ \text{from } 4\% \\ \text{account} \end{pmatrix} = \$622.50$$

$$x = 1500 + y$$

$$0.065x + 0.04y = 622.50$$

Using substitution:

$$0.065(1500 + y) + 0.04y = 622.50$$

$$97.5 + 0.065y + 0.04y = 622.50$$

$$0.105\,y = 525$$

$$y = 5000$$

$$x = 1500 + 5000 = 6500$$

Mercedes invested $6500 at 6.5% and $5000 at 4%.

Section 3.3—Systems of Linear Equations in Three Variables

Key Concepts:

A linear equation in three variables can be written in the form: $ax + by + cz = d$, where a, b, and c are not all zero. The graph of a linear equation in three variables is a plane in space.

A solution to a system of linear equations in three variables is an ordered triple that satisfies each equation. Graphically, a solution is a point of intersection among three planes.

Examples:

$\boxed{A}$ $x + 2y - z = 4$

$\boxed{B}$ $3x - y + z = 5$

$\boxed{C}$ $2x + 3y + 2z = 7$

$\boxed{A}$ and $\boxed{B}$ $x + 2y - z = 4$

$\phantom{\boxed{A} \text{ and } \boxed{B} \;\;} 3x - y + z = 5$

$\phantom{\boxed{A} \text{ and } \boxed{B} \;\;} 4x + y = 9 \;\; \boxed{D}$

$\boxed{A}$ and $\boxed{C}$ $2x + 4y - 2z = 8$

$\phantom{\boxed{A} \text{ and } \boxed{C} \;\;} 2x + 3y + 2z = 7$

$\phantom{\boxed{A} \text{ and } \boxed{C} \;\;} 4x + 7y = 15 \;\; \boxed{E}$

A system of linear equations in three variables may have one unique solution, infinitely many solutions (dependent system), or no solution (inconsistent system).

KEY TERMS:

linear equation in three variables
ordered triple

solution to a system of linear equations in three variables

$$\boxed{D} \quad 4x + y = 9 \rightarrow -4x - y = -9$$

$$\boxed{E} \quad 4x + 7y = 15 \rightarrow \underline{\quad 4x + 7y = 15}$$

$$6y = 6$$

$$y = 1$$

Substitute $y = 1$ into either equation $\boxed{D}$ or $\boxed{E}$.

$$\boxed{D} \quad 4x + (1) = 9$$

$$4x = 8$$

$$x = 2$$

Substitute $x = 2$ and $y = 1$ into either equation $\boxed{A}$, $\boxed{B}$, or $\boxed{C}$.

$$\boxed{A} \quad (2) + 2(1) - z = 4$$

$$z = 0$$

The solution is $(2, 1, 0)$.

SECTION 3.4—SOLVING SYSTEMS OF LINEAR EQUATIONS USING MATRICES

KEY CONCEPTS:

A matrix is a rectangular array of numbers displayed in rows and columns. Every number or entry within a matrix is called an element of the matrix.

The order of a matrix is determined by the number of rows and number of columns. A matrix with m rows and n columns is an $m \times n$ matrix.

A system of equations written in standard form can be represented by an augmented matrix consisting of the coefficients of the terms of each equation in the system.

The Gauss-Jordan method can be used to solve a system of equations by using the following elementary row operations on an augmented matrix.

1. Interchange two rows.
2. Multiply every element in a row by a nonzero real number.
3. Add a multiple of one row to another row.

EXAMPLES:

$[1 \quad 2 \quad 5]$ is a 1×3 matrix (called a row matrix).

$\begin{bmatrix} -1 & 8 \\ 1 & 5 \end{bmatrix}$ is a 2×2 matrix (called a square matrix).

$\begin{bmatrix} 4 \\ 1 \end{bmatrix}$ is a 2×1 matrix (called a column matrix).

Write the augmented matrix for the system.

$$\begin{aligned} 4x + y &= -12 \\ x - 2y &= 6 \end{aligned} \qquad \begin{bmatrix} 4 & 1 & | & -12 \\ 1 & -2 & | & 6 \end{bmatrix}$$

Solve the system using the Gauss-Jordan method.

$$R_1 \Leftrightarrow R_2 \qquad \begin{bmatrix} 1 & -2 & | & 6 \\ 4 & 1 & | & -12 \end{bmatrix}$$

$$\xrightarrow{-4R_1 + R_2 \Rightarrow R_2} \begin{bmatrix} 1 & -2 & | & 6 \\ 0 & 9 & | & -36 \end{bmatrix}$$

$$\xrightarrow{\frac{1}{9}R_2 \Rightarrow R_2} \begin{bmatrix} 1 & -2 & | & 6 \\ 0 & 1 & | & -4 \end{bmatrix}$$

These operations are used to write the matrix in reduced row echelon form.

$$\begin{bmatrix} 1 & 0 & | & a \\ 0 & 1 & | & b \end{bmatrix}$$

which represents the solution, $x = a$ and $y = b$.

KEY TERMS:

augmented matrix
coefficient matrix
column matrix
elementary row
  operations
Gauss-Jordan method

matrix
order of a matrix
reduced row echelon
  form
row matrix
square matrix

$$\xrightarrow{2R_2 + R_1 \Rightarrow R_1} \begin{bmatrix} 1 & 0 & | & -2 \\ 0 & 1 & | & -4 \end{bmatrix}$$

Solution:

$$x = -2 \quad \text{and} \quad y = -4$$

SECTION 3.5—ALGEBRA OF MATRICES

KEY CONCEPTS:

Given two matrices of the same order, $\mathbf{A} = [a_{ij}]$ and $\mathbf{B} = [b_{ij}]$, then $\mathbf{A} = \mathbf{B}$ if and only if $a_{ij} = b_{ij}$ for every i and j.

Given two matrices of order $m \times n$, $\mathbf{A} = [a_{ij}]$ and $\mathbf{B} = [b_{ij}]$, then the sum is the $m \times n$ matrix defined by:

$$\mathbf{A} + \mathbf{B} = [a_{ij} + b_{ij}] \quad \text{for all } i \text{ and } j.$$

Given two matrices of the same order, $\mathbf{A} - \mathbf{B}$ is defined as:

$$\mathbf{A} - \mathbf{B} = \mathbf{A} + (-\mathbf{B})$$

The product of a real number, k, and an $m \times n$ matrix matrix, $\mathbf{A} = [a_{ij}]$ is given by

$$k\mathbf{A} = [k \cdot a_{ij}]$$

If $\mathbf{A}$ is an $m \times p$ matrix and $\mathbf{B}$ is a $p \times n$ matrix, then the product $\mathbf{AB}$ is an $m \times n$ matrix. For the matrix $\mathbf{AB}$, the element in the ith row and jth column is the sum of the products of the corresponding elements in the ith row of $\mathbf{A}$ and the jth column of $\mathbf{B}$. *Note*: If the number of columns in $\mathbf{A}$ does not equal the number of rows in $\mathbf{B}$, then the product $\mathbf{AB}$ is not defined.

EXAMPLES:

Given that A = B, find *x* and *y*:

$$\mathbf{A} = \begin{bmatrix} x & -3 & 2 \\ -1 & 4 & 9 \end{bmatrix}, \quad \mathbf{B} = \begin{bmatrix} 8 & -3 & 2 \\ -1 & y & 9 \end{bmatrix}$$

Then $x = 8$ and $y = 4$

For matrices A and B:

$$\mathbf{A} = \begin{bmatrix} -3 & 4 \\ 9 & 0 \\ 11 & -1 \end{bmatrix}, \quad \mathbf{B} = \begin{bmatrix} 8 & -1 \\ 2 & 2 \\ -3 & -2 \end{bmatrix}$$

$$\mathbf{A} + \mathbf{B} = \begin{bmatrix} 5 & 3 \\ 11 & 2 \\ 8 & -3 \end{bmatrix}, \quad \mathbf{A} - \mathbf{B} = \begin{bmatrix} -11 & 5 \\ 7 & -2 \\ 14 & 1 \end{bmatrix}$$

$$3\mathbf{A} = \begin{bmatrix} -9 & 12 \\ 27 & 0 \\ 33 & -3 \end{bmatrix}$$

For matrices A and B:

$$\mathbf{A} = \begin{bmatrix} 2 & 5 \\ -1 & 4 \end{bmatrix} \quad \text{and} \quad \mathbf{B} = \begin{bmatrix} 7 & -1 & 6 \\ -2 & 5 & 1 \end{bmatrix}$$

$$\mathbf{AB} = \begin{bmatrix} 4 & 23 & 17 \\ -15 & 21 & -2 \end{bmatrix}$$

BA is not defined.

SECTION 3.6—DETERMINANTS

KEY CONCEPTS:

The determinant of a matrix $\mathbf{A}$ is denoted $\det\mathbf{A} = |a_{ij}|$.

The determinant of a 2×2 matrix is defined as:

$$\begin{vmatrix} a & b \\ c & d \end{vmatrix} = ad - bc$$

The determinant of a 3×3 matrix is defined by:

$$\begin{vmatrix} a_1 & b_1 & c_1 \\ a_2 & b_2 & c_2 \\ a_3 & b_3 & c_3 \end{vmatrix} = a_1 \cdot \begin{vmatrix} b_2 & c_2 \\ b_3 & c_3 \end{vmatrix} - a_2 \cdot \begin{vmatrix} b_1 & c_1 \\ b_3 & c_3 \end{vmatrix} +$$

$$a_3 \cdot \begin{vmatrix} b_1 & c_1 \\ b_2 & c_2 \end{vmatrix}$$

KEY TERMS:

determinant
minor

EXAMPLES:

Find the determinant of matrix A:

$$\mathbf{A} = \begin{bmatrix} 7 & -2 \\ 3 & 2 \end{bmatrix}, \quad \det\mathbf{A} = \begin{vmatrix} 7 & -2 \\ 3 & 2 \end{vmatrix}$$

$$= 14 - (-6)$$

$$= 20$$

Find the determinant of matrix B:

$$\mathbf{B} = \begin{bmatrix} 3 & -1 & 4 \\ 0 & 5 & 1 \\ 6 & -2 & -3 \end{bmatrix}$$

$\det\mathbf{B}$

$$= 3 \cdot \begin{vmatrix} 5 & 1 \\ -2 & -3 \end{vmatrix} - 0 \cdot \begin{vmatrix} -1 & 4 \\ -2 & -3 \end{vmatrix} + 6 \cdot \begin{vmatrix} -1 & 4 \\ 5 & 1 \end{vmatrix}$$

$$= 3(-15 + 2) - 0(3 + 8) + 6(-1 - 20)$$

$$= -39 - 0 + (-126)$$

$$= -165$$

SECTION 3.7—CRAMER'S RULE

KEY CONCEPTS:

Cramer's Rule for a 2 × 2 System of Linear Equations
The solution to the system

$$a_1x + b_1y = c_1$$

$$a_2x + b_2y = c_2$$

EXAMPLES:

Use Cramer's rule to solve the system.

$$2x + 8y = 0$$

$$x + 3y = 1$$

$$\mathbf{D} = \begin{vmatrix} 2 & 8 \\ 1 & 3 \end{vmatrix} = -2 \quad \mathbf{D}_x = \begin{vmatrix} 0 & 8 \\ 1 & 3 \end{vmatrix} = -8$$

is given by

$$x = \frac{\mathbf{D}_x}{\mathbf{D}} \quad \text{and} \quad y = \frac{\mathbf{D}_y}{\mathbf{D}}$$

where

$$\mathbf{D} = \begin{vmatrix} a_1 & b_1 \\ a_2 & b_2 \end{vmatrix} \quad (\text{and } \mathbf{D} \neq 0),$$

$$\mathbf{D}_x = \begin{vmatrix} c_1 & b_1 \\ c_2 & b_2 \end{vmatrix}, \quad \text{and} \quad \mathbf{D}_y = \begin{vmatrix} a_1 & c_1 \\ a_2 & c_2 \end{vmatrix}$$

Cramer's Rule for a 3 × 3 System of Linear Equations

The solution to the system

$$a_1 x + b_1 y + c_1 z = d_1$$
$$a_2 x + b_2 y + c_2 z = d_2$$
$$a_3 x + b_3 y + c_3 z = d_3$$

is given by

$$x = \frac{\mathbf{D}_x}{\mathbf{D}}, y = \frac{\mathbf{D}_y}{\mathbf{D}}, \text{ and } z = \frac{\mathbf{D}_z}{\mathbf{D}}$$

where

$$\mathbf{D} = \begin{vmatrix} a_1 & b_1 & c_1 \\ a_2 & b_2 & c_2 \\ a_3 & b_3 & c_3 \end{vmatrix} \quad (\text{and } \mathbf{D} \neq 0),$$

$$\mathbf{D}_x = \begin{vmatrix} d_1 & b_1 & c_1 \\ d_2 & b_2 & c_2 \\ d_3 & b_3 & c_3 \end{vmatrix}, \quad \mathbf{D}_y = \begin{vmatrix} a_1 & d_1 & c_1 \\ a_2 & d_2 & c_2 \\ a_3 & d_3 & c_3 \end{vmatrix},$$

$$\text{and } \mathbf{D}_z = \begin{vmatrix} a_1 & b_1 & d_1 \\ a_2 & b_2 & d_2 \\ a_3 & b_3 & d_3 \end{vmatrix}$$

If $\mathbf{D} = 0$, use the addition method or substitution method to solve the system.

KEY TERM:

Cramer's rule

$$\mathbf{D}_y = \begin{vmatrix} 2 & 0 \\ 1 & 1 \end{vmatrix} = 2$$

Therefore,

$$x = \frac{-8}{-2} = 4, y = \frac{2}{-2} = -1$$

Use Cramer's rule to solve for x.

$$x + 3y \qquad = 3$$
$$2y + z = 3$$
$$x \qquad - 3z = 2$$

$$\mathbf{D} = \begin{vmatrix} 1 & 3 & 0 \\ 0 & 2 & 1 \\ 1 & 0 & -3 \end{vmatrix} = -3$$

$$\mathbf{D}_x = \begin{vmatrix} 3 & 3 & 0 \\ 3 & 2 & 1 \\ 2 & 0 & -3 \end{vmatrix} = 15$$

Therefore,

$$x = \frac{15}{-3} = -5$$

chapter 3	REVIEW EXERCISES

Section 3.1

For Exercises 1–4, solve the systems using the substitution method.

1. $y = \dfrac{3}{4}x - 4$

    $-x + 2y = -6$

2. $3x = 11y - 9$

    $y = \dfrac{3}{11}x + \dfrac{6}{11}$

3. $4x + y = 7$

    $x = -\dfrac{1}{4}y + \dfrac{7}{4}$

4. $6x + y = 5$

    $5x + y = 3$

For Exercises 5–8, solve the systems using the addition method.

5. $\dfrac{2}{5}x + \dfrac{3}{5}y = 1$

    $x - \dfrac{2}{3}y = \dfrac{1}{3}$

6. $4x + 3y = 5$

    $3x - 4y = 10$

7. $3x + 4y = 2$

    $2x + 5y = -1$

8. $3x + y = 1$

    $-x - \dfrac{1}{3}y = -\dfrac{1}{3}$

Section 3.2

9. Antonio invested twice as much money in an account paying 5% simple interest as he did in an account paying 3.5% simple interest. If his total interest at the end of one year is $303.75, find the amount he invested in the 5% account.

10. A school carnival sold tickets to ride on a Ferris wheel. The charge was $1.50 for an adult and $1.00 for students. If 54 tickets were sold for a total of $70.50, how many of each type of ticket were sold?

11. It takes a pilot $1\frac{3}{4}$ h to travel with the wind to get from Jacksonville, Florida, to Myrtle Beach, South Carolina. Her return trip takes 2 h flying against the wind. What is the speed of the wind and the speed of the plane in still air if the distance between Jacksonville and Myrtle Beach is 280 miles?

12. Two angles are complementary. One angle is 6° more than 5 times the other. What are the measures of the two angles?

13. Two phone companies offer discount rates to students.

Company 1: $9.95 per month, plus $0.10 per minute for long distance calls

Company 2: $12.95 per month, plus $0.08 per minute for long distance calls

a. Write a linear model describing the total cost, y, for x minutes of long distance calls from company 1.

b. Write a linear model describing the total cost, y, for x minutes of long distance calls from company 2.

c. How many minutes of long distance calls would result in equal cost for both offers?

Section 3.3

For Exercises 14–16, solve the systems of equations.

14. $5x + 5y + 5z = 30$

    $-x + y + z = 2$

    $10x + 6y - 2z = 4$

15. $5x + 3y - z = 5$

    $x + 2y + z = 6$

    $-x - 2y - z = 8$

16. $3x + 4z = 5$

    $2y + 3z = 2$

    $2x - 5y = 8$

17. The perimeter of a right triangle is 30 ft. One leg is 2 ft more than twice the shortest leg. The hypotenuse is 2 ft less than 3 times the shortest leg. Find the lengths of the sides of this triangle.

18. Find a general solution to the system:

$$x + y + z = 4$$
$$-x - 2y - 3z = -6$$
$$2x + 4y + 6z = 12$$

Section 3.4

For Exercises 19–22, determine the order of each matrix.

19. $\begin{bmatrix} 2 & 4 & -1 \\ 5 & 0 & -3 \\ -1 & 6 & 10 \end{bmatrix}$ 20. $\begin{bmatrix} -5 & 6 \\ 9 & 2 \\ 0 & -3 \end{bmatrix}$

21. $\begin{bmatrix} 0 & 13 & -4 & 16 \end{bmatrix}$ 22. $\begin{bmatrix} 7 \\ 12 \\ -4 \end{bmatrix}$

For Exercises 23–24, set up the augmented matrix.

23. $\begin{aligned} x + y &= 3 \\ x - y &= -1 \end{aligned}$

24. $\begin{aligned} x - y + z &= 4 \\ 2x - y + 3z &= 8 \\ -2x + 2y - z &= -9 \end{aligned}$

For Exercises 25–26, write a corresponding system of equations from the augmented matrix.

25. $\left[\begin{array}{cc|c} 1 & 0 & 9 \\ 0 & 1 & -3 \end{array}\right]$

26. $\left[\begin{array}{ccc|c} 1 & 0 & 0 & -5 \\ 0 & 1 & 0 & 2 \\ 0 & 0 & 1 & -8 \end{array}\right]$

27. Given the matrix **A**:

$$\mathbf{A} = \left[\begin{array}{cc|c} 2 & 0 & 5 \\ 1 & 3 & -11 \end{array}\right]$$

a. What is the element in the second row and first column?

b. Write the matrix obtained by interchanging rows 1 and 2.

28. Given the matrix **B**:

$$\mathbf{B} = \left[\begin{array}{cc|c} 5 & 5 & 10 \\ 1 & -4 & 6 \end{array}\right]$$

a. What is the element in the first row and second column?

b. Write the matrix obtained by multiplying the first row by $-\frac{1}{5}$.

29. Given the matrix **C**:

$$\mathbf{C} = \left[\begin{array}{cc|c} 1 & 3 & 1 \\ 4 & -1 & 6 \end{array}\right]$$

a. What is the element in the second row and first column?

b. Write the matrix obtained by multiplying the first row by -4 and adding the result to row 2.

30. Given the matrix **D**:

$$\mathbf{D} = \left[\begin{array}{ccc|c} 1 & 2 & 0 & -3 \\ 4 & -1 & 1 & 0 \\ -3 & 2 & 2 & 5 \end{array}\right]$$

a. Write the matrix obtained by multiplying the first row by -4 and adding the result to row 2.

b. Using the matrix obtained in part (a), write the matrix obtained by multiplying the first row by 3 and adding the result to row 3.

For Exercises 31–32, solve the system by using the Gauss-Jordan method.

31. $\begin{aligned} x + y &= 3 \\ x - y &= -1 \end{aligned}$

32. $\begin{aligned} x - y + z &= 4 \\ 2x - y + 3z &= 8 \\ -2x + 2y - z &= -9 \end{aligned}$

Section 3.5

For Exercises 33–34, given that the matrices are equal, solve for the variables.

33. $\begin{bmatrix} -3 & x & 5 \\ 0 & 3 & 4 \end{bmatrix} = \begin{bmatrix} -3 & 1 & y \\ 0 & 3 & 4 \end{bmatrix}$

34. $\begin{bmatrix} 4 & 8 \\ z & -1 \end{bmatrix} = \begin{bmatrix} w & 8 \\ 6 & -1 \end{bmatrix}$

For Exercises 35–44, perform the indicated operations, if possible.

$$\mathbf{A} = \begin{bmatrix} 4 & 3 \\ -1 & 5 \end{bmatrix} \qquad \mathbf{B} = \begin{bmatrix} 2 & 1 & 8 \\ 0 & 3 & -2 \\ 6 & 4 & -4 \end{bmatrix}$$

$$\mathbf{C} = \begin{bmatrix} 4 & -1 \\ 0 & 6 \\ 5 & 1 \end{bmatrix} \qquad \mathbf{D} = \begin{bmatrix} 2 & 2 & -1 \\ 1 & 6 & 12 \end{bmatrix}$$

$$\mathbf{E} = \begin{bmatrix} 0 & 8 \\ 2 & -1 \end{bmatrix} \qquad \mathbf{F} = \begin{bmatrix} 8 & 1 & 1 \\ 0 & 2 & -3 \end{bmatrix}$$

35. **A** + **E**

36. **D** − **F**

37. **A** + **B**

38. 6**C**

39. **BC**

40. **DB**

41. $3\mathbf{A} - \mathbf{E}$ 42. $\mathbf{AC}$

43. $\mathbf{DC} + \mathbf{E}$ 44. $\mathbf{CF} + 2\mathbf{B}$

45. A citrus farmer grows oranges and grapefruits that are shipped to three markets. The 2×3 matrix, $\mathbf{C}$, represents the number of bushels of oranges and grapefruit that are shipped to three markets.

$$\mathbf{C} = \begin{array}{c} \begin{array}{ccc} 1 & 2 & 3 \end{array} \\ \begin{bmatrix} 20 & 45 & 30 \\ 35 & 25 & 30 \end{bmatrix} \begin{array}{l} \text{Oranges} \\ \text{Grapefruit} \end{array} \end{array}$$

The matrix, $\mathbf{M}$, represents the profit per bushel.

Profits (\$)
Oranges   Grapefruit

$$\mathbf{M} = [2.75 \quad 2.00]$$

Find the product $\mathbf{MC}$ and interpret the results in the context of the problem.

Section 3.6

For Exercises 46–49, evaluate the determinant.

46. $\begin{vmatrix} 5 & -2 \\ 2 & -3 \end{vmatrix}$ 47. $\begin{vmatrix} -6 & 1 \\ 0 & 10 \end{vmatrix}$

48. $\begin{vmatrix} \frac{1}{2} & 3 \\ 1 & 8 \end{vmatrix}$ 49. $\begin{vmatrix} 9 & 3 \\ -2 & \frac{2}{3} \end{vmatrix}$

For Exercises 50–53, evaluate the minor corresponding to the given element from matrix $\mathbf{A}$.

$$\mathbf{A} = \begin{vmatrix} 8 & 2 & 0 \\ -1 & 4 & -2 \\ 3 & -3 & 6 \end{vmatrix}$$

50. 8 51. 2

52. -2 53. 4

For Exercises 54–57, evaluate the determinant.

54. $\begin{vmatrix} 2 & 1 & 0 \\ -4 & 3 & -1 \\ 3 & 0 & 1 \end{vmatrix}$ 55. $\begin{vmatrix} 1 & 0 & 2 \\ 3 & -2 & 4 \\ 0 & 1 & 1 \end{vmatrix}$

56. $\begin{vmatrix} 4 & -2 & 0 \\ 9 & 5 & 4 \\ 1 & 2 & 0 \end{vmatrix}$ 57. $\begin{vmatrix} -1 & 0 & 2 \\ 5 & -2 & 6 \\ 3 & 0 & -4 \end{vmatrix}$

For Exercises 58–59, find the area of the triangle given its vertices.

58. $(3, 8), (-1, 2), (-3, -3)$

59. $(0, -5), (2, 1), (-3, 4)$

Section 3.7

For Exercises 60–61, evaluate the determinants represented by $\mathbf{D}, \mathbf{D}_x$, and $\mathbf{D}_y$. Then use Cramer's rule to solve for x and y.

60. $\begin{aligned} 3x + 2y &= 9 \\ x - 3y &= 1 \end{aligned}$ 61. $\begin{aligned} -x + 3y &= -8 \\ 2x - y &= -2 \end{aligned}$

For Exercises 62–65, solve the system using Cramer's rule.

62. $\begin{aligned} 3x - 4y &= 1 \\ 2x + 3y &= 12 \end{aligned}$ 63. $\begin{aligned} 3x + 2y &= 11 \\ -x + y &= 3 \end{aligned}$

64. $\begin{aligned} 2x + 3y - z &= -7 \\ x + 3z &= 10 \\ 2y + z &= -1 \end{aligned}$

65. $\begin{aligned} 6y + 4z &= -12 \\ 3x + 3y &= 9 \\ 2x - 3z &= 10 \end{aligned}$

For Exercises 66–67, solve the system of equations using Cramer's rule if possible. If not possible, use another method.

66. $\begin{aligned} 2x - y &= 1 \\ 4x - 2y &= 2 \end{aligned}$

67. $\begin{aligned} x + y - 3z &= -1 \\ y - z &= 6 \\ -x + 2y &= 1 \end{aligned}$

For Exercises 68, use Cramer's rule to solve the problem.

68. At the bottom of Akita's purse there are 13 coins, consisting of nickels, dimes, and quarters. There are three more dimes than nickels and the total value is \$1.40. How many nickels are there?

chapter 3   TEST

For Exercises 1–4, solve the system of equations.

1. $-2x - 6y = -98$
    $9x - 2y = 6$

2. $3x - 5y = -7$
    $-18x + 30y = 42$

3. $2x + 2y + 4z = -6$
    $3x + y + 2z = 29$
    $x - y - z = 44$

4. $3x - 2y - 4z = 1$
    $x + y - z = 6$
    $6x - 4y - 8z = 3$

5. How many liters of a 20% acid solution should be mixed with a 60% acid solution to produce 200 L of a 44% acid solution?

6. A rectangle has a perimeter of 72 cm. The length is 9 cm less than twice the width. Find the length and the width.

7. Working together Joanne, Kent, and Geoff can process 504 orders per day for their business. Kent can process 20 more orders per day than Joanne can process. Geoff can process 104 fewer orders per day than Kent and Joanne combined. Find the number of orders that each person can process per day.

8. Write an example of a 3 × 2 matrix.

9. Given the matrix **A**:

$$\mathbf{A} = \left[\begin{array}{ccc|c} 1 & 2 & 1 & -3 \\ 4 & 0 & 1 & -2 \\ -5 & -6 & 3 & 0 \end{array}\right]$$

   a. Write the matrix obtained by multiplying the first row by -4 and adding the result to row 2.

   b. Using the matrix obtained in part (a), write the matrix obtained by multiplying the first row by 5 and adding the result to row 3.

10. Solve the system using the Gauss-Jordan method.

$$5x - 4y = 34$$
$$x - 2y = 8$$

11. Solve the system using the Gauss-Jordan elimination method.

$$2x - y = 5$$
$$y + 3z = 9$$
$$-x + z = -2$$

12. Add the matrices: $\begin{bmatrix} -2 & 7 \\ 3 & -1 \end{bmatrix} + \begin{bmatrix} 2 & 0 \\ 3 & 8 \end{bmatrix}$

13. Multiply the matrices: $\begin{bmatrix} -2 & 7 \\ 3 & -1 \end{bmatrix} \cdot \begin{bmatrix} 2 & 0 \\ 3 & 8 \end{bmatrix}$

14. Given,

$$\mathbf{A} = \begin{bmatrix} -3 & 1 & 6 \\ 4 & -2 & 1 \end{bmatrix} \quad \text{and} \quad \mathbf{B} = \begin{bmatrix} 9 & 3 \\ -6 & 10 \end{bmatrix}$$

   find **AB** if possible. If not possible, explain why.

15. In general, does **AB** = **BA**? Explain.

For Exercises 16–18, find the determinant of the matrix.

16. $\begin{bmatrix} 2 & -3 \\ 1 & 2 \end{bmatrix}$

17. $\begin{bmatrix} 0 & 3 \\ 2 & -4 \end{bmatrix}$

18. $\begin{bmatrix} 0 & 5 & -2 \\ 0 & 0 & 2 \\ 2 & 3 & 1 \end{bmatrix}$

19. Do all matrices have a determinant? Explain.

For Exercises 20–21, use Cramer's rule to solve for y.

20. $6x - 5y = 13$
    $-2x - 2y = 9$

21. $2x + 2z = 2$
    $5x + 3y = 4$
    $3y - 4z = 4$

22. Solve the system:
    $6x - 2y = 0$
    $3x - y = 0$

CUMULATIVE REVIEW EXERCISES, CHAPTERS 1–3

1. Use the order of operations to simplify:
   $|6 - 9| + (12 \div 4 \cdot 2) - 3^2$

2. Simplify: $7(x + 2) - 4x^2 + 8x(x - 1)$

3. Solve for x: $2(x + 2) + 5 = 5(x + 3)$

4. Solve for x: $\frac{1}{2}x + 2y = -3$

5. A rectangular room is 1.5 times as long as it is wide. If its perimeter is 75 ft, find the length of the room.

6. Solve the inequality and write the answer in interval notation.
   $$-5 \le 2 - 4(x + 2) < 6$$

7. Find the slope and y-intercept of the line $2x + 3y = 0$ and graph the line.

8. Write an equation of the line with slope $m = \frac{1}{3}$ and x-intercept $(2, 0)$. Write the equation in slope-intercept form.

9. Solve the system using the addition method:
   $$2x - 3y = 6$$
   $$\frac{1}{2}x - \frac{3}{4}y = 1$$

10. Solve the system using the substitution method:
    $$2x + y = 4$$
    $$y = 3x - 1$$

11. A child's piggy bank contains 19 coins consisting of nickels, dimes, and quarters. The total amount of money in the bank is $3.05. If the number of quarters is 1 more than twice the number of nickels, find the number of each type of coin in the bank.

12. Two video clubs rent tapes according to the following fee schedules:

    Club 1: $25 initiation fee, plus $2.50 per tape

    Club 2: $10 initiation fee, plus $3.00 per tape

    a. Write a linear model describing the total cost, y, of renting x tapes from club 1.

    b. Write a linear model describing the total cost, y, of renting x tapes from club 2.

    c. How many tapes would have to be rented so that the cost for club 1 is the same as the cost for club 2?

13. Solve the system:
    $$3x + 2y + 3z = 3$$
    $$4x - 5y + 7z = 1$$
    $$2x + 3y - 2z = 6$$

14. Determine the order of the matrix:
    $$\begin{bmatrix} 4 & 5 & 1 \\ -2 & 6 & 0 \end{bmatrix}$$

15. Write an example of a 2 by 4 matrix.

16. List at least two different row operations.

17. Solve the system using the Gauss-Jordan method:
    $$2x - 4y = -2$$
    $$4x + y = 5$$

Introduction to Relations and Functions

The graphical representation of numerical data can give insight to the relationship among two or more variables. Furthermore, advances in technology have made graphing equations and functions a fast and efficient process. For an equation in two variables, we can plot points by hand. For complicated functions, however, a graphing calculator or computer graphing utility is a convenient tool for analysis.

For more information visit xyplot at

www.mhhe.com/miller_oneill

In this chapter, we investigate several basic functions and their graphs.

$$f(x) = x^6 - 7.25x^4 + 15.25x^2 - 9$$

section

4.1   INTRODUCTION TO RELATIONS

1. Definition of a Relation

In many naturally occurring phenomena, two variables may be linked or paired by some relationship. For example, Table 4-1 shows a correspondence between the length of a woman's femur and her height. (The femur is the large bone in the thigh attached to the knee and hip.)

Table 4-1

Length of Femur (cm) x	Height (in.) y		Ordered Pair
45.5	65.5	$\rightarrow$	(45.5, 65.5)
48.2	68.0	$\rightarrow$	(48.2, 68.0)
41.8	62.2	$\rightarrow$	(41.8, 62.2)
46.0	66.0	$\rightarrow$	(46.0, 66.0)
50.4	70.0	$\rightarrow$	(50.4, 70.0)

Each data point from Table 4-1 may be represented as an ordered pair. In this case, the first value represents the length of a woman's femur and the second the woman's height. The set of ordered pairs: {(45.5, 65.5), (48.2, 68.0), (41.8, 62.2), (46.0, 66.0), (50.4, 70.0)} defines a relation between femur length and height.

Definition of a Relation in x and y

Any set of ordered pairs, (x, y), is called a **relation in x and y**. Furthermore:

- The set of first components in the ordered pairs is called the **domain of the relation**.
- The set of second components in the ordered pairs is called the **range of the relation**.

2. Finding the Domain and Range of a Relation

example 1

Finding the Domain and Range of a Relation

Find the domain and range of the relation linking the length of a woman's femur to her height: {(45.5, 65.5), (48.2, 68.0), (41.8, 62.2), (46.0, 66.0), (50.4, 70.0)}

Solution:

Domain: {45.5, 48.2, 41.8, 46.0, 50.4}   Set of first coordinates

Range: {65.5, 68.0, 62.2, 66.0, 70.0}   Set of second coordinates

The *x*- and *y*-components that constitute the ordered pairs in a relation do not need to be numerical. For example, Table 4-2 depicts 10 states in the United States and the corresponding number of representatives in the House of Representatives as of July 1998.

Table 4-2

State *x*	Number of Representatives *y*
Arizona	6
California	52
Colorado	6
Florida	23
Kansas	4
New York	31
North Carolina	12
Oregon	5
Texas	30
Virginia	11

These data define a relation:

{(Arizona, 6), (California, 52), (Colorado, 6), (Florida, 23), (Kansas, 4),

(New York, 31), (North Carolina, 12), (Oregon, 5), (Texas, 30), (Virginia, 11)}

example 2

Finding the Domain and Range of a Relation

Find the domain and range of the relation:
{(Arizona, 6), (California, 52), (Colorado, 6), (Florida, 23), (Kansas, 4),
(New York, 31), (North Carolina, 12), (Oregon, 5), (Texas, 30), (Virginia, 11)}

Solution:

Domain: {Arizona, California, Colorado, Florida, Kansas, New York,
          North Carolina, Oregon, Texas, Virginia}

Range: {6, 52, 23, 4, 31, 12, 5, 30, 11}   (*Note:* The element 6 is not listed
                                                twice.)

A relation may consist of a finite number of ordered pairs or an infinite number of ordered pairs. Furthermore, a relation may be defined by several different methods: by a list of ordered pairs, by a "mapping" between the domain and range, by a graph, or by an equation.

Figure 4-1

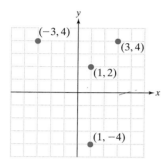

Figure 4-2

- A relation may be defined as a set of ordered pairs.
$$\{(1, 2), (-3, 4), (1, -4), (3, 4)\}$$

- A relation may be defined by a mapping (Figure 4-1). The corresponding ordered pairs are $\{(1, 2), (1, -4), (-3, 4), (3, 4)\}$.

- A relation may be defined by a graph (Figure 4-2). The corresponding ordered pairs are $\{(1, 2), (-3, 4), (1, -4), (3, 4)\}$.

- A relation may be expressed by an equation such as $x = y^2$. The solutions to this equation define an infinite set of ordered pairs of the form $\{(x, y) \mid x = y^2\}$. The solutions can also be represented by a graph in a rectangular coordinate system (Figure 4-3).

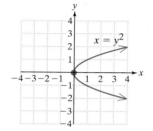

Figure 4-3

Tip: Some of the solutions to the relation $x = y^2$ are shown here. These points can be used to sketch a graph of the relation.

$$(0, 0), (1, 1), (1, -1), (4, 2), \text{ and } (4, -2)$$

---

example 3

Finding the Domain and Range of a Relation

Find the domain and range of the following relations:

a.

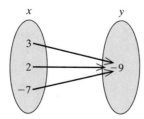

Domain: $\{3, 2, -7\}$

Range: $\{-9\}$

b.

Domain: $\{-2, -1, 0, 1, 2\}$

Range: $\{-3, 0, 1\}$

c.

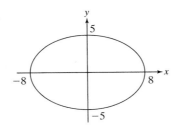

The domain consists of an infinite number of x-values extending from −8 to 8. The range consists of all y-values from −5 to 5. Thus, the domain and range must be expressed in set-builder notation or in interval notation.

Domain: $\{x | -8 \le x \le 8\}$ or $[-8, 8]$

Range: $\{y | -5 \le y \le 5\}$ or $[-5, 5]$

d. $x = y^2$

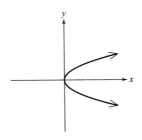

The arrows on the curve indicate that the graph extends infinitely far up and to the right and infinitely far down and to the right.

Domain: $\{x | x \ge 0\}$ or $[0, \infty)$

Range: All real numbers or $(-\infty, \infty)$

3. Graphing a Relation

example 4

Graphing a Relation and Identifying the Domain and Range

Graph the relation $y = |x|$, and state the domain and range.

Solution:

To graph the relation, $y = |x|$, a sufficient number of points must be found to establish its shape. To find points, we may choose arbitrary values of x and use the equation to solve for y. In Table 4-3, we chose both positive and negative values of x to determine the behavior of the function to the right and to the left of the origin.

Table 4-3

x	$y = |x|$
0	0
1	1
2	2
3	3
−1	1
−2	2
−3	3

> ### Graphing Calculator Box
>
> Try using a *Table* feature to find several ordered pairs of the relation $y = |x|$.
> Enter $Y_1 = abs(x)$

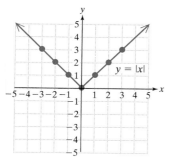

Figure 4-4

Several ordered pairs were used to determine the shape of the relation. It is important to realize, however, that the relation represents an *infinite* number of points whose coordinates satisfy the equation. The graph represents all such ordered pairs. Based on the pattern of the points, it appears that the graph is a V shape that extends infinitely far to the right and up, and infinitely far to the left and up (Figure 4-4).

The graph extends infinitely far to the left and right, so the domain is all real numbers. Notice that the y-values never extend below zero. Hence, the range is $\{y \mid y \geq 0\}$.

Domain: All real numbers   or $(-\infty, \infty)$

Range: $\{y \mid y \geq 0\}$ or $[0, \infty)$

4.   Applications Involving Relations

example 5

Analyzing a Relation

The data in Table 4-4 depict the length of a woman's femur and her corresponding height.

Table 4-4

Length of Femur (cm) x	Height (in.) y
45.5	65.5
48.2	68.0
41.8	62.2
46.0	66.0
50.4	70.0

After collecting the data, a medical researcher finds the following linear relationship between height, y, and femur length, x:

$$y = 0.906x + 24.3 \quad 40 \leq x \leq 51$$

a. Find the height of a woman whose femur is 46.0 cm.
b. Find the height of a woman whose femur is 51.0 cm.
c. Why is the domain restricted to $40 \leq x \leq 51$?

Solution:

a. $y = 0.906x + 24.3$
    $= 0.906(46.0) + 24.3$ Substitute $x = 46.0$ cm.
    $= 65.976$ The woman is approximately 66.0 in. tall.

b. $y = 0.906x + 24.3$
    $= 0.906(51.0) + 24.3$ Substitute $x = 51.0$ cm.
    $= 70.506$ The woman is approximately 70.5 in. tall.

Graphing Calculator Box

Use a *Table* feature and the relation
$Y_1 = 0.906x + 24.3$ to confirm the solutions
to Example 5.

X	Y₁
46	65.976
47	66.882
48	67.788
49	68.694
50	69.6
51	70.506
52	71.412

X=46

---

c. The domain restricts femur length to values between 40 cm and 51 cm, inclusive. These values are within the normal lengths for an adult female and are in the proximity of the observed data (Figure 4-5).

Figure 4-5

section 4.1   PRACTICE EXERCISES

For Exercises 1–4, write each relation as a set of ordered pairs.

1.

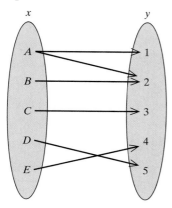

2.

State x	Year of Statehood y
Connecticut	1788
Colorado	1876
Maryland	1788
Illinois	1818
Missouri	1821

3. Reference daily intake (RDI) for proteins

Group (x)	RDI in Grams (y)
Pregnant women	60
Nursing mothers	65
Infants younger than 1 year old	14
Children from 1 to 4 years	16
Adults	50

4.

x	y
0	3
−2	$\frac{1}{2}$
5	10
−7	1
−2	8
5	1

5. List the domain and range of Exercise 1.

6. List the domain and range of Exercise 2.

7. List the domain and range of Exercise 3.

8. List the domain and range of Exercise 4.

9. a. Define a relation with four ordered pairs such that the first element of the ordered pair is the name of a friend, the second element is your friend's place of birth.

   b. State the domain and range of this relation.

10. a. Define a relation with four ordered pairs such that the first element is a state and the second element is its capital.

    b. State the domain and range of this relation.

11. a. Use a mathematical equation to define a relation whose second component, y, is 1 less than 2 times the first component, x.

    b. Sketch the relation.

    c. Write the domain and range of this relation in interval notation.

12. a. Use a mathematical equation to define a relation whose second component, y, is 3 more than the first component, x.

    b. Sketch the relation.

    c. Write the domain and range of this relation in interval notation.

For Exercises 13–26, find the domain and range of the relations. Use interval notation where appropriate.

13.

14.

15.

16.

17.

18.

19.

20.

21.

22.

23.

24.

25.

26.

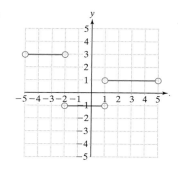

27. The following table gives a relation between the month of the year and the average precipitation for that month for Miami, Florida.

Month x	Precipitation (in.) y
Jan.	2.01
Feb.	2.08
Mar.	2.39
Apr.	2.85
May	6.21
June	9.33
July	5.70
Aug.	7.58
Sept.	7.63
Oct.	5.64
Nov.	2.66
Dec.	1.83

Source: U.S. National Oceanic and Atmospheric Administration

a. What is the range element corresponding to April?

b. What is the range element corresponding to June?

c. Which element in the domain corresponds to the lowest range value?

d. Complete the ordered pair: (, 2.66)

e. Complete the ordered pair: (Sept.,)

f. What is the domain of this relation?

28. The following table gives a relation between the month of the year and the average precipitation for that month for Portland, Oregon.

Month x	Precipitation (in.) y
Jan.	5.35
Feb.	3.85
Mar.	3.56
Apr.	2.39
May	2.06
June	1.48
July	0.63
Aug.	1.09
Sept.	1.75
Oct.	2.67
Nov.	5.34
Dec.	6.13

Source: U.S. National Oceanic and Atmospheric Administration.

a. What is the domain?

b. What is the range?

c. Which element in the domain corresponds to the highest element in the range?

d. Complete the ordered pair: (July,)

e. Complete the ordered pair: (, 1.09)

f. Graph the ordered pairs defining this relation by plotting the month on the horizontal axis and the amount of precipitation on the vertical axis.

29. The percentage of male high school students, *y*, who participated in an organized physical activity for the year 1995 is approximated by $y = -12.64x + 195.22$. For this model, *x* represents the grade level ($9 \leq x \leq 12$). (*Source: Centers for Disease Control*)

Figure for Exercise 29

a. Approximate the percentage of males who participated in organized physical activity for grades 9, 10, 11, and 12, respectively.

b. Can we use this model to predict seventh-grade participation? Explain your answer.

30. As of March 1998, the world record times for selected women's track and field events are shown in the table.

Distance (m)	Time (s)	Winner's Name and Country
100	10.49 (0:10:49)	Florence Griffith Joyner (U.S.)
200	21.34 (0:21:34)	Florence Griffith Joyner (U.S.)
400	47.60 (0:47:60)	Marita Koch (East Germany)
800	113.28 (1:53:28)	Jarmila Kratochvilova (Czechoslovakia)
1000	149.34 (2:29:34)	Maria Mutola (Mozambique)
1500	230.46 (3:50:46)	Qu Yunxia (China)

The women's world record time, *y* (in seconds) required to run *x* meters can be approximated by the relation $y = -10.78 + 0.159x$.

a. Predict the time required for a 500-m race.

b. Use this model to predict the time for a 1000-m race. Is this value exactly the same as the data value given in the table? Explain.

EXPANDING YOUR SKILLS

31. Write the domain and the range for the relation $y = |x|$ from the graph.

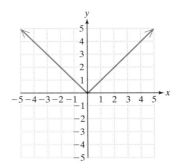

32. Write the domain and the range for the relation $y = |x - 2|$ from the graph.

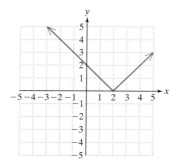

33. Write the domain and the range for the relation $y = |x + 2|$ from the graph.

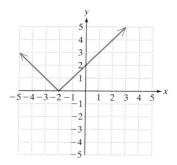

34. By comparing the domains and ranges for Exercises 31–33, what can you say about the domain and the range for the relation $y = |x + c|$, where c is any real number?

35. Write the domain and the range for the relation $y = |x| - 2$ from the graph.

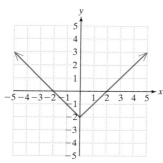

36. Write the domain and the range for the relation $y = |x| + 2$ from the graph.

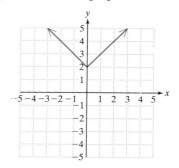

37. By comparing the domains and ranges for Exercises 31, 35–36, what can you say about the domain and the range for the relation $y = |x| + c$, where c is any real number?

GRAPHING CALCULATOR EXERCISES

38. a. Use a graphing calculator to graph the relation $Y_1 = -12.64x + 195.22$ on a viewing window defined by $9 \le x \le 12$ and $0 \le y \le 100$.

    b. Use a *Table* feature to evaluate the relation for $x = 9, 10, 11$, and 12. Do these values agree with your solutions from Exercise 29?

39. a. Use a graphing calculator to graph the relation $Y_1 = -10.78 + 0.159x$ on a viewing window defined by $0 \le x \le 2000$ and $0 \le y \le 350$.

    b. Use a *Table* feature to evaluate the relation for $x = 500, 1000$, and 1500. Do these values agree with your solutions from Exercise 30?

section

4.2 INTRODUCTION TO FUNCTIONS

1. Definition of a Function

In this section we introduce a special type of relation called a function.

Definition of a Function

Given a relation in x and y, we say "y is a *function* of x" if for every element x in the domain, there corresponds exactly one element y in the range.

To understand the difference between a relation that is a function and a relation that is not a function, consider the following example.

example 1   **Determining Whether a Relation Is a Function**

Determine which of the relations define y as a function of x.

a.

b.

c.
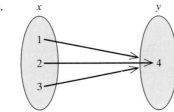

Solution:

a.   This relation is defined by the set of ordered pairs: $\{(1, 4), (2, -1), (3, 2)\}$.

Notice that each x in the domain corresponds to only *one y* in the range. Therefore, this relation is a function.

When $x = 1$, there is only one possibility for y: $y = 4$

When $x = 2$, there is only one possibility for y: $y = -1$

When $x = 3$, there is only one possibility for y: $y = 2$

b. This relation is defined by the set of ordered pairs:

For the domain element $x = 1$, there are *two* possible range elements: $y = 3$ and $y = 4$. Therefore, this relation is *not* a function.

c. This relation is defined by the set of ordered pairs: $\{(1, 4), (2, 4), (3, 4)\}$.

When $x = 1$, there is only one possibility for y: $y = 4$

When $x = 2$, there is only one possibility for y: $y = 4$

When $x = 3$, there is only one possibility for y: $y = 4$

Because each value of x in the domain corresponds to only *one* y-value, this relation is a function.

2. Vertical Line Test

A relation that is not a function has at least one domain element, x, paired with more than one range value, y. For example, the ordered pairs $(1, 3)$ and $(1, 4)$ do not constitute a function. These two points are aligned vertically in the xy-plane, and a vertical line drawn through one point also intersects the other point. Thus if a vertical line drawn through a graph of a relation intersects the graph in more than one point, the relation cannot be a function. This idea is stated formally as the **vertical line test**.

The Vertical Line Test

Consider a relation defined by a set of points (x, y) in a rectangular coordinate system. Then the graph defines y as a function of x if no vertical line intersects the graph in more than one point.

The vertical line test also implies that if any vertical line drawn through the graph of a relation intersects the relation in more than one point, then the relation does *not define y as a function of x*.

The vertical line test can be demonstrated by graphing the ordered pairs from the relations in Example 1.

a. {(1, 4), (2, −1), (3, 2)}   b. {(1, 3), (1, 4), (2, −1), (3, −2)}

Function
No vertical line
intersects more than once.

Not a Function
A vertical line intersects
in more than one point.

c. {(1, 4), (2, 4), (3, 4)}

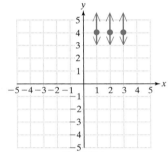

Function
No vertical line
intersects more than once.

example 2   **Using the Vertical Line Test**

Use the vertical line test to determine whether the following relations define *y*
as a function of *x*.

a.

b.

c.

Solution:

a.

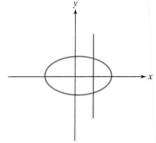

Not a Function
A vertical line intersects
in more than one point.

b.

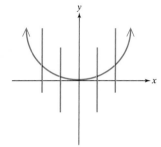

Function
No vertical line intersects
in more than one point.

c.

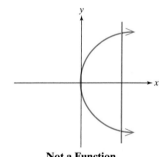

Not a Function
A vertical line intersects
in more than one point.

3.   Function Notation

A function is defined as a relation with the added restriction that each value in the domain corresponds to only one value in the range. In mathematics, functions are often given by rules or equations to define the relationship between two or more variables. For example, the equation $y = 2x$ defines the set of ordered pairs such that the y-value is twice the x-value.

When a function is defined by an equation, we often use **function notation**. For example, the equation $y = 2x$ may be written in function notation as

$f(x) = 2x,$ where f is the name of the function, x is an input value from the domain of the function, and $f(x)$ is the function value (or y-value) corresponding to x.

The notation $f(x)$ is read as "f of x" or "the value of the function, f, at x."

4. Evaluating Functions

A function may be evaluated at different values of x by substituting x values from the domain into the function. For example, to evaluate the function defined by $f(x) = 2x$ at $x = 5$, substitute $x = 5$ into the function.

$$f(x) = 2x$$

$$f(5) = 2(5)$$

$$f(5) = 10$$

Tip: The function value $f(5) = 10$ can be written as the ordered pair $(5, 10)$.

Thus, when $x = 5$, the corresponding function value is 10. We say "f of 5 is 10" or "f at 5 is 10."

The names of functions are often given by either lowercase or uppercase letters, such as f, g, h, p, K, M, and so on.

---

example 3

Evaluating a Function

Given the function defined by $g(x) = \frac{1}{2}x - 1$, find the function values.

a. $g(0)$ b. $g(2)$ c. $g(4)$ d. $g(-2)$

Solution:

a. $g(x) = \frac{1}{2}x - 1$

$g(0) = \frac{1}{2}(0) - 1$
$= 0 - 1$
$= -1$ We say, "g of 0 is -1" or "g at 0 is -1." This is equivalent to the ordered pair $(0, -1)$.

b. $g(x) = \frac{1}{2}x - 1$

$g(2) = \frac{1}{2}(2) - 1$
$= 1 - 1$
$= 0$ We say "g of 2 is 0" or "g at 2 is 0." This is equivalent to the ordered pair $(2, 0)$.

c. $g(x) = \frac{1}{2}x - 1$

$g(4) = \frac{1}{2}(4) - 1$
$= 2 - 1$
$= 1$ We say "g of 4 is 1" or "g at 4 is 1." This is equivalent to the ordered pair $(4, 1)$.

d. $g(x) = \dfrac{1}{2}x - 1$

$$g(-2) = \dfrac{1}{2}(-2) - 1$$

$$= -1 - 1$$

$$= -2$$

We say "g of -2 is -2" or "g at -2 is -2." This is equivalent to the ordered pair $(-2, -2)$.

Graphing Calculator Box

The values of $g(x)$ in Example 3 can be found using a *Table* feature.

$$Y_1 = \tfrac{1}{2}x - 1$$

Function values can also be evaluated by using a *Value* (or *Eval*) feature. The value of $g(4)$ is shown here.

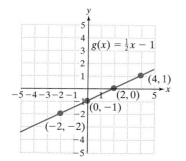

Figure 4-6

Notice that the function values $g(0)$, $g(2)$, $g(4)$, and $g(-2)$ correspond to the ordered pairs $(0, -1)$, $(2, 0)$, $(4, 1)$, and $(-2, -2)$. In the graph, these points "line up." The graph of *all* ordered pairs defined by this function is a line with a slope of $\frac{1}{2}$, and y-intercept of $(0, -1)$ (Figure 4-6). This should not be surprising because the function defined by $g(x) = \frac{1}{2}x - 1$ is equivalent to $y = \frac{1}{2}x - 1$.

A function may be evaluated at numerical values or at algebraic expressions as shown in the next example.

example 4   **Evaluating Functions**

Given the functions defined by $f(x) = x^2 - 2x$ and $g(x) = 3x + 5$, find the function values.

a. $f(t)$ b. $g(w + 4)$ c. $f(x + h)$

Solution:

a. $f(x) = x^2 - 2x$

$$f(t) = (t)^2 - 2(t)$$ Substitute $x = t$ for all values of x in the function.

$$= t^2 - 2t$$ Simplify.

b. $g(x) = 3x + 5$

$$g(w + 4) = 3(w + 4) + 5$$ Substitute $x = w + 4$ for all
$$= 3w + 12 + 5$$ values of x in the function.

$$= 3w + 17$$ Simplify.

c. $f(x) = x^2 - 2x$ Substitute the quantity $x + h$ for x.

$$f(x + h) = (x + h)^2 - 2(x + h)$$
$$= x^2 + 2xh + h^2 - 2x - 2h$$ Simplify.

5. Finding Function Values from a Graph

example 5

Finding Function Values from a Graph

Consider the function pictured in Figure 4-7.

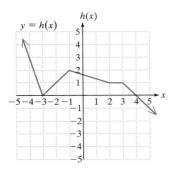

Figure 4-7

a.   Find $h(-1)$.

b.   Find $h(2)$.

c.   For what value of x is $h(x) = 3$?

d.   For what values of x is $h(x) = 0$?

Solution:

a. $h(-1) = 2$ This corresponds to the ordered pair $(-1, 2)$.

b. $h(2) = 1$ This corresponds to the ordered pair $(2, 1)$.

c. $h(x) = 3$ for $x = -4$ This corresponds to the ordered pair $(-4, 3)$.

d. $h(x) = 0$ for $x = -3$ and for $x = 4$.   These are the ordered pairs $(-3, 0)$ and $(4, 0)$.

6. Domain of a Function

A function is a relation and it is often necessary to determine its domain and range. Consider a function defined by the equation $y = f(x)$. The **domain** of f is the set of all x-values that when substituted into the function produce a real number. The **range** of f is the set of all y-values corresponding to the values of x in the domain.

Tip: Thus far in your study of algebra, you have seen two situations in which an expression will not be a real number. The first case is dividing by zero. The second case is taking a square root of a negative number.

To find the domain of a function defined by $y = f(x)$, you must keep the following tips in mind:

- Exclude values of x that make the denominator of a fraction zero.
- Exclude values of x that make the radicand of a square root negative.

example 6 — Finding the Domain of a Function

Find the domain of the following functions. Write the answers in interval notation.

a. $f(x) = \dfrac{x + 7}{2x - 1}$

b. $h(x) = \dfrac{x - 4}{x^2 + 9}$

c. $k(t) = \sqrt{t + 4}$

d. $g(t) = t^2 - 3t$

Solution:

a. The function will not be a real number when the denominator is zero. That is when,

$$2x - 1 = 0$$
$$2x = 1$$
$$x = \frac{1}{2}$$ The value $x = \frac{1}{2}$ must be *excluded* from the domain.

The domain of f is the set of all real numbers *excluding* $\frac{1}{2}$: $\{x \mid x \neq \frac{1}{2}\}$.

Interval notation: $\left(-\infty, \dfrac{1}{2}\right) \cup \left(\dfrac{1}{2}, \infty\right)$

b. The quantity x^2 is greater than or equal to zero for all real numbers x, and the number 9 is positive. Therefore, the sum, $x^2 + 9$, must be *positive* for all real numbers x. The denominator of $h(x) = (x - 4)/(x^2 + 9)$ will never be zero; the domain is therefore the set of all real numbers.

Interval notation: $(-\infty, \infty)$

c. The function defined by $k(t) = \sqrt{t + 4}$ will be not be a real number when the radicand is negative; hence the domain is the set of all t-values that make the radicand *greater than or equal to zero:*

$$t + 4 \geq 0$$
$$t \geq -4$$

Interval notation: $[-4, \infty)$

d. The function defined by $g(t) = t^2 - 3t$ has no restrictions on its domain because any real number substituted for t will produce a real number. The domain is the set of all real numbers.

Interval notation: $(-\infty, \infty)$

7. Algebra of Functions

Addition, subtraction, multiplication, and division may be used to combine two or more functions.

Sum, Difference, Product, and Quotient of Functions

Given two functions, f and g, the functions $f + g$, $f - g$, $f \cdot g$, and $\frac{f}{g}$ are defined as:

$$(f + g)(x) = f(x) + g(x)$$
$$(f - g)(x) = f(x) - g(x)$$
$$(f \cdot g)(x) = f(x) \cdot g(x)$$
$$\left(\frac{f}{g}\right)(x) = \frac{f(x)}{g(x)} \qquad \text{provided } g(x) \neq 0$$

The domain of the functions $f + g$, $f - g$, $f \cdot g$, and $\frac{f}{g}$ is the *intersection* of the domain of f and the domain of g.

---

example 7 **Combining Functions**

Given the functions defined by $f(x) = 4x - 5$, $g(x) = 5x + 2$, and $h(x) = x^2 - 3x$, find

a. $(f - g)(x)$ b. $(g + h)(-2)$ c. $\left(\dfrac{g}{h}\right)(x)$ d. $(f \cdot h)(3)$

Solution:

a. $(f - g)(x) = f(x) - g(x)$

$$= (4x - 5) - (5x + 2)$$
$$= 4x - 5 - 5x - 2$$
$$= -x - 7$$

b. $(g + h)(-2) = g(-2) + h(-2)$

$$= [5(-2) + 2] + [(-2)^2 - 3(-2)] \qquad \text{Evaluate the functions}$$
$$= -10 + 2 + 4 + 6 \qquad\qquad\qquad g \text{ and } h \text{ at } x = -2.$$
$$= 2$$

Tip: The expression $(5x + 2)/(x^2 - 3x)$ can be written as $(5x + 2)/[x(x - 3)]$. Therefore the domain of the function defined by

$$\left(\frac{g}{h}\right)(x) = \frac{5x + 2}{x(x - 3)} \quad \text{is}$$

$\{x \mid x \neq 0, x \neq 3\}$

c. $\left(\dfrac{g}{h}\right)(x) = \dfrac{g(x)}{h(x)}$

$$= \frac{5x + 2}{x^2 - 3x} \qquad \text{for } x \neq 0, x \neq 3$$

d. $(f \cdot h)(3) = f(3) \cdot h(3)$

$\qquad = [4(3) - 5][(3)^2 - 3(3)]$ Evaluate the functions

$\qquad = [12 - 5][9 - 9]$ f and h at $x = 3$.

$\qquad = (7)(0)$

$\qquad = 0$

8. Composition of Functions

Another way to combine functions is by finding the composition of two functions.

Composition of Functions

The **composition** of f and g, denoted $f \circ g$, is defined by the rule:

$$(f \circ g)(x) = f(g(x)) \quad \text{provided that } g(x) \text{ is in the domain of } f.*$$

The composition of g and f, denoted $g \circ f$, is defined by the rule:

$$(g \circ f)(x) = g(f(x)) \quad \text{provided that } f(x) \text{ is in the domain of } g.^\dagger$$

*$f \circ g$ is also read as "f compose g."
$^\dagger g \circ f$ is also read as "g compose f."

For example, given $f(x) = 2x - 3$ and $g(x) = x + 5$, we have

$(f \circ g)(x) = f(g(x))$

$\qquad = f(x + 5)$ Substitute $g(x) = x + 5$ into the function f.

$\qquad = 2(x + 5) - 3$

$\qquad = 2x + 10 - 3$

$\qquad = 2x + 7$

In this composition, the function g is the innermost operation and acts on x first. Then the output value of function g becomes the domain element of the function f (Figure 4-8).

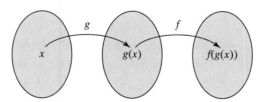

Figure 4-8

---

example 8   **Composing Functions**

Given the functions defined by $h(x) = 3x - 7$, $k(x) = 2x$, and $m(x) = 2x^2 - 1$, find

a. $(h \circ k)(x)$ b. $(k \circ h)(x)$ c. $(m \circ h)(4)$

Tip: Examples 8(a) and 8(b), illustrate that the order in which two functions are composed may result in different functions. That is, $f \circ g$ does not necessarily equal $g \circ f$.

Solution:

a. $(h \circ k)(x) = h(k(x))$
    $= h(2x)$ Substitute $k(x) = 2x$ into function h.
    $= 3(2x) - 7$
    $= 6x - 7$

b. $(k \circ h)(x) = k(h(x))$
    $= k(3x - 7)$ Substitute $h(x) = 3x - 7$ into function k.
    $= 2(3x - 7)$
    $= 6x - 14$

c. $(m \circ h)(4) = m(h(4))$ Evaluate $h(4)$ first. $h(4) = 3(4) - 7 = 5$
    $= m(5)$ Because $h(4) = 5$, substitute $x = 5$ into the function m.

    $= 2(5)^2 - 1$
    $= 2(25) - 1$
    $= 50 - 1$
    $= 49$

---

example 9

Evaluating Functions

Given the functions $w = \{(0, 3), (1, 7), (-2, -4)\}$ and $z = \{(1, -2), (-2, 0), (7, 3), (4, -2)\}$, find the function values:

a. $w(1)$ b. $(w \circ z)(-2)$ c. $(z \circ w)(1)$ d. $w(1) + z(1)$

Solution:

a.   From the function, w, the ordered pair $(1, 7)$ implies that $w(1) = 7$.

b. $(w \circ z)(-2)$

    $= w(z(-2))$ Evaluate $z(-2)$ first. $z(-2) = 0$.
    $= w(0)$
    $= 3$

c. $(z \circ w)(1)$

    $= z(w(1))$ Evaluate $w(1)$ first. $w(1) = 7$.
    $= z(7)$
    $= 3$

d. $w(1) + z(1)$ Evaluate $w(1)$ and $z(1)$ separately and then take the sum.
    $= 7 + (-2)$

    $= 5$ Hence $w(1) + z(1) = 5$.

section 4.2   PRACTICE EXERCISES

For Exercises 1–4, (a) Write the relation as a set of ordered pairs. (b) Identify the domain. (c) Identify the range. (d) Is the relation a function?

1.

Parent (x)	Child (y)
Doris	Mike
Richard	Nora
Doris	Molly
Richard	Mike

2.

3.

4.

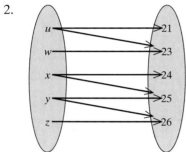

For Exercises 5–8, state the domain and range.

5.

6.

7.

8.

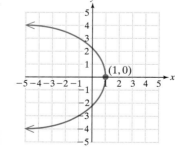

For Exercises 9–14, use the vertical line test to determine whether the relation defines *y* as a function of *x*.

9.

10.

11.

12.

13.

14.

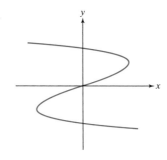

Consider the functions defined by $f(x) = 6x - 2$, $g(x) = x^2$, and $h(x) = 7$. For Exercises 15–46, find the function values.

15. $f(2)$	16. $g(2)$
17. $h(2)$	18. $f(0)$
19. $g(0)$	20. $h(0)$
21. $f(t)$	22. $g(a)$
23. $h(b)$	24. $f(x + k)$
25. $g(x + k)$	26. $h(x + k)$
27. $f(a + 1)$	28. $g(a + 1)$
29. $h(a + 1)$	30. $(f \circ g)(-3)$
31. $(g \circ f)(-3)$	32. $(h \circ g)(1)$
33. $(f \circ h)(2)$	34. $g(h(2))$
35. $g(f(0))$	36. $f(-1) + g(-1)$
37. $f(2) - h(0)$	38. $g(0) - f(2)$
39. $g(3) + h(6)$	40. $f(-3) \cdot h(1)$
41. $g(3) \cdot h(3)$	42. $h(-4) \cdot f(-3)$

43. $f(0) \cdot g(0)$

44. $\dfrac{f(5)}{h(-2)}$

45. $\dfrac{g(2)}{f(1)}$

46. $\dfrac{g(0)}{h(0)}$

For Exercises 47–60, let $f(x) = \frac{2}{3}$, $g(x) = x - 6$, $h(x) = -4x + 1$, and $k(x) = x^2 - 3$. Find

47. $(h + g)(x)$

48. $(g - h)(x)$

49. $(k - f)(x)$

50. $(f + g)(x)$

51. $(f \cdot g)(x)$

52. $(h \cdot f)(x)$

53. $\left(\dfrac{h}{k}\right)(x)$

54. $\left(\dfrac{k}{g}\right)(x)$

55. $(g \circ h)(x)$

56. $(h \circ g)(x)$

57. $(g \circ f)(x)$

58. $(k \circ f)(x)$

59. $(g \circ k)(x)$

60. $(h \circ k)(x)$

Consider the functions $p = \{(\frac{1}{2}, 6), (2, -7), (1, 0), (3, 2\pi)\}$ and $q = \{(6, 4), (2, -5), (\frac{3}{4}, \frac{1}{5}), (0, 9)\}$. For Exercises 61–76, find the function values.

61. $p(2)$

62. $p(1)$

63. $p(3)$

64. $p\left(\dfrac{1}{2}\right)$

65. $q(2)$

66. $q\left(\dfrac{3}{4}\right)$

67. $p\left(\dfrac{1}{2}\right) + q(0)$

68. $q\left(\dfrac{3}{4}\right) - p(2)$

69. $q(2) - p(1)$

70. $p(3) + q(6)$

71. $(q \circ p)\left(\dfrac{1}{2}\right)$

72. $(q \circ p)(1)$

73. $p(2) \cdot q(0)$

74. $p(1) \cdot q\left(\dfrac{3}{4}\right)$

75. $\dfrac{p(1)}{q(0)}$

76. $\dfrac{p(3)}{q(6)}$

77. The graph of $y = f(x)$ is shown below.

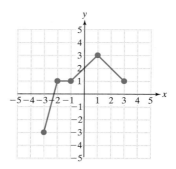

a. Evaluate $f(0)$.
b. Evaluate $f(3)$.
c. Evaluate $f(-2)$.
d. For what value(s) of x is $f(x) = -3$?
e. For what value(s) of x is $f(x) = 3$?

78. The graph of $y = g(x)$ is shown below.

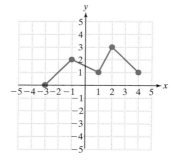

a. Evaluate $g(-1)$.
b. Evaluate $g(1)$.
c. Evaluate $g(4)$.
d. For what value(s) of x is $g(x) = 3$?
e. For what value(s) of x is $g(x) = 0$?

79. Explain how to determine the domain of the function defined by

$$f(x) = \frac{x + 6}{x - 2}$$

For Exercises 80–85, find the domain. Write the answers in interval notation.

80. $k(x) = \dfrac{x - 3}{x + 6}$

81. $m(x) = \dfrac{x - 1}{x - 4}$

82. $f(t) = \dfrac{5}{t}$

83. $g(t) = \dfrac{t - 7}{t}$

84. $h(p) = \dfrac{p - 4}{p^2 + 1}$

85. $n(p) = \dfrac{p + 8}{p^2 + 2}$

86. Explain how to determine the domain of the function defined by $g(x) = \sqrt{x - 3}$.

For Exercises 87–92, find the domain. Write the answers in interval notation.

87. $h(t) = \sqrt{t + 7}$

88. $k(t) = \sqrt{t - 5}$

89. $f(a) = \sqrt{a - 3}$

90. $g(a) = \sqrt{a + 2}$

91. $m(x) = \sqrt{2x + 1}$

92. $n(x) = \sqrt{6x - 12}$

93. Explain how to determine the domain of the function defined by $h(x) = 2x^2 + 3$.

For Exercises 94–97, find the domain. Write the answers in interval notation.

94. $p(t) = 2t^2 + t - 1$

95. $q(t) = t^3 + t - 1$

96. $f(x) = x + 6$

97. $g(x) = 8x - \pi$

98. The height of a ball that is dropped from an 80-ft building is given by $h(t) = -16t^2 + 80$, where t is time in seconds.

  a. Find $h(1)$ and $h(1.5)$

  b. Interpret the meaning of the function values found in part (a).

99. A ball is dropped from a 50-m building. The height after t seconds is given by $h(t) = -4.9t^2 + 50$.

  a. Find $h(1)$ and $h(1.5)$.

  b. Interpret the meaning of the function values found in part (a).

100. If Alicia rides a bike at an average of 11.5 mph, the distance that she rides can be represented by $d(t) = 11.5t$, where t is the time in hours.

  a. Find $d(1)$ and $d(1.5)$.

  b. Interpret the meaning of the function values found in part (a).

101. If Miguel walks at an average of 5.9 km/h, the distance that he walks can be represented by $d(t) = 5.9t$, where t is the time in hours.

  a. Find $d(1)$ and $d(2)$.

  b. Interpret the meaning of the function values found in part (a).

102. Brian's score on an exam is a function of the number of hours he spends studying. The function defined by $P(x) = (100x^2)/(50 + x^2)$ $(x \geq 0)$ indicates that he will achieve a score of $P\%$ if he studies for x hours.

  a. Evaluate $P(0)$, $P(5)$, $P(10)$, $P(15)$, $P(20)$, and $P(25)$. (Round to one decimal place.) Interpret the results in the context of this problem.

  b. Match the function values found in part (a) with the points A, B, C, D, E, and F on the graph.

Student Score (Percent) as a Function of Study Time

Figure for Exercise 102

103. The function P approximates the percentage of the population that reads the newspaper as a function of annual income, x.

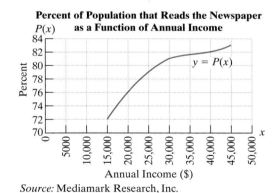

Percent of Population that Reads the Newspaper as a Function of Annual Income

Source: Mediamark Research, Inc.

Figure for Exercise 103

Use the graph to answer the questions.

  a. What is the domain of P?

  b. From the graph, approximate $P(20,000)$, $P(30,000)$, and $P(40,000)$. Interpret the results in the context of this problem.

104. The number of households that own a television and have cable service is shown in the following graph as a function of the year between 1970 and 1996. Let the $N(t)$ represent the number of households in millions and let t represent the year.

The Number of TV Households that Have Cable Television (1970–1996)

Figure for Exercise 104

Source: Mediamark Research, Inc.

a. From the graph, approximate $N(1976)$, $N(1980)$, and $N(1992)$. Interpret the results in the context of the problem.

b. To the nearest year, approximate the year when $N(t) = 20$.

c. To the nearest year, approximate the year when $N(t) = 50$.

105. The average number of visits to office-based physicians depends on the age of the patient according to

$N(a) = 0.0014a^2 - 0.0658a + 2.65$

where a is a patient's age in years and $N(a)$ is the average number of doctor visits per year.

a. Evaluate $N(1)$, $N(20)$, $N(40)$, and $N(75)$. (Round to one decimal place.) Interpret the results in the context of this problem.

b. Locate the function values from part (a) on the graph shown on the top right.

c. Based on the graph, approximately what age corresponds to the fewest doctor visits per year?

Average Number of Visits to a Doctor's Office per Year Based on Age of Patient

Source: U.S. National Center for Health Statistics.

Figure for Exercise 105

■ EXPANDING YOUR SKILLS

For Exercises 106–109, find the domain. Write the answers in interval notation.

106. $f(x) = \dfrac{x + 1}{3x + 1}$

107. $g(x) = \dfrac{x - 5}{6x - 2}$

108. $q(x) = \dfrac{2}{\sqrt{x + 2}}$

109. $p(x) = \dfrac{8}{\sqrt{x - 4}}$

■ GRAPHING CALCULATOR EXERCISES

110. Graph $h(t) = \sqrt{t + 7}$. Use the graph to confirm the domain found in Exercise 87.

111. Graph $k(t) = \sqrt{t - 5}$. Use the graph to confirm the domain found in Exercise 88.

112. Graph $p(t) = 2t^2 + t - 1$. Use the graph to confirm the domain found in Exercise 94.

113. Graph $q(t) = t^3 + t - 1$. Use the graph to confirm the domain found in Exercise 95.

114. a. Graph $h(t) = -16t^2 + 80$ on a viewing window defined by $0 \le t \le 2$ and $0 \le y \le 100$.

b. Use the graph to approximate the function at $t = 1$ and $t = 1.5$. Use these values to support your answer to Exercise 98

115. a. Graph $h(t) = -4.9t^2 + 50$ on a viewing window defined by $0 \le t \le 3$ and $0 \le y \le 60$.

b. Use the graph to approximate the function at $t = 1$ and $t = 1.5$. Use these values to support your answer to Exercise 99.

section

4.3   GRAPHS OF BASIC FUNCTIONS

1.   Linear and Constant Functions

A function may be expressed as a mathematical equation that relates two or more variables. In this section, we will look at several elementary functions.

We know from Section 2.1 that an equation in the form $y = k$ is a horizontal line. In function notation, this can be written as $f(x) = k$. For example, the function defined by $f(x) = 3$ is a horizontal line as shown in Figure 4-9.

We say that a function defined by $f(x) = k$ is a **constant function** because for any value of x, the function value is constant.

An equation of the form $y = mx + b$ is represented graphically by a line with slope, m, and y-intercept $(0, b)$. In function notation, this may be written as $f(x) = mx + b$. A function in this form is called a linear function. For example, the function defined by $f(x) = 2x - 3$ is a linear function with slope $m = 2$ and y-intercept $(0, -3)$ (Figure 4-10).

Figure 4-9

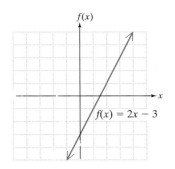

Figure 4-10

Definition of a Linear Function

Let m and b represent real numbers; then,

A function that can be written in the form $f(x) = mx + b$ is a **linear function**.
A function that can be written in the form $f(x) = b$ is a constant (linear) function.

---

2.   Applications of Linear Functions

example 1   **Solving an Application Involving a Linear Function**

The number of students receiving financial aid at a certain community college in the Midwest has grown between 1970 and 1998 according to

$$N(x) = 58x + 2050 \quad 0 \le x \le 28$$

For this function x represents the number of years since 1970 ($x = 0$ corresponds to 1970, $x = 1$ corresponds to 1971, and so on).

a.   Is this function linear or nonlinear?
b.   Find $N(0)$. Interpret the meaning of $N(0)$ in the context of this problem.
c.   Find $N(20)$. Interpret the meaning of $N(20)$ in the context of this problem.
d.   Find the year in which 2804 students received financial aid.

Solution:

a.   The function $N(x) = 58x + 2050$ is linear, with $m = 58$ and $b = 2050$. The slope is 58 and the y-intercept is $(0, 2050)$.

b.
$$N(0) = 58(0) + 2050$$
$$= 2050$$

Substitute $x = 0$.
This value indicates that in the year $x = 0$ (1970), 2050 students received financial aid.

c.
$$N(20) = 58(20) + 2050$$
$$= 1160 + 2050$$
$$= 3210$$

Substitute $x = 20$.

This value indicates that in the year $x = 20$ (1990), 3210 students received financial aid.

d.
$$N(x) = 58x + 2050$$
$$2804 = 58x + 2050$$
$$2804 - 2050 = 58x$$
$$754 = 58x$$
$$\frac{754}{58} = \frac{58x}{58}$$
$$x = 13$$

Substitute $N(x) = 2804$.

In the year $x = 13$ (1983), 2804 students received financial aid.

The answers to Example 1 can be confirmed from the graph of $N(x) = 58x + 2050$ (Figure 4-11).

The Number of Students on Financial Aid for a Selected Community College, 1970–1998

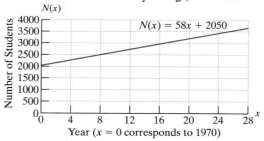

Year ($x = 0$ corresponds to 1970)

Figure 4-11

3. Graphs of Basic Functions

At this point, we are able to recognize the equations and graphs of linear and constant functions. In addition to linear and constant functions, the following equations define six basic functions that will be encountered in the study of algebra:

Equation		Function Notation
$y = x$		$f(x) = x$
$y = x^2$	equivalent function notation	$f(x) = x^2$
$y = x^3$	$\longrightarrow$	$f(x) = x^3$
$y = |x|$		$f(x) = |x|$
$y = \sqrt{x}$		$f(x) = \sqrt{x}$
$y = \dfrac{1}{x}$		$f(x) = \dfrac{1}{x}$

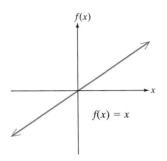

Figure 4-12

The graph of the function defined by $f(x) = x$ is linear, with slope $m = 1$, and y-intercept $(0, 0)$ (Figure 4-12).

To determine the shapes of the other basic functions, we can plot several points to establish the pattern of the graph. Analyzing the equation itself may also provide insight to the domain, range, and shape of the function. To demonstrate this, we will graph $f(x) = x^2$ and $g(x) = \frac{1}{x}$. The remaining functions in this list are left to the reader to graph in the homework exercises.

example 2

Graphing Basic Functions

Graph the functions defined by

a. $f(x) = x^2$

b. $g(x) = \dfrac{1}{x}$

Solution:

a.   The domain of the function given by $f(x) = x^2$ (or equivalently $y = x^2$) is all real numbers.

To graph the function, choose arbitrary values of x within the domain of the function. Be sure to choose values of x that are positive and values that are negative to determine the behavior of the function to the right and left of the origin (Table 4-5). The graph of $f(x) = x^2$ is shown in Figure 4-13. The function values are equated to the square of x, so $f(x)$ will always be greater than or equal to zero. Hence, the y-coordinates on the graph will never be negative. The range of the function is $\{y \mid y \geq 0\}$. The arrows on each branch of the graph imply that the pattern continues indefinitely.

Table 4-5	
x	$f(x) = x^2$
0	0
1	1
2	4
3	9
−1	1
−2	4
−3	9

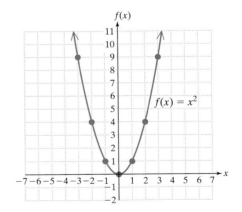

Figure 4-13

b. $g(x) = \dfrac{1}{x}$ Notice that $x = 0$ is not part of the domain of the function. From the equation $y = \frac{1}{x}$, the y-values will be the reciprocal of the x-values. The graph defined by $g(x) = \frac{1}{x}$ is shown in Figure 4-14.

x	$g(x) = \dfrac{1}{x}$
1	1
2	$\dfrac{1}{2}$
3	$\dfrac{1}{3}$
-1	-1
-2	$-\dfrac{1}{2}$
-3	$-\dfrac{1}{3}$

x	$g(x) = \dfrac{1}{x}$
$\dfrac{1}{2}$	2
$\dfrac{1}{3}$	3
$\dfrac{1}{4}$	4
$-\dfrac{1}{2}$	-2
$-\dfrac{1}{3}$	-3
$-\dfrac{1}{4}$	-4

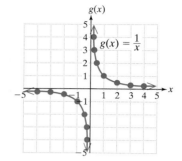

Figure 4-14

Notice that as x approaches ∞ and $-\infty$, the y-values approach zero, and the graph approaches the x-axis. In this case, the x-axis is called a **horizontal asymptote**. Similarly, the graph of the function approaches the y-axis as x gets close to zero. In this case, the y-axis is called a **vertical asymptote**.

Graphing Calculator Box

The graphs of the functions defined by $f(x) = x^2$ and $g(x) = \frac{1}{x}$ are shown in the following calculator displays.

Summary of Six Basic Functions and Their Graphs

Function	Graph	Domain and Range
1. $f(x) = x$		Domain $(-\infty, \infty)$ Range $(-\infty, \infty)$
2. $f(x) = x^2$		Domain $(-\infty, \infty)$ Range $[0, \infty)$
3. $f(x) = x^3$		Domain $(-\infty, \infty)$ Range $(-\infty, \infty)$
4. $f(x) = |x|$		Domain $(-\infty, \infty)$ Range $[0, \infty)$
5. $f(x) = \sqrt{x}$		Domain $[0, \infty)$ Range $[0, \infty)$
6. $f(x) = \dfrac{1}{x}$		Domain $(-\infty, 0) \cup (0, \infty)$ Range $(-\infty, 0) \cup (0, \infty)$

The shapes of these six graphs will be developed in the homework exercises. These functions will be used often in the study of algebra. We therefore recommend that you associate an equation with its graph and commit each to memory.

4. Finding the *x*- and *y*-Intercepts of a Function Defined by $y = f(x)$

In Section 2.1, we learned that to find the *x*-intercept of an equation, we substitute $y = 0$ and solve for *x*. Using function notation, this is equivalent to finding the real solutions of the equation $f(x) = 0$. To find the *y*-intercept of an equation, substitute $x = 0$ and solve for *y*. Using function notation, this is equivalent to finding $f(0)$.

Finding the *x*- and *y*-Intercepts of a Function

Given a function defined by $y = f(x)$,

1. The **x-intercepts** are the real solutions to the equation $f(x) = 0$.
2. The **y-intercept** is given by $f(0)$.

---

example 3

Finding the *x*- and *y*-Intercepts of a Function

Given the function defined by $f(x) = 2x - 4$,

a. Find the *x*-intercept(s).
b. Find the *y*-intercept.
c. Graph the function.

Solution:

a. To find the *x*-intercept(s), find the real solutions to the equation $f(x) = 0$.

$$f(x) = 2x - 4$$

$$0 = 2x - 4 \qquad \text{Substitute } f(x) = 0.$$

$$4 = 2x$$

$$2 = x \qquad \text{The } x\text{-intercept is } (2, 0).$$

b. To find the *y*-intercept, evaluate $f(0)$.

$$f(0) = 2(0) - 4 \qquad \text{Substitute } x = 0.$$

$$f(0) = -4 \qquad \text{The } y\text{-intercept is } (0, -4).$$

c. This function is linear, with a *y*-intercept of $(0, -4)$, an *x*-intercept of $(2, 0)$, and a slope of 2 (Figure 4-15).

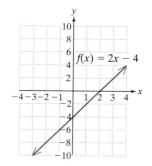

Figure 4-15

example 4

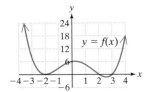

Figure 4-16

Finding the *x*- and *y*-Intercepts of a Function

For the function pictured in Figure 4-16 find

a. The real values of *x* for which $f(x) = 0$.
b. The value of $f(0)$.

Solution:

a. The real values of *x* for which $f(x) = 0$ are the *x*-intercepts of the function. For this graph, the *x*-intercepts are located at $x = -2$, $x = 2$, and $x = 3$.
b. The value of $f(0)$ is the value of *y* at $x = 0$. That is, $f(0)$ is the *y*-intercept. $f(0) = 6$.

example 5

Finding the *x*- and *y*-Intercepts of a Function

For the function pictured in Figure 4-17, find

a. The real values of *x* for which $f(x) = 0$.
b. The value of $f(0)$.

Solution:

a. There are no *x*-intercepts for this graph; therefore, there are no real values of *x* for which $f(x) = 0$.
b. From the graph, the value of $f(0)$ is 3.

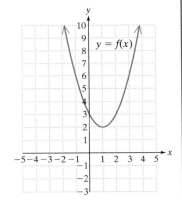

Figure 4-17

5. Equations of Functions and Nonfunctions

We have seen several equations that represent *y* as a function of *x*. In each case, notice the *y*-variable is expressed in terms of *x*, and for every *x* in the domain, there is only one *y*-value produced by the equation. Some equations, however, do not represent *y* as a function of *x*.

example 6

Determining Whether an Equation Represents a Function

Determine whether the following equations represent *y* as a function of *x*.

a. $x = |y|$ b. $y = x^3 - 4$ c. $y = \pm\sqrt{x}$

Solution:

a. $x = |y|$

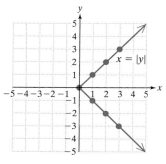

Figure 4-18

We know that $y = |x|$ is a function. Its graph is a **V** shape opening up with the vertex at the origin. In this example, however, the x- and y-variables have been interchanged. To determine if this is a function, we ask the question, "For any arbitrary value of x, will there be exactly one corresponding y-value?"

If $x = 1$, we have $\qquad x = |y|$

$$1 = |y|$$

$$y = 1 \qquad \text{or} \qquad y = -1$$

Because two values of y correspond to $x = 1$, this equation is not a function.

We can graph the equation $x = |y|$ by plotting several solutions to the equation. By the vertical line test, this relation is not a function (Figure 4-18).

b. $y = x^3 - 4$

For any value of x, the cube of x is unique. Therefore, only one y-value corresponds to a given value of x. The equation is a function.

The graph of $y = x^3 - 4$ is shown in Figure 4-19. By the vertical line test, this relation is a function.

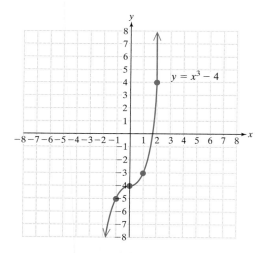

Figure 4-19

c. $y = \pm\sqrt{x}$

The symbol, $\pm$ is read as "plus or minus." Therefore, $y = \pm\sqrt{x}$ is read as "y equals plus or minus the square root of x." For any value of $x > 0$, there will be two corresponding values of y. For example, if $x = 4$, then we have:

$$y = \pm\sqrt{x}$$
$$= \pm\sqrt{4}$$
$$= \pm 2$$

Because two values of y correspond to $x = 4$, this equation is not a function. The graph of $y = \pm\sqrt{x}$ is shown in Figure 4-20. By the vertical line test, this relation is not a function.

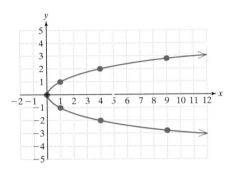

Figure 4-20

section 4.3   PRACTICE EXERCISES

1. For $g = \{(6, 1), (5, 2), (4, 3), (3, 4), (2, 5), (1, 6)\}$
   a. Is this relation a function?
   b. List the elements of the domain.
   c. List the elements of the range.

2. For $f = \{(7, 3), (2, 3), (-5, 3), (9, 3)\}$
   a. Is this relation a function?
   b. List the elements of the domain.
   c. List the elements of the range.

Consider $k(x) = x^2 - 2$. For Exercises 3–10, find the function values.

3. $k(0)$

4. $k(6)$

5. $k(a)$

6. $k(a + 2)$

7. $k(-2)$

8. $k(2)$

9. $k(b)$

10. $k(b - 1)$

For Exercises 11–14, write the domain in interval notation.

11. $f(x) = x - 6$

12. $g(x) = \dfrac{x + 2}{x - 6}$

13. $h(x) = \sqrt{x - 6}$

14. $k(x) = x^2 - 6$

15. The force (measured in pounds) to stretch a certain spring x inches is given by $f(x) = 3x$.
   a. Evaluate $f(3)$ and interpret the results in the context of the problem.
   b. Evaluate $f(0)$ and interpret the results in the context of the problem.

16. The acceleration (measured in feet per second squared) of a falling object is given by $A(x) = 32$, where x is the number of seconds after the object was released.

    a. Evaluate $A(1)$ and interpret the results in the context of the problem.

    b. Evaluate $A(4)$ and interpret the results in the context of the problem.

For Exercises 17–22, sketch a graph by completing the table and plotting the points.

17. $g(x) = |x|$

x	$g(x)$
-2	
-1	
0	
1	
2	

18. $f(x) = \dfrac{1}{x}$

x	$f(x)$
-2	
-1	
$-\dfrac{1}{2}$	
$-\dfrac{1}{4}$	
$\dfrac{1}{4}$	
$\dfrac{1}{2}$	
1	
2	

19. $h(x) = x^3$

x	$h(x)$
-2	
-1	
0	
1	
2	

20. $k(x) = x$

x	$k(x)$
-2	
-1	
0	
1	
2	

21. $p(x) = \sqrt{x}$

x	$p(x)$
0	
1	
4	
9	
16	

22. $q(x) = x^2$

x	$q(x)$
-2	
-1	
0	
1	
2	

23. For $f(x) = \sqrt{x + 4}$

    a. Write the domain of f in interval notation.

    b. Find $f(0), f(2), f(-2)$.

24. For $g(x) = \sqrt{x - 3}$

    a. Write the domain of g in interval notation.

    b. Find $g(4), g(8), g(3)$.

25. For $h(x) = -x^2 + 2$

    a. Write the domain of h in interval notation.

    b. Find $h(1), h(-1), h(0)$.

26. For $k(x) = x^2 + 2$

    a. Write the domain of k in interval notation.

    b. Find $k(2), k(-2), k(0)$.

27. For $p(x) = \dfrac{2}{x-3}$

    a. Write the domain of p in interval notation.

    b. Find $p(0), p(1), p(2), p(4), p(5), p(6)$.

28. For $q(x) = \dfrac{3}{x-2}$

    a. Write the domain of q in interval notation.

    b. Find $q(-1), q(0), q(1), q(3), q(4), q(5)$.

For Exercises 29–34, use the graph of the function to determine the x- and y-intercepts (if they exist).

29. $g(x) = x^3 + 1$

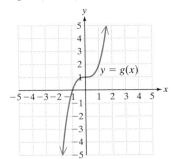

30. $h(x) = x^3 - 1$

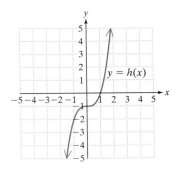

31. $f(x) = |x| - 2$

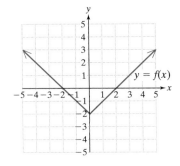

32. $P(x) = |x| + 1$

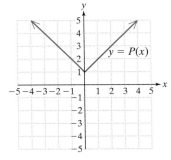

33. $r(x) = x^2 + 2$

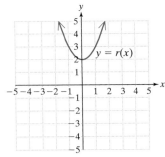

34. $q(x) = -x^2 + 1$

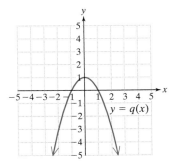

35. a. Sketch the relation $y = x^2$ from memory.

b. Does $y = x^2$ define y as a function of x? Why or why not?

c. Sketch the relation $x = y^2$ by completing the table and plotting the points.

x	y
	-2
	-1
	0
	1
	2

d. Does $x = y^2$ define y as a function of x? Why or why not?

36. a. Sketch the relation $y = |x|$ from memory.

b. Does $y = |x|$ define y as a function of x? Why or why not?

c. Sketch the relation $x = |y|$ by completing the table and plotting the points.

x	y
	-2
	-1
	0
	1
	2

d. Does $x = |y|$ define y as a function of x? Why or why not?

For Exercises 37–46,

a. Identify the domain of the function.

b. Identify the y-intercept of the function.

c. Match the function with its graph by recognizing the basic shape of the function and using the results from parts (a) and (b). Plot additional points if necessary.

37. $q(x) = 2x^2$

38. $p(x) = -2x^2 + 1$

39. $h(x) = x^3 + 1$ **40.** $k(x) = x^3 - 2$

41. $r(x) = \sqrt{x + 1}$ **42.** $s(x) = \sqrt{x + 4}$

43. $f(x) = \dfrac{1}{x - 3}$ **44.** $g(x) = \dfrac{1}{x + 1}$

45. $k(x) = |x + 2|$

46. $h(x) = |x - 1| + 2$

i.

ii.

iii.

iv.

v.

vi.

vii.

viii.

ix.

x.
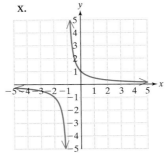

EXPANDING YOUR SKILLS

For Exercises 47–52, sketch parts (a) and (b) on the same coordinate axes.

47. a. $h(x) = x$
    b. $k(x) = 2x$

48. a. $h(x) = x^2$
    b. $k(x) = 2x^2$

49. a. $h(x) = |x|$
    b. $k(x) = 2|x|$

50. a. $h(x) = \sqrt{x}$
    b. $k(x) = 2\sqrt{x}$

51. a. $h(x) = x^3$
    b. $k(x) = 2x^3$

52. a. $h(x) = \dfrac{1}{x}$
    b. $k(x) = \dfrac{2}{x}$

53. Based on Exercises 47–52, explain the difference between the graph of $y = h(x)$ and $y = 2h(x)$.

▨ GRAPHING CALCULATOR EXERCISES

54. Repeat Exercise 23b using a *Table* feature of your graphing calculator.

55. Repeat Exercise 24b using a *Table* feature of your graphing calculator.

56. Repeat Exercise 25b using a *Table* feature of your graphing calculator.

57. Repeat Exercise 26b using a *Table* feature of your graphing calculator.

58. Repeat Exercise 27b using a *Table* feature of your graphing calculator.

59. Repeat Exercise 28b using a *Table* feature of your graphing calculator.

---

chapter 4   MIDCHAPTER REVIEW

For Exercises 1–6, list the domain and range of each relation. Then determine if the relation defines y as a function of x.

1.

State x	Percent Change in Population Since 1990 y
Colorado	16
Rhode Island	−1.3
Kentucky	5.3
Alabama	5.8

2.
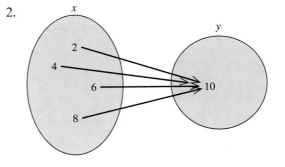

3.

x	y
1	1
-1	-1
2	8
-2	-8
0	0

4.

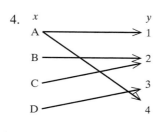

5. $\{(13, 6), (8, 2), (-6, 4\pi), (\sqrt{2}, 1), (13, 2)\}$

6. $\{(0.1, -6.4), (0.1, 9.0), (0.1, -2.7), (0.1, 3.0)\}$

For Exercises 7–10, use the vertical line test to determine if the relation defines y as a function of x.

7.

8.

9.

10.

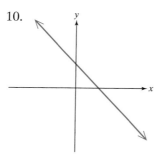

11. Let $g(x) = -6x + 1$

    a. Find $g(3)$, $g(0)$, $g\left(\frac{1}{2}\right)$, $g\left(-\frac{1}{3}\right)$, $g(-2)$.

    b. Write the domain of g in interval notation.

12. Let $f(x) = \dfrac{1}{x - 5}$

    a. Find $f(0)$, $f(2)$, $f(4)$, $f(4\frac{1}{2})$, $f(5\frac{1}{2})$, $f(6)$, $f(8)$.

    b. Write the domain of f in interval notation.

13. Let $p(x) = \sqrt{x + 1}$

    a. Find $p(-1)$, $p(0)$, $p(3)$, $p(5)$.

    b. Write the domain of p in interval notation.

14. Let $k(x) = |3 - x| + 1$

    a. Find $k(0)$, $k(1)$, $k(2)$, $k(3)$, $k(4)$, $k(5)$.

    b. Write the domain of k in interval notation.

For Exercises 15–20, graph the function from memory.

15. $y = x^2$

16. $y = |x|$

17. $y = \sqrt{x}$

18. $y = \dfrac{1}{x}$

19. $y = x$

20. $y = x^3$

section

4.4   ADDITIONAL TOPICS ON FUNCTIONS

1.   Increasing and Decreasing Functions

The function shown in Figure 4-21 represents the average cost of a gallon of gasoline in the United States from 1976 to 1993.

Notice that between the years 1976 and 1981 and between 1988 and 1990, gasoline prices increased. We say that the function is *increasing* on the intervals (1976, 1981) and (1988, 1990).

Figure 4-21

Source: American Petroleum Institute.

Between the years 1981 and 1986 and between 1990 and 1993, gasoline prices decreased. We say that the function is *decreasing* on the intervals (1981, 1986) and (1990, 1993).

Between the years 1986 and 1988, the cost of gasoline remained relatively constant. We say that the function is *constant* on the interval (1986, 1988).

In many applications, it is important to note the open intervals where a function is increasing, decreasing, or constant. An open interval is an interval on the real number line that is not bounded by an endpoint.

Intervals Over Which a Function Is Increasing, Decreasing, or Constant

Let I be an open interval in the domain of a function f. Then,

1. f is **increasing** on I if $f(a) < f(b)$ for all $a < b$ on I.
2. f is **decreasing** on I if $f(a) > f(b)$ for all $a < b$ on I.
3. f is **constant** on I if $f(a) = f(b)$ for all a and b on I.

Tip:

- A function is *increasing* on an interval if it goes "uphill" from left to right.
- A function is *decreasing* on an interval if it goes "downhill" from left to right.
- A function is *constant* on an interval if it is "level" or "flat."

2.   Determining Where a Function Is Increasing, Decreasing, or Constant

example 1

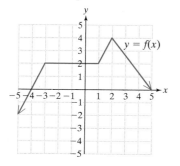

Figure 4-22

Tip: The intervals over which a function given by $y = f(x)$ is increasing, decreasing, or constant are always expressed in terms of x.

Determining Where a Function Is Increasing, Decreasing, or Constant

For the function pictured in Figure 4-22. determine the open interval(s) for which the function is

a.   increasing   b.   decreasing   c.   constant

Solution:

a.   A function is increasing on an interval if the y-values increase from left to right (the function goes uphill). This function is increasing on the intervals $(-\infty, -3)$ and $(1, 2)$.

b.   A function is decreasing on an interval if the y-values decrease from left to right (the function goes downhill). This function is decreasing on the interval $(2, \infty)$.

c.   A function is constant on an interval if the y-values remain unchanged (the function is level). This function is constant on the interval $(-3, 1)$.

■

example 2

Comparing Two Functions

Figure 4-23 depicts the number of bachelor's degrees earned by males and by females between 1971 and 1998.

Figure 4-23

Let $x = 0$ correspond to the year 1971. Then for $0 \le x \le 27$, the values of $M(x)$ and $F(x)$ approximate the number of bachelor's degrees earned by males and females, respectively.

a.   On what interval is $M(x) > F(x)$?
b.   On what interval is $M(x) < F(x)$?
c.   At what point is $M(x) = F(x)$?

Solution:

a. From the graph, we want to determine the interval(s) on the *x*-axis for which the *y*-values of *M* exceed the *y*-values of *F*.

$$M(x) > F(x) \text{ on the interval } [0, 11]$$

The number of bachelor's degrees earned by men exceeded the number earned by women from 1971 to 1982.

b. From the graph, we want to determine the interval(s) on the *x*-axis for which the *y*-values of *M* are less than the *y*-values of *F*.

$$M(x) < F(x) \text{ on the interval } (11, 27]$$

Men earned fewer bachelor's degrees than women from 1982 through 1998.

c. $M(x) = F(x)$ at $x = 11$

The number of bachelor's degrees earned by men and women was approximately the same in 1982.

3. Piecewise-Defined Functions

Sometimes a function may be defined by more than one rule on different intervals within the domain of the function. Such a function is called a **piecewise-defined function**. For example,

$$k(x) = \begin{cases} 4 & \text{if} & x \le -2 \\ x^2 & \text{if} & -2 < x \le 1 \\ x + 2 & \text{if} & x > 1 \end{cases} \quad \text{is pictured in Figure 4-24}$$

- For *x*-values less than or equal to -2, the function is constant and follows the first rule, $k(x) = 4$ (pictured in red).
- For *x*-values greater than -2 and less than or equal to 1, the function follows the second rule, $k(x) = x^2$ (pictured in blue).
- For *x*-values greater than 1, the function follows the third rule, $k(x) = x + 2$ (pictured in black).

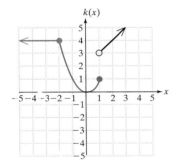

$k(x)$

Figure 4-24

Tip: The open dot indicates that the point $(1, 3)$ is *not* included in the graph.

4. Evaluating a Piecewise-Defined Function

example 3

Interpreting a Piecewise-Defined Function

For the function defined by

$$k(x) = \begin{cases} 4 & \text{if} & x \le -2 \\ x^2 & \text{if} & -2 < x \le 1 \\ x + 2 & \text{if} & x > 1 \end{cases} \quad \text{evaluate the function values:}$$

a. $k(0)$ b. $k(-3)$ c. $k(5)$ d. $k(1)$ e. $k(-2)$

Solution:

To evaluate a piecewise-defined function, the value of *x* determines which rule to use in the function.

a. $k(0)$. Because $x = 0$ is on the interval $-2 < x \le 1$, use the *second rule* to evaluate the function.

$$k(x) = x^2 \quad \text{for } -2 < x \le 1$$

$$k(0) = (0)^2$$

$$= 0$$

b. $k(-3)$. Because $x = -3$ is on the interval $x \le -2$, use the *first rule* to evaluate the function.

$$k(x) = 4 \quad \text{for } x \le -2$$

$$k(-3) = 4$$

c. $k(5)$. Because $x = 5$ is on the interval $x > 1$, use the *third rule* to evaluate the function.

$$k(x) = x + 2 \quad \text{for } x > 1$$

$$k(5) = 5 + 2$$

$$= 7$$

d. $k(1)$. Because $x = 1$ is on the interval $-2 < x \le 1$ use the *second rule*. (*Note:* $x = 1$ is *not* included on the interval $x > 1$)

$$k(x) = x^2$$

$$k(1) = (1)^2$$

$$= 1$$

e. $k(-2)$.   Because $x = -2$ is on the interval $x \le -2$, use the *first rule*. (*Note:* $x = -2$ is *not* included on the interval $-2 < x \le 1$)

$$k(-2) = 4$$

5.   Graphing a Piecewise-Defined Function

example 4

Graphing a Piecewise-Defined Function

A taxi company in New York City charges the following fee schedule during daylight hours:

$2.00 for the first mile

$1.50 for each mile after the first mile.

(*Note:* Prices do not include waiting time)

The function may be defined piecewise as

$$f(x) = \begin{cases} 2.00 & \text{if } 0 \le x \le 1 \\ 2.00 + 1.50(x-1) & \text{if } x > 1 \end{cases}$$

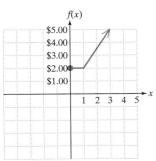

Figure 4-25

a. Graph the function.
b. Find $f(7)$ and interpret the meaning of this function value in the context of this problem.

Solution:

a. To graph a piecewise-defined function, graph each component function, showing only the portion of that function over the indicated domain.

$f(x) = 2.00$ is constant on the interval, $0 \leq x \leq 1$.

$f(x) = 2.00 + 1.50(x - 1)$ or
$f(x) = 1.50x + 0.50$

$f(x)$ is linear on the interval $x > 1$.

To graph the entire function, f, superimpose each component on the same graph (Figure 4-25).

b. $f(x) = 1.50x + 0.50$ Because $x = 7$ is on the interval $x > 0$, use the *second* rule.

$f(7) = 1.50(7) + 0.50$
$= 10.50 + 0.50$
$= 11.00$ A taxi ride of 7 miles will cost $11.00.

Graphing Calculator Box

One way to graph a piecewise-defined function on a graphing calculator is to graph each "piece" of the graph over its designated domain. For example, the function from Example 4 may be entered into the calculator as follows.

$$f(x) = \begin{cases} 2.00 & \text{if} \quad 0 \leq x \leq 1 \\ 2.00 + 1.50(x - 1) & \text{if} \quad x > 1 \end{cases}$$

The calculator will graph the function
$Y_1 = 2.00*(x \geq 0)*(x \leq 1)$ only for values of x greater than or equal to zero and less than or equal to 1.

The calculator will graph the function
$Y_2 = (2.00 + 1.50(x - 1))*(x > 1)$ only for values of x greater than 1.

Most calculators have an option to graph a function in a *Dot* mode or in a *Connected* mode. To view an image of a piecewise-defined function, it is recommended that you use *Dot* mode.

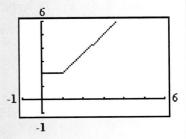

---

section 4.4   PRACTICE EXERCISES

For Exercises 1–4, write the domain of each function in interval notation.

1. $h(x) = \dfrac{6}{x + 5}$

2. $g(x) = \sqrt{x - 3}$

3. $f(x) = x^2 + 4$

4. $k(x) = x^3 - 7$

Consider $q(x) = x^2 + 3x$ and $p(x) = 3/(x - 1)$. For Exercises 5–16, find the function values.

5. $q(2)$

6. $q(-1)$

7. $p(0)$

8. $p(4)$

9. $\dfrac{q(-2)}{p(-2)}$

10. $\dfrac{q(0)}{p(2)}$

11. $q(2) + p(2)$

12. $q(-2) - p(-1)$

13. $q(1) \cdot p(3)$

14. $q(0) \cdot p(0)$

15. $q(p(4))$

16. $p(q(2))$

For Exercises 17–22, sketch the functions from memory. Then determine the open intervals where the function is increasing or decreasing.

17. $f(x) = |x|$

18. $g(x) = x$

19. $k(x) = x^3$

20. $h(x) = \sqrt{x}$

21. $q(x) = \dfrac{1}{x}$

22. $p(x) = x^2$

23. The following graph depicts the number of reported tuberculosis cases in the United States between 1976 and 1996.

Number of Reported Tuberculosis Cases—United States,* 1976–1996

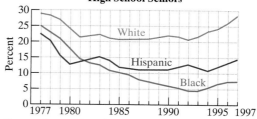

Year

*Comprises the 50 states, the District of Columbia, and New York City.
Source: Centers for Disease Control.

Figure for Exercise 23

a. Let N be the function represented by the graph. Approximate $N(1978)$ and $N(1984)$.

b. Approximate the open intervals where N is increasing.

c. Approximate the open intervals where N is decreasing.

24. The following graph depicts the federal budget outlay (in billions of dollars) for the Defense Department military between the years 1980 and 1998.

Federal Budget Outlay for Defense Department Military (1980–1998)

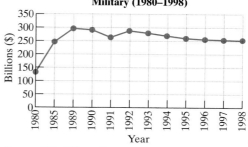

Year

Source: U.S. Office of Management and Budget.

Figure for Exercise 24

a. On what open interval(s) did the federal budget show an increase in defense spending for the military?

b. On what open interval(s) did the federal budget show a decrease in defense spending for the military?

25. The following graph represents the percentage of Black, Hispanic, and White high school seniors who smoke.

Daily Cigarette Smoking Among High School Seniors

White

Hispanic

Black

1977 1980   1985   1990   1995 1997

Source: Centers for Disease Control.

Figure for Exercise 25

Let x represent the year where $1977 \leq x \leq 1997$.

Let $W(x)$ represent the percentage of White high school seniors who smoke.

Let $H(x)$ represent the percentage of Hispanic high school seniors who smoke.

Let $B(x)$ represent the percentage of Black high school seniors who smoke.

Assume that $H(x) = B(x)$ for the year 1981.

a. Approximate the open intervals for which $H(x) > B(x)$.

b. Approximate the open intervals for which $W(x) > B(x)$.

c. Approximate the open intervals for which $W(x) < H(x)$.

d. Approximate the open intervals for which B is increasing.

e. Approximate the open intervals for which H is decreasing.

26. a. What can be said about the slope of an increasing line?

b. What can be said about the slope of a decreasing line?

27. Given the function defined by

$$f(x) = \begin{cases} x^2 & \text{for } x < 0 \\ x & \text{for } x \geq 0 \end{cases}$$

Find $f(-2)$, $f(0)$, and $f(6)$.

28. Given the function defined by

$$g(x) = \begin{cases} |x| & \text{for } x \leq 2 \\ 3 & \text{for } x > 2 \end{cases}$$

Find $g(-3)$, $g(0)$, $g(2)$, $g(3)$, and $g(4)$.

29. Given the function defined by

$$h(x) = \begin{cases} x + 2 & \text{for } x < -3 \\ 4 & \text{for } -3 \leq x \leq 3 \\ x^3 & \text{for } x > 3 \end{cases}$$

Find $h(-4)$, $h(-3)$, $h(0)$, $h(3)$, $h(4)$.

30. Given the function defined by

$$k(x) = \begin{cases} -2 & \text{for } x \leq -4 \\ x & \text{for } -4 < x < 6 \\ \sqrt{x+3} & \text{for } x \geq 6 \end{cases}$$

Find $k(-5)$, $k(-4)$, $k(-3)$, $k(0)$, $k(2)$, $k(6)$, and $k(8)$.

31. a. Graph $f(x) = x$ for $x < 0$.

b. Graph $g(x) = \sqrt{x}$ for $x \geq 0$.

c. Draw both $y = f(x)$ and $y = g(x)$ on the same axes to graph the piecewise-defined function.

$$h(x) = \begin{cases} x & \text{for } x < 0 \\ \sqrt{x} & \text{for } x \geq 0 \end{cases}$$

d. Find $h(-3)$, $h(0)$, and $h(4)$.

32. a. Graph $p(x) = |x|$ for $x \leq 1$.

b. Graph $q(x) = 1$ for $x > 1$.

c. Draw both $y = p(x)$ and $y = q(x)$ on the same axes to graph the piecewise-defined function.

$$r(x) = \begin{cases} |x| & \text{for } x \leq 1 \\ 1 & \text{for } x > 1 \end{cases}$$

d. Find $r(-2)$, $r(0)$, $r(1)$, and $r(4)$.

33. Graph the function defined by

$$Q(x) = \begin{cases} x & x \geq 0 \\ -x & x < 0 \end{cases}$$

34. Which basic function from page 231 resembles the function Q from Exercise 33?

35. Graph the function defined by

$$G(x) = \begin{cases} 3 & \text{for } x \leq -1 \\ x^3 & \text{for } x > -1 \end{cases}$$

36. Graph the function defined by

$$H(x) = \begin{cases} \dfrac{1}{x} & \text{for } x < 0 \\ x + 1 & \text{for } x \geq 0 \end{cases}$$

For Exercises 37–40, produce a rule for a function f. Answers may vary.

37.

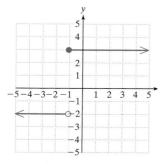

$$f(x) = \begin{cases} \end{cases}$$

38.

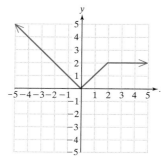

$$f(x) = \begin{cases} \end{cases}$$

39.

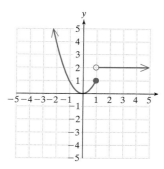

$$f(x) = \begin{cases} \end{cases}$$

40.

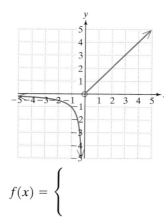

$$f(x) = \begin{cases} \end{cases}$$

41. A bicyclist rides at a steady speed of 16 mph for 35 min. Then she encounters a hill and her average speed immediately slows to 10 mph for the next 25 min. Then, after reaching the summit, she rides down the hill and her speed increases at a rate of 2 mph per minute until she reaches the finish line 7 min later.

    The bicyclist's speed can be approximated by the piecewise-defined function.

$$S(t) = \begin{cases} 16 & 0 \le t \le 35 \\ 10 & 35 < t \le 60 \\ 10 + 2(t - 60) & 60 < t \le 67 \end{cases}$$

where t is in minutes and S is in miles per hour.

    a. Find $S(30)$, $S(35)$, $S(60)$, and $S(65)$.

    b. Find the bicyclist's speed at the end of the ride.

    c. Sketch the function $y = S(t)$.

42. A sled accelerates (gains speed) down a hill and then slows down after it reaches a flat portion of ground. The speed of the sled can be approximated by the piecewise-defined function.

$$S(t) = \begin{cases} 1.5t & 0 \le t \le 16 \\ \dfrac{24}{t - 15} & t > 16 \end{cases}$$

where t is in seconds and S is in feet per second.

    a. Evaluate $S(0)$, $S(10)$, $S(16)$, $S(20)$, and $S(25)$.

b. Locate the points defined by the function
    values in part (a) on the graph of $y = S(t)$.

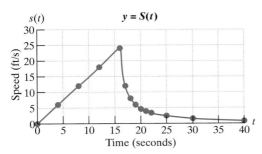

Figure for Exercise 42

43. A shopping cart rolls across a parking lot at a
     constant speed and then crashes into a tree and
     stops. Which graph of speed as a function of time
     represents this scenario? Explain your answer.

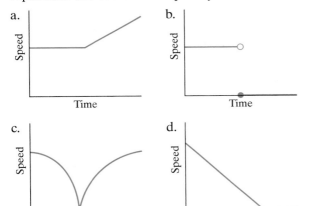

44. A student makes $8 per hour for the first 40 h
     worked in a week. Then she makes time and a
     half ($12/h) for the work exceeding 40 h. Which
     graph best depicts her total salary as a function
     of time? Explain your reasoning.

a.

b.

c.

d.

45.

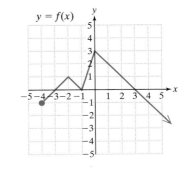

Figure for Exercise 45

a. Find the domain of f.

b. Find the range of f.

c. Find $f(-4)$.

d. Find $f(3)$.

e. For what value(s) of x is $f(x) = 0$?

f. For what value(s) of x is $f(x) = 3$?

g. On what open interval(s) is f increasing?

h. On what open interval(s) is f decreasing?

i. On what open interval(s) is f constant?

j. True or false: $f(3) < f(-4)$?

k. True or false: $f(-1) < f(3)$?

46.

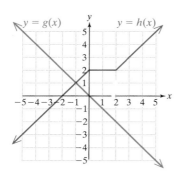

Figure for Exercise 46

a. Find the domain and range of h.

b. Find the domain and range of g.

c. On what open interval(s) is h increasing?

d. On what open interval(s) is h decreasing?

e. On what open interval(s) is h constant?

f. On what open interval(s) is g increasing?

g. On what open interval(s) is g decreasing?

h. On what open interval(s) is g constant?

i. On what open interval(s) is $h(x) > g(x)$?

j. On what open interval(s) is $h(x) < g(x)$?

k. Find the point where $h(x) = g(x)$.

l. Find $h(0)$.

m. Find $g(0)$.

n. For what value of x is $h(x) = 1$?

o. For what value of x is $g(x) = -1$?

47. The following graph depicts the rural and urban populations in the southern United States between 1900 and 1970.

Rural and Urban Populations in the South, 1900–1970

Source: Historical Abstract of the United States.

Figure for Exercise 47

Let $r(t)$ represent the rural population and let $u(t)$ represent the urban population. Assume that $r(t) = u(t)$ for the year 1950.

a. Approximate the open interval where $r(t) > u(t)$.

b. Approximate the open interval where $r(t) < u(t)$.

c. Approximate the open interval(s) where r is increasing.

d. Approximate the open interval(s) where u is increasing.

48. Some of the crude oil used in the United States is imported from other countries around the globe.

The following graph depicts the amount of crude oil imported from Saudi Arabia and Venezuela (1970–1997).

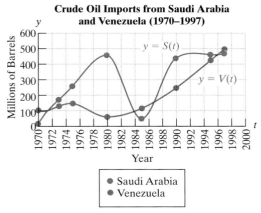

Crude Oil Imports from Saudi Arabia and Venezuela (1970–1997)

Source: U.S. Energy Information Administration.

Figure for Exercise 48

Let $V(t)$ represent the amount of oil imported from Venezuela and let $S(t)$ represent the amount of oil imported from Saudi Arabia. Assume that $V(t) = S(t)$ for the years 1972, 1984, 1987, and 1996.

a.   Approximate the open interval(s) where $V(t) > S(t)$.

b.   Approximate the open interval(s) where $V(t) < S(t)$.

▪ EXPANDING YOUR SKILLS

For Exercises 49–54, graph each of the following functions.

49. $g(x) = x^2$

50. $h(x) = x^3$

51. $j(x) = x^4$

52. $f(x) = x^5$

53. $k(x) = x^6$

54. $p(x) = x^7$

55.   What conjecture can you make about graphs of the function defined by $q(x) = x^n$, where n is a natural number?

▪ GRAPHING CALCULATOR EXERCISES

For Exercises 56–59, use a graphing calculator to graph the function, then use the graph to find the following: (round to two decimal places if necessary)

a.   The domain.

b.   The range.

c.   The open interval(s) over which the function is increasing.

d.   The open interval(s) over which the function is decreasing.

56. $m(x) = x^2 - 2x + 4$

57. $n(x) = x^2 + 8x + 14$

58. $p(x) = \sqrt{3x + 6} + 1$

59. $q(x) = -\sqrt{3 - x}$

60.   Graph the function defined by

$$h(x) = \begin{cases} x & \text{for } x < 0 \\ \sqrt{x} & \text{for } x \geq 0 \end{cases}$$

by entering each piece into your graphing calculator.

$$Y_1 = x*(x < 0)$$
$$Y_2 = \sqrt{x}*(x \geq 0)$$

Use dot mode and graph the function on the standard viewing window. Does the graph match your answer from Exercise 31?

61.   Graph the function defined by

$$r(x) = \begin{cases} |x| & \text{for } x \leq 1 \\ 1 & \text{for } x > 1 \end{cases}$$

by entering each piece into your graphing calculator.

$$Y_1 = \text{abs}(x)*(x \leq 1)$$
$$Y_2 = 1*(x > 1)$$

Use dot mode and graph the function on the standard viewing window. Does the graph match your answer from Exercise 32?

section

4.5 VARIATION

1. Definition of Direct and Inverse Variation

In this section, we introduce the concept of variation. Direct and inverse variation models can show how one quantity varies in proportion to another.

Definition of Direct and Inverse Variation

Let k be a nonzero constant real number. Then the following statements are equivalent:

1. y varies **directly** as x.
    y is directly proportional to x. $\Big\}$ $y = kx$

2. y varies **inversely** as x.
    y is inversely proportional to x. $\Big\}$ $y = \dfrac{k}{x}$

Note: The value of k is called the constant of variation.

For a car traveling at 30 mph, the equation $d = 30t$ indicates that the distance traveled is *directly proportional* to the time of travel. For positive values of k, when two variables are directly related, as one variable increases, the other variable will also increase. Likewise, if one variable decreases, the other will decrease. In the equation $d = 30t$, the longer the time of the trip, the greater the distance traveled. The shorter the time of the trip, the shorter the distance traveled.

For positive values of k, when two variables are *inversely related,* as one variable increases, the other will decrease, and vice versa. Consider a car traveling between Toronto and Montreal, a distance of 500 km. The time required to make the trip is inversely proportional to the speed of travel: $t = 500/r$. As the rate of speed, r, increases, the quotient $500/r$ will decrease. Hence the time will decrease. Similarly, as the rate of speed decreases, the trip will take longer.

2. Translations Involving Variation

The first step in using a variation model is to translate an English phrase into an equivalent mathematical equation.

example 1

Translating a Variation Model

Translate each expression into an equivalent mathematical model.

a. The circumference of a circle varies directly as the radius.
b. At a constant temperature, the volume of a gas varies inversely as the pressure.
c. The length of time of a meeting is directly proportional to the *square* of the number of people present.

Solution:

a. Let C represent circumference and r represent radius. The variables are directly related, so use the model $C = kr$.

b. Let V represent volume and P represent pressure. Because the variables are inversely related, use the model $V = k/P$.

c. Let t represent time and let N be the number of people present at a meeting. Because t is directly related to N^2, use the model $t = kN^2$.

3. Definition of Joint Variation

Sometimes a variable varies directly as the product of two or more other variables. In this case, we have joint variation.

Definition of Joint Variation
_____

Let k be a nonzero constant real number. Then the following statements are equivalent:

$$\left.\begin{array}{l} y \text{ varies } \textbf{jointly} \text{ as } w \text{ and } z. \\[6pt] y \text{ is jointly proportional to } w \text{ and } z. \end{array}\right\} \quad y = kwz$$

---

4. Creating a Variation Model

example 2

Creating a Variation Model

Translate each expression into an equivalent mathematical model.

a. y varies jointly as u and the square root of v.

b. The gravitational force of attraction between two planets varies jointly as the product of their masses and inversely as the square of the distance between them.

Solution:

a. $y = ku\sqrt{v}$

b. Let m_1 and m_2 represent the masses of the two planets. Let F represent the gravitational force of attraction and d represent the distance between the planets.

The variation model is

$$F = \frac{km_1m_2}{d^2}$$

5. Applications of Variation

Consider the variation models $y = kx$ and $y = k/x$. In either case, if values for x and y are known, we can solve for k. Once k is known, we can use the variation equation to find y if x is known, or to find x if y is known. This concept is the basis for solving many problems involving variation.

Steps to Find a Variation Model

1. Write a general variation model that relates the variables given in the problem. Let k represent the constant of variation.
2. Solve for k by substituting known values of the variables into the model from step 1.
3. Substitute the value of k into the original variation model from step 1.

example 3

Solving an Application Involving Direct Variation

The speed of a racing canoe in still water varies directly as the square root of the length of the canoe.

a. If a 16-ft canoe can travel 6.2 mph in still water, find a variation model that relates the speed of a canoe to its length.
b. Find the speed of a 20-ft canoe. (Round the answer to the nearest tenth of a mile per hour.)

Solution:

a. Let s represent the speed of the canoe, and L represent the length. The general variation model is $s = k\sqrt{L}$. To solve for k, substitute the known values for s and L.

$$s = k\sqrt{L}$$

$$6.2 = k\sqrt{16} \qquad \text{Substitute } s = 6.2 \text{ mph and } L = 16 \text{ ft.}$$

$$6.2 = k \cdot 4$$

$$\frac{6.2}{4} = \frac{\cancel{4}k}{\cancel{4}} \qquad \text{Solve for } k.$$

$$k = 1.55$$

$$s = 1.55\sqrt{L} \qquad \text{Substitute } k = 1.55 \text{ into the model } s = k\sqrt{L}.$$

b. $\quad s = 1.55\sqrt{L}$

$$= 1.55\sqrt{20} \qquad \text{Find the speed when } L = 20 \text{ ft.}$$

$$= 6.9 \text{ mph}$$

example 4

Solving an Application Involving Inverse Variation

The loudness of sound measured in decibels varies inversely as the square of the distance between the listener and the source of the sound. If the loudness of sound is 17.92 decibels at a distance of 10 ft from a stereo speaker, what is the decibel level 20 ft from the speaker? (Round the answer to the nearest hundredth of a decibel.)

Solution:

Let L represent the loudness of sound in decibels and d represent the distance in feet. The inverse relationship between decibel level and the square of the distance is modeled by

$$L = \frac{k}{d^2}$$

$$17.92 = \frac{k}{(10)^2} \qquad \text{Substitute } L = 17.92 \text{ decibels and } d = 10 \text{ ft.}$$

$$17.92 = \frac{k}{100}$$

$$(17.92)100 = \frac{k}{100} \cdot 100 \qquad \text{Solve for } k \text{ (clear fractions).}$$

$$k = 1792$$

$$L = \frac{1792}{d^2} \qquad \text{Substitute } k = 1792 \text{ into the original model}$$
$$L = \frac{k}{d^2}.$$

With the value of k known, we can find the value of L for any value of d.

$$L = \frac{1792}{(20)^2} \qquad \text{Find the loudness when } d = 20 \text{ ft.}$$

$$= 4.48 \text{ decibels}$$

Notice that the loudness of sound is 17.92 decibels at a distance 10 ft from the speaker. When the distance from the speaker is increased to 20 ft, the decibel level decreases to 4.48 decibels. This is consistent with an inverse relationship. For $k > 0$, as one variable is increased, the other is decreased. It also seems reasonable that the further one moves away from the source of a sound, the softer the sound becomes.

---

example 5

Solving an Application Involving Joint Variation

From August 23 to August 28, 1992, Hurricane Andrew carved a path of destruction from the Caribbean to South Florida and from the Louisiana coast to the North Carolina mountains. The destructive power of a hurricane or other severe storm is related to the *square* of the wind speed. During Hurricane Andrew, the National Weather Service reported wind gusts over 180 mph. These winds were strong enough to send a piece of plywood through a tree.

The kinetic energy of an object varies jointly as the mass of the object and as the square of its velocity. During a hurricane, a 0.225-kg stone (approximately $\frac{1}{2}$ lb) traveling at 22.352 m/s (approximately 50 mph) generates a kinetic energy of 56.2 J (joules). Suppose the wind speed increases and the same stone now travels three times as fast at 67.056 m/s (150 mph). Find the kinetic energy (round to the nearest tenth of a joule).

Solution:

Let E represent the kinetic energy, let m represent the mass, and let v represent the velocity of the object. The variation model is

$$E = kmv^2$$

$$56.2 = k(0.225)(22.352)^2 \qquad \text{Substitute } E = 56.2 \text{ J,}$$
$$\qquad\qquad\qquad\qquad\qquad\qquad\qquad m = 0.225 \text{ kg, and } v = 22.352 \text{ m/s.}$$

$$\frac{56.2}{(0.225)(22.352)^2} = k$$

$$0.5 \approx k \qquad\qquad\qquad \text{Solve for } k.$$

$$E = 0.5\,mv^2 \qquad\qquad \text{Substitute } k = 0.5 \text{ back into the}$$
$$\qquad\qquad\qquad\qquad\qquad \text{original equation.}$$

$$E = 0.5(0.225)(67.056)^2 \qquad \text{To find the kinetic energy of the}$$
$$\qquad\qquad\qquad\qquad\qquad\qquad \text{same stone, now traveling 3 times}$$
$$\qquad\qquad\qquad\qquad\qquad\qquad \text{as fast, substitute } m = 0.225 \text{ kg}$$
$$\qquad\qquad\qquad\qquad\qquad\qquad \text{and } v = 67.056 \text{ m/s.}$$

$$\approx 505.9 \text{ J}$$

In Example 5, when the velocity was increased by 3 times, the kinetic energy increased by 9 times (ignoring round-off error). This factor of 9 occurs because the kinetic energy is proportional to the *square* of the velocity. When the velocity is increased by 3 times, the kinetic energy is increased by 3^2 times.

section 4.5   PRACTICE EXERCISES

For Exercises 1–6, use the graphs to find the function values.

1. $f(1) + g(2)$

2. $f(-1) - g(-1)$

3. $f(0) \cdot g(0)$

4. $\dfrac{g(0)}{f(0)}$

5. $f(g(3))$

6. $g(f(-4))$

$y = f(x)$

$y = g(x)$

For Exercises 7–14, determine if the relation defines y as a function of x.

7.

8.

9.

10.

11.

12.

13.

14.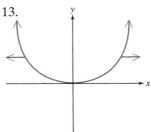

15. Suppose y varies directly as x, and $k > 0$.

   a. If x increases, then y will (increase or decrease)?

   b. If x decreases, then y will (increase or decrease)?

16. Suppose y varies inversely as x, and $k > 0$.

   a. If x increases, then y will (increase or decrease)?

   b. If x decreases, then y will (increase or decrease)?

For Exercises 17–24, write a variation model. Use k as the constant of variation.

17. T varies directly as q.

18. P varies inversely as r.

19. W varies inversely as the square of p.

20. Y varies directly as the square root of z.

21. Q is directly proportional to x and inversely proportional to the cube of y.

22. M is directly proportional to the square of p and inversely proportional to the cube of n.

23. L varies jointly as w and the square root of v.

24. X varies jointly as the square of y and w.

For Exercises 25–30, find the constant of variation, k.

25. y varies directly as x and when x is 4, y is 18.

26. m varies directly as x and when x is 8, m is 22.

27. p varies inversely as q and when q is 16, p is 32.

28. T varies inversely as x and when x is 40, T is 200.

29. y varies jointly as w and v. When w is 50 and v is 0.1, y is 8.75.

30. N varies jointly as t and p. When t is 1 and p is 7.5, N is 330.

Solve Exercises 31–36 using the steps found on page 292.

31. Z varies directly as the square of w. $Z = 14$ when $w = 4$. Find Z when $w = 8$.

32. Q varies inversely as the square of p. $Q = 4$ when $p = 3$. Find Q when $p = 2$.

33. L varies jointly as a and the square root of b. $L = 72$ when $a = 8$ and $b = 9$. Find L when $a = \frac{1}{2}$ and $b = 36$.

34. Y varies jointly as the cube of x and the square root of w. $Y = 128$ when $x = 2$ and $w = 16$. Find Y when $x = \frac{1}{2}$ and $w = 64$.

35. B varies directly as m and inversely as n. $B = 20$ when $m = 10$ and $n = 3$. Find B when $m = 15$ and $n = 12$.

36. R varies directly as s and inversely as t. $R = 14$ when $s = 2$ and $t = 9$. Find R when $s = 4$ and $t = 3$.

For Exercises 37–48, use a variation model to solve for the unknown value.

37. The amount of pollution entering the atmosphere varies directly as the number of people living in an area. If 80,000 people cause 56,800 tons of pollutants, how many tons enter the atmosphere in a city with a population of 500,000?

38. The area of a picture projected on a wall varies directly as the square of the distance from the projector to the wall. If a 10-ft distance produces a 16-ft^2 picture, what is the area of a picture produced when the projection unit is moved to a distance 20 ft from the wall?

39. The stopping distance of a car varies directly as the square of the speed of the car. If a car traveling at 40 mph has a stopping distance of 109 ft, find the stopping distance of a car that is traveling at 25 mph. (Round your answer to one decimal place.)

40. The intensity of a light source varies inversely as the square of the distance from the source. If the intensity is 48 lumens at a distance of 5 ft, what is the intensity when the distance is 8 ft?

41. The current in a wire varies directly as the voltage and inversely as the resistance. If the current is 9 A (amperes) when the voltage is 90 V (volts) and the resistance is 10 Ω (ohms), find the current when the voltage is 185 V and the resistance is 10 Ω.

42. The power in an electric circuit varies jointly as the current and the square of the resistance. If the power is 144 W (watts) when the current is 4 A and the resistance is 6 Ω, find the power when the current is 3 A and the resistance is 10 Ω.

43. The resistance of a wire varies directly as its length and inversely as the square of its diameter. A 40-ft wire 0.1 in. in diameter has a resistance of 4 Ω. What is the resistance of a 50-ft wire with a diameter of 0.20 in.?

44. The frequency of a vibrating string varies inversely as its length. A 24-in. piano string vibrates at 252 cycles/s. What would be the frequency of an 18-in. string?

45. The weight of a medicine ball varies directly as the cube of its radius. A ball with a radius of 3 in. weighs 4.32 lb. How much would a medicine ball weigh if its radius is 5 in.?

46. The surface area of a cube varies directly as the square of the length of an edge. The surface area is 24 ft^2 when the length of an edge is 2 ft. Find the surface area of a cube with an edge that is 5 ft.

47. The strength of a wooden beam varies jointly as the width of the beam and the square of the thickness of the beam and inversely as the length of the beam. A beam that is 48 in. long, 6 in. wide, and 2 in. thick can support a load of 417 lb. Find the maximum load that can be safely supported by a board that is 12 in. wide, 72 in. long, and 4 in. thick.

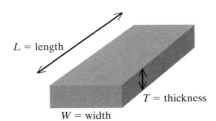

Figure for Exercise 47

48. The period of a pendulum is the length of time required to complete one swing back and forth. The period varies directly as the square root of the length of the pendulum. If it takes 1.4 s for a 0.5-m pendulum to complete one period, what is the period of a 1.5-m pendulum. (Round your answer to two decimal places.)

■ EXPANDING YOUR SKILLS

49. The area, A, of a square varies directly as the square of the length, l, of its sides.

    a. Write a general variation model with k as the constant of variation.

    b. If the length of the sides are doubled, what effect will that have on the area?

    c. If the length of a side is tripled, what effect will that have on the area?

d. Use your answers from parts (b) and (c) to explain why the following graph might be misleading.

The value of the dollar was twice as strong in 1980 as it was in 1998. This means that $1 in 1980 would buy twice what it would buy in 1998.

1980 dollars   1998 dollars

Figure for Exercise 49

50. In a physics laboratory, a spring is fixed to the ceiling. With no weight attached to the end of the spring, the spring is said to be in its equilibrium position. As weights are applied to the end of the spring, the force stretches the spring a distance, d, from its equilibrium position. A student in the laboratory collects the following data:

Force, F (lb)	2	4	6	8	10
Distance, d (cm)	2.5	5.0	7.5	10.0	12.5

a. Based on the data, do you suspect a direct relationship between force and distance or an inverse relationship?

b. Find a variation model that describes the relationship between force and distance.

chapter 4   SUMMARY

SECTION 4.1—INTRODUCTION TO RELATIONS

KEY CONCEPTS:

Any set of ordered pairs, (x, y), is called a **relation in x and y**.

The **domain of a relation** is the set of first components in the ordered pairs in the relation. The **range of a relation** is the set of second components in the ordered pairs.

KEY TERMS:

domain of a relation
range of a relation
relation in x and y

EXAMPLES:

Find the Domain and Range of the Relation:

$$\{(0, 0), (1, 1), (2, 4), (3, 9), (-1, 1), (-2, 4), (-3, 9)\}$$

Domain: $\{0, 1, 2, 3, -1, -2, -3\}$

Range: $\{0, 1, 4, 9\}$

Find the domain and range of the relation:

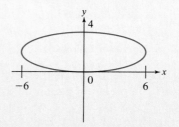

Domain: $[-6, 6]$

Range: $[0, 4]$

SECTION 4.2—INTRODUCTION TO FUNCTIONS

KEY CONCEPTS:

Given a relation in x and y, we say "y is a function of x" if for every element x in the domain, there corresponds exactly one element y in the range.

The Vertical Line Test for Functions:
Consider a relation defined by a set of points (x, y) in a rectangular coordinate system. Then the graph defines y as a function of x if no vertical line intersects the graph in more than one point.

Function Notation:
$f(x)$ is the value of the function, f, at x.

EXAMPLES:

Function $\{(1, 3), (2, 5), (6, 3)\}$

Nonfunction $\{(1, 3), (2, 5), (1, 4)\}$

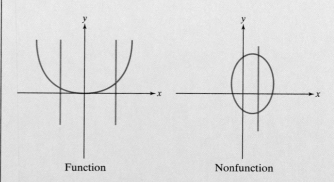

Function   Nonfunction

Given $f(x) = -3x^2 + 5x$, find $f(-2)$:

$$f(-2) = -3(-2)^2 + 5(-2)$$
$$= -12 - 10$$
$$= -22$$

The domain of a function defined by $y = f(x)$ is the set of x-values that when substituted into the function produces a real number. In particular,

- Exclude values of x that make the denominator of a fraction zero.
- Exclude values of x that make the radicand of a square root negative.

Find the domain:

1. $f(x) = \dfrac{x + 4}{(x - 5)}; (-\infty, 5) \cup (5, \infty)$

2. $f(x) = \sqrt{x - 3}; [3, \infty)$

3. $f(x) = 3x^2 - 5; (-\infty, \infty)$

The Algebra of Functions:

Given two functions, f and g, the functions $f + g, f - g, f \cdot g$, and $\dfrac{f}{g}$ are defined as:

$$(f + g)(x) = f(x) + g(x)$$

$$(f - g)(x) = f(x) - g(x)$$

$$(f \cdot g)(x) = f(x) \cdot g(x)$$

$$\left(\frac{f}{g}\right)(x) = \frac{f(x)}{g(x)} \quad \text{provided } g(x) \neq 0$$

Let $g(x) = 5x + 1$ and $h(x) = x^3$. Find:

1. $g(0) + h(3) = 1 + 27 = 28$

2. $g(4) \cdot h(-1) = 21 \cdot (-1) = -21$

3. $(g - h)(x) = 5x + 1 - x^3$

4. $\left(\dfrac{g}{h}\right)(x) = \dfrac{5x + 1}{x^3}$

Composition of Functions:

The composition of f and g, denoted $f \circ g$, is defined by the rule:

$(f \circ g)(x) = f(g(x))$ provided that $g(x)$ is in the domain of f

$(g \circ f)(x) = g(f(x))$ provided that $f(x)$ is in the domain of g

Find $(f \circ g)(x)$ and $(g \circ f)(x)$ given the functions defined by $f(x) = 4x + 3$ and $g(x) = 7x$.

$$(f \circ g)(x) = f(g(x)) = 4(7x) + 3 = 28x + 3$$

$$(g \circ f)(x) = g(f(x)) = 7(4x + 3) = 28x + 21$$

KEY TERMS:

composition of functions	function notation
domain of a function	range of a function
function	vertical line test

SECTION 4.3—GRAPHS OF BASIC FUNCTIONS

KEY CONCEPTS:

A function of the form $f(x) = mx + b$ is a linear function. Its graph is a line with slope m and y-intercept $(0, b)$.

A function of the form $f(x) = k$ is a constant function. Its graph is a horizontal line.

EXAMPLES:

$f(x) = 2x - 3$

$f(x) = 5$

Graphs of basic functions:

$$f(x) = x \qquad f(x) = x^2 \qquad f(x) = x^3$$

$$f(x) = |x| \qquad f(x) = \sqrt{x} \qquad f(x) = \frac{1}{x}$$

The x-intercepts of a function are determined by finding the real solutions to the equation $f(x) = 0$.

The y-intercept of a function is at $f(0)$.

Key Terms:

constant function   vertical asymptote
horizontal asymptote x-intercept
linear function y-intercept

Find the x- and y-intercepts:

$$f(x) = |x - 3| - 2$$

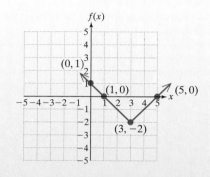

$f(x) = 0$, when $x = 1$ and $x = 5$.

Therefore, the x-intercepts are $(1, 0)$ and $(5, 0)$.
$f(0) = 1$. Therefore, the y-intercept is $(0, 1)$.

Section 4.4—Additional Topics on Functions

Key Concepts:

f is increasing on an open interval I if
$f(a) < f(b)$ for all $a < b$ on I.

Examples:

f is increasing on $(3, 4)$

f is decreasing on $(-\infty, -1)$

f is constant on $(-1, 3) \cup (4, \infty)$

f is decreasing on an open interval I if
$f(a) > f(b)$ for all $a < b$ on I.

f is constant on an open interval I if
$f(a) = f(b)$ for all a and b on I.

A piecewise-defined function is defined by more than one rule.

KEY TERMS:

constant function
decreasing function
increasing function
piecewise-defined function

Graph the piecewise-defined function:

$$f(x) = \begin{cases} x^2 & \text{if } x < 2 \\ -1 & \text{if } x \geq 2 \end{cases}$$

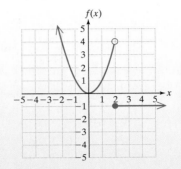

$$f(-1) = (-1)^2 = 1$$
$$f(0) = 0^2 = 0$$
$$f(1) = 1^2 = 1$$
$$f(2) = -1$$
$$f(3) = -1$$

SECTION 4.5—VARIATION

KEY CONCEPTS:

Direct Variation:
y varies directly as x. $y = k \times x$
y is directly proportional to x.

Inverse Variation:
y varies inversely as x. $y = \frac{k}{x}$
y is inversely proportional to x.

Joint Variation:
y varies jointly as w and z. $y = kwz$
y is jointly proportional to w and z.

EXAMPLES:

t varies directly as the square root of u.
$t = k\sqrt{u}$

W is inversely proportional to the cube of x.
$W = \frac{k}{x^3}$

y is jointly proportional to x and the square of z.
$y = kxz^2$

Steps to Find a Variation Model:

1. Write a general variation model that relates the variables given in the problem. Let k represent the constant of variation.

2. Solve for k by substituting known values of the variables into the model from step 1.

3. Substitute the value of k into the original variation model from step 1.

KEY TERMS:

direct variation
inverse variation
joint variation

C varies directly as the square root of d and inversely as t. If $C = 12$ when d is 9 and t is 6, find C if d is 16 and t is 12.

1. $C = \dfrac{k\sqrt{d}}{t}$

2. $12 = \dfrac{k\sqrt{9}}{6} \Rightarrow 12 = \dfrac{k \cdot 3}{6} \Rightarrow k = 24$

3. $C = \dfrac{24\sqrt{d}}{t} \Rightarrow C = \dfrac{24\sqrt{16}}{12} \Rightarrow C = 8$

---

chapter 4   REVIEW EXERCISES

Section 4.1

1. Write a relation with four ordered pairs for which the first element is the name of a parent and the second element is the name of the parent's child.

For Exercises 2–5, find the domain and range.

2. $\left\{ \left(\dfrac{1}{3}, 10\right), \left(6, -\dfrac{1}{2}\right), \left(\dfrac{1}{4}, 4\right), \left(7, \dfrac{2}{5}\right) \right\}$

3.

4.

5.

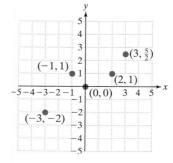

Section 4.2

6. Draw a sketch of a relation that is *not* a function. (Answers may vary.)

7. Draw a sketch of a relation that *is* a function. (Answers may vary.)

For Exercises 8–13:

    a. Determine whether the relation defines y as a function of x.

    b. Find the domain.

    c. Find the range.

8.

9.

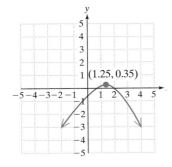

(1.25, 0.35)

10. $\{(1, 3), (2, 3), (3, 3), (4, 3)\}$

11. $\{(0, 2), (0, 3), (4, 4), (0, 5)\}$

12.

13.

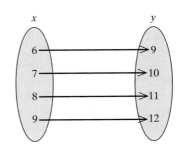

For Exercises 14–21, find the function values given $f(x) = 6x^2 - 4$.

14. $f(0)$ 15. $f(1)$

16. $f(-1)$ 17. $f(t)$

18. $f(b)$ 19. $f(\pi)$

20. $f(\square)$ 21. $f(x + h)$

For Exercises 22–25, write the domain of each function in interval notation.

22. $g(x) = 7x^3 + 1$ 23. $h(x) = \dfrac{x + 10}{x - 11}$

24. $k(x) = \sqrt{x - 8}$ 25. $w(x) = \sqrt{x + 2}$

26. Anita is a waitress and makes \$6/h plus tips. Her tips average \$5 per table. In one 8-h shift, Anita's pay can be described by $p(x) = 48 + 5x$, where x represents the number of tables she waits on. How much will Anita earn if she waits on

    a. 10 tables   b. 15 tables   c. 20 tables

Section 4.3

For Exercises 27–32, sketch the functions from memory.

27. $h(x) = x$ 28. $f(x) = x^2$

29. $g(x) = x^3$ 30. $w(x) = |x|$

31. $s(x) = \sqrt{x}$ 32. $r(x) = \dfrac{1}{x}$

For Exercises 33–34, sketch the linear functions.

33. $q(x) = 3$ 34. $k(x) = 2x + 1$

35. For $s(x) = (x - 2)^2$
    a. Find $s(4)$, $s(3)$, $s(2)$, $s(1)$, and $s(0)$.
    b. What is the domain of s?
    c. Sketch the graph of $y = s(x)$.

36. For $r(x) = 2\sqrt{x} - 4$
    a. Find $r(4)$, $r(5)$, and $r(8)$.
    b. What is the domain of r?
    c. Sketch the graph of $y = r(x)$.

37. For $h(x) = 3/(x - 3)$
    a. Find $h(-3)$, $h(-1)$, $h(0)$, $h(2)$, $h(4)$, $h(5)$, and $h(7)$.
    b. What is the domain of h?
    c. Sketch the graph of $y = h(x)$.

38. For $k(x) = -|x + 3|$
    a. Find $k(-5)$, $k(-4)$, $k(-3)$, $k(-2)$, and $k(-1)$.
    b. What is the domain of k?
    c. Sketch the graph of $y = k(x)$.

39. The function defined by $b(t) = 0.7t + 4.5$ represents the per capita consumption of bottled water in the United States between 1985 and 1995. The values of $b(t)$ are measured in gallons and $t = 0$ corresponds to the year 1985. (*Source:* U.S. Department of Agriculture)
    a. Evaluate $b(0)$ and $b(7)$ and interpret the results in the context of the problem.
    b. What is the slope of this function? Interpret the slope in the context of the problem.
    c. Sketch the function.

Section 4.4

40. The average number of visits to office-based physicians fluctuates with the age of the patient according to the function defined by
    $$N(a) = 0.0014a^2 - 0.0658a + 2.65 \quad 0 \le a \le 85$$
    where a is a patient's age in years and $N(a)$ is the average number of doctor visits per year.

    Use the following graph to answer the questions.
    a. Find the open interval where the function is increasing. Interpret this result in the context of the problem.

b. Find the open interval where the function is decreasing. Interpret this result in the context of the problem.

Average Number of Visits to a Doctor's Office per Year Based on Age of Patient

Source: U.S. National Center for Health Statistics.

Figure for Exercise 40

41. The function M represents the total number of murder victims in the United States according to the age a of the victim for 1996.

Number of Murder Victims by Age (1996)

$y = M(a)$

Source: U.S. Federal Bureau of Investigation.

Figure for Exercise 41

Use the graph of $y = M(a)$ to answer the following questions:
a. What is the domain of the function?
b. Approximate the open interval(s) where M is increasing.
c. Approximate the open interval(s) where M is decreasing.
d. Approximate the age(s) for which $M(a) = 2000$. (Give the answer(s) to the nearest year.)
e. Approximate the age(s) for which $M(a) = 1000$. (Give the answer(s) to the nearest year.)

42. Draw a function that increases on the interval (1, 3), decreases on the interval (3, 5), and is constant on the interval (5, 7). (Answers may vary.)

43. For

$$k(x) = \begin{cases} x^2 & \text{for } x \le -1 \\ 7 & \text{for } -1 < x < 3 \\ \sqrt{x-3} & \text{for } x \ge 3 \end{cases}$$

Find $k(-2)$, $k(-1)$, $k(0)$, $k(3)$, and $k(5)$.

44. Graph the piecewise-defined function

$$f(x) = \begin{cases} 3 & \text{for } x < 2 \\ x & \text{for } x \ge 2 \end{cases}$$

45. Graph the piecewise-defined function

$$g(x) = \begin{cases} x^3 & \text{for } x < 0 \\ x+1 & \text{for } x \ge 0 \end{cases}$$

Section 4.5

46. The force applied to a spring varies directly with the distance that the spring is stretched. When 6 lb of force is applied, the spring stretches 2 ft.

   a. Write a variation model using k as the constant of variation.

   b. Find k.

   c. How many feet will the spring stretch when 5 lb of pressure are applied?

47. Suppose y varies directly with the cube of x, and $y = 32$ when $x = 2$. Find y when $x = 4$.

48. Suppose y varies jointly with x and the square root of z, and $y = 3$ when $x = 3$ and $z = 4$. Find y when $x = 8$ and $z = 9$.

49. The distance, d, that one can see to the horizon varies directly as the square root of the height above sea level. If a person 19.5 m above sea level can see 28.96 km, how far can a person see if she is 68 m above sea level? (Round to the nearest tenth of a kilometer.)

---

chapter 4   TEST

For Exercises 1–3, (a) Determine if the relation defines y as a function of x. (b) Identify the domain. (c) Identify the range.

1.

2.

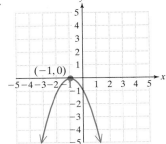

3. The percentage of mothers in the workforce who have children under 18 years old is shown for selected years.

Year x	Percentage y
1975	47.4
1985	62.2
1997	72.1

Source: U.S. Bureau of Labor Statistics

4. For $f(x) = \frac{1}{3}x + 6$ and $g(x) = |x|$, find

   a. $f(-3)$ b. $g(-3)$

   c. $f(0) + g(6)$ d. $(f \circ g)(-9)$

   e. $(g \circ f)(-9)$ f. $\dfrac{f(3)}{g(-1)}$

5. Let $k(x) = 8$

   a. Find $k(0)$, $k(-2)$, and $k(15)$.

   b. Write the domain of k.

   c. Sketch a graph of $y = k(x)$.

   d. Write the range of k.

6. For $r(x) = (x - 1)^3$

   a. Find $r(-2), r(-1), r(0), r(1), r(2),$ and $r(3)$.

   b. What is the domain of r?

   c. Sketch a graph of $y = r(x)$.

7. The function defined by $s(t) = 1.6t + 36$ approximates the per capita consumption of soft drinks in the United States between 1985 and 1995. The values of $s(t)$ are measured in gallons and $t = 0$ corresponds to the year 1985. (*Source:* U.S. Department of Agriculture)

   a. Evaluate $s(0)$ and $s(7)$ and interpret the results in the context of the problem.

   b. What is the slope of the function? Interpret the slope in the context of the problem.

   c. Sketch the function.

8. Graph $g(x) = \begin{cases} |x| & \text{for } x < 0 \\ \sqrt{x} & \text{for } x \geq 0 \end{cases}$

9. For the graph of $y = f(x)$ below

   a. List the open intervals where f is decreasing.

   b. List the open intervals where f is increasing.

   c. List the open intervals where f is constant.

   d. Find $f(1)$, $f(4)$, and $f(7)$.

   e. For what value(s) of x is $f(x) = 0$?

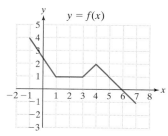

Figure for Exercise 9

10. Match the set defined on the left with the appropriate interval on the right.

    a. The domain of the function given by $f(x) = \dfrac{1}{x - 3}$ i. $(-\infty, 0)$

    b. The open interval for which $g(x) = \sqrt{x}$ is increasing   ii. $(-\infty, 3) \cup (3, \infty)$

    c. The range of the function given by $g(x) = \sqrt{x}$ iii. $(0, \infty)$

    d. The domain of the function given by $h(x) = |x|$ iv. $(-\infty, \infty)$

    e. The open interval for which $h(x) = |x|$ is decreasing   v. $[0, \infty)$

11. The following graph depicts the per capita consumption of refined sugar (cane and beet) and the per capita consumption of corn sweeteners as a function of the year from 1980 to 1996.

Per Capita Consumption of Refined Sugar (Cane and Beet) and Corn Sweeteners (1980–1996)

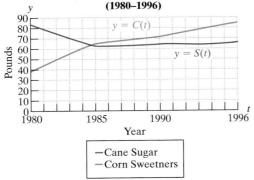

Source: U.S. Department of Agriculture.

Figure for Exercise 11

Let the function C represent the amount of corn sweeteners consumed per capita, and let the function S represent the amount of refined sugar (cane and beet) consumed per capita. Both functions measure sugar consumption in pounds. The variable t represents the year where $1980 \leq t \leq 1996$.

a. To the nearest year, where does $C(t) = S(t)$?

b. On what open interval is $C(t) > S(t)$?

c. On what open interval is $C(t) < S(t)$?

d. Suppose the function G is defined as $G(t) = C(t) + S(t)$. What does the function G represent?

12. The period of a pendulum varies directly as the square root of the length of the pendulum. If the period of the pendulum is 1.5 s when the length is 2 ft, find the period when the length is 5 ft. (Round to the nearest hundredth of a second.)

CUMULATIVE REVIEW EXERCISES, CHAPTERS 1–4

1. Solve the equation.
$$\frac{1}{3}t + \frac{1}{5} = \frac{1}{10}(t - 2)$$

2. Simplify: $5 - 3(2 - \sqrt{25}) + 2 - 10 \div 5$

3. Write the inequalities in interval notation:

    a. x is greater than or equal to 6.

    b. x is less than 17.

    c. x is between -2 and 3, inclusive.

4. Solve the inequality. Graph the answer and write the solution set in interval notation.
$$4 \leq -6y + 5$$

5. Determine the volume of the cone pictured here. Round your answer to two decimal places.

Figure for Exercise 5

6. Find an equation of the line passing through the origin and perpendicular to $3x - 4y = 1$. Write your final answer in slope-intercept form.

7. Find the pitch (slope) of the roof.

Figure for Exercise 7

8. a. Explain how to find the x- and y-intercepts of a function, $y = f(x)$.

    b. Find the y-intercept of the function defined by $f(x) = 3x + 2$

    c. Find the x-intercept(s) of the function defined by $f(x) = 3x + 2$

9. Is the ordered triple, $(2, 1, 0)$ a solution to the following system of equations? Why or why not?
$$x + 2y - z = 4$$
$$2x - 3y - z = 1$$
$$-3x + 2y + 2z = 8$$

10. An advanced math student has two work-study jobs. She is a math tutor, and she also serves as a note-taker for visually impaired students. One week, she earns $161.00 tutoring for 10 h and taking notes for 8 h. Another week, she earns $164.40 tutoring for 12 h and taking notes for 6 h. What is her hourly wage for tutoring and what is her hourly wage as a note-taker?

11. Set up the augmented matrix for the system

$$8x - 9y = 3$$

$$3x + 2y = -4$$

12. Identify the element in the second row and fourth column of the matrix.

$$\begin{bmatrix} -1 & 4 & 5 & -1 & 0 \\ 4 & -6 & -3 & 6 & 5 \\ 0 & 3 & -9 & 10 & -5 \end{bmatrix}$$

13. The linear function defined by $N(x) = 420x + 5260$ provides a model for the number of full-time-equivalent (FTE) students attending a community college from 1988 to 1998. Assume that $x = 0$ corresponds to the year 1988.

    a. Use this model to find the number of FTE students who attended the college in 1996.

    b. If this linear trend continues, predict the year in which the number of FTE students will reach 14,902.

14. State the domain and range of the relation. Is the relation a function?

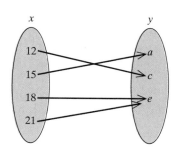

Figure for Exercise 14

15. Given $f(x) = \frac{1}{2}x - 1$ and $g(x) = 3x^2 - 2x$

    a. Find $f(4)$

    b. Find $g(-3)$

    c. Find $f(6) + g(-2)$

    d. Find $(g \circ f)(0)$

16. Given $f(x) = 3x - 2$ and $g(x) = -4x$

    a. Find $(f + g)(x)$

    b. Find $(f - g)(x)$

    c. Find $(f \circ g)(x)$

17. Write the domain of the functions in interval notation.

    a. $f(x) = \dfrac{1}{x - 15}$ b. $g(x) = \sqrt{x - 6}$

18. Simple interest varies jointly as the interest rate and as the time the money is invested. If an investment yields $1120 interest at 8% for 2 years, how much interest will the investment yield at 10% for 5 years?

19. Evaluate the determinants:

    a. $\begin{vmatrix} 5 & -2 \\ -8 & 9 \end{vmatrix}$ b. $\begin{vmatrix} 2 & 3 & 0 \\ 0 & -1 & 4 \\ 1 & 0 & 6 \end{vmatrix}$

20. Solve the system for y using Cramer's rule.

$$12x + 9y = -2$$

$$10x - 3y = 5$$

POLYNOMIALS

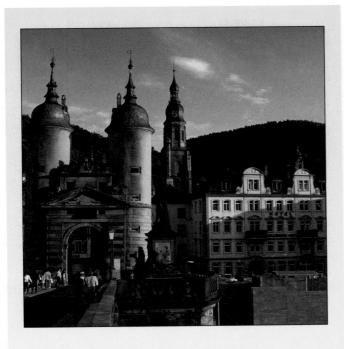

To plan a vacation overseas, an understanding of currency exchange rates is important. For example, if you visit Frankfurt, Germany, you will need to know how many Euros (the main unit of currency in Germany as well as 11 other European countries) may be exchanged for $1. If you visit Japan, you will need to know how many Yen may be exchanged for $1.

Because many countries outside the United States use the metric system, it is also helpful to know unit conversions for some common units of measurement. For example, 1 kilometer (km) is approximately 0.622 miles. Therefore, the distance of 305 km between Frankfurt, Germany, and Munich, Germany, is approximately 190 miles.

A linear function can be used to perform unit conversions. If x is a distance measured in kilometers, then the function defined by

$$m(x) = 0.622x$$

gives the corresponding distance in miles.

For more information about currency exchange and unit conversion, visit currencyex and unitconv at

www.mhhe.com/miller_oneill

section

5.1   PROPERTIES OF INTEGER EXPONENTS AND SCIENTIFIC NOTATION

1.   Properties of Exponents

In Section 1.2, we learned that exponents are used to represent repeated multiplication. The following properties of exponents are often used to simplify algebraic expressions.

Properties of Exponents*			
Description	**Property**	**Example**	**Details/Notes**
Multiplication of Like Bases	$b^m \cdot b^n = b^{m+n}$	$b^2 \cdot b^4 = b^{2+4}$ $= b^6$	$b^2 \cdot b^4 = (b \cdot b)(b \cdot b \cdot b \cdot b)$ $= b^6$
Division of Like Bases	$\dfrac{b^m}{b^n} = b^{m-n}$	$\dfrac{b^5}{b^2} = b^{5-3}$ $= b^3$	$\dfrac{b^5}{b^2} = \dfrac{b \cdot b \cdot b \cdot b \cdot b}{b \cdot b}$ $= b^3$
Power Rule	$(b^m)^n = b^{m \cdot n}$	$(b^4)^2 = b^{4 \cdot 2}$ $= b^8$	$(b^4)^2 = (b \cdot b \cdot b \cdot b)(b \cdot b \cdot b \cdot b)$ $= b^8$
Power of a Product	$(ab)^m = a^m b^m$	$(ab)^3 = a^3 b^3$	$(ab)^3 = (ab)(ab)(ab)$ $= (a \cdot a \cdot a)(b \cdot b \cdot b) = a^3 b^3$
Power of a Quotient	$\left(\dfrac{a}{b}\right)^m = \dfrac{a^m}{b^m}$	$\left(\dfrac{a}{b}\right)^3 = \dfrac{a^3}{b^3}$	$\left(\dfrac{a}{b}\right)^3 = \left(\dfrac{a}{b}\right)\left(\dfrac{a}{b}\right)\left(\dfrac{a}{b}\right)$ $= \dfrac{a \cdot a \cdot a}{b \cdot b \cdot b} = \dfrac{a^3}{b^3}$

*Assume that a and b are real numbers ($b \neq 0$) and that m and n represent positive integers.

In addition to the properties of exponents, two definitions are used to simplify algebraic expressions.

b^0 and b^{-n}

Let n be an integer and let b be a real number such that $b \neq 0$, then

1. $b^0 = 1$

2. $b^{-n} = \left(\dfrac{1}{b}\right)^n = \dfrac{1}{b^n}$

The definition of b^0 is consistent with the properties of exponents. For example, if b is a nonzero real number and n is an integer, then:

$$\frac{b^n}{b^n} = 1 \longleftarrow$$

The expression $b^0 = 1$

$$\frac{b^n}{b^n} = b^{n-n} = b^0 \longrightarrow$$

The definition of b^{-n} is also consistent with the properties of exponents. If b is a nonzero real number, then:

$$\frac{b^3}{b^5} = \frac{\cancel{b} \cdot \cancel{b} \cdot \cancel{b}}{\cancel{b} \cdot \cancel{b} \cdot \cancel{b} \cdot b \cdot b} = \frac{1}{b^2} \longleftarrow$$

The expression $b^{-2} = \dfrac{1}{b^2}$

$$\frac{b^3}{b^5} = b^{3-5} = b^{-2} \underline{\hspace{2cm}}$$

2. Simplifying Expressions with Exponents

example 1   **Simplifying Expressions with Exponents**

Simplify the following expressions. Write the final answer with positive exponents only.

a. $(x^7 x^{-3})^2$

b. $\left(\dfrac{1}{5}\right)^{-3} - (2)^{-2} + 3^0$

c. $\left(\dfrac{y^3 w^{10}}{y^5 w^4}\right)^{-1}$

d. $\left(\dfrac{2a^7 b^{-4}}{8a^9 b^{-2}}\right)^{-3} (-6a^{-1} b^0)^{-2}$

Solution:

a. $(x^7 x^{-3})^2$

$\qquad = (x^{7+(-3)})^2$ Multiply like bases by adding exponents.

$\qquad = (x^4)^2$ Apply the power rule.

$\qquad = x^8$ Multiply exponents.

b. $\left(\dfrac{1}{5}\right)^{-3} - (2)^{-2} + 3^0$

$\qquad = 5^3 - \left(\dfrac{1}{2}\right)^2 + 3^0$ Simplify negative exponents.

$\qquad = 125 - \dfrac{1}{4} + 1$ Evaluate the exponents.

$\qquad = \dfrac{500}{4} - \dfrac{1}{4} + \dfrac{4}{4}$ Write the expressions with a common denominator.

$\qquad = \dfrac{503}{4}$ Simplify.

c. $\left(\dfrac{y^3 w^{10}}{y^5 w^4}\right)^{-1}$ Work within the parentheses first.

$\qquad = (y^{3-5} w^{10-4})^{-1}$ Divide like bases by subtracting exponents.

$$= (y^{-2}w^6)^{-1} \qquad \text{Simplify within parentheses.}$$

$$= (y^{-2})^{-1}(w^6)^{-1} \qquad \text{Apply the power rule.}$$

$$= y^2 w^{-6} \qquad \text{Multiply exponents.}$$

$$= y^2\left(\frac{1}{w^6}\right) \quad \text{or} \quad \frac{y^2}{w^6} \qquad \text{Simplify negative exponents.}$$

d. $\left(\dfrac{2a^7 b^{-4}}{8a^9 b^{-2}}\right)^{-3}(-6a^{-1}b^0)^{-2}$ Subtract exponents within first parentheses. Reduce $\frac{2}{8}$ to $\frac{1}{4}$.

$$= \left(\frac{a^{7-9}b^{-4-(-2)}}{4}\right)^{-3}(-6a^{-1}\cdot 1)^{-2} \qquad \text{In the second parentheses, replace } b^0 \text{ by 1.}$$

$$= \left(\frac{a^{-2}b^{-2}}{4}\right)^{-3}(-6a^{-1})^{-2} \qquad \text{Simplify inside parentheses.}$$

$$= \left[\frac{(a^{-2})^{-3}(b^{-2})^{-3}}{4^{-3}}\right](-6)^{-2}(a^{-1})^{-2} \qquad \text{Apply the power rule.}$$

$$= \left(\frac{a^6 b^6}{4^{-3}}\right)(-6)^{-2}a^2 \qquad \text{Multiply exponents.}$$

$$= 4^3 a^6 b^6\left[\frac{a^2}{(-6)^2}\right] \qquad \text{Simplify negative exponents.}$$

$$= \frac{64a^8 b^6}{36} \qquad \text{Multiply factors in the numerator and denominator.}$$

$$= \frac{16a^8 b^6}{9} \qquad \text{Reduce.}$$

3.   Scientific Notation

Scientists in a variety of fields often work with very large or very small numbers. For instance, the distance between the earth and the sun is approximately 93,000,000 miles. The national debt in the United States in 1997 was approximately $4,600,000,000,000. The mass of an electron is 0.000 000 000 000 000 000 000 000 000 911 kg.

Scientific notation was devised as a shortcut method of expressing very large and very small numbers. The principle behind scientific notation is to use a power of 10 to express the magnitude of the number. Consider the following powers of 10:

$$10^0 = 1$$

$$10^1 = 10 \qquad\qquad 10^{-1} = \frac{1}{10^1} = \frac{1}{10} = 0.1$$

$$10^2 = 100 \qquad\qquad 10^{-2} = \frac{1}{10^2} = \frac{1}{100} = 0.01$$

$$10^3 = 1000 \qquad\qquad 10^{-3} = \frac{1}{10^3} = \frac{1}{1000} = 0.001$$

$$10^4 = 10,000 \qquad 10^{-4} = \frac{1}{10^4} = \frac{1}{10,000} = 0.0001$$

Each power of 10 represents a place value in the base 10 numbering system. A number such as 50,000 may therefore be written as $5 \times 10,000$ or equivalently as 5.0×10^4. Similarly, the number 0.035 is equal to $3.5 \times \frac{1}{1000}$ or equivalently, 3.5×10^{-3}.

Definition of a Number Written in Scientific Notation

A number expressed in the form $a \times 10^n$, where $1 \le |a| < 10$ and n is an integer is said to be written in **scientific notation**.

Consider the following numbers in scientific notation:

The distance between the sun and the earth: 93,000,000 miles $= 9.3 \times 10^7$ miles

7 places

The national debt of the United States in 1997: $\$4,600,000,000,000 = \$4.6 \times 10^{12}$

12 places

The mass of an electron: 0.000 000 000 000 000 000 000 000 000 000 911 kg

$$= 9.11 \times 10^{-31} \text{ kg} \qquad 31 \text{ places}$$

In each case, the power of 10 corresponds to the number of place positions that the decimal point is moved. The power of 10 is sometimes called the order of magnitude (or simply the magnitude) of the number. The order of magnitude of the national debt is 10^{12} dollars (trillions). The order of magnitude of the distance between the earth and sun is 10^7 miles (tens of millions). The mass of an electron has an order of magnitude of 10^{-31} kg.

4.   **Writing a Number in Scientific Notation and in Expanded Form**

---

example 2

Writing Numbers in Scientific Notation

Fill in the table by writing the numbers in scientific notation or expanded notation as indicated.

Quantity	Expanded Notation	Scientific Notation
Attendance at NASCAR Winston Cup races in 1996	5,600,000 people	
Width of an influenza virus	0.000000001 m	
Cost of Hurricane Andrew		$\$2.65 \times 10^{10}$
Probability of winning the Florida state lottery		$4.35587878 \times 10^{-8}$
Approximate width of a human red blood cell	0.000007 m	
The salary of the highest paid CEO in 1996		$\$1.024 \times 10^8$

Solution:

Quantity	Expanded Notation	Scientific Notation
Attendance at NASCAR Winston Cup races in 1996	5,600,000 people	5.6×10^6 people
Width of an influenza virus	0.000000001 m	1.0×10^{-9} m
Cost of Hurricane Andrew	$26,500,000,000	2.65×10^{10}
Probability of winning the Florida state lottery	0.0000000435587878	$4.35587878 \times 10^{-8}$
Approximate width of a human red blood cell	0.000007 m	7.0×10^{-6} m
The salary of the highest paid CEO in 1996	$102,400,000	1.024×10^8

Graphing Calculator Box

Calculators use scientific notation to display very large or very small numbers. To enter scientific notation in a calculator, try using the EE key or the EXP key to express the power of 10.

```
9.3E7
              93000000
7.25E-2
                  .0725
```

5.   Applications of Exponents and Scientific Notation

example 3

Applying Scientific Notation

a. The U.S. national debt in 1997 was approximately $4,600,000,000,000. Assuming there were approximately 260,000,000 people in the United States at that time, determine how much each individual would have to pay to pay off the debt.

b. The mean distance between the earth and the Andromeda Galaxy is approximately 1.8×10^6 lightyears. Assuming a lightyear is 6.0×10^{12} miles, what is the distance in miles to the Andromeda Galaxy?

Solution:

a. Divide the total U.S. national debt by the number of people:

$$\frac{4.6 \times 10^{12}}{2.6 \times 10^8}$$

$$= \left(\frac{4.6}{2.6}\right) \times \left(\frac{10^{12}}{10^8}\right) \quad \text{Divide 4.6 by 2.6 and subtract the powers of 10.}$$

$$\approx 1.7692 \times 10^4$$

In expanded form, this amounts to approximately $17,692 per person.

b.   Multiply the number of lightyears by the number of miles per lightyear.

$$(1.8 \times 10^6)(6.0 \times 10^{12})$$
$$= (1.8)(6.0) \times (10^6)(10^{12})$$
$$= 10.8 \times 10^{18} \qquad \text{Multiply 1.8 and 6.0 and add the powers of 10.}$$

The number 10.8×10^{18} is not in proper scientific notation because 10.8 is not between 1 and 10.

$$= (1.08 \times 10^1) \times 10^{18} \qquad \text{Rewrite 10.8 as } 1.08 \times 10^1.$$

$$= 1.08 \times (10^1 \times 10^{18}) \qquad \text{Apply the associative property of multiplication.}$$

$$= 1.08 \times 10^{19}$$

The distance between the earth and the Andromeda Galaxy is 1.08×10^{19} miles.

Graphing Calculator Box

Use a calculator to check the solutions to Example 3.

```
(4.6E12)/(2.6E8)
        17692.30769
(1.8E6)*(6.0E12)
            1.08E19
```

---

example 4

Applications and Calculations Involving Scientific Notation

The distribution of income for the United States federal government in 1998 is shown in Figure 5-1. If the total budget was 1.7×10^{12} ($1.7 trillion), determine the percentage that each source of income contributed to the federal budget.

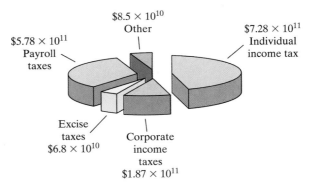

Income Sources for Federal Budget, 1998
(Total budget, 1.7×10^{12})

8.5×10^{10}
Other

7.28×10^{11}
Individual
income tax

5.78×10^{11}
Payroll
taxes

Excise
taxes
6.8×10^{10}

Corporate
income
taxes
1.87×10^{11}

Figure 5-1

Source: Information Please Almanac.

Solution:

The total revenue for 1998 was \$1.7 trillion. To find the percentage contribution for each source of income, divide that dollar amount by \$1.7 $\times$ 10^{12}.

Individual Income Taxes: (\$7.82 $\times$ 10^{11}) $\div$ (\$1.7 $\times$ 10^{12}) = 0.46 = 46%

Excise Taxes: (\$6.8 $\times$ 10^{10}) $\div$ (\$1.7 $\times$ 10^{12}) = 0.04 = 4%

Payroll Taxes: (\$5.78 $\times$ 10^{11}) $\div$ (\$1.7 $\times$ 10^{12}) = 0.34 = 34%

Corporate Income Taxes: (\$1.87 $\times$ 10^{11}) $\div$ (\$1.7 $\times$ 10^{12}) = 0.11 = 11%

Other: (\$8.5 $\times$ 10^{10}) $\div$ (\$1.7 $\times$ 10^{12}) = 0.05 = 5%

---

section 5.1   PRACTICE EXERCISES

1. Explain the difference between $b^4 \cdot b^3$ and $(b^4)^3$. (*Hint*: Expand both expressions and compare.)

2. Explain the difference between ab^3 and $(ab)^3$.

For Exercises 3–8, write two examples of each property. Include examples with and without variables. (Answers may vary.)

3. $b^n \cdot b^m = b^{n+m}$

4. $(ab)^n = a^n b^n$

5. $(b^n)^m = b^{nm}$

6. $\dfrac{b^n}{b^m} = b^{n-m}$ $(b \neq 0)$

7. $\left(\dfrac{a}{b}\right)^n = \dfrac{a^n}{b^n}$ $(b \neq 0)$

8. $b^0 = 1$ $(b \neq 0)$

For Exercises 9–42, simplify and write the answer with positive exponents only.

9. $6^3 \cdot 6^5$

10. $x^4 \cdot x^8$

11. $\dfrac{13^8}{13^2}$

12. $\dfrac{5^7}{5^3}$

13. $(y^2)^4$

14. $(z^3)^4$

15. $(3x^2)^4$

16. $(2y^5)^3$

17. p^{-3}

18. q^{-5}

19. $7^{10} \cdot 7^{-13}$

20. $11^{-9} \cdot 11^7$

21. $\dfrac{w^3}{w^5}$

22. $\dfrac{t^4}{t^8}$

23. $(6xyz^2)^0$

24. $(-7ab^3)^0$

25. $\left(\dfrac{2}{3}\right)^{-2} - \left(\dfrac{1}{2}\right)^2 + \left(\dfrac{1}{3}\right)^0$

26. $\left(\dfrac{4}{5}\right)^{-1} + \left(\dfrac{3}{2}\right)^2 - \left(\dfrac{2}{7}\right)^0$

27. $\dfrac{p^2 q}{p^5 q^{-1}}$

28. $\dfrac{m^{-1} n^3}{m^4 n^{-2}}$

29. $\dfrac{-48ab^{10}}{32a^4 b^3}$

30. $\dfrac{25x^2 y^{12}}{10x^5 y^7}$

31. $(-8x^{-4} y^5 z^2)^{-4}$

32. $(-6a^{-2} b^3 c)^{-2}$

33. $(4m^{-2}n)(-m^6 n^{-3})$

34. $(-6pq^{-3})(2p^4 q)$

35. $(p^{-2}q)^3 (2pq^4)^2$

36. $(mn^3)^2 (5m^{-2} n^2)$

37. $\left(\dfrac{x^2}{y}\right)^3 (5x^2 y)$

38. $\left(\dfrac{a}{b^2}\right)^2 (3a^2 b^3)$

39. $\dfrac{(-8a^2 b^2)^4}{(16a^3 b^7)^2}$

40. $\dfrac{(-3x^2 y^3)^2}{(-2xy^4)^3}$

41. $\left(\dfrac{2x^6 y^{-5}}{3x^{-2} y^4}\right)^{-3}$

42. $\left(\dfrac{6a^2 b^{-3}}{5a^{-1} b}\right)^{-2}$

43. Write the numbers in scientific notation.

   a. Paper is 0.0042 in. thick.

   b. One mole is 602,200,000,000,000,000,000,000 particles.

   c. The dissociation constant for nitrous acid is 0.00046.

44. Write the numbers in scientific notation.

    a. In April 1999, the population of the United States was approximately 272,000,000.

    b. As of October 1998, the net worth of Bill Gates was $79,250,000,000.

    c. A trillion is defined as 1,000,000,000,000.

45. Write the numbers in expanded notation.

    a. The number of $20 bills printed in 1998 was 1.8816×10^9.

    b. The dissociation constant for acetic acid is 1.8×10^{-5}.

    c. On April 24, 1999, the population of the world was approximately 5.981×10^9.

46. Write the numbers in expanded notation.

    a. The U.S. national debt as of April 24, 1999, was approximately $\$5.631 \times 10^{12}$.

    b. The mass of a neutron is 1.67×10^{-24} g.

    c. The number of $2 bills printed in 1997 was 1.024×10^8.

For Exercises 47–54, perform the indicated operations and write the answer in scientific notation.

47. $(6.5 \times 10^3)(5.2 \times 10^{-8})$

48. $(3.26 \times 10^{-6})(8.2 \times 10^9)$

49. $(0.0000024)(6700000000)$

50. $(3400000000)(70000000000000)$

51. $(8.5 \times 10^{-2}) \div (2.5 \times 10^{-15})$

52. $(3 \times 10^9) \div (1.5 \times 10^{13})$

53. $(900000000) \div (360000)$

54. $(0.0000000002) \div (8000000)$

For Exercises 55–60, determine which numbers are in proper scientific notation. If the number is not in proper scientific notation, correct it.

55. 35×10^4

56. 0.469×10^{-7}

57. 7.0×10^0

58. 8.12×10^1

59. 9×10^{23}

60. 6.9×10

61. If one H_2O molecule contains 2 hydrogen atoms and 1 oxygen atom, and 10 H_2O molecules con-

tain 20 hydrogen atoms and 10 oxygen atoms, how many hydrogen atoms and oxygen atoms are contained in 6.02×10^{23} H_2O molecules?

62. At one count per second, how many days would it take to count to 1 million? (Round to one decimal place.)

63. Do you know anyone who is more than 1.0×10^9 seconds old? If so, who?

64. Do you know anyone who is more than 4.5×10^5 hours old? If so, who?

Fun Facts:

65. What is the heaviest recorded weight of a blue whale?

    a. 3.8×10^3 lb

    b. 3.8×10^5 lb

    c. 3.8×10^2 lb

    d. 3.8×10^8 lb

Answer: 380,000 lb or 190 tons

66. What is the approximate number of red blood cells in an average adult?

    a. 3.0×10^5

    b. 3.0×10^{12}

    c. 3.0×10^{10}

    d. 3.0×10^3

Answer: 30,000,000,000

67. The brain cells in the cerebellum are among the smallest cells in the human body. What is the average width of these cells?

    a. 5.0×10^{-5} mm

    b. 5.0×10^{-1} mm

c. 5.0×10^{-3} mm

d. 5.0×10^{-9} mm

Answer: 0.005 mm

68. What is the mass of the lightest insect?

a. 5×10^{1} mg

b. 5×10^{-1} mg

c. 5×10^{-3} mg

d. 5×10^{-5} mg

Answer: 0.005 mg

■ EXPANDING YOUR SKILLS

For Exercises 69–74, simplify the expression. Assume that a and b represent positive integers.

69. $x^{a+1}x^{a+5}$

70. $y^{a-5}y^{a+7}$

71. $\dfrac{y^{2a+1}}{y^{a-1}}$

72. $\dfrac{x^{3a-3}}{x^{a+1}}$

73. $\dfrac{x^{3b-2}y^{b+1}}{x^{2b+1}y^{2b+2}}$

74. $\dfrac{x^{2a-2}y^{a-3}}{x^{a+4}y^{a+3}}$

For Exercises 75–78, simplify and write the answer with positive exponents only.

75. $\left(\dfrac{2x^{-3}y^{0}}{4x^{6}y^{-5}}\right)^{-2}$

76. $\left(\dfrac{a^{3}b^{2}c^{0}}{a^{-1}b^{-2}c^{-3}}\right)^{-2}$

77. $3xy^{5}\left(\dfrac{2x^{4}y}{6x^{5}y^{3}}\right)^{-2}$

78. $7x^{-3}y^{-4}\left(\dfrac{3x^{-1}y^{5}}{9x^{3}y^{-2}}\right)^{-3}$

Concepts

1. **Polynomials: Basic Definitions**

2. **Definition of a Polynomial Function**

3. **Evaluating a Polynomial Function**

4. **Applications of Polynomial Functions**

section

5.2   POLYNOMIAL FUNCTIONS AND APPLICATIONS

1. Polynomials: Basic Definitions

One commonly used algebraic expression is called a polynomial. A **polynomial** in x is defined as a finite sum of terms of the form ax^{n}, where a is a real number and the exponent, n, is a nonnegative integer. For each term, a is called the **coefficient**, and n is called the **degree of the term**. For example:

Term (expressed in the form ax^{n})	Coefficient	Degree
$3x^{5}$	3	5
$x^{14} \rightarrow$ rewrite as $1x^{14}$	1	14
$7 \rightarrow$ rewrite as $7x^{0}$	7	0
$\dfrac{1}{2}p \rightarrow$ rewrite as $\frac{1}{2}p^{1}$	$\dfrac{1}{2}$	1

If a polynomial has exactly one term, it is categorized as a **monomial**. A two-term polynomial is called a **binomial**, and a three-term polynomial is called a **trinomial**. Usually the terms of a polynomial are written in descending order according to degree. The term with highest degree is called the **leading term**, and its coefficient is called the **leading coefficient**. The **degree of a polynomial** is the largest degree of all of its terms. Thus, the leading term determines the degree of the polynomial.

	Expression	Descending Order	Leading Coefficient	Degree of Polynomial
Monomials	$2x^9$	$2x^9$	2	9
	-49	-49	-49	0
Binomials	$10y - 7y^2$	$-7y^2 + 10y$	-7	2
	$6 - \dfrac{2}{3}b$	$-\dfrac{2}{3}b + 6$	$-\dfrac{2}{3}$	1
Trinomials	$w + 2w^3 + 9w^6$	$9w^6 + 2w^3 + w$	9	6
	$2.5a^4 - a^8 + 1.3a^3$	$-a^8 + 2.5a^4 + 1.3a^3$	-1	8

Polynomials may have more than one variable. In such a case, the degree of a term is the sum of the exponents of the variables contained in the term. For example, the term, $2x^3y^4z$, has degree 8 because the exponents applied to x, y, and z are 3, 4, and 1, respectively.

The following polynomial has a degree of 12 because the highest degree of its terms is 12.

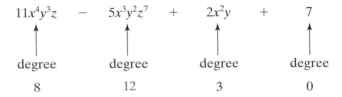

$$11x^4y^3z \quad - \quad 5x^3y^2z^7 \quad + \quad 2x^2y \quad + \quad 7$$

degree	degree	degree	degree
8	12	3	0

2.   Definition of a Polynomial Function

A **polynomial function** is a function defined by a finite sum of terms of the form ax^n, where a is a real number and n is a whole number. For example, the functions defined here are polynomial functions:

$$f(x) = 3x - 8 \qquad\qquad g(x) = 4x^5 - 2x^3 + 5x - 3$$

$$h(x) = -\frac{1}{2}x^4 + \frac{3}{5}x^3 - 4x^2 + \frac{5}{9}x - 1 \qquad k(x) = 7$$

The following functions are *not* polynomial functions:

$$m(x) = \frac{1}{x} - 8 \qquad n(x) = 3x^4 + \sqrt{x}$$

$$q(x) = |x|$$

3.   Evaluating a Polynomial Function

example 1

Evaluating a Polynomial Function

Given $P(x) = x^3 + 2x^2 - x - 2$, find the function values.

a. $P(-3)$ b. $P(-1)$ c. $P(0)$ d. $P(2)$

Solution:

a. $P(x) = x^3 + 2x^2 - x - 2$
    $P(-3) = (-3)^3 + 2(-3)^2 - (-3) - 2$
    $ = -27 + 2(9) + 3 - 2$
    $ = -27 + 18 + 3 - 2$
    $ = -8$

b. $P(-1) = (-1)^3 + 2(-1)^2 - (-1) - 2$
    $ = -1 + 2(1) + 1 - 2$
    $ = -1 + 2 + 1 - 2$
    $ = 0$

c. $P(0) = (0)^3 + 2(0)^2 - (0) - 2$
    $ = -2$

d. $P(2) = (2)^3 + 2(2)^2 - (2) - 2$
    $ = 8 + 2(4) - 2 - 2$
    $ = 8 + 8 - 2 - 2$
    $ = 12$

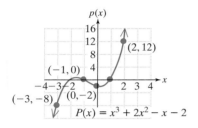

Figure 5-2

The function values from Example 1 can be confirmed from the graph of $y = P(x)$ (Figure 5-2).

4. Applications of Polynomial Functions

example 2

Applying a Polynomial Function

The percentage of female smokers, $S(t)$, in the United States between 1955 and 1994 can be approximated by $S(t) = -0.016t^2 + 0.422t + 29.6$, where t is the number of years since 1955 ($t = 0$ corresponds to the year 1955 and $0 \leq t \leq 39$; see Figure 5-3).

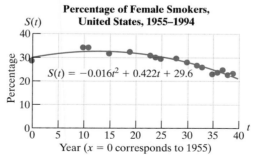

Source: Centers for Disease Control.

Figure 5-3

a. Use the function S to approximate the percentage of female smokers in the United States in the year 1955.
b. Use the function S to approximate the percentage of female smokers in the year 1988.

Solution:

a. $S(t) = -0.016t^2 + 0.422t + 29.6$ The year 1955 corresponds to $t = 0$.

     $S(0) = -0.016(0)^2 + 0.422(0) + 29.6$ Substitute $t = 0$.

          $= 29.6$ Simplify.

Approximately 29.6% of females in the United States were smokers in the year 1955.

b. $S(t) = -0.016t^2 + 0.422t + 29.6$ 1988 is 33 years after 1955.

     $S(33) = -0.016(33)^2 + 0.422(33) + 29.6$ Substitute $t = 33$.

          ≈ 26.1 Simplify.

Approximately 26.1% of females in the United States were smokers in the year 1988.

---

example 3

An Application of a Polynomial Function

An engineering student has a radio-controlled model airplane. The student flies the plane over an open field and has a programmed flight path for landing. Four hundred horizontal feet from the landing point, the plane begins its descent (Figure 5-4). The flight path for landing can be modeled by

$$f(x) = -\frac{1}{320,000}x^3 + \frac{3}{1600}x^2$$ where x is the horizontal distance from the landing point, and $f(x)$ is the altitude (all units are in feet).

Figure 5-4

Find the function values and interpret their meaning in the context of this problem.

a. $f(400)$ b. $f(300)$ c. $f(100)$

Solution:

a. $\quad f(x) = -\dfrac{1}{320,000}x^3 + \dfrac{3}{1600}x^2$

$\quad f(400) = -\dfrac{1}{320,000}(400)^3 + \dfrac{3}{1600}(400)^2$ Substitute 400 for x.

$\qquad\qquad = -\dfrac{1}{320,000}(64,000,000) + \dfrac{3}{1600}(160,000)$

$\qquad\qquad = -200 + 300$

$\qquad\qquad = 100$

$f(400) = 100$ means that when the plane is 400 horizontal feet from the landing point, its altitude is 100 ft.

b. $\quad f(300) = -\dfrac{1}{320,000}(300)^3 + \dfrac{3}{1600}(300)^2$ Substitute 300 for x.

$\qquad\qquad = -\dfrac{1}{320,000}(27,000,000) + \dfrac{3}{1600}(90,000)$

$\qquad\qquad = -84.375 + 168.75$

$\qquad\qquad = 84.375$

$f(300) = 84.375$ means that when the plane is 300 horizontal feet from the landing point, its altitude is 84.375 ft.

c. $\quad f(100) = -\dfrac{1}{320,000}(100)^3 + \dfrac{3}{1600}(100)^2$ Substitute 100 for x.

$\qquad\qquad = 15.625$

$f(100) = 15.625$ means that when the plane is 100 horizontal feet from the landing point, its altitude is 15.625 ft.

---

section 5.2   PRACTICE EXERCISES

For Exercises 1–10, simplify the expression and write the answer with positive exponents only.

1. p^3p^5 2. q^4q^3

3. $(p^3)^5$ 4. $(q^4)^3$

5. $\dfrac{p^5}{p^3}$ 6. $\dfrac{q^4}{q^3}$

7. $\dfrac{p^3}{p^5}$ 8. $\dfrac{q^3}{q^4}$

9. $\dfrac{p^5}{p^5}$ 10. $\dfrac{q^4}{q^4}$

For Exercises 11–16, write the polynomial in descending order. Then identify the leading coefficient and the degree.

11. $a^2 - 6a^3 - a$ 12. $2b - b^4 + 5b^2$

13. $6x^2 - x + 3x^4 - 1$ 14. $8 - 4y + y^5 - y^2$

15. $100 - t^2$ 16. $-51 + s^2$

For Exercises 17–28, write a polynomial in one variable that is described by the following. (Answers may vary.)

17. A monomial of degree 5

18. A monomial of degree 4

19. A trinomial of degree 2

20. A trinomial of degree 3

21. A binomial of degree 4

22. A binomial of degree 2

23. A monomial of degree 0

24. A monomial of degree 1

25. A trinomial with leading coefficient -3

26. A trinomial with leading coefficient 1

27. A binomial with leading coefficient 1

28. A binomial with leading coefficient -2

29. Given $M(x) = x^2 + 2x - 1$, find the function values.

   a. $M(2)$ b. $M(1)$

   c. $M(0)$ d. $M(-2)$

30. Given $Q(x) = x^2 - 4x$, find the function values.

   a. $Q(-2)$ b. $Q(0)$

   c. $Q(3)$ d. $Q(-1)$

31. Given $P(x) = -x^3 + 2x - 5$, find the function values.

   a. $P(2)$ b. $P(-1)$

   c. $P(0)$ d. $P(4)$

32. Given $N(x) = -x^2 + 5x$, find the function values.

   a. $N(1)$ b. $N(-1)$

   c. $N(2)$ d. $N(0)$

33. Given $H(x) = \frac{1}{2}x^3 - x + \frac{1}{4}$, find the function values.

   a. $H(0)$ b. $H(2)$

   c. $H(-2)$ d. $H(-1)$

34. Given $K(x) = \frac{2}{3}x^2 + \frac{1}{9}$, find the function values.

   a. $K(0)$ b. $K(3)$

   c. $K(-3)$ d. $K(-1)$

35. Given $S(t) = -0.03t^3 + 1.01t + 6.1$, find the function values.

   a. $S(1)$ b. $S(-1)$

   c. $S(0)$ d. $S(2)$

36. Given $D(t) = -1.1t^2 - 0.3t + 4$, find the function values.

   a. $D(1)$ b. $D(0)$

   c. $D(-1)$ d. $D(-2)$

37. The function defined by $D(x) = 4x^2 + 129x + 1741$ approximates the yearly dormitory charges for private 4-year colleges between the years 1985 and 1997. $D(x)$ is measured in dollars and $x = 0$ corresponds to the year 1985. Find the function values and interpret their meaning in the context of this problem.

   a. $D(0)$ b. $D(2)$

   c. $D(4)$ d. $D(6)$

Yearly Dormitory Charge for Private 4-Year Colleges 1985–1997

$D(x) = 4x^2 + 129x + 1741$

Year ($x = 0$ corresponds to 1985)

Source: U.S. National Center for Education Statistics.

Figure for Exercise 37

38. The number of tuberculosis cases (in thousands) in the United States between 1976 and 1998 can be approximated by

$$T(x) = -0.0039x^3 + 0.168x^2 - 2.2054x + 32.1$$

where x represents the year ($x = 0$ corresponds to 1976).

   a. Evaluate $T(0)$, $T(8)$, and $T(20)$. (Round to the nearest whole unit.)

b. Interpret the function values from part (a) in the context of this problem.

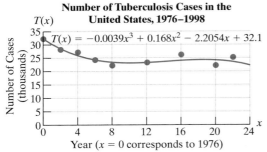

Number of Tuberculosis Cases in the United States, 1976–1998

$T(x) = -0.0039x^3 + 0.168x^2 - 2.2054x + 32.1$

Source: Centers for Disease Control.

Figure for Exercise 38

39. The number of women, w, who were due child support in the United States between 1985 and 1989 can be approximated by

    $W(t) = 143t + 4435$ where t is the number of years after 1985 and $W(t)$ is measured in thousands. (*Source:* U.S. Bureau of the Census.)

    a. Evaluate $W(0)$, $W(1)$, and $W(2)$.

    b. Interpret the meaning of the function values found in part (a).

40. The total amount of child support due (in billions of dollars) in the United States between 1985 and 1989 can be approximated by

    $D(t) = 0.925t + 13.083$ where t is the number of years after 1985 and $D(t)$ is the amount due (in billions of dollars).

    a. Evaluate $D(0)$, $D(2)$, and $D(4)$. Match the function values with points on the graph.

    b. Interpret the meaning of the function values found in part (a).

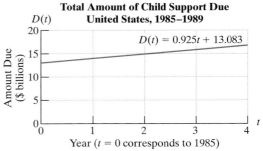

Total Amount of Child Support Due United States, 1985–1989

$D(t) = 0.925t + 13.083$

Source: U.S. Bureau of the Census.

Figure for Exercise 40

41. The percentage of white high school seniors who engaged in daily cigarette smoking in the United States can be approximated by

    $W(x) = 0.0835x^2 - 1.6556x + 28.3$ where x is the year ($x = 0$ corresponds to 1977) and $W(x)$ is measured as a percentage.

    Use the function W to approximate the percentage of white high school seniors who engaged in daily cigarette smoking in the year 1980 and in the year 1994. (Round to the nearest tenth of a percent.)

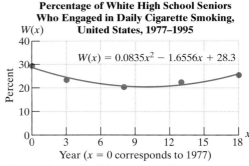

Percentage of White High School Seniors Who Engaged in Daily Cigarette Smoking, United States, 1977–1995

$W(x) = 0.0835x^2 - 1.6556x + 28.3$

Source: Centers for Disease Control.

Figure for Exercise 41

42. The percentage of black high school seniors who engaged in daily cigarette smoking in the United States can be approximated by

$B(x) = 0.101x^2 - 2.717x + 23.4$ where x is the year ($x = 0$ corresponds to 1977) and $B(x)$ is measured as a percentage.

Use the function B to approximate the percentage of black high school seniors who engaged in daily cigarette smoking in the year 1980 and in the year 1994. (Round to the nearest tenth of a percent.)

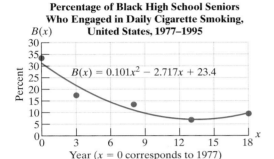

Percentage of Black High School Seniors Who Engaged in Daily Cigarette Smoking, United States, 1977–1995

Source: Centers for Disease Control.

Figure for Exercise 42

■ Expanding Your Skills

43. A toy rocket is shot from ground level at an angle of 60° from the horizontal. See figure. The x- and y-positions of the rocket (measured in feet) vary with time t according to

$$x(t) = 25t$$
$$y(t) = -16t^2 + 43.3t$$

a. Evaluate $x(0)$ and $y(0)$, and write the values as an ordered pair. Interpret the meaning of these function values in the context of this problem. Match the ordered pair with a point on the graph.

b. Evaluate $x(1)$ and $y(1)$ and write the values as an ordered pair. Interpret the meaning of these function values in the context of this problem. Match the ordered pair with a point on the graph.

c. Evaluate $x(2)$ and $y(2)$, and write the values as an ordered pair. Match the ordered pair with a point on the graph.

Figure for Exercise 43

44. A baseball is thrown at an angle of 30° from the horizontal. See figure. The x- and y-positions of the ball (measured in feet) vary with time t according to

$$x(t) = 60.6t$$
$$y(t) = -16t^2 + 35t + 5$$ where t is the number of seconds after the ball is released

a. Evaluate $x(0)$ and $y(0)$ and write the values as an ordered pair. Interpret the meaning of these function values in the context of this problem. Match the ordered pair with a point on the graph.

b. Evaluate $x(1)$ and $y(1)$, and write the values as an ordered pair. Interpret the meaning of these function values in the context of this problem. Match the ordered pair with a point on the graph.

c. Evaluate $x(2)$ and $y(2)$, and write the values as an ordered pair. Match the ordered pair with a point on the graph.

Figure for Exercise 44

45. a. Graph $D(x) = 4x^2 + 129x + 1741$ on a viewing window defined by $0 \le x \le 12$ and $0 \le y \le 5000$.

    b. Use a *Table* feature to evaluate $D(0)$, $D(2)$, $D(4)$, $D(6)$, and $D(8)$. Do these values agree with your solution to Exercise 37?

46. a. Graph $T(x) = -0.0039x^3 + 0.168x^2 - 2.2054x + 32.1$ on a viewing window defined by $0 \le x \le 24$ and $0 \le y \le 40$.

    b. Use a *Table* feature to evaluate $T(0)$, $T(4)$, $T(8)$, and $T(12)$. Do these values agree with your solution to Exercise 38?

---

section

Concepts

1. Addition of Polynomials
2. Opposite of a Polynomial
3. Subtraction of Polynomials
4. Adding and Subtracting Polynomial Functions
5. Applications of Polynomials

5.3   ADDITION AND SUBTRACTION OF POLYNOMIALS

1.   Addition of Polynomials

To add or subtract two polynomials, we combine *like* terms. Recall that two terms are ***like* terms** if they each have the same variables and the corresponding variables are raised to the same powers. The distributive property is used to combine *like* terms.

example 1

Adding Polynomials

Add the polynomials.

a. $-5t^2 - 7t^2 + 3t^2$
b. $-4.1x^2yz^3 + (-6.8x^2yz^3)$
c. $(a^2b + 7ab + 6) + (5a^2b - 2ab - 7)$

Solution:

a. $-5t^2 - 7t^2 + 3t^2$

   $= t^2(-5 - 7 + 3)$ Apply the distributive property.

   $= t^2(-9)$ Simplify.

   $= -9t^2$

Tip: Although the distributive property is used to combine *like* terms, the process is simplified by combining the coefficients of *like* terms.

$-5t^2 - 7t^2 + 3t^2 = -9t^2$

b. $-4.1x^2yz^3 + (-6.8x^2yz^3)$

   $= -10.9x^2yz^3$ Add *like* terms.

c. $(a^2b + 7ab + 6) + (5a^2b - 2ab - 7)$

   $= a^2b + 5a^2b + 7ab + (-2ab) + 6 + (-7)$ Group *like* terms.

   $= 6a^2b + 5ab - 1$ Add *like* terms.

Tip: Addition of polynomials can be performed vertically by vertically aligning *like* terms.

$$(a^2b + 7ab + 6) + (5a^2b - 2ab - 7) \longrightarrow$$

$$\begin{array}{r} a^2b + 7ab + 6 \\ + \ 5a^2b - 2ab - 7 \\ \hline 6a^2b + 5ab - 1 \end{array}$$

2. Opposite of a Polynomial

The opposite (or additive inverse) of a real number a is $-a$. Similarly, if A is a polynomial, then $-A$ is its opposite.

example 2

Finding the Opposite of a Polynomial

Find the opposite of the polynomials.

a. $4x$ b. $5a - 2b - c$ c. $5.5y^4 - 2.4y^3 + 1.1y - 3$

Solution:

a.   The opposite of $4x$ is $-(4x)$ or $-4x$.

b.   The opposite of $5a - 2b - c$ is $-(5a - 2b - c)$
     or equivalently $-5a + 2b + c$.

c.   The opposite of $5.5y^4 - 2.4y^3 + 1.1y - 3$ is $-(5.5y^4 - 2.4y^3 + 1.1y - 3)$ or
     equivalently $-5.5y^4 + 2.4y^3 - 1.1y + 3$.

Tip: Notice that the sign of each term is changed when finding the opposite of a polynomial.

3. Subtraction of Polynomials

Subtraction of two polynomials is similar to subtracting real numbers. Add the opposite of the second polynomial to the first polynomial.

Definition of Subtraction of Polynomials

If A and B are polynomials, then $A - B = A + (-B)$.

example 3

Subtracting Polynomials

Subtract the polynomials.

a. $(3x^2 + 2x - 5) - (4x^2 - 7x + 2)$ b. $(x^2y - 2xy + 5) - (x^2y - 3)$

Solution:

a. $(3x^2 + 2x - 5) - (4x^2 - 7x + 2)$

$$= (3x^2 + 2x - 5) + (-4x^2 + 7x - 2) \qquad \text{Add the opposite of the second polynomial.}$$

$$= 3x^2 + (-4x^2) + 2x + 7x + (-5) + (-2) \qquad \text{Group } like \text{ terms.}$$

$$= -x^2 + 9x - 7 \qquad \text{Combine } like \text{ terms.}$$

Graphing Calculator Box

A graphing calculator can be used to determine whether two algebraic expressions are equivalent. Consider the polynomial operations in Example 3a. By graphing the equations

$$y = (3x^2 + 2x - 5) - (4x^2 - 7x + 2)$$

and

$$y = -x^2 + 9x - 7$$

we see that the graphs coincide. This suggests that the polynomials are equivalent.

b. $(6x^2y - 2xy + 5) - (x^2y - 3)$

$\qquad = (6x^2y - 2xy + 5) + (-x^2y + 3)$ Add the opposite of the second polynomial.

$\qquad = 6x^2y + (-x^2y) + (-2xy) + 5 + 3$ Group *like* terms.

$\qquad = 5x^2y - 2xy + 8$ Combine *like* terms.

Tip: Subtraction of polynomials can be performed vertically by vertically aligning *like* terms. Then add the opposite of the second polynomial. "Place holders," (shown in bold) may be used to help line up *like* terms.

$$(6x^2y - 2xy + 5) - (x^2y - 3) \longrightarrow \begin{array}{r} 6x^2y - 2xy + 5 \\ -(x^2y + \mathbf{0}xy - 3) \end{array} \xrightarrow[\text{opposite}]{\text{add the}} \begin{array}{r} 6x^2y - 2xy + 5 \\ + -x^2y - \mathbf{0}xy + 3 \\ \hline 5x^2y - 2xy + 8 \end{array}$$

example 4   **Subtracting Polynomials**

Subtract

$$\frac{1}{2}x^4 - \frac{3}{4}x^2 + \frac{1}{5} \qquad \text{from} \qquad \frac{3}{2}x^4 + \frac{1}{2}x^2 - 4x$$

and simplify the result.

Solution:

In general, to subtract a from b we write $b - a$. Therefore, to subtract

$$\frac{1}{2}x^4 - \frac{3}{4}x^2 + \frac{1}{5} \qquad \text{from} \qquad \frac{3}{2}x^4 + \frac{1}{2}x^2 - 4x$$

we have:

$$\left(\frac{3}{2}x^4 + \frac{1}{2}x^2 - 4x\right) - \left(\frac{1}{2}x^4 - \frac{3}{4}x^2 + \frac{1}{5}\right)$$

$$= \frac{3}{2}x^4 + \frac{1}{2}x^2 - 4x - \frac{1}{2}x^4 + \frac{3}{4}x^2 - \frac{1}{5} \qquad \text{Subtract the polynomials.}$$

$$= \frac{3}{2}x^4 - \frac{1}{2}x^4 + \frac{1}{2}x^2 + \frac{3}{4}x^2 - 4x - \frac{1}{5} \qquad \text{Group } \textit{like} \text{ terms.}$$

$$= \frac{3}{2}x^4 - \frac{1}{2}x^4 + \frac{2}{4}x^2 + \frac{3}{4}x^2 - 4x - \frac{1}{5} \qquad \begin{array}{l}\text{Write } \textit{like} \text{ terms with a} \\ \text{common denominator.}\end{array}$$

$$= \frac{2}{2}x^4 + \frac{5}{4}x^2 - 4x - \frac{1}{5} \qquad \text{Combine } \textit{like} \text{ terms.}$$

$$= x^4 + \frac{5}{4}x^2 - 4x - \frac{1}{5} \qquad \text{Reduce.}$$

4. Adding and Subtracting Polynomial Functions

Recall that functions may be defined in terms of other functions through addition, subtraction, multiplication, division, and composition. For example, recall that

$$(f + g)(x) = f(x) + g(x)$$

$$(f - g)(x) = f(x) - g(x)$$

example 5

Adding and Subtracting Polynomial Functions

Given

$$f(t) = 4t^3 - 3t^2 - 5, \quad g(t) = -2t^3 + 7t^2 + 11, \quad \text{and} \quad h(t) = -t^3 + 4t - 2$$

Find $(f + g - h)(t)$.

Solution:

$$(f + g - h)(t) = f(t) + g(t) - h(t)$$

$$= (4t^3 - 3t^2 - 5) + (-2t^3 + 7t^2 + 11) - (-t^3 + 4t - 2)$$

$$= 4t^3 - 3t^2 - 5 - 2t^3 + 7t^2 + 11 + t^3 - 4t + 2 \qquad \text{Clear parentheses.}$$

$$= \underbrace{4t^3 - 2t^3 + t^3}_{} \underbrace{- 3t^2 + 7t^2}_{} \underbrace{- 4t}_{} \underbrace{- 5 + 11 + 2}_{} \qquad \text{Group } \textit{like} \text{ terms.}$$

$$= 3t^3 + 4t^2 - 4t + 8 \qquad \text{Combine } \textit{like} \text{ terms.}$$

5.   Applications of Polynomials

example 6

An Application of Adding Polynomial Functions

Figure 5-5 depicts the number of bachelor's degrees (in thousands) earned by males and by females between 1971 and 1998.

Number of Bachelor's Degrees Earned (thousands) by Males and Females, 1971–1998

Source: National Center for Education Statistics.

Figure 5-5

Let x represent the numbers of years since 1971 ($x = 0$ corresponds to 1971). Then for $0 \le x \le 27$, the functions defined by

$$M(x) = 0.1075x^2 - 0.8759x + 474.1 \quad \text{and} \quad F(x) = 0.0472x^2 + 9.694x + 361.7$$

approximate the number of bachelor's degrees earned by males and females, respectively.

a.   Find the function defined by $T(x) = (M + F)(x)$. What does $T(x)$ represent in the context of this problem?
b.   Evaluate $T(5)$ and interpret the meaning of the function value in the context of this problem.

Solution:

a. $T(x) = (M + F)(x) = M(x) + F(x)$ represents the total number of bachelor's degrees (in thousands) earned by *both* men and women, x years after 1971 (Figure 5-6).

$$T(x) = \overbrace{\qquad\qquad M(x) \qquad\qquad}^{} + \overbrace{\qquad\qquad F(x) \qquad\qquad}^{}$$

$$= (0.1075x^2 - 0.8759x + 474.1) + (0.0472x^2 + 9.694x + 361.7)$$
$$= 0.1547x^2 + 8.8181x + 835.8$$

b. $T(5) = 0.1547(5)^2 + 8.8181(5) + 835.8 \qquad$ Substitute $x = 5$.
$$\approx 884$$

$T(5) \approx 884$ indicates that in the year 1976 ($x = 5$), the total number of bachelor's degrees earned by both men and women was approximately 884,000.

**Number of Bachelor's Degrees Earned
(thousands) by Males and Females,
1971–1998**

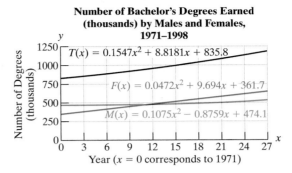

Figure 5-6

example 7

Using Polynomials in Applications and Translations

One angle in a triangle is twice as large as the smallest angle. The third angle is four degrees more than the smallest angle. Let x represent the smallest angle. Find a polynomial function, S, that represents the sum of the angles in the triangle and simplify the result.

Solution:

Let x represent the smallest angle. Then the three angles of the triangle can be expressed in terms of x as follows:

Smallest angle:	x
Second angle:	$2x$
Third angle:	$x + 4$

The sum of the angles is given by

$$S(x) = (x) + (2x) + (x + 4)$$
$$= 4x + 4$$

example 8

Using Polynomials in Applications and Translations

The length of a rectangle is 4 m less than 3 times the width. Let x represent the width. Write a polynomial function, P, that represents the perimeter of the rectangle and simplify the result.

Solution:

Let x represent the width. Then $3x - 4$ is the length.
The perimeter of a rectangle is given by: $P = 2L + 2W$.
Thus:

$$P(x) = 2(3x - 4) + 2(x)$$
$$= 6x - 8 + 2x$$
$$= 8x - 8$$

section 5.3   PRACTICE EXERCISES

For Exercises 1–6, simplify the expression and write the answer with positive exponents only.

1. $(2a^2b^{-1}c)^4$

2. $(5p^{-4}q^3)^{-2}$

3. $\left(\dfrac{x^{-3}}{3y^4}\right)^{-3}$

4. $\left(\dfrac{u^5}{4v^{-1}}\right)^{-2}$

5. $\left(\dfrac{r^2s^{-1}}{r^0s^{-4}}\right)(r^{-3}s)$

6. $(s^{-3}t^6)\left(\dfrac{s^0t^{-4}}{s^4t^{-5}}\right)$

7. Explain in words the difference between a binomial and a second-degree polynomial.

8. Explain in words the difference between a trinomial and a third-degree polynomial.

9. Write an example of a binomial of degree 7. (Answers may vary.)

10. Write an example of a trinomial with leading coefficient -6. (Answers may vary.)

For Exercises 11–34, add or subtract the polynomials and simplify. Write the answers in descending order.

11. $(4m - 4m^2) + (6m + 5m^2)$

12. $(3n^3 + 5n) + (2n^3 - 2n)$

13. $(13z^5 - z^2) - (7z^5 + 5z^2)$

14. $(8w^4 + 3w^2) - (12w^4 - w^2)$

15. $(8y^2 - 4y^3) - (3y^2 - 8y^3)$

16. $(-9y^2 - 8) - (4y^2 + 3)$

17. $(-2r - 6r^4) + (-9r - r^4)$

18. $(-8s^9 + 7s^2) + (7s^9 - s^2)$

19. $(3x^4 - x^3 - x^2) + (3x^3 - 7x^2 + 2x)$

20. $(6x^3 - 2x^2 - 12) + (x^2 + 3x + 9)$

21. $(-3x^3 + 2x^2 - x + 6) - (x^3 - x^2 - x + 1)$

22. $(-8x^3 + 6x + 7) + (-5x^3 - 2x - 4)$

23. $\left(\dfrac{1}{5}a^2 - \dfrac{1}{2}ab + \dfrac{1}{10}b^2 + 3\right)$
$- \left(-\dfrac{3}{10}a^2 + \dfrac{2}{5}ab - \dfrac{1}{2}b^2 - 5\right)$

24. $\left(\dfrac{4}{7}a^2 - \dfrac{1}{7}ab + \dfrac{1}{14}b^2 - 7\right)$
$- \left(\dfrac{1}{2}a^2 - \dfrac{2}{7}ab - \dfrac{9}{14}b^2 + 1\right)$

25. $\left(\dfrac{1}{2}w^3 + \dfrac{2}{9}w^2 - 1.8w\right) + \left(\dfrac{3}{2}w^3 - \dfrac{1}{9}w^2 + 2.7w\right)$

26. $\left(2.9t^4 - \dfrac{7}{8}t + \dfrac{5}{3}\right) + \left(-8.1t^4 - \dfrac{1}{8}t - \dfrac{1}{3}\right)$

27. $[2p - (3p + 5)] + (4p - 6) + 2$

28. $-(q - 2) - [4 - (2q - 3) + 5]$

29. Add $(9x^2 - 5x + 1)$ to $(8x^2 + x - 15)$

30. Add $(-x^3 + 5x)$ to $(10x^3 + x^2 - 10)$

31. Subtract $(9x^2 - 5x + 1)$ from $(8x^2 + x - 15)$

32. Subtract $(-x^3 + 5x)$ from $(10x^3 + x^2 - 10)$

33. Find the difference of $3x^5 - 2x^3 + 4$ and $x^4 + 2x^3 - 7$

34. Find the difference of $7x^{10} - 2x^4 - 3x$ and $-4x^3 - 5x^4 + x + 5$

For Exercises 35–38, find $(f + g)(x)$ and $(f - g)(x)$ and simplify.

35. $f(x) = 5x + 13x^2 + 3$, $g(x) = 4x^2 - 8$

36. $f(x) = 6x^3 - 2x$, $g(x) = -2x^3 + 13$

37. $f(x) = 11x - 23$, $g(x) = 7x - 19$

38. $f(x) = -4x^2 + 9$, $g(x) = 8x^2 - 12$

39. A rectangular garden is designed to be 3 ft longer than it is wide. Let x represent the width of the garden. Find a function P that represents the perimeter in terms of x. (*Hint:* Add all sides.)

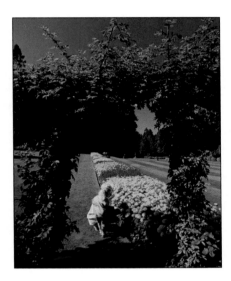

40. A flower bed is in the shape of a triangle with the larger side 3 times the middle side and the smallest side 2 ft shorter than the middle side. Let x represent the length of the middle side. Find a function P that represents the perimeter in terms of x.

41. The cost in dollars of producing x toy cars is $C(x) = 2.2x + 1$. The revenue received is $R(x) = 5.98x$. To calculate profit, subtract the cost from the revenue.

    a. Write and simplify a function P that represents profit in terms of x.

    b. Find the profit of producing 50 toy cars.

42. The cost in dollars of producing x lawn chairs is $C(x) = 2.5x + 10.1$. The revenue for selling x chairs is $R(x) = 6.99x$. To calculate profit, subtract the cost from the revenue.

    a. Write and simplify a function P that represents profit in terms of x.

    b. Find the profit of producing 100 lawn chairs.

43. The functions defined by $D(t) = 0.925t + 13.083$ and $R(t) = 0.725t + 8.683$ approximate the amount of child support (in billions of dollars) that was due and the amount of child support actually received in the United States between 1985 and 1989. In each case, $t = 0$ corresponds to 1985.

    a. Find the function F defined by $F(t) = D(t) - R(t)$. What does F represent in the context of this problem?

    b. Find $F(0)$, $F(2)$, and $F(4)$. What do these function values represent in the context of this problem?

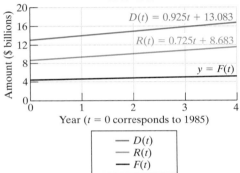

The Difference Between Child Support Due and Child Support Paid, United States, 1985–1989

Source: U.S. Bureau of the Census.

Figure for Exercise 43

44. If t represents the number of years after 1900, then the rural and urban populations in the South (United States) between 1900 and 1970 can be approximated by

    $$r(t) = -3.497t^2 + 266.2t + 20{,}220$$

    $t = 0$ corresponds to 1900 and $r(t)$ represents the rural population in thousands.

    $$u(t) = 0.0566t^3 + 0.952t^2 + 177.8t + 4593$$

    $t = 0$ corresponds to 1900 and $u(t)$ represents the urban population in thousands.

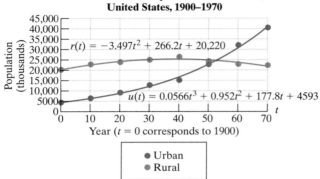

Rural and Urban Populations in the South, United States, 1900–1970

$r(t) = -3.497t^2 + 266.2t + 20{,}220$

$u(t) = 0.0566t^3 + 0.952t^2 + 177.8t + 4593$

Year ($t = 0$ corresponds to 1900)

● Urban
● Rural

Source: Historical Abstract of the United States.

Figure for Exercise 44

a. Find the function T defined by $T(t) = r(t) + u(t)$. What does the function T represent in the context of this problem.

b. Use the function T to approximate the total population in the South for the year 1940.

45. Write a polynomial that represents the missing angle.

Figure for Exercise 45

46. Write a polynomial that represents the missing angle.

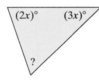

Figure for Exercise 46

47. Write a polynomial that represents the missing angle.

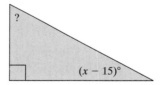

Figure for Exercise 47

48. Write a polynomial that represents the missing angle.

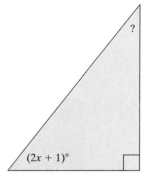

Figure for Exercise 48

49. The two angles pictured are complementary. Find a polynomial that represents the missing angle.

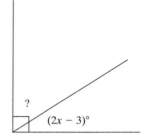

Figure for Exercise 49

50. The two angles pictured are complementary. Find a polynomial that represents the missing angle.

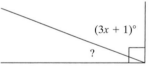

Figure for Exercise 50

51. The two angles pictured are supplementary. Find a polynomial that represents the missing angle.

Figure for Exercise 51

52. The two angles pictured are supplementary. Find a polynomial that represents the missing angle.

Figure for Exercise 52

EXPANDING YOUR SKILLS

For Exercises 53–58, add or subtract as indicated.

53. $[x - (x^2 + 4x - 5)] - [-(x + 3)]$

54. $[5x - [-(2x - 4)] + 6x^2] - [x - (2x - 7)]$

55. $[4y^2 - (y + 2) + (4 - y^2)] - [y - (6y + y^2)]$

56. $[(t^3 + 6) - (2t^2 + 1) + (t^2 - 3t)]$
    $- [t^3 - (5t + 3)]$

57. $(7.23x^3 - 4.71x^2 + 4.52)$
    $- (-2.14x^3 + 5.62x^2 - 1.01)$

58. $(2.1x^5 + 1.7x^3) - (4.06x^3 - 8.1x^4)$

GRAPHING CALCULATOR EXERCISES

59. Refer to Exercise 19. Graph Y_1 and Y_2 on a viewing window defined by $-5 \le x \le 5$ and $-20 \le y \le 20$.

    $Y_1 = (3x^4 - x^3 - x^2) + (3x^3 - 7x^2 + 2x)$

    $Y_2 = 3x^4 + 2x^3 - 8x^2 + 2x$

Do the graphs appear to coincide? What does this suggest about the following expressions?

$$(3x^4 - x^3 - x^2) + (3x^3 - 7x^2 + 2x)$$
$$\text{and} \quad 3x^4 + 2x^3 - 8x^2 + 2x$$

60. Refer to Exercise 20. Graph Y_1 and Y_2 on a viewing window defined by $-4 \le x \le 4$ and $-15 \le y \le 15$.

    $Y_1 = (6x^3 - 2x^2 - 12) + (x^2 + 3x + 9)$

    $Y_2 = 6x^3 - x^2 + 3x - 3$

Do the graphs appear to coincide? What does this suggest about the following expressions?

$$(6x^3 - 2x^2 - 12) + (x^2 + 3x + 9)$$
$$\text{and} \quad 6x^3 - x^2 + 3x - 3$$

---

chapter 5   MIDCHAPTER REVIEW

For Exercises 1–15, simplify the expression and leave the answer with positive exponents.

1. $\left(\dfrac{x^5}{x^2}\right)^3$

2. $\left(\dfrac{y^3}{y^2}\right)^4$

3. $\left(\dfrac{6^5}{6^2}\right)^3$

4. $\left(\dfrac{2^3}{2^2}\right)^4$

5. $\dfrac{x^4}{x^{-6}}$

6. $\dfrac{y^5}{y^{-2}}$

7. $\dfrac{(b^5)^3}{b^{10}}$

8. $\dfrac{(c^3)^4}{c^7}$

9. $\dfrac{(a^6)^2 a^4}{(a^5)^8}$

10. $\dfrac{(x^3)^2 x^5}{(x^4)^3}$

11. $\dfrac{(2m^3 n^4)^5}{(m^2 n^6)^3}$

12. $\dfrac{(5a^3 b^{10})^2}{(a^8 b^4)^3}$

13. $\left(\dfrac{a^{-8} b^{-3}}{a^{-5} b^6}\right)^{-2}$

14. $\left(\dfrac{x^{-3} y^5}{x^{-5} y^2}\right)^{-2}$

15. $\left(\dfrac{x^{-3} y^2}{x^4 y^{-5}}\right)^{-2}\left(\dfrac{x^3 y^{-1}}{xy^0}\right)$

16. The federal debt was $290,525,000,000 in 1990. Write this number in scientific notation.

17. The federal debt is predicted to be $6,063,900,000,000 in 2003. Write this number in scientific notation.

18. Earth travels around the sun in an elliptical orbit that is nearly circular. The average distance between earth and the sun is approximately 9.3×10^7 miles.

    a. Find the circumference of the earth's orbit. $(C = 2\pi r)$ (Round to the nearest million.)

    b. If earth travels around the sun in 365 days, determine the number of hours this represents.

    c. Find the speed that earth travels around the sun. (*Hint:* divide the number of miles found in part (a) by the number of hours found in part (b).)

19. The profit (in dollars) that a company makes selling calculators is a function of the number of calculators produced, x. The profit function is defined as

$$P(x) = -\frac{1}{10,000}x^2 + 5x$$

    a. What is the profit in producing 10,000 calculators?

    b. What is the profit in producing 30,000 calculators?

20. The average annual income for physicians specializing in obstetrics and gynecology between 1985 and 1995 can be approximated by

$I(x) = 11.828x + 135.32$ where $I(x)$ is measured in thousands of dollars and x is the time in years after 1985 ($x = 0$ corresponds to the year 1985).

Most physicians purchase malpractice insurance to provide financial protection against expensive law-suits. The average annual malpractice premium for physicians specializing in obstetrics and gynecology between 1985 and 1995 can be approximated by

$M(x) = 1.3996x + 24.882$ where $M(x)$ is measured in thousands of dollars, and x is the time in years after 1985 ($x = 0$ corresponds to the year 1985).

The graphs of $y = I(x)$ and $y = M(x)$ are shown in the following figure.

Annual Income and Annual Malpractice Premiums for Physicians Specializing in Obstetrics and Gynecology (1985–1995)

Source: American Medical Association.

Figure for Exercise 20

a. What is the slope of the function I? Interpret the slope in the context of this problem.

b. What is the slope of the function M? Interpret the slope in the context of this problem.

c. Find an expression for the function defined by $P(x) = I(x) - M(x)$. What does the function P represent in the context of the problem?

d. Find $I(10)$, $M(10)$, and $P(10)$. Interpret the results in the context of the problem.

section

5.4   MULTIPLICATION OF POLYNOMIALS

1. Multiplying Monomials

The properties of exponents covered in Section 5.1 can be used to simplify many algebraic expressions including the multiplication of monomials. To multiply monomials, first use the associative and commutative properties of multiplication to group coefficients and *like* bases. Then simplify the result by using the properties of exponents.

---

example 1   **Multiplying Monomials**

Multiply the monomials.

a. $(3x^2y^7)(5x^3y)$

b. $(-3x^4y^3)(-2x^6yz^8)$

Solution:

a. $(3x^2y^7)(5x^3y)$

$\quad = (3 \cdot 5)(x^2 \cdot x^3)(y^7 \cdot y)$ Group coefficients and like bases.

$\quad = 15x^5y^8$ Add exponents and simplify.

b. $(-3x^4y^3)(-2x^6yz^8)$

$\quad = [(-3)(-2)](x^4 \cdot x^6)(y^3 \cdot y)(z^8)$ Group coefficients and like bases.

$\quad = 6x^{10}y^4z^8$ Add exponents and simplify.

---

2. Multiplying a Polynomial by a Monomial

The distributive property is used to multiply polynomials: $a(b + c) = ab + ac$.

---

example 2   **Multiplying a Polynomial by a Monomial**

Multiply the polynomials.

a. $5y^3(2y^2 - 7y + 6)$

b. $-4a^3b^7c\left(2ab^2c^4 - \dfrac{1}{2}a^5b\right)$

Solution:

a. $5y^3(2y^2 - 7y + 6)$

$\quad = (5y^3)(2y^2) + (5y^3)(-7y) + (5y^3)(6)$ Apply the distributive property.

$\quad = 10y^5 - 35y^4 + 30y^3$ Simplify each term.

b. $-4a^3b^7c\left(2ab^2c^4 - \dfrac{1}{2}a^5b\right)$

$= (-4a^3b^7c)(2ab^2c^4) + (-4a^3b^7c)\left(-\dfrac{1}{2}a^5b\right)$ Apply the distributive property.

$= -8a^4b^9c^5 + 2a^8b^8c$ Simplify each term.

Thus far, we have illustrated polynomial multiplication involving monomials. Next, the distributive property will be used to multiply polynomials with more than one term. For example:

$(x + 3)(x + 5) = (x + 3)x + (x + 3)5$ Apply the distributive property.

$= (x + 3)x + (x + 3)5$ Apply the distributive property again.

$= x \cdot x + 3 \cdot x + x \cdot 5 + 3 \cdot 5$

$= x^2 + 3x + 5x + 15$

$= x^2 + 8x + 15$ Combine *like* terms.

Note: Using the distributive property results in multiplying each term of the first polynomial by each term of the second polynomial:

$(x + 3)(x + 5) = x \cdot x + x \cdot 5 + 3 \cdot x + 3 \cdot 5$

$= x^2 + 5x + 3x + 15$

$= x^2 + 8x + 15$

3.   Multiplying Polynomials

example 3   **Multiplying Polynomials**

Multiply the polynomials.

a. $(2x^2 + 4)(3x^2 - x + 5)$ b. $(3y + 2)(7y - 6)$

Solution:

a. $(2x^2 + 4)(3x^2 - x + 5)$ Multiply each term in the first polynomial by each term in the second.

$= (2x^2)(3x^2) + (2x^2)(-x) + (2x^2)(5)$
$\qquad + (4)(3x^2) + (4)(-x) + (4)(5)$ Apply the distributive property.

$$= 6x^4 - 2x^3 + 10x^2 + 12x^2 - 4x + 20 \qquad \text{Simplify each term.}$$

$$= 6x^4 - 2x^3 + 22x^2 - 4x + 20 \qquad \text{Combine } like \text{ terms.}$$

Tip: Multiplication of polynomials can be performed vertically by a process similar to column multiplication of real numbers.

$$(2x^2 + 4)(3x^2 - x + 5) \longrightarrow \begin{array}{r} 3x^2 - x + 5 \\ \times\ 2x^2 \qquad + 4 \\ \hline 12x^2 - 4x + 20 \\ 6x^4 - 2x^3 + 10x^2 \\ \hline 6x^4 - 2x^3 + 22x^2 - 4x + 20 \end{array}$$

Note: When multiplying by the column method, it is important to align *like* terms vertically before adding terms.

b. $(3y + 2)(7y - 6)$ — Multiply each term in the first polynomial by each term in the second.

$$= (3y)(7y) + (3y)(-6) + (2)(7y) + (2)(-6) \qquad \text{Apply the distributive property.}$$

$$= 21y^2 - 18y + 14y - 12 \qquad \text{Simplify each term.}$$

$$= 21y^2 - 4y - 12 \qquad \text{Combine } like \text{ terms.}$$

Tip: The acronym, FOIL (First Outer Inner Last) can be used as a memory device to multiply the terms of two binomials.

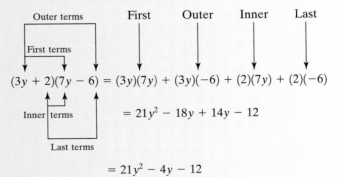

$$(3y + 2)(7y - 6) = (3y)(7y) + (3y)(-6) + (2)(7y) + (2)(-6)$$

$$= 21y^2 - 18y + 14y - 12$$

$$= 21y^2 - 4y - 12$$

Note: It is important to realize that the acronym FOIL may only be used when finding the product of two *binomials*.

4. Special Case Products: Difference of Squares and Perfect Square Trinomials

In some cases the product of two binomials takes on a special pattern.

I. The first special case occurs when multiplying the sum and difference of the same two terms. For example:

$$(2x + 3)(2x - 3)$$
$$= 2x^2 - 6x + 6x - 9$$
$$= 4x^2 - 9$$

Notice that the "middle terms" are opposites. This leaves only the difference between the square of the first term and the square of the second term. For this reason, the product is called a **difference of squares**.

Note: The sum and difference of the same two terms are called **conjugates**. Thus, the expressions $2x + 3$ and $2x - 3$ are conjugates of each other.

II. The second special case involves the square of a binomial. For example:

$$(3x + 7)^2$$
$$= (3x + 7)(3x + 7)$$
$$= 9x^2 + 21x + 21x + 49$$
$$= 9x^2 + 42x + 49$$
$$= (3x)^2 + 2(3x)(7) + (7)^2$$

When squaring a binomial, the product will be a trinomial called a **perfect square trinomial**. The first and third terms are formed by squaring the terms of the binomial. The middle term is twice the product of the terms in the binomial.

Note: The expression $(3x - 7)^2$ also results in a perfect square trinomial, but the middle term is negative.

$$(3x - 7)(3x - 7) = 9x^2 - 21x - 21x + 49 = 9x^2 - 42x + 49$$

The following table summarizes these special case products.

Special Case Product Formulas

1. $(a + b)(a - b) = a^2 - b^2$ The product is called a difference of squares.

2. $(a + b)^2 = a^2 + 2ab + b^2$
    $(a - b)^2 = a^2 - 2ab + b^2$ The product is called a perfect square trinomial.

It is advantageous for you to become familiar with these special case products because they will be presented again when we factor polynomials.

---

example 4   **Finding Special Products**

Use the special product formulas to multiply the polynomials.

a. $(5x - 2)^2$ b. $(6c - 7d)(6c + 7d)$ c. $(4x^3 + 3y^2)^2$

Solution:

a. $(5x - 2)^2$ $a = 5x, b = 2$

     $= (5x)^2 - 2(5x)(2) + (2)^2$ Apply the formula: $a^2 - 2ab + b^2$.

     $= 25x^2 - 20x + 4$ Simplify each term.

b. $(6c - 7d)(6c + 7d)$ $a = 6c, b = 7d$

     $= (6c)^2 - (7d)^2$ Apply the formula: $a^2 - b^2$.

     $= 36c^2 - 49d^2$ Simplify each term.

c. $(4x^3 + 3y^2)^2$ $a = 4x^3, b = 3y^2$

     $= (4x^3)^2 + 2(4x^3)(3y^2) + (3y^2)^2$ Apply the formula: $a^2 + 2ab + b^2$.

     $= 16x^6 + 24x^3y^2 + 9y^4$ Simplify each term.

The special case products can be used to simplify more complicated algebraic expressions.

example 5

Using Special Products

Multiply the following expressions.

a. $(x + y)^3$ b. $[x + (y + z)][x - (y + z)]$

Solution:

a. $(x + y)^3$

     $= (x + y)^2(x + y)$ Rewrite as the square of a binomial and another factor.

     $= (x^2 + 2xy + y^2)(x + y)$ Expand $(x + y)^2$ using the special case product formula.

     $= (x^2)(x) + (x^2)(y) + (2xy)(x)$ Apply the distributive
        $+ (2xy)(y) + (y^2)(x) + (y^2)(y)$ property.

     $= x^3 + x^2y + 2x^2y + 2xy^2 + xy^2 + y^3$ Simplify each term.

     $= x^3 + 3x^2y + 3xy^2 + y^3$ Combine *like* terms.

b. $[x + (y + z)][x - (y + z)]$ This product is in the form $(a + b)(a - b)$ where $a = x$ and $b = (y + z)$.

     $= (x)^2 - (y + z)^2$ Apply the formula: $a^2 - b^2$.

     $= (x)^2 - (y^2 + 2yz + z^2)$ Expand $(y + z)^2$ using the special case product formula.

     $= x^2 - y^2 - 2yz - z^2$ Apply the distributive property.

5.   Translations Involving Polynomials

example 6

Translating Between English Form and Algebraic Form

Complete the table.

English Form	Algebraic Form
The square of the sum of x and y.	
	$x^2 + y^2$
The square of the product of three and x.	

Solution:

English Form	Algebraic Form	Notes
The square of the sum of x and y.	$(x + y)^2$	The *sum* is squared, not the individual terms.
The sum of the squares of x and y.	$x^2 + y^2$	The individual terms x and y are squared first. Then the sum is taken.
The square of the product of three and x.	$(3x)^2$	The product of three and x is taken. Then the result is squared.

6.   Applications Involving a Product of Polynomials

example 7

Applying a Product of Polynomials

A box is created from a sheet of cardboard 20 in. on a side by cutting a square from each corner and folding up the sides (Figures 5-7 and 5-8). Let x represent the length of the sides of the squares removed from each corner.

a.   Find an expression for the volume of the box in terms of x.
b.   Find the volume if a 4-in. square is removed.

Figure 5-7   **Figure 5-8**

Solution:

a. The volume of a rectangular box is given by the formula: $V = lwh$. The length and width can both be expressed as $20 - 2x$. The height of the box is x. Hence the volume is given by

$$V = l \cdot w \cdot h$$
$$= (20 - 2x)(20 - 2x)x$$
$$\text{or} \quad = (20 - 2x)^2 x$$

b. If a 4-in. square is removed from the corners of the box, we have $x = 4$ in. Thus the volume is

$$V = (20 - 2(4))^2(4)$$
$$= (20 - 8)^2(4)$$
$$= (12)^2(4)$$
$$= (144)(4)$$
$$= 576$$

The volume is 576 in.^{3}

---

section 5.4   PRACTICE EXERCISES

For Exercises 1–4, simplify the expression and write the answer with positive exponents only.

1. $\left(\dfrac{z^2 z^{-3}}{3z^{-5}}\right)^4$

2. $\left(\dfrac{5w^4}{w^{-6}w^2}\right)^{-2}$

3. $(a^6 b^{-2})(ab^3)^{-1}$

4. $(x^3 y)^{-2}(x^{-1}y^3)$

5. Given $f(x) = 4x^3 - 5$, find the function values.
    a. $f(3)$ b. $f(0)$ c. $f(-2)$

6. Given $g(x) = x^4 - x^2 - 3$, find the function values.
    a. $g(-1)$ b. $g(2)$ c. $g(0)$

7. Given the polynomial functions defined by $P(x) = 3x^2 - 7x - 2$ and $Q(x) = -x^2 + 3x - 5$
    a. Find $P(x) + Q(x)$ and simplify.
    b. Find $P(x) - Q(x)$ and simplify.
    c. Find $Q(x) - P(x)$ and simplify.

8. Given the polynomial functions defined by $H(x) = 6x + 7$ and $K(x) = -3x^2 - x + 1$
    a. Find $H(x) + K(x)$ and simplify.
    b. Find $H(x) - K(x)$ and simplify.
    c. Find $K(x) - H(x)$ and simplify.

9. Can the terms $2x^3$ and $3x^2$ be combined by addition? Can they be combined by multiplication? Explain.

10. Write the distributive property of multiplication over addition. Give an example of the distributive property. (Answers may vary.)

For Exercises 11–46, multiply the polynomials using the distributive property and the special product formulas.

11. $3ab(a + b)$

12. $2a(3 - a)$

13. $\dfrac{1}{5}(2a - 3)$

14. $\dfrac{1}{3}(6b + 4)$

15. $2m^3 n^2(m^2 n^3 - 3mn^2 + 4n)$

16. $3p^2 q(p^3 q^3 - pq^2 - 4p)$

17. $(x + y)(x - 2y)$

18. $(3a + 5)(a - 2)$

19. $(1.3a - 4b)(2.5a + 7b)$

20. $(2.1x - 3.5y)(4.7x + 2y)$

21. $(2x + y)(3x^2 + 2xy + y^2)$

22. $(h - 5k)(h^2 - 2hk + 3k^2)$

23. $(x - 7)(x^2 + 7x + 49)$

24. $(x + 3)(x^2 - 3x + 9)$

25. $(4a - b)(a^3 - 4a^2b + ab^2 - b^3)$

26. $(3m + 2n)(m^3 + 2m^2n - mn^2 + 2n^3)$

27. $\left(\frac{1}{2}a - 2b + c\right)(a + 6b - c)$

28. $(x + y - 2z)(5x - y + z)$

29. $(-x^2 + 2x + 1)(3x - 5)$

30. $\left(\frac{1}{2}a^2 - 2ab + b^2\right)(2a + b)$

31. $(a - 8)(a + 8)$

32. $(b + 2)(b - 2)$

33. $(3p + 1)(3p - 1)$

34. $(5q - 3)(5q + 3)$

35. $\left(x - \frac{1}{3}\right)\left(x + \frac{1}{3}\right)$

36. $\left(\frac{1}{2}x + \frac{1}{3}\right)\left(\frac{1}{2}x - \frac{1}{3}\right)$

37. $(3h - k)(3h + k)$

38. $(x - 7y)(x + 7y)$

39. $(3h - k)^2$

40. $(x - 7y)^2$

41. $(t - 7)^2$

42. $(w + 9)^2$

43. $(u + 3v)^2$

44. $(a - 4b)^2$

45. $\left(h + \frac{1}{6}k\right)^2$

46. $\left(\frac{2}{5}x + 1\right)^2$

47. Multiply the expressions. Explain their similarities.
    a. $(A - B)(A + B)$
    b. $[(x + y) - B][(x + y) + B]$

48. Multiply the expressions. Explain their similarities.
    a. $(A + B)(A - B)$
    b. $[A + (3h + k)][A - (3h + k)]$

For Exercises 49–54, multiply the expressions.

49. $[(w + v) - 2][(w + v) + 2]$

50. $[(x + y) - 6][(x + y) + 6]$

51. $[2 - (x + y)][2 + (x + y)]$

52. $[a - (b + 1)][a + (b + 1)]$

53. $[(3a - 4) + b][(3a - 4) - b]$

54. $[(5p - 7) - q][(5p - 7) + q]$

55. Explain how to multiply $(x + y)^3$.

56. Explain how to multiply $(a - b)^3$.

For Exercises 57–60, multiply the expressions.

57. $(2x + y)^3$

58. $(x - 5y)^3$

59. $(4a - b)^3$

60. $(3a + 4b)^3$

61. Explain how you would multiply the following binomials:

$$(x - 2)(x + 6)(2x + 1)$$

62. Explain how you would multiply the following binomials:

$$(a + b)(a - b)(2a + b)(2a - b)$$

For Exercises 63–66, find $(f \cdot g)(x)$ and simplify.

63. $f(x) = 2x - 9, g(x) = -4x + 2$

64. $f(x) = 8x + 1, g(x) = x - 3$

65. $f(x) = x^2, g(x) = 9x^3 - 3x + 10$

66. $f(x) = -x^2, g(x) = 4x^2 + 3x - 5$

67. A rectangular garden has a walk around it of width x. The garden is 20 ft by 15 ft. Find a function, f, in terms of x that represents the combined area of the garden and walk. Simplify the result.

Figure for Exercise 67

68. An 8 in. by 10 in. photograph is in a frame of width x. Find a function, g, in terms of x that represents the area of the frame. Simplify the result.

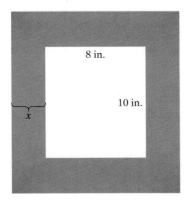

Figure for Exercise 68

For Exercises 69–76, write an expression for the area and simplify your answer.

69. Square

$x - 2$

70. Square

$x + 3$

71. Rectangle

$x - 2$

$x + 2$

72. Rectangle

$2x - 3$

$2x + 3$

73. Triangle

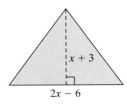

$x + 3$

$2x - 6$

74. Triangle

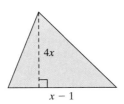

$4x$

$x - 1$

75. Parallelogram

$0.25x - 1.5$

4

76. Parallelogram

$2x - 5$

$\frac{1}{2}x$

For Exercises 77–80, write an expression for the volume and simplify your answer.

77.

$3x + 10$

$3x$

x

78.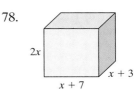

$2x$

$x + 3$

$x + 7$

79. Cube

$x + 4$

80. Cube

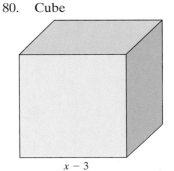

$x - 3$

■ EXPANDING YOUR SKILLS

81. Explain how to multiply $(x + 2)^4$.

82. Explain how to multiply $(y - 3)^4$.

83. $(2x - 3)$ multiplied by what binomial will result in the trinomial $10x^2 - 27x + 18$? Check your answer by multiplying the binomials.

84. $(4x + 1)$ multiplied by what binomial will result in the trinomial $12x^2 - 5x - 2$? Check your answer by multiplying the binomials.

85. $(4y + 3)$ multiplied by what binomial will result in the trinomial $8y^2 + 2y - 3$? Check your answer by multiplying the binomials.

86. $(3y - 2)$ multiplied by what binomial will result in the trinomial $3y^2 - 17y + 10$? Check your answer by multiplying the binomials.

87. Refer to Exercise 23. Graph Y_1 and Y_2 on a viewing window defined by $-10 \le x \le 10$ and $-1000 \le y \le 1000$.

$$Y_1 = (x - 7)(x^2 + 7x + 49)$$

$$Y_2 = x^3 - 343$$

Do the graphs appear to coincide? What does this suggest about the expressions $(x - 7)(x^2 + 7x + 49)$ and $x^3 - 343$?

88. Refer to Exercise 24. Graph Y_1 and Y_2 on a viewing window defined by $-10 \le x \le 10$ and $-100 \le y \le 100$.

$$Y_1 = (x + 3)(x^2 - 3x + 9)$$

$$Y_2 = x^3 + 27$$

Do the graphs appear to coincide? What does this suggest about the expressions $(x + 3)(x^2 - 3x + 9)$ and $x^3 + 27$?

89. Refer to Exercise 35. Graph Y_1 and Y_2 on a viewing window defined by $-5 \le x \le 5$ and $-5 \le y \le 5$.

$$Y_1 = \left(x - \frac{1}{3} \right)\left(x + \frac{1}{3} \right)$$

$$Y_2 = x^2 - \frac{1}{9}$$

Do the graphs appear to coincide? What does this suggest about the expressions

$$\left(x - \tfrac{1}{3}\right)\left(x + \tfrac{1}{3}\right) \quad \text{and} \quad x^2 - \tfrac{1}{9}?$$

90. Refer to Exercise 36. Graph Y_1 and Y_2 on a viewing window defined by $-5 \le x \le 5$ and $-5 \le y \le 5$.

$$Y_1 = \left(\frac{1}{2}x + \frac{1}{3} \right)\left(\frac{1}{2}x - \frac{1}{3} \right)$$

$$Y_2 = \frac{1}{4}x^2 - \frac{1}{9}$$

Do the graphs appear to coincide? What does this suggest about the expressions

$$\left(\tfrac{1}{2}x + \tfrac{1}{3}\right)\left(\tfrac{1}{2}x - \tfrac{1}{3}\right) \quad \text{and} \quad \tfrac{1}{4}x^2 - \tfrac{1}{9}?$$

---

section

5.5   DIVISION OF POLYNOMIALS

Concepts

1. **Division by a Monomial**
2. **Dividing a Polynomial by a Monomial**
3. **Long Division**
4. **Long Division Requiring Place Holders**

1. Division by a Monomial

Division of polynomials will be presented in this section as two separate cases. The first case illustrates division by a monomial divisor. The second case illustrates division by a polynomial with two or more terms.

To divide a polynomial by a monomial, divide each individual term in the polynomial by the divisor and simplify the result.

To Divide a Polynomial by a Monomial

If a, b, and c are polynomials such that $c \ne 0$, then

$$\frac{a + b}{c} = \frac{a}{c} + \frac{b}{c} \qquad \text{Similarly,} \qquad \frac{a - b}{c} = \frac{a}{c} - \frac{b}{c}$$

2.   Dividing a Polynomial by a Monomial

example 1

Dividing a Polynomial by a Monomial

Divide the polynomials.

a. $\dfrac{3x^4 - 6x^3 + 9x}{3x}$

b. $(10c^3d - 15c^2d^2 + 2cd^3) \div (5c^2d^2)$

Solution:

a. $\dfrac{3x^4 - 6x^3 + 9x}{3x}$

$= \dfrac{3x^4}{3x} - \dfrac{6x^3}{3x} + \dfrac{9x}{3x}$ Divide each term in the numerator by $3x$.

$= x^3 - 2x^2 + 3$ Simplify each term using the properties of exponents.

b. $(10c^3d - 15c^2d^2 + 2cd^3) \div (5c^2d^2)$

$= \dfrac{10c^3d - 15c^2d^2 + 2cd^3}{5c^2d^2}$

$= \dfrac{10c^3d}{5c^2d^2} - \dfrac{15c^2d^2}{5c^2d^2} + \dfrac{2cd^3}{5c^2d^2}$ Divide each term in the numerator by $5c^2d^2$.

$= \dfrac{2c}{d} - 3 + \dfrac{2d}{5c}$ Simplify each term.

3.   Long Division

If the divisor has two or more terms, a long division process similar to the division of real numbers is used.

example 2

Using Long Division to Divide Polynomials

Divide the polynomials using long division.

$$(3x^2 - 14x - 10) \div (x - 2)$$

Solution:

$x - 2 \,\overline{)\,3x^2 - 14x - 10}$ Divide the leading term in the dividend by the leading term in the divisor.

$(3x^2)/x = 3x$. This is the first term in the quotient.

$\begin{array}{r} 3x \\ x - 2 \,\overline{)\,3x^2 - 14x - 10} \\ \underline{3x^2 - 6x} \end{array}$ Multiply $3x$ by the divisor and record the result: $3x(x - 2) = 3x^2 - 6x$.

$$
\begin{array}{r}
3x \\
x - 2 \overline{\smash{\big)}\, 3x^2 - 14x - 10} \\
\underline{-3x^2 + 6x} \\
-8x
\end{array}
$$

Next, subtract the quantity $3x^2 - 6x$. To do this, add its opposite.

$$
\begin{array}{r}
3x - 8 \\
x - 2 \overline{\smash{\big)}\, 3x^2 - 14x - 10} \\
\underline{-3x^2 + 6x} \\
-8x - 10 \\
\underline{-8x + 16}
\end{array}
$$

Bring down the next column and repeat the process.

Divide the leading term by x: $-8x/x = -8$

Multiply the divisor by -8 and record the result: $-8(x - 2) = -8x + 16$.

$$
\begin{array}{r}
3x - 8 \\
x - 2 \overline{\smash{\big)}\, 3x^2 - 14x - 10} \\
\underline{-3x^2 + 6x} \\
-8x - 10 \\
\underline{+8x - 16} \\
-26
\end{array}
$$

Subtract the quantity $(-8x + 16)$ by adding its opposite.

The remainder is -26.

Summary:

The quotient is	$3x - 8$
The remainder is	-26
The divisor is	$x - 2$
The dividend is	$3x^2 - 14x - 10$

The solution to a long division problem is often written in the form: Quotient + remainder/divisor. Hence:

$$
(3x^2 - 14x - 10) \div (x - 2) = \mathbf{3x - 8} + \frac{\mathbf{-26}}{\mathbf{x - 2}}
$$

The division of polynomials can be checked in the same fashion as the division of real numbers. To check, we know that:

$$
\text{Dividend} = (\text{divisor})(\text{quotient}) + \text{remainder}
$$

$$
3x^2 - 14x - 10 \stackrel{?}{=} (x - 2)(3x - 8) + (-26)
$$
$$
\stackrel{?}{=} 3x^2 - 8x - 6x + 16 + (-26)
$$
$$
\stackrel{?}{=} 3x^2 - 14x - 10 \ ✔
$$

4. Long Division Requiring Place Holders

example 3

Using Long Division to Divide Polynomials

Divide the polynomials using long division: $(-2x^3 - 10x^2 + 56) \div (2x - 4)$.

Solution:

Tip: Both the divisor and dividend must be written in descending order before doing polynomial division.

First note that the dividend has a missing power of x and can be written as $-2x^3 - 10x^2 + 0x + 56$. The term $0x$ is a place holder for the missing term. It is helpful to use the place holder to keep the powers of x lined up.

$$\begin{array}{r} -x^2 \\ 2x - 4 \overline{\smash{\big)}\, -2x^3 - 10x^2 + 0x + 56} \\ \underline{-2x^3 + 4x^2} \end{array}$$

Leave space for the missing power of x.
Divide $-2x^3/2x = -x^2$ to get the first term of the quotient.

$$\begin{array}{r} -x^2 - 7x \\ 2x - 4 \overline{\smash{\big)}\, -2x^3 - 10x^2 + 0x + 56} \\ \underline{2x^3 - 4x^2} \\ -14x^2 + 0x \\ -14x^2 + 28x \end{array}$$

Subtract by adding the opposite.
Bring down the next column.

Divide $-14x^2/2x = 7x$ to get the next term in the quotient.

$$\begin{array}{r} -x^2 - 7x - 14 \\ 2x - 4 \overline{\smash{\big)}\, -2x^3 - 10x^2 + 0x + 56} \\ \underline{2x^3 - 4x^2} \\ -14x^2 + 0x \\ \underline{14x^2 - 28x} \\ -28x + 56 \\ -28x + 56 \end{array}$$

Subtract by adding the opposite.
Bring down the next column.

Divide $-28x/2x = -14$ to get the next term in the quotient.

$$\begin{array}{r} -x^2 - 7x - 14 \\ 2x - 4 \overline{\smash{\big)}\, -2x^3 - 10x^2 + 0x + 56} \\ \underline{2x^3 - 4x^2} \\ -14x^2 + 0x \\ \underline{14x^2 - 28x} \\ -28x + 56 \\ \underline{28x - 56} \\ 0 \end{array}$$

Subtract by adding the opposite.

$0 \longleftarrow$ The remainder is 0.

The quotient is $-x^2 - 7x - 14$ and the remainder is 0.

Because the remainder is zero, $2x - 4$ divides *evenly* into $-2x^3 - 10x^2 + 56$. For this reason, the divisor and quotient are *factors* of $-2x^3 - 10x^2 + 56$. To check, we have:

$$\text{Dividend} = (\text{divisor})(\text{quotient}) + \text{remainder}$$

$$-2x^3 - 10x^2 + 56 \stackrel{?}{=} (2x - 4)(-x^2 - 7x - 14) + 0$$
$$\stackrel{?}{=} -2x^3 - 14x^2 - 28x + 4x^2 + 28x + 56$$
$$\stackrel{?}{=} -2x^3 - 10x^2 + 56 \quad \checkmark$$

example 4   **Using Long Division to Divide Polynomials**

Divide

$$(6x^4 + 15x^3 - 5x^2 - 4) \div (3x^2 - 4)$$

Solution:

The dividend has a missing power of x and can be written as $6x^4 + 15x^3 - 5x^2 + 0x - 4$.

The divisor has a missing power of x and can be written as $3x^2 + 0x - 4$.

$$
\begin{array}{r}
2x^2 \\
3x^2 + 0x - 4 \overline{\smash{)}\,6x^4 + 15x^3 - 5x^2 + 0x - 4} \\
\underline{6x^4 + 0x^3 - 8x^2}
\end{array}
$$

Leave space for missing powers of x.

Divide $6x^4/3x^2 = 2x^2$ to get the first term of the quotient.

$$
\begin{array}{r}
2x^2 + 5x \\
3x^2 + 0x - 4 \overline{\smash{)}\,6x^4 + 15x^3 - 5x^2 + 0x - 4} \\
\underline{-6x^4 - 0x^3 + 8x^2} \\
15x^3 + 3x^2 + 0x \\
15x^3 + 0x^2 - 20x
\end{array}
$$

Subtract by adding the opposite.

Bring down the next column.

$$
\begin{array}{r}
2x^2 + 5x + 1 \\
3x^2 + 0x - 4 \overline{\smash{)}\,6x^4 + 15x^3 - 5x^2 + 0x - 4} \\
\underline{-6x^4 - 0x^3 + 8x^2} \\
15x^3 + 3x^2 + 0x \\
\underline{-15x^3 - 0x^2 + 20x} \\
3x^2 + 20x - 4 \\
3x^2 + 0x - 4
\end{array}
$$

Subtract by adding the opposite.

Bring down the next column.

$$
\begin{array}{r}
2x^2 + 5x + 1 \\
3x^2 + 0x - 4\overline{\smash{\big)}\,6x^4 + 15x^3 - 5x^2 + 0x - 4} \\
\underline{-6x^4 - 0x^3 + 8x^2} \\
15x^3 + 3x^2 + 0x \\
\underline{-15x^3 - 0x^2 + 20x} \\
3x^2 - 20x - 4 \\
\underline{-3x^2 - 0x + 4} \\
20x
\end{array}
$$

Subtract by adding the opposite.

The remainder is $20x$.

Therefore,

$$(6x^4 + 15x^3 - 5x^2 - 4) \div (3x^2 - 4) = 2x^2 + 5x + 1 + \frac{20x}{3x^2 - 4}$$

---

section 5.5   PRACTICE EXERCISES

1. a. Add $(3x + 1) + (2x - 5)$
   b. Multiply $(3x + 1)(2x - 5)$

2. a. Subtract $(a - 10b) - (5a + b)$
   b. Multiply $(a - 10b)(5a + b)$

3. a. Subtract $(2y^2 + 1) - (y^2 - 5y + 1)$
   b. Multiply $(2y^2 + 1)(y^2 - 5y + 1)$

4. a. Add $(x^2 - x) + (6x^2 + x + 2)$
   b. Multiply $(x^2 - x)(6x^2 + x + 2)$

For Exercises 5–10, answers may vary.

5. Write an example of a product of a monomial and a binomial and simplify.

6. Write an example of a product of two binomials and simplify.

7. Write an example of a sum of two trinomials and simplify.

8. Write an example of a sum of a binomial and a trinomial and simplify.

9. Write an example of the square of a binomial and simplify.

10. Write an example of the product of conjugates and simplify.

For Exercises 11–24, divide the polynomials. Check your answer by multiplication.

11. $(36y + 24y^2 + 6y^3) \div (3y)$

12. $(6p^2 - 18p^4 + 30p^5) \div (6p)$

13. $(4x^3y + 12x^2y^2 - 4xy^3) \div (4xy)$

14. $(25m^5n - 10m^4n + m^3n) \div (5m^3n)$

15. $(-8y^4 - 12y^3 + 32y^2) \div (-4y^2)$

16. $(12y^5 - 8y^6 + 16y^4 - 10y^3) \div (2y^3)$

17. $(3p^4 - 6p^3 + 2p^2 - p) \div (-6p)$

18. $(-4q^3 + 8q^2 - q) \div (-12q)$

19. $(a^3 + 5a^2 + a - 5) \div (a)$

20. $(2m^5 - 3m^4 + m^3 - m^2 + 9m) \div (m^2)$

21. $(6s^3t^5 - 8s^2t^4 + 10st^2) \div (-2st^4)$

22. $(-8r^4w^2 - 4r^3w + 2w^3) \div (-4r^3w)$

23. $(8p^4q^7 - 9p^5q^6 - 11p^3q - 4) \div (p^2q)$

24. $(20a^5b^5 - 20a^3b^2 + 5a^2b + 6) \div (a^2b)$

25. a. Divide $(2x^3 - 7x^2 + 5x - 1) \div (x - 2)$, and identify the divisor, quotient, and remainder.
    b. Explain how to check using multiplication.

26. a. Divide $(x^3 + 4x^2 + 7x - 3) \div (x + 3)$, and identify the divisor, quotient, and remainder.
    b. Explain how to check using multiplication.

For Exercises 27–42, divide the polynomials using long division. Check your answer by multiplication.

27. $(x^2 + 11x + 19) \div (x + 4)$

28. $(x^3 - 7x^2 + 13x + 3) \div (x - 2)$

29. $(3y^3 - 7y^2 - 4y + 3) \div (y - 3)$

30. $(z^3 - 2z^2 + 2z - 5) \div (z - 4)$

31. $(-12a^2 + 77a - 121) \div (3a - 11)$

32. $(28x^2 - 29x + 6) \div (4x - 3)$

33. $(18y^2 + 9y - 20) \div (3y + 4)$

34. $(-3y^2 + 2y + 1) \div (-y + 1)$

35. $(8a^3 + 1) \div (2a + 1)$

36. $(81x^4 - 1) \div (3x + 1)$

37. $(x^4 - x^3 - x^2 + 4x - 2) \div (x^2 + x - 1)$

38. $(2a^5 - 7a^4 + 11a^3 - 22a^2 + 29a - 10)$
    $\div (2a^2 - 5a + 2)$

39. $(x^4 - 3x^2 + 10) \div (x^2 - 2)$

40. $(3y^4 - 25y^2 - 18) \div (y^2 - 3)$

41. $(n^4 - 16) \div (n - 2)$

42. $(m^3 + 27) \div (m + 3)$

For Exercises 43–54, divide the polynomials using an appropriate method.

43. $(-x^3 - 8x^2 - 3x - 2) \div (x + 4)$

44. $(8xy^2 - 9x^2y + 6x^2y^2) \div (x^2y^2)$

45. $(22x^2 - 11x + 33) \div (11x)$

46. $(2m^3 - 4m^2 + 5m - 33) \div (m - 3)$

47. $(12y^3 - 17y^2 + 30y - 10) \div (3y^2 - 2y + 5)$

48. $(90h^{12} - 63h^9 + 45h^8 - 36h^7) \div (9h^9)$

49. $(4x^4 + 6x^3 + 3x - 1) \div (2x^2 + 1)$

50. $(y^4 - 3y^3 - 5y^2 - 2y + 5) \div (y + 2)$

51. $(16k^{11} - 32k^{10} + 8k^8 - 40k^4) \div (8k^8)$

52. $(4m^3 - 18m^2 + 22m - 10) \div (2m^2 - 4m + 3)$

53. $(5x^3 + 9x^2 + 10x) \div (5x^2)$

54. $(15k^4 + 3k^3 + 4k^2 + 4) \div (3k^2 - 1)$

For Exercises 55–56, use long division to find $\left(\frac{f}{g}\right)(x)$.

55. $f(x) = 3x^3 - 11x^2 + 11x + 5, g(x) = 3x + 1$

56. $f(x) = 4x^3 + 2x^2 - 22x + 10, g(x) = 4x - 2$

5.6 SYNTHETIC DIVISION

Concepts

1. **Introduction to Synthetic Division**

2. **Using Synthetic Division to Divide Polynomials**

3. **Choosing Synthetic Division or Long Division**

1. Introduction to Synthetic Division

In Section 5.5 we introduced the process of long division to divide two polynomials. In this section, we will learn another technique, called **synthetic division**, to divide two polynomials. Synthetic division may be used when dividing a polynomial by a first-degree divisor of the form, $x - r$, where r is a constant. Synthetic division is considered a "short cut" because it uses the coefficients of the divisor and dividend without writing the variables.

From Example 2 in Section 5.5, we used long division to divide $(3x^2 - 14x - 10) \div (x - 2)$

$$
\begin{array}{r}
3x - 8 \\
x - 2\overline{\smash)3x^2 - 14x - 10} \\
\underline{-3x^2 + 6x} \\
-8x - 10 \\
\underline{+8x - 16} \\
-26
\end{array}
$$

First note that the divisor, $x - 2$, is in the form $x - r$, where $r = 2$. Hence synthetic division can also be used to find the quotient and remainder.

Step 1: Write the value of r in a box. ⟶ $\underline{2}|\ 3\ -14\ -10$ ⟵ **Step 2:** Write the coefficients of the dividend to the right of the box.

$$3$$

Step 3: Skip a line and draw a horizontal line below the list of coefficients.

Step 4: Bring down the leading coefficient from the dividend and write it below the line.

$$\underline{2}|\ 3\ -14\ -10$$

Step 5: Multiply the value of r by the number below the line $(2 \times 3 = 6)$. Write the result in the next column above the line.

$$
\begin{array}{l}
6 \\
\overline{3\quad -8}
\end{array}
$$

Step 6: Add the numbers in the column above the line $(-14 + 6)$ and write the result below the line.

Repeat Steps 5 and 6 until all columns have been completed.

Step 7: To get the final result, we use the numbers below the line. The number in the last column is the remainder. The other numbers are the coefficients of the quotient.

$$
\begin{array}{l}
\underline{2}|\ 3\ -14\ -10 \\
\ 6\ -16 \\
\overline{3\quad -8\ |-26}
\end{array}
$$

A box is usually drawn around the remainder.

quotient: $3x - 8$, remainder $= -26$

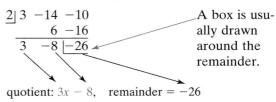

The degree of the quotient will always be one less than that of the dividend. Because the dividend is a second-degree polynomial, the quotient will be a first-degree polynomial. Hence, the quotient is $3x - 8$ and the remainder is -26.

2. Using Synthetic Division to Divide Polynomials

example 1

Using Synthetic Division to Divide Polynomials

Divide the polynomials $(x^4 + 4x^3 + 5x - 6) \div (x + 3)$ using synthetic division.

Solution:
As with long division, missing powers in the dividend must be accounted for using place holders (shown in bold). Hence $x^4 + 4x^3 + 5x - 6 = x^4 + 4x^3 + \mathbf{0}x^2 + 5x - 6$.

To use synthetic division, the divisor must be in the form, $(x - r)$. The divisor, $x + 3$, can be written as $x - (-3)$. Hence, $r = -3$.

Step 1: Write the value of r in a box.

Step 2: Write the coefficients of the dividend to the right of the box.

$$-3 \underline{|\ 1\ \ 4\ \ 0\ \ 5\ \ -6}$$
$$1$$

Step 3: Skip a line and draw a horizontal line below the list of coefficients.

Step 4: Bring down the leading co-efficient from the dividend and write it below the line.

Step 5: Multiply the value of r by the number below the line ($-3 \times 1 = -3$). Write the result in the next column above the line.

Step 6: Add the numbers in the column above the line $4 + (-3)$.

Repeat Steps 5 and 6:

$$
\begin{array}{r|rrrrr}
-3 & 1 & 4 & 0 & 5 & -6 \\
   &   & -3 & -3 & 9 & -42 \\
\hline
   & 1 & 1 & -3 & 14 & \boxed{-48}
\end{array}
$$

← remainder

constant

x-term coefficient

x^2-term coefficient

x^3-term coefficient

The quotient is

$x^3 + x^2 - 3x + 14$.

The remainder is -48.

Tip: It is interesting to compare the long division process to the synthetic division process. For Example 1, long division is shown on the left, and synthetic division is shown on the right. Notice that the same pattern of coefficients used in long division appears in the synthetic division process.

$$x + 3 \overline{) x^4 + 4x^3 + 0x^2 + 5x - 6}$$
$$\quad\quad x^3 + x^2 - 3x + 14$$
$$-(x^4 + 3x^3)$$
$$\quad\quad x^3 + 0x^2$$
$$\quad -(x^3 + 3x^2)$$
$$\quad\quad\quad -3x^2 + 5x$$
$$\quad\quad -(-3x^2 - 9x)$$
$$\quad\quad\quad\quad 14x - 6$$
$$\quad\quad\quad -(14x + 42)$$
$$\quad\quad\quad\quad\quad -48$$

$$\underline{-3|}\quad 1\quad 4\quad 0\quad 5\quad -6$$
$$\quad\quad\quad -3\quad -3\quad 9\quad -42$$
$$\quad\quad 1\quad 1\quad -3\quad 14\quad \underline{|-48}$$

$$\quad\quad x^3\quad x^2\quad x\quad \text{constant}\quad \text{remainder}$$

Quotient: $x^3 + x^2 - 3x + 14$
Remainder: -48

---

example 2

Using Synthetic Division to Divide Polynomials

Divide the polynomials using synthetic division. Identify the quotient and remainder.

a. $(2m^7 - 3m^5 + 4m^4 - m + 8) \div (m + 2)$ b. $(p^4 - 81) \div (p - 3)$

Solution:

a. Insert place holders (bold) for missing powers of m.

$(2m^7 - 3m^5 + 4m^4 - m + 8) \div (m + 2)$

$(2m^7 + \mathbf{0m^6} - 3m^5 + 4m^4 + \mathbf{0m^3} + \mathbf{0m^2} - m + 8) \div (m + 2)$

Because $m + 2$ can be written as $m - (-2)$, $r = -2$

$$\underline{-2|}\quad 2\quad 0\quad -3\quad 4\quad 0\quad 0\quad -1\quad 8$$
$$\quad\quad\quad -4\quad 8\quad -10\quad 12\quad -24\quad 48\quad -94$$
$$\quad\quad 2\quad -4\quad 5\quad -6\quad 12\quad -24\quad 47\quad \underline{|-86}$$

Quotient: $2m^6 - 4m^5 + 5m^4 - 6m^3 + 12m^2 - 24m + 47$ (the quotient is one degree less than dividend)

Remainder: -86

b. $(p^4 - 81) \div (p - 3)$

$(p^4 + \mathbf{0}p^3 + \mathbf{0}p^2 + \mathbf{0}p - 81) \div (p - 3)$ Insert place holders (bold) for missing powers of p.

$$\underline{3\rfloor}\ \ 1 \quad 0 \quad 0 \quad 0 \quad -81$$
$$\quad\quad\quad\ 3 \quad 9 \quad 27 \quad 81$$
$$\overline{\quad\quad 1 \quad 3 \quad 9 \quad 27 \quad \underline{\rfloor 0}}$$

Quotient: $p^3 + 3p^2 + 9p + 27$
Remainder: 0

3.   Choosing Synthetic Division or Long Division

Synthetic division is a time-saving shortcut. It is important to remember, however, that we will only use synthetic division if the divisor is in the form $(x - r)$, where r is a constant.

example 3   **Choosing Long Division or Synthetic Division**

Determine whether synthetic division can be used to divide the following polynomials.

a. $(x^3 - 4x^2 + 5) \div (x - 7)$
b. $(w^8 - w^2) \div (w^2 - 3)$
c. $\left(x^2 - 4x + \dfrac{1}{2}\right) \div (2x + 3)$

Solution:

a.   Yes. The divisor $(x - 7)$ is in the form $(x - r)$, where $r = 7$. Either long division or synthetic division may be used.
b.   No. $(w^2 - 3)$ is a second-degree divisor instead of first degree. Long division must be used.
c.   No. The leading coefficient in the divisor is not 1. Hence $(2x + 3)$ is not in the form $(x - r)$. Long division must be used.

section 5.6   PRACTICE EXERCISES

For Exercises 1–8, multiply or divide as indicated.

1. $(3x + 2)(x - 5)$

2. $(6y + 1)(5y - 4)$

3. $(8x^5y^4 + 4x^3y^2 - 12x^6y^3) \div (4x^2y^2)$

4. $(-10a^4b^3 + 5a^3b^4 - 15a^3b^3) \div (-5a^2b^3)$

5. $-3p^2q(2p + 4pq - 5q^2)$

6. $2rs(4r^2 - 7r^2s + 3rs^3)$

7. $(3y^3 + 2y^2 + 6y - 11) \div (y - 1)$

8. $(5x^3 + 11x^2 - 5x - 14) \div (x + 2)$

9.   Can synthetic division be used to divide $(4x^4 + 3x^3 - 7x + 9)$ by $(2x + 5)$? Explain why or why not.

10.   Can synthetic division be used to divide $(6y^5 - 3y^2 + 2y - 14)$ by $(y^2 - 3)$? Explain why or why not.

11. The following table represents the result of a synthetic division.

$$\underline{5|}\ \begin{array}{rrrr} 1 & -2 & -4 & 3 \\ & 5 & 15 & 55 \\ \hline 1 & 3 & 11 & \underline{|58} \end{array}$$

Using x as the variable,

a. Identify the divisor.

b. Identify the quotient.

c. Identify the remainder.

12. The following table represents the result of a synthetic division.

$$\underline{-2|}\ \begin{array}{rrrrr} 2 & 3 & 0 & -1 & 6 \\ & -4 & 2 & -4 & 10 \\ \hline 2 & -1 & 2 & -5 & \underline{|16} \end{array}$$

Using x as the variable,

a. Identify the divisor.

b. Identify the quotient.

c. Identify the remainder.

13. The following table represents the result of a synthetic division.

$$\underline{-3|}\ \begin{array}{rrrrr} 2 & 9 & 7 & -1 & 15 \\ & -6 & -9 & 6 & -15 \\ \hline 2 & 3 & -2 & 5 & \underline{|0} \end{array}$$

Using x as the variable,

a. Identify the divisor.

b. Identify the quotient.

c. Identify the remainder.

14. The following table represents the result of a synthetic division.

$$\underline{4|}\ \begin{array}{rrrrr} 1 & 4 & -34 & 11 & -12 \\ & 4 & 32 & -8 & 12 \\ \hline 1 & 8 & -2 & 3 & \underline{|0} \end{array}$$

Using x as the variable,

a. Identify the divisor.

b. Identify the quotient.

c. Identify the remainder.

For Exercises 15–38, divide using synthetic division. Check your answer by multiplication.

15. $(x^2 - 2x - 48) \div (x - 8)$

16. $(x^2 - 4x - 12) \div (x - 6)$

17. $(t^2 - 3t - 4) \div (t + 1)$

18. $(h^2 + 7h + 12) \div (h + 3)$

19. $(5y^2 + 5y + 1) \div (y - 1)$

20. $(3w^2 + w - 5) \div (w + 2)$

21. $(x^2 + 11x + 28) \div (x + 4)$

22. $(x^3 - 7x^2 + 13x - 6) \div (x - 2)$

23. $(3y^3 + 7y^2 - 4y + 3) \div (y + 3)$

24. $(z^3 - 2z^2 + 2z - 5) \div (z + 3)$

25. $(x^3 - 3x^2 + 4) \div (x - 2)$

26. $(3y^4 - 25y^2 - 18) \div (y - 3)$

27. $(m^3 + 27) \div (m + 3)$

28. $(n^4 - 16) \div (n - 2)$

29. $(a^4 - 2a^2 - 8) \div (a + 2)$

30. $(b^4 - 6b^2 - 27) \div (b + 3)$

31. $(3p^4 - 11p^3 - 14p - 10) \div (p - 4)$

32. $(t^4 + 3t^3 - 3t + 4) \div (t + 2)$

33. $(x^4 + 10x^3 + 11x^2 + 17x - 6) \div (x + 9)$

34. $(2k^4 - 19k^3 + 25k^2 - 13k + 42) \div (k - 8)$

35. $(4w^4 - w^2 + 6w - 3) \div \left(w - \dfrac{1}{2}\right)$

36. $(-12y^4 - 5y^3 - y^2 + y + 3) \div \left(y + \dfrac{3}{4}\right)$

37. $(8x^3 - 2x^2 + 1) \div \left(x + \dfrac{1}{4}\right)$

38. $(3x^3 + 4x^2 - x - 4) \div \left(x - \dfrac{2}{3}\right)$

■ EXPANDING YOUR SKILLS

39. Given the polynomial function defined by
$P(x) = 2x^3 + 4x - 5$,

   a. Evaluate $P(3)$.

   b. Divide $(2x^3 + 4x - 5) \div (x - 3)$.

   c. Compare the value found in part (a) to the remainder found in part (b).

40. Given the polynomial function defined by
$Q(x) = 3x^3 - 2x + 9$,

   a. Evaluate $Q(5)$.

   b. Divide $(3x^3 - 2x + 9) \div (x - 5)$.

   c. Compare the value found in part (a) to the remainder found in part (b).

41. Given the polynomial function defined by
$T(x) = 4x^3 + 10x^2 - 8x - 20$,

   a. Evaluate $T(-4)$.

   b. Divide $(4x^3 + 10x^2 - 8x - 20) \div (x + 4)$.

   c. Compare the value found in part (a) to the remainder found in part (b).

42. Given the polynomial function defined by
$M(x) = -3x^3 - 12x^2 + 5x - 8$,

   a. Evaluate $M(-6)$.

   b. Divide $(-3x^3 - 12x^2 + 5x - 8) \div (x + 6)$.

   c. Compare the value found in part (a) to the remainder found in part (b).

43. Based on your solutions to Exercises 39–42, make a conjecture about the relationship between the value of a polynomial function, $P(x)$ at $x = r$ and the value of the remainder of $P(x) \div (x - r)$.

44. a. Use synthetic division to divide
$(12x^2 + 6x - 36) \div (x + 2)$.

   b. Based on your solution to part (a), is $x + 2$ a *factor* of $12x^2 + 6x - 36$?

45. a. Use synthetic division to divide
$(10x^2 - 28x - 6) \div (x - 3)$.

   b. Based on your solution to part (a), is $x - 3$ a *factor* of $10x^2 - 28x - 6$?

46. a. Use synthetic division to divide
$(7x^2 - 16x + 9) \div (x - 1)$.

   b. Based on your solution to part (a), is $x - 1$ a *factor* of $7x^2 - 16x + 9$?

47. a. Use synthetic division to divide
$(8x^2 + 13x + 5) \div (x + 1)$.

   b. Based on your solution to part (a), is $x + 1$ a *factor* of $8x^2 + 13x + 5$?

chapter 5   SUMMARY

SECTION 5.1—PROPERTIES OF INTEGER EXPONENTS AND SCIENTIFIC NOTATION

KEY CONCEPTS:

Let a and b ($b \neq 0$) represent real numbers and m and n represent positive integers.

$$b^m \cdot b^n = b^{m+n} \qquad \frac{b^m}{b^n} = b^{m-n}$$

$$(b^m)^n = b^{mn} \qquad (ab)^m = a^m b^m$$

$$\left(\frac{a}{b}\right)^m = \frac{a^m}{b^m} \qquad b^0 = 1$$

$$b^{-n} = \left(\frac{1}{b}\right)^n$$

A number expressed in the form $a \times 10^n$ where $1 \leq |a| < 10$ and n is an integer is said to be written in scientific notation.

KEY TERMS:

b^0

b^{-n}

scientific notation

EXAMPLES:

Simplify:

$$\left(\frac{2x^2 y}{z^{-1}}\right)^{-3} (x^{-4} y^0)$$

$$= \left(\frac{2^{-3} x^{-6} y^{-3}}{z^3}\right) x^{-4}(1)$$

$$= \frac{2^{-3} x^{-10} y^{-3}}{z^3}$$

$$= \frac{1}{2^3 x^{10} y^3 z^3} \quad \text{or} \quad \frac{1}{8 x^{10} y^3 z^3}$$

Simplify:

$$0.0000002 \times 35{,}000$$

$$= (2.0 \times 10^{-7})(3.5 \times 10^4)$$

$$= 7.0 \times 10^{-3} \quad \text{or} \quad 0.007$$

SECTION 5.2—POLYNOMIAL FUNCTIONS AND APPLICATIONS

KEY CONCEPTS:

A polynomial function in x is defined by a finite sum of terms of the form ax^n, where a is a real number and n is a whole number.

- a is the coefficient of the term.
- n is the degree of the term.

The degree of a polynomial is the largest degree of its terms.

The term of a polynomial with the largest degree is the leading term. Its coefficient is the leading coefficient.

A one-term polynomial is a monomial.

A two-term polynomial is a binomial.

A three-term polynomial is a trinomial.

EXAMPLES:

$$f(x) = 4x^3 - 6x - 11$$

f is a polynomial function with leading term $4x^3$ and leading coefficient 4. The degree of f is 3.

Find the function values:

$f(2), f(-1)$, and $f(0)$ for $f(x) = 4x^3 - 6x - 11$

$$f(2) = 4(2)^3 - 6(2) - 11 = 9$$

$$f(-1) = 4(-1)^3 - 6(-1) - 11 = -9$$

$$f(0) = 4(0)^3 - 6(0) - 11 = -11$$

KEY TERMS:

binomial   leading term
coefficient   monomial
degree of a polynomial   polynomial
degree of a term   polynomial function
leading coefficient   trinomial

SECTION 5.3—ADDITION AND SUBTRACTION OF POLYNOMIALS

KEY CONCEPTS:

To add or subtract polynomials, add or subtract *like* terms.

KEY TERMS:

like terms

EXAMPLES:

Perform the indicated operations:

$$(-4x^3y + 3x^2y^2) - (7x^3y - 5x^2y^2)$$
$$= -4x^3y + 3x^2y^2 - 7x^3y + 5x^2y^2$$
$$= -11x^3y + 8x^2y^2$$

SECTION 5.4—MULTIPLICATION OF POLYNOMIALS

KEY CONCEPTS:

To multiply polynomials, multiply each term in the first polynomial by each term in the second polynomial.

Special Products:

1. Multiplication of conjugates

$$(x + y)(x - y) = x^2 - y^2$$

The product is called the difference of squares.

2. Square of a binomial

$$(x + y)^2 = x^2 + 2xy + y^2 \qquad \text{and}$$
$$(x - y)^2 = x^2 - 2xy + y^2$$

The product is called a perfect square trinomial.

KEY TERMS:

conjugates
difference of squares
perfect square trinomial

EXAMPLES:

Multiply:

$$(x - 2)(3x^2 - 4x + 11)$$
$$= 3x^3 - 4x^2 + 11x - 6x^2 + 8x - 22$$
$$= 3x^3 - 10x^2 + 19x - 22$$

Multiply:

$$(3x + 5)(3x - 5)$$
$$= (3x)^2 - (5)^2$$
$$= 9x^2 - 25$$

Multiply:

$$(4y + 3)^2$$
$$= (4y)^2 + (2)(4y)(3) + (3)^2$$
$$= 16y^2 + 24y + 9$$

SECTION 5.5—DIVISION OF POLYNOMIALS

KEY CONCEPTS:

Division of polynomials:

1. Division by a monomial, use the properties:

$$\frac{a+b}{c} = \frac{a}{c} + \frac{b}{c} \quad \text{and} \quad \frac{a-b}{c} = \frac{a}{c} - \frac{b}{c}$$

for $c \neq 0$.

2. If the divisor has more than one term, use long division.

KEY TERMS:

long division
monomial division

EXAMPLES:

Divide:

$$\frac{-12a^2 - 6a + 9}{-3a}$$
$$= \frac{-12a^2}{-3a} - \frac{6a}{-3a} + \frac{9}{-3a}$$
$$= 4a + 2 - \frac{3}{a}$$

Divide:

$$(3x^2 - 5x + 1) \div (x + 2)$$

$$
\begin{array}{r}
3x - 11 \\
x + 2 \overline{\smash{\big)}\ 3x^2 - 5x + 1} \\
-(3x^2 + 6x) \\
\hline
-11x + 1 \\
-(-11x - 22) \\
\hline
23
\end{array}
$$

Answer: $3x - 11 + \dfrac{23}{x + 2}$

SECTION 5.6—SYNTHETIC DIVISION

KEY CONCEPTS:

Synthetic division may be used to divide a polynomial by a binomial in the form $x - r$, where r is a constant.

KEY TERMS:

synthetic division

EXAMPLES:

Divide using synthetic division:

$$(3x^2 - 5x + 1) \div (x + 2)$$

$$
\begin{array}{r}
-2 \,\underline{|\ 3 \quad -5 \quad 1} \\
-6 \quad 22 \\
\hline
3 \quad -11 \ \underline{|23}
\end{array}
$$

Answer: $3x - 11 + \dfrac{23}{x + 2}$

| **chapter 5** | **REVIEW EXERCISES** |

Section 5.1

For Exercises 1–14, simplify the expression and write the answer with positive exponents.

1. $(3x)^3(3x)^2$

2. $(-6x^{-4})(3x^{-8})$

3. $\dfrac{m^3}{m^{-2}}$

4. $\dfrac{m^{-7}}{m^{-5}}$

5. $\dfrac{24x^5y^3}{-8x^4y}$

6. $\dfrac{-18x^{-2}y^3}{-12x^{-5}y^5}$

7. $(-2a^2b^{-5})^{-3}$

8. $(-4a^{-2}b^3)^{-2}$

9. $\left(\dfrac{-4x^4y^{-2}}{5x^{-1}y^4}\right)^{-4}$

10. $\left(\dfrac{25x^2y^{-3}}{5x^4y^{-2}}\right)^{-5}$

11. $\dfrac{x^{a+4}y^{b+1}}{x^{a+3}y^{2+b}}$

12. $\dfrac{x^{b+5}y^{4+c}}{x^{b-5}y^{c-4}}$

13. $(x^{2a})^{3b}$

14. $(y^a)^{2b}$

15. Write the numbers in scientific notation.

   a. The population of Asia was 3,362,994,000 in 1998.

   b. The population of Asia is predicted to be 4,247,079,000 by 2020.

16. Write the numbers in scientific notation.

   a. A millimeter is 0.001 of a meter.

   b. A nanometer is 0.000001 of a millimeter.

17. Write the numbers in expanded form.

   a. A micrometer is 1×10^{-3} of a millimeter.

   b. A nanometer is 1×10^{-9} of a meter.

18. Write the numbers in expanded form.

   a. The total square footage of shopping centers in the United States in 1997 was 5.23×10^9 ft^2.

   b. The total sales of those shopping centers in 1997 was $\$1.091 \times 10^{12}$. (*Source:* International Council of Shopping Centers.)

For Exercises 19–22, perform the indicated operations. Write the answer in scientific notation.

19. $\dfrac{(0.00005)(2,500,000)}{0.0004}$

20. $\dfrac{(725,000,000,000)(0.0005)}{25,000}$

21. $\dfrac{(3.6 \times 10^8)(9.0 \times 10^{-2})}{1.5 \times 10^{10}}$

22. $\dfrac{(7.0 \times 10^{-12})(5.2 \times 10^3)}{4.0 \times 10^{-18}}$

Section 5.2

For Exercises 23–26, identify the polynomial as a monomial, binomial, or trinomial, then give the degree of the polynomial.

23. $6x^4 + 10x - 1$

24. $a^2 - 5a^6$

25. $-3c^5$

26. 18

27. Given the polynomial function defined by $g(x) = 4x - 7$, find the function values.

   a. $g(0)$ b. $g(-4)$ c. $g(3)$

28. Given the polynomial function defined by $p(x) = -x^4 - x + 12$, find the function values.

   a. $p(0)$ b. $p(1)$ c. $p(-2)$

29. If x represents the number of years after 1977, then the percentage of white high school seniors who engaged in daily cigarette smoking in the United States can be approximated by

   $$W(x) = 0.0835x^2 - 1.6556x + 28.3$$

   ($x = 0$ corresponds to 1977)

   Similarly, the percentage of black high school seniors who engaged in daily cigarette smoking in the United States can be approximated by

   $$B(x) = 0.101x^2 - 2.717x + 23.4$$

   ($x = 0$ corresponds to 1977)

   a. Based on the graphs of the two functions (see the following figure), which group has a higher percentage who smoke, white or black high school seniors?

b. For the year 1995, determine the percentage of white high school seniors who smoked by evaluating $W(18)$. (Round to the nearest tenth of a percent.)

c. For the year 1995, determine the percentage of black high school seniors who smoked by evaluating $B(18)$.

d. For the year 1995, what is the difference in the percentage of white high school seniors who smoked and the percentage of black high school seniors who smoked?

Percentage of White and Black U.S. High School Seniors Who Engaged in Daily Cigarette Smoking, 1977–1995

$W(x) = 0.0835x^2 - 1.6556x + 28.3$

$B(x) = 0.101x^2 - 2.717x + 23.4$

Year ($x = 0$ corresponds to 1977)

Source: Centers for Disease Control.

Figure for Exercise 29

Section 5.3

For Exercises 30–41, add or subtract the polynomials as indicated.

30. $(x^2 - 2x - 3xy - 7) + (-3x^2 - x + 2xy + 6)$

31. $(7xy - 3xz + 5yz) + (13xy - 15xz - 8yz)$

32. $(8a^2 - 4a^3 - 3a) - (3a^2 - 9a - 7a^3)$

33. $(3a^2 - 2a - a^3) - (5a^2 - a^3 - 8a)$

34. $(a + 8b - 4c) + (4a + 6c - 3b)$

35. $(-9a^2 + 4b + 8) + (4a^2 + 2b - 3)$

36. $\left(\dfrac{5}{8}x^4 - \dfrac{1}{4}x^2 - \dfrac{1}{2}\right) - \left(-\dfrac{3}{8}x^4 + \dfrac{3}{4}x^2 + \dfrac{1}{2}\right)$

37. $\left(\dfrac{5}{6}x^4 + \dfrac{1}{2}x^2 - \dfrac{1}{3}\right) - \left(-\dfrac{1}{6}x^4 - \dfrac{1}{4}x^2 - \dfrac{1}{3}\right)$

38. $(2.8a^3 + 7.1a - 6.7) - (1.1a^3 - 2.5a^2 - 6.8)$

39. $(0.6a^4 - 3.1a^2 + 17.1) - (-3.1a^3 + 2.2a^2 - 6.8)$

40. $(7x - y) - [-(2x + y) - (-3x - 6y)]$

41. $-(4x - 4y) - [(4x + 2y) - (3x + 7y)]$

42. Add $-4x + 6$ to $-7x - 5$

43. Add $2x^2 - 4x$ to $2x^2 - 7x$

44. Subtract $-4x + 6$ from $-7x - 5$

45. Subtract $2x^2 - 4x$ from $2x^2 - 7x$

46. Subtract $-7x - 5$ from $-4x + 6$

47. Subtract $2x^2 - 7x$ from $2x^2 - 4x$

48. Write an expression for the missing angle and simplify.

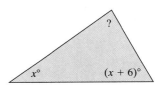

Figure for Exercise 48

49. The two angles are supplementary. Write an expression for the missing angle and simplify.

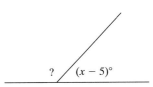

Figure for Exercise 49

Section 5.4

For Exercises 50–77, multiply the polynomials.

50. $2x(x^2 - 7x - 4)$ 51. $-3x(6x^2 - 5x + 4)$

52. $-2x^2y(x^3 - xy + y^3)$

53. $5y^2z^2(8y^2 - 2yz + z^2)$

54. $(x + 6)(x - 7)$ 55. $(x - 2)(x - 9)$

56. $\left(\dfrac{1}{2}x + 1\right)\left(\dfrac{1}{2}x - 5\right)$

57. $\left(-\dfrac{1}{5} + 2y\right)\left(\dfrac{1}{5} + y\right)$

58. $(3x + 5)(9x^2 - 15x + 25)$

59. $(x - y)(x^2 + xy + y^2)$

60. $(a^2 - 1)(a^3 + 2a^2 - a + 6)$

61. $(a^2 + 2)(-4a^3 + 2a + 5)$

62. $(6a + 3b - 9)\left(\dfrac{1}{3}a - b - 4\right)$

63. $\left(a - \dfrac{1}{2}b + c\right)(4a - 2b - 6c)$

64. $(x + 7)^2$ 65. $(2x - 5)^2$

66. $\left(\dfrac{1}{2}x + 4\right)^2$ 67. $\left(\dfrac{1}{3}x - 5\right)^2$

68. $(2x + 3)^2 - (2x - 3)^2$

69. $(x - 3)^2 - (x + 3)^2$

70. $(3y - 11)(3y + 11)$

71. $(6w - 1)(6w + 1)$

72. $\left(\dfrac{2}{3}t + 4\right)\left(\dfrac{2}{3}t - 4\right)$ 73. $\left(z + \dfrac{1}{4}\right)\left(z - \dfrac{1}{4}\right)$

74. $[(x + 2) - b][(x + 2) + b]$

75. $[c - (w + 3)][c + (w + 3)]$

76. $(2x + 1)^3$ 77. $(y^2 - 3)^3$

78. A square garden is surrounded by a walkway of uniform width, x. If the sides of the garden are given by the expression $2x + 3$, find and simplify a polynomial that represents

    a. The area of the garden.

    b. The area of the walkway and garden.

    c. The area of the walkway only.

Figure for Exercise 78

79. The length of a rectangle is 2 ft more than 3 times the width. Let x represent the width of the rectangle.

    a. Write a function P that represents the perimeter of the rectangle.

    b. Write a function A that represents the area of the rectangle.

80. One of the statements is true and the other is false. Identify the true statement and explain why the false statement is incorrect.

    a. $2x^2 + 5x = 7x^3$ $(2x^2)(5x) = 10x^3$

    b. $4x - 7x = -3x$ $4x - 7x = -3$

Section 5.5

For Exercises 81–86, divide the polynomials.

81. $(6x^3 + 12x^2 - 9x) \div (3x)$

82. $(10x^4 + 15x^3 - 20x^2) \div (-5x^2)$

83. $(-9x^5 + 10x^3 - 12x) \div (6x^4)$

84. $(6y^4 - 3y^3 + 18y^2) \div (9y^2)$

85. $(9x^4y^4 + 18x^3y^4 - 27x^2y^4) \div (-9xy^3)$

86. $(10x^3y^2 - 20x^2y^3 - 30x^3y^3) \div (-10x^2y)$

87. a. Divide $(9y^4 + 14y^2 - 8) \div (3y + 2)$

    b. Identify the quotient and the remainder.

    c. Explain how you can check your answer.

For Exercises 88–95, divide the polynomials using long division.

88. $(x^2 + 7x + 10) \div (x + 5)$

89. $(x^2 + 8x - 16) \div (x + 4)$

90. $(9y^2 + 15y - 8) \div (3y + 2)$

91. $(3y^2 - 11y + 6) \div (y - 3)$

92. $(2x^5 - 4x^4 + 2x^3 - 4) \div (x^2 - 3x)$

93. $(2x^5 + 3x^3 + x^2 - 4) \div (x^2 + x)$

94. $(2x^6 + 5x^4 - x^3 + 1) \div (x^2 + x + 1)$

95. $(2y^5 - 11y^3 - 2y - 3) \div (y^2 - 3y + 1)$

Section 5.6

96. Explain the conditions under which you may use synthetic division.

97. The following table is the result of a synthetic division.

$$3\rvert\ \ 2\quad\ \ 5\quad -2\quad\ \ 6\quad\ \ 1$$
$$\underline{\qquad\ \ 6\quad 33\quad 93\quad 297}$$
$$\ \ \ \ \ 2\quad 11\quad 31\quad 99\ \rvert 298$$

Using x as the variable,

a. Identify the divisor.

b. Identify the quotient.

c. Identify the remainder.

For Exercises 98–105, divide the polynomials using synthetic division.

98. $(z^3 + 4z^2 + 5z + 2) \div (z + 1)$

99. $(t^3 - 3t^2 + 8t - 12) \div (t - 2)$

100. $(x^2 + 7x + 14) \div (x + 5)$

101. $(x^2 + 8x + 20) \div (x + 4)$

102. $(w^3 - 6w^2 + 8) \div (w - 3)$

103. $(3y^4 - y - 4) \div (y + 1)$

104. $(y^5 + 1) \div (y + 1)$

105. $(p^4 - 16) \div (p - 2)$

chapter 5   TEST

For Exercises 1–4, simplify the expression, and write the answer with positive exponents only.

1. $\dfrac{20a^7}{4a^{-6}}$

2. $\dfrac{x^6 x^3}{x^{-2}}$

3. $\left(\dfrac{-3x^6}{5y^7}\right)^2$

4. $\dfrac{(2^{-1}xy^{-2})^{-3}(x^{-4}y)}{(x^0 y^5)^{-1}}$

5. Multiply $(8.0 \times 10^{-6})(7.1 \times 10^5)$

6. Divide: (Write the answer in scientific notation.)
   $(9{,}200{,}000) \div (0.004)$

7. To approximate the number of times your heart beats per year, first find your heart rate for 1 min (or use 65 beats per minute). Then multiply using the formula:

$$\begin{pmatrix}\text{Number of}\\\text{beats per}\\\text{year}\end{pmatrix} = \begin{pmatrix}\text{number of}\\\text{beats per}\\\text{minute}\end{pmatrix}$$

$$\times \begin{pmatrix}\text{number of}\\\text{minutes per}\\\text{hour}\end{pmatrix} \times \begin{pmatrix}\text{number of}\\\text{hours per}\\\text{day}\end{pmatrix}$$

$$\times \begin{pmatrix}\text{number of}\\\text{days per}\\\text{year}\end{pmatrix}$$

Express the answer in scientific notation.

8. For the function defined by $F(x) = 5x^3 - 2x^2 + 8$, find the function values: $F(-1)$, $F(2)$, and $F(0)$.

9. The total amount of child support paid (in billions of dollars) in the United States between 1985 and 1989 can be approximated by

$$R(t) = 0.725t + 8.683, \qquad$$ where t is the number of years after 1985 and $R(t)$ is the amount paid (in $ billions).

a. Evaluate $R(0)$, $R(2)$, and $R(4)$. Match the function values with points on the graph (see the following figure).

b. Interpret the meaning of the function values found in part (a).

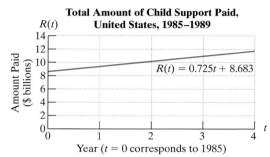

Total Amount of Child Support Paid, United States, 1985–1989

$R(t) = 0.725t + 8.683$

Year ($t = 0$ corresponds to 1985)

Source: U.S. Bureau of the Census.

Figure for Exercise 9

10. Perform the indicated operations. Write the answer in descending order.

$$(5x^2 - 7x + 3) - (x^2 + 5x - 25)$$
$$+ (4x^2 + 4x - 20)$$

For Exercises 11–13, multiply the polynomials. Write the answer in descending order.

11. $(2a - 5)(a^2 - 4a - 9)$

12. $\left(\dfrac{1}{3}x - \dfrac{3}{2}\right)(6x + 4)$

13. $(5x - 4y^2)(5x + 4y^2)$

14. Explain why $(5x + 7)^2 \neq 25x^2 + 49$.

15. Write and simplify an expression that describes the area of the square.

$7x - 4$

Figure for Exercise 15

16. Divide the polynomials

$$(2x^3y^4 + 5x^2y^2 - 6xy^3 - xy) \div (2xy)$$

17. Divide the polynomials

$$(10p^3 + 13p^2 - p + 3) \div (2p + 3)$$

18. Divide the polynomials using synthetic division.
$(y^4 - 2y + 5) \div (y - 2)$

CUMULATIVE REVIEW EXERCISES, CHAPTERS 1–5

1. Graph the inequality and express the set in interval notation: All real numbers at least 5, but not more than 12.

2. Simplify the expression $3x^2 - 5x + 2 - 4(x^2 + 3)$.

3. Graph from memory.

   a. $y = x^2$ b. $y = |x|$

4. Simplify the expression $\left(\frac{1}{3}\right)^{-2} - \left(\frac{1}{2}\right)^{3}$.

5. In 1998, the population of Mexico was approximately 9.85×10^7. At the current growth rate of 1.7%, this number is expected to double after 42 years. How many people does this represent? Express your answer in scientific notation.

6. In the 1990 Orange Bowl football championship, Florida State scored 5 points more than Notre Dame. The total number of points scored was 57. Find the number of points scored by each team.

7. Find the value of each angle in the triangle.

Figure for Exercise 7

8. Divide: $(x^3 + 64) \div (x + 4)$.

9. Determine the slope and y-intercept of the line $4x - 3y = -9$, and graph the line.

10. If y varies directly with x and inversely with z, and $y = 6$ when $x = 9$ and $z = \frac{1}{2}$, find y when $x = 3$ and $z = 4$.

11. Simplify the expression
$$\left(\frac{36a^{-2}b^4}{18b^{-6}}\right)^{-3}$$

12. Solve the system:
$$2x - y + 2z = 1$$
$$-3x + 5y - 2z = 11$$
$$x + y - 2z = -1$$

13. Determine whether the relation is a function.
   a. $\{(2, 1), (3, 1), (-8, 1), (5, 1)\}$
   b.

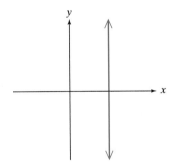

14. A telephone pole is leaning after a storm (see figure). What is the slope of the pole?

Figure for Exercise 14

15. Given $P(x) = \frac{1}{6}x^2 + x - 5$, find the function value $P(6)$.

16. Solve for x: $\frac{1}{3}x - \frac{1}{6} = \frac{1}{2}(x - 3)$.

17. Given $3x - 2y = 5$, solve for y.

18. A student scores 76, 85, and 92 on her first three algebra tests.
   a. Is it possible for her to score high enough on the fourth test to bring her test average up to 90? Assume that each test is weighted equally and that the maximum score on a test is 100 points.
   b. What is the range of values required for the fourth test so that the student's test average will be between 80 and 89, inclusive?

19. How many liters of a 40% acid solution and how many liters of a 15% acid solution must be mixed to obtain 25 L of a 30% acid solution?

20. Multiply the polynomials $(4b - 3)(2b^2 + 1)$.

21. Add the polynomials
$$(5a^2 + 3a - 1) + (3a^3 - 5a + 6).$$

22. Divide the polynomials $(6w^3 - 5w^2 - 2w) \div (2w^2)$

For Exercises 23–25, perform the indicated operations (if possible) using the matrices:

$$A = \begin{bmatrix} -3 & 5 & 0 \\ 1 & -2 & 9 \end{bmatrix} \quad B = \begin{bmatrix} 5 \\ 7 \\ 1 \end{bmatrix} \quad C = \begin{bmatrix} 8 & -3 & -3 \\ 10 & 2 & 4 \end{bmatrix}$$

23. $A + B$ 24. AB 25. $C - A$

RADICALS AND COMPLEX NUMBERS

Conditions of extreme cold can lead to frostbite, hypothermia, and even death, if proper precautions are not taken. Therefore, many weather forecasters report temperatures as well as the *wind chill factor* (WCF) to measure the effects of cold. The WCF (measured in kilocalories) is a means of quantifying the amount of heat that can be lost to the air in one hour from an exposed surface area of one square meter.

For more information visit weatherinfo at

www.mhhe.com/miller_oneill

The value of the wind chill factor, K, can be measured by

$$K = (\sqrt{100v} - v + k)(33 - T),$$

where v is the velocity of the wind measured in meters per second (m/s), T is the temperature measured in degrees Celsius (°C), and k is a constant equal to 10.45.

This and other radical expressions are presented in this chapter.

section

6.1   DEFINITION OF AN *n*th ROOT

1. Definition of a Square Root

The reverse operation to squaring a number is to find its square roots. For example, finding a square root of 36 is equivalent to asking: "What number when squared equals 36?"

One obvious answer to this question is 6 because $(6)^2 = 36$, but -6 will also work, because $(-6)^2 = 36$.

Definition of a Square Root

b is a square root of a if $b^2 = a$.

---

2. Identifying Square Roots of a Real Number

example 1   **Identifying Square Roots**

Identify the square roots of the real numbers

a. 25   b. 49   c. 0   d. -9

Solution:

a. 5 is a square root of 25 because $(5)^2 = 25$
    -5 is a square root of 25 because $(-5)^2 = 25$
b. 7 is a square root of 49 because $(7)^2 = 49$
    -7 is a square root of 49 because $(-7)^2 = 49$
c. 0 is a square root of 0 because $(0)^2 = 0$
d. There are no real numbers that when squared will equal a negative number; therefore, there are no real-valued square roots of -9.

Tip: All positive real numbers have two real-valued square roots: one positive and one negative. Zero has only one square root, which is 0 itself. Finally, for any negative real number, there are no real-valued square roots.

Recall from Section 1.2, that the positive square root of a real number can be denoted with a **radical sign**, $\sqrt{}$.

Notation for Positive and Negative Square Roots

Let a represent a positive real number. Then,

1. $\sqrt{a}$ is the *positive* square root of a. The positive square root is also called the **principal square root**.
2. $-\sqrt{a}$ is the *negative* square root of a.
3. $\sqrt{0} = 0$

---

example 2 — Simplifying a Square Root

Simplify the square roots.

a. $\sqrt{36}$ b. $\sqrt{\dfrac{4}{9}}$ c. $\sqrt{0.04}$

Solution:

a. $\sqrt{36}$ denotes the positive square root of 36.
$$\sqrt{36} = 6$$

b. $\sqrt{\dfrac{4}{9}}$ denotes the positive square root of $\dfrac{4}{9}$.
$$\sqrt{\dfrac{4}{9}} = \dfrac{2}{3}$$

c. $\sqrt{0.04}$ denotes the positive square root of 0.04.
$$\sqrt{0.04} = 0.2$$

Avoiding Mistakes

a. $\sqrt{36} = 6$ (not -6)

b. $\sqrt{\dfrac{4}{9}} = \dfrac{2}{3}$ $\left(\text{not } -\dfrac{2}{3}\right)$

c. $\sqrt{0.04} = 0.2$ (not -0.2)

The numbers 36, $\frac{4}{9}$ and 0.04 are **perfect squares** because their square roots are rational numbers. Radicals that cannot be simplified to rational numbers are irrational numbers. Recall that an irrational number cannot be written as a terminating or repeating decimal. For example, the symbol, $\sqrt{13}$, is used to represent the *exact* value of the square root of 13. The symbol, $\sqrt{42}$, is used to represent the *exact* value of the square root of 42. These values can be approximated by a rational number by using a calculator.

$$\sqrt{13} \approx 3.605551275 \qquad \sqrt{42} \approx 6.480740698$$

Tip: Before using a calculator to evaluate a square root, try estimating the value first.

$\sqrt{13}$ must be a number between 3 and 4 because $\sqrt{9} < \sqrt{13} < \sqrt{16}$.

$\sqrt{42}$ must be a number between 6 and 7 because $\sqrt{36} < \sqrt{42} < \sqrt{49}$.

Graphing Calculator Box

Use a calculator to approximate the values of $\sqrt{13}$ and $\sqrt{42}$

```
√(13)
          3.605551275
√(42)
          6.480740698
```

A negative number cannot have a real number as a square root because no real number when squared is negative. For example, $\sqrt{-25}$ is *not* a real number because there is no real number, b, for which $(b)^2 = -25$.

| example 3 | **Evaluating Square Roots** |

Simplify the square roots if possible.

a. $\sqrt{-144}$ b. $-\sqrt{144}$ c. $\sqrt{-0.01}$

Solution:

a. $\sqrt{-144}$ is *not* a real number.

b. $-\sqrt{144}$

$$= -1 \cdot \sqrt{144}$$

$$= -1 \cdot \quad 12$$

$$= -12$$

c. $\sqrt{-0.01}$ is *not* a real number.

Tip: For the expression $-\sqrt{144}$, the factor of -1 is *outside* the radical.

3.   Definition of an *n*th Root

Finding a square root of a number is the reverse process of squaring a number. This concept can be extended to finding a third root (called a cube root), a fourth root, and in general, an **nth root**.

Definition of an *n*th Root

$$b \text{ is an } n\text{th root of } a \text{ if } b^n = a$$

The radical sign $\sqrt{\ }$ is used to denote the principal square root of a number. The symbol, $\sqrt[n]{\ }$, is used to denote the principal *n*th root of a number. In the expression, $\sqrt[n]{a}$, *n* is called the **index** of the radical, and *a* is called the **radicand**. For a square root, the index is 2, but it is usually not written ($\sqrt[2]{a}$ is denoted simply as $\sqrt{a}$). A radical with an index of 3 is called a **cube root**, $\sqrt[3]{a}$.

Definition of $\sqrt[n]{a}$
---

1. If *n* is a positive *even* integer and $a > 0$, then $\sqrt[n]{a}$ is the principal (positive) *n*th root of *a*.
2. If *n* is a positive *odd* integer, then $\sqrt[n]{a}$ is the *n*th root of *a*.
3. If *n* is any positive integer, then $\sqrt[n]{0} = 0$.

For the purpose of simplifying radicals, it is helpful to know the following powers:

Perfect Cubes	Perfect Fourth Powers	Perfect Fifth Powers
$1^3 = 1$	$1^4 = 1$	$1^5 = 1$
$2^3 = 8$	$2^4 = 16$	$2^5 = 32$
$3^3 = 27$	$3^4 = 81$	$3^5 = 243$
$4^3 = 64$	$4^4 = 256$	$4^5 = 1024$
$5^3 = 125$	$5^4 = 625$	$5^5 = 3125$

4. Identifying the Principal *n*th Root of a Real Number

example 4

Identifying the Principal *n*th Root of a Real Number

Simplify the expressions (if possible).

a. $\sqrt{4}$ b. $\sqrt[3]{64}$ c. $\sqrt[5]{-32}$ d. $\sqrt[4]{81}$

e. $\sqrt[6]{1{,}000{,}000}$ f. $\sqrt{-100}$ g. $\sqrt[4]{-16}$

Solution:

a. $\sqrt{4} = 2$ because $(2)^2 = 4$

b. $\sqrt[3]{64} = 4$ because $(4)^3 = 64$

c. $\sqrt[5]{-32} = -2$ because $(-2)^5 = -32$

d. $\sqrt[4]{81} = 3$ because $(3)^4 = 81$

e. $\sqrt[6]{1{,}000{,}000} = 10$ because $(10)^6 = 1{,}000{,}000$

f. $\sqrt{-100}$ is not a real number.   No real number when squared equals -100.

g. $\sqrt[4]{-16}$ is not a real number.   No real number when raised to the fourth power equals -16.

◆ **Avoiding Mistakes**

When evaluating $\sqrt[n]{a}$, where *n* is even, always choose the principal (positive) root. Hence:

$$\sqrt[4]{81} = 3 \quad (\text{not } -3)$$

$$\sqrt[6]{1{,}000{,}000} = 10 \quad (\text{not } -10)$$

Examples 4f and 4g illustrate that an *n*th root of a negative quantity is not a real number if the index is even because no real number raised to an even power is negative.

Graphing Calculator Box

A calculator can be used to approximate *n*th roots by using the $\boxed{\sqrt[\square]{}}$ key. On most calculators, the index is entered first.

5. Radical Functions

If n is an integer greater than 1, then a function written in the form $f(x) = \sqrt[n]{x}$ is called a **radical function**. Note that if n is an even integer, then the function will be a real number only if the radicand is nonnegative. Therefore, the domain is restricted to nonnegative real numbers, or equivalently, $\{x \mid x \geq 0\}$. If n is an odd integer, then the domain is all real numbers.

example 5

Determining the Domain of Radical Functions

For each function defined here, write the domain in interval notation.

a. $g(t) = \sqrt[4]{t - 2}$ b. $h(a) = \sqrt[3]{a - 4}$ c. $k(x) = \sqrt{3 - 5x}$

Solution:

a. $\quad g(t) = \sqrt[4]{t - 2}$ The index is even. The radicand must be nonnegative.

$\quad\quad t - 2 \geq 0$ Set the radicand greater than or equal to zero.

$\quad\quad\quad t \geq 2$ Solve for t.

The domain is $[2, \infty)$.

Graphing Calculator Box

The domain of $g(t) = \sqrt[4]{t - 2}$ can be confirmed from its graph.

---

b. $h(a) = \sqrt[3]{a - 4}$ The index is odd; therefore, the domain is all real numbers.

The domain is $(-\infty, \infty)$.

Graphing Calculator Box

The domain of $h(a) = \sqrt[3]{a - 4}$ can be confirmed from its graph.

c. $k(x) = \sqrt{3 - 5x}$ The index is even; therefore, the radicand must be nonnegative.

$3 - 5x \geq 0$ Set the radicand greater than or equal to zero.

$-5x \geq -3$ Solve for x.

$\dfrac{-5x}{-5} \leq \dfrac{-3}{-5}$ Reverse the inequality sign.

$x \leq \dfrac{3}{5}$

The domain is $\left(-\infty, \frac{3}{5}\right]$

Graphing Calculator Box

The domain of the function defined by $k(x) = \sqrt{3 - 5x}$ can be confirmed from its graph.

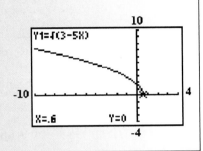

---

example 6   **Applying Radical Functions**

Ignoring air resistance, the velocity, v, (in feet/second) of an object in free fall is a function of the distance it has fallen, x, (in feet):

$$v(x) = 8\sqrt{x} \quad (x \geq 0)$$

Evaluate the function values and interpret their meaning in the context of the problem.

a. $v(25)$ b. $v(100)$

Solution:

a. $v(25) = 8\sqrt{25}$
     $= 8 \cdot 5$
     $= 40$ $v(25) = 40$ means that if an object has fallen 25 ft, its velocity is 40 ft/s.

b. $v(100) = 8\sqrt{100}$
     $= 8 \cdot 10$
     $= 80$ $v(100) = 80$ means that if an object has fallen 100 ft, its velocity is 80 ft/s.

6. Roots of Variable Expressions

Finding an *n*th root of a variable expression is similar to finding an *n*th root of a numerical expression. For roots with an even index, however, particular care must be taken to obtain a nonnegative solution.

Definition of $\sqrt[n]{a^n}$

1. If *n* is a positive *odd* integer, then $\sqrt[n]{a^n} = a$.
2. If *n* is a positive *even* integer, then $\sqrt[n]{a^n} = |a|$.

The absolute value bars are necessary for roots with an even index because the variable, *a*, may represent a positive quantity or a negative quantity. By using absolute value bars, $\sqrt[n]{a^n} = |a|$ is nonnegative and represents the principal *n*th root of *a*.

---

example 7   **Simplifying Expressions of the Form $\sqrt[n]{a^n}$**

Simplify the expressions.

a. $\sqrt[4]{(-3)^4}$ b. $\sqrt[5]{(-3)^5}$ c. $\sqrt{(x + 2)^2}$ d. $\sqrt[3]{(a + b)^3}$

Solution:

a. $\sqrt[4]{(-3)^4} = |-3| = 3$ Because this is an *even*-indexed root, absolute value bars are necessary to make the answer positive.

b. $\sqrt[5]{(-3)^5} = -3$ This is an *odd*-indexed root, so absolute value bars are not necessary.

c. $\sqrt{(x + 2)^2} = |x + 2|$ Because this is an *even*-indexed root, absolute value bars are necessary. The sign of the quantity $x + 2$ is unknown, however, $|x + 2| \geq 0$ regardless of the value of *x*.

d. $\sqrt[3]{(a + b)^3} = a + b$ This is an *odd*-indexed root, so absolute value bars are not necessary.

If *n* is an even integer, then $\sqrt[n]{a^n} = |a|$; however, if the variable *a* is assumed to be *nonnegative,* then the absolute value bars may be dropped. That is, $\sqrt[n]{a^n} = a$ provided $a \geq 0$. In many examples and exercises, we will make the assumption that the variables within a radical expression are positive real numbers. In such a case, the absolute value bars are not needed to evaluate $\sqrt[n]{a^n}$.

It is helpful to become familiar with the patterns associated with perfect squares and perfect cubes involving variable expressions.

The following powers of x are perfect squares:

Perfect Squares

$$(x^1)^2 = x^2$$
$$(x^2)^2 = x^4$$
$$(x^3)^2 = x^6$$
$$(x^4)^2 = x^8$$

. . .

Tip: In general, any expression raised to an even power (a multiple of 2) is a perfect square.

The following powers of x are perfect cubes:

Perfect Cubes

$$(x^1)^3 = x^3$$
$$(x^2)^3 = x^6$$
$$(x^3)^3 = x^9$$
$$(x^4)^3 = x^{12}$$

. . .

Tip: In general, any expression raised to a power that is a multiple of 3 is a perfect cube.

These patterns may be extended to higher powers.

example 8

Simplifying *n*th Roots

Simplify the expressions. Assume that all variables are positive real numbers.

a. $\sqrt{y^8}$ b. $\sqrt[3]{27a^3}$ c. $\sqrt[5]{\dfrac{a^5}{b^5}}$ d. $-\sqrt[4]{\dfrac{81x^4y^8}{16}}$

Solution:

a. $\sqrt{y^8} = \sqrt{(y^4)^2} = y^4$

b. $\sqrt[3]{27a^3} = \sqrt[3]{(3a)^3} = 3a$

c. $\sqrt[5]{\dfrac{a^5}{b^5}} = \sqrt[5]{\left(\dfrac{a}{b}\right)^5} = \dfrac{a}{b}$

d. $-\sqrt[4]{\dfrac{81x^4y^8}{16}} = -\sqrt[4]{\left(\dfrac{3xy^2}{2}\right)^4} = -\dfrac{3xy^2}{2}$

7. Pythagorean Theorem

A right triangle is a triangle that contains a 90° angle. Furthermore, the sum of the squares of the two legs (the shorter sides) of a right triangle equals the square of the **hypotenuse** (the longest side). This important fact is known as the Pythagorean theorem, an enduring landmark of mathematical history from which many mathematical ideas have been built. Although the theorem is named after the Greek mathematician and philosopher Pythagoras (circa 560–480 B.C.), it is thought that the ancient Babylonians were familiar with the principle more than a thousand years earlier.

b
(leg) c (hypotenuse)

a
(leg)

Figure 6-1

For the triangle shown in Figure 6-1, the **Pythagorean theorem** is stated as: $a^2 + b^2 = c^2$.

In this formula, a and b are the legs of the right triangle and c is the hypotenuse. Notice that the hypotenuse is the longest side of the right triangle and is opposite the 90° angle.

8.   Applications of the Pythagorean Theorem

example 9

Applying the Pythagorean Theorem

Use the Pythagorean theorem and the definition of the principal square root of a positive real number to find the length of the unknown side of the triangle shown to the left.

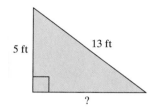

5 ft   13 ft

?

Solution:

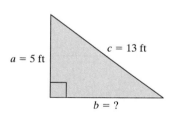

$a = 5$ ft $c = 13$ ft

$b = ?$

Label the sides of the triangle.

$$a^2 + b^2 = c^2$$

$$(5)^2 + b^2 = (13)^2 \qquad \text{Apply the Pythagorean theorem.}$$

$$25 + b^2 = 169 \qquad \text{Simplify.}$$

$$b^2 = 169 - 25 \qquad \text{Isolate } b^2.$$

$$b^2 = 144 \qquad$$

By definition, b must be one of the square roots of 144. Because b represents the length of a side of a triangle, choose the positive square root of 144.

$$b = 12$$

The third side is 12 ft long.

example 10

Applying the Pythagorean Theorem

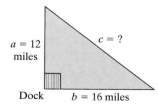

$a = 12$
miles $c = ?$

Dock $b = 16$ miles

Figure 6-2

Two boats leave a dock at 12:00 noon. One travels due north at 6 mph, and the other travels due east at 8 mph (Figure 6-2). How far apart are the two boats after 2 h?

Solution:

The boat traveling north travels a distance of (6 mph)(2 h) = 12 miles. The boat traveling east travels a distance of (8 mph)(2 h) = 16 miles. The course of the boats forms a right triangle where the hypotenuse represents the distance between them.

$$a^2 + b^2 = c^2$$

$$(12)^2 + (16)^2 = c^2 \qquad \text{Apply the Pythagorean theorem.}$$

$$144 + 256 = c^2 \quad \text{Simplify.}$$

$$400 = c^2$$

$$\sqrt{400} = c \quad$$ By definition, c must be one of the square roots of 400. Choose the positive square root of 400 to represent distance between the two boats.

$$20 = c$$

The boats are 20 miles apart.

section 6.1 PRACTICE EXERCISES

1. a. Find the square roots of 64.

    b. Find $\sqrt{64}$.

    c. Explain the difference between the answers in part (a) and part (b).

2. a. Find the square roots of 121.

    b. Find $\sqrt{121}$.

    c. Explain the difference between the answers in part (a) and part (b).

3. a. What is the principal square root of 81?

    b. What is the negative square root of 81?

4. a. What is the principal square root of 100?

    b. What is the negative square root of 100?

5. Using the definition of a square root, explain why $\sqrt{-36}$ does not have a real-valued square root.

6. Using the definition of an nth root, explain why $\sqrt[4]{-36}$ does not have a real-valued fourth root.

For Exercises 7–26, evaluate the roots without a calculator. Identify those that are not real numbers.

7. $\sqrt{25}$

8. $-\sqrt{36}$

9. $\sqrt[3]{-27}$

10. $\sqrt{-9}$

11. $\sqrt[4]{16}$

12. $\sqrt{16}$

13. $\sqrt[3]{\dfrac{1}{8}}$

14. $\sqrt[5]{32}$

15. $\sqrt[6]{64}$

16. $\sqrt{64}$

17. $\sqrt[3]{64}$

18. $\sqrt{\dfrac{49}{100}}$

19. $\sqrt[4]{-81}$

20. $\sqrt[6]{-1}$

21. $\sqrt[6]{1,000,000}$

22. $-\sqrt[4]{625}$

23. $-\sqrt[3]{0.008}$

24. $-\sqrt{25}$

25. $-\sqrt{0.0144}$

26. $\sqrt[3]{\dfrac{27}{1000}}$

For Exercises 27–34, use a calculator to evaluate the expressions to four decimal places.

27. $\sqrt{69}$

28. $\sqrt{5798}$

29. $2 + \sqrt[3]{5}$

30. $3 - 2\sqrt[4]{10}$

31. $\sqrt{\sqrt{17}}$

32. $\sqrt{\sqrt{8}}$

33. $\dfrac{3 - \sqrt{19}}{11}$

34. $\dfrac{5 + 2\sqrt{15}}{12}$

35. Use a calculator to evaluate (if possible) $h(x) = \sqrt{x - 2}$ for the given values of x (round to two decimal places). Then use interval notation to state the domain of h.

    a. $h(-1)$ b. $h(0)$ c. $h(1)$ d. $h(2)$

    e. $h(3)$ f. $h(4)$ g. $h(5)$ h. $h(6)$

36. Use a calculator to evaluate (if possible) $k(x) = \sqrt{x + 1}$ for the given values of x (round to two decimal places). Then use interval notation to state the domain of k.

    a. $k(-4)$ b. $k(-3)$

    c. $k(-2)$ d. $k(-1)$

    e. $k(0)$ f. $k(1)$

    g. $k(2)$ h. $k(3)$

37. Use a calculator to evaluate (if possible) $g(x) = \sqrt[3]{x} - 2$ for the given values of x (round to two decimal places). Then use interval notation to state the domain of g.

   a. $g(-1)$ b. $g(0)$ c. $g(1)$ d. $g(2)$

   e. $g(3)$ f. $g(4)$ g. $g(5)$ h. $g(6)$

38. Use a calculator to evaluate (if possible) $f(x) = \sqrt[3]{x} + 1$ for the given values of x (round to two decimal places). Then use interval notation to state the domain of f.

   a. $f(-4)$ b. $f(-3)$

   c. $f(-2)$ d. $f(-1)$

   e. $f(0)$ f. $f(1)$

   g. $f(2)$ h. $f(3)$

For each function defined in Exercises 39–42, write the domain in interval notation.

39. $p(x) = \sqrt{x - 1}$

40. $q(x) = \sqrt{x + 5}$

41. $R(x) = \sqrt[3]{x + 1}$

42. $T(x) = \sqrt{x - 10}$

For Exercises 43–46, match the function with the graph. Use the domain information from Exercises 39–42.

43. $p(x) = \sqrt{x - 1}$

44. $q(x) = \sqrt{x + 5}$

45. $T(x) = \sqrt{x - 10}$

46. $R(x) = \sqrt[3]{x + 1}$

   a.

b.

c.

d.

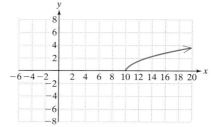

For Exercises 47–64, simplify the radical expressions.

47. $\sqrt{a^2}$ 48. $\sqrt[4]{a^4}$

49. $\sqrt[3]{a^3}$ 50. $\sqrt[5]{a^5}$

51. $\sqrt[6]{a^6}$ 52. $\sqrt[7]{a^7}$

53. $\sqrt{x^4}$ 54. $\sqrt[3]{y^{12}}$

55. $\sqrt{x^2 y^4 z^{10}}$ 56. $\sqrt[3]{(u + v)^3}$

57. $-\sqrt[3]{\dfrac{x^3}{y^3}}, \quad y \neq 0$ 58. $\sqrt[4]{\dfrac{a^4}{b^8}}, \quad b \neq 0$

59. $\dfrac{2}{\sqrt[4]{x^4}}, \quad x \neq 0$ 60. $\sqrt{(-5)^2}$

61. $\sqrt[3]{(-9)^3}$ 62. $\sqrt[6]{(50)^6}$

63. $\sqrt[5]{(-2)^5}$ 64. $\sqrt[10]{(-2)^{10}}$

For Exercises 65–80, simplify the expressions. Assume all variables are positive real numbers.

65. $\sqrt{x^2y^4}$

66. $\sqrt{16p^2}$

67. $\sqrt{\dfrac{a^6}{b^2}}$

68. $\sqrt{\dfrac{w^2}{z^4}}$

69. $-\sqrt{\dfrac{25}{q^2}}$

70. $-\sqrt{\dfrac{p^6}{81}}$

71. $\sqrt{9x^2y^4z^2}$

72. $\sqrt{4a^4b^2c^6}$

73. $\sqrt{\dfrac{h^2k^4}{16}}$

74. $\sqrt{\dfrac{4x^2}{y^8}}$

75. $-\sqrt[3]{\dfrac{t^3}{27}}$

76. $\sqrt[4]{\dfrac{16}{w^4}}$

77. $\sqrt[5]{32y^{10}}$

78. $\sqrt[3]{64x^6y^3}$

79. $\sqrt[6]{64p^{12}q^{18}}$

80. $\sqrt[4]{16r^{12}s^8}$

For Exercises 81–84, translate the English phrase into an algebraic expression.

81. The sum of q and the square of p.

82. The product of 11 and the cube root of x.

83. The quotient of 6 and the fourth root of x.

84. The difference of y and the square root of x.

For Exercises 85–88, translate the algebraic expression into an English phrase. Answers may vary.

85. $a^2 + \sqrt{b}$

86. $\sqrt[3]{\dfrac{x}{y}}$

87. $\dfrac{1}{(c+d)^2}$

88. $2(t + \sqrt{t})$

89. If a square has an area of 64 in.², then what are the lengths of the sides?

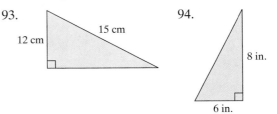

Figure for Exercise 89

90. If a square has an area of 121 m², then what are the lengths of the sides?

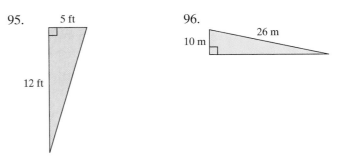

Figure for Exercise 90

91. If a square has an area of 97 in.², use a calculator to find the lengths of the sides. Round to the nearest tenth of an inch.

$A = 97$ in.² $s = ?$

$s = ?$

Figure for Exercise 91

92. If a square has an area of 45 cm², use a calculator to find the lengths of the sides. Round to the nearest tenth of a centimeter.

$A = 45$ cm² $s = ?$

$s = ?$

Figure for Exercise 92

For Exercises 93–96, find the length of the third side of each triangle using the Pythagorean theorem.

93.

12 cm   15 cm

94.

8 in.

6 in.

95.   5 ft

12 ft

96.

10 m   26 m

■ **EXPANDING YOUR SKILLS**

97. Construct four squares of different sizes. For each square, measure the length of the sides of the square and the diagonal of the square. Record the values of the length, L, and the diagonal, D. Then compute the ratio, D/L.

Square Number	Length, L	Diagonal, D	$\dfrac{D}{L}$
1			
2			
3			
4			

a. What observation can you make about the ratio D/L? Does it appear to be constant?

b. Find a decimal approximation for $\sqrt{2}$ and compare that value to the values of D/L.

98. Follow the steps to provide a proof of the Pythagorean theorem.

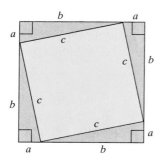

Note: The length of each side of the large outer square is $(a + b)$. Therefore, the area of the large outer square is $(a + b)^2$.

The area of the large outer square can also be found by adding the area of the inner square (pictured in yellow) plus the area of the four right triangles (pictured in blue).

Area of inner square: c^2 Area of the four right triangles: $4 \cdot \left(\frac{1}{2} ab\right)$

$\frac{1}{2}$ base $\cdot$ height

Now equate the two expressions representing the area of the large outer square:

$$\left(\begin{array}{c}\text{Area of outer}\\ \text{square}\end{array}\right) = \left(\begin{array}{c}\text{area of inner}\\ \text{square}\end{array}\right) + \left(\begin{array}{c}\text{area of the}\\ \text{four right triangles}\end{array}\right)$$

$(a + b)^2 = c^2 + 4\left(\frac{1}{2}ab\right)$

_____ = _____ + _____   Clear parentheses on both sides.

_____ = _____   Subtract $2ab$ from both sides.

GRAPHING CALCULATOR EXERCISES

99. Graph $h(x) = \sqrt{x - 2}$ on the standard viewing window. Use the graph to confirm the domain found in Exercise 35.

100. Graph $k(x) = \sqrt{x + 1}$ on the standard viewing window. Use the graph to confirm the domain found in Exercise 36.

101. Graph $g(x) = \sqrt[3]{x - 2}$ on the standard viewing window. Use the graph to confirm the domain found in Exercise 37.

102. Graph $f(x) = \sqrt[3]{x + 1}$ on the standard viewing window. Use the graph to confirm the domain found in Exercise 38.

section

6.2 RATIONAL EXPONENTS

1. Evaluating Expressions of the Form $a^{1/n}$

In Section 5.1 the properties for simplifying expressions with integer exponents were presented. In this section, the properties are expanded to include expressions with rational exponents. We begin by defining expressions of the form: $a^{1/n}$

Definition of $a^{1/n}$

Let a be a real number, and let n be an integer such that $n > 1$. If $\sqrt[n]{a}$ is a real number, then

$$a^{1/n} = \sqrt[n]{a}$$

---

example 1

Evaluating Expressions of the Form $a^{1/n}$

Evaluate the expressions.

a. $(-8)^{1/3}$ b. $81^{1/4}$ c. $-100^{1/2}$ d. $(-100)^{1/2}$

Solution:

a. $(-8)^{1/3} = \sqrt[3]{-8} = -2$
b. $81^{1/4} = \sqrt[4]{81} = 3$
c. $-100^{1/2} = -\sqrt{100} = -10$
d. $(-100)^{1/2}$ is not a real number because $\sqrt{-100}$ is not a real number.

---

2. Evaluating Expressions of the Form $a^{m/n}$

If $\sqrt[n]{a}$ is a real number, then we can define an expression of the form $a^{m/n}$ in such a way that the multiplication property of exponents still holds true. For example,

$$16^{3/4} \begin{cases} (16^{1/4})^3 = (\sqrt[4]{16})^3 = (2)^3 = 8 \\ (16^3)^{1/4} = \sqrt[4]{16^3} = \sqrt[4]{4096} = 8 \end{cases}$$

Definition of $a^{m/n}$

Let a be a real number, and let m and n be positive integers such that m and n share no common factors and $n > 1$. If $\sqrt[n]{a}$ is a real number, then

$$a^{m/n} = (a^{1/n})^m = (\sqrt[n]{a})^m \qquad \text{and} \qquad a^{m/n} = (a^m)^{1/n} = \sqrt[n]{a^m}$$

The rational exponent in the expression $a^{m/n}$ is essentially performing two operations. The numerator of the exponent raises the base to the mth power. The denominator takes the nth root.

example 2

Evaluating Expressions of the Form $a^{m/n}$

Simplify the expressions.

a. $8^{2/3}$ b. $100^{5/2}$ c. $\left(\dfrac{1}{25}\right)^{3/2}$

Solution:

a. $8^{2/3} = (\sqrt[3]{8})^2$ Take the cube root of 8 and square the result.

$\quad\quad = (2)^2$ Simplify.
$\quad\quad = 4$

b. $100^{5/2} = (\sqrt{100})^5$ Take the square root of 100 and raise the result to the fifth power.

$\quad\quad = (10)^5$ Simplify.
$\quad\quad = 100{,}000$

c. $\left(\dfrac{1}{25}\right)^{3/2} = \left(\sqrt{\dfrac{1}{25}}\right)^3$ Take the square root of $\frac{1}{25}$ and cube the result.

$\quad\quad = \left(\dfrac{1}{5}\right)^3$ Simplify.

$\quad\quad = \dfrac{1}{125}$

Graphing Calculator Box

A calculator can be used to confirm the results of Example 2.

```
(8)^(2/3)
                    4
(100)^(5/2)
               100000
(1/25)^(3/2)
                 .008
```

---

3. Converting Between Rational Exponents and Radical Notation

example 3

Using Radical Notation and Rational Exponents

Convert each expression to radical notation.

a. $a^{3/5}$ b. $(5x^2)^{1/3}$ c. $3y^{1/4}$

Solution:

a. $a^{3/5} = \sqrt[5]{a^3}$ or $\left(\sqrt[5]{a}\right)^3$

b. $(5x^2)^{1/3} = \sqrt[3]{5x^2}$

c. $3y^{1/4} = 3\sqrt[4]{y}$

example 4   **Using Radical Notation and Rational Exponents**

Convert each expression to an equivalent expression using rational exponents. Assume that all variables represent positive real numbers.

a. $\sqrt[4]{b^3}$ b. $\sqrt{7a}$

Solution:

a. $\sqrt[4]{b^3} = b^{3/4}$
b. $\sqrt{7a} = (7a)^{1/2}$

---

4.   Properties of Rational Exponents

In Section 5.1, several properties and definitions were introduced to simplify expressions with integer exponents. These properties also apply to rational exponents.

Properties of Exponents and Definitions

Let a and b be real numbers. Let m and n be rational numbers such that a^m, a^n, and b^n are real numbers. Then,

Description	Property	Example
1. Multiplying like bases	$a^m a^n = a^{m+n}$	$x^{1/3} x^{4/3} = x^{5/3}$
2. Dividing like bases	$\dfrac{a^m}{a^n} = a^{m-n}$	$\dfrac{x^{3/5}}{x^{1/5}} = x^{2/5}$
3. The power rule	$(a^m)^n = a^{mn}$	$(2^{1/3})^{1/2} = 2^{1/6}$
4. Power of a product	$(ab)^m = a^m b^m$	$(xy)^{1/2} = x^{1/2} y^{1/2}$
5. Power of a quotient	$\left(\dfrac{a}{b}\right)^m = \dfrac{a^m}{b^m} \quad (b \ne 0)$	$\left(\dfrac{4}{25}\right)^{1/2} = \dfrac{4^{1/2}}{25^{1/2}} = \dfrac{2}{5}$

Description	Definition	Example
1. Negative exponents	$a^{-m} = \left(\dfrac{1}{a}\right)^m = \dfrac{1}{a^m} \quad (a \ne 0)$	$(8)^{-1/3} = \left(\dfrac{1}{8}\right)^{1/3} = \dfrac{1}{2}$
2. Zero exponent	$a^0 = 1 \quad (a \ne 0)$	$5^0 = 1$

5.   Simplifying Expressions with Rational Exponents

example 5   **Simplifying Expressions with Rational Exponents**

Use the properties of exponents to simplify the expressions. Assume all variables represent positive real numbers.

a. $y^{2/5} y^{3/5}$ b. $(s^4 t^8)^{1/4}$ c. $\left(\dfrac{81cd^{-2}}{3c^{-2}d^4}\right)^{1/3}$ d. $\left(\dfrac{x^{-2/3}}{y^{-1/2}}\right)^6 (x^{-1/5})^{10}$

Solution:

a. $y^{2/5}y^{3/5} = y^{(2/5)+(3/5)}$ Multiply like bases by adding exponents.

$= y^{5/5}$ Simplify.

$= y$ Reduce.

b. $(s^4t^8)^{1/4} = s^{4/4}t^{8/4}$ Apply the power rule. Multiply exponents.

$= st^2$ Reduce.

c. $\left(\dfrac{81cd^{-2}}{3c^{-2}d^4}\right)^{1/3} = (27c^{1-(-2)}d^{-2-4})^{1/3}$ Simplify inside parentheses. Subtract exponents.

$= (27c^3d^{-6})^{1/3}$

$= \left(\dfrac{27c^3}{d^6}\right)^{1/3}$ Simplify negative exponent.

$= \dfrac{27^{1/3}c^{3/3}}{d^{6/3}}$ Apply the power rule. Multiply exponents.

$= \dfrac{3c}{d^2}$ Simplify.

d. $\left(\dfrac{x^{-2/3}}{y^{-1/2}}\right)^6 (x^{-1/5})^{10} = \left(\dfrac{x^{-2/3 \cdot 6}}{y^{-1/2 \cdot 6}}\right)(x^{-1/5 \cdot 10})$ Apply the power rule. Multiply exponents.

$= \left(\dfrac{x^{-4}}{y^{-3}}\right)(x^{-2})$ Simplify.

$= \dfrac{x^{-4}}{y^{-3}} \cdot \dfrac{x^{-2}}{1}$

$= \dfrac{x^{-6}}{y^{-3}}$ Multiply like bases by adding exponents.

$= \dfrac{y^3}{x^6}$ Simplify negative exponents.

6.   Applications Involving Rational Exponents

example 6

Applying Rational Exponents

Suppose P dollars in principal is invested in an account that earns interest annually. If after t years the investment grows to A dollars, then the annual rate of return, r, on the investment is given by

$$r = \left(\dfrac{A}{P}\right)^{1/t} - 1$$

Find the annual rate of return on $5000 which grew to $12,500 after 6 years.

Solution:

$$r = \left(\frac{A}{P}\right)^{1/t} - 1 \qquad \text{Where } A = \$12,500, P = \$5000 \text{ and } t = 6. \text{ Hence}$$

$$= \left(\frac{12,500}{5000}\right)^{1/6} - 1$$

$$= (2.5)^{1/6} - 1$$

$$\approx 1.165 - 1$$

$$\approx 0.165 \text{ or } 16.5\%$$

The annual rate of return is 16.5%.

Graphing Calculator Box

The expression

$$r = \left(\frac{12,500}{5000}\right)^{1/6} - 1$$

is easily evaluated on a graphing calculator.

```
(12500/5000)^(1/
6)-1
        .1649930508
```

---

section 6.2   PRACTICE EXERCISES

For the exercises in this set, assume that all variables represent positive real numbers unless otherwise stated.

1. Given $\sqrt[3]{27}$:
   a. Identify the index
   b. Identify the radicand

2. Given $\sqrt{18}$:
   a. Identify the index
   b. Identify the radicand

For Exercises 3–10, evaluate the radicals (if possible).

3. $\sqrt{25}$

4. $\sqrt[3]{8}$

5. $\sqrt[4]{81}$

6. $(\sqrt[4]{16})^3$

7. $\sqrt{-9}$

8. $-\sqrt{9}$

9. $\sqrt[3]{(a+1)^3}$

10. $\sqrt[5]{(x+y)^5}$

11. Explain how to interpret the expression $a^{m/n}$ as a radical.

12. Explain why $(\sqrt[3]{8})^4$ is easier to evaluate than $\sqrt[3]{8^4}$.

For Exercises 13–36, simplify the expression.

13. $25^{1/2}$

14. $81^{1/2}$

15. $8^{1/3}$

16. $125^{1/3}$

17. $81^{1/4}$

18. $16^{3/4}$

19. $(-8)^{1/3}$

20. $(-9)^{1/2}$

21. $-8^{1/3}$

22. $-9^{1/2}$

23. $4^{-1/2}$

24. $121^{-1/2}$

25. $27^{-2/3}$

26. $125^{-1/3}$

27. $\dfrac{1}{36^{-1/2}}$

28. $\dfrac{1}{16^{-1/2}}$

29. $\dfrac{1}{1000^{-1/3}}$

30. $\dfrac{1}{81^{-3/4}}$

31. $\left(\dfrac{1}{8}\right)^{2/3} + \left(\dfrac{1}{4}\right)^{1/2}$

32. $\left(\dfrac{1}{8}\right)^{-2/3} + \left(\dfrac{1}{4}\right)^{-1/2}$

33. $\left(\dfrac{1}{16}\right)^{-1/4} - \left(\dfrac{1}{49}\right)^{-1/2}$

34. $\left(\dfrac{1}{16}\right)^{1/4} - \left(\dfrac{1}{49}\right)^{1/2}$

35. $\left(\dfrac{1}{4}\right)^{1/2} + \left(\dfrac{1}{64}\right)^{-1/3}$

36. $\left(\dfrac{1}{36}\right)^{1/2} + \left(\dfrac{1}{64}\right)^{-5/6}$

For Exercises 37–60, simplify the expressions using the properties of rational exponents. Write the final answer using positive exponents only.

37. $x^{1/4}x^{3/4}$

38. $2^{2/3}2^{1/3}$

39. $\dfrac{p^{5/3}}{p^{2/3}}$

40. $\dfrac{q^{5/4}}{q^{1/4}}$

41. $(y^{1/5})^{10}$

42. $(x^{1/2})^{8}$

43. $6^{-1/5}6^{6/5}$

44. $a^{-1/3}a^{2/3}$

45. $\dfrac{4t^{1/2}}{t^{-1/2}}$

46. $\dfrac{5s^{1/3}}{s^{-5/3}}$

47. $(a^{1/3}a^{1/4})^{12}$

48. $(x^{2/3}x^{1/2})^{6}$

49. $(5a^2c^{-1/2}d^{1/2})^2$

50. $(2x^{-1/3}y^2z^{5/3})^3$

51. $\left(\dfrac{x^{-2/3}}{y^{-3/4}}\right)^{12}$

52. $\left(\dfrac{m^{-1/4}}{n^{-1/2}}\right)^{-4}$

53. $\left(\dfrac{16w^{-2}z}{2wz^{-8}}\right)^{1/3}$

54. $\left(\dfrac{50p^{-1}q}{2pq^{-3}}\right)^{1/2}$

55. $(25x^2y^4z^6)^{1/2}$

56. $(8a^6b^3c^9)^{2/3}$

57. $\left(\dfrac{x^2y^{-1/3}z^{2/3}}{x^{2/3}y^{1/4}z}\right)^{12}$

58. $\left(\dfrac{a^2b^{1/2}c^{-2}}{a^{-3/4}b^0c^{1/8}}\right)^8$

59. $\left(\dfrac{x^{3m}y^{2m}}{z^{5m}}\right)^{1/m}$

60. $\left(\dfrac{a^{4n}b^{3n}}{c^n}\right)^{1/n}$

For Exercises 61–64, write the expressions in radical notation.

61. $(2x^2y)^{1/3}$

62. $(16abc)^{1/4}$

63. $\left(\dfrac{2}{y}\right)^{1/2}$

64. $(6x)^{1/2}$

For Exercises 65–68, write the expressions using rational exponents rather than radical notation.

65. $\sqrt[3]{x}$

66. $\sqrt[4]{a^2b^3}$

67. $5\sqrt{x}$

68. $\sqrt[3]{y^2}$

For Exercises 69–76, use a calculator to approximate the expressions and round to four decimal places, if necessary.

69. $9^{1/2}$

70. $125^{-1/3}$

71. $50^{-1/4}$

72. $(172)^{3/5}$

73. $\sqrt[3]{5^2}$

74. $\sqrt[4]{6^3}$

75. $\sqrt{10^3}$

76. $\sqrt[3]{16}$

77. If the area, A, of a square is known, then the length of its sides, s, can be computed by the formula: $s = A^{1/2}$

a. Compute the length of the sides of a square having an area of 100 in.^{2}

b. Compute the length of the sides of a square having an area of 72 in.^{2} Round your answer to the nearest 0.1 in.

78. The radius, r, of a sphere of volume, V, is given by $r = (3V/4\pi)^{1/3}$. Find the radius of a sphere having a volume of 85 in.^{3} Round your answer to the nearest 0.1 in.

79. If P dollars in principal grows to A dollars after t years with annual interest, then the interest rate of return is given by: $r = (A/P)^{1/t} - 1$

a. In one account, $10,000 grows to $16,802 after 5 years. Compute the interest rate. Round your answer to a tenth of a percent.

b. In another account $10,000 grows to $18,000 after 7 years. Compute the interest rate. Round your answer to a tenth of a percent.

c. Which account produced a higher average yearly return?

80. Is $(a + b)^{1/2}$ the same as $a^{1/2} + b^{1/2}$? Why or why not?

EXPANDING YOUR SKILLS

For Exercises 81–86, write the expression as a single radical.

81. $\sqrt{\sqrt[3]{x}}$

82. $\sqrt[3]{\sqrt{x}}$

83. $\sqrt[4]{\sqrt{y}}$

84. $\sqrt{\sqrt[4]{y}}$

85. $\sqrt[5]{\sqrt[3]{w}}$

86. $\sqrt[3]{\sqrt[4]{w}}$

section

6.3   PROPERTIES OF RADICALS

1.   Multiplication and Division Properties of Radicals

You may have already recognized certain properties of radicals involving a product or quotient:

Multiplication and Division Properties of Radicals

Let a and b represent real numbers such that $\sqrt[n]{a}$ and $\sqrt[n]{b}$ are both real. Then,

1. $\sqrt[n]{ab} = \sqrt[n]{a} \cdot \sqrt[n]{b}$ **Multiplication property of radicals**

2. $\sqrt[n]{\dfrac{a}{b}} = \dfrac{\sqrt[n]{a}}{\sqrt[n]{b}}$ $b \neq 0$ **Division property of radicals**

Properties 1 and 2 follow from the properties of rational exponents.

$$\sqrt[4]{ab} = (ab)^{1/n} = a^{1/n}b^{1/n} = \sqrt[n]{a} \cdot \sqrt[n]{b}$$

$$\sqrt[n]{\frac{a}{b}} = \left(\frac{a}{b}\right)^{1/n} = \frac{a^{1/n}}{b^{1/n}} = \frac{\sqrt[n]{a}}{\sqrt[n]{b}}$$

The multiplication and division properties of radicals indicate that a product or quotient within a radicand can be written as a product or quotient of radicals, provided the roots are real numbers. For example:

$$\sqrt{144} = \sqrt{16} \cdot \sqrt{9}$$

$$\sqrt{\frac{25}{36}} = \frac{\sqrt{25}}{\sqrt{36}}$$

The reverse process is also true. A product or quotient of radicals can be written as a single radical provided the roots are real numbers and they have the same indices.

$$\sqrt{3} \cdot \sqrt{12} = \sqrt{36}$$

$$\frac{\sqrt[3]{8}}{\sqrt[3]{125}} = \sqrt[3]{\frac{8}{125}}$$

2.   Simplified Form of a Radical

In algebra it is customary to simplify radical expressions as much as possible. A radical expression is in simplified form if all of the following conditions are true:

Simplified Form of a Radical

Consider any radical expression where the radicand is written as a product of prime factors. The expression is in **simplified form** if all of the following conditions are met:

1. The radicand has no factor raised to a power greater than or equal to the index.
2. There are no radicals in the denominator of a fraction.
3. The radicand does not contain a fraction.

3. Simplifying Radicals Using the Multiplication Property of Radicals

The expression $\sqrt{x^2}$ is not simplified because it fails condition 1. Because x^2 is a perfect square, $\sqrt{x^2}$ is easily simplified:

$$\sqrt{x^2} = x \quad (\text{for } x \geq 0)$$

However, how is an expression such as $\sqrt{x^9}$ simplified? This and many other radical expressions are simplified using the multiplication property of radicals. The following examples illustrate how nth powers can be removed from the radicands of nth roots.

---

example 1

Using the Multiplication Property to Simplify a Radical Expression

Use the multiplication property of radicals to simplify the expression $\sqrt{x^9}$. Assume $x \geq 0$.

Solution:

The expression $\sqrt{x^9}$ is equivalent to $\sqrt{x^8 \cdot x}$. By applying the multiplication property of radicals, we have

$$\sqrt{x^9} = \sqrt{x^8 \cdot x}$$

$$= \sqrt{x^8} \cdot \sqrt{x} \qquad \text{Apply the multiplication property of radicals.}$$

Note that x^8 is a perfect square because $x^8 = (x^4)^2$.

$$= x^4\sqrt{x} \qquad \text{Simplify.}$$

In Example 1, the expression x^9 is not a perfect square. Therefore, to simplify $\sqrt{x^9}$, it was necessary to write the expression as the product of the largest perfect square and a remaining or "leftover" factor: $\sqrt{x^9} = \sqrt{x^8 \cdot x}$. This process also applies to simplifying nth roots as shown in the next example.

---

example 2

Using the Multiplication Property to Simplify a Radical Expression

Use the multiplication property of radicals to simplify each expression. Assume all variables represent positive real numbers.

a. $\sqrt[4]{b^7}$

b. $\sqrt[3]{w^7 z^9}$

Solution:

The goal is to rewrite each radicand as the product of the largest perfect square (perfect cube, perfect fourth power, and so on) and a leftover factor.

a. $\sqrt[4]{b^7} = \sqrt[4]{(b^4) \cdot (b^3)}$ b^4 is the largest perfect fourth power in the radicand.

$= \sqrt[4]{b^4} \cdot \sqrt[4]{b^3}$ Apply the multiplication property of radicals.

$= b\sqrt[4]{b^3}$ Simplify.

b. $\sqrt[3]{w^7 z^9} = \sqrt[3]{(w^6 z^9) \cdot (w)}$ $w^6 z^9$ is the largest perfect cube in the radicand.

$= \sqrt[3]{w^6 z^9} \cdot \sqrt[3]{w}$ Apply the multiplication property of radicals.

$= w^2 z^3 \sqrt[3]{w}$ Simplify.

Each expression in Example 2 involves a radicand that is a product of variable factors. If a numerical factor is present, sometimes it is necessary to factor the coefficient before simplifying the radical.

example 3   **Using the Multiplication Property to Simplify Radicals**

Use the multiplication property of radicals to simplify the expressions. Assume all variables represent positive real numbers.

a. $\sqrt{56}$ b. $\sqrt[3]{40x^3 y^5 z^7}$

Solution:

a. $\sqrt{56} = \sqrt{2^3 7}$ Factor the radicand.

$= \sqrt{(2^2) \cdot (2 \cdot 7)}$ 2^2 is the largest perfect square in the radicand.

$= \sqrt{2^2} \cdot \sqrt{2 \cdot 7}$ Apply the multiplication property of radicals.

$= 2 \cdot \sqrt{14}$ Simplify.

```
2|56
2|28
2|14
2|7
 1
```

Graphing Calculator Box

A calculator can be used to support the solution to Example 3(a). The decimal approximation for $\sqrt{56}$ and $2 \cdot \sqrt{14}$ agree for the first 10 digits. This in itself does not make $\sqrt{56} = 2 \cdot \sqrt{14}$. It is the multiplication of property of radicals that guarantees that the expressions are equal.

```
√(56)
          7.483314774
2*√(14)
          7.483314774
```

b. $\sqrt[3]{40x^3y^5z^7}$

$= \sqrt[3]{2^3 5 x^3 y^5 z^7}$ Factor the radicand.

$= \sqrt[3]{(2^3 x^3 y^3 z^6) \cdot (5y^2 z)}$ $2^3 x^3 y^3 z^6$ is the largest perfect cube.

$= \sqrt[3]{2^3 x^3 y^3 z^6} \cdot \sqrt[3]{5y^2 z}$ Apply the multiplication property of radicals.

$= 2xyz^2 \sqrt[3]{5y^2 z}$ Simplify.

2	40
2	20
2	10
5	5
	1

Avoiding Mistakes

The multiplication property of radicals allows us to simplify a product of factors within a radical. For example:

$\sqrt{x^2 y^2} = \sqrt{x^2} \cdot \sqrt{y^2} = xy$
(for $x \geq 0$ and $y \geq 0$)

However, this rule does not apply to *terms* that are added or subtracted within the radical. For example,

$\sqrt{x^2 + y^2}$ and $\sqrt{x^2 - y^2}$
cannot be simplified.

4. Simplifying Radicals Using the Division Property of Radicals

The division property of radicals indicates that a radical of a quotient can be written as the quotient of the radicals and vice versa provided all roots are real numbers.

example 4

Using the Division Property to Simplify Radicals

Use the division property of radicals to simplify the expressions. Assume all variables represent positive real numbers.

a. $\sqrt{\dfrac{a^7}{a^3}}$ b. $\dfrac{\sqrt[3]{3}}{\sqrt[3]{81}}$ c. $\dfrac{7\sqrt{50}}{15}$ d. $\sqrt[4]{\dfrac{2c^5}{32cd^8}}$

Solution:

a. $\sqrt{\dfrac{a^7}{a^3}}$ The radicand contains a fraction. However, the fraction can be reduced.

$= \sqrt{a^4}$ Reduce.

$= a^2$ Simplify the radical.

b. $\dfrac{\sqrt[3]{3}}{\sqrt[3]{81}}$ The expression has a radical in the denominator.

$= \sqrt[3]{\dfrac{3}{81}}$ Because the radicands have a common factor, write the expression as a single radical and reduce (division property of radicals).

$= \sqrt[3]{\dfrac{1}{27}}$ Reduce.

$= \dfrac{1}{3}$ Simplify.

c. $\dfrac{7\sqrt{50}}{15}$ Simplify $\sqrt{50}$.

$= \dfrac{7\sqrt{5^2 \cdot 2}}{15}$ 5^2 is the largest perfect square in the radicand.

$$= \frac{7\sqrt{5^2} \cdot \sqrt{2}}{15}$$ Multiplication property of radicals.

$$= \frac{7 \cdot 5\sqrt{2}}{15}$$ Simplify the radicals.

$$= \frac{7 \cdot \overset{1}{\cancel{5}}\sqrt{2}}{\underset{3}{\cancel{15}}}$$ Reduce.

$$= \frac{7\sqrt{2}}{3}$$

Avoiding Mistakes

The division property of radicals allows us to reduce a ratio of two radicals provided they have the same index. For example:

$$\frac{\sqrt{15}}{\sqrt{5}} = \sqrt{\frac{15}{5}} = \sqrt{3}$$

However, a factor within the radicand cannot be simplified with a factor outside the radicand. For example,

$$\frac{\sqrt{15}}{2}$$ cannot be simplified.

d. $\sqrt[4]{\dfrac{2c^5}{32cd^8}}$ The radicand contains a fraction.

$$= \sqrt[4]{\frac{c^4}{16d^8}}$$ Reduce the factors in the radicand.

$$= \frac{\sqrt[4]{c^4}}{\sqrt[4]{16d^8}}$$ Apply the division property of radicals.

$$= \frac{c}{2d^2}$$ Simplify.

section 6.3   PRACTICE EXERCISES

For the exercises in this set, assume that all variables represent positive real numbers unless otherwise stated.

For Exercises 1–4, simplify the expression. Write the answer with positive exponents only.

1. $(a^2b^{-4})^{1/2}\left(\dfrac{a}{b^{-3}}\right)$

2. $\left(\dfrac{p^4}{q^{-6}}\right)^{-1/2}(p^3q^{-2})$

3. $(r^{-1/4}s^{3/4})^8$

4. $(x^{1/3}y^{5/6})^{-6}$

5. Write $x^{4/7}$ in radical notation.

6. Write $y^{2/5}$ in radical notation.

7. Write $\sqrt{y^9}$ using rational exponents.

8. Write $\sqrt[3]{x^2}$ using rational exponents.

9. Approximate the expression $(2 - \sqrt{y})/4$ to two decimal places for:
   a. $y = 3$ b. $y = 5$

10. Approximate the expression $\sqrt{\frac{1}{2}x + 3}$ to two decimal places for:
   a. $x = -2$ b. $x = 3$

For Exercises 11–18, use the multiplication property of radicals to multiply the expressions. Then simplify the result.

   Example: $\sqrt{3x} \cdot \sqrt{3x} = \sqrt{9x^2} = 3x$

11. $\sqrt{4x} \cdot \sqrt{25x}$ 12. $\sqrt{2z} \cdot \sqrt{8z}$

13. $\sqrt[3]{2x} \cdot \sqrt[3]{4x^2}$ 14. $\sqrt[3]{a^2b} \cdot \sqrt[3]{ab^3}$

15. $\sqrt[4]{(x+2)^3} \cdot \sqrt[4]{(x+2)}$ 16. $\sqrt[4]{8w^2} \cdot \sqrt[4]{2w^2}$

17. $\sqrt[5]{2y^2} \cdot \sqrt[5]{16y^3}$

18. $\sqrt[5]{8(t-1)^2} \cdot \sqrt[5]{4(t-1)^3}$

For Exercises 19–26, use the division property of radicals to divide the expressions. Then simplify the result.

Example: $\dfrac{\sqrt{18x}}{\sqrt{2x}} = \sqrt{\dfrac{18x}{2x}} = \sqrt{9} = 3$

19. $\dfrac{\sqrt{27y}}{\sqrt{3y}}$

20. $\dfrac{\sqrt{24r}}{\sqrt{6r}}$

21. $\dfrac{\sqrt[4]{2^5a^3b^7}}{\sqrt[4]{2a^3b^3}}$

22. $\dfrac{\sqrt[4]{8^5x^6y^3}}{\sqrt[4]{8x^2y^3}}$

23. $\dfrac{\sqrt[3]{(3x+1)^5}}{\sqrt[3]{(3x+1)^2}}$

24. $\dfrac{\sqrt[3]{(6-w)^7}}{\sqrt[3]{(6-w)^4}}$

25. $\dfrac{\sqrt{(a+b)}}{\sqrt{(a+b)^3}}$

26. $\dfrac{\sqrt{(x-3)^2}}{\sqrt{(x-3)^4}}$

For Exercises 27–46, simplify the radicals.

27. $\sqrt{28}$

28. $\sqrt{63}$

29. $\sqrt{80}$

30. $\sqrt{108}$

31. $5\sqrt{18}$

32. $2\sqrt{24}$

33. $\sqrt[3]{54}$

34. $\sqrt[3]{48}$

35. $\sqrt{25x^4y^3}$

36. $\sqrt{125p^3q^2}$

37. $\sqrt[3]{27x^2y^3z^4}$

38. $\sqrt[3]{108a^3bc^2}$

39. $\sqrt[3]{\dfrac{16a^2b}{2a^2b^4}}$

40. $\sqrt[4]{\dfrac{3s^2t^4}{10,000}}$

41. $\sqrt[5]{\dfrac{32x}{y^{10}}}$

42. $\sqrt[3]{\dfrac{-16j^3}{k^3}}$

43. $\dfrac{\sqrt{50x^3y}}{\sqrt{9y^4}}$

44. $\dfrac{\sqrt[3]{-27a^4}}{\sqrt[3]{8a}}$

45. $\sqrt{2^3a^{14}b^8c^{31}d^{22}}$

46. $\sqrt{7^5u^{12}v^{20}w^{65}x^{80}}$

For Exercises 47–50, write a mathematical expression for the English phrase and simplify.

47. The quotient of one and the cube root of w^6.

48. The square root of the quotient of h and 49.

49. The square root of k raised to the third power.

50. The cube root of $2x^4$.

For Exercises 51–54, find the third side of the right triangle. Write your answer as a radical and simplify.

51.

10 ft
?
8 ft

52.

?
6 in.
12 in.

53.

?
18 m
12 m

54.
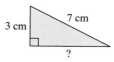
3 cm
7 cm
?

55. On a baseball diamond, the bases are 90 ft apart. Find the distance from home plate to second base. Round to one decimal place.

2nd base

90 ft

90 ft

Home plate

Figure for Exercise 55

56. Linda is at the beach flying a kite. The kite is directly over a sand castle 60 ft away from Linda. If 100 ft of kite string is out (ignoring any sag in the string), how high is the kite? (Assume that Linda is 5 ft tall.) See figure.

Figure for Exercise 56

■ EXPANDING YOUR SKILLS

57. Tom has to travel from town A to town C across a small mountain range. He can travel one of two routes. He can travel on a four-lane highway from A to B and then from B to C at an average speed of 55 mph. Or he can travel on a two-lane road directly from town A to town C, but his average speed will only be 35 mph. If Tom is in a hurry, which route will take him to town C the fastest?

Figure for Exercise 57

58. One side of a rectangular pasture is 80 ft in length. The diagonal distance is 110 yds. If fencing costs \$3.29 per foot, how much will it cost to fence the pasture?

Figure for Exercise 58

---

chapter 6   MIDCHAPTER REVIEW

In the following exercises, assume all variables represent positive real numbers.

For Exercises 1–10, simplify the expressions.

1. $\sqrt[3]{64}$ 2. $\sqrt{81}$

3. $\sqrt[4]{\dfrac{1}{16}}$ 4. $\sqrt[3]{\dfrac{27}{125}}$

5. $\sqrt[3]{54x^2w^4}$ 6. $\sqrt{20t^2u^3v^7}$

7. $\sqrt{\dfrac{50x^3y^5}{x}}$ 8. $\sqrt[3]{\dfrac{16w^5z^{10}}{2w^2}}$

9. $\sqrt[3]{(4r-3)^3}$ 10. $\sqrt{\dfrac{a^2b^2}{(a+b)^2}}$

11. Explain how to simplify $\sqrt[5]{x^{51}}$.

For Exercises 12–19, simplify the exponential expressions. Leave no negative exponents in your final answer.

12. $8^{2/3}$ 13. $16^{3/4}$

14. $\left(\dfrac{1}{25}\right)^{-1/2}$ 15. $\left(\dfrac{4}{25}\right)^{-1/2}$

16. $\left(\dfrac{s^{-2}t^4}{r^6}\right)^{1/2}$ 17. $\left(\dfrac{p^2q^{-3}}{r^{-5}}\right)^{1/2}$

18. $(u^2v^3)^{-1/6}(u^3v^6)^{1/3}$ 19. $(x^{1/2}y^{1/4})(x^{1/2}y^{1/3})$

20. Explain how to simplify $125^{2/3}$.

21. Rewrite the expressions using rational exponents and simplify.

     a. $\sqrt[3]{8x^6}$ b. $\sqrt{25b^4}$

22. Rewrite the expressions in radical notation.

     a. $x^{2/3}$ b. $(c^{1/4})^3$

Concepts

1. Definition of *Like* Radicals
2. Addition and Subtraction of Radicals
3. Recognizing Un*like* Radicals

6.4   ADDITION AND SUBTRACTION OF RADICALS

1.   Definition of *Like* Radicals

Definition of *Like* Radicals

Two radical expressions are said to be ***like* radicals** if their radical factors have the same index and the same radicand.

The following are pairs of *like* radicals:

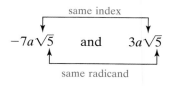

$-7a\sqrt{5}$ and $3a\sqrt{5}$ Indices and radicands are the same.

$-\dfrac{1}{2}\sqrt[3]{15b}$ and $4\sqrt[3]{15b}$ Indices and radicands are the same.

These pairs are not *like* radicals:

$-2\sqrt{6}$ and $13\sqrt[4]{6}$ Radicals have different indices.

$1.3cd\sqrt{3}$ and $-3.7cd\sqrt{10}$ Radicals have different radicands.

2.   Addition and Subtraction of Radicals

Expressions with radicals can be added or subtracted if they are *like* radicals. To add or subtract *like* radicals, use the distributive property. For example:

$$2\sqrt{5} + 6\sqrt{5} = (2 + 6)\sqrt{5}$$
$$= 8\sqrt{5}$$

$$9\sqrt[3]{2y} - 4\sqrt[3]{2y} = (9 - 4)\sqrt[3]{2y}$$
$$= 5\sqrt[3]{2y}$$

---

example 1   **Adding and Subtracting Radicals**

Add or subtract the radicals as indicated.

a. $6\sqrt{11} + 2\sqrt{11}$ b. $\sqrt{3} + \sqrt{3}$

c. $-2\sqrt[3]{ab} + 7\sqrt[3]{ab} - \sqrt[3]{ab}$ d. $\dfrac{1}{4}x\sqrt{3y} - \dfrac{3}{2}x\sqrt{3y}$

Solution:

a. $6\sqrt{11} + 2\sqrt{11}$

   $= (6 + 2)\sqrt{11}$ Apply the distributive property.

   $= 8\sqrt{11}$ Simplify.

b. $\sqrt{3} + \sqrt{3}$

   $= 1\sqrt{3} + 1\sqrt{3}$ Note that $\sqrt{3} = 1\sqrt{3}$.

   $= (1 + 1)\sqrt{3}$ Apply the distributive property.

   $= 2\sqrt{3}$ Simplify.

c. $-2\sqrt[3]{ab} + 7\sqrt[3]{ab} - \sqrt[3]{ab}$

   $= (-2 + 7 - 1)\sqrt[3]{ab}$ Apply the distributive property.

   $= 4\sqrt[3]{ab}$ Simplify.

d. $\dfrac{1}{4}x\sqrt{3y} - \dfrac{3}{2}x\sqrt{3y}$

   $= \left(\dfrac{1}{4} - \dfrac{3}{2}\right)x\sqrt{3y}$ Apply the distributive property.

   $= \left(\dfrac{1}{4} - \dfrac{6}{4}\right)x\sqrt{3y}$ Get a common denominator.

   $= -\dfrac{5}{4}x\sqrt{3y}$ Simplify.

Avoiding Mistakes

The process of adding *like* radicals with the distributive property is similar to adding *like* terms. The end result is that the numerical coefficients are added and the radical factor is unchanged.

$\sqrt{5} + \sqrt{5} = 1\sqrt{5} + 1\sqrt{5} = 2\sqrt{5}$

(correct)

Be careful: $\sqrt{5} + \sqrt{5} \neq \sqrt{10}$

In general: $\sqrt{x} + \sqrt{y} \neq \sqrt{x + y}$

Sometimes it is necessary to simplify radicals before adding or subtracting.

---

example 2   **Adding and Subtracting Radicals**

Simplify the radicals and add or subtract as indicated.

a. $3\sqrt{8} + \sqrt{2}$ b. $8\sqrt{x^3y^2} - 3y\sqrt{x^3}$

c. $\sqrt{50x^2y^5} - 13y\sqrt{2x^2y^3} + xy\sqrt{98y^3}$

Solution:

a. $3\sqrt{8} + \sqrt{2}$ The radicands are different. Try simplifying the radicals first.

   $= 3 \cdot 2\sqrt{2} + \sqrt{2}$ Simplify: $\sqrt{8} = 2\sqrt{2}$

   $= 6\sqrt{2} + \sqrt{2}$

   $= (6 + 1)\sqrt{2}$ Apply the distributive property.

   $= 7\sqrt{2}$ Simplify.

Graphing Calculator Box

To check the solution to Example 2(a), use
a calculator to evaluate the expressions
$3\sqrt{8} + \sqrt{2}$ and $7\sqrt{2}$. The decimal approximations agree to 10 digits.

```
3√(8)+√(2)
           9.899494937
7√(2)
           9.899494937
```

b. $8\sqrt{x^3y^2} - 3y\sqrt{x^3}$

The radicands are different.
Simplify the radicals first.

$= 8xy\sqrt{x} - 3xy\sqrt{x}$

Simplify: $\sqrt{x^3y^2} = xy\sqrt{x}$
and $\sqrt{x^3} = x\sqrt{x}$

$= (8 - 3)xy\sqrt{x}$

Apply the distributive property.

$= 5xy\sqrt{x}$

Simplify.

Simplify each radical.

c. $\sqrt{50x^2y^5} - 13y\sqrt{2x^2y^3} + xy\sqrt{98y^3}$

$= 5xy^2\sqrt{2y} - 13xy^2\sqrt{2y} + 7xy^2\sqrt{2y}$

$$\begin{cases} \sqrt{50x^2y^5} = \sqrt{5^2 2x^2y^5} \\ \quad = 5xy^2\sqrt{2y} \\ -13y\sqrt{2x^2y^3} = -13xy^2\sqrt{2y} \\ xy\sqrt{98y^3} = xy\sqrt{7^2 2y^3} \\ \quad = 7xy^2\sqrt{2y} \end{cases}$$

$= (5 - 13 + 7)xy^2\sqrt{2y}$

Apply the distributive property.

$= -xy^2\sqrt{2y}$

3.   Recognizing Un*like* Radicals

It is important to keep in mind that only *like* radicals may be added or subtracted.
The next example provides extra practice for recognizing un*like* radicals.

example 3   **Recognizing Un*like* Radicals**

The following radicals cannot be added or subtracted to form a single radical.
Explain why.

a. $\sqrt{2} + \sqrt[3]{2}$ Un*like* radicals. Indices are not the same.

b. $5\sqrt{3} - 2\sqrt{5}$ Un*like* radicals. Radicands are not the same.

c. $12\sqrt{7} - 12$ Un*like* radicals. One term has a radical, one does not.

d. $2\sqrt{50} - 3\sqrt{75}$ Simplify.

$10\sqrt{2} - 15\sqrt{3}$ Un*like* radicals. Radicands are not the same.

section 6.4 PRACTICE EXERCISES

For the exercises in this set, assume that all variables represent positive real numbers unless otherwise stated.

For Exercises 1–4, simplify the radicals.

1. $\sqrt[3]{-16s^4t^9}$

2. $-\sqrt[4]{x^7y^4}$

3. $\sqrt{3p^2} \cdot \sqrt{12p^4}$

4. $\dfrac{\sqrt[3]{7b^8}}{\sqrt[3]{56b^2}}$

5. Write the expression $(4x^2)^{3/2}$ as a radical and simplify.

6. Convert to rational exponents and simplify.
   $\sqrt[5]{3^5x^{15}y^{10}}$

For Exercises 7–8, simplify the expressions. Write the answer with positive exponents only.

7. $y^{2/3}y^{1/4}$

8. $(x^{1/2}y^{-3/4})^{-4}$

For Exercises 9–10, use a calculator to approximate the expressions. Round to two decimal places.

9. $(2.718)^{2/3}$

10. $\sqrt[4]{90}$

11. Explain the similarities and differences between the following pairs of expressions.

    a. $7\sqrt{5} + 4\sqrt{5}$ and $7x + 4x$

    b. $-2\sqrt{6} - 9\sqrt{3}$ and $-2x - 9y$

12. Explain the similarities and differences between the following pairs of expressions.

    a. $-4\sqrt{3} + 5\sqrt{3}$ and $-4z + 5z$

    b. $13\sqrt{7} - 6\sqrt{9}$ and $13a - 18$

For Exercises 13–30, add or subtract the radical expressions (if possible).

13. $3\sqrt{5} + 6\sqrt{5}$

14. $5\sqrt{a} + 3\sqrt{a}$

15. $3\sqrt[3]{t} - 2\sqrt[3]{t}$

16. $6\sqrt[3]{7} - 2\sqrt[3]{7}$

17. $6\sqrt{10} - \sqrt{10}$

18. $13\sqrt{11} - \sqrt{11}$

19. $\sqrt[4]{3} + 7\sqrt[4]{3} - \sqrt[4]{14}$

20. $2\sqrt{11} + 3\sqrt{13} + 5\sqrt{11}$

21. $8\sqrt{x} + 2\sqrt{y} - 6\sqrt{x}$

22. $10\sqrt{10} - 8\sqrt{10} + \sqrt{2}$

23. $\sqrt[3]{ab} + a\sqrt[3]{b}$

24. $x\sqrt[4]{y} - y\sqrt[4]{x}$

25. $\sqrt{2t} + \sqrt[3]{2t}$

26. $\sqrt[4]{5c} + \sqrt[3]{5c}$

27. $\dfrac{5}{6}z\sqrt[3]{6} + \dfrac{7}{9}z\sqrt[3]{6}$

28. $\dfrac{3}{4}a\sqrt[4]{b} + \dfrac{1}{6}a\sqrt[4]{b}$

29. $0.81x\sqrt{y} - 0.11x\sqrt{y}$

30. $7.5\sqrt{pq} - 6.3\sqrt{pq}$

31. Explain the process for adding the two radicals.
    $3\sqrt{2} + 7\sqrt{50}$.

32. Explain the process for adding the two radicals.
    $\sqrt{8} + \sqrt{32}$.

For Exercises 33–50, add or subtract the radical expressions as indicated.

33. $\sqrt{36} + \sqrt{81}$

34. $3\sqrt{80} - 5\sqrt{45}$

35. $2\sqrt{12} + \sqrt{48}$

36. $5\sqrt{32} + 2\sqrt{50}$

37. $4\sqrt{7} + \sqrt{63} - 2\sqrt{28}$

38. $8\sqrt{3} - 2\sqrt{27} + \sqrt{75}$

39. $3\sqrt{2a} - \sqrt{8a} - \sqrt{72a}$

40. $\sqrt{12t} - \sqrt{27t} + 5\sqrt{3t}$

41. $2s^2\sqrt[3]{s^2t^6} + 3t^2\sqrt[3]{8s^8}$

42. $4\sqrt[3]{x^4} - 2x\sqrt[3]{x}$

43. $7\sqrt[3]{x^4} - x\sqrt[3]{x}$

44. $6\sqrt[3]{y^{10}} - 3y^2\sqrt[3]{y^4}$

45. $5p\sqrt{20p^2} + p^2\sqrt{80}$

46. $2q\sqrt{48q^2} - \sqrt{27q^4}$

47. $\dfrac{3}{2}ab\sqrt{24a^3} + \dfrac{4}{3}\sqrt{54a^5b^2} - a^2b\sqrt{150a}$

48. $mn\sqrt{72n} + \dfrac{2}{3}n\sqrt{8m^2n} - \dfrac{5}{6}\sqrt{50m^2n^3}$

49. $x\sqrt[3]{16} - 2\sqrt[3]{27x} + \sqrt[3]{54x^3}$

50. $5\sqrt[4]{y^5} - 2y\sqrt[4]{y} + \sqrt[4]{16y^7}$

For Exercises 51–56, answer true or false. If an answer is false, explain why.

51. $\sqrt{x} + \sqrt{y} = \sqrt{x + y}$

52. $\sqrt{x} + \sqrt{x} = 2\sqrt{x}$

53. $5\sqrt[3]{x} + 2\sqrt[3]{x} = 7\sqrt[3]{x}$

54. $6\sqrt{x} + 5\sqrt[3]{x} = 11\sqrt{x}$

55. $\sqrt{y} + \sqrt{y} = \sqrt{2y}$

56. $\sqrt{c^2 + d^2} = c + d$

For Exercises 57–60, translate the English phrase into an algebraic expression. Simplify each expression if possible.

57. The sum of the square root of 48 and the square root of 12.

58. The sum of the cube root of 16 and the cube root of 2.

59. The difference of 5 times the cube root of x^6 and the square of x.

60. The sum of the cube of y and the fourth root of y^{12}.

For Exercises 61–64, write an English phrase that translates the mathematical expression. (Answers may vary.)

61. $\sqrt{18} - 5^2$

62. $4^3 - \sqrt[3]{4}$

63. $\sqrt[4]{x} + y^3$

64. $a^4 + \sqrt{a}$

■ EXPANDING YOUR SKILLS

65. a. An irregularly shaped garden is shown in the figure. All distances are expressed in yards. Find the perimeter. *Hint:* Use the Pythagorean theorem to find the length of each side. Write the final answer in radical form.

    b. Approximate your answer to two decimal places.

    c. If edging costs \$1.49 per foot and sales tax is 6%, find the total cost of edging the garden.

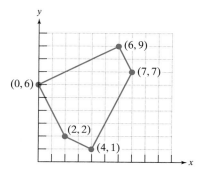

Figure for Exercise 65

66. a. An irregularly shaped garden is shown in the figure. All distances are expressed in yards. Find the perimeter. Write the final answer in radical form.

    b. Approximate your answer to two decimal places.

    c. If edging costs \$1.69 per foot and sales tax is 6%, find the total cost of edging the garden.

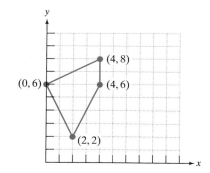

Figure for Exercise 66

Concepts

1. **Multiplication Property of Radicals**

2. **Multiplying Radicals with Different Indices**

3. **Multiplying Radical Expressions Involving Multiple Terms**

4. **Expressions of the Form $(\sqrt[n]{a})^n$**

5. **Special Case Products**

section 6.5   MULTIPLICATION OF RADICALS

1. Multiplication Property of Radicals

In this section we will learn how to multiply radicals by using the **multiplication property of radicals** first introduced in Section 6.3.

The Multiplication Property of Radicals

Let a and b represent real numbers such that $\sqrt[n]{a}$ and $\sqrt[n]{b}$ are both real. Then,
$$\sqrt[n]{ab} = \sqrt[n]{a} \cdot \sqrt[n]{b}$$

To multiply two radical expressions, we use the multiplication property of radicals along with the commutative and associative properties of multiplication.

---

example 1   **Multiplying Radical Expressions**

Multiply the expressions and simplify the result. Assume all variables represent positive real numbers.

a. $(3\sqrt{2})(5\sqrt{6})$ b. $(2x\sqrt{y})(-7\sqrt{xy})$ c. $(15c\sqrt[3]{cd})\left(\dfrac{1}{3}\sqrt[3]{cd^2}\right)$

Solution:

a. $(3\sqrt{2})(5\sqrt{6})$

$= (3 \cdot 5)(\sqrt{2} \cdot \sqrt{6})$ Commutative and associative properties of multiplication

$= 15\sqrt{12}$ Multiplication property of radicals

$= 15\sqrt{2^2 3}$

$= 15 \cdot 2\sqrt{3}$ Simplify the radical.

$= 30\sqrt{3}$

b. $(2x\sqrt{y})(-7\sqrt{xy})$

$= (2x)(-7)(\sqrt{y} \cdot \sqrt{xy})$ Commutative and associative properties of multiplication

$= -14x\sqrt{xy^2}$ Multiplication property of radicals

$= -14xy\sqrt{x}$ Simplify the radical.

c. $(15c\sqrt[3]{cd})\left(\dfrac{1}{3}\sqrt[3]{cd^2}\right)$

$= \left(15c \cdot \dfrac{1}{3}\right)(\sqrt[3]{cd} \cdot \sqrt[3]{cd^2})$ Commutative and associative properties of multiplication

$= 5c\sqrt[3]{c^2 d^3}$ Multiplication property of radicals

$= 5cd\sqrt[3]{c^2}$ Simplify the radical.

2. Multiplying Radicals with Different Indices

The product of two radicals can be simplified provided the radicals have the same index. If the radicals have different indices, then we can use the properties of rational expressions to obtain a common index.

---

example 2   **Multiplying Radicals with Different Indices**

Multiply the expressions:

a. $\sqrt[3]{5} \cdot \sqrt[4]{5}$ b. $\sqrt[3]{7} \cdot \sqrt{2}$

Solution:

a. $\sqrt[3]{5} \cdot \sqrt[4]{5}$

$\quad = 5^{1/3}5^{1/4}$ $\qquad$ Rewrite each expression with rational exponents.

$\quad = 5^{(1/3)+(1/4)}$ $\qquad$ Because the bases are equal, we can add the exponents.

$\quad = 5^{(4/12)+(3/12)}$ $\qquad$ Write the fractions with a common denominator.

$\quad = 5^{7/12}$

$\quad = \sqrt[12]{5^7}$ $\qquad$ Rewrite the expression as a radical.

b. $\sqrt[3]{7} \cdot \sqrt{2}$

$\quad = 7^{1/3}2^{1/2}$ $\qquad$ Rewrite each expression with rational exponents.

$\quad = 7^{2/6}2^{3/6}$ $\qquad$ Write the rational exponents with a common denominator.

$\quad = (7^2 2^3)^{1/6}$ $\qquad$ Apply the power rule of exponents.

$\quad = \sqrt[6]{7^2 2^3}$ $\qquad$ Rewrite the expression as a single radical.

$\quad = \sqrt[6]{392}$ $\qquad$ Simplify.

---

3. Multiplying Radical Expressions Involving Multiple Terms

When multiplying radical expressions with more than one term, we use the distributive property.

---

example 3   **Multiplying Radical Expressions**

Multiply the radical expressions. Assume all variables represent positive real numbers.

a. $3\sqrt{11}(2 + \sqrt{11})$ $\qquad\qquad$ b. $(\sqrt{5} + 3\sqrt{2})(2\sqrt{5} - \sqrt{2})$

c. $(2\sqrt{14} + \sqrt{7})(6 - \sqrt{14} + 8\sqrt{7})$ $\qquad$ d. $(-10a\sqrt{b} + 7b)(a\sqrt{b} + 2b)$

Solution:

a. $3\sqrt{11}(2 + \sqrt{11})$

$= 3\sqrt{11} \cdot (2) + 3\sqrt{11} \cdot \sqrt{11}$ Apply the distributive property.

$= 6\sqrt{11} + 3\sqrt{11^2}$ Multiplication property of radicals

$= 6\sqrt{11} + 3 \cdot 11$ Simplify the radical.

$= 6\sqrt{11} + 33$

b. $(\sqrt{5} + 3\sqrt{2})(2\sqrt{5} - \sqrt{2})$

$= 2\sqrt{5^2} - \sqrt{10} + 6\sqrt{10} - 3\sqrt{2^2}$ Apply the distributive property.

$= 2 \cdot 5 + 5\sqrt{10} - 3 \cdot 2$ Simplify radicals and combine *like* radicals.

$= 10 + 5\sqrt{10} - 6$

$= 4 + 5\sqrt{10}$ Combine *like* terms.

Graphing Calculator Box

To check the solution to Example 3(b), use a calculator to evaluate the expressions $(\sqrt{5} + 3\sqrt{2})(2\sqrt{5} - \sqrt{2})$ and $4 + 5\sqrt{10}$. The decimal approximations agree to 9 digits.

```
(√(5)+3√(2))*(2√
(5)-√(2))
           19.8113883
4+5√(10)
           19.8113883
```

---

c. $(2\sqrt{14} + \sqrt{7})(6 - \sqrt{14} + 8\sqrt{7})$

$= 12\sqrt{14} - 2\sqrt{14^2} + 16\sqrt{98} + 6\sqrt{7} - \sqrt{98} + 8\sqrt{7^2}$ Apply the distributive property.

$= 12\sqrt{14} - 2 \cdot 14 + 16 \cdot 7\sqrt{2} + 6\sqrt{7} - 7\sqrt{2} + 8 \cdot 7$ Simplify the radicals.

(*Note:* $\sqrt{98}$
$= \sqrt{7^2 \cdot 2}$
$= 7\sqrt{2})$

$= 12\sqrt{14} - 28 + 112\sqrt{2} + 6\sqrt{7} - 7\sqrt{2} + 56$ Simplify.

$= 12\sqrt{14} + 105\sqrt{2} + 6\sqrt{7} + 28$ Combine *like* terms.

d. $(-10a\sqrt{b} + 7b)(a\sqrt{b} + 2b)$

$= -10a^2\sqrt{b^2} - 20ab\sqrt{b} + 7ab\sqrt{b} + 14b^2$ Apply the distributive property.

$= -10a^2b - 13ab\sqrt{b} + 14b^2$ Simplify and combine *like* terms.

4. Expressions of the Form $(\sqrt[n]{a})^n$

The multiplication property of radicals can be used to simplify an expression of the form $(\sqrt{a})^2$, where $a \geq 0$.

$$(\sqrt{a})^2 = \sqrt{a} \cdot \sqrt{a} = \sqrt{a^2} = a, \text{ where } a \geq 0$$

This logic can be applied to nth roots. If $\sqrt[n]{a}$ is a real number, then, $(\sqrt[n]{a})^n = a$.

example 4

Simplifying Radical Expressions

Simplify the expressions. Assume all variables represent positive real numbers.

a. $(\sqrt{11})^2$ b. $(\sqrt[5]{z})^5$ c. $(\sqrt[3]{pq})^3$

Solution:

a. $(\sqrt{11})^2 = 11$ b. $(\sqrt[5]{z})^5 = z$ c. $(\sqrt[3]{pq})^3 = pq$

5. Special Case Products

From Example 3, you may have noticed a similarity between multiplying radical expressions and multiplying polynomials.

Recall from Section 5.4 that the square of a binomial results in a perfect square trinomial:

$$(a + b)^2 = a^2 + 2ab + b^2$$

$$(a - b)^2 = a^2 - 2ab + b^2$$

The same patterns occur when squaring a radical expression with two terms.

example 5

Squaring a Two-Term Radical Expression

Square the radical expressions.

a. $(\sqrt{d} + 3)^2$ b. $(5\sqrt{y} - \sqrt{2})^2$

Solution:

a. $(\sqrt{d} + 3)^2$ This expression is in the form $(a + b)^2$, where $a = \sqrt{d}$ and $b = 3$.

$$\overset{a^2 + 2ab + b^2}{\diagdown}$$

$$= (\sqrt{d})^2 + 2(\sqrt{d})(3) + (3)^2$$ Apply the formula $(a + b)^2 = a^2 + 2ab + b^2$.

$$= d + 6\sqrt{d} + 9$$ Simplify.

Tip: The product $(\sqrt{d} + 3)^2$ can also be found using the distributive property:

$$(\sqrt{d} + 3)^2 = (\sqrt{d} + 3)(\sqrt{d} + 3) = \sqrt{d} \cdot \sqrt{d} + \sqrt{d} \cdot 3 + 3 \cdot \sqrt{d} + 3 \cdot 3$$
$$= \sqrt{d^2} + 3\sqrt{d} + 3\sqrt{d} + 9$$
$$= d + 6\sqrt{d} + 9$$

b. $(5\sqrt{y} - \sqrt{2})^2$ This expression is in the form $(a - b)^2$, where $a = 5\sqrt{y}$ and $b = \sqrt{2}$.

$$\overset{a^2 - 2ab + b^2}{\diagdown}$$

$$= (5\sqrt{y})^2 - 2(5\sqrt{y})(\sqrt{2}) + (\sqrt{2})^2$$ Apply the formula $(a - b)^2 = a^2 - 2ab + b^2$.

$$= 25y - 10\sqrt{2y} + 2$$ Simplify.

Recall from Section 5.4, that the product of two conjugate binomials results in a difference of squares.

$$(a + b)(a - b) = a^2 - b^2$$

The same pattern occurs when multiplying two conjugate radical expressions.

example 6   **Multiplying Conjugate Radical Expressions**

Multiply the radical expressions. Assume all variables represent positive real numbers.

a. $(\sqrt{3} + 2)(\sqrt{3} - 2)$ b. $\left(\frac{1}{3}\sqrt{s} - \frac{3}{4}\sqrt{t}\right)\left(\frac{1}{3}\sqrt{s} + \frac{3}{4}\sqrt{t}\right)$

Solution:

a. $(\sqrt{3} + 2)(\sqrt{3} - 2)$ The expression is in the form $(a + b)(a - b)$, where $a = \sqrt{3}$ and $b = 2$.

$$\overset{\displaystyle a^2 - b^2}{\Big\downarrow \quad \Big\downarrow}$$

$= (\sqrt{3})^2 - (2)^2$ Apply the formula $(a + b)(a - b) = a^2 - b^2$.

$= 3 - 4$ Simplify.

$= -1$

Tip: The product $(\sqrt{3} + 2)(\sqrt{3} - 2)$ can also be found using the distributive property.

$$(\sqrt{3} + 2)(\sqrt{3} - 2) = \sqrt{3} \cdot \sqrt{3} + \sqrt{3} \cdot (-2) + 2 \cdot \sqrt{3} + 2 \cdot (-2)$$
$$= 3 - 2\sqrt{3} + 2\sqrt{3} - 4$$
$$= 3 - 4$$
$$= -1$$

b. $\left(\dfrac{1}{3}\sqrt{s} - \dfrac{3}{4}\sqrt{t}\right)\left(\dfrac{1}{3}\sqrt{s} + \dfrac{3}{4}\sqrt{t}\right)$ This expression is in the form $(a - b)(a + b)$, where $a = \frac{1}{3}\sqrt{s}$ and $b = \frac{3}{4}\sqrt{t}$.

$$\overset{\displaystyle a^2 - b^2}{\Big\downarrow \quad \Big\downarrow}$$

$= \left(\dfrac{1}{3}\sqrt{s}\right)^2 - \left(\dfrac{3}{4}\sqrt{t}\right)^2$ Apply the formula $(a + b)(a - b) = a^2 - b^2$.

$= \dfrac{1}{9}s - \dfrac{9}{16}t$ Simplify.

---

section 6.5   PRACTICE EXERCISES

For the exercises in this set, assume that all variables represent positive real numbers unless otherwise stated.

1. Given $f(x) = \sqrt{-3x + 1}$, evaluate
   a. $f(-1)$ b. $f(-5)$

2. Given $g(x) = \sqrt{5 - x}$, evaluate
   a. $g(-20)$ b. $g(-11)$

For Exercises 3–6, simplify the radicals.

3. $\sqrt[3]{(x - y)^3}$ 4. $\sqrt[5]{(2 + h)^5}$

5. $\sqrt[3]{-16x^5y^6z^7}$ 6. $-\sqrt{20a^2b^3c}$

For Exercises 7–12, simplify the expressions. Write the answer with positive exponents only.

7. $\dfrac{1}{9^{-1/2}}$ 8. $\left(\dfrac{1}{8}\right)^{-1/3}$

9. $x^{1/3}y^{1/4}x^{-1/6}y^{1/3}$

10. $p^{1/8}q^{1/2}p^{-1/4}q^{3/2}$

11. $\dfrac{a^{2/3}}{a^{1/2}}$

12. $\dfrac{b^{1/4}}{b^{3/2}}$

Exercises 13–14, add or subtract as indicated.

13. $-2\sqrt[3]{7} + 4\sqrt[3]{7}$

14. $4\sqrt{8x^3} - x\sqrt{50x}$

For Exercises 15–40, multiply the radical expression.

15. $\sqrt{2} \cdot \sqrt{10}$

16. $\sqrt[3]{4} \cdot \sqrt[3]{12}$

17. $\sqrt[4]{16} \cdot \sqrt[4]{64}$

18. $\sqrt{5x^3} \cdot \sqrt{10x^4}$

19. $(2\sqrt{5})(3\sqrt{7})$

20. $(4\sqrt[3]{4})(2\sqrt[3]{5})$

21. $(8a\sqrt{b})(-3\sqrt{ab})$

22. $(p\sqrt[4]{q^3})(\sqrt[4]{pq})$

23. $\sqrt{3}(4\sqrt{3} - 6)$

24. $3\sqrt{5}(2\sqrt{5} + 4)$

25. $\sqrt{2}(\sqrt{6} - \sqrt{3})$

26. $\sqrt{5}(\sqrt{3} + \sqrt{7})$

27. $-3\sqrt{x}(\sqrt{x} + 7)$

28. $-2\sqrt{y}(8 - \sqrt{y})$

29. $(\sqrt{3} + 2\sqrt{10})(4\sqrt{3} - \sqrt{10})$

30. $(8\sqrt{7} - \sqrt{5})(\sqrt{7} + 3\sqrt{5})$

31. $(\sqrt{x} + 4)(\sqrt{x} - 9)$

32. $(\sqrt{w} - 2)(\sqrt{w} - 9)$

33. $(\sqrt[3]{y} + 2)(\sqrt[3]{y} - 3)$

34. $(4 + \sqrt[5]{p})(5 + \sqrt[5]{p})$

35. $(\sqrt{a} - 3\sqrt{b})(9\sqrt{a} - \sqrt{b})$

36. $(11\sqrt{m} + 4\sqrt{n})(\sqrt{m} + \sqrt{n})$

37. $(\sqrt{7} + 3)(\sqrt{7} + \sqrt{2} - 5)$

38. $(\sqrt{2} - 6)(\sqrt{2} - \sqrt{3} - 4)$

39. $(\sqrt{p} + 2\sqrt{q})(8 + 3\sqrt{p} - \sqrt{q})$

40. $(5\sqrt{s} - \sqrt{t})(\sqrt{s} + 5 + 6\sqrt{t})$

For Exercises 41–50, multiply or divide the radicals with different indices. Write the answers in radical form and simplify.

41. $\sqrt{x} \cdot \sqrt[4]{x}$

42. $\sqrt[3]{y} \cdot \sqrt{y}$

43. $\sqrt[5]{2z} \cdot \sqrt[3]{2z}$

44. $\sqrt[3]{5w} \cdot \sqrt[4]{5w}$

45. $\sqrt[3]{p^2} \cdot \sqrt{p^3}$

46. $\sqrt[4]{q^3} \cdot \sqrt[3]{q^2}$

47. $\dfrac{\sqrt{u^3}}{\sqrt[3]{u}}$

48. $\dfrac{\sqrt{v^5}}{\sqrt[4]{v}}$

49. $\dfrac{\sqrt{(a + b)}}{\sqrt[3]{(a + b)}}$

50. $\dfrac{\sqrt[3]{(q - 1)}}{\sqrt[4]{(q - 1)}}$

51. a. Write the formula for the product of two conjugates: $(x + y)(x - y) =$

   b. Multiply $(x + 5)(x - 5)$

52. a. Write the formula for squaring a binomial: $(x + y)^2 =$

   b. Multiply $(x + 5)^2$

For Exercises 53–64, multiply the special products.

53. $(\sqrt{3} + x)(\sqrt{3} - x)$

54. $(y + \sqrt{6})(y - \sqrt{6})$

55. $(\sqrt{6} + \sqrt{2})(\sqrt{6} - \sqrt{2})$

56. $(\sqrt{15} + \sqrt{5})(\sqrt{15} - \sqrt{5})$

57. $(8\sqrt{x} + 2\sqrt{y})(8\sqrt{x} - 2\sqrt{y})$

58. $(4\sqrt{s} + 11\sqrt{t})(4\sqrt{s} - 11\sqrt{t})$

59. $(\sqrt{13} + 4)^2$

60. $(6 - \sqrt{11})^2$

61. $(\sqrt{p} - \sqrt{7})^2$

62. $(\sqrt{q} + \sqrt{2})^2$

63. $(\sqrt{2a} - 3\sqrt{b})^2$

64. $(\sqrt{3w} + 4\sqrt{z})^2$

For Exercises 65–72, identify each statement as true or false. If an answer is false, explain why.

65. $\sqrt{3} \cdot \sqrt{2} = \sqrt{6}$

66. $\sqrt{5} \cdot \sqrt[3]{2} = \sqrt{10}$

67. $(x - \sqrt{5})^2 = x - 5$

68. $3(2\sqrt{5x}) = 6\sqrt{5x}$

69. $5(3\sqrt{4x}) = 15\sqrt{20x}$

70. $\dfrac{\sqrt{5x}}{5} = \sqrt{x}$

71. $\dfrac{3\sqrt{x}}{3} = \sqrt{x}$

72. $(\sqrt{t} - 1)(\sqrt{t} + 1) = t - 1$

For Exercises 73–78, find the exact area.

73.

$\sqrt{40}$ ft

$3\sqrt{2}$ ft

74.

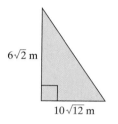

$6\sqrt{2}$ m

$10\sqrt{12}$ m

75.

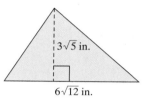

$3\sqrt{5}$ in.

$6\sqrt{12}$ in.

76.

$2\sqrt{18}$ yd

$7\sqrt{6}$ yd

77.

$\sqrt{32}$ m

$5\sqrt{2}$ m

78.

$\sqrt{20}$ ft

$\sqrt{20}$ ft

■ **EXPANDING YOUR SKILLS**

79. Multiply: $(\sqrt[3]{a} + \sqrt[3]{b})(\sqrt[3]{a^2} - \sqrt[3]{ab} + \sqrt[3]{b^2})$

80. Multiply: $(\sqrt[3]{a} - \sqrt[3]{b})(\sqrt[3]{a^2} + \sqrt[3]{ab} + \sqrt[3]{b^2})$

For Exercises 81–88, multiply the radicals with different indices (see Example 2(b)).

81. $\sqrt[3]{x} \cdot \sqrt[6]{y}$

82. $\sqrt{a} \cdot \sqrt[6]{b}$

83. $\sqrt[4]{8} \cdot \sqrt{3}$

84. $\sqrt{11} \cdot \sqrt[6]{2}$

85. $\sqrt[4]{6} \cdot \sqrt{2}$

86. $\sqrt[3]{10} \cdot \sqrt{3}$

87. $\sqrt[5]{p} \cdot \sqrt[3]{q}$

88. $\sqrt[6]{h} \cdot \sqrt[4]{k}$

section

6.6 RATIONALIZATION

1. Simplified Form of a Radical

Recall that for a radical expression to be in simplified form the following three conditions must be met.

Simplified Form of a Radical

Consider any radical expression in which the radicand is written as a product of prime factors. The expression is in simplified form if all of the following conditions are met:

1. The radicand has no factor raised to a power greater than or equal to the index.
2. No radicals are in the denominator of a fraction.
3. The radicand does not contain a fraction.

The basis of the second and third conditions, which restrict radicals from the denominator of an expression, are largely historical. In some cases, removing a radical from the denominator of a fraction will create an expression that is computationally simpler. For example, we will show that

$$\frac{6}{\sqrt{3}} = 2\sqrt{3} \quad \text{and} \quad \frac{-2}{2 + \sqrt{6}} = 2 - \sqrt{6}$$

The process to remove a radical from the denominator is called rationalizing the denominator. In this section we will consider two cases:

1. **Rationalizing the denominator (one term)**
2. **Rationalizing the denominator (two terms involving square roots)**

2. Rationalizing the Denominator—One Term

To begin the first case, recall that the nth root of a perfect nth power simplifies completely.

$$\sqrt{x^2} = x \quad x \geq 0$$
$$\sqrt[3]{x^3} = x$$
$$\sqrt[4]{x^4} = x \quad x \geq 0$$
$$\sqrt[5]{x^5} = x$$

. . .

Therefore, to rationalize a radical expression, use the multiplication property of radicals to create an nth root of an nth power.

example 1

Rationalizing Radical Expressions

Fill in the blanks to rationalize the radical expressions. Assume all variables represent positive real numbers.

a. $\sqrt{a} \cdot \sqrt{?} = \sqrt{a^2} = a$ b. $\sqrt[3]{y} \cdot \sqrt[3]{?} = \sqrt[3]{y^3} = y$

c. $\sqrt[4]{2z^3} \cdot \sqrt[4]{?} = \sqrt[4]{2^4 z^4} = 2z$

Solution:

a. $\sqrt{a} \cdot \sqrt{?} = \sqrt{a^2} = a$ What multiplied by $\sqrt{a}$ will equal $\sqrt{a^2}$?

$\sqrt{a} \cdot \sqrt{a} = \sqrt{a^2} = a$

b. $\sqrt[3]{y} \cdot \sqrt[3]{?} = \sqrt[3]{y^3} = y$ What multiplied by $\sqrt[3]{y}$ will equal $\sqrt[6]{y^3}$?

$\sqrt[3]{y} \cdot \sqrt[3]{y^2} = \sqrt[3]{y^3} = y$

c. $\sqrt[4]{2z^3} \cdot \sqrt[4]{?} = \sqrt[4]{2^4 z^4} = 2z$ What multiplied by $\sqrt[4]{2z^3}$ will equal $\sqrt[4]{2^4 z^4}$?

$\sqrt[4]{2z^3} \cdot \sqrt[4]{2^3 z} = \sqrt[4]{2^4 z^4} = 2z$

To rationalize the denominator of a radical expression, multiply the numerator and denominator by an appropriate expression to create an nth root of an nth power in the denominator.

example 2

Rationalizing the Denominator—One Term

Simplify the expression

$$\frac{5}{\sqrt[3]{a}}, \quad (a \neq 0)$$

Solution:

To remove the radical from the denominator, a cube root of a perfect cube is needed in the denominator. Multiply numerator and denominator by $\sqrt[3]{a^2}$ because $\sqrt[3]{a} \cdot \sqrt[3]{a^2} = \sqrt[3]{a^3} = a$

Tip: Notice that for $a \neq 0$, the expression $\dfrac{\sqrt[3]{a^2}}{\sqrt[3]{a^2}} = 1$. Multiplying the original expression $5/\sqrt[3]{a}$ by this ratio does not change its value.

$$\frac{5}{\sqrt[3]{a}} = \frac{5}{\sqrt[3]{a}} \cdot \frac{\sqrt[3]{a^2}}{\sqrt[3]{a^2}}$$

$$= \frac{5\sqrt[3]{a^2}}{\sqrt[3]{a^3}} \qquad \text{Multiply the radicals.}$$

$$= \frac{5\sqrt[3]{a^2}}{a} \qquad \text{Simplify.}$$

example 3   **Rationalizing the Denominator—One Term**

Simplify the expressions. Assume all variables represent positive real numbers.

a. $\dfrac{6}{\sqrt{3}}$ b. $\sqrt{\dfrac{y^5}{7}}$ c. $\dfrac{15}{\sqrt[3]{25s}}$ d. $\dfrac{\sqrt{125p^3}}{\sqrt{5p}}$

Solution:

a.   To rationalize the denominator, a square root of a perfect square is needed. Multiply numerator and denominator by $\sqrt{3}$ because $\sqrt{3} \cdot \sqrt{3} = \sqrt{3^2} = 3$.

$$\dfrac{6}{\sqrt{3}} = \dfrac{6}{\sqrt{3}} \cdot \dfrac{\sqrt{3}}{\sqrt{3}} \qquad \text{Rationalize the denominator.}$$

$$= \dfrac{6\sqrt{3}}{\sqrt{3^2}} \qquad \text{Multiply the radicals.}$$

$$= \dfrac{6\sqrt{3}}{3} \qquad \text{Simplify.}$$

$$= 2\sqrt{3} \qquad \text{Reduce.}$$

Graphing Calculator Box

A calculator can be used to support the solution to a simplified radical. The calculator approximations of the expressions $6/\sqrt{3}$ and $2\sqrt{3}$ agree to 10 decimal places.

```
6/√(3)
         3.464101615
2√(3)
         3.464101615
```

---

b. $\sqrt{\dfrac{y^5}{7}}$ The radical contains an irreducible fraction.

$$= \dfrac{\sqrt{y^5}}{\sqrt{7}} \qquad \text{Apply the division property of radicals.}$$

$$= \dfrac{y^2\sqrt{y}}{\sqrt{7}} \qquad \text{Remove factors from the radical in the numerator.}$$

$$= \dfrac{y^2\sqrt{y}}{\sqrt{7}} \cdot \dfrac{\sqrt{7}}{\sqrt{7}} \qquad \begin{array}{l}\text{Rationalize the denominator.}\\ \textit{Note: } \sqrt{7} \cdot \sqrt{7} = \sqrt{7^2} = 7.\end{array}$$

$$= \dfrac{y^2\sqrt{7y}}{\sqrt{7^2}}$$

$$= \dfrac{y^2\sqrt{7y}}{7} \qquad \text{Simplify.}$$

⬣ **Avoiding Mistakes**

A factor within a radicand cannot be simplified with a factor outside the radicand. For example, $\sqrt{7y}/7$ cannot be simplified

c. $\dfrac{15}{\sqrt[3]{25s}}$

$= \dfrac{15}{\sqrt[3]{5^2 s}} \cdot \dfrac{\sqrt[3]{5s^2}}{\sqrt[3]{5s^2}}$ Because $25 = 5^2$, one additional factor of 5 is needed to form a perfect cube. Two additional factors of s are needed to make a perfect cube. Multiply numerator and denominator by $\sqrt[3]{5s^2}$.

$= \dfrac{15\sqrt[3]{5s^2}}{\sqrt[3]{5^3 s^3}}$

$= \dfrac{15\sqrt[3]{5s^2}}{5s}$ Simplify the perfect cube.

$= \dfrac{\overset{3}{\cancel{15}}\sqrt[3]{5s^2}}{\underset{1}{\cancel{5}s}}$ Reduce.

$= \dfrac{3\sqrt[3]{5s^2}}{s}$

Tip: In the expression

$$\frac{15\sqrt[3]{s^2}}{5s},$$

the factor of 15 and the factor of 5 may be reduced because both are outside the radical.

$$\frac{15\sqrt[3]{5s^2}}{5s} = \frac{15}{5} \cdot \frac{\sqrt[3]{5s^2}}{s} = \frac{3\sqrt[3]{5s^2}}{s}$$

d. $\dfrac{\sqrt{125p^3}}{\sqrt{5p}}$ Notice that the radicands in the numerator and denominator share common factors.

$= \sqrt{\dfrac{125p^3}{5p}}$ Rewrite the expression using the division property of radicals.

$= \sqrt{25p^2}$ Reduce the fraction within the radicand.

$= 5p$ Simplify the radical.

3. Rationalizing the Denominator—Two Terms

The next example demonstrates how to rationalize a two-term denominator involving square roots.

First recall from the multiplication of polynomials that the product of two conjugates results in a difference of squares.

$$(a + b)(a - b) = a^2 - b^2$$

If either a or b has a square root factor, the expression will simplify without a radical. That is, the expression is *rationalized*. For example,

$$(2 + \sqrt{6})(2 - \sqrt{6}) = (2)^2 - (\sqrt{6})^2$$
$$= 4 - 6$$
$$= -2$$

example 4

Rationalizing the Denominator—Two Terms

Simplify the expression by rationalizing the denominator.

$$\frac{-2}{2 + \sqrt{6}}$$

Solution:

$$\frac{-2}{2 + \sqrt{6}}$$

$$= \frac{(-2)}{(2 + \sqrt{6})} \cdot \frac{(2 - \sqrt{6})}{(2 - \sqrt{6})} \qquad \text{Multiply the numerator and denominator by the conjugate of the denominator.}$$

conjugates

$$= \frac{-2(2 - \sqrt{6})}{(2)^2 - (\sqrt{6})^2} \qquad \text{In the denominator, apply the formula } (a + b)(a - b) = a^2 - b^2.$$

$$= \frac{-2(2 - \sqrt{6})}{4 - 6} \qquad \text{Simplify.}$$

$$= \frac{-2(2 - \sqrt{6})}{-2}$$

$$= \frac{-2(2 - \sqrt{6})}{-2}$$

$$= 2 - \sqrt{6}$$

Graphing Calculator Box

A calculator can be used to support the solution to a simplified radical. The calculator approximations of the expressions $-2/(2 + \sqrt{6})$ and $2 - \sqrt{6}$ agree to 10 decimal places.

```
-2/(2+√(6))
           -.4494897428
2-√(6)
           -.4494897428
```

example 5

Rationalizing the Denominator—Two Terms

Rationalize the denominator of the expression.

$$\frac{\sqrt{c} + \sqrt{d}}{\sqrt{c} - \sqrt{d}}$$

Solution:

$$\frac{\sqrt{c} + \sqrt{d}}{\sqrt{c} - \sqrt{d}}$$

$$= \frac{(\sqrt{c} + \sqrt{d})}{(\sqrt{c} - \sqrt{d})} \cdot \frac{(\sqrt{c} + \sqrt{d})}{(\sqrt{c} + \sqrt{d})}$$ Multiply numerator and denominator by the conjugate of the denominator.

conjugates

$$= \frac{(\sqrt{c} + \sqrt{d})^2}{(\sqrt{c})^2 - (\sqrt{d})^2}$$ In the denominator apply the formula $(a + b)(a - b) = a^2 - b^2$.

$$= \frac{(\sqrt{c} + \sqrt{d})^2}{c - d}$$ Simplify.

$$= \frac{(\sqrt{c})^2 + 2\sqrt{c}\sqrt{d} + (\sqrt{d})^2}{c - d}$$ In the numerator apply the formula $(a + b)^2 = a^2 + 2ab + b^2$.

$$= \frac{c + 2\sqrt{cd} + d}{c - d}$$

---

section 6.6   PRACTICE EXERCISES

For the exercises in this set, assume that all variables represent positive real numbers unless otherwise stated.
   For Exercises 1–10, perform the indicated operations.

1. $2y\sqrt{45} + 3\sqrt{20y^2}$

2. $3x\sqrt{72x} - 9\sqrt{50x^3}$

3. $(-6\sqrt{y} + 3)(3\sqrt{y} + 1)$

4. $(\sqrt{w} + 12)(2\sqrt{w} - 4)$

5. $4\sqrt{3} + \sqrt{5} \cdot \sqrt{15}$

6. $\sqrt{7} \cdot \sqrt{21} + 2\sqrt{27}$

7. $(8 - \sqrt{t})^2$

8. $(\sqrt{p} + 4)^2$

9. $(\sqrt{2} + \sqrt{7})(\sqrt{2} - \sqrt{7})$

10. $(\sqrt{3} + 5)(\sqrt{3} - 5)$

The radical expressions in Exercises 11–18 have radicals in the denominator. Multiply the numerator and denominator by an appropriate expression to rationalize the denominator. Then simplify the result.

11. $\dfrac{x}{\sqrt{5}} = \dfrac{x}{\sqrt{5}} \cdot \dfrac{\sqrt{?}}{\sqrt{?}}$

12. $\dfrac{2}{\sqrt{x}} = \dfrac{2}{\sqrt{x}} \cdot \dfrac{\sqrt{?}}{\sqrt{?}}$

13. $\dfrac{7}{\sqrt[3]{x}} = \dfrac{7}{\sqrt[3]{x}} \cdot \dfrac{\sqrt[3]{?}}{\sqrt[3]{?}}$

14. $\dfrac{5}{\sqrt[4]{y}} = \dfrac{5}{\sqrt[4]{y}} \cdot \dfrac{\sqrt[4]{?}}{\sqrt[4]{?}}$

15. $\dfrac{8}{\sqrt{3z}} = \dfrac{8}{\sqrt{3z}} \cdot \dfrac{\sqrt{??}}{\sqrt{??}}$

16. $\dfrac{10}{\sqrt{7w}} = \dfrac{10}{\sqrt{7w}} \cdot \dfrac{\sqrt{??}}{\sqrt{??}}$

17. $\dfrac{1}{\sqrt[4]{2a^2}} = \dfrac{1}{\sqrt[4]{2a^2}} \cdot \dfrac{\sqrt[4]{??}}{\sqrt[4]{??}}$

18. $\dfrac{1}{\sqrt[3]{6b^2}} = \dfrac{1}{\sqrt[3]{6b^2}} \cdot \dfrac{\sqrt[3]{??}}{\sqrt[3]{??}}$

For Exercises 19–42, rationalize the denominator.

19. $\dfrac{1}{\sqrt{3}}$

20. $\dfrac{1}{\sqrt{7}}$

21. $\dfrac{10}{\sqrt{5}}$

22. $\dfrac{12}{\sqrt{6}}$

23. $\dfrac{1}{\sqrt{x}}$

24. $\dfrac{1}{\sqrt{z}}$

25. $\dfrac{6}{\sqrt{2y}}$

26. $\dfrac{9}{\sqrt{3t}}$

27. $\dfrac{-2a}{\sqrt{a}}$

28. $\dfrac{-7b}{\sqrt{b}}$

29. $\dfrac{7}{\sqrt[3]{4}}$

30. $\dfrac{1}{\sqrt[3]{9}}$

31. $\dfrac{4}{\sqrt[3]{w^2}}$

32. $\dfrac{5}{\sqrt[3]{z^2}}$

33. $\sqrt[4]{\dfrac{16}{3}}$

34. $\sqrt[4]{\dfrac{81}{8}}$

35. $\dfrac{1}{\sqrt[10]{x^7}}$

36. $\dfrac{1}{\sqrt[9]{y^4}}$

37. $\dfrac{2}{\sqrt[3]{4x^2}}$

38. $\dfrac{6}{\sqrt[3]{3y^2}}$

39. $\sqrt[3]{\dfrac{16x^3}{y}}$

40. $\sqrt{\dfrac{5}{9x}}$

41. $\dfrac{\sqrt{x^4 y^5}}{\sqrt{10x}}$

42. $\sqrt[4]{\dfrac{10x^2}{15xy^3}}$

43. What is the conjugate of $\sqrt{2} - \sqrt{6}$?

44. What is the conjugate of $\sqrt{11} + \sqrt{5}$?

45. What is the conjugate of $\sqrt{x} + 23$?

46. What is the conjugate of $17 - \sqrt{y}$?

For Exercises 47–50, multiply the conjugates.

47. $(\sqrt{2} + 3)(\sqrt{2} - 3)$

48. $(4 - \sqrt{3})(4 + \sqrt{3})$

49. $(\sqrt{5} - \sqrt{2})(\sqrt{5} + \sqrt{2})$

50. $(\sqrt{3} + \sqrt{7})(\sqrt{3} - \sqrt{7})$

For Exercises 51–62, rationalize the denominators.

51. $\dfrac{4}{\sqrt{2} + 3}$

52. $\dfrac{6}{4 - \sqrt{3}}$

53. $\dfrac{1}{\sqrt{5} - \sqrt{2}}$

54. $\dfrac{1}{\sqrt{3} + \sqrt{7}}$

55. $\dfrac{\sqrt{7}}{\sqrt{3} + 2}$

56. $\dfrac{\sqrt{8}}{\sqrt{3} + 1}$

57. $\dfrac{-1}{\sqrt{p} + \sqrt{q}}$

58. $\dfrac{6}{\sqrt{a} - \sqrt{b}}$

59. $\dfrac{2\sqrt{3} + \sqrt{7}}{3\sqrt{3} - \sqrt{7}}$

60. $\dfrac{5\sqrt{2} - \sqrt{5}}{5\sqrt{2} + \sqrt{5}}$

61. $\dfrac{\sqrt{5} + 4}{2 - \sqrt{5}}$

62. $\dfrac{3 + \sqrt{2}}{\sqrt{2} - 5}$

For Exercises 63–66, translate the English phrase into an algebraic expression. Then simplify the expression.

63. Sixteen divided by the cube root of 4.

64. Twenty-one divided by the fourth root of 27.

65. Four divided by the difference of x and the square root of 2.

66. Eight divided by the sum of y and the square root of 3.

67. The approximate time, T (in seconds) for a pendulum to make one complete swing back and forth is given by

$$T(x) = 2\pi\sqrt{\dfrac{x}{32}},$$ where x is the length of the pendulum in feet.

a. Determine the time required for one swing for a pendulum that is 2 ft long. (Round the answer to two decimal places.)

b. Determine the time required for one swing for a pendulum that is 1 ft long. (Round the answer to two decimal places.)

c. Determine the time required for one swing for a pendulum that is $\frac{1}{2}$ ft long. (Round the answer to two decimal places.)

68. An object is dropped off a building x meters tall. The time, T, (in seconds) required for the object to hit the ground is given by

$$T(x) = \sqrt{\frac{10x}{49}}$$

a. Find the time required for the object to hit the ground if it is dropped off a 50-m building. (Round the answer to two decimal places.)

b. Find the time required for the object to hit the ground if it is dropped off a 25-m building. (Round the answer to two decimal places.)

c. Find the time required for the object to hit the ground if it is dropped off a 10-m building. (Round the answer to two decimal places.)

EXPANDING YOUR SKILLS

For Exercises 69–74, simplify the expression. Then add or subtract as indicated.

69. $\dfrac{\sqrt{6}}{2} + \dfrac{1}{\sqrt{6}}$

70. $\dfrac{1}{\sqrt{7}} + \sqrt{7}$

71. $\sqrt{15} - \sqrt{\dfrac{3}{5}} + \sqrt{\dfrac{5}{3}}$

72. $\sqrt{\dfrac{6}{2}} - \sqrt{12} + \sqrt{\dfrac{2}{6}}$

73. $\sqrt[3]{25} + \dfrac{3}{\sqrt[3]{5}}$

74. $\dfrac{1}{\sqrt[3]{4}} + \sqrt[3]{54}$

For Exercises 75–78, rationalize the numerator by multiplying both numerator and denominator by the conjugate of the numerator.

75. $\dfrac{\sqrt{3} + 6}{2}$

76. $\dfrac{\sqrt{7} - 2}{5}$

77. $\dfrac{\sqrt{a} - \sqrt{b}}{\sqrt{a} + \sqrt{b}}$

78. $\dfrac{\sqrt{p} + \sqrt{q}}{\sqrt{p} - \sqrt{q}}$

GRAPHING CALCULATOR EXERCISES

79. a. Graph $Y_1 = 3/\sqrt{x}$
    b. Graph $Y_2 = 3\sqrt{x}/x$
    c. Do the graphs from parts (a) and (b) appear to coincide? What does this suggest about the expressions $3/\sqrt{x}$ and $3\sqrt{x}/x$?

80. a. Graph $Y_1 = 5/\sqrt[3]{x}$
    b. Graph $Y_2 = 5\sqrt[3]{x^2}/x$
    c. Do the graphs from parts (a) and (b) appear to coincide? What does this suggest about the expressions $5/\sqrt[3]{x}$ and $5\sqrt[3]{x^2}/x$?

---

section

6.7   RADICAL EQUATIONS

Concepts

1. Solutions to Radical Equations

2. Solving Radical Equations Involving One Radical

3. Solving Radical Equations Involving More than One Radical

4. Applications of Radical Equations and Functions

1. Solutions to Radical Equations

An equation with one or more radicals containing a variable is called a **radical equation**. For example, $\sqrt[3]{x} = 5$ is a radical equation. Recall that $(\sqrt[n]{a})^n = a$, provided $\sqrt[n]{a}$ is a real number. The basis of solving a radical equation is to eliminate the radical by raising both sides of the equation to a power equal to the index of the radical.

To solve the equation $\sqrt[3]{x} = 5$, cube both sides of the equation.

$$\sqrt[3]{x} = 5$$

$$(\sqrt[3]{x})^3 = (5)^3$$

$$x = 125$$

By raising each side of a radical equation to a power equal to the index of the radical, a new equation is produced. It is important to note, however, that the new equation may have extraneous solutions. That is, some or all of the solutions to the new equation may *not* be solutions to the original radical equation. For this reason, it is necessary to *check all potential solutions* in the original equation. For example, consider the equation $x = 4$. By squaring both sides we produce a quadratic equation.

$$x = 4$$

square both sides → $$(x)^2 = (4)^2$$ ← Squaring both sides produces a quadratic equation.

$$x^2 = 16$$ ← Solving this equation, we find two solutions. However, the solution $x = -4$ does not check in the original equation.

$$x^2 - 16 = 0$$

$$(x - 4)(x + 4) = 0$$

$$x = 4 \quad \text{or} \quad x \neq -4 \text{ (does not check)}$$

Steps to Solve a Radical Equation

1. Isolate the radical. If an equation has more than one radical, choose one of the radicals to isolate.
2. Raise each side of the equation to a power equal to the index of the radical.
3. Solve the resulting equation. If the equation still has a radical, repeat steps 1 and 2.
*4. Check the potential solutions in the original equation.

*Extraneous solutions can only arise when both sides of the equation are raised to an *even power*. An equation with odd-index roots will, therefore, not have an extraneous solution. However, it is still recommended that you check *all* potential solutions regardless of the type of root.

2.   Solving Radical Equations Involving One Radical

example 1   **Solving Equations Containing One Radical**

Solve the equations.

a. $\sqrt{3x - 2} + 4 = 5$

b. $(w - 1)^{1/3} - 2 = 2$

c. $7 = \sqrt[4]{x + 3} + 9$

d. $y + \sqrt{y^2 + 5} = 7$

Solution:

a. $\sqrt{3x - 2} + 4 = 5$

$\sqrt{3x - 2} = 1$ Isolate the radical.

$(\sqrt{3x - 2})^2 = (1)^2$ Because the index is 2, square both sides.

$3x - 2 = 1$ Simplify.

$3x = 3$ Solve the resulting equation.

$x = 1$

Check: $x = 1$ Check $x = 1$ as a potential solution.

$\sqrt{3x - 2} + 4 = 5$

$\sqrt{3(1) - 2} + 4 \overset{?}{=} 5$

$\sqrt{1} + 4 \overset{?}{=} 5$

$5 = 5$ ✔   Therefore, $x = 1$ is a solution to the original equation.

b. $(w - 1)^{1/3} - 2 = 2$ Note that $(w - 1)^{1/3} = \sqrt[3]{w - 1}$.

$\sqrt[3]{w - 1} - 2 = 2$

$\sqrt[3]{w - 1} = 4$ Isolate the radical.

$(\sqrt[3]{w - 1})^3 = (4)^3$ Because the index is 3, cube both sides.

$w - 1 = 64$ Simplify.

$w = 65$

Check: $w = 65$

$(w - 1)^{1/3} - 2 = 2$ Check $w = 65$ as a potential solution.

$\sqrt[3]{65 - 1} - 2 \overset{?}{=} 2$

$\sqrt[3]{64} - 2 \overset{?}{=} 2$

$4 - 2 \overset{?}{=} 2$

$2 = 2$ ✔   Therefore, $w = 65$ is a solution to the original equation.

c. $7 = \sqrt[4]{x + 3} + 9$

$-2 = \sqrt[4]{x + 3}$ Isolate the radical.

$(-2)^4 = (\sqrt[4]{x + 3})^4$ Because the index is 4, raise both sides to the fourth power.

$16 = x + 3$

$x = 13$ Solve for x.

Tip: After isolating the radical in Example 1(c), the equation shows a fourth root equated to a negative number:

$$-2 = \sqrt[4]{x + 3}$$

By definition, a principal fourth root of any real number must be nonnegative. Therefore, there can be no real solution to this equation.

Check: $x = 13$

$$7 = \sqrt[4]{x + 3} + 9$$

$$7 \stackrel{?}{=} \sqrt[4]{(13) + 3} + 9$$

$$7 \stackrel{?}{=} \sqrt[4]{16} + 9$$

$$7 \neq 2 + 9 \qquad \text{Therefore, } x = 13 \text{ is } not \text{ a solution to the original equation.}$$

The equation $7 = \sqrt[4]{x + 3} + 9$ has no solution.

d. $\quad y + \sqrt{y^2 + 5} = 7$

$$\sqrt{y^2 + 5} = 7 - y \qquad \text{Isolate the radical.}$$

$$(\sqrt{y^2 + 5})^2 = (7 - y)^2 \qquad \text{Because the index is 2, square both sides.}$$

$$\text{Note that } (7 - y)^2 = (7 - y)(7 - y)$$
$$= 49 - 14y + y^2.$$

$$y^2 + 5 = 49 - 14y + y^2 \qquad \text{Simplify.}$$

$$5 = 49 - 14y \qquad \text{Subtract } y^2 \text{ from both sides.}$$

$$-44 = -14y \qquad \text{Solve for } y.$$

$$\frac{-44}{-14} = \frac{-14y}{-14}$$

$$\frac{22}{7} = y$$

Check: $y = \dfrac{22}{7}$

$$y + \sqrt{y^2 + 5} = 7 \qquad \text{Check } y = 22/7 \text{ as a potential solution.}$$

$$\frac{22}{7} + \sqrt{\left(\frac{22}{7}\right)^2 + 5} \stackrel{?}{=} 7$$

$$\frac{22}{7} + \sqrt{\frac{484}{49} + 5} \stackrel{?}{=} 7$$

$$\frac{22}{7} + \sqrt{\frac{484}{49} + \frac{245}{49}} \stackrel{?}{=} 7$$

$$\frac{22}{7} + \sqrt{\frac{729}{49}} \stackrel{?}{=} 7$$

$$\frac{22}{7} + \frac{27}{7} \stackrel{?}{=} 7$$

$$\frac{49}{7} = 7 \ ✔ \qquad \text{Therefore, } y = 22/7 \text{ is a solution to the original equation.}$$

3. Solving Radical Equations Involving More than One Radical

---

example 2

Solving Equations with Two Radicals

Solve the radical equations.

a. $\sqrt[3]{2x - 4} = \sqrt[3]{1 - 8x}$

b. $\sqrt{2t - 5} + 1 = \sqrt{2t + 2}$

Solution:

a.

$$\sqrt[3]{2x - 4} = \sqrt[3]{1 - 8x}$$

$$(\sqrt[3]{2x - 4})^3 = (\sqrt[3]{1 - 8x})^3 \qquad \text{Because the index is 3, cube both sides.}$$

$$2x - 4 = 1 - 8x \qquad \text{Simplify.}$$

$$2x + 8x - 4 = 1 \qquad \text{Solve the resulting equation. Add } 8x \text{ to both sides.}$$

$$10x = 5 \qquad \text{Combine } like \text{ terms and add 4 to both sides.}$$

$$\frac{10x}{10} = \frac{5}{10}$$

$$x = \frac{1}{2}$$

Check: $x = \frac{1}{2}$

$$\sqrt[3]{2x - 4} = \sqrt[3]{1 - 8x}$$

$$\sqrt[3]{2\left(\frac{1}{2}\right) - 4} \stackrel{?}{=} \sqrt[3]{1 - 8\left(\frac{1}{2}\right)}$$

$$\sqrt[3]{1 - 4} \stackrel{?}{=} \sqrt[3]{1 - 4}$$

$$\sqrt[3]{-3} = \sqrt[3]{-3} \ \checkmark \qquad \text{Therefore, } x = \frac{1}{2} \text{ is a solution to the original equation.}$$

Graphing Calculator Box

The expressions on the right- and left-hand sides of the equation $\sqrt[3]{2x - 4} = \sqrt[3]{1 - 8x}$ are each functions of x. Consider the graphs of the functions:

$$Y_1 = \sqrt[3]{2x - 4} \qquad \text{and} \qquad Y_2 = \sqrt[3]{1 - 8x}$$

The x-coordinate of the point of intersection of the two functions is the solution to the equation $\sqrt[3]{2x - 4} = \sqrt[3]{1 - 8x}$. The point of intersection can be approximated by using *Zoom* and *Trace* or by using an *Intersect* function.

b. $$\sqrt{2t-5}+1 = \sqrt{2t+2}$$ The radical on the right is already isolated.

$$(\sqrt{2t-5}+1)^2 = (\sqrt{2t+2})^2$$ Because the index is 2, square both sides.

Tip: To square the quantity $(\sqrt{2t-5}+1)^2$, use the formula: $(a+b)^2 = a^2 + 2ab + b^2$.

$$(\sqrt{2t-5}+1)^2 = (\sqrt{2t-5})^2 + 2 \cdot (\sqrt{2t-5}) \cdot (1) + (1)^2$$
$$= 2t - 5 + 2\sqrt{2t-5} + 1$$

$$2t - 5 + 2\sqrt{2t-5} + 1 = 2t + 2$$

$$2t - 4 + 2\sqrt{2t-5} = 2t + 2$$ Combine *like* terms.

$$-4 + 2\sqrt{2t-5} = 2$$ Subtract $2t$ from both sides.

$$2\sqrt{2t-5} = 6$$ Add 4 to both sides.

$$\frac{2\sqrt{2t-5}}{2} = \frac{6}{2}$$ Isolate the radical. Divide both sides by 2.

$$\sqrt{2t-5} = 3$$

$$(\sqrt{2t-5})^2 = (3)^2$$ Because the index is 2, square both sides.

$$2t - 5 = 9$$

$$2t = 14$$

$$t = 7$$

Check: $t = 7$

$$\sqrt{2t-5} + 1 = \sqrt{2t+2}$$

$$\sqrt{2(7)-5} + 1 \stackrel{?}{=} \sqrt{2(7)+2}$$

$$\sqrt{14-5} + 1 \stackrel{?}{=} \sqrt{14+2}$$

$$\sqrt{9} + 1 \stackrel{?}{=} \sqrt{16}$$

$$3 + 1 = 4 \checkmark$$ Therefore, $t = 7$ is a solution to the original equation.

Graphing Calculator Box

To approximate the solution of the equation $\sqrt{2t-5}+1 = \sqrt{2t+2}$, graph the functions

$$Y_1 = \sqrt{2x-5}+1 \quad \text{and} \quad Y_2 = \sqrt{2x+2}$$

and find the *x*-coordinate of their point of intersection.

4.   Applications of Radical Equations and Functions

example 3

Applying a Radical Equation in Geometry

For a pyramid with a square base, the length of a side of the base, b, is given by:

$$b = \sqrt{\frac{3V}{h}}$$

The Pyramid of the Pharoah Khufu (known as the Great Pyramid) at Giza has a square base (Figure 6-3). If the distance around the bottom of the pyramid is 921.6 m and the height is 146.6 m, what is the volume of the pyramid?

Figure 6-3

Solution:

The length of a side, b, (in meters) is given by $921.6/4 \approx 230.4$ m

$$b = \sqrt{\frac{3V}{h}}$$

$$230.4 = \sqrt{\frac{3V}{146.6}} \qquad \text{Substitute } b = 230.4 \text{ and } h = 146.6.$$

$$(230.4)^2 = \left(\sqrt{\frac{3V}{146.6}}\right)^2 \qquad \text{Because the index is 2, square both sides.}$$

$$53{,}084.16 = \frac{3V}{146.6} \qquad \text{Simplify.}$$

$$(53{,}084.16)(146.6) = \frac{3V}{146.6}(146.6) \qquad \text{Multiply both sides by 146.6.}$$

$$(53{,}084.16)(146.6) = 3V$$

$$\frac{(53{,}084.16)(146.6)}{3} = \frac{3V}{3} \qquad \text{Divide both sides by 3.}$$

$$2{,}594{,}046 \approx V$$

The volume of the Great Pyramid at Giza is approximately 2,594,046 m^3.

example 4   **Applying a Radical Function**

On a certain surface, the speed of a car, s, (in miles per hour) before the brakes were applied can be approximated from the length of its skid marks, x, (in feet) by:

$$s(x) = 3.8\sqrt{x} \quad x \geq 0$$

See Figure 6-4.

Figure 6-4

a. Find the speed of a car before the brakes were applied if its skid marks are 361 ft long.
b. How long would you expect the skid marks to be if the car had been traveling the speed limit of 50 mph? (Round to the nearest foot)

Solution:

a. $s(x) = 3.8\sqrt{x}$

$s(361) = 3.8\sqrt{361}$ Substitute $x = 361$.

$\qquad = 3.8(19)$

$\qquad = 72.2$

If the skid marks are 361 ft, the car was traveling approximately 72.2 mph before the brakes were applied.

b. $s(x) = 3.8\sqrt{x}$

$\quad\ 50 = 3.8\sqrt{x}$ Substitute $s(x) = 50$ and solve for x.

$\dfrac{50}{3.8} = \sqrt{x}$ Isolate the radical.

$\left(\dfrac{50}{3.8}\right)^2 = x$

$\qquad x \approx 173$

If the car had been going the speed limit (50 mph), then the stopping distance would have been approximately 173 ft.

section 6.7 PRACTICE EXERCISES

For Exercises 1–12, simplify the radical expressions, if possible. Assume all variables represent positive real numbers.

1. $\sqrt{48}$

2. $\sqrt{18w^4}$

3. $\sqrt{\dfrac{9w^3}{16}}$

4. $\sqrt{\dfrac{a^2}{3}}$

5. $\sqrt{-25}$

6. $\sqrt[3]{54c^4}$

7. $\sqrt[3]{\dfrac{p^5}{q^2}}$

8. $\sqrt[4]{\dfrac{x^4y^2}{16y^{10}}}$

9. $\sqrt{\dfrac{49}{5t^3}}$

10. $\sqrt[3]{-\dfrac{8}{27}}$

11. $\sqrt[4]{\dfrac{5m^2n}{40mn^3}}$

12. $\sqrt{x^3yz^6}$

For Exercises 13–20, simplify each expression. Assume all radicands represent positive real numbers.

13. $(\sqrt{4x-6})^2$

14. $(\sqrt{5y+2})^2$

15. $(\sqrt[3]{9p+7})^3$

16. $(\sqrt[3]{4t+13})^3$

17. $(\sqrt{w^2+2w-17})^2$

18. $(\sqrt{6x^2-x+8})^2$

19. $(\sqrt[4]{7r})^4$

20. $(\sqrt[4]{3s})^4$

For Exercises 21–38, solve the equations.

21. $\sqrt{4x}=6$

22. $\sqrt{2x}=8$

23. $\sqrt{5y+1}=4$

24. $\sqrt{9z-5}=11$

25. $(2z-3)^{1/2}=9$

26. $(8+3a)^{1/2}=5$

27. $\sqrt[3]{x-2}=3$

28. $\sqrt[3]{2x-5}=2$

29. $(15-w)^{1/3}=-5$

30. $(k+18)^{1/3}=-2$

31. $\sqrt{x-16}=-3$

32. $\sqrt{2x+1}=-12$

33. $\sqrt[4]{h+4}=\sqrt[4]{2h-5}$

34. $\sqrt[4]{3b+6}=\sqrt[4]{7b-6}$

35. $\sqrt[3]{5a+3}=\sqrt[3]{a-13}$

36. $\sqrt[3]{k-8}=\sqrt[3]{4k+1}$

37. $\sqrt[4]{2x-5}=-1$

38. $\sqrt[4]{x+16}=-4$

39. Solve for V: $r=\sqrt[3]{\dfrac{3V}{4\pi}}$

40. Solve for V: $r=\sqrt{\dfrac{V}{h\pi}}$

41. Solve for h^2: $r=\pi\sqrt{r^2+h^2}$

42. Solve for d: $s=1.3\sqrt{d}$

For Exercises 43–48, use $(a+b)^2=a^2+2ab+b^2$ to practice squaring a binomial.

43. $(a+5)^2=$

44. $(b+7)^2=$

45. $(5w-4)^2=$

46. $(2p-3)^2=$

47. $(\sqrt{5a}-3)^2=$

48. $(2+\sqrt{b})^2=$

For Exercises 49–66, solve the radical equations, if possible.

49. $\sqrt{a^2+2a+1}=a+5$

50. $\sqrt{b^2-5b-8}=b+7$

51. $\sqrt{25w^2-2w-3}=5w-4$

52. $\sqrt{4p^2-2p+1}=2p-3$

53. $\sqrt{9z^2-z+6}=3z-1$

54. $\sqrt{16x^2-2x-9}=4x+1$

55. $\sqrt{5a-9}=\sqrt{5a}-3$

56. $\sqrt{8+b}=2+\sqrt{b}$

57. $\sqrt{2h+5}-\sqrt{2h}=1$

58. $\sqrt{3k-5}-\sqrt{3k}=-1$

59. $\sqrt{t-9}=3+\sqrt{t}$

60. $\sqrt{y-16}=\sqrt{y}+4$

61. $\sqrt{x^2+3}=6+x$

62. $\sqrt{y^2+5}=2+y$

63. $\sqrt{3t-7}=2-\sqrt{3t+1}$

64. $\sqrt{p-6}=\sqrt{p+2}-4$

65. $\sqrt{8b - 3} = 4 + \sqrt{8b + 1}$

66. $\sqrt{2w + 5} = \sqrt{2w - 1} + 3$

67. The time, t, in seconds it takes an object to drop d meters is given by

$$t(d) = \sqrt{\frac{d}{4.9}}$$

   a. Approximate the height of the Texas Commerce Tower in Houston, if it takes an object 7.89 s to drop from the top. Round to the nearest meter.

   b. Approximate the height of the Shanghai World Financial Center, if it takes an object 9.69 s to drop from the top. Round to the nearest meter.

68. If an object is dropped from an initial height h, its velocity at impact with the ground is given by

   $v = \sqrt{2gh}$, where g is the acceleration due to gravity and h is the initial height.

   a. Find the initial height (in feet) of an object if its velocity at impact is 44 ft/s. (Assume that the acceleration due to gravity is $g = 32$ ft/s^2)

   b. Find the initial height (in meters) of an object if its velocity at impact is 26 m/s. (Assume that the acceleration due to gravity is $g = 9.8$ m/s^2) Round to the nearest tenth of a meter.

69. The airline cost for x thousand passengers to travel round trip from New York to Atlanta is given by

   $C(x) = \sqrt{0.3x + 1}$, where $C(x)$ is measured in millions of dollars and $x \geq 0$.

   a. Find the airline's cost for 10,000 passengers ($x = 10$) to travel from New York to Atlanta.

b. If the airline charges $320 per passenger, find the profit made by the airline for flying 10,000 passengers from New York to Atlanta.

   c. Approximate the number of passengers who traveled from New York to Atlanta if the total cost for the airline was $4 million.

70. The time, T (in seconds), required for a pendulum to make one complete swing back and forth is approximated by

   $T = 2\pi\sqrt{\dfrac{L}{g}}$, where g is the acceleration due to gravity and L is the length of the pendulum (in feet).

   a. Find the length of a pendulum that requires 1.36 s to make one complete swing back and forth. (Assume that the acceleration due to gravity is $g = 32$ ft/s^2) Round to the nearest tenth of a foot.

   b. Find the time required for a pendulum to complete one swing back and forth if the length of the pendulum is 4 ft. (Assume that the acceleration due to gravity is $g = 32$ ft/s^2) Round to the nearest tenth of a second.

71. a. For $x = 3$, evaluate the two expressions $\sqrt{x^2 + 4}$ and $x + 2$.

   b. Are these expressions equal?

72. a. For $x = 3$, evaluate the two expressions $\sqrt{x^2 + 16}$ and $x + 4$.

   b. Are these expressions equal?

■ EXPANDING YOUR SKILLS

73. The number of hours needed to cook a turkey that weighs x pounds can be approximated by

   $t(x) = 0.90\sqrt[5]{x^3}$, where t is the time in hours and x is the weight of the turkey in pounds.

   a. Find the weight of a turkey that cooked for 4 h. Round to the nearest pound.

   b. Find $t(18)$ and interpret the result. Round to the nearest tenth of an hour.

For Exercises 74–79, use the Pythagorean theorem to find a, b, or c.

$$a^2 + b^2 = c^2$$

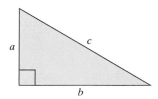

Figure for Exercises 74–79

74. Find c when $a = 6$ and $b = x$.

75. Find c when $a = k$ and $b = 9$.

76. Find b when $a = 2$ and $c = y$.

77. Find b when $a = h$ and $c = 5$.

78. Find a when $b = x$ and $c = 8$.

79. Find a when $b = 14$ and $c = k$.

GRAPHING CALCULATOR EXERCISES

80. Refer to Exercise 21. Graph Y_1 and Y_2 on a viewing window defined by $-10 \le x \le 20$ and $-5 \le y \le 10$.

$$Y_1 = \sqrt{4x} \qquad \text{and} \qquad Y_2 = 6$$

Use an *Intersect* feature to approximate the x-coordinate of the point of intersection of the two graphs to support your solution to Exercise 21.

81. Refer to Exercise 22. Graph Y_1 and Y_2 on a viewing window defined by $-10 \le x \le 40$ and $-5 \le y \le 10$.

$$Y_1 = \sqrt{2x} \qquad \text{and} \qquad Y_2 = 8$$

Use an *Intersect* feature to approximate the x-coordinate of the point of intersection of the two graphs to support your solution to Exercise 22.

82. Refer to Exercise 33. Graph Y_1 and Y_2 on a viewing window defined by $-5 \le x \le 20$ and $-1 \le y \le 4$.

$$Y_1 = \sqrt[4]{x + 4} \qquad \text{and} \qquad Y_2 = \sqrt[4]{2x - 5}$$

Use an *Intersect* feature to approximate the x-coordinate of the point of intersection of the two graphs to support your solution to Exercise 33.

83. Refer to Exercise 34. Graph Y_1 and Y_2 on a viewing window defined by $-5 \le x \le 20$ and $-1 \le y \le 4$.

$$Y_1 = \sqrt[4]{3x + 6} \qquad \text{and} \qquad Y_2 = \sqrt[4]{7x - 6}$$

Use an *Intersect* feature to approximate the x-coordinate of the point of intersection of the two graphs to support your solution to Exercise 34.

84. Refer to Exercise 49. Graph Y_1 and Y_2 on the standard viewing window.

$$Y_1 = \sqrt{x^2 + 2x + 1} \qquad \text{and} \qquad Y_2 = x + 5$$

Use an *Intersect* feature to approximate the x-coordinate of the point of intersection of the two graphs to support your solution to Exercise 49.

85. Refer to Exercise 50. Graph Y_1 and Y_2 on the standard viewing window.

$$Y_1 = \sqrt{x^2 - 5x - 8} \qquad \text{and} \qquad Y_2 = x + 7$$

Use an *Intersect* feature to approximate the x-coordinate of the point of intersection of the two graphs to support your solution to Exercise 50.

86. Refer to Exercise 59. Graph Y_1 and Y_2 on a viewing window defined by $-5 \le x \le 100$ and $-2 \le y \le 20$.

$$Y_1 = \sqrt{x - 9} \qquad \text{and} \qquad Y_2 = 3 + \sqrt{x}$$

Use an *Intersect* feature to approximate the x-coordinate of the point of intersection of the two graphs to support your solution to Exercise 59.

87. Refer to Exercise 60. Graph Y_1 and Y_2 on a viewing window defined by $-5 \le x \le 100$ and $-2 \le y \le 20$.

$$Y_1 = \sqrt{x - 16} \qquad \text{and} \qquad Y_2 = \sqrt{x} + 4$$

Use an *Intersect* feature to approximate the x-coordinate of the point of intersection of the two graphs to support your solution to Exercise 60.

88. Graph $C(x) = \sqrt{0.3x + 1}$ on a viewing window defined by $0 \le x \le 60$ and $-2 \le y \le 6$. Use a

Table feature to find the following function values:

$$C(10), C(20), C(30), C(40), \text{ and } C(50)$$

Use these values to support your answers to Exercises 69(a) and 69(c).

89. Graph $t(x) = 0.9\sqrt[5]{x^3}$ on a viewing window defined by $0 \leq x \leq 30$ and $-2 \leq y \leq 10$. Use a *Table* feature to find the following function values:

$$t(10), t(12), t(14), t(16), t(18), \text{ and } t(20)$$

Use these values to support your answers to Exercise 73.

---

section

6.8   COMPLEX NUMBERS

Concepts

1. Definition of *i*

2. Simplifying Expressions in Terms of *i*

3. The Powers of *i*

4. Definition of a Complex Number

5. Addition, Subtraction, and Multiplication of Complex Numbers

6. Division of Complex Numbers

7. Simplifying Negative Powers of *i*

1.   Definition of *i*

In Section 6.1, we learned that there are no real-valued square roots of a negative number. For example, $\sqrt{-9}$ is not a real number because no real number when squared equals -9. However, the square roots of a negative number are defined over another set of numbers called the **imaginary numbers**. The foundation of the set of imaginary numbers is the definition of the imaginary number, i, as: $i = \sqrt{-1}$.

Definition of *i*

$$i = \sqrt{-1}$$

Note: From the definition of i, it follows that $i^2 = -1$.

2.   Simplifying Expressions in Terms of *i*

Using the imaginary number i, we can define the square root of any negative real number.

Definition of $\sqrt{-b}, b > 0$

Let b be a real number such that $b > 0$, then $\sqrt{-b} = i\sqrt{b}$.

example 1

Simplifying Expressions in Terms of *i*

Simplify the expressions in terms of i.

a. $\sqrt{-64}$ b. $\sqrt{-100}$ c. $\sqrt{-29}$

Solution:

a. $\sqrt{-64} = 8i$

b. $\sqrt{-100} = 10i$

c. $\sqrt{-29} = i\sqrt{29}$

■

⬡ **Avoiding Mistakes**

In an expression such as $i\sqrt{29}$ the i is usually written in front of the square root. The expression $\sqrt{29}\,i$ is also correct, but may be misinterpreted as $\sqrt{29i}$ (with i incorrectly placed under the square root).

The multiplication and division properties of radicals were presented in Sections 6.3 and 6.5 as follows:

If a and b represent real numbers such that $\sqrt[n]{a}$ and $\sqrt[n]{b}$ are both real, then

$$\sqrt[n]{ab} = \sqrt[n]{a} \cdot \sqrt[n]{b} \qquad \text{and} \qquad \sqrt[n]{\frac{a}{b}} = \frac{\sqrt[n]{a}}{\sqrt[n]{b}} \qquad b \neq 0.$$

The conditions that $\sqrt[n]{a}$ and $\sqrt[n]{b}$ must both be real numbers prevent us from applying the multiplication and division properties of radicals for square roots with a negative radicand. Therefore, to multiply or divide radicals with a negative radicand, write the radical in terms of the imaginary number i first. This is demonstrated in the following example.

example 2

Simplifying a Product of Expressions in Terms of *i*

Simplify the expressions.

a. $\dfrac{\sqrt{-100}}{\sqrt{-25}}$ b. $\sqrt{-25} \cdot \sqrt{-9}$

Solution:

a. $\dfrac{\sqrt{-100}}{\sqrt{-25}}$

$= \dfrac{10i}{5i}$ Simplify each radical in terms of i *before* dividing.

$= 2$ Reduce.

⬡ **Avoiding Mistakes**

In Example 2(b), the radical expressions were written in terms of i first *before* multiplying. If we had mistakenly applied the multiplication property first we would obtain an incorrect answer.

Correct: $\sqrt{-25} \cdot \sqrt{-9}$
$= (5i)(3i) = 15i^2$
$= 15(-1) = -15$
          ↑ correct

Be careful: $\sqrt{-25} \cdot \sqrt{-9}$
$\neq \sqrt{225} = 15$
      ↑ (incorrect answer)

b. $\sqrt{-25} \cdot \sqrt{-9}$

$= 5i \cdot 3i$ Simplify each radical in terms of i first *before* multiplying.

$= 15i^2$ Multiply.

$= 15(-1)$ Recall that $i^2 = -1$

$= -15$ Simplify.

■

3. The Powers of i

From the definition of $i = \sqrt{-1}$, it follows that

$$i = i$$
$$i^2 = -1$$
$$i^3 = -i \qquad \text{because } i^3 = i^2 \cdot i = (-1)i = -i$$
$$i^4 = 1 \qquad \text{because } i^4 = i^2 \cdot i^2 = (-1)(-1) = 1$$
$$i^5 = i \qquad \text{because } i^5 = i^4 \cdot i = (1)i = i$$
$$i^6 = -1 \qquad \text{because } i^6 = i^4 \cdot i^2 = (1)(-1) = -1$$

This pattern of values $i, -1, -i, 1, i, -1, -i, 1, \ldots$ continues for all subsequent powers of i. Here is a list of several powers of i.

Powers of i

$i^1 = i$	$i^5 = i$	$i^9 = i$
$i^2 = -1$	$i^6 = -1$	$i^{10} = -1$
$i^3 = -i$	$i^7 = -i$	$i^{11} = -i$
$i^4 = 1$	$i^8 = 1$	$i^{12} = 1$

To simplify higher powers of i, we can decompose the expression into multiples of i^4 ($i^4 = 1$) and write the remaining factors as i, i^2, or i^3.

example 3

Simplifying Powers of i

Simplify the powers of i.

a. i^{13} b. i^{18} c. i^{107} d. i^{32}

Solution:

a. $i^{13} = (i^{12}) \cdot (i)$

$\qquad = (i^4)^3 \cdot (i)$

$\qquad = (1)^3(i)$ Recall that $i^4 = 1$.

$\qquad = i$ Simplify.

b. $i^{18} = (i^{16}) \cdot (i^2)$

$\qquad = (i^4)^4 \cdot (i^2)$

$\qquad = (1)^4 \cdot (-1)$ $i^4 = 1$ and $i^2 = -1$

$\qquad = -1$ Simplify.

c. $i^{107} = (i^{104}) \cdot (i^3)$

$\qquad = (i^4)^{26}(i^3)$

$\qquad = (1)^{26}(-i)$ $i^4 = 1$ and $i^3 = -i$

$\qquad = -i$ Simplify.

d. $i^{32} = (i^4)^8$

$\quad = (1)^8 \qquad i^4 = 1$

$\quad = 1 \qquad \quad$ Simplify.

4. Definition of a Complex Number

We have already learned the definitions of the integers, rational numbers, irrational numbers, and real numbers. In this section, we define the complex numbers.

Definition of a Complex Number

A **complex number** is a number of the form $a + bi$, where a and b are real numbers and $i = \sqrt{-1}$.

Notes:

- If $b = 0$, then the complex number, $a + bi$ is a real number.
- If $b \neq 0$, then we say that $a + bi$ is an imaginary number.
- The complex number $a + bi$ is said to be written in standard form. The quantities a and b are called the **real** and **imaginary parts** (respectively) **of the complex number**.
- The complex numbers $a - bi$ and $a + bi$ are called the **conjugates**.

From the definition of a complex number, it follows that all real numbers are complex numbers and all imaginary numbers are complex numbers. Figure 6-5 illustrates the relationship among the sets of numbers we have learned so far.

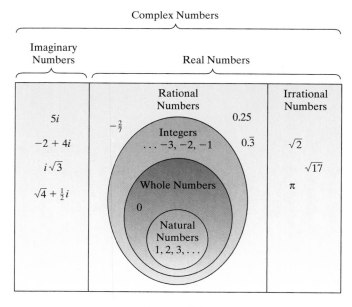

Figure 6-5

example 4

Identifying the Real and Imaginary Parts of a Complex Number

Identify the real and imaginary parts of the complex numbers.

a. $-8 + 2i$ b. $\dfrac{3}{2}$ c. $-1.75i$

Solution:

a. $-8 + 2i$ -8 is the real part, and 2 is the imaginary part.

b. $\dfrac{3}{2}$

> **Tip:** This example illustrates that a real number is also a complex number.

$\; = \dfrac{3}{2} + 0i$ Rewrite $\frac{3}{2}$ in the form $a + bi$.
$\frac{3}{2}$ is the real part, and 0 is the imaginary part.

c. $-1.75i$

> **Tip:** This example illustrates that an imaginary number is also a complex number.

$\; = 0 + -1.75i$ Rewrite $1.75i$ in the form $a + bi$.
0 is the real part, and -1.75 is the imaginary part.

5. Addition, Subtraction, and Multiplication of Complex Numbers

The operations of addition, subtraction, and multiplication of real numbers also apply to imaginary numbers. To add or subtract complex numbers, combine the real parts and combine the imaginary parts. The commutative, associative, and distributive properties that apply to real numbers also apply to complex numbers.

example 5

Adding, Subtracting, and Multiplying Complex Numbers

a. Add: $(1 - 5i) + (-3 + 7i)$
b. Subtract: $\left(-\frac{1}{4} + \frac{3}{5}i\right) - \left(\frac{1}{2} - \frac{1}{10}i\right)$
c. Multiply: $(10 - 5i)(2 + 3i)$
d. Multiply: $(1.2 + 0.5i)(1.2 - 0.5i)$

Solution:

           real parts

a. $(1 - 5i) + (-3 + 7i) = (1 + -3) + (-5 + 7)i$ Add real parts. Add imaginary parts.

       imaginary parts

$ = -2 + 2i$ Simplify.

b. $\left(-\dfrac{1}{4} + \dfrac{3}{5}i\right) - \left(\dfrac{1}{2} - \dfrac{1}{10}i\right) = -\dfrac{1}{4} + \dfrac{3}{5}i - \dfrac{1}{2} + \dfrac{1}{10}i$ Apply the distributive property.

$= \left(-\dfrac{1}{4} - \dfrac{1}{2}\right) + \left(\dfrac{3}{5} + \dfrac{1}{10}\right)i$ Add real parts. Add imaginary parts.

$= \left(-\dfrac{1}{4} - \dfrac{2}{4}\right) + \left(\dfrac{6}{10} + \dfrac{1}{10}\right)i$ Get a common denominator.

$= -\dfrac{3}{4} + \dfrac{7}{10}i$ Simplify.

c. $(10 - 5i)(2 + 3i)$

$= (10)(2) + (10)(3i) + (-5i)(2) + (-5i)(3i)$ Apply the distributive property.

$= 20 + 30i - 10i - 15i^2$

$= 20 + 20i - (15)(-1)$ Recall $i^2 = -1$.

$= 20 + 20i + 15$

$= 35 + 20i$ Write in the form $a + bi$.

d. $(1.2 + 0.5i)(1.2 - 0.5i)$

The expressions $(1.2 + 0.5i)$ and $(1.2 - 0.5i)$ are conjugates. The product is a difference of squares:

$(a + b)(a - b) = a^2 - b^2$

$(1.2 + 0.5i)(1.2 - 0.5i) = (1.2)^2 - (0.5i)^2$ Apply the formula, where $a = 1.2$ and $b = 0.5i$.

$= 1.44 - 0.25i^2$

$= 1.44 - 0.25(-1)$ Recall $i^2 = -1$.

$= 1.44 + 0.25$

$= 1.69$

Tip: The complex numbers $(1.2 + 0.5i)$ and $(1.2 - 0.5i)$ can also be multiplied by using the distributive property:

$(1.2 + 0.5i)(1.2 - 0.5i) = 1.44 - 0.6i + 0.6i - 0.25i^2$
$= 1.44 - 0.25(-1)$
$= 1.69$

Graphing Calculator Box

Some calculators with advanced mathematical functions can perform operations over the set of complex numbers. (Consult your user's manual to determine if your calculator has this feature.)

On many calculators, a complex number is written in parentheses with the real part written first, followed by a comma, followed by the imaginary part. For example, the number $1 - 5i$ is entered as $(1, -5)$.

The operations performed in Example 5 are shown here:

a. $(1 - 5i) + (-3 + 7i)$
b. $(-\frac{1}{4} + \frac{3}{5}i) - (\frac{1}{2} - \frac{1}{10}i)$
c. $(10 - 5i)(2 + 3i)$
d. $(1.2 + 0.5i)(1.2 - 0.5i)$

Notice that the solution to part (d) $(1.69, 0)$ represents the real number $1.69 + 0i$ or simply 1.69.

```
(1,-5)+(-3,7)
              (-2,2)
(-1/4,3/5)-(1/2,-1/10
)
           (-.75,.7)
```

```
(10,-5)(2,3)
             (35,20)
(1.2,0.5)(1.2,-0.5)
            (1.69,0)
```

---

6.   Division of Complex Numbers

The product of a complex number and its conjugate produces a real number. For example:

$$
\begin{aligned}
(5 + 3i)(5 - 3i) &= 25 - 9i^2 \\
&= 25 - 9(-1) \\
&= 25 + 9 \\
&= 34
\end{aligned}
$$

To divide by a complex number, multiply the numerator and denominator by the conjugate of the denominator. This produces a real number in the denominator so that the resulting expression can be written in the form $a + bi$.

---

example 6   **Dividing by a Complex Number**

Divide the complex numbers.

$$\frac{4 - 3i}{5 + 2i}$$

Solution:

a. $\dfrac{4 - 3i}{5 + 2i}$ Multiply the numerator and denominator by the conjugate of the denominator:

$$\frac{(4 - 3i)}{(5 + 2i)} \cdot \frac{(5 - 2i)}{(5 - 2i)} = \frac{(4)(5) + (4)(-2i) + (-3i)(5) + (-3i)(-2i)}{(5)^2 - (2i)^2}$$

$$= \frac{20 - 8i - 15i + 6i^2}{25 - 4i^2} \qquad \text{Simplify numerator and denominator.}$$

$$= \frac{20 - 23i + 6(-1)}{25 - 4(-1)} \qquad \text{Recall } i^2 = -1.$$

$$= \frac{20 - 23i - 6}{25 + 4}$$

$$= \frac{14 - 23i}{29} \qquad \text{Simplify.}$$

$$= \frac{14}{29} - \frac{23i}{29}$$

7. Simplifying Negative Powers of i

example 7

Simplifying Negative Powers of i

Simplify the expression $-5i^{-9}$.

Solution:

$$-5i^{-9} = \frac{-5}{i^9}$$

$$= \frac{-5}{i^9} \qquad i^9 \text{ can be simplified as } i^9 = (i^4)^2 \cdot i = (1) \cdot i = i.$$

$$= \frac{-5}{i} \qquad \begin{array}{l}\text{The denominator is equivalent to } 0 + i. \text{ The conjugate} \\ \text{is } 0 - i \text{ or simply } -i. \text{ Multiply numerator and} \\ \text{denominator by the conjugate of the denominator.}\end{array}$$

$$= \frac{-5}{i} \cdot \frac{-i}{-i}$$

$$= \frac{5i}{-i^2}$$

$$= \frac{5i}{-(-1)} \qquad \text{Recall } i^2 = -1.$$

$$= \frac{5i}{1} \qquad \text{Simplify.}$$

$$= 5i$$

section 6.8   Practice Exercises

For Exercises 1–4, perform the indicated operations.

1. $-2\sqrt{5} - 3\sqrt{50} + \sqrt{125}$

2. $\sqrt[3]{2x}(\sqrt[3]{2x} - \sqrt[3]{4x^2})$

3. $(3 - \sqrt{x})(3 + \sqrt{x})$ 4. $(\sqrt{5} + \sqrt{2})^2$

For Exercises 5–10, solve the equations.

5. $\sqrt{5y - 4} - 2 = 4$

6. $\sqrt{3w + 4} - 3 = 2$

7. $\sqrt[3]{3p + 7} - \sqrt[3]{2p - 1} = 0$

8. $\sqrt[3]{t - 5} - \sqrt[3]{2t + 1} = 0$

9. $\sqrt{36c + 15} = 6\sqrt{c} + 1$

10. $\sqrt{4a + 29} = 2\sqrt{a} + 5$

11. Define the imaginary number i.

12. Simplify i^2.

13. What is the conjugate of a complex number, $a + bi$?

14. True or False.

   a. Every real number is a complex number.

   b. Every complex number is a real number.

For Exercises 15–34, simplify the expressions:

15. $\sqrt{-144}$ 16. $\sqrt{-81}$

17. $\sqrt{-3}$ 18. $\sqrt{-17}$

19. $\sqrt{-20}$ 20. $\sqrt{-75}$

21. $3\sqrt{-18} + 5\sqrt{-32}$ 22. $5\sqrt{-45} + 3\sqrt{-80}$

23. $7\sqrt{-63} - 4\sqrt{-28}$ 24. $7\sqrt{-3} - 4\sqrt{-27}$

25. $\sqrt{-7} \cdot \sqrt{-7}$ 26. $\sqrt{-11} \cdot \sqrt{-11}$

27. $\sqrt{-9} \cdot \sqrt{-16}$ 28. $\sqrt{-25} \cdot \sqrt{-36}$

29. $\sqrt{-15} \cdot \sqrt{-6}$ 30. $\sqrt{-12} \cdot \sqrt{-50}$

31. $\dfrac{\sqrt{-50}}{\sqrt{-25}}$ 32. $\dfrac{\sqrt{-27}}{\sqrt{-9}}$

33. $\dfrac{\sqrt{-90}}{\sqrt{10}}$ 34. $\dfrac{\sqrt{-125}}{\sqrt{45}}$

For Exercises 35–42, add or subtract as indicated. Write the answer in the form $a + bi$.

35. $(2 - i) + (5 + 7i)$

36. $(5 - 2i) + (3 + 4i)$

37. $\left(\dfrac{1}{2} + \dfrac{2}{3}i\right) - \left(\dfrac{1}{5} - \dfrac{5}{6}i\right)$

38. $\left(\dfrac{11}{10} - \dfrac{7}{5}i\right) - \left(-\dfrac{2}{5} + \dfrac{3}{5}i\right)$

39. $(1 + 3i) + (4 - 3i)$

40. $(-2 + i) + (1 - i)$

41. $(2 + 3i) - (1 - 4i) + (-2 + 3i)$

42. $(2 + 5i) - (7 - 2i) + (-3 + 4i)$

For Exercises 43–54, simplify the powers of i.

43. i^7 44. i^{38}

45. i^{64} 46. i^{75}

47. i^{41} 48. i^{25}

49. i^{52} 50. i^0

51. i^{23} 52. i^{103}

53. i^6 54. i^{82}

For Exercises 55–66, multiply the complex numbers. Write the answer in the form $a + bi$.

55. $(8i)(3i)$ 56. $(2i)(4i)$

57. $6i(1 - 3i)$ 58. $-i(3 + 4i)$

59. $(2 - 10i)(3 + 2i)$ 60. $(4 + 7i)(1 - i)$

61. $(-5 + 2i)(5 + 2i)$ 62. $(4 - 11i)(-4 - 11i)$

63. $(4 + 5i)^2$ 64. $(3 - 2i)^2$

65. $(2 + i)(3 - 2i)(4 + 3i)$

66. $(3 - i)(3 + i)(4 - i)$

For Exercises 67–70, find the conjugate. Then find the product of the number and its conjugate.

67. $(1 + 3i)$

68. $(3 + i)$

69. $(4 - 3i)$

70. $(1 - i)$

For Exercises 71–80, divide the complex numbers. Write the answer in the form $a + bi$.

71. $\dfrac{2}{1 + 3i}$

72. $\dfrac{-2}{3 + i}$

73. $\dfrac{-i}{4 - 3i}$

74. $\dfrac{3 - 3i}{1 - i}$

75. $\dfrac{5 + 2i}{5 - 2i}$

76. $\dfrac{7 + 3i}{4 - 2i}$

77. $\dfrac{3}{2i}$

78. $\dfrac{-2}{7i}$

79. $\dfrac{3}{-i}$

80. $\dfrac{-2}{-i}$

For Exercises 81–86, simplify the expression and write the answer in the form $a + bi$.

81. $7i^{-5}$

82. $9i^{-7}$

83. $12i^{-8}$

84. $-6i^{-12}$

85. i^{-10}

86. i^{-22}

GRAPHING CALCULATOR EXERCISES

Some calculators have the capability to perform operations over the set of complex numbers. Consult your user's manual to determine if your calculator has this feature. If so, use the calculator to check the solutions to the following exercises:

87. Exercise 15

88. Exercise 16

89. Exercise 27

90. Exercise 28

91. Exercise 35

92. Exercise 36

93. Exercise 43

94. Exercise 44

95. Exercise 55

96. Exercise 56

97. Exercise 59

98. Exercise 60

99. Exercise 61

100. Exercise 62

101. Exercise 63

102. Exercise 64

103. Exercise 71

104. Exercise 72

---

chapter 6   SUMMARY

SECTION 6.1—DEFINITION OF AN nth ROOT

KEY CONCEPTS:

b is an nth root of a if $b^n = a$.

The expression $\sqrt{a}$ represents the principal square root of a.

The expression $\sqrt[n]{a}$ represents the principal nth root of a.

$\sqrt[n]{a^n} = |a|$ if n is even.

$\sqrt[n]{a^n} = a$ if n is odd.

$\sqrt[n]{a}$ is not a real number if $a < 0$ and n is even.

$f(x) = \sqrt[n]{x}$ defines a radical function.

EXAMPLES:

2 is a square root of 4.

-2 is a square root of 4.

-3 is a cube root of -27.

$$\sqrt{36} = 6 \qquad\qquad \sqrt[3]{-64} = -4$$

$$\sqrt[4]{(x + 3)^4} = |x + 3| \qquad \sqrt[5]{(x + 3)^5} = x + 3$$

$\sqrt[4]{-16}$ is not a real number.

For $g(x) = \sqrt{x}$ the domain is $[0, \infty)$.

For $h(x) = \sqrt[3]{x}$ the domain is $(-\infty, \infty)$.

The Pythagorean Theorem

$$a^2 + b^2 = c^2$$

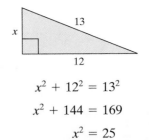

$$x^2 + 12^2 = 13^2$$
$$x^2 + 144 = 169$$
$$x^2 = 25$$
$$x = 5$$

KEY TERMS:

cube root	principal square root
hypotenuse	Pythagorean theorem
index	radical function
perfect square	radical sign
principal nth root	radicand

SECTION 6.2—RATIONAL EXPONENTS

KEY CONCEPTS:

Let a be a real number and n be an integer such that $n > 1$. If $\sqrt[n]{a}$ exists, then

$$a^{1/n} = \sqrt[n]{a}$$
$$a^{m/n} = (\sqrt[n]{a})^m = \sqrt[n]{a^m}$$

KEY TERMS:

$a^{1/n}$
$a^{m/n}$

EXAMPLES:

$$121^{1/2} = \sqrt{121} = 11$$
$$27^{2/3} = (\sqrt[3]{27})^2 = (3)^2 = 9$$

SECTION 6.3—PROPERTIES OF RADICALS

KEY CONCEPTS:

Let a and b represent real numbers such that $\sqrt[n]{a}$ and $\sqrt[n]{b}$ are both real. Then

$$\sqrt[n]{ab} = \sqrt[n]{a} \cdot \sqrt[n]{b} \quad \text{Multiplication property}$$

$$\sqrt[n]{\frac{a}{b}} = \frac{\sqrt[n]{a}}{\sqrt[n]{b}} \quad \text{Division property}$$

EXAMPLES:

$$\sqrt{3} \cdot \sqrt{5} = \sqrt{15}$$

$$\sqrt{\frac{x}{9}} = \frac{\sqrt{x}}{\sqrt{9}} = \frac{\sqrt{x}}{3}$$

A radical expression whose radicand is written as a product of prime factors is in simplified form if all of the following conditions are met:

1. The radicand has no factor raised to a power greater than or equal to the index.
2. No radicals are in the denominator of a fraction.
3. The radicand does not contain a fraction.

KEY TERMS:

division property of radicals
multiplication property of radicals
simplified form of a radical

Simplify:

$$\sqrt[3]{16x^5y^7}$$
$$= \sqrt[3]{2^4x^5y^7}$$
$$= \sqrt[3]{2^3x^3y^6} \cdot \sqrt[3]{2x^2y}$$
$$= 2xy^2\sqrt[3]{2x^2y}$$

SECTION 6.4—ADDITION AND SUBTRACTION OF RADICALS

KEY CONCEPTS:

Like radicals have radical factors with the same index and the same radicand.

Use the distributive property to add and subtract *like* radicals.

KEY TERMS:

like radicals

EXAMPLES:

Perform the indicated operations:

$$3x\sqrt{7} - 5x\sqrt{7} + x\sqrt{7}$$
$$= (3 - 5 + 1) \cdot x\sqrt{7}$$
$$= -x\sqrt{7}$$

Subtract:

$$x\sqrt[4]{16x} - 3\sqrt[4]{x^5}$$
$$= 2x\sqrt[4]{x} - 3x\sqrt[4]{x}$$
$$= -x\sqrt[4]{x}$$

SECTION 6.5—MULTIPLICATION OF RADICALS

KEY CONCEPTS:

The Multiplication Property of Radicals

If $\sqrt[n]{a}$ and $\sqrt[n]{b}$ are real numbers, then $\sqrt[n]{ab} = \sqrt[n]{a} \cdot \sqrt[n]{b}$

To multiply or divide radicals with different indices, convert to rational exponents and use the properties of exponents.

KEY TERMS:

multiplication property of radicals

EXAMPLES:

Multiply:

$$3\sqrt{2}(\sqrt{2} + 5\sqrt{7} - \sqrt{6})$$
$$= 3\sqrt{4} + 15\sqrt{14} - 3\sqrt{12}$$
$$= 3 \cdot 2 + 15\sqrt{14} - 3 \cdot 2\sqrt{3}$$
$$= 6 + 15\sqrt{14} - 6\sqrt{3}$$

Divide:

$$\frac{\sqrt{p}}{\sqrt[5]{p^2}}$$
$$= \frac{p^{1/2}}{p^{2/5}}$$
$$= p^{1/2-2/5}$$
$$= p^{1/10} = \sqrt[10]{p}$$

SECTION 6.6—RATIONALIZATION

KEY CONCEPTS:

Rationalizing a denominator with one term

Rationalizing a denominator with two terms

KEY TERMS:

rationalizing the denominator (one term)
rationalizing the denominator (two terms involving square roots)

EXAMPLES:

Simplify:

$$\frac{4}{\sqrt[4]{2y^3}}$$

$$= \frac{4}{\sqrt[4]{2y^3}} \cdot \frac{\sqrt[4]{2^3 y}}{\sqrt[4]{2^3 y}} = \frac{4\sqrt[4]{8y}}{\sqrt[4]{2^4 y^4}}$$

$$= \frac{4\sqrt[4]{8y}}{2y} = \frac{2\sqrt[4]{8y}}{y}$$

Rationalize the denominator:

$$\frac{\sqrt{2}}{\sqrt{x} - \sqrt{3}}$$

$$= \frac{\sqrt{2}}{(\sqrt{x} - \sqrt{3})} \cdot \frac{(\sqrt{x} + \sqrt{3})}{(\sqrt{x} + \sqrt{3})}$$

$$= \frac{\sqrt{2x} + \sqrt{6}}{x - 3}$$

SECTION 6.7—RADICAL EQUATIONS

KEY CONCEPTS:

Steps to Solve a Radical Equation

1. Isolate the radical. If an equation has more than one radical, choose one of the radicals to isolate.
2. Raise each side of the equation to a power equal to the index of the radical.
3. Solve the resulting equation. If the equation still has a radical, repeat steps 1 and 2.
4. Check the potential solutions in the original equation.

KEY TERMS:

radical equation

EXAMPLES:

Solve:

$$\sqrt{b - 5} - \sqrt{b + 3} = 2$$
$$\sqrt{b - 5} = \sqrt{b + 3} + 2$$
$$(\sqrt{b - 5})^2 = (\sqrt{b + 3} + 2)^2$$
$$b - 5 = b + 3 + 4\sqrt{b + 3} + 4$$
$$b - 5 = b + 7 + 4\sqrt{b + 3}$$
$$-12 = 4\sqrt{b + 3}$$
$$-3 = \sqrt{b + 3}$$
$$(-3)^2 = (\sqrt{b + 3})^2$$
$$9 = b + 3$$
$$6 = b$$

Check:

$$\sqrt{6 - 5} - \sqrt{6 + 3} \stackrel{?}{=} 2$$
$$\sqrt{1} - \sqrt{9} \stackrel{?}{=} 2$$
$$1 - 3 \neq 2 \qquad \text{Does not check.}$$

No solution

SECTION 6.8—COMPLEX NUMBERS

KEY CONCEPTS:

$i = \sqrt{-1}$ and $i^2 = -1$

For a real number $b > 0$, $\sqrt{-b} = i\sqrt{b}$

A complex number is in the form $a + bi$, where a and b are real numbers. a is called the real part, and b is called the imaginary part.

To add or subtract complex numbers, combine the real parts and combine the imaginary parts.

Multiply complex numbers by using the distributive property.

Divide complex numbers by multiplying the numerator and denominator by the conjugate of the denominator.

KEY TERMS:

complex numbers
conjugate
i
imaginary numbers
imaginary part of a complex number
real part of a complex number

EXAMPLES:

Simplify:

$$\sqrt{-4} \cdot \sqrt{-9}$$
$$= (2i)(3i)$$
$$= 6i^2$$
$$= -6$$

Perform the indicated operations:

$$(3 - 5i) - (2 + i) + (3 - 2i)$$
$$= 3 - 5i - 2 - i + 3 - 2i$$
$$= 4 - 8i$$

Multiply:

$$(1 + 6i)(2 + 4i)$$
$$= 2 + 4i + 12i + 24i^2$$
$$= 2 + 16i + 24(-1)$$
$$= -22 + 16i$$

Divide:

$$\frac{3}{2 - 5i}$$
$$= \frac{3}{2 - 5i} \cdot \frac{(2 + 5i)}{(2 + 5i)} = \frac{6 + 15i}{4 - 25i^2}$$
$$= \frac{6 + 15i}{29} \quad \text{or} \quad \frac{6}{29} + \frac{15}{29}i$$

---

chapter 6   REVIEW EXERCISES

For the exercises in this set, assume that all variables represent positive real numbers unless otherwise stated.

Section 6.1

1. True or false:

    a. The principal nth root of an even indexed root is always positive.

    b. The principal nth root of an odd indexed root is always positive.

2. Explain why $\sqrt{(-3)^2} = 3$ and $\sqrt{(-3)^2} \neq -3$.

3. Are the following statements true or false?

    a. $\sqrt{a^2 + b^2} = a + b$

    b. $\sqrt{(a + b)^2} = a + b$

For Exercises 4–6, simplify the radicals.

4. $\sqrt{\dfrac{50}{32}}$ 5. $\sqrt[4]{625}$ 6. $\sqrt{(-6)^2}$

7. Evaluate the function values for $f(x) = \sqrt{x} - 1$.

   a. $f(10)$ b. $f(1)$ c. $f(8)$

   d. Given $f(x) = \sqrt{x} - 1$, write the domain of f in interval notation.

8. Use a calculator to approximate the expression $-3 - 3\sqrt{5}$ to two decimal places.

9. Translate the English sentence into an algebraic expression: Four more than the quotient of the cube root of $2x$ and the fourth root of $2x$.

10. State the Pythagorean theorem and explain the theorem in your own words.

11. Use the Pythagorean theorem to find the length of the third side of the triangle.

Figure for Exercise 11

12. Three sides of a right triangle are related as shown in the figure.

   a. Find the lengths of the sides when $x = 3$ in.

   b. Find the lengths of the sides when $x = 12$ in.

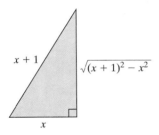

Figure for Exercise 12

Section 6.2

13. Are the properties of exponents the same for rational exponents and integer exponents? Give an example. (Answers may vary.)

14. In the expression $x^{m/n}$ what does n represent? What does m represent?

15. Explain the process of eliminating a negative exponent from an algebraic expression.

For Exercises 16–20, simplify the expressions. Write the answer with positive exponents only.

16. $(-125)^{1/3}$

17. $16^{-1/4}$

18. $\left(\dfrac{1}{16}\right)^{-3/4} - \left(\dfrac{1}{8}\right)^{-2/3}$

19. $(b^{1/2} \cdot b^{1/3})^{12}$

20. $\left(\dfrac{x^{-1/4}y^{-1/3}z^{3/4}}{2^{1/3}x^{-1/3}y^{2/3}}\right)^{-12}$

For Exercises 21–22, rewrite the expressions using rational exponents.

21. $\sqrt[4]{x^3}$

22. $\sqrt[3]{2y^2}$

For Exercises 23–25, use a calculator to approximate the expressions to four decimal places.

23. $10^{/3}$ 24. $17.8^{2/3}$ 25. $147^{4/5}$

26. An initial investment of P dollars is made into an account in which the return is compounded quarterly. The amount in the account can be determined by

$$A = P\left(1 + \frac{r}{4}\right)^{t/3},$$

where r is the annual rate of return, and t is the time in months.

When she is 20 years old, Jenna invests $5000 in a mutual fund that grows by an average of 11% per year. How much money does she have

   a. After 6 months?   b. After 1 year?

   c. At age 40?   d. At age 50?

   e. At age 65?

Section 6.3

27. List the criteria for a rational expression to be simplified.

For Exercises 28–31, simplify the radicals.

28. $\sqrt{108}$

29. $\sqrt[4]{x^5yz^4}$

30. $\sqrt{5x} \cdot \sqrt{20x}$

31. $\sqrt[3]{\dfrac{-16x^7y^6}{z^9}}$

32. Write an English phrase that describes the following mathematical expressions: (Answers may vary.)

   a. $\sqrt{\dfrac{2}{x}}$ b. $(x + 1)^3$

33. An engineering firm made a mistake when building a $\frac{1}{4}$-mile bridge in the Florida Keys. The bridge was made without adequate expansion joints to prevent buckling during the heat of summer. During mid-June, the bridge expanded 1.5 ft causing a vertical bulge in the middle. Calculate the height of the bulge, h, in feet. (*Note*: 1 mile = 5280 ft) Round to the nearest foot.

Figure for Exercise 33

Section 6.4

34. Complete the following statement: Radicals may be added or subtracted if. . . .

For Exercises 35–38, determine whether the radicals may be combined, and explain your answer.

35. $\sqrt[3]{2x} - 2\sqrt{2x}$

36. $2 + \sqrt{x}$

37. $\sqrt[4]{3xy} + 2\sqrt[4]{3xy}$

38. $-4\sqrt{32} + 7\sqrt{50}$

For Exercises 39–42, add or subtract as indicated.

39. $4\sqrt{7} - 2\sqrt{7} + 3\sqrt{7}$

40. $2\sqrt[3]{64} + 3\sqrt[3]{54} - 16$

41. $\sqrt{50} + 7\sqrt{2} - \sqrt{8}$

42. $x\sqrt[3]{16x^2} - 4\sqrt[3]{2x^5} + 5x\sqrt[3]{54x^2}$

For Exercises 43–44, answer true or false. If an answer is false, explain why. Assume all variables represent positive real numbers.

43. $5 + 3\sqrt{x} = 8\sqrt{x}$

44. $\sqrt{y} + \sqrt{y} = \sqrt{2y}$

Section 6.5

45. Define the conjugate of a binomial expression.

46. Explain why $x - y = (\sqrt{x} + \sqrt{y})(\sqrt{x} - \sqrt{y})$.

For Exercises 47–55, multiply the radicals and simplify the answer.

47. $\sqrt{3} \cdot \sqrt{12}$

48. $\sqrt[4]{4} \cdot \sqrt[4]{8}$

49. $-2\sqrt{3}(\sqrt{3} - 3\sqrt{3})$

50. $(\sqrt{y} + 4)(\sqrt{y} - 4)$

51. $(\sqrt[3]{2x} - \sqrt[3]{4x})^2$

52. $(3\sqrt{a} - \sqrt{5})(\sqrt{a} + 2\sqrt{5})$

53. $\sqrt[3]{u} \cdot \sqrt{u^5}$

54. $\sqrt[4]{w^3} \cdot \sqrt{w}$

55. $\sqrt[3]{(a + b)} \cdot \sqrt[6]{(a + b)^5}$

Section 6.6

For Exercises 56–59, rationalize the denominator.

56. $\dfrac{-2}{\sqrt[3]{2x}}$

57. $\dfrac{2\sqrt{x} + \sqrt{5}}{\sqrt{5x}}$

58. $\dfrac{-2}{\sqrt{x} - 4}$

59. $\dfrac{2\sqrt{b} - 1}{3\sqrt{b} - 1}$

60. Tr nslate the mathematical expression into an English phrase. (Answers may vary.)

$$\frac{\sqrt{2}}{x^2}$$

Section 6.7

Solve the radical equations in Exercises 61–66, if possible.

61. $\sqrt{2y} = 7$

62. $\sqrt{a - 6} = 5$

63. $\sqrt[3]{2w - 3} + 5 = 2$

64. $\sqrt[4]{p + 12} = \sqrt[4]{5p - 16}$

65. $\sqrt{t} + \sqrt{t - 5} = 5$

66. $\sqrt{8x + 1} = -\sqrt{x - 13}$

67. The velocity, v, of an ocean wave depends on the water depth, d, as the wave approaches land.

$v(d) = \sqrt{32d}$, where v is in feet/second and d is in feet.

a. Find $v(20)$ and interpret its value. Round to one decimal place.

b. Find the depth of the water at a point where a wave is traveling at 16 ft/s.

68. A Pony league baseball field is larger than a Little League diamond but still smaller than a Major League diamond. The Pony League field is a square that measures 80 ft on each side. Find the distance from home plate to second base on this field.

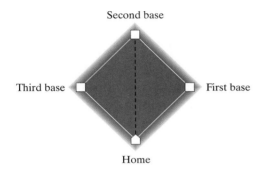

Second base

Third base   First base

Home

Section 6.8

69. Define a complex number.

70. Define an imaginary number.

71. Consider the following expressions.

$$\frac{3}{4 + 6i} \quad \text{and} \quad \frac{3}{\sqrt{4} + \sqrt{6}}$$

Compare the process of dividing by a complex number to the process of rationalizing the denominator.

For Exercises 72–74, rewrite the expressions in terms of i.

72. $\sqrt{-16}$

73. $-\sqrt{-5}$

74. $\sqrt{-x}$ if $x \geq 0$

For Exercises 75–79, simplify the powers of i.

75. i^{38} 76. i^{101} 77. i^{19} 78. $i^{1000} + i^{1002}$

79. $2i^{17} - 3i^{23} + 2i^{24} + 4i^{34}$

For Exercises 80–83, perform the indicated operations. Write the final answer in the form $a + bi$.

80. $(-3 + i) - (2 - 4i)$ 81. $(2i + 4)(2i - 4)$

82. $(4 - 3i)(4 + 3i)$ 83. $(5 - i)^2$

For Exercises 84–85, write the expressions in the form $a + bi$, and determine the real and imaginary parts.

84. $\dfrac{17 - 4i}{-4}$ 85. $\dfrac{-16 - 8i}{8}$

For Exercises 86–87, divide and simplify. Write the final answer in the form $a + bi$.

86. $\dfrac{2 - i}{3 + 2i}$ 87. $\dfrac{2 + i}{i^5}$

---

chapter 6   TEST

1. a. What is the principal square root of 36?
    b. What is the negative square root of 36?

2. Which of the following are real numbers?
    a. $-\sqrt{100}$ b. $\sqrt{-100}$
    c. $-\sqrt[3]{1000}$ d. $\sqrt[3]{-1000}$

3. Simplify.
    a. $\sqrt[3]{y^3}$ b. $\sqrt[4]{y^4}$

For Exercises 4–11, simplify the radicals. Assume that all variables represent positive numbers.

4. $\sqrt[4]{81}$ 5. $\sqrt{\dfrac{16}{9}}$

6. $\sqrt[3]{32}$ 7. $\sqrt{a^4 b^3 c^5}$

8. $\sqrt{3x} \cdot \sqrt{6x^3}$ 9. $\sqrt{\dfrac{32w^6}{3w}}$

10. $\sqrt{7y} \cdot \sqrt[5]{7y}$

11. $\dfrac{\sqrt[3]{10}}{\sqrt[4]{10}}$

12. a. Evaluate the function values $f(-8), f(-6)$, $f(-4)$, and $f(-2)$ for $f(x) = \sqrt{-2x - 4}$.

  b. Write the domain of f in interval notation.

13. Use a calculator to evaluate $(-3 - \sqrt{5})/17$ to four decimal places.

For Exercises 14–15, simplify the expressions. Assume that all variables represent positive numbers.

14. $-27^{1/3}$

15. $\dfrac{t^{-1} \cdot t^{1/2}}{t^{1/4}}$

16. Add or subtract as indicated:
$3\sqrt{5} + 4\sqrt{5} - 2\sqrt{20}$

17. Multiply the radicals.

  a. $3\sqrt{x}(\sqrt{2} - \sqrt{5})$

  b. $(\sqrt{2x} - 3)^2$

18. Rationalize the denominator. Assume $x > 0$.

  a. $\dfrac{-2}{\sqrt[3]{x}}$

  b. $\dfrac{\sqrt{x} + 2}{3 - \sqrt{x}}$

19. Rewrite the expressions in terms of i.

  a. $\sqrt{-8}$

  b. $2\sqrt{-16}$

20. Perform the indicated operation and simplify completely. Write the final answer in the form $a + bi$.

$(10 + 3i)[(-5i + 8) - (5 - 3i)]$

21. Divide and write the final answers in the form $a + bi$.

  a. $\dfrac{-4 + i}{i^5}$

  b. $\dfrac{3 - 2i}{3 - 4i}$

22. If the volume, V, of a sphere is known, the radius of the sphere can be computed by $r(V) = \sqrt[3]{(3V)/(4\pi)}$. Find $r(10)$ to two decimal places. Interpret the meaning in the context of the problem.

23. A patio 20 ft wide has a slanted roof as shown in the picture. Find the length of the roof if there is an 8-in. overhang. Round the answer to the nearest foot.

Figure for Exercise 23

For Exercises 24–25, solve the radical equations.

24. $\sqrt[3]{2x + 5} = -3$

25. $\sqrt{5x + 8} = \sqrt{5x - 1} + 1$

CUMULATIVE REVIEW EXERCISES, CHAPTERS 1–6

1. Simplify the expression:
$6^2 - 2[5 - 8(3 - 1) + 4 \div 2]$

2. Simplify the expression:
$3x - 3(-2x + 5) - 4y + 2(3x + 5) - y$

3. Solve the equation: $9(2y + 8) = 20 - (y + 5)$

4. Solve the inequality. Write the answer in interval notation. $2a - 4 < -14$

5. Write an equation of the line that is parallel to the line $2x + y = 9$ and passes through the point $(3, -1)$. Write the answer in slope-intercept form.

6. On the same coordinate system, graph the line $2x + y = 9$ and the line that you derived in Exercise 5. Verify that these two lines are indeed parallel.

7. Solve the system of equations using the addition method.
$$2x - 3y = 0$$
$$-4x + 3y = -1$$

8. Determine if $(2, -2, \frac{1}{2})$ is a solution to the system.
$$2x + y - 4z = 0$$
$$x - y + 2z = 5$$
$$3x + 2y + 2z = 4$$

9. Write a system of linear equations from the augmented matrix. Use x, y, and z for the variables.
$$\begin{bmatrix} 1 & 0 & 0 & | & 6 \\ 0 & 1 & 0 & | & 3 \\ 0 & 0 & 1 & | & 8 \end{bmatrix}$$

10. Given the function defined by $f(x) = 4x - 2$.
    a. Find $f(-2)$, $f(0)$, $f(4)$, and $f(\frac{1}{2})$.
    b. Write the ordered pairs that correspond to the function values in part (a).
    c. Graph the function $y = f(x)$.

11. Determine if the graph of $y = h(x)$ defines y as a function of x.

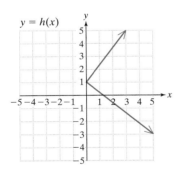

12. Simplify the expression. Write the final answer with positive exponents only.
$$\left(\frac{a^3 b^{-1} c^3}{ab^{-5} c^2} \right)^2$$

13. Simplify the expression. Write the final answer with positive exponents only.
$$\left(\frac{a^{3/2} b^{-1/4} c^{1/3}}{ab^{-5/4} c^0} \right)^{12}$$

14. The escape velocity of an object is the minimum initial velocity needed to escape a planet's gravitational pull. The escape velocity, v (in meters per second) is related to the mass of the planet and the radius of the planet according to the formula:

$V = \sqrt{\dfrac{2GM}{R}}$, where M is the mass of the planet in kilograms; R is the radius of the planet in meters; and G is a constant equal to 6.672×10^{-11} m^3/s$^2 \cdot$ kg

Find the escape velocity of the earth whose mass is 5.97×10^{27} kg and whose radius is 6.37×10^7 m.

15. Multiply the polynomials: $(2x + 5)(x - 3)$. What is the degree of the product?

16. Perform the indicated operations and simplify:
$\sqrt{3} \cdot (\sqrt{5} + \sqrt{6} + \sqrt{3})$

17. Divide: $(x^2 - x - 12) \div (x + 3)$. Is $(x + 3)$ a factor of $x^2 - x - 12$?

18. Simplify and subtract: $\sqrt[4]{1/16} - \sqrt[3]{8/27}$.

19. Simplify: $\sqrt[3]{\dfrac{54c^4}{cd^3}}$.

20. Add: $4\sqrt{45b^3} + 5b\sqrt{80b}$.

21. Divide: $13i/(3 + 2i)$. Write the answer in the form $a + bi$.

22. Can the matrices **E** and **F** be added? Can they be multiplied? Explain.

$$\mathbf{E} = \begin{bmatrix} -1 & 8 \\ 10 & 3 \\ -3 & 1 \\ 0 & 4 \end{bmatrix} \qquad \mathbf{F} = \begin{bmatrix} 3 & 7 & 2 \\ 12 & 4 & -5 \end{bmatrix}$$

FACTORING AND QUADRATIC FUNCTIONS

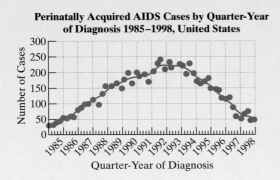

Perinatally Acquired AIDS Cases by Quarter-Year of Diagnosis 1985–1998, United States

Quarter-Year of Diagnosis

Source: Centers for Disease Control.

The Centers for Disease Control provide surveillance reports documenting the number of AIDS cases for various exposure categories. In the 1980s and 1990s, the number of children who acquired the HIV virus *perinatally* (around the time of birth) rose significantly. Then in 1992, public health organizations recommended new preventative treatments and the number of perinatally acquired AIDS cases declined.

For more information visit CDCAIDSinfo at

www.mhhe.com/miller_oneill

Between 1985 and 1998, the number of perinatally acquired AIDS cases, N, can be approximated by the *quadratic function*:

$$N(t) = -3.483t^2 + 51.64t + 35$$

where t is the number of years since 1985 and N is the number of cases.

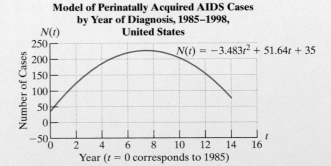

Model of Perinatally Acquired AIDS Cases by Year of Diagnosis, 1985–1998, United States

$N(t) = -3.483t^2 + 51.64t + 35$

Year ($t = 0$ corresponds to 1985)

section

7.1 GREATEST COMMON FACTOR AND FACTORING BY GROUPING

1. Factoring Out the Greatest Common Factor

The first three sections of Chapter 7 are devoted to a mathematical operation called factoring. To factor an integer means to write the integer as a product of two or more integers. To factor a polynomial means to express the polynomial as a product of two or more polynomials.

In the product $5 \cdot 7 = 35$, for example, 5 and 7 are factors of 35.

In the product $(2x + 1)(x - 6) = 2x^2 - 11x - 6$, the quantities $(2x + 1)$ and $(x - 6)$ are factors of $2x^2 - 11x - 6$.

The **greatest common factor (GCF)** of a polynomial is the greatest factor common to all terms of the polynomial. For example, the greatest common factor of $9x^4 + 18x^3 - 6x^2$ is $3x^2$. In other words, $3x^2$ is the greatest factor that divides evenly into each term. To factor out the greatest common factor from a polynomial, follow these steps:

Steps to Remove the Greatest Common Factor

1. Identify the greatest common factor of all terms of the polynomial.
2. Write each term as the product of the GCF and another factor.
3. Use the distributive property to remove the greatest common factor.

Note: To check the factorization, multiply the polynomials.

---

example 1

Factoring Out the Greatest Common Factor

Factor out the greatest common factor.

a. $12x^3 + 30x^2$ b. $12c^2d^3 - 30c^3d^2 - 3cd$

Tip: Any factoring problem can be checked by multiplying the factors:

Check: $6x^2(2x + 5) = 12x^3 + 30x^2$ ✓

Solution:

a. $12x^3 + 30x^2$ The GCF is $6x^2$.

$= 6x^2(2x) + 6x^2(5)$ Write each term as the product of the GCF and another factor.

$= 6x^2(2x + 5)$ Remove $6x^2$ by using the distributive property.

b. $12c^2d^3 - 30c^3d^2 - 3cd$ The GCF is $3cd$.

$= 3cd(4cd^2) - 3cd(10c^2d) - 3cd(1)$ Write each term as the product of the GCF and another factor.

$= 3cd(4cd^2 - 10c^2d - 1)$ Remove $3cd$ by using the distributive property.

⬡ **Avoiding Mistakes**

In Example 1(b), the GCF, $3cd$, is equal to one of the terms of the polynomial. In such a case, you must leave a 1 in place of that term after the GCF is factored out.

$3cd(4cd^2 - 10c^2d - 1)$

Check: $3cd(4cd^2 - 10c^2d - 1) = 12c^2d^3 - 30c^3d^2 - 3cd$ ✓

2. Factoring Out a Negative Factor

Sometimes it is advantageous to factor out the *opposite* of the GCF, particularly when the leading coefficient of the polynomial is negative. This is demonstrated in the next example. Notice that this *changes the signs* of the remaining terms inside the parentheses.

---

example 2

Factoring Out a Negative Factor

Factor out the quantity $-5a^2b$ from the polynomial $-5a^4b - 10a^3b^2 + 15a^2b^3$.

Solution:

$$-5a^4b - 10a^3b^2 + 15a^2b^3$$

The GCF is $5a^2b$. However, in this case we will factor out the opposite of the GCF, $-5a^2b$.

$$= -5a^2b(a^2) + -5a^2b(2ab) + -5a^2b(-3b^2)$$

Write each term as the product of $-5a^2b$ times another factor.

$$= -5a^2b(a^2 + 2ab - 3b^2)$$

Remove $-5a^2b$ by using the distributive property.

Check: $-5a^2b(a^2 + 2ab - 3b^2) = -5a^4b - 10a^3b^2 + 15a^2b^3$ ✓

---

3. Factoring Out a Binomial Factor

The distributive property may also be used to factor out a common factor that consists of more than one term. This is shown in the following example.

---

example 3

Factoring Out a Binomial Factor

Factor out the greatest common factor.

$$x^3(x + 2) - x(x + 2) - 9(x + 2)$$

Solution:

$$x^3(x + 2) - x(x + 2) - 9(x + 2)$$

The GCF is the quantity $(x + 2)$.

$$= (x + 2)(x^3) - (x + 2)(x) - (x + 2)(9)$$

Write each term as the product of $(x + 2)$ and another factor.

$$= (x + 2)(x^3 - x - 9)$$

Remove $(x + 2)$ by using the distributive property.

---

4. Factoring by Grouping

When two binomials are multiplied, the product before simplifying contains four terms. For example:

$$(3a + 2)(2b - 7) = (3a + 2)(2b) + (3a + 2)(-7)$$
$$= (3a + 2)(2b) + (3a + 2)(-7)$$
$$= 6ab + 4b - 21a - 14$$

In the next example, we learn how to reverse this process. That is, given a four-term polynomial, we will factor it as a product of two binomials. The process is called **factoring by grouping**.

Steps to Factor by Grouping

To factor a four-term polynomial by grouping:

1. Identify and factor out the GCF from all four terms.
2. Factor out the GCF from the first pair of terms. Factor out the GCF from the second pair of terms. (Sometimes it is necessary to factor out the *opposite* of the GCF.)
3. If the two terms share a common binomial factor, factor out the binomial factor.

---

example 4   **Factoring by Grouping**

Factor by grouping.

$$6ab - 21a + 4b - 14$$

Solution:

 Avoiding Mistakes

In step 2, the expression $3a(2b - 7) + 2(2b - 7)$ is not yet factored because it is a *sum*, not a product. To factor the expression, you must carry it one step further.

$$3a(2b - 7) + 2(2b - 7)$$

$$= (2b - 7)(3a + 2)$$

The factored form must be represented as a product.

$$6ab - 21a + 4b - 14$$

$$= 6ab - 21a \mid + 4b - 14$$

$$= 3a(2b - 7) + 2(2b - 7)$$

$$= (2b - 7)(3a + 2)$$

Step 1: Identify and factor out the GCF from all four terms. In this case the GCF is 1.

Group the first pair of terms and the second pair of terms.

Step 2: Factor out the GCF from each pair of terms.

Note: The two terms now share a common binomial factor of $(2b - 7)$.

Step 3: Factor out the common binomial factor.

Check: $(2b - 7)(3a + 2) = 2b(3a) + 2b(2) - 7(3a) - 7(2)$
$$= 6ab + 4b - 21a - 14 \checkmark$$

example 5

Factoring by Grouping

Factor by grouping.

$$x^3 + 3x^2 - 3x - 9$$

Solution:

$x^3 + 3x^2 - 3x - 9$	**Step 1:** Identify and factor out the GCF from all four terms. In this case the GCF is 1.
$= x^3 + 3x^2 \; \vdots \; - 3x - 9$	Group the first pair of terms and the second pair of terms.
$= x^2(x + 3) - 3(x + 3)$	**Step 2:** Factor out x^2 from the first pair of terms. Factor out -3 from the second pair of terms (this causes the signs to change in the second parentheses). The terms now contain a common binomial factor.
$= (x + 3)(x^2 - 3)$	**Step 3:** Factor out the common binomial, $(x + 3)$.

Check: $(x + 3)(x^2 - 3) = x(x^2) + x(-3) + 3(x^2) + 3(-3)$
$$= x^3 - 3x + 3x^2 - 9 \checkmark$$

Tip: One frequently asked question is whether the order can be switched between factors. The answer is yes. Because multiplication is commutative, the order in which two or more factors are written does not matter. Thus, the following factorizations are equivalent:

$$(x + 3)(x^2 - 3) = (x^2 - 3)(x + 3)$$

example 6

Factoring by Grouping

Factor by grouping.

$$24p^2q^2 - 18p^2q + 60pq^2 - 45pq$$

Solution:

$$24p^2q^2 - 18p^2q + 60pq^2 - 45pq$$

$$= 3pq(8pq - 6p + 20q - 15) \qquad \textbf{Step 1:} \quad \text{Remove the GCF from all four terms, } 3pq.$$

$$= 3pq(8pq - 6p \;\vert\; + 20q - 15) \qquad\qquad \text{Group the first pair of terms and the second pair of terms.}$$

$$= 3pq[2p(4q - 3) + 5(4q - 3)] \qquad \textbf{Step 2:} \quad \text{Factor out the GCF from each pair of terms. The terms share the binomial factor, } (4q - 3).$$

$$= 3pq[(4q - 3)(2p + 5)] \qquad \textbf{Step 3:} \quad \text{Factor out the common binomial, } (4q - 3).$$

$\underline{\text{Check:}}$ $\quad 3pq[(4q - 3)(2p + 5)] = 3pq[4q(2p) + 4q(5) - 3(2p) - 3(5)]$

$$= 3pq[8pq + 20q - 6p - 15]$$

$$= 24p^2q^2 + 60pq^2 - 18p^2q - 45pq \checkmark$$

5.   Factoring by Grouping—Rearranging Terms

Notice that in step 3 of factoring by grouping, a common binomial is factored from the two terms. These binomials must be *exactly* the same in each term. If the two binomial factors differ, try rearranging the original four terms.

example 7   **Factoring by Grouping Where Rearranging Terms Is Necessary**

Factor the polynomial.

$$4x + 6pa - 8a - 3px$$

Solution:

$$4x + 6pa - 8a - 3px \qquad\qquad \textbf{Step 1:} \quad \text{Identify and factor out the GCF from all four terms. In this case the GCF is 1.}$$

$$= 4x + 6pa \;\vert\; - 8a - 3px$$

$$= 2(2x + 3pa) - 1(8a + 3px) \qquad \textbf{Step 2:} \quad \text{The binomial factors in each term are different.}$$

$$= 4x - 8a \;\vert\; - 3px + 6pa \qquad\qquad \textit{Try rearranging the original four terms} \text{ in such a way that the first pair of coefficients is in the same ratio as the second pair of coefficients. Notice that the ratio 4 to 8 is the same as the ratio 3 to 6.}$$

$= 4(x - 2a) - 3p(x - 2a)$ **Step 3:** Factor out 4 from the first pair of terms.

Factor out $-3p$ from the second pair of terms.

$= (x - 2a)(4 - 3p)$ **Step 4:** Factor out the common binomial factor.

Check: $(x - 2a)(4 - 3p) = x(4) + x(-3p) - 2a(4) - 2a(-3p)$

$= 4x - 3xp - 8a + 6ap$ ✓

section 7.1   PRACTICE EXERCISES

1. What is meant by a common factor in a polynomial? What is meant by the greatest common factor?

2. Explain how to find the greatest common factor of a polynomial.

For Exercises 3–26, factor out the greatest common factor.

3. $3x + 12$

4. $15x - 10$

5. $6z^2 + 4z$

6. $49y^3 - 35y^2$

7. $4p^6 - 4p$

8. $5q^2 - 5q$

9. $12x^4 - 36x^2$

10. $-51w^4 - 34w^3$

11. $-9st^2 + 27t$

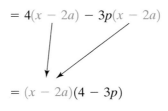 12. $8a^2b^3 + 12a^2b$

13. $9a^2 + 27a + 18$

14. $3x^2 - 15x + 9$

15. $10x^2y + 15xy^2 - 35xy$

16. $12c^3d - 15c^2d + 3cd$

17. $13b^2 - 11a^2b - 12ab$

18. $6a^3 - 2a^2b + 5a^2$

19. $2a(3z - 2b) - 5(3z - 2b)$

20. $5x(3x + 4) + 2(3x + 4)$

21. $2x^2(2x - 3) + (2x - 3)$

22. $z(w - 9) + (w - 9)$

23. $y(2x + 1)^2 - 3(2x + 1)^2$

24. $a(b - 7)^2 + 5(b - 7)^2$

25. $3y(x - 2)^2 + 6(x - 2)^2$

26. $10z(z + 3)^2 - 2(z + 3)^2$

27. Solve the equation: $U = Av + Acw$ for A by first factoring out A.

28. Solve the equation: $S = rt + wt$ for t by first factoring out t.

29. Solve the equation: $ay + bx = cy$ for y.

30. Solve the equation: $cd + 2x = ac$ for c.

31. Construct a polynomial that has a greatest common factor of $3x^2$. (Answers may vary.)

32. Construct two different trinomials that have a greatest common factor of $5x^2y^3$. (Answers may vary.)

33. Construct a binomial that has a greatest common factor of $(c + d)$. (Answers may vary.)

34. If a polynomial has four terms, what technique would you use to factor it?

35. Factor the polynomials by grouping:

a. $2ax - ay + 6bx - 3by$

b. $10w^2 - 5w - 6bw + 3b$

c. Explain why you factored out $3b$ from the second pair of terms in part (a) but factored out the quantity $-3b$ from the second pair of terms in part (b).

36. Factor the polynomials by grouping:

a. $3xy + 2bx + 6by + 4b^2$

b. $15ac + 10ab - 6bc - 4b^2$

c. Explain why you factored out $2b$ from the second pair of terms in part (a) but factored out the quantity $-2b$ from the second pair of terms in part (b).

For Exercises 37–52, factor each polynomial by grouping (if possible).

37. $y^3 + 4y^2 + 3y + 12$ 38. $ab + b + 2a + 2$

39. $6p - 42 + pq - 7q$ 40. $2t - 8 + st - 4s$

41. $2mx + 2nx + 3my + 3ny$

42. $4x^2 + 6xy - 2xy - 3y^2$

43. $10ax - 15ay - 8bx + 12by$

44. $35a^2 - 15a + 14a - 6$

45. $6p^2q + 18pq - 30p^2 - 90p$

46. $5s^2t + 20st - 15s^2 - 60s$

47. $100x^3 - 300x^2 + 200x - 600$

48. $2x^5 - 10x^4 + 6x^3 - 30x^2$

49. $6ax - by + 2bx - 3ay$

50. $5pq - 12 - 4q + 15p$

51. $7y^3 - 21y^2 + 5y - 10$

52. $5ax + 10bx - 2ac + 4bc$

53. Explain why the grouping method failed for Exercise 51.

54. Explain why the grouping method failed for Exercise 52.

55. The area of a rectangle of width, w, is given by $A = 2w^2 + w$. Factor the right-hand side of the equation to find an expression for the length of the rectangle.

56. The area of a triangle of base, b, is given by $A = \frac{1}{2}(b^2 - 2b)$. Factor the right-hand side of the equation to find an expression for the height of the triangle.

57. The amount in a savings account bearing simple interest at an interest rate, r, for t years is given by

$A = P + Prt$, where P is the principal amount invested.

a. Solve the equation for P.

b. Compute the amount of principal originally invested if the account is worth \$12,705 after 3 years at a 7% interest rate.

58. Consider a savings account that earns compound interest annually. The amount in the account after two compound periods is given by

$A = P(1 + r) + P(1 + r)r$, where $A =$ the amount in the account, $r =$ the annual interest rate, $P =$ principal amount invested.

a. Factor the right-hand side of the equation.

b. Solve for P.

c. Compute the principal amount initially invested, P, if after two compound periods the total amount in the account is \$6415.20 and the interest rate is 8%.

EXPANDING YOUR SKILLS

For Exercises 59–66, factor out the greatest common factor and simplify.

59. $(a + 3)^4 + 6(a + 3)^5$

60. $(4 - b)^4 - 2(4 - b)^3$

61. $24(3x + 5)^3 - 30(3x + 5)^2$

62. $10(2y + 3)^2 + 15(2y + 3)^3$

63. $(t + 4)^2 - (t + 4)$

64. $(p + 6)^2 - (p + 6)$

65. $15w^2(2w - 1)^3 + 5w^3(2w - 1)^2$

66. $8z^4(3z - 2)^2 + 12z^3(3z - 2)^3$

GRAPHING CALCULATOR EXERCISES

For Exercises 67–70, graph Y_1 and Y_2 on a standard viewing window to give evidence that the two expressions are equivalent.

67. $Y_1 = 6x^2 + 4x$
     $Y_2 = 2x(3x + 2)$

68. $Y_1 = 7x^3 - 35x^2$
     $Y_2 = 7x^2(x - 5)$

69. $Y_1 = 5x(3x + 4) + 2(3x + 4)$
      $Y_2 = (3x + 4)(5x + 2)$

70. $Y_1 = 2x(x - 6) + 7(x - 6)$
      $Y_2 = (x - 6)(2x + 7)$

Concepts

1. **Factoring Trinomials: Grouping Method**

2. **Factoring Trinomials: Trial-and-Error Method**

3. **Factoring Trinomials with a Leading Coefficient of 1**

4. **Factoring Perfect Square Trinomials**

5. **Summary of Factoring Trinomials**

section

7.2   FACTORING TRINOMIALS

1.   Factoring Trinomials: Grouping Method

In Section 7.1, we learned how to factor out the greatest common factor from a polynomial and how to factor a four-term polynomial by grouping. In this section we present two methods to factor trinomials. The first method is called the grouping method (sometimes referred to as the "ac" method). The second method is called the trial-and-error method.

The product of two binomials results in a four-term expression that can sometimes be simplified to a trinomial. To factor the trinomial, we want to reverse the process.

Multiply the binomials.

Multiply: $(2x + 3)(x + 2) = \longrightarrow 2x^2 + 4x + 3x + 6$

Add the middle terms.

$= \longrightarrow 2x^2 + 7x + 6$

Factor: $2x^2 + 7x + 6 = \longrightarrow 2x^2 + 4x + 3x + 6$

Rewrite the middle term as a sum or difference of terms.

$= \longrightarrow (2x + 3)(x + 2)$

Factor by grouping.

To factor a trinomial, $ax^2 + bx + c$, by the grouping method, we rewrite the middle term, bx, as a sum or difference of terms. The goal is to produce a four-term polynomial that can be factored by grouping. The process is outlined as follows.

The Grouping Method to Factor $ax^2 + bx + c$ $(a \neq 0)$

1. Multiply the coefficients of the first and last terms (ac).
2. Find two integers whose product is ac and whose sum is b. (If no pair of integers can be found, then the trinomial cannot be factored further and is called a prime polynomial.)
3. Rewrite the middle term (bx) as the sum of two terms whose coefficients are the integers found in step 2.
4. Factor by grouping.

The grouping method for factoring trinomials is illustrated in the next example. Before we begin, however, keep these two important guidelines in mind.

- For any factoring problem you encounter, always factor out the GCF from all terms first.
- To factor a trinomial, write the trinomial in the form $ax^2 + bx + c$.

---

example 1   **Factoring a Trinomial by the Grouping Method**

Factor the trinomial by the grouping method.

$$6x^2 + 19x + 10$$

Solution:

$6x^2 + 19x + 10$ Factor out the GCF from all terms. In this case, the GCF is 1.

$6x^2 + 19x + 10$

$a = 6, b = 19, c = 10$ **Step 1:**   The trinomial is written in the form $ax^2 + bx + c$. Find the product of a and c: $ac = (6)(10) = 60$.

Factors of 60	Factors of 60
$1 \cdot 60$	$(-1)(-60)$
$2 \cdot 30$	$(-2)(-30)$
$3 \cdot 20$	$(-3)(-20)$
$4 \cdot 15$	$(-4)(-15)$
$5 \cdot 12$	$(-5)(-12)$
$6 \cdot 10$	$(-6)(-10)$

Step 2:   List all the factors of ac and search for the pair whose sum equals the value of b.
That is, list the factors of 60 and find the pair whose *sum* equals 19.
The numbers 4 and 15 satisfy both conditions: $4 \cdot 15 = 60$ and $4 + 15 = 19$.

$6x^2 + 19x + 10$

$= 6x^2 + 4x + 15x + 10$

Step 3:   Write the middle term of the trinomial as the sum of two terms whose coefficients are the selected pair of numbers 4 and 15.

$= 6x^2 + 4x \ \vdots \ + 15x + 10$ **Step 4:**   Factor by grouping.

$= 2x(3x + 2) + 5(3x + 2)$

$= (3x + 2)(2x + 5)$

Check: $(3x + 2)(2x + 5) = 6x^2 + 15x + 4x + 10$

$= 6x^2 + 19x + 10 \ \checkmark$

Tip: One frequently asked question is whether the order matters when we rewrite the middle term of the trinomial as two terms (step 3). The answer is *no*. From the previous example, the two middle terms in step 3 could have been reversed to obtain the same result.

$$6x^2 + 19x + 10$$
$$= 6x^2 + 15x + 4x + 10$$
$$= 3x(2x + 5) + 2(2x + 5)$$
$$= (2x + 5)(3x + 2)$$

This example also points out that the order in which two factors are written does not matter. The expression $(3x + 2)(2x + 5)$ is equivalent to $(2x + 5)(3x + 2)$ because multiplication is a commutative operation.

---

example 2

Factoring a Trinomial by the Grouping Method

Factor the function defined by

$$f(x) = 12x^2 - 5x - 2$$

Solution:

$f(x) = 12x^2 - 5x - 2$ The GCF is 1.

$a = 12, b = -5, c = -2$ **Step 1:** The function is written in the form $f(x) = ax^2 + bx + c$. Find the product $ac = 12(-2) = -24$.

Factors of -24	Factors of -24
$(1)(-24)$	$(-1)(24)$
$(2)(-12)$	$(-2)(12)$
$(3)(-8)$	$(-3)(8)$
$(4)(-6)$	$(-4)(6)$

Step 2: List all the factors of -24 and find the pair whose sum equals -5. The numbers 3 and -8 produce a product of -24 and a sum of -5.

$f(x) = 12x^2 - 5x - 2$

$= 12x^2 + 3x - 8x - 2$

Step 3: Write the middle term of the trinomial as two terms whose coefficients are the selected numbers 3 and -8.

$= 12x^2 + 3x \quad - 8x - 2$ **Step 4:** Factor by grouping.

$= 3x(4x + 1) - 2(4x + 1)$

$= (4x + 1)(3x - 2)$ The check is left for the reader.

example 3

Factoring a Trinomial by the Grouping Method

Factor the trinomial by the grouping method.

$$-5p^3 + 50p^2 - 125p$$

Solution:

$$-5p^3 + 50p^2 - 125p$$

$$= -5p(p^2 - 10p + 25) \qquad \text{Factor out } -5p.$$

Step 1: Find the product $a \cdot c = (1)(25) = 25$.

Factors of 25	Factors of 25
$1 \cdot 25$	$(-1)(-25)$
$5 \cdot 5$	$(-5)(-5)$

Step 2: The numbers -5 and -5 form a product of 25 and a sum of -10.

$$-5p(p^2 - 10p + 25)$$

Step 3: Write the middle term of the trinomial as two terms whose coefficients are -5 and -5.

$$= -5p[p^2 - 5p \mid -5p + 25] \qquad \textbf{Step 4:} \quad \text{Factor by grouping.}$$

$$= -5p[p(p - 5) - 5(p - 5)]$$
$$= -5p[(p - 5)(p - 5)]$$
$$= -5p(p - 5)^2$$

Check: $-5p(p - 5)^2 = -5p(p^2 - 10p + 25)$
$$= -5p^3 + 50p^2 - 125p \checkmark$$

Tip: Notice when the GCF is removed from the original trinomial, the new trinomial has smaller coefficients. This makes the factoring process simpler because the product ac is smaller. It is much easier to list the factors of 25 than the factors of 625.

Original trinomial	With the GCF factored out
$-5p^3 + 50p^2 - 125p$	$-5p(p^2 - 10p + 25)$
$ac = (-5)(-125) = 625$	$ac = (1)(25) = 25$

2. Factoring Trinomials: Trial-and-Error Method

Another method that is widely used to factor trinomials of the form $ax^2 + bx + c$ is the trial-and-error method. To understand how the trial-and-error method works, first consider the multiplication of two binomials:

Product of $2 \cdot 1$ Product of $3 \cdot 2$

$$(2x + 3)(1x + 2) = 2x^2 \underbrace{+ 4x + 3x}_{\substack{\text{sum of products} \\ \text{of inner terms} \\ \text{and outer terms}}} + 6 = 2x^2 + 7x + 6$$

To factor the trinomial, $2x^2 + 7x + 6$ this operation is reversed. Hence:

$$2x^2 + 7x + 6 = (\overset{\text{factors of 2}}{\square x} \quad \square)(\square x \quad \underset{\text{factors of 6}}{\square})$$

We need to fill in the blanks so that the product of the first terms in the binomials is $2x^2$ and the product of the last terms in the binomials is 6. Furthermore, the factors of $2x^2$ and 6 must be chosen so that the sum of the products of the inner terms and outer terms equals $7x$.

To produce the product $2x^2$ we might try the factors $2x$ and x within the binomials.

$$(2x \quad \square)(x \quad \square)$$

To produce a product of 6, the remaining terms in the binomials must either both be positive or both be negative. To produce a positive middle term, we will try positive factors of 6 in the remaining blanks until the correct product is found. The possibilities are $1 \cdot 6, 2 \cdot 3, 3 \cdot 2$, and $6 \cdot 1$.

$(2x + 1)(x + 6) = 2x^2 + 12x + 1x + 6 = 2x^2 + 13x + 6$ Wrong middle term

$(2x + 2)(x + 3) = 2x^2 + 6x + 2x + 6 = 2x^2 + 8x + 6$ Wrong middle term

$\mathbf{(2x + 3)(x + 2) = 2x^2 + 4x + 3x + 6 = 2x^2 + 7x + 6}$ Correct!

$(2x + 6)(x + 1) = 2x^2 + 2x + 6x + 6 = 2x^2 + 8x + 6$ Wrong middle term

The correct factorization of $2x^2 + 7x + 6$ is $(2x + 3)(x + 2)$. ✓

As this example shows, we factor a trinomial of the form $ax^2 + bx + c$ by shuffling the factors of a and c within the binomials until the correct product is obtained. However, sometimes it is not necessary to test all the possible combinations of factors. In the previous example, the GCF of the original trinomial is 1. Therefore, any binomial factor that shares a common factor *greater than 1* does not need to be considered. In this case the possibilities $(2x + 2)(x + 3)$ and $(2x + 6)(x + 1)$ cannot work.

$\underbrace{(2x + 2)}_{\substack{\text{common} \\ \text{factor of 2}}}(x + 3)$ $\underbrace{(2x + 6)}_{\substack{\text{common} \\ \text{factor of 2}}}(x + 1)$

The steps to factor a trinomial by the trial-and-error method are outlined as follows.

The Trial-and-Error Method to Factor $ax^2 + bx + c$

1. Factor out the greatest common factor (GCF).
2. List all pairs of positive factors of a and pairs of positive factors of c. Consider the reverse order for either list of factors.
3. Construct two binomials of the form:

Test each combination of factors and signs until the correct product is found. If no combination of factors produces the correct product, the trinomial cannot be factored further and is a prime polynomial.

example 4

Factoring a Trinomial by the Trial-and-Error Method

Factor the trinomial by the trial-and-error method.

$$10x^2 - 9x - 1$$

Solution:

$10x^2 - 9x - 1$ **Step 1:** Factor out the GCF from all terms. The GCF is 1. The trinomial is written in the form $ax^2 + bx + c$.

To factor $10x^2 - 9x - 1$, two binomials must be constructed in the form

      Step 2: To produce the product $10x^2$, we might try $5x$ and $2x$ or $10x$ and $1x$. To produce a product of -1, we will try the factors $1(-1)$ and $-1(1)$.

     Step 3: Construct all possible binomial factors using different combinations of the factors of $10x^2$ and -1.

$(5x + 1)(2x - 1) = 10x^2 - 5x + 2x - 1 = 10x^2 - 3x - 1$ Wrong middle term

$(5x - 1)(2x + 1) = 10x^2 + 5x - 2x - 1 = 10x^2 + 3x - 1$ Wrong middle term

The numbers 1 and -1 did not produce the correct trinomial when coupled with $5x$ and $2x$, so try using $10x$ and $1x$.

$\mathbf{(10x + 1)(1x - 1)} = 10x^2 - 10x + 1x - 1 = \mathbf{10x^2 - 9x - 1}$ Correct!

$(10x - 1)(1x + 1) = 10x^2 + 10x - 1x - 1 = 10x^2 + 9x - 1$ Wrong middle term

Hence $10x^2 - 9x - 1 = (10x + 1)(x - 1)$

In Example 4, the factors of -1 must have opposite signs to produce a negative product. Therefore, one binomial factor is a sum and one is a difference. Determining the correct signs is an important aspect of factoring trinomials. We suggest the following guidelines:

Tip: Given the trinomial $ax^2 + bx + c, (a > 0)$ the signs can be determined as follows:

1. If c is *positive*, then the signs in the binomials must be the same (either both positive or both negative). The correct choice is determined by the middle term. If the middle term is positive, then both signs must be positive. If the middle term is negative, then both signs must be negative.

c is positive

Example: $20x^2 + 43x + 21$
$(4x + 3)(5x + 7)$
same signs

c is positive

Example: $20x^2 - 43x + 21$
$(4x - 3)(5x - 7)$
same signs

2. If c is *negative*, then the signs in the binomials must be different. The middle term in the trinomial determines which factor gets the positive sign and which factor gets the negative sign.

c is negative

Example: $x^2 + 3x - 28$
$(x + 7)(x - 4)$
different signs

c is negative

Example: $x^2 - 3x - 28$
$(x - 7)(x + 4)$
different signs

---

example 5

Factoring a Trinomial

Factor the trinomial by the trial-and-error method.

$$8y^2 + 13y - 6$$

Solution:

$8y^2 + 13y - 6$

$(\Box y \ \Box)(\Box y \ \Box)$

Step 1: The GCF is 1.

Factors of 8	**Factors of 6**
$1 \cdot 8$	$1 \cdot 6$
$2 \cdot 4$	$2 \cdot 3$
	$3 \cdot 2$
	$6 \cdot 1$

(reverse order) — for $3 \cdot 2$ and $6 \cdot 1$

Step 2: List the positive factors of 8 and positive factors of 6. Consider the reverse order in one list of factors.

Step 3: Construct all possible binomial factors using different combinations of the factors of 8 and 6.

$$
\left.\begin{array}{l}
(2y \quad 1)(4y \quad 6) \\
(2y \quad 2)(4y \quad 3) \\
(2y \quad 3)(4y \quad 2) \\
(2y \quad 6)(4y \quad 1) \\
(1y \quad 1)(8y \quad 6) \\
(1y \quad 3)(8y \quad 2)
\end{array}\right\}
$$

Without regard to signs, these factorizations cannot work because the terms in the binomial share a common factor greater than 1.

Test the remaining factorizations. Keep in mind that to produce a product of -6, the signs within the parentheses must be opposite (one positive and one negative). Also, the sum of the products of the inner terms and outer terms must be combined to form $13y$.

$(1y \quad 6)(8y \quad 1)$ *Incorrect.*   Wrong middle term.

Regardless of signs, the product of inner terms, $48y$, and the product of outer terms, $1y$, cannot be combined to form the middle term $13y$.

$(1y \quad 2)(8y \quad 3)$ *Correct.*   The terms $16y$ and $3y$ can be combined to form the middle term $13x$, provided the signs are applied correctly. We require $+16y$ and $-3y$.

Hence, the correct factorization is $(y + 2)(8y - 3)$.

---

example 6

Factoring a Trinomial by the Trial-and-Error Method

Factor the trinomial by the trial-and-error method.

$$-80x^3y + 208x^2y^2 - 20xy^3$$

Solution:

$$-80x^3y + 208x^2y^2 - 20xy^3$$

Step 1: Factor out $-4xy$.

$$= -4xy(20x^2 - 52xy + 5y^2)$$

$$= -4xy(\square x \;\; \square y)(\square x \;\; \square y)$$

Factors of 20	**Factors of 5**
$1 \cdot 20$	$1 \cdot 5$
$2 \cdot 10$	$5 \cdot 1$
$4 \cdot 5$	

Step 2: List the positive factors of 20 and positive factors of 5. Consider the reverse order in one list of factors.

Step 3: Construct all possible binomial factors using different combinations of the factors of 20 and factors of 5. The signs in the parentheses must both be negative.

$-4xy(1x - 1y)(20x - 5y)$

$-4xy(2x - 1y)(10x - 5y)$ *Incorrect.*   Each of these binomials contains a common factor.

$-4xy(4x - 1y)(5x - 5y)$

$-4xy(1x - 5y)(20x - 1y)$ *Incorrect.*   Wrong middle term.

$$-4xy(x - 5y)(20x - 1y)$$
$$= -4xy(20x^2 - 101xy + 5y^2)$$

$-4xy(2x - 5y)(10x - 1y)$ ***Correct.***
$$-4xy(2x - 5y)(10x - 1y)$$
$$= \mathbf{-4xy(20x^2 - 52xy + 5y^2)}$$
$$= -80x^3y + 208x^2y^2 - 20xy^3$$

$-4xy(4x - 5y)(5x - 1y)$ *Incorrect.*   Wrong middle term.

$$-4xy(4x - 5y)(5x - 1y)$$
$$= -4xy(20x^2 - 29x + 5y^2)$$

The correct factorization is $-4xy(2x - 5y)(10x - y)$.

3. Factoring Trinomials with a Leading Coefficient of 1

If a trinomial has a leading coefficient of 1, the factoring process simplifies significantly. Consider the trinomial $x^2 + bx + c$. To produce a leading term of x^2, we can construct binomials of the form $(x + \square)(x + \square)$. The remaining terms may be satisfied by two numbers p and q whose product is c and whose sum is b:

$$\overbrace{(x + p)(x + q)}^{\text{factors of } c} = x^2 + qx + px + pq = x^2 + \underbrace{(p + q)}_{\text{sum} = b}x + \underbrace{pq}_{\text{product} = c}$$

This process is demonstrated in the next example.

---

example 7

Factoring a Trinomial with a Leading Coefficient of 1

Factor the trinomial.

$$x^2 - 10x + 16$$

Solution:

$x^2 - 10x + 16$ Factor out the GCF from all terms. In this case, the GCF is 1.

$= (x \ \square)(x \ \square)$ The trinomial is written in the form $x^2 + bx + c$. To form the product x^2, use the factors x and x.

Next, look for two numbers whose product is 16 and whose sum is -10. Because the middle term is negative, we will consider only the negative factors of 16.

Factors of 16	**Sum**
$-1(-16)$	$-1 + (-16) = -17$
$\mathbf{-2(-8)}$	$\mathbf{-2 + (-8) = -10}$
$-4(-4)$	$-4 + (-4) = -8$

The numbers are -2 and -8.

Hence $x^2 - 10x + 16 = (x - 2)(x - 8)$

$\underline{\text{Check:}} \ (x - 2)(x - 8) = x^2 - 8x - 2x + 16$
$= x^2 - 10x + 16 \ \checkmark$

4. Factoring Perfect Square Trinomials

Recall from Section 5.4 that the square of a binomial always results in a **perfect square trinomial**.

$$(a + b)^2 = (a + b)(a + b) = a^2 + ab + ab + b^2 = a^2 + 2ab + b^2$$
$$(a - b)^2 = (a - b)(a - b) = a^2 - ab - ab + b^2 = a^2 - 2ab + b^2$$

For example, $(2x + 7)^2 = (2x)^2 + 2(2x)(7) + (7)^2 = 4x^2 + 28x + 49$

$a = 2x \quad b = 7 \qquad\qquad a^2 + 2ab + b^2$

To factor the trinomial $4x^2 + 28x + 49$, the grouping method or the trial-and-error method can be used. However, recognizing that the trinomial is a perfect square trinomial, we can use one of the following patterns to reach a quick solution.

Factored Form of a Perfect Square Trinomial

$$a^2 + 2ab + b^2 = (a + b)^2$$
$$a^2 - 2ab + b^2 = (a - b)^2$$

Tip: To determine if a trinomial is a perfect square trinomial, follow these steps:

1. Check if the first and third terms are both perfect squares with positive coefficients.
2. If this is the case, identify a and b, and determine if the middle term equals $2ab$.

example 8   Factoring Perfect Square Trinomials

Factor the trinomials completely.

a. $x^2 + 12x + 36$ b. $4x^2 - 36x + 81$

Solution:

a. $x^2 + 12x + 36$ The GCF is 1.

* The first and third terms are positive.
* The first term is a perfect square: $x^2 = (x)^2$

perfect squares

$= x^2 + 12x + 36$

* The third term is a perfect square: $36 = (6)^2$
* The middle term is twice the product of x and 6:

$$12x = 2(x)(6)$$

$= (x)^2 + 2(x)(6) + (6)^2$ Hence the trinomial is in the form $a^2 + 2ab + b^2$, where $a = x$ and $b = 6$.

$= (x + 6)^2$ Factor as $(a + b)^2$.

b. $4x^2 - 36x + 81$ The GCF is 1.

* The first and third terms are positive.
* The first term is a perfect square: $4x^2 = (2x)^2$.

perfect squares

$= 4x^2 - 36x + 81$

* The third term is a perfect square: $81 = (-9)^2$.
* The middle term is twice the product of $2x$ and -9:

$$-36x = 2(2x)(-9)$$

$= (2x)^2 - 2(2x)(9) + (9)^2$ The trinomial is in the form $a^2 - 2ab + b^2$, where $a = 2x$ and $b = 9$.

$= (2x - 9)^2$ Factor as $(a - b)^2$.

5.   Summary of Factoring Trinomials

Summary: Factoring Trinomials of the Form $ax^2 + bx + c$ $(a \neq 0)$

When factoring trinomials, the following guidelines should be considered:

1. Factor out the greatest common factor.
2. Check to see if the trinomial is a perfect square trinomial. If so, factor it as either $(a + b)^2$ or $(a - b)^2$. (With a perfect square trinomial, you do not need to use the grouping method or trial-and-error method.)
3. If the trinomial is not a perfect square, use either the grouping method or the trial-and-error method to factor.
4. Check the factorization by multiplication.

example 9   Factoring Trinomials

Factor the trinomials completely.

a. $80s^3t + 80s^2t^2 + 20st^3$ b. $5w^2 + 50w + 45$ c. $2p^2 + 9p + 14$

Solution:

a. $80s^3t + 80s^2t^2 + 20st^3$

   $= 20st(4s^2 + 4st + t^2)$ The GCF is $20st$.

perfect squares

   $= 20st(4s^2 + 4st + t^2)$

   $= 20st(2s + t)^2$

- The first and third terms are positive.
- The first and third terms are perfect squares.
- Because $4st = 2(2s)(t)$, the trinomial is in the form $a^2 + 2ab + b^2$, where $a = 2s$ and $b = t$.

Factor as $(a + b)^2$.

b. $5w^2 + 50w + 45$

   $= 5(w^2 + 10w + 9)$ The GCF is 5.

perfect squares

   $= 5(w^2 + 10w + 9)$

The first and third terms are perfect squares: $w^2 = (w)^2$ and $9 = (3)^2$.

However, the middle term, $10w \neq 2(w)(3)$. Therefore, this is *not* a perfect square trinomial.

   $= 5(w + 9)(w + 1)$ To factor, use either the grouping method or the trial-and-error method.

c. $2p^2 + 9p + 14$

The GCF is 1. The trinomial is not a perfect square trinomial because neither 2 nor 14 is a perfect square. Therefore, try factoring by either the grouping method or the trial-and-error method. We will use the trial-and-error method here.

Factors of 2	**Factors of 14**
$2 \cdot 1$	$1 \cdot 14$
	$14 \cdot 1$
	$2 \cdot 7$
	$7 \cdot 2$

After constructing all factors of 2 and 14, we see that no combination of factors will produce the correct result.

$(2p + 14)(p + 1)$ *Incorrect:* $(2p + 14)$ contains a common factor of 2.

$(2p + 2)(p + 7)$ *Incorrect:* $(2p + 2)$ contains a common factor of 2.

$$(2p + 1)(p + 14) = 2p^2 + 28p + p + 14 \longrightarrow 2p^2 + 29p + 14 \qquad \textit{Incorrect.}$$

$29p$ (wrong middle term)

$$(2p + 7)(p + 2) = 2p^2 + 4p + 7p + 14 \longrightarrow 2p^2 + 11p + 14 \qquad \textit{Incorrect.}$$

$11p$ (wrong middle term)

Because none of the combinations of factors resulted in the correct product, we say that the trinomial $2p^2 + 9p + 14$ is prime. This polynomial cannot be factored by the techniques presented here.

---

section 7.2 PRACTICE EXERCISES

For Exercises 1–6, factor the polynomial completely.

1. $36c^2d^7e^{11} + 12c^3d^5e^{15} - 6c^2d^4e^7$

2. $5x^3y^3 + 15x^4y^2 - 35x^2y^4$

3. $2x(3a - b) - (3a - b)$

4. $6(v - 8) - 3u(v - 8)$

5. $wz^2 + 2wz - 33az - 66a$

6. $3a^2x + 9ab - abx - 3b^2$

In Exercises 7–28, factor the trinomial completely, if possible, using any method. Remember to look for a common factor first.

7. $b^2 - 12b + 32$

8. $a^2 - 12a + 27$

9. $y^2 + 10y - 24$

10. $w^2 + 3w - 54$

11. $2x^2 - 7x - 15$

12. $2y^2 - 13y + 15$

13. $6a^2 + a - 5$

14. $10b^2 - 29b - 3$

15. $s^2 + st - 6t^2$

16. $p^2 - pq - 20q^2$

17. $3x^2 - 60x + 108$

18. $4c^2 + 12c - 72$

19. $2c^2 - 2c - 24$

20. $3x^2 + 12x - 15$

21. $2x^2 + 8xy - 10y^2$

22. $20z^2 + 26zw - 28w^2$

23. $33t^2 - 18t + 2$

24. $5p^2 - 10p + 7$

25. $3x^2 + 14xy + 15y^2$

26. $2a^2 + 15ab - 27b^2$

27. $5u^3v - 30u^2v^2 + 45uv^3$

28. $3a^3 + 30a^2b + 75ab^2$

29. a. Multiply the binomials $(x + 5)(x + 5)$.

    b. How do you factor $x^2 + 10x + 25$?

30. a. Multiply the binomials $(2w - 5)(2w - 5)$.

    b. How do you factor $4w^2 - 20w + 25$?

31. a. Multiply the binomials $(3x - 2y)^2$.

    b. How do you factor $9x^2 - 12xy + 4y^2$?

32. a. Multiply the binomials $(x + 7y)^2$.

    b. How do you factor $x^2 + 14xy + 49y^2$?

For Exercises 33–38, fill in the blank to make the trinomial a perfect square trinomial.

33. $9x^2 + (\underline{\hspace{1cm}}) + 25$

34. $16x^4 - (\underline{\hspace{1cm}}) + 1$

35. $b^2 - 12b + (\underline{\hspace{1cm}})$

36. $4w^2 + 28w + (\underline{\hspace{1cm}})$

37. $(\underline{\hspace{1cm}})z^2 + 16z + 1$

38. $(\underline{\hspace{1cm}})x^2 - 42x + 49$

For Exercises 39–46, remove the greatest common factor. Then determine if the polynomial is a perfect square trinomial. If it is, factor it.

39. $y^2 - 8y + 16$

40. $x^2 + 10x + 25$

41. $w^2 - 5w + 9$

42. $2a^2 + 14a + 98$

43. $9a^2 - 30ab + 25b^2$

44. $16x^4 - 48x^2y + 9y^2$

45. $16t^2 - 80tv + 20v^2$

46. $12x^2 - 12xy + 3y^2$

For Exercises 47–58, factor completely using an appropriate method.

47. $3x^3 - 9x^2 + 5x - 15$

48. $ay + ax - 5cy - 5cx$

49. $a^2 + 12a + 36$

50. $9 - 6b + b^2$

51. $81w^2 + 90w + 25$

52. $49a^2 - 28ab + 4b^2$

53. $3x(a + b) - 6(a + b)$

54. $4p(t - 8) + 2(t - 8)$

55. $x^4 + 15x^2 + 36$

56. $t^6 - 16t^3 + 63$

57. $12a^2bc^2 + 4ab^2c^2 - 6abc^3$

58. $18x^2z - 6xyz + 30xz^2$

For Exercises 59–66, factor the function completely.

59. $f(x) = 2x^2 + 13x - 7$

60. $g(x) = 3x^2 + 14x + 8$

61. $m(t) = t^2 - 22t + 121$

62. $n(t) = t^2 + 20t + 100$

63. $P(x) = x^3 + 4x^2 + 3x$

64. $Q(x) = x^4 + 6x^3 + 8x^2$

65. $h(a) = a^3 + 5a^2 - 6a - 30$

66. $k(a) = a^3 - 4a^2 + 2a - 8$

■ EXPANDING YOUR SKILLS

67. Factor completely using substitution. Let $u = (3x - 1)$.
$$(3x - 1)^2 - (3x - 1) - 6$$

68. Factor completely using substitution. Let $u = (2x + 5)$.
$$(2x + 5)^2 - (2x + 5) - 12$$

69. Factor completely using substitution. Let $u = (x - 5)$.
$$2(x - 5)^2 + 9(x - 5) + 4$$

70. Factor completely using substitution. Let $u = (x - 3)$.
$$4(x - 3)^2 + 7(x - 3) + 3$$

■ GRAPHING CALCULATOR EXERCISES

For Exercises 71–74, graph Y_1 and Y_2 to provide evidence that the two expressions are equivalent.

71. $Y_1 = 2x^2 - 7x - 15$ $Y_2 = (2x + 3)(x - 5)$

72. $Y_1 = 2x^2 - 13x - 15$ $Y_2 = (2x - 15)(x + 1)$

73. $Y_1 = x^2 + 6x + 9$ $Y_2 = (x + 3)^2$

74. $Y_1 = x^2 - 10x + 25$ $Y_2 = (x - 5)^2$

Concepts

1. Difference of Squares

2. Using a Difference of Squares in Grouping

3. Sum and Difference of Cubes

4. Summary of Factoring Binomials

5. Factoring Binomials of the Form $x^6 - y^6$

section

7.3   FACTORING BINOMIALS

1.   Difference of Squares

Up to this point we have learned to

- Factor out the greatest common factor from a polynomial
- Factor a four-term polynomial by grouping
- Recognize and factor perfect square trinomials
- Factor trinomials by the grouping method and by the trial-and-error method

Next, we will learn how to factor binomials that fit the pattern of a difference of squares. Recall from Section 5.4 that the product of two conjugates results in a **difference of squares**:

$$(a + b)(a - b) = a^2 - b^2$$

Therefore, to factor a difference of squares, the process is reversed. Identify a and b and construct the conjugate factors.

Factored Form of a Difference of Squares

$$a^2 - b^2 = (a + b)(a - b)$$

---

example 1

Factoring the Difference of Squares

Factor the binomials completely.

a. $16x^2 - 9$ b. $98c^2d - 50d^3$ c. $(3x + 2)^2 - y^2$

Solution:

a. $16x^2 - 9$ The GCF is 1. The binomial is a difference of squares.

$\quad = (4x)^2 - (3)^2$ Write in the form $a^2 - b^2$, where $a = 4x$ and $b = 3$.

$\quad = (4x + 3)(4x - 3)$ Factor as $(a + b)(a - b)$

Check: $(4x + 3)(4x - 3) = 4x^2 - 12x + 12x - 9$

$\qquad\qquad\qquad\qquad\quad = 4x^2 - 9 \checkmark$

b. $98c^2d - 50d^3$

$\quad = 2d(49c^2 - 25d^2)$ The GCF is $2d$. The resulting binomial is a difference of squares.

$\quad = 2d[(7c)^2 - (5d)^2]$ Write in the form $a^2 - b^2$, where $a = 7c$ and $b = 5d$.

$\quad = 2d(7c + 5d)(7c - 5d)$ Factor as $(a + b)(a - b)$.

c. $(3x + 2)^2 - y^2$ The GCF is 1. The binomial is a difference of squares.

$\quad = [(3x + 2)^2 - (y)^2]$ Write in the form $a^2 - b^2$, where $a = (3x + 2)$ and $b = y$.

$\quad = [(3x + 2) + y][(3x + 2) - y]$ Factor as $(a + b)(a - b)$.

$\quad = (3x + 2 + y)(3x + 2 - y)$

Tip: If you have trouble recognizing that the binomial $(3x + 2)^2 - y^2$ is a difference of squares, consider making a substitution. For example, let $u = (3x + 2)$. Then the binomial becomes

$$(3x + 2)^2 - y^2$$

$$= u^2 - y^2 \qquad \text{Substitute } u = (3x + 2).$$

$$= (u + y)(u - y) \qquad \text{Factor.}$$

$$= [(3x + 2) + y][(3x + 2) - y] \qquad \text{Substitute back.}$$

$$= (3x + 2 + y)(3x + 2 - y)$$

Suppose a and b share no common factors. Then the difference of squares $a^2 - b^2$ can be factored as $(a + b)(a - b)$. However, the sum of squares $a^2 + b^2$ cannot be factored over the real numbers. To see why, consider the expression $a^2 + b^2$. The factored form would require two binomials of the form:

$$(a \quad b)(a \quad b) \overset{?}{=} a^2 + b^2$$

If all possible combinations of signs are considered, none produces the correct product.

$$(a + b)(a - b) = a^2 - b^2 \qquad \text{Wrong sign}$$

$$(a + b)(a + b) = a^2 + 2ab + b^2 \qquad \text{Wrong middle term}$$

$$(a - b)(a - b) = a^2 - 2ab + b^2 \qquad \text{Wrong middle term}$$

After exhausting all possibilities, we see that if a and b share no common factors, then the sum of squares $a^2 + b^2$ is a prime polynomial.

Sometimes a difference of squares can be used along with other factoring techniques.

example 2   **Factoring Polynomials**

Factor completely.

a. $z^4 - 81$

b. $y^3 - 6y^2 - 4y + 24$

Solution:

a. $z^4 - 81$

The GCF is 1. The binomial is a difference of squares.

$$= (z^2)^2 - (9)^2$$

Write in the form $a^2 - b^2$, where $a = z^2$ and $b = 9$.

$$= (z^2 + 9)(z^2 - 9)$$

Factor as $(a + b)(a - b)$.

$z^2 - 9$ is also a difference of squares.

$$= (z^2 + 9)(z + 3)(z - 3)$$

b. $y^3 - 6y^2 - 4y + 24$

The GCF is 1.

$$= y^3 - 6y^2 \mid - 4y + 24$$

The polynomial has four terms. Factor by grouping.

$$= y^2(y - 6) - 4(y - 6)$$

$$= (y - 6)(y^2 - 4)$$

$y^2 - 4$ is a difference of squares.

$$= (y - 6)(y + 2)(y - 2)$$

2.   Using a Difference of Squares in Grouping

example 3

Using a Difference in Squares in Grouping

Factor completely.

$$25w^2 + 90w + 81 - p^2$$

Solution:

With a four-term polynomial, we recommend "2 by 2" grouping—that is, to group the first pair of terms and the second pair of terms. However, in this case, no common binomial factor is shared by both pair of terms. (Even rearranging terms does not help.)

Because this polynomial is not factorable with "2 by 2" grouping, try grouping three terms. Notice the first three terms constitute a perfect square trinomial. Hence, we will use "3 by 1" grouping.

$$\underbrace{25w^2 + 90w + 81} \mid - p^2$$

Group "3 by 1."

Factor $25w^2 + 90w + 81 = (5w + 9)^2$.

$$= (5w + 9)^2 - p^2$$

$(5w + 9)^2 - p^2$ is a difference of squares $a^2 - b^2$, where $a = (5w + 9)$ and $b = p$.

$$= [(5w + 9) + p][(5w + 9) - p]$$

Factor as $a^2 - b^2 = (a + b)(a - b)$.

$$= (5w + 9 + p)(5w + 9 - p)$$

Simplify.

Tip: The expression $(5w + 9)^2 - p^2$ can also be factored using substitution. Let $u = 5w + 9$. Then

$$(5w + 9)^2 - p^2$$

$$= u^2 - p^2 \qquad\qquad\qquad \text{Substitute } u = 5w + 9.$$

$$= [u + p][u - p] \qquad\qquad \text{Factor as a difference of squares.}$$

$$= [(5w + 9) + p][(5w + 9) - p] \qquad \text{Substitute back.}$$

$$= (5w + 9 + p)(5w + 9 - p)$$

3. Sum and Difference of Cubes

For binomials that represent the sum or difference of cubes, factor using the following formulas.

Factoring a Sum and Difference of Cubes

Sum of Cubes: $a^3 + b^3 = (a + b)(a^2 - ab + b^2)$

Difference of Cubes: $a^3 - b^3 = (a - b)(a^2 + ab + b^2)$

Multiplication can be used to confirm the formulas for factoring a sum or difference of cubes.

$$(a + b)(a^2 - ab + b^2) = a^3 - a^2b + ab^2 + a^2b - ab^2 + b^3 = a^3 + b^3 \checkmark$$

$$(a - b)(a^2 + ab + b^2) = a^3 + a^2b + ab^2 - a^2b - ab^2 - b^3 = a^3 - b^3 \checkmark$$

To help you remember the formulas for factoring a sum or difference of cubes, keep the following guidelines in mind.

- The factored form is the product of a binomial and a trinomial.
- The first and third terms in the trinomial are the squares of the terms within the binomial factor.
- Without regard to sign, the middle term in the trinomial is the product of terms in the binomial factor.

$$x^3 + 8 = (x)^3 + (2)^3 = (x + 2)[(x)^2 - (x)(2) + (2)^2]$$

Square the first term of the binomial.

product of terms in the binomial

Square the last term of the binomial.

- The sign within the binomial factor is the same as the sign of the original binomial.
- The first and third terms in the trinomial are always positive.

- The sign of the middle term in the trinomial is opposite the sign within the binomial.

$$x^3 + 8 = (x)^3 + (2)^3 = (x + 2)[(x)^2 - (x)(2) + (2)^2]$$

same sign   positive

opposite signs

---

example 4

Factoring a Difference of Cubes

Factor: $8x^3 - 27$

Solution:

$8x^3 - 27$	$8x^3$ and 27 are perfect cubes.
$= (2x)^3 - (3)^3$	Write as $a^3 - b^3$, where $a = 2x$ and $b = 3$.

$$a^3 - b^3 = (a - b)(a^2 + ab + b^2)$$

$(2x)^3 - (3)^3 = (2x - 3)[(2x)^2 + (2x)(3) + (3)^2]$	Apply the difference of cubes formula.
$= (2x - 3)(4x^2 + 6x + 9)$	Simplify.

Check: $(2x - 3)(4x^2 + 6x + 9) = 8x^3 + 12x^2 + 18x - 12x^2 - 18x - 27$
$$= 8x^3 - 27 \checkmark$$

---

example 5

Factoring the Sum of Cubes

Factor: $125t^3 + 64z^6$

Solution:

$125t^3 + 64z^6$	$125t^3$ and $64z^6$ are perfect cubes.
$= (5t)^3 + (4z^2)^3$	Write as $a^3 + b^3$, where $a = 5t$ and $b = 4z^2$.

$$a^3 + b^3 = (a + b)(a^2 - ab + b^2)$$

Apply the sum of cubes formula.

$$(5t)^3 + (4z^2)^3 = [(5t) + (4z^2)][(5t)^2 - (5t)(4z^2) + (4z^2)^2]$$

$= (5t + 4z^2)(25t^2 - 20tz^2 + 16z^4)$	Simplify.

4. Summary of Factoring Binomials

After removing the greatest common factor, the next step in any factoring problem is to recognize what type of pattern it follows. Exponents that are divisible by two are perfect squares and those divisible by three are perfect cubes. The formulas for factoring binomials are summarized below:

Factoring Binomials

1. Difference of Squares: $a^2 - b^2 = (a + b)(a - b)$
2. Difference of Cubes: $a^3 - b^3 = (a - b)(a^2 + ab + b^2)$
3. Sum of Cubes: $a^3 + b^3 = (a + b)(a^2 - ab + b^2)$

---

example 6

Review of Factoring Binomials

Factor the binomials.

a. $m^3 - \dfrac{1}{8}$ b. $9k^2 + 24m^2$ c. $128y^6 + 54x^3$ d. $50y^6 - 8x^2$

Solution:

a. $m^3 - \dfrac{1}{8}$ $\qquad$ m^3 is a perfect cube: $m^3 = (m)^3$.

$\dfrac{1}{8}$ is a perfect cube: $\dfrac{1}{8} = \left(\dfrac{1}{2}\right)^3$.

$= (m)^3 - \left(\dfrac{1}{2}\right)^3$ $\qquad$ This is a difference of cubes, where $a = m$ and $b = \dfrac{1}{2}$:
$a^3 - b^3 = (a - b)(a^2 + ab + b^2)$.

$= \left(m - \dfrac{1}{2}\right)\left(m^2 + \dfrac{1}{2}m + \dfrac{1}{4}\right)$ $\qquad$ Factor.

b. $9k^2 + 24m^2$ $\qquad$ Factor out the GCF.

$= 3(3k^2 + 8m^2)$ $\qquad$ The resulting binomial is not a difference of squares or a sum or difference of cubes. It cannot be factored further over the real numbers.

c. $128y^6 + 54x^3$ $\qquad$ Factor out the GCF.

$= 2(64y^6 + 27x^3)$ $\qquad$ 64 and 27 are both perfect cubes and the exponents of both x and y are multiples of three. This is a sum of cubes, where $a = 4y^2$ and $b = 3x$.

$= 2[(4y^2)^3 + (3x)^3]$ $\qquad$ $a^3 + b^3 = (a + b)(a^2 - ab + b^2)$.

$= 2(4y^2 + 3x)(16y^4 - 12xy^2 + 9x^2)$ $\qquad$ Factor.

d. $50y^6 - 8x^2$ Factor out the GCF.

   $= 2(25y^6 - 4x^2)$ 25 and 4 are perfect squares. The exponents of both x and y are both multiples of 2. This is a difference of squares, where $a = 5y^3$ and $b = 2x$.

   $= 2[(5y^3)^2 - (2x)^2]$ $a^2 - b^2 = (a + b)(a - b)$.

   $= 2(5y^3 + 2x)(5y^3 - 2x)$

5. Factoring Binomials of the Form $x^6 - y^6$

example 7

Factoring Binomials

Factor the binomial $x^6 - y^6$ as

a.   A difference of cubes
b.   A difference of squares

Solution:

Notice that the expressions x^6 and y^6 are both perfect squares and perfect cubes because the exponents are both multiples of 2 and of 3. Consequently, $x^6 - y^6$ can be factored initially as either a difference of cubes or as a difference of squares.

a. $x^6 - y^6$

difference
of cubes

   $= (x^2)^3 - (y^2)^3$ Write as $a^3 - b^3$, where $a = x^2$ and $b = y^2$.

   $= (x^2 - y^2)[(x^2)^2 + (x^2)(y^2) + (y^2)^2]$ Apply the formula $a^3 - b^3 = (a - b)(a^2 + ab + b^2)$.

   $= (x^2 - y^2)(x^4 + x^2y^2 + y^4)$ Factor $x^2 - y^2$ as a difference of squares.

   $= (x + y)(x - y)(x^4 + x^2y^2 + y^4)$

b. $x^6 - y^6$

$$= (x^3)^2 - (y^3)^2 \qquad \text{Write as } a^2 - b^2, \text{ where } a = x^3 \text{ and } b = y^3.$$

$$= (x^3 + y^3)(x^3 - y^3) \qquad \text{Apply the formula } a^2 - b^2 = (a + b)(a - b).$$

Factor $x^3 + y^3$ as a sum of cubes.
Factor $x^3 - y^3$ as a difference of cubes.

$$= (x + y)(x^2 - xy + y^2)(x - y)(x^2 + xy + y^2)$$

If given a choice between factoring a binomial as a difference of squares or as a difference of cubes, it is recommended that you factor initially as a difference of squares. As this example illustrates, factoring as a difference of squares leads to a more complete factorization. Hence,

$$a^6 - b^6 = (a - b)(a^2 + ab + b^2)(a + b)(a^2 - ab + b^2)$$

---

section 7.3   PRACTICE EXERCISES

1. Explain how to recognize a perfect square trinomial.

2. Can a perfect square trinomial be factored using the grouping method? Explain.

For Exercises 3–10, factor completely.

3. $4x^2 - 20x + 25$ 4. $9t^2 - 42t + 49$

5. $10x + 6xy + 5 + 3y$

6. $21a + 7ab - 3b - b^2$

7. $32p^2 - 28p - 4$ 8. $6q^2 + 37q - 35$

9. $45a^2 - 9ac$ 10. $11xy^2 - 55y^3$

11. Explain how to identify and factor a difference of squares.

12. Explain how to identify and factor a sum of cubes.

13. Explain how to identify and factor a difference of cubes.

14. Can you factor $25x^2 + 4$? Explain your answer.

For Exercises 15–48, factor the binomials. Identify the binomials that are prime.

15. $x^2 - 9$ 16. $y^2 - 25$

17. $16 - w^2$ 18. $81 - b^2$

19. $36y^2 - \dfrac{1}{25}$ 20. $16p^2 - \dfrac{1}{9}$

21. $8a^2 - 162b^2$ 22. $50c^2 - 72d^2$

23. $18d^{12} - 32$ 24. $3z^8 - 12$

25. $25u^2 + 1$ 26. $w^2 + 4$

27. $242v^2 + 32$ 28. $8p^2 + 200$

29. $(2m - 5)^2 - 36$ 30. $(3n + 1)^2 - 49$

31. $8x^3 - 1$ (check by multiplying)

32. $y^3 + 64$ (check by multiplying)

33. $125c^3 - 27$ (check by multiplying)

34. $216u^3 - v^3$ (check by multiplying)

35. $27a^3 + \dfrac{1}{8}$

36. $b^3 + \dfrac{27}{125}$

37. $2m^3 + 16$

38. $3x^3 - 375$

39. $x^6 - y^6$ (*Hint:* Treat as the difference of squares)

40. $64a^6 - b^6$

41. $h^6 + k^6$ (*Hint:* Treat as a sum of cubes)

42. $27q^6 + 125p^6$

43. $x^4 - y^4$

44. $81u^4 - 16v^4$

45. $a^9 + b^9$

46. $27m^9 - 8n^9$

47. $(p - 3)^3 - 64$

48. $(q - 1)^3 + 125$

For Exercises 49–52, factor the polynomials by using the difference of squares with grouping.

49. $x^2 + 12x + 36 - a^2$

50. $b^2 - (x^2 + 4x + 4)$

51. $p^2 - (y^2 - 6y + 9)$

52. $a^2 + 10a + 25 - b^2$

53. Find a difference of squares that has $(2x + 3)$ as one of its factors.

54. Find a difference of squares that has $(4 - p)$ as one of its factors.

55. Find a difference of cubes that has $(4a^2 + 6a + 9)$ as its trinomial factor.

56. Find a sum of cubes that has $(25c^2 - 10cd + 4d^2)$ as its trinomial factor.

57. Find a sum of cubes that has $(4x^2 + y)$ as its binomial factor.

58. Find a difference of cubes that has $(3t - r^2)$ as its binomial factor.

59. Consider the area of the following shaded region:

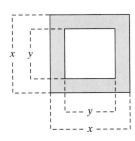

Figure for Exercise 59

a. Find an expression that represents the area of the shaded region.

b. Factor the expression found in part (a).

c. Find the area of the shaded region if $x = 6$ in. and $y = 4$ in.

60. A manufacturer needs to know the area of a metal washer. The outer radius of the washer is R and the inner radius is r.

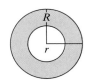

Figure for Exercise 60

a. Find an expression that represents the area of the washer.

b. Factor the expression found in part (a).

c. Find the area of the washer if $R = \frac{1}{2}$ in. and $r = \frac{1}{4}$ in. (Round to the nearest 0.01 in.^{2})

■ EXPANDING YOUR SKILLS

For Exercises 61–64, factor the polynomials by using the difference of squares, sum of cubes, or difference of cubes with grouping.

61. $x^2 - y^2 + x + y$

62. $25c^2 - 9d^2 + 5c - 3d$

63. $5wx^3 + 5wy^3 - 2zx^3 - 2zy^3$

64. $3xu^3 - 3xv^3 - 5yu^3 + 5yv^3$

▦ GRAPHING CALCULATOR EXERCISES

65. a. Graph $Y_1 = x^2 - x - 2$ and use the *Zoom* and *Trace* features to approximate the x-intercepts.

    b. Factor the function.

66. a. Graph $Y_1 = x^2 - x - 12$ and use the *Zoom* and *Trace* features to approximate the x-intercepts.

    b. Factor the function.

67. a. Graph $Y_1 = x^2 - 5x + 4$ and use the *Zoom* and *Trace* features to approximate the x-intercepts.

    b. Factor the function.

68. a. Graph $Y_1 = x^2 + 3x + 2$ and use the *Zoom* and *Trace* features to approximate the x-intercepts.

    b. Factor the function.

chapter 7   MIDCHAPTER REVIEW: A FACTORING STRATEGY

Factoring Strategy

1. Factor out the greatest common factor, GCF (Section 7.1).
2. Identify whether the polynomial has two terms, three terms, or more than three terms.
3. If the polynomial has two terms, determine if it fits the pattern for a difference of squares, difference of cubes, or sum of cubes. Remember, a sum of squares is not factorable over the real numbers (Section 7.3).
4. If the polynomial has three terms, check first for a perfect square trinomial. Otherwise factor the trinomial with the grouping method or the trial-and-error method (Section 7.2).
5. If the polynomial has more than three terms, try factoring by grouping (Section 7.1 and Section 7.3).

1. What is meant by a prime factor?

2. What is the first step in factoring any polynomial?

3. When factoring a binomial, what patterns do you look for?

4. When factoring a trinomial what pattern do you look for first before using the grouping method or trial-and-error method?

5. What do you look for when factoring a perfect square trinomial?

6. What do you look for when factoring a four-term polynomial?

For Exercises 7–26,

   a. Identify by inspection what type of factoring pattern would be most appropriate:

   Difference of squares   Perfect square trinomial

   Sum of cubes   Trinomial (grouping or trial-and-error)

   Difference of cubes   Grouping

   b. Factor the polynomial completely.

7. $6x^2 - 21x - 45$

8. $8m^3 - 10m^2 - 3m$

9. $8a^2 - 50$

10. $ab + ay - b^2 - by$

11. $14u^2 - 11uv + 2v^2$

12. $9p^2 - 12pq + 4q^2$

13. $16x^3 - 2$

14. $9m^2 + 16n^2$

15. $27y^3 + 125$

16. $3x^2 - 16$

17. $128p^6 + 54q^3$

18. $5b^2 - 30b + 45$

19. $16a^4 - 1$

20. $81u^2 - 90uv + 25v^2$

21. $p^2 - 12p + 36 - c^2$

22. $4x^2 + 16$

23. $12ax - 6ay + 4bx - 2by$

24. $125y^3 - 8$

25. $5y^2 + 14y - 3$

26. $2m^4 - 128$

section

7.4   ZERO PRODUCT RULE

1.   Definition of a Quadratic Equation

In Section 1.4 we defined a linear equation in one variable as an equation of the form $ax + b = 0\, (a \neq 0)$. A linear equation in one variable is sometimes called a first-degree polynomial equation because the highest degree of all its terms is 1. A second-degree polynomial equation is called a quadratic equation.

Definition of a Quadratic Equation in One Variable

If a, b, and c are real numbers such that $a \neq 0$, then a **quadratic equation** is an equation that can be written in the form

$$ax^2 + bx + c = 0$$

The following equations are quadratic because they can each be written in the form $ax^2 + bx + c,\, (a \neq 0)$

$$-4x^2 + 4x = 1 \qquad x(x - 2) = 3 \qquad (x - 4)(x + 4) = 9$$
$$-4x^2 + 4x - 1 = 0 \qquad x^2 - 2x = 3 \qquad x^2 - 16 = 9$$
$$x^2 - 2x - 3 = 0 \qquad x^2 - 25 = 0$$
$$x^2 + 0x - 25 = 0$$

2.   Zero Product Rule

One method to solve a quadratic equation is to factor the equation and apply the zero product rule. The **zero product rule** states that if the product of two factors is zero, then one or both of its factors is zero.

The Zero Product Rule

If $ab = 0$, then $a = 0$ or $b = 0$

For example, the quadratic equation $x^2 - x - 12 = 0$ can be written in factored form as $(x - 4)(x + 3) = 0$. By the zero product rule, one or both factors must be zero. Hence, either $x - 4 = 0$ or $x + 3 = 0$. Therefore, to solve the quadratic equation, set each factor to zero and solve for x.

$$(x - 4)(x + 3) = 0 \qquad \text{Apply the zero product rule.}$$

$$x - 4 = 0 \text{ or } x + 3 = 0 \qquad \text{Set each factor to zero.}$$

$$x = 4 \text{ or } x = -3 \qquad \text{Solve each equation for } x.$$

3. Solving Quadratic Equations Using the Zero Product Rule

Quadratic equations, like linear equations, arise in many applications of mathematics, science, and business. The following steps summarize the factoring method to solve a quadratic equation.

Steps to Solve a Quadratic Equation by Factoring

1. Write the equation in the form: $ax^2 + bx + c = 0$
2. Factor the equation completely.
3. Apply the zero product rule. That is, set each factor equal to zero and solve the resulting equations.[*]

*The solution(s) found in step 3 may be checked by substitution in the original equation.

---

example 1

Solving Quadratic Equations

Solve the quadratic equations.

a. $2x^2 - 5x = 12$ b. $\frac{1}{2}x^2 + \frac{2}{3}x = 0$ c. $9x(4x + 2) - 10x = 8x + 25$

Solution:

a.
$$2x^2 - 5x = 12$$

$$2x^2 - 5x - 12 = 0$$ Write the equation in the form: $ax^2 + bx + c = 0$.

$$(2x + 3)(x - 4) = 0$$ Factor the polynomial completely.

$2x + 3 = 0$ or $x - 4 = 0$ Set each factor equal to zero.

$2x = -3$ or $x = 4$ Solve each equation.

$x = -\dfrac{3}{2}$ or $x = 4$

Check: $x = -\frac{3}{2}$

$$2x^2 - 5x = 12$$

$$2\left(-\frac{3}{2}\right)^2 - 5\left(-\frac{3}{2}\right) \stackrel{?}{=} 12$$

$$2\left(\frac{9}{4}\right) + \frac{15}{2} \stackrel{?}{=} 12$$

$$\frac{18}{4} + \frac{30}{4} \stackrel{?}{=} 12$$

$$\frac{48}{4} = 12 \checkmark$$

Check: $x = 4$

$$2x^2 - 5x = 12$$

$$2(4)^2 - 5(4) \stackrel{?}{=} 12$$

$$2(16) - 20 \stackrel{?}{=} 12$$

$$32 - 20 = 12 \checkmark$$

b. $\dfrac{1}{2}x^2 + \dfrac{2}{3}x = 0$ The equation is already in the form $ax^2 + bx + c = 0$ (*Note: c = 0*).

$6\left(\dfrac{1}{2}x^2 + \dfrac{2}{3}x\right) = 6(0)$ Clear fractions.

$3x^2 + 4x = 0$

$x(3x + 4) = 0$ Factor completely.

$x = 0$ or $3x + 4 = 0$ Set each factor equal to zero.

$x = 0$ or $x = -\dfrac{4}{3}$ Solve each equation for x.

Check: $x = 0$ Check: $x = -\frac{4}{3}$

$\dfrac{1}{2}x^2 + \dfrac{2}{3}x = 0$ $\dfrac{1}{2}x^2 + \dfrac{2}{3}x = 0$

$\dfrac{1}{2}(0)^2 + \dfrac{2}{3}(0) \stackrel{?}{=} 0$ $\dfrac{1}{2}\left(-\dfrac{4}{3}\right)^2 + \dfrac{2}{3}\left(-\dfrac{4}{3}\right) \stackrel{?}{=} 0$

$0 = 0 \checkmark$ $\dfrac{1}{2}\left(\dfrac{16}{9}\right) - \dfrac{8}{9} \stackrel{?}{=} 0$

$\dfrac{8}{9} - \dfrac{8}{9} = 0 \checkmark$

c. $9x(4x + 2) - 10x = 8x + 25$

$36x^2 + 18x - 10x = 8x + 25$ Clear parentheses.

$36x^2 + 8x = 8x + 25$ Combine *like* terms.

$36x^2 - 25 = 0$ Set the equation equal to zero. The equation is in the form $ax^2 + bx + c = 0$ (*Note: b = 0*).

$(6x - 5)(6x + 5) = 0$ Factor completely.

$6x - 5 = 0$ or $6x + 5 = 0$ Set each factor equal to zero.

$6x = 5$ or $6x = -5$ Solve each equation.

$\dfrac{6x}{6} = \dfrac{5}{6}$ or $\dfrac{6x}{6} = \dfrac{-5}{6}$

$x = \dfrac{5}{6}$ or $x = -\dfrac{5}{6}$ The check is left to the reader.

4. Solving Higher Degree Polynomial Equations

The zero product rule can be used to solve higher degree polynomial equations provided the equations can be set to zero and written in factored form.

example 2   **Solving Higher Degree Polynomial Equations**

Solve the equations.

a. $-2(y + 7)(y - 1)(10y + 3) = 0$ b. $z^3 + 3z^2 - 4z - 12 = 0$

Solution:

a. $-2(y + 7)(y - 1)(10y + 3) = 0$

The equation is already in factored form and is equal to zero.

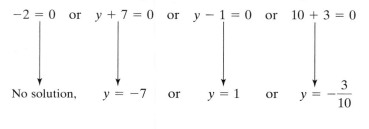

| $-2 = 0$ or | $y + 7 = 0$ or | $y - 1 = 0$ or | $10 + 3 = 0$ | Set each factor equal to zero. |

| No solution, | $y = -7$ or | $y = 1$ or | $y = -\dfrac{3}{10}$ | Solve each equation for y. |

Notice that when the constant factor is set to zero, the result is a contradiction $-2 = 0$. The constant factor does not produce a solution to the equation. Therefore, the only solutions are $y = -7$, $y = 1$, and $y = -\frac{3}{10}$. Each solution can be checked in the original equation.

b. $z^3 + 3z^2 - 4z - 12 = 0$ This is a higher degree polynomial equation.

$z^3 + 3z^2 \mid - 4z - 12 = 0$ The equation is already set to zero. Now factor. Because there are four terms, try factoring by grouping.

$z^2(z + 3) - 4(z + 3) = 0$

$(z + 3)(z^2 - 4) = 0$ $z^2 - 4$ can be factored further as a difference of squares.

$(z + 3)(z - 2)(z + 2) = 0$

$z + 3 = 0$ or $z - 2 = 0$ or $z + 2 = 0$ Set each factor equal to zero.

$z = -3$ or $z = 2$ or $z = -2$ Solve each equation.

5.   Definition of a Quadratic Function

In Section 4.3, we graphed several basic functions by plotting points, including $f(x) = x^2$. This function is called a quadratic function, and its graph is in the shape of a **parabola**. In general, any second-degree polynomial function is a quadratic function.

Definition of a Quadratic Function

Let a, b, and c represent real numbers such that $a \neq 0$. Then a function in the form, $f(x) = ax^2 + bx + c$ is called a **quadratic function**.

The graph of a quadratic function is a parabola that opens up or down. The leading coefficient, a, determines the direction of the parabola. For the quadratic function defined by $f(x) = ax^2 + bx + c$:

If $a > 0$, the parabola opens up. For example: $f(x) = x^2$

If $a < 0$, the parabola opens down. For example: $g(x) = -x^2$

6. Finding the *x*- and *y*-Intercepts of a Quadratic Function

Recall from Section 4.3 that the *x*-intercepts of a function $y = f(x)$ are the real solutions to the equation $f(x) = 0$. The *y*-intercept is found by evaluating $f(0)$.

example 3

Finding the *x*- and *y*-Intercepts of a Quadratic Function

Find the *x*- and *y*-intercepts.

$$f(x) = x^2 - x - 12$$

Solution:

To find the *x*-intercept, substitute $f(x) = 0$:

$f(x) = x^2 - x - 12$

$0 = x^2 - x - 12$ Substitute 0 for $f(x)$. The result is a quadratic equation.

$0 = (x - 4)(x + 3)$ Factor.

$x - 4 = 0$ or $x + 3 = 0$ Set each factor equal to zero.

$x = 4$ or $x = -3$ Solve each equation.

The *x*-intercepts are $(4, 0)$ and $(-3, 0)$.

To find the y-intercept, substitute $x = 0$:

$$f(x) = x^2 - x - 12$$
$$= (0)^2 - (0) - 12$$
$$= -12$$

The y-intercept is $(0, -12)$.

Graphing Calculator Box

The solution to Example 3 can be supported from the graph of

$$f(x) = x^2 - x - 12$$

7. Applications of Quadratic Functions

example 4

Applications of Quadratic Functions

A concession stand at a community ballpark sells personal pizzas during summer softball games. The profit realized by the concession stand is a function of the number of pizzas it produces. The profit function is given by

$$P(x) = -\frac{1}{40}x^2 + 5x - 90,$$ where x is the number of pizzas produced and P is the profit measured in dollars.

a. Find $P(0)$, $P(50)$, $P(100)$, and $P(150)$ and interpret the meaning of these function values in the context of the number of pizzas produced and the profit.
b. Find the x-intercepts and interpret their meaning in the context of the problem.

Solution:

a. $\quad P(x) = -\dfrac{1}{40}x^2 + 5x - 90$

$$P(0) = -\frac{1}{40}(0)^2 + 5(0) - 90 = -90$$

$$P(50) = -\frac{1}{40}(50)^2 + 5(50) - 90 = 97.50$$

$$P(100) = -\frac{1}{40}(100)^2 + 5(100) - 90 = 160$$

$$P(150) = -\frac{1}{40}(150)^2 + 5(150) - 90 = 97.50$$

$P(0) = -90$ indicates that if 0 pizzas are produced, there is a *loss* of $90.00.

$P(50) = 97.5$ indicates that if 50 pizzas are produced, there is a profit of $97.50.

$P(100) = 160$ indicates that if 100 pizzas are produced, there is a profit of $160.00.

$P(150) = 97.5$ indicates that if 150 pizzas are produced, there is a profit of $97.50.

b.   To find the *x*-intercepts, find the real solutions of the equation $P(x) = 0$.

$$-\frac{1}{40}x^2 + 5x - 90 = 0 \qquad\qquad \text{Set } P(x) = 0.$$

$$-40\left(-\frac{1}{40}x^2 + 5x - 90\right) = -40(0) \qquad \text{Multiply by } -40 \text{ to clear fractions.}$$

$$x^2 - 200x + 3600 = 0$$

$$(x - 20)(x - 180) = 0 \qquad\qquad \text{Factor.}$$

$$x = 20 \quad\text{ or }\quad x = 180 \qquad\qquad \text{Apply the zero product rule.}$$

The *x*-intercepts are $(20, 0)$ and $(180, 0)$. The *x*-intercepts represent the number of pizzas required to make a profit of 0. That is, if 20 pizzas are produced or 180 pizzas are produced, the concession stand will break even (Figure 7-1).

Figure 7-1

Notice that the concession stand does not begin to make a profit until more than 20 pizzas are produced. The revenue generated by the first 20 pizzas probably covers the cost of operating the stand such as employee wages and the cost of ingredients. After 20 pizzas are produced, the profit will rise, but only to a point. After approximately 100 pizzas, profit declines. Beyond that point, the concession stand is probably not able to sell all the pizzas it produces, resulting in smaller profit.

example 5   **Applications of Quadratic Functions**

A rocket is shot vertically upward with an initial velocity of 288 ft/s. The function given by $h(t) = -16t^2 + 288t$ relates the rocket's height, h, (in feet) to the time, t, after launch (in seconds).

a. Find $h(0), h(5), h(10),$ and $h(15)$ and interpret the meaning of these function values in the context of the rocket's height and time after launch.
b. Find the t-intercepts of the function and interpret their meaning in the context of the rocket's height and time after launch.
c. Find the time(s) at which the rocket is at a height of 1152 ft.

Solution:

a. $h(t) = -16t^2 + 288t$

$h(0) = -16(0)^2 + 288(0) = 0$

$h(5) = -16(5)^2 + 288(5) = 1040$

$h(10) = -16(10)^2 + 288(10) = 1280$

$h(15) = -16(15)^2 + 288(15) = 720$

$h(0) = 0$ indicates that at $t = 0$ s, the height of the rocket is 0 ft.

$h(5) = 1040$ indicates that 5 s after launch, the height of the rocket is 1040 ft.

$h(10) = 1280$ indicates that 10 s after launch, the height of the rocket is 1280 ft.

$h(15) = 720$ indicates that 15 s after launch, the height of the rocket is 720 ft.

b. The t-intercepts of the function are represented by the real solutions of the equation $h(t) = 0$.

$-16t^2 + 288t = 0$	Set $h(t) = 0$.
$-16t(t - 18) = 0$	Factor.
$-16t = 0$ $\quad$ or $\quad$ $t - 18 = 0$	Apply the zero product rule.
$t = 0$ $\quad$ or $\quad$ $t = 18$	

The rocket is at ground level initially (at $t = 0$ s) and then again after 18 s when it hits the ground.

c. Set $h(t) = 1152$ and solve for t.

$$h(t) = -16t^2 + 288t$$

$$1152 = -16t^2 + 288t \qquad \text{Substitute } 1152 \text{ for } h(t).$$

$$16t^2 - 288t + 1152 = 0 \qquad \text{Set the equation equal to zero.}$$

$$16(t^2 - 18t + 72) = 0 \qquad \text{Factor out the GCF.}$$

$$16(t - 6)(t - 12) = 0 \qquad \text{Factor.}$$

$$t = 6 \qquad \text{or} \qquad t = 12$$

The rocket will reach a height of 1152 ft after 6 s (on the way up) and after 12 s (on the way down). (See Figure 7-2.)

Height of Rocket versus Time after Launch

$h(t) = -16t^2 + 288t$

Figure 7-2

8. Applications of Quadratic Equations and Geometry

example 6

Application Problem

The length of a basketball court is 6 ft less than 2 times the width. If the total area is 4700 ft², find the dimensions of the court.

Solution:

Figure 7-3

If the width of the court is represented by w, then the length can be represented by $2w - 6$ (Figure 7-3).

$$A = (\text{length})(\text{width}) \qquad \text{Area of a rectangle}$$

$$4700 = (2w - 6)w \qquad \text{Mathematical equation}$$

$$4700 = 2w^2 - 6w$$

$$2w^2 - 6w - 4700 = 0 \qquad \text{Set the equation equal to zero and factor.}$$

$$2(w^2 - 3w - 2350) = 0 \qquad \text{Factor out GCF.}$$

$$2(w - 50)(w + 47) = 0$$ Factor the trinomial.

$2 \neq 0$ or $w - 50 = 0$ or $w + 47 = 0$ Set each factor equal to zero.

contradiction $w = 50$ or $w \neq -47$ A negative width is not possible.

The width is 50 ft.

The length is $2w - 6 = 2(50) - 6 = 94$ ft.

---

example 7

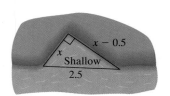

Figure 7-4

An Application of a Quadratic Equation

A region of coastline off Biscayne Bay is approximately in the shape of a right angle. The corresponding triangular area has sandbars and is marked off on navigational charts as being shallow water. If one leg of the triangle is $\frac{1}{2}$ mile shorter than the other leg, and the hypotenuse is 2.5 miles, find the lengths of the legs of the triangle (Figure 7-4).

Solution:

Let x represent the longer leg.

Then $x - 0.5$ represents the shorter leg.

$$a^2 + b^2 = c^2$$ Pythagorean theorem

$$x^2 + (x - 0.5)^2 = (2.5)^2$$

$$x^2 + (x)^2 - 2(x)(0.5) + (0.5)^2 = 6.25$$

Tip: Recall that the square of a binomial results in a perfect square trinomial.

$$(a - b)^2 = a^2 - 2ab + b^2$$

$$(x - 0.5)^2 = (x)^2 - 2(x)(0.5) + (0.5)^2$$

$$= x^2 - x + 0.25$$

$$x^2 + x^2 - x + 0.25 = 6.25$$

$$2x^2 - x - 6 = 0$$ Write the equation in the form $ax^2 + bx + c = 0$.

$$(2x + 3)(x - 2) = 0$$ Factor.

$2x + 3 = 0$ or $x - 2 = 0$ Set both factors to zero.

$x \neq -\dfrac{3}{2}$ or $x = 2$ Solve both equations for x.

The side of a triangle may not be $-\frac{3}{2}$ miles, so we reject the solution $x = -\frac{3}{2}$.

Therefore, one leg of the triangle is 2 miles.

The other leg is $x - 0.5 = 2 - 0.5 = 1.5$ miles.

section 7.4   PRACTICE EXERCISES

1. What conditions are necessary to solve an equation by using the zero product rule?

2. State the zero product rule.

For Exercises 3–8, determine which of the equations are written in the correct form to apply the zero product rule directly. If an equation is not in the correct form, explain what is wrong.

3. $2x(x - 3) = 0$

4. $(u + 1)(u - 3) = 10$

5. $(p + 2)(3p - 1) = 1$ 6. $t^2 - t - 12 = 0$

7. $a(a + 3)^2 = 5$

8. $\left(\frac{2}{3}x - 5\right)\left(x + \frac{1}{2}\right) = 0$

For Exercises 9–30, solve the equation.

9. $(x + 3)(x + 5) = 0$

10. $(x + 7)(x - 4) = 0$

11. $(2w + 9)(5w - 1) = 0$

12. $(3a + 1)(4a - 5) = 0$

13. $x(x + 4)(10x - 3) = 0$

14. $t(t - 6)(3t - 11) = 0$

15. $0 = 5(y - 0.4)(y + 2.1)$

16. $0 = -4(z - 7.5)(z - 9.3)$

17. $x^2 + 6x - 27 = 0$

18. $2x^2 + x - 15 = 0$

19. $2x^2 + 5x = 3$ 20. $-11x = 3x^2 - 4$

21. $10x^2 = 15x$ 22. $5x^2 = 7x$

23. $-9 = y(y + 6)$

24. $-62 = t(t - 16) + 2$

25. $(x + 1)(2x - 1)(x - 3) = 0$

26. $2x(x - 4)^2(4x + 3) = 0$

27. $(y - 3)(y + 4) = 8$

28. $(t + 10)(t + 5) = 6$

29. $p^2 + (p + 7)^2 = 169$

30. $x^2 + (x + 2)^2 = 100$

For Exercises 31–38,
  a. Find the values of x for which $f(x) = 0$.
  b. Find $f(0)$.

31. $f(x) = x^2 - 3x$ 32. $f(x) = 4x^2 + 2x$

33. $f(x) = 5(x - 7)$ 34. $f(x) = 4(x + 5)$

35. $f(x) = \frac{1}{2}(x - 2)(x + 1)(2x)$

36. $f(x) = (x + 1)(x - 2)(x + 3)^2$

37. $f(x) = x^2 - 2x + 1$

38. $f(x) = x^2 + 4x + 4$

For Exercises 39–44, sketch the parabola by finding and plotting the x-intercepts, y-intercept, and determining if the parabola opens up or down.

39. $g(x) = 2x^2 - 9x - 5$

40. $h(x) = x^2 + x - 12$

41. $k(x) = -x^2 - 2x + 3$

42. $p(x) = -3x^2 - 13x + 10$

43. $m(x) = x^2 - 4$ 44. $n(x) = x^2 - 9$

For Exercises 45–48, find the x-intercepts of each function and use that information to match the function with its graph (shown on page 490).

45. $g(x) = (x + 3)(x - 3)$

46. $h(x) = x(x - 2)(x + 4)$

47. $f(x) = 4(x + 1)$

48. $k(x) = (x + 1)(x + 3)(x - 2)(x - 1)$

a.

b.

c.

d.
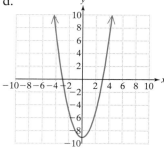

49. If 5 is added to the square of a number, the result is 30. Find all such numbers.

50. Four less than the square of a number is 77. Find all such numbers.

51. The square of a number is equal to 12 more than the number. Find all such numbers.

52. The square of a number is equal to 20 more than the number. Find all such numbers.

53. The product of two consecutive integers is 42. Find the integers.

54. The product of two consecutive integers is 110. Find the integers.

55. The product of two consecutive even integers is 120. Find the integers.

56. The product of two consecutive odd integers is 63. Find the integers.

57. The height of a triangle is 1 in. more than the base. If the height is increased by 2 in. while the base remains the same, the new area becomes 20 in.²

   a. Find the base and height of the original triangle.

   b. Find the area of the original triangle.

58. The base of a triangle is 2 cm more than the height. If the base is increased by 4 cm while the height remains the same, the new area is 56 cm².

   a. Find the base and height of the original triangle.

   b. Find the area of the original triangle.

59. The sum of the squares of two consecutive positive integers is 41. Find the integers.

60. The sum of the squares of two consecutive, positive even integers is 164. Find the integers.

61. A certain company makes water purification systems. The factory can produce x water systems per year. The profit, $P(x)$, the company makes is a function of the number of systems it produces, x.

   $$P(x) = -2x^2 + 1000x$$

   a. Is this function linear or quadratic?

   b. Find the number of water systems, x, that would produce a zero profit.

   c. What points on the graph do the answers in part (b) represent?

   d. Find the number of systems for which the profit is $80,000.

Figure for Exercise 61

62. A rocket is fired upward from ground level with an initial velocity of 490 m/s. The height of the rocket in meters, $s(t)$, is a function of the time in seconds, t, after launch.

   $$s(t) = -4.9t^2 + 490t$$

   a. What characteristics of s indicate that it is a quadratic function?

   b. Find the t-intercepts of the function and label them on the graph.

c. What do the *t*-intercepts mean in the context of this problem?

d. At what times is the rocket at a height of 485.1 m?

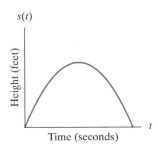

Figure for Exercise 62

63. A rectangular pen is to contain 35 ft² of area. If the width is 2 ft less than the length, find the dimensions of the pen.

64. The height of a triangle is 1 in. more than twice the base. If the area is 18 in.², find the base and height of the triangle.

65. Justin must travel from Summersville to Clayton. He can drive 10 miles through the mountains at 40 mph. Or he can drive east and then north on superhighways at 60 mph. The alternative route forms a right angle as shown in the diagram. The eastern leg is 2 miles less than the northern leg.

a. Find the total distance Justin would travel going the alternative route.

b. If Justin wants to minimize the time of the trip, which route should he take?

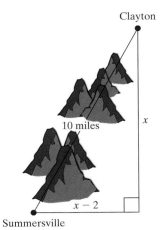

Figure for Exercise 65

66. The hypotenuse of a right triangle is 3 m more than twice the shortest leg. The longer leg is 2 m more than twice the shortest leg. Find the lengths of the sides.

For Exercises 67–72, factor the functions. Explain how the factored form relates to the graph of the function. Can the graph of the functions help you determine the factors of the function?

67. $f(x) = x^2 - 7x + 10$

68. $f(x) = x^2 - 2x - 3$

69. $f(x) = 2x^2 - x - 10$

70. $f(x) = x^2 - 3x$

71. $f(x) = x^2 + 4x + 4$

72. $f(x) = x^2 - 6x + 9$

For Exercises 73–78, find an equation that has the given solutions. For example: 2 and -1 are solutions to $(x - 2)(x + 1) = 0$ or $x^2 - x - 2 = 0$. In general, x_1 and x_2 are solutions to the equation $a(x - x_1)(x - x_2) = 0$, where a can be any nonzero real number. For each problem, there is more than one correct answer depending on your choice of a.

73. $x = -3$ and $x = 1$

74. $x = 2$ and $x = -2$

75. $x = \dfrac{2}{3}$ and $x = -\dfrac{1}{2}$

76. $x = \dfrac{3}{4}$ and $x = -\dfrac{1}{5}$

77. $x = 0$ and $x = -5$

78. $x = 0$ and $x = -3$

🖩 **GRAPHING CALCULATOR EXERCISES**

For Exercises 79–84, graph Y_1. Use the *Zoom* and *Trace* features to approximate the *x*-intercepts. Then solve $Y_1 = 0$ and compare the solutions to the *x*-intercepts.

79. $Y_1 = -x^2 + x + 2$

80. $Y_1 = -x^2 - x + 20$

81. $Y_1 = 2x^2 - x - 3$

82. $Y_1 = 5x^2 + 9x - 2$

83. $Y_1 = x^2 - 6x + 9$

84. $Y_1 = x^2 + 4x + 4$

Concepts

1. Square Root Property

2. Solving Quadratic Equations Using the Square Root Property

3. Completing the Square

4. Solving Quadratic Equations by Completing the Square

5. Applications of Quadratic Functions

6. Find the *x*- and *y*-Intercepts of a Quadratic Function

section

7.5 COMPLETING THE SQUARE AND THE SQUARE ROOT PROPERTY

1. Square Root Property

In Section 7.4, we learned to solve quadratic equations by factoring and applying the zero product rule; however, the zero product rule can only be used if the equation is factorable. In this section and the next, we will learn two techniques to solve *all* quadratic equations, factorable and nonfactorable.

The first technique will use the **square root property**.

The Square Root Property

For any real number, k, if $x^2 = k$, then $x = \sqrt{k}$ or $x = -\sqrt{k}$

Note: The solution may also be written as $x = \pm\sqrt{k}$, read *x* equals plus or minus the square root of *k*.

2. Solving Quadratic Equations Using the Square Root Property

example 1

Tip: The equation $x^2 = 81$ can also be solved by using the zero product rule.

$$x^2 = 81$$
$$x^2 - 81 = 0$$
$$(x - 9)(x + 9) = 0$$
$$x = 9 \quad \text{or} \quad x = -9$$

Solving Quadratic Equations Using the Square Root Property

Use the square root property to solve the equations.

a. $x^2 = 81$ b. $3x^2 + 75 = 0$ c. $(w + 3)^2 = 20$

Solution:

a. $x^2 = 81$ The equation is in the form $x^2 = k$.

   $x = \pm\sqrt{81}$ Apply the square root property.

   $x = \pm 9$

The solutions are $x = 9$ and $x = -9$.

b. $3x^2 + 75 = 0$ Rewrite the equation to fit the form $x^2 = k$.

$\qquad 3x^2 = -75$

$\qquad x^2 = -25$ The equation is now in the form $x^2 = k$.

$\qquad x = \pm\sqrt{-25}$ Apply the square root property.

◆ Avoiding Mistakes

$\qquad\quad = \pm 5i$

The solutions are $x = 5i$ and $x = -5i$.

A common mistake is to forget the $\pm$ symbol when solving the equation $x^2 = k$

$$x = \pm\sqrt{k}$$

Check: $x = 5i$ Check: $x = -5i$

$\quad 3x^2 + 75 = 0$ $\quad 3x^2 + 75 = 0$

$\quad 3(5i)^2 + 75 \stackrel{?}{=} 0$ $\quad 3(-5i)^2 + 75 \stackrel{?}{=} 0$

$\quad 3(25i^2) + 75 \stackrel{?}{=} 0$ $\quad 3(25i^2) + 75 \stackrel{?}{=} 0$

$\quad 3(-25) + 75 \stackrel{?}{=} 0$ $\quad 3(-25) + 75 = 0$

$\quad\;\; -75 + 75 \stackrel{?}{=} 0 \checkmark$ $\quad\;\; -75 + 75 \stackrel{?}{=} 0 \checkmark$

c. $(w + 3)^2 = 20$ The equation is in the form $x^2 = k$, where $x = (w + 3)$.

$\qquad w + 3 = \pm\sqrt{20}$ Apply the square root property.

$\qquad w + 3 = \pm\sqrt{2^2 \cdot 5}$ Simplify the radical.

$\qquad w + 3 = \pm 2\sqrt{5}$

$\qquad\qquad w = -3 \pm 2\sqrt{5}$ Solve for w.

The solutions are $w = -3 + 2\sqrt{5}$ and $w = -3 - 2\sqrt{5}$.

Check: $w = -3 + 2\sqrt{5}$ Check: $w = -3 - 2\sqrt{5}$

$\quad (w + 3)^2 = 20$ $\quad (w + 3)^2 = 20$

$(-3 + 2\sqrt{5} + 3)^2 \stackrel{?}{=} 20$ $(-3 - 2\sqrt{5} + 3)^2 \stackrel{?}{=} 20$

$\quad (2\sqrt{5})^2 \stackrel{?}{=} 20$ $\quad (-2\sqrt{5})^2 \stackrel{?}{=} 20$

$\quad\;\; 4 \cdot 5 \stackrel{?}{=} 20$ $\quad\;\; 4 \cdot 5 \stackrel{?}{=} 20$

$\quad\;\; 20 = 20 \checkmark$ $\quad\;\; 20 = 20 \checkmark$

3.   Completing the Square

In Example 1(c), we used the square root property to solve an equation where the square of a binomial was equal to a constant.

$$(w + 3)^2 = 20$$

$$w + 3 = \pm\sqrt{20}$$

$$w = -3 \pm 2\sqrt{5}$$

In general, an equation of the form $(x - h)^2 = k$ can be solved using the square root property. Furthermore, any equation $ax^2 + bx + c = 0 \; (a \neq 0)$ can be rewritten in the form $(x - h)^2 = k$ by using a process called **completing the square**.

We begin our discussion of completing the square with some vocabulary. For a trinomial $ax^2 + bx + c, (a \neq 0)$, the term ax^2 is called the quadratic term. The term bx is called the linear term, and the term, c, is called the constant term.

Next, notice that the factored form of a perfect square trinomial is the square of a binomial.

Perfect Square Trinomial	**Factored Form**
$x^2 + 10x + 25$ ⟶	$(x + 5)^2$
$t^2 - 6t + 9$ ⟶	$(t - 3)^2$
$p^2 - 14p + 49$ ⟶	$(p - 7)^2$

Furthermore, for a perfect square trinomial with a leading coefficient of 1, the constant term is the square of half the coefficient of the linear term. For example:

$$x^2 + 10x + 25 \qquad\qquad t^2 - 6t + 9 \qquad\qquad p^2 - 14p + 49$$

$$\left[\frac{1}{2}(10)\right]^2 = (5)^2 = 25 \qquad \left[\frac{1}{2}(-6)\right]^2 = (-3)^2 = 9 \qquad \left[\frac{1}{2}(-14)\right]^2 = (-7)^2 = 49$$

In general, an expression of the form $x^2 + bx$ will be a perfect square trinomial if the square of half the linear term coefficient, $(\frac{1}{2}b)^2$, is added to the expression.

example 2

Completing the Square

Complete the square for each expression. Then factor the expression as the square of a binomial.

a. $x^2 + 12x$ b. $x^2 - 26x$ c. $x^2 + 11x$ d. $x^2 - \frac{4}{7}x$

Solution:

The expressions are in the form $x^2 + bx$. Add the square of half the linear term coefficient, $(\frac{1}{2}b)^2$.

a. $x^2 + 12x$

     $x^2 + 12x + 36$ Add $\frac{1}{2}$ of 12, squared: $[\frac{1}{2}(12)]^2 = (6)^2 = 36$.

     $(x + 6)^2$ Factored form

b. $x^2 - 26x$

     $x^2 - 26x + 169$ Add $\frac{1}{2}$ of -26, squared: $[\frac{1}{2}(-26)]^2 = (-13)^2 = 169$.

     $(x - 13)^2$ Factored form

c. $x^2 + 11x$

     $x^2 + 11x + \dfrac{121}{4}$ Add $\frac{1}{2}$ of 11, squared: $[\frac{1}{2}(11)]^2 = (\frac{11}{2})^2 = \frac{121}{4}$.

     $\left(x + \dfrac{11}{2}\right)^2$ Factored form

d. $x^2 - \dfrac{4}{7}x$

$x^2 - \dfrac{4}{7}x + \dfrac{4}{49}$ Add $\frac{1}{2}$ of $-\frac{4}{7}$, squared. $[\frac{1}{2}(-\frac{4}{7})]^2 = (-\frac{2}{7})^2 = \frac{4}{49}$

$\left(x - \dfrac{2}{7}\right)^2$ Factored form

4. Solving Quadratic Equations by Completing the Square

The process of completing the square can be used to write a quadratic equation $ax^2 + bx + c = 0$ $(a \neq 0)$ in the form $(x - h)^2 = k$. Then, the square root property can be used to solve the equation. The following steps outline the procedure.

> **Solving a Quadratic Equation in the Form $ax^2 + bx + c = 0$ $(a \neq 0)$ by Completing the Square and Applying the Square Root Property**
>
> 1. Divide both sides by a to make the leading coefficient 1.
> 2. Isolate the variable terms on one side of the equation.
> 3. Complete the square. (Add the square of $\frac{1}{2}$ the linear term coefficient to both sides of the equation. Then factor the resulting perfect square trinomial.)
> 4. Apply the square root property and solve for x.

example 3

Solving Quadratic Equations by Completing the Square and Applying the Square Root Property

Solve the quadratic equations by completing the square and applying the square root property.

a. $3x^2 = 18x - 39$ b. $2x(2x - 10) = -30 + 6x$

Solution:

a. $3x^2 = 18x - 39$

$3x^2 - 18x + 39 = 0$ Write the equation in the form $ax^2 + bx + c = 0$.

$\dfrac{3x^2}{3} - \dfrac{18x}{3} + \dfrac{39}{3} = \dfrac{0}{3}$ **Step 1:** Divide both sides by the coefficient, 3.

$x^2 - 6x + 13 = 0$

$x^2 - 6x = -13$ **Step 2:** Isolate the variable terms on one side.

$x^2 - 6x + 9 = -13 + 9$ **Step 3:** To complete the square, add $[\frac{1}{2}(-6)]^2 = 9$ to both sides of the equation.

$(x - 3)^2 = -4$ Factor the perfect square trinomial.

$$x - 3 = \pm\sqrt{-4} \qquad \textbf{Step 4:} \quad \text{Apply the square root property.}$$

$$x - 3 = \pm 2i \qquad\qquad \text{Simplify the radical.}$$

$$x = 3 \pm 2i \qquad\qquad \text{Solve for } x.$$

The solutions are imaginary numbers and can be written as $x = 3 + 2i$ and $x = 3 - 2i$.

Check: $x = 3 + 2i$

$$3x^2 = 18x - 39$$

$$3(3 + 2i)^2 \overset{?}{=} 18(3 + 2i) - 39$$

$$3(9 + 12i + 4i^2) \overset{?}{=} 54 + 36i - 39$$

$$3(9 + 12i - 4) \overset{?}{=} 15 + 36i$$

$$3(5 + 12i) \overset{?}{=} 15 + 36i$$

$$15 + 36i = 15 + 36i \checkmark$$

Check: $x = 3 - 2i$

$$3x^2 = 18x - 39$$

$$3(3 - 2i)^2 \overset{?}{=} 18(3 - 2i) - 39$$

$$3(9 - 12i + 4i^2) \overset{?}{=} 54 - 36i - 39$$

$$3(9 - 12i - 4) \overset{?}{=} 15 - 36i$$

$$3(5 - 12i) \overset{?}{=} 15 - 36i$$

$$15 - 36i = 15 - 36i \checkmark$$

b.
$$2x(2x - 10) = -30 + 6x$$

$$4x^2 - 20x = -30 + 6x \qquad \text{Clear parentheses.}$$

$$4x^2 - 26x + 30 = 0 \qquad \text{Write the equation in the form } ax^2 + bx + c = 0.$$

$$\frac{4x^2}{4} - \frac{26x}{4} + \frac{30}{4} = \frac{0}{4} \qquad \textbf{Step 1:} \quad \text{Divide both sides by the coefficient, 4.}$$

$$x^2 - \frac{13}{2}x + \frac{15}{2} = 0$$

$$x^2 - \frac{13}{2}x = -\frac{15}{2} \qquad \textbf{Step 2:} \quad \text{Isolate the variable terms on one side.}$$

$$x^2 - \frac{13}{2}x + \frac{169}{16} = -\frac{15}{2} + \frac{169}{16} \qquad \textbf{Step 3:} \quad \text{Add } [\tfrac{1}{2}(-\tfrac{13}{2})]^2 = (\tfrac{13}{4})^2 = \tfrac{169}{16} \text{ to both sides.}$$

$$\left(x - \frac{13}{4}\right)^2 = -\frac{120}{16} + \frac{169}{16} \qquad \text{Factor the perfect square trinomial. Rewrite the right-hand side with a common denominator.}$$

$$\left(x - \frac{13}{4}\right)^2 = \frac{49}{16}$$

$$x - \frac{13}{4} = \pm\sqrt{\frac{49}{16}} \qquad \textbf{Step 4:} \quad \text{Apply the square root property.}$$

$$x - \frac{13}{4} = \pm\frac{7}{4} \qquad\qquad \text{Simplify the radical.}$$

$$x = \frac{13}{4} + \frac{7}{4} = \frac{20}{4} = 5$$

$$x = \frac{13}{4} \pm \frac{7}{4}$$

$$x = \frac{13}{4} - \frac{7}{4} = \frac{6}{4} = \frac{3}{2}$$

The solutions are rational numbers: $x = \frac{3}{2}$ and $x = 5$. The check is left to the reader.

Tip: Because the solutions to the equation $2x(2x - 10) = -30 + 6x$ are rational numbers, the equation could have been solved by factoring and using the zero product rule.

$$2x(2x - 10) = -30 + 6x$$

$$4x^2 - 20x = -30 + 6x$$

$$4x^2 - 26x + 30 = 0$$

$$2(2x^2 - 13x + 15) = 0$$

$$2(x - 5)(2x - 3) = 0$$

$$x = 5 \quad \text{or} \quad x = \frac{3}{2}$$

5.   Applications of Quadratic Functions

example 4

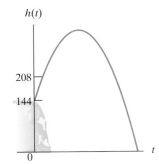

Figure 7-5

Applying a Quadratic Function

A model rocket is launched straight up from the side of a 144-ft cliff (Figure 7-5). The initial velocity is 112 ft/s. The height of the rocket, $h(t)$, is given by

$$h(t) = -16t^2 + 112t + 144, \text{ where } h(t) \text{ is measured in feet}$$
$$\text{and } t \text{ is the time in seconds.}$$

Find the time(s) at which the rocket is 208 ft above the ground.

Solution:

$$h(t) = -16t^2 + 112t + 144$$

$$208 = -16t^2 + 112t + 144 \qquad \text{Substitute 208 for } h(t).$$

$$16t^2 - 112t + 64 = 0 \qquad \text{The equation is quadratic.}$$

$$\frac{16t^2}{16} - \frac{112t}{16} + \frac{64}{16} = \frac{0}{16} \qquad \text{Divide by 16.}$$

$$t^2 - 7t + 4 = 0$$

The equation is not factorable. Complete the square and apply the square root property.

$$t^2 - 7t = -4$$

Isolate the variable terms.

$$t^2 - 7t + \frac{49}{4} = -4 + \frac{49}{4}$$

Add $[\frac{1}{2}(-7)]^2 = [-\frac{7}{2}]^2 = \frac{49}{4}$ to both sides.

$$\left(t - \frac{7}{2}\right)^2 = -\frac{16}{4} + \frac{49}{4}$$

Factor on the left and rewrite the right-hand side with a common denominator.

$$\left(t - \frac{7}{2}\right)^2 = \frac{33}{4}$$

$$t - \frac{7}{2} = \pm\sqrt{\frac{33}{4}}$$

Apply the square root property.

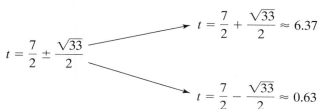

$$t = \frac{7}{2} + \frac{\sqrt{33}}{2} \approx 6.37$$

$$t = \frac{7}{2} \pm \frac{\sqrt{33}}{2}$$

$$t = \frac{7}{2} - \frac{\sqrt{33}}{2} \approx 0.63$$

The rocket will reach a height of 208 ft after approximately 0.63 s (on the way up) and after 6.37 s (on the way down).

---

example 5   **Solving a Literal Equation**

Ignoring air resistance, the distance, d (in meters), that an object falls in t seconds is given by the equation:

$$d = 4.9t^2, \text{ where } t \geq 0$$

a.   Solve the equation for t. Do not rationalize the denominator.
b.   Using the equation from part (a), determine the amount of time required for an object to fall 500 m. Round to the nearest second.

Solution:

a. $d = 4.9t^2$

$$\frac{d}{4.9} = t^2$$ Isolate the quadratic term. The equation is in the form $t^2 = k$.

$$t = \pm\sqrt{\frac{d}{4.9}}$$ Apply the square root property.

$$= \sqrt{\frac{d}{4.9}}$$ Because $t \geq 0$, reject the negative solution.

b. $t = \sqrt{\frac{d}{4.9}}$

$$= \sqrt{\frac{500}{4.9}}$$ Substitute $d = 500$.

$t \approx 10.1$

The object will require approximately 10.1 s to fall 500 m.

6.   Finding the *x*- and *y*-Intercepts of a Quadratic Function

example 6

Finding the *x*- and *y*-Intercepts of a Quadratic Function

Find the *x*- and *y*-intercepts of the function given by $f(x) = x^2 - 8x + 10$.

Solution:

To find the *x*-intercepts, solve the equation $f(x) = 0$:

$$f(x) = x^2 - 8x + 10$$

$$0 = x^2 - 8x + 10$$ Substitute $f(x) = 0$.

$$x^2 - 8x + 10 = 0$$ **Step 1:** The leading coefficient is already 1.

$$x^2 - 8x = -10$$ **Step 2:** Isolate the variable terms on one side.

$$x^2 - 8x + 16 = -10 + 16$$ **Step 3:** Add $[\frac{1}{2}(-8)]^2 = 16$ to both sides.

$$(x - 4)^2 = 6$$ Factor the perfect square trinomial.

$$x - 4 = \pm\sqrt{6}$$ **Step 4:** Apply the square root property.

$$x = 4 \pm \sqrt{6}$$ Solve for *x*.

The x-intercepts are $(4 + \sqrt{6}, 0) \approx (6.45, 0)$

and $(4 - \sqrt{6}, 0) \approx (1.55, 0)$

To find the y-intercept, find $f(0)$:

$$f(x) = x^2 - 8x + 10$$
$$f(0) = (0)^2 - 8(0) + 10$$
$$f(0) = 10$$

The y-intercept is $(0, 10)$.

The graph of $f(x) = x^2 - 8x + 10$ is shown in Figure 7-6.

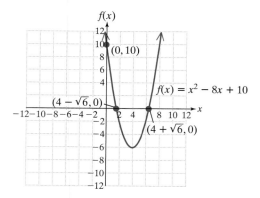

Figure 7-6

Graphing Calculator Box

The real solutions to a quadratic equation $ax^2 + bx + c = 0$ can be interpreted graphically as the x-intercepts of the function given by $f(x) = ax^2 + bx + c$. Consequently, we can use the graph of f to approximate the real solutions to the equation $ax^2 + bx + c = 0$. As the following examples indicate, a quadratic function may have zero, one, or two x-intercepts.

Case 1: Two x-Intercepts

Approximate the real solutions to the equation $-x^2 - 3x + 6 = 0$ from the graph of $f(x) = -x^2 - 3x + 6$.

A *Trace* option or a *Zero* or *Root* feature can be used to find decimal approximations of the x-intercepts. From the graphs, we have $x \approx 1.3722813$ and $x \approx -4.372281$.

Figure 7-7   **Figure 7-8**

The exact solutions to the equation

$$-x^2 - 3x + 6 = 0 \text{ are } x = \frac{-3 \pm \sqrt{33}}{2}$$

where

$$x = \frac{-3 + \sqrt{33}}{2} \approx 1.3722813 \quad \text{and} \quad x = \frac{-3 - \sqrt{33}}{2} \approx -4.372281$$

Case 2: One x-Intercept

Approximate the real solution(s) to the equation $x^2 - 6x + 9 = 0$ from the graph of $f(x) = x^2 - 6x + 9$.

From the graph, it appears that the function has only one x-intercept at $x \approx 2.9999992$. Because the equation can be easily factored, we can confirm our results analytically.

Figure 7-9

$$x^2 - 6x + 9 = 0$$

$$(x - 3)^2 = 0 \qquad \text{The repeated factor, } x - 3 \text{ yields only one solution.}$$

$$x - 3 = 0$$

$$x = 3$$

Case 3: Zero x-Intercepts

Find the real solution(s) to the equation $2x^2 - 16x + 40 = 0$ from the graph of $f(x) = 2x^2 - 16x + 40$.

The equation $f(x) = 2x^2 - 16x + 40$ has no x-intercepts. Therefore, the equation $2x^2 - 16x + 40 = 0$ has no real solutions.

The exact solutions to the equation $2x^2 - 16x + 40 = 0$ are the imaginary numbers $x = 4 + 2i$ and $x = 4 - 2i$.

Figure 7-10

section 7.5   PRACTICE EXERCISES

For Exercises 1–6, match the expression with the type of factoring pattern. Then factor the expression.

    a.   Difference of squares

    b.   Difference of cubes

    c.   Sum of cubes

    d.   Perfect square trinomial

    e.   Trinomial (grouping or trial-and-error)

    f.   Grouping

1. $-t^2 + 6t + 16$ 2. $25u^3 - 9uv^2$

3. $8y^3 - \dfrac{1}{1000}$ 4. $16a^4 - 8a^2 + 1$

5. $9ax + 9ay - 9cx - 9cy$ 6. $x^3 + 27y^6$

7.   How do you recognize a perfect square trinomial?

8.   How do you factor a difference of cubes?

9.   How do you factor a difference of squares?

10.   How do you factor a sum of cubes?

For Exercises 11–26, solve the equations by using the square root property.

11. $x^2 = 100$ 12. $y^2 = 4$

13. $a^2 = 5$ 14. $k^2 - 7 = 0$

15. $v^2 + 11 = 0$ 16. $m^2 = -25$

17. $(p - 5)^2 = 9$ 18. $(q + 3)^2 = 4$

19. $(x - 2)^2 = 5$ 20. $(y + 3)^2 - 7 = 0$

21. $(h - 4)^2 = -8$ 22. $(t + 5)^2 = -18$

23. $\left(a - \dfrac{1}{2}\right)^2 = \dfrac{3}{4}$ 24. $\left(y + \dfrac{2}{3}\right)^2 = -\dfrac{5}{9}$

25. $\left(x - \dfrac{3}{2}\right)^2 + \dfrac{7}{4} = 0$

26. $\left(m + \dfrac{4}{5}\right)^2 - \dfrac{3}{25} = 0$

27.   State two methods that can be used to solve the equation: $x^2 - 81 = 0$. Then solve the equation using both methods.

28.   State two methods that can be used to solve the equation: $x^2 - 9 = 0$. Then solve the equation using both methods.

29.   A corner shelf is to be made from a triangular piece of plywood as shown in the diagram. Find the distance, x, that the shelf will extend along the walls. Assume that the walls are at right angles. Round the answer to a tenth of a foot.

Figure for Exercise 29

30.   A square has an area of 50 in.^{2} What are the lengths of the sides? (Round to one decimal place.)

31.   The amount of money, A, in an account with an interest rate, r, compounded annually is given by

$A = P(1 + r)^t$, where P is the initial principal and t is the number of years the money is invested.

    a.   If a \$10,000 investment grows to \$11,664 after 2 years, find the interest rate.

    b.   If a \$6000 investment grows to \$7392.60 after 2 years, find the interest rate.

    c.   Jamal wants to invest \$5000. He wants the money to grow to at least \$6500 in 2 years to cover the cost of his son's first year at college. What interest rate does Jamal need for his investment to grow to \$6500 in 2 years? Round to the nearest hundredth of a percent.

32. The volume of a box with a square bottom and a height of 4 in. is given by $V(x) = 4x^2$, where x is the length (in inches) of the sides of the bottom of the box.

a. If the volume of the box is 289 in.³, find the dimensions of the box.

b. Are there two possible answers to part (a)? Why or why not?

Figure for Exercise 32

For Exercises 33–38, find the value of k so that the expression is a perfect square trinomial. Then factor the trinomial.

33. $x^2 - 6x + k$

34. $x^2 + 12x + k$

35. $y^2 + 5y + k$

36. $a^2 - 7a + k$

37. $b^2 + \frac{2}{5}b + k$

38. $m^2 - \frac{2}{7}m + k$

39. Summarize the steps used in solving a quadratic equation by completing the square and applying the square root property.

40. What types of quadratic equations can be solved by completing the square and applying the square root property?

For Exercises 41–58, solve the quadratic equation by completing the square and applying the square root property.

41. $t^2 + 8t + 15 = 0$

42. $m^2 + 6m + 8 = 0$

43. $x^2 + 6x = 16$

44. $x^2 - 4x = -3$

45. $p^2 + 4p + 6 = 0$

46. $q^2 + 2q + 2 = 0$

47. $y^2 - 3y - 10 = 0$

48. $-24 = -2y^2 + 2y$

49. $2a^2 + 4a + 5 = 0$

50. $3a^2 + 6a - 7 = 0$

51. $9x^2 - 36x + 40 = 0$

52. $9y^2 - 12y + 5 = 0$

53. $p^2 - \frac{2}{5}p = \frac{2}{25}$

54. $n^2 - \frac{2}{3}n = \frac{1}{9}$

55. $(2w + 5)(w - 1) = 2$

56. $(3p - 5)(p + 1) = -3$

57. $n(n - 4) = 7$

58. $m(m + 10) = 2$

For Exercises 59–66, solve for the indicated variable.

59. $A = \pi r^2$ for r $(r > 0)$

60. $E = mc^2$ for c $(c > 0)$

61. $a^2 + b^2 + c^2 = d^2$ for a $(a > 0)$

62. $a^2 + b^2 = c^2$ for b $(b > 0)$

63. $V = \frac{1}{3}\pi r^2 h$ for r $(r > 0)$

64. $A = 6x^2$ for x $(x > 0)$

65. $s = 2\sqrt{x}$ for x

66. $A = 1.5\sqrt{x - 1}$ for x

67. A textbook company has discovered that the profit for selling its books is given by

$$P(x) = -\frac{1}{8}x^2 + 5x,$$ where x is the number of textbooks produced (in thousands) and $P(x)$ is the corresponding profit (in thousands of dollars)

The graph of the function is shown below.

a. Approximate the number of books required to make a profit of $20,000. (*Hint:* Let $P(x) = 20$. Then complete the square to solve for x.) Round to one decimal place.

b. Why are there two answers to part (a)?

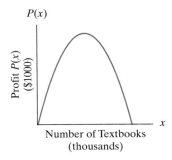

Figure for Exercise 67

68. Ignoring air resistance, the distance, d, (in feet) that an object travels in free fall can be approximated by $d(t) = 16t^2$, where t is the time in seconds after the object was dropped.

    a. If the CN Tower in Toronto is 1815 ft high, how long will it take an object to fall from the top of the building? Round to one decimal place.

    b. If the Renaissance Tower in Dallas is 886 ft high, how long will it take an object to fall from the top of the building? Round to one decimal place.

GRAPHING CALCULATOR EXERCISES

For Exercises 69–76,

    a. Graph Y_1 and use a *Zero* or *Root* feature of the calculator to approximate the *x*-intercepts, if they exist.

    b. Solve $Y_1 = 0$ by using the square root property, completing the square if necessary. Round to four decimal places.

    c. Compare your answers from parts (a) and (b).

69. $Y_1 = 3(x - 2)^2 - 5$

70. $Y_1 = 2(x - 1)^2 - 3$

71. $Y_1 = x^2 + 4x - 9$

72. $Y_1 = x^2 + 3x - 11$

73. $Y_1 = x^2 + x + 6$

74. $Y_1 = x^2 + 2x + 8$

75. $Y_1 = x^2 - 2x + 1$

76. $Y_1 = x^2 - 6x + 9$

Concepts

1. **Derivation of the Quadratic Formula**

2. **Solving Quadratic Equations Using the Quadratic Formula**

3. **Using the Quadratic Formula in Applications**

4. **Discriminant**

5. **Review of the Methods to Solve a Quadratic Equation**

section

7.6   QUADRATIC FORMULA

1.   Derivation of the Quadratic Formula

If we solve a general quadratic equation $ax^2 + bx + c = 0 \, (a \neq 0)$ by completing the square and using the square root property, the result is a formula that gives the solutions for x in terms of a, b, and c.

$$ax^2 + bx + c = 0$$

Begin with a quadratic equation in standard form.

$$x^2 + \frac{b}{a}x + \frac{c}{a} = 0$$

Divide by the leading coefficient.

$$x^2 + \frac{b}{a}x = -\frac{c}{a}$$

Isolate the terms containing x.

$$x^2 + \frac{b}{a}x + \left(\frac{1}{2} \cdot \frac{b}{a}\right)^2 = \left(\frac{1}{2} \cdot \frac{b}{a}\right)^2 - \frac{c}{a}$$

Add the square of $\frac{1}{2}$ the linear term coefficient to both sides of the equation.

$$\left(x + \frac{b}{2a}\right)^2 = \frac{b^2}{4a^2} - \frac{c}{a}$$

Factor the left side as a perfect square.

$$\left(x + \frac{b}{2a}\right)^2 = \frac{b^2 - 4ac}{4a^2}$$

Combine fractions on the right side by getting a common denominator.

$$x + \frac{b}{2a} = \pm\sqrt{\frac{b^2 - 4ac}{4a^2}}$$

Apply the square root property.

$$x + \frac{b}{2a} = \frac{\pm\sqrt{b^2 - 4ac}}{2a}$$

Simplify the denominator.

$$x = -\frac{b}{2a} \pm \frac{\sqrt{b^2 - 4ac}}{2a}$$

Subtract $\frac{b}{2a}$ from both sides.

$$= \frac{-b \pm \sqrt{b^2 - 4ac}}{2a}$$

Combine fractions.

The solution to the equation, $ax^2 + bx + c = 0$, for x in terms of the coefficients a, b, and c, is given by the **quadratic formula**.

The Quadratic Formula

For any quadratic equation of the form $ax^2 + bx + c = 0$ $(a \neq 0)$ the solutions are

$$x = \frac{-b \pm \sqrt{b^2 - 4ac}}{2a}$$

---

2. Solving Quadratic Equations Using the Quadratic Formula

example 1

Solving a Quadratic Equation Using the Quadratic Formula

Solve the quadratic equation using the quadratic formula.

$$3x^2 + 8x = -5$$

Solution:

$$3x^2 + 8x = -5$$

$$3x^2 + 8x + 5 = 0$$

Write the equation in the form $ax^2 + bx + c = 0$.

$$a = 3, b = 8, c = 5$$

Identify a, b, and c.

$$x = \frac{-(8) \pm \sqrt{(8)^2 - 4(3)(5)}}{2(3)}$$

Apply the quadratic formula.

$$= \frac{-8 \pm \sqrt{64 - 60}}{6}$$

Simplify.

$$= \frac{-8 \pm \sqrt{4}}{6}$$

$$= \frac{-8 \pm 2}{6}$$

There are two rational solutions.

$$x = \frac{-8 + 2}{6} = \frac{-6}{6} = -1$$

$$x = \frac{-8 - 2}{6} = \frac{-10}{6} = -\frac{5}{3}$$

Both solutions check in the original equation.

Tip: Because the solutions to the equation $3x^2 + 8x = -5$ are rational numbers, the equation could have been solved by factoring and using the zero product rule.

$$3x^2 + 8x = -5$$

$$3x^2 + 8x + 5 = 0$$

$$(3x + 5)(x + 1) = 0$$

$$x = -\tfrac{5}{3} \quad \text{or} \quad x = -1$$

---

example 2   **Solving a Quadratic Equation Using the Quadratic Formula**

Solve the quadratic equation using the quadratic formula.

$$x(x + 7) + 4 = 0$$

Solution:

$$x(x + 7) + 4 = 0$$
$$x^2 + 7x + 4 = 0$$ Write the equation in the form $ax^2 + bx + c = 0$.

$$a = 1, b = 7, c = 4$$ Identify a, b, and c.

$$x = \frac{-(7) \pm \sqrt{(7)^2 - 4(1)(4)}}{2(1)}$$ Apply the quadratic formula.

$$= \frac{-7 \pm \sqrt{49 - 16}}{2}$$ Simplify.

$$= \frac{-7 \pm \sqrt{33}}{2}$$ The solutions are irrational numbers.

The solutions can be written as

$$x = \frac{-7 + \sqrt{33}}{2} \approx -0.628 \quad \text{and} \quad x = \frac{-7 - \sqrt{33}}{2} \approx -6.372$$

Graphing Calculator Box

Consider the equation $x(x + 7) + 4 = 0$ from Example 2. In standard form, this equation is written as $x^2 + 7x + 4 = 0$. Using the quadratic formula, we have

$$x = \frac{-(7) \pm \sqrt{(7)^2 - 4(1)(4)}}{2(1)}$$

A calculator can be used to apply the quadratic formula directly; however, each solution must be entered separately. The solution can be checked on the calculator by using the *Ans* variable. This contains the result of the calculator's most recent computation.

$$x = \frac{-(7) + \sqrt{(7)^2 - 4(1)(4)}}{2(1)} \approx -0.6277186767$$

```
(-(7)+√((7)²-4*1
*4))/(2*1)
          -.6277186767     ← Solution
Ans²+7Ans+4
                     0     ← Check
```

$$x = \frac{-(7) - \sqrt{(7)^2 - 4(1)(4)}}{2(1)} \approx -6.372281323$$

```
(-(7)-√((7)²-4*1
*4))/(2*1)
          -6.372281323     ← Solution
Ans²+7Ans+4
                     0     ← Check
```

---

example 3

Solving a Quadratic Equation Using the Quadratic Formula

Solve the quadratic equation using the quadratic formula.

$$\frac{1}{4}z^2 + \frac{1}{4}z = -\frac{1}{2}$$

Solution:

$$\frac{1}{4}z^2 + \frac{1}{4}z = -\frac{1}{2}$$

$$4\left(\frac{1}{4}z^2 + \frac{1}{4}z\right) = 4\left(-\frac{1}{2}\right) \qquad \text{Multiply by 4 to clear fractions.}$$

$$z^2 + z = -2$$

$$z^2 + z + 2 = 0$$

Write the equation in the form $ax^2 + bx + c = 0$.

$$a = 1, b = 1, c = 2$$

Identify a, b, and c.

$$z = \frac{-(1) \pm \sqrt{(1)^2 - 4(1)(2)}}{2(1)}$$

Apply the quadratic formula.

$$= \frac{-1 \pm \sqrt{-7}}{2}$$

Simplify.

$$= -\frac{1}{2} \pm \frac{\sqrt{7}}{2}i$$

These solutions are *imaginary numbers*.

3. Using the Quadratic Formula in Applications

example 4

Using the Quadratic Formula in an Application

A delivery truck travels south from Hartselle, Alabama, to Birmingham along Interstate 65. The truck then heads east to Atlanta, Georgia, along Interstate 20. The distance from Birmingham to Atlanta is 8 miles less than twice the distance from Hartselle to Birmingham. If the straight-line distance from Hartselle to Atlanta is 165 miles, find the distance from Hartselle to Birmingham and from Birmingham to Atlanta. (Round the answers to the nearest mile.)

Solution:

The motorist travels due south and then due east, the three cities therefore form the vertices of a right triangle (Figure 7-11).

Let x represent the distance between Hartselle and Birmingham.

Then $2x - 8$ represents the distance between Birmingham and Atlanta.

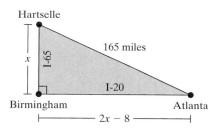

Figure 7-11

Use the Pythagorean theorem to establish a relationship among the three sides of the triangle.

$$(x)^2 + (2x - 8)^2 = (165)^2$$

$$x^2 + 4x^2 - 32x + 64 = 27{,}225$$

$$5x^2 - 32x - 27{,}161 = 0$$

Write the equation in the form $ax^2 + bx + c = 0$.

$$a = 5, b = -32, c = -27{,}161$$

Identify a, b, and c.

$$x = \frac{-(-32) \pm \sqrt{(-32)^2 - 4(5)(-27{,}161)}}{2(5)}$$

Apply the quadratic formula.

$$= \frac{32 \pm \sqrt{1024 + 543{,}220}}{10}$$

Simplify.

$$= \frac{32 \pm \sqrt{544{,}244}}{10}$$

$$x = \frac{32 + \sqrt{544{,}244}}{10} \approx 76.97 \text{ miles} \qquad \text{or}$$

$$x = \frac{32 - \sqrt{544{,}244}}{10} \approx -70.57 \text{ miles} \qquad \text{We reject the negative distance.}$$

Recall that x represents the distance from Hartselle to Birmingham; therefore, to the nearest mile, the distance between Hartselle and Birmingham is 77 miles.

The distance between Birmingham and Atlanta is $2x - 8 = 2(77) - 8 = 146$ miles.

example 5

Applying a Quadratic Function

The recent population, P, of Costa Rica (in thousands of people), can be approximated by

$$P(t) = 0.524t^2 + 46.3t + 2603 \quad t \geq 0, \text{ where } t \text{ represents the number of}$$
$$\text{years after 1980 (Figure 7-12).}$$

a. Use the function to predict the population of Costa Rica in the year 2010.
b. In what year was the population 3,500,000 (3500 thousands)? (Round the answer to the nearest year.)

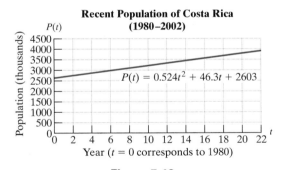

Figure 7-12

Solution:

a. $P(t) = 0.524t^2 + 46.3t + 2603$

$P(30) = 0.524(30)^2 + 46.3(30) + 2603$ The year 2010 corresponds to $t = 30$.

$= 4463.6$

The population of Costa Rica is predicted to be 4463.6 thousands (4,463,600) in the year 2010.

b. $P(t) = 0.524t^2 + 46.3t + 2603$

$3500 = 0.524t^2 + 46.3t + 2603$ Substitute 3500 for $P(t)$.

$0 = 0.524t^2 + 46.3t - 897$ Write the equation in the form $ax^2 + bx + c = 0$.

$a = 0.524, b = 46.3, c = -897$ Identify a, b, and c.

$$t = \frac{-(46.3) \pm \sqrt{(46.3)^2 - 4(0.524)(-897)}}{2(0.524)}$$ Apply the quadratic formula.

$$\approx \frac{-46.3 \pm \sqrt{4023.802}}{1.048}$$

$$t \approx \frac{-46.3 + 63.433}{1.048} \approx 16 \text{ (rounded to the nearest year)}$$

$$t \approx \frac{-46.3 \pm 63.433}{1.048}$$

$$t \approx \frac{-46.3 - 63.433}{1.048} \approx -105 \text{ (rounded to the nearest year)}$$

We reject the negative solution; therefore, the population of Costa Rica was approximately 3,500,000 for $x = 16$. This is the year 1996.

4. Discriminant

From Examples 1–3, we see that the solutions to a quadratic equation may be rational, irrational, or imaginary numbers. The *number* and the *type* of solution can be determined by noting the value of the square root term in the quadratic formula. The radicand of the square root, $b^2 - 4ac$, is called the discriminant.

Using the Discriminant to Determine the Number and Type of Solutions of a Quadratic Equation

Consider the equation, $ax^2 + bx + c = 0$, where a, b, and c are rational numbers and $a \neq 0$. The expression $b^2 - 4ac$, is called the **discriminant**. Furthermore,

1.   If $b^2 - 4ac > 0$ then there will be two real solutions. Moreover,
     a. If $b^2 - 4ac$ is a perfect square, the solutions will be rational numbers.
     b. If $b^2 - 4ac$ is not a perfect square, the solutions will be irrational numbers.

2.   If $b^2 - 4ac < 0$ then there will be two imaginary solutions.

3.   If $b^2 - 4ac = 0$ then there will be one rational solution.

example 6

Using the Discriminant

Use the discriminant to determine the type and number of solutions for each equation.

a. $2x^2 - 5x + 9 = 0$ b. $3x^2 = -x + 2$

c. $-2x(2x - 3) = -1$ d. $3.6x^2 = -1.2x - 0.1$

Solution:

For each equation, first write the equation in standard form, $ax^2 + bx + c = 0$. Then determine the discriminant.

Equation	Discriminant	Solution Type and Number
a. $2x^2 - 5x + 9 = 0$	$b^2 - 4ac$ $= (-5)^2 - 4(2)(9)$ $= 25 - 72$ $= -47$	Because $-47 < 0$, there will be two imaginary solutions.
b. $\quad\quad 3x^2 = -x + 2$ $3x^2 + x - 2 = 0$	$b^2 - 4ac$ $= (1)^2 - 4(3)(-2)$ $= 1 - (-24)$ $= 25$	Because $25 > 0$ and 25 is a perfect square, there will be two rational solutions.
c. $\quad -2x(2x - 3) = -1$ $\quad\quad -4x^2 + 6x = -1$ $-4x^2 + 6x + 1 = 0$	$b^2 - 4ac$ $= (6)^2 - 4(-4)(1)$ $= 36 - (-16)$ $= 52$	Because $52 > 0$, but 52 is *not* a perfect square, there will be two irrational solutions.
d. $\quad\quad 3.6x^2 = -1.2x - 0.1$ $\quad\quad 36x^2 = -12x - 1$ Clear decimals first. $36x^2 + 12x + 1 = 0$	$b^2 - 4ac$ $= (12)^2 - 4(36)(1)$ $= 144 - 144$ $= 0$	Because the discriminant equals 0, there will be only one rational solution.

5. Review of the Methods to Solve a Quadratic Equation

Three methods have been presented to solve quadratic equations.

Methods to Solve a Quadratic Equation

- Factor and use the zero product rule (Section 7.4).
- Use the square root property. Complete the square if necessary (Section 7.5).
- Use the quadratic formula (Section 7.6).

Using the zero product rule is the simplest method, but it only works if you can factor the equation. The square root property and the quadratic formula can be used to solve any quadratic equation. Before solving a quadratic equation, take a minute to analyze it first. Each problem must be evaluated individually before choosing the most efficient method to find its solutions.

example 7   **Solving Quadratic Equations Using Any Method**

Solve the quadratic equations using any method.

a. $(x + 3)^2 + x^2 - 9x = 8$ b. $\dfrac{x^2}{2} + \dfrac{5}{2} = -x$ c. $(p - 2)^2 - 11 = 0$

Solution:

a.
$$(x + 3)^2 + x^2 - 9x = 8$$

$x^2 + 6x + 9 + x^2 - 9x - 8 = 0$ Clear parentheses and write the equation in the form $ax^2 + bx + c = 0$.

$2x^2 - 3x + 1 = 0$ This equation is factorable.

$(2x - 1)(x - 1) = 0$ Factor.

$2x - 1 = 0$ or $x - 1 = 0$ Apply the zero product rule.

$x = \frac{1}{2}$ or $x = 1$ Solve for x.

This equation could have been solved using any of the three methods but factoring was the most efficient method.

b.
$$\frac{x^2}{2} + \frac{5}{2} = -x$$

Clear fractions and write the equation in the form $ax^2 + bx + c = 0$.

$$x^2 + 5 = -2x$$

$$x^2 + 2x + 5 = 0$$

This equation does not factor. Use the quadratic formula.

$$a = 1, b = 2, c = 5$$

Identify a, b, and c.

$$x = \frac{-(2) \pm \sqrt{(2)^2 - 4(1)(5)}}{2(1)}$$

Apply the quadratic formula.

$$= \frac{-2 \pm \sqrt{-16}}{2}$$

Simplify.

$$= \frac{-2 \pm 4i}{2}$$

Simplify the radical.

$$= -1 + 2i$$

Reduce the expression.

$$\frac{-2 \pm 4i}{2} = \frac{2(-1 \pm 2i)}{2}$$

This equation could also have been solved by completing the square and applying the square root property.

c. $(p - 2)^2 - 11 = 0$

$$(p - 2)^2 = 11$$

The equation is in the form $x^2 = k$, where $x = (p - 2)$.

$$p - 2 = \pm\sqrt{11}$$

Apply the square root property.

$$p = 2 \pm \sqrt{11}$$

Solve for p.

This problem could have been solved by the quadratic formula but that would have involved clearing parentheses and collecting *like* terms first.

---

section 7.6   PRACTICE EXERCISES

For Exercises 1–8, either factor the polynomial or solve the polynomial equation as the directions indicate.

1. Solve: $(x + 5)^2 = 49$

2. Solve: $16 = (2x - 3)^2$

3. Factor: $x^3 - 1$

4. Factor: $y^4 - \frac{1}{81}$

5. Solve: $x^3 - 2x^2 - 9x + 18 = 0$

6. Solve: $k^3 + 2k^2 - 3k = 0$

7. Factor: $8uv - 6u + 12v - 9$

8. Factor: $4t^2 - 20t + 25 - s^2$

For Exercises 9–12, simplify the expressions.

9. $\frac{16 - \sqrt{640}}{4}$

10. $\frac{18 + \sqrt{180}}{3}$

11. $\dfrac{14 - \sqrt{-147}}{7}$

12. $\dfrac{10 - \sqrt{-175}}{5}$

For Exercises 13–20, write the equation in the form $ax^2 + bx + c = 0$, $a > 0$, and identify a, b, and c.

13. $x^2 + 2x = -1$

14. $12y - 9 = 4y^2$

15. $19m^2 = 8m$

16. $2n - 5n^2 = 0$

17. $5p^2 - 21 = 0$

18. $3k^2 = 7$

19. $4n(n - 2) - 5n(n - 1) = 4$

20. $(2x + 1)(x - 3) = -9$

For Exercises 21–28, use the discriminant, $b^2 - 4ac$, to determine the number and type of solutions to the indicated exercise. Choose from two rational solutions, one rational solution, two irrational solutions, or two imaginary solutions.

21. Exercise 13

22. Exercise 14

23. Exercise 15

24. Exercise 16

25. Exercise 17

26. Exercise 18

27. Exercise 19

28. Exercise 20

29. Describe the circumstances in which factoring can be used as a method for solving a quadratic equation.

30. Describe the circumstances in which the square root property can be used as a method for solving a quadratic equation.

31. Describe the circumstances in which the quadratic formula can be used as a method for solving a quadratic equation.

32. Write the quadratic formula from memory.

For Exercises 33–56, solve the equation using the quadratic formula.

33. $a^2 + 11a - 12 = 0$

34. $5b^2 - 14b - 3 = 0$

35. $9y^2 - 2y + 5 = 0$

36. $2t^2 + 3t - 7 = 0$

37. $12p^2 - 4p + 5 = 0$

38. $5n^2 - 4n + 6 = 0$

39. $z^2 = 2z + 35$

40. $12x^2 - 5x = 2$

41. $a^2 + 3a = 8$

42. $k^2 + 4 = 6k$

43. $25x^2 - 20x + 4 = 0$

44. $9y^2 = -12y - 4$

45. $w^2 - 6w + 14 = 0$

46. $2m^2 + 3m = -2$

47. $(x + 2)(x - 3) = 1$

48. $3y(y + 1) - 7y(y + 2) = 6$

49. $\dfrac{1}{2}y^2 + \dfrac{2}{3} = -\dfrac{2}{3}y$

(*Hint:* Clear the fractions first.)

50. $\dfrac{2}{3}p^2 - \dfrac{1}{6}p + \dfrac{1}{2} = 0$

51. $\dfrac{1}{5}h^2 + h + \dfrac{3}{5} = 0$

52. $\dfrac{1}{4}w^2 + \dfrac{7}{4}w + 1 = 0$

53. $0.01x^2 + 0.06x + 0.08 = 0$

(*Hint:* Clear the decimals first.)

54. $0.5y^2 - 0.7y + 0.2 = 0$

55. $0.3t^2 + 0.7t - 0.5 = 0$

56. $0.01x^2 + 0.04x - 0.07 = 0$

57. a. Factor: $x^3 - 27$.

    b. Use the zero product rule and the quadratic formula to solve $x^3 - 27 = 0$. There should be three solutions (one real and two imaginary).

58. a. Factor: $64x^3 + 1$.

    b. Use the zero product rule and the quadratic formula to solve $64x^3 + 1 = 0$. There should be three solutions (one real and two imaginary).

59. a. Factor: $3x^3 - 6x^2 + 6x$.

    b. Use the zero product rule and the quadratic formula to solve $3x^3 - 6x^2 + 6x = 0$. There should be three complex solutions.

60. a. Factor: $5x^3 + 5x^2 + 10x$.

    b. Use the zero product rule and the quadratic formula to solve $5x^3 + 5x^2 + 10x = 0$. There should be three complex solutions.

61. The volume of a cube is 27 ft³. Find the lengths of the sides.

Figure for Exercise 61

62. The volume of a rectangular box is 64 ft³. If the width is 3 times longer than the height, and the length is 9 times longer than the height, find the dimensions of the box.

Figure for Exercise 62

For Exercises 63–70, solve the quadratic equations using any method.

63. $a^2 + 3a + 4 = 0$

64. $4z^2 + 7z = 0$

65. $x^2 - 2 = 0$

66. $b^2 + 7 = 0$

67. $4y^2 + 8y - 5 = 0$

68. $k^2 - k + 8 = 0$

69. $\left(x + \dfrac{1}{2}\right)^2 + 4 = 0$

70. $(2y + 3)^2 = 9$

71. The braking distance, d (in feet), of a car going v miles per hour is given by

$$d(v) = \frac{v^2}{20} + v \quad v \geq 0$$

a. How fast would a car be traveling if its braking distance is 150 ft? Round to the nearest mile per hour.

b. How fast would a car be traveling if its braking distance is 100 ft? Round to the nearest mile per hour.

72. The number of lawyers, N, in the United States from the year 1951 through 1989 can be approximated by $N(t) = 1060t^2 - 7976t + 202{,}209$ where t represents the number of years after 1951 (*Source:* Datapedia of the United States).

a. Approximate the number of lawyers in the United States in the year 1978. Round to the nearest thousand.

b. In what year after 1951 did the number of lawyers in the United States hit 400,000. (Round to the nearest year.)

c. In what year after 1951 did the number of lawyers hit a half-million? (Round to the nearest year.)

d. If this trend continues, predict the approximate number of lawyers in the United States in the year 2010. Round to the nearest thousand.

73. The hypotenuse of a right triangle is 10.2 m long. One leg is 2.1 m shorter than the other leg. Find the lengths of the legs. Round to one decimal place.

74. The hypotenuse of a right triangle is 17 ft long. One leg is 3.4 ft longer than the other leg. Find the lengths of the legs.

75. The number of farms in the United States increased between 1890 and 1920 and then began a downward trend.

The number of farms, N, can be approximated as a function of time by $N(t) = -1.43t^2 + 94.56t + 4825$, where $t = 0$ corresponds to the year 1890 and N is measured in thousands of farms.

a. Use the function to approximate the number of farms in the year 1930. Round to the nearest whole unit.

b. Why is the function value slightly different from the observed data value of 6295?

c. Approximate the years when the number of farms in the United States was 5,000,000 ($N = 5000$ thousands).

▪ EXPANDING YOUR SKILLS

76. An artist has been commissioned to make a stained glass window in the shape of a regular octagon. The octagon must fit inside an 18-in. square space. See the figure.

Figure for Exercise 76

a. Let x represent the length of each side of the octagon. Verify that the legs of the small triangles formed by the corners of the square can be expressed as $\dfrac{18 - x}{2}$.

b. Use the Pythagorean theorem to set up an equation in terms of x that represents the relationship between the legs of the triangle and the hypotenuse.

c. Simplify the equation by clearing parentheses and clearing fractions.

d. Solve the resulting quadratic equation by using the quadratic formula. Use a calculator and round your answers to the nearest tenth of an inch.

e. There are two solutions for x. Which one is appropriate and why?

▪ GRAPHING CALCULATOR EXERCISES

77. Graph $Y_1 = x^3 - 27$. Compare the x-intercepts with the solutions to the equation $x^3 - 27 = 0$ found in Exercise 57.

78. Graph $Y_1 = 64x^3 + 1$. Compare the x-intercepts with the solutions to the equation $64x^3 + 1 = 0$ found in Exercise 58.

79. Graph $Y_1 = 3x^3 - 6x^2 + 6x$. Compare the x-intercepts with the solutions to the equation $3x^3 - 6x^2 + 6x = 0$ found in Exercise 59.

80. Graph $Y_1 = 5x^3 + 5x^2 + 10x$. Compare the x-intercepts with the solutions to the equation $5x^3 + 5x^2 + 10x = 0$ found in Exercise 60.

81. The recent population, P (in thousands), of Ecuador can be approximated by $P(t) = 1.12t^2 + 204.4t + 6697$, where $t = 0$ corresponds to the year 1974.

a. Approximate the number of people in Ecuador in the year 1980.

b. If this trend continues, approximate the number of people in Ecuador in the year 2010.

c. In what year after 1974 did the population of Ecuador reach 10 million? Round to the nearest year. (*Hint:* 10 million equals 10,000 thousands.)

d. Use a graphing calculator to graph the function, P on the window $0 \le x \le 20$, $4000 \le y \le 12{,}000$. Use a *Trace* feature to determine the year when the population in Ecuador was 10 million (10,000 thousands).

82. The recent population, P (in thousands), of New Zealand can be approximated by $P(t) = 0.089t^2 + 25.7t + 3601$, where $t = 0$ corresponds to the year 1995.

a. Approximate the number of people in New Zealand in the year 1999.

b. If this trend continues, approximate the number of people in New Zealand in the year 2005.

c. In what year after 1995 did the population of New Zealand reach 3.8 million? Round to the nearest year. (*Hint:* 3.8 million equals 3800 thousands.)

d. Use a graphing calculator to graph the function, $P(t)$ on the window $0 \leq x \leq 10$, $2000 \leq y \leq 6000$. Use the *Trace* feature to determine the year when the population in New Zealand was 3.8 million.

---

section

7.7 EQUATIONS IN QUADRATIC FORM

Concepts

1. **Equations Reducible to a Quadratic**

2. **Solving Equations Using Substitution**

1. Equations Reducible to a Quadratic

We have learned to solve a variety of different types of equations, including linear, radical, and polynomial equations. Sometimes, however, it is necessary to use a quadratic equation as a tool to solve other types of equations. For instance, the equation in Example 1 is a radical equation that reduces to a quadratic equation after squaring both sides.

example 1   **Solving an Equation in Quadratic Form**

Solve the equation.

$$x - \sqrt{x} - 12 = 0$$

Solution:

$x - \sqrt{x} - 12 = 0$	This is a radical equation.
$x - 12 = \sqrt{x}$	Isolate the radical.
$(x - 12)^2 = (\sqrt{x})^2$	Square both sides.
$x^2 - 24x + 144 = x$	The resulting equation is quadratic.
$x^2 - 25x + 144 = 0$	Write the equation in the form $ax^2 + bx + c = 0$.
$(x - 9)(x - 16) = 0$	The equation is factorable.
$x = 9 \quad$ or $\quad x = 16$	Apply the zero product rule.

Avoiding Mistakes

Recall that if we raise both sides of a radical equation to an even power, the potential solutions must be checked in the original equation.

Check: $x = 9$

$x - \sqrt{x} - 12 = 0$

$(9) - \sqrt{9} - 12 \stackrel{?}{=} 0$

$9 - 3 - 12 \neq 0$

Check: $x = 16$

$x - \sqrt{x} - 12 = 0$

$(16) - \sqrt{16} - 12 \stackrel{?}{=} 0$

$16 - 4 - 12 = 0 \checkmark$

$x = 16$ is the only solution. ($x = 9$ does not check.)

example 2

Solving an Equation Quadratic in Form

Solve the equation. $w^4 - 81 = 0$

Solution:

This equation is a higher order polynomial equation.

$$w^4 - 81 = 0$$

$$(w^2 - 9)(w^2 + 9) = 0 \qquad \text{The equation is factorable.}$$

$$(w + 3)(w - 3)(w^2 + 9) = 0$$

$$w + 3 = 0 \quad \text{or} \quad w - 3 = 0 \quad \text{or} \quad w^2 + 9 = 0 \qquad \text{Apply the zero product rule.}$$

$$w = -3 \quad \text{or} \qquad w = 3 \quad \text{or} \quad w^2 = -9 \qquad \text{Solve for } w.$$

$$w = \pm\sqrt{-9}$$

$$w = \pm 3i$$

The solutions are $w = 3$, $w = -3$, $w = 3i$, and $w = -3i$.

2. Solving Equations Using Substitution

In this section, we will see that some equations that are not quadratic can be manipulated to appear as **equations in quadratic form** by using substitution.

example 3

Solving an Equation Quadratic in Form

Solve the equation.

$$(2x^2 - 5)^2 - 16(2x^2 - 5) + 39 = 0$$

Solution:

$$(2x^2 - 5)^2 - 16(2x^2 - 5) + 39 = 0 \qquad \text{Notice this equation is a trinomial. If the substitution } u = (2x^2 - 5) \text{ is made, the equation becomes quadratic in the variable } u.$$

substitute $u = (2x^2 - 5)$

$$u^2 - 16u + 39 = 0 \qquad \text{The equation is in the form } au^2 + bu + c = 0.$$

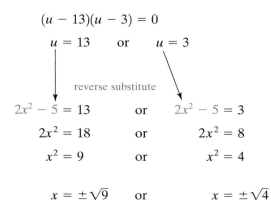

$$(u - 13)(u - 3) = 0 \qquad \text{The equation is factorable.}$$

$$u = 13 \quad \text{or} \quad u = 3 \qquad \text{Apply the zero product rule.}$$

reverse substitute

Avoiding Mistakes

When using substitution, it is critical to reverse substitute to solve the equation in terms of the original variable.

$$2x^2 - 5 = 13 \quad \text{or} \quad 2x^2 - 5 = 3$$

$$2x^2 = 18 \quad \text{or} \quad 2x^2 = 8$$

$$x^2 = 9 \quad \text{or} \quad x^2 = 4 \qquad \text{Write the equations in the form } x^2 = k.$$

$$x = \pm\sqrt{9} \quad \text{or} \quad x = \pm\sqrt{4} \qquad \text{Apply the square root property.}$$

$$= \pm 3 \quad \text{or} \quad = \pm 2$$

The solutions are $x = 3, x = -3, x = 2, x = -2.$ Substituting these values in the original equation verifies that these are all valid solutions.

---

example 4   **Solving an Equation Quadratic in Form**

Solve the equation.

$$p^{2/3} - 2p^{1/3} = 8$$

Solution:

$$p^{2/3} - 2p^{1/3} = 8$$

$$p^{2/3} - 2p^{1/3} - 8 = 0 \qquad \text{Set the equation equal to zero.}$$

$$(p^{1/3})^2 - 2(p^{1/3})^1 - 8 = 0 \qquad \text{Make the substitution } u = p^{1/3}.$$

substitute $u = p^{1/3}$ Then, the equation is in the form $au^2 + bu + c = 0.$

$$u^2 \quad - \quad 2u \quad - 8 = 0$$

$$(u - 4)(u + 2) = 0 \qquad \text{The equation is factorable.}$$

$$u = 4 \quad \text{or} \quad u = -2 \qquad \text{Apply the zero product rule.}$$

reverse substitute

$$p^{1/3} = 4 \quad \text{or} \quad p^{1/3} = -2$$

$$\sqrt[3]{p} = 4 \quad \text{or} \quad \sqrt[3]{p} = -2 \qquad \text{The equations are radical equations.}$$

$$(\sqrt[3]{p})^3 = (4)^3 \quad \text{or} \quad (\sqrt[3]{p})^3 = (-2)^3 \qquad \text{Cube both sides.}$$

$$p = 64 \quad \text{or} \quad p = -8$$

$$\text{Check: } p = 64 \qquad\qquad \text{Check: } p = -8$$

$$p^{2/3} - 2p^{1/3} = 8 \qquad\qquad p^{2/3} - 2p^{1/3} = 8$$

$$(64)^{2/3} - 2(64)^{1/3} \stackrel{?}{=} 8 \qquad (-8)^{2/3} - 2(-8)^{1/3} \stackrel{?}{=} 8$$

$$16 - 2(4) \stackrel{?}{=} 8 \qquad\qquad 4 - 2(-2) \stackrel{?}{=} 8$$

$$8 = 8 \checkmark \qquad\qquad 4 + 4 = 8 \checkmark$$

The solutions are $p = 64$ and $p = -8$.

---

example 5

Solving a Quadratic Equation Using Substitution

Solve the equation $(t - 5)^2 - 4(t - 5) + 13 = 0$ by using the substitution $u = t - 5$.

Solution:

$(t - 5)^2 - 4(t - 5) + 13 = 0$ This equation is quadratic; however, we can make it a simpler quadratic equation by letting $u = (t - 5)$.

substitute $u = t - 5$

$u^2 - 4u + 13 = 0$ This equation does not factor.

$u = \dfrac{-(-4) \pm \sqrt{(-4)^2 - 4(1)(13)}}{2(1)}$ Apply the quadratic formula: $a = 1$, $b = -4$, $c = 13$.

$= \dfrac{4 \pm \sqrt{16 - 52}}{2}$

$= \dfrac{4 \pm \sqrt{-36}}{2}$

$u = \dfrac{4 + 6i}{2}$

$u = \dfrac{4 + 6i}{2} = 2 + 3i$

$u = \dfrac{4 - 6i}{2} = 2 - 3i$

$u = 2 + 3i$ or $u = 2 - 3i$

reverse substitute

$t - 5 = 2 + 3i$ or $t - 5 = 2 - 3i$

$t = 7 + 3i$ or $t = 7 - 3i$ Both values check in the original equation.

The solutions are $t = 7 + 3i$ and $t = 7 - 3i$.

section 7.7 PRACTICE EXERCISES

For Exercises 1–14, factor the polynomial, solve the polynomial equation, or find the x-intercepts as the directions indicate. Pay close attention to the directions and how you should express your final answer. See the following examples.

Factor the polynomial: $x^2 - 16$	Solve the equation: $x^2 - 16 = 0$	Find the x-intercepts $f(x) = x^2 - 16$
Solution:	Solution:	Solution:
$(x - 4)(x + 4)$	$(x - 4)(x + 4) = 0$	Solve: $f(x) = 0$
	$x - 4 = 0$ or $x + 4 = 0$	$0 = (x - 4)(x + 4)$
	$x = 4$ or $x = -4$	$x - 4 = 0$ or $x + 4 = 0$
		$x = 4$ or $x = -4$
		x-intercepts: $(4, 0)$ and $(-4, 0)$

1. Solve: $16 = (2x - 3)^2$

2. Solve: $\left(x - \dfrac{3}{2}\right)^2 = \dfrac{7}{4}$

3. Factor: $a^4 - \dfrac{1}{16}$

4. Factor: $u^2 - \dfrac{1}{16}$

5. Find the x-intercept(s): $f(x) = -6x^2 + 11x - 4$

6. Find the x-intercept(s): $g(x) = 10x^2 - 26x + 12$

7. Solve: $n(n - 6) = -13$

8. Solve: $x(x + 8) = -16$

9. Factor: $12x^2 - 12x + 3$

10. Factor: $21x^4y + 41x^3y + 10x^2y$

11. Find the x-intercept(s): $h(x) = x^2 - 10$

12. Find the x-intercept(s): $k(x) = 8x^3 + 125$

13. Solve: $6k^2 + 7k = 6$

14. Solve: $2x^2 - 8x - 44 = 0$

For Exercises 15–30, solve the equation. For the equations involving radicals, be sure that you check all solutions in the original equation.

15. $y + 6\sqrt{y} = 16$

16. $p - 8\sqrt{p} = -15$

17. $2x + 3\sqrt{x} - 2 = 0$

18. $3t + 5\sqrt{t} - 2 = 0$

19. $\sqrt{4b + 1} - \sqrt{b - 2} = 3$

20. $\sqrt{6a + 7} - \sqrt{3a + 3} = 1$

21. $\sqrt{w - 6} + 3 = \sqrt{w + 9}$

22. $\sqrt{z + 15} - \sqrt{2z + 7} = 1$

23. $x^4 - 16 = 0$

24. $t^4 - 625 = 0$

25. $m^4 - 81 = 0$

26. $n^4 - 256$

27. $a^3 + 8 = 0$

28. $b^3 - 1 = 0$

29. $5p^3 - 5 = 0$

30. $2t^3 + 54 = 0$

31. a. Solve the quadratic equation by factoring: $u^2 + 10u + 24 = 0$

    b. Solve the equation using substitution: $(y^2 + 5y)^2 + 10(y^2 + 5y) + 24 = 0$

32. a. Solve the quadratic equation by factoring: $u^2 - 2u - 35 = 0$

    b. Solve the equation using substitution: $(w^2 - 6w)^2 - 2(w^2 - 6w) - 35 = 0$

33. a. Solve the quadratic equation by factoring:
    $u^2 - 2u - 24 = 0$

    b. Solve the equation using substitution:
    $(x^2 - 5x)^2 - 2(x^2 - 5x) - 24 = 0$

34. a. Solve the quadratic equation by factoring:
    $u^2 - 4u + 3 = 0$

    b. Solve the equation using substitution:
    $(2p^2 + p)^2 - 4(2p^2 + p) + 3 = 0$

For Exercises 35–48, solve using substitution.

35. $(4x + 5)^2 + 3(4x + 5) + 2 = 0$

36. $2(5x + 3)^2 - (5x + 3) - 28 = 0$

37. $16\left(\dfrac{x + 6}{4}\right)^2 + 8\left(\dfrac{x + 6}{4}\right) + 1 = 0$

38. $9\left(\dfrac{x + 3}{2}\right)^2 - 6\left(\dfrac{x + 3}{2}\right) + 1 = 0$

39. $(x^2 - 2x)^2 + 2(x^2 - 2x) = 3$

40. $(x^2 + x)^2 - 8(x^2 + x) = -12$

41. $x^4 - 13x^2 + 36 = 0$

42. $y^4 - 5y^2 + 4 = 0$

43. $x^6 - 9x^3 + 8 = 0$

44. $x^6 - 26x^3 - 27 = 0$

45. $m^{2/3} - m^{1/3} - 6 = 0$

46. $2n^{2/3} + 7n^{1/3} - 15 = 0$

47. $2t^{2/5} + 7t^{1/5} + 3 = 0$

48. $p^{2/5} + p^{1/5} - 2 = 0$

EXPANDING YOUR SKILLS

49. Solve $x^2 - 4 = 0$ three ways:
    a. By factoring
    b. By using the square root property
    c. By using the quadratic formula

50. Solve $9x^2 - 16 = 0$ three ways:
    a. By factoring

b. By using the square root property

c. By using the quadratic formula

For Exercises 51–54, solve the equation. *Hint*: Factor by grouping first.

51. $a^3 + 16a - a^2 - 16 = 0$

52. $b^3 + 9b - b^2 - 9 = 0$

53. $x^3 + 5x - 4x^2 - 20 = 0$

54. $y^3 + 8y - 3y^2 - 24 = 0$

GRAPHING CALCULATOR EXERCISES

55. a. Solve the equation $x^4 + 4x^2 + 4 = 0$.

    b. How many solutions are real and how many solutions are imaginary?

    c. How many x-intercepts do you anticipate for the function defined by $y = x^4 + 4x^2 + 4$?

    d. Graph $Y_1 = x^4 + 4x^2 + 4$ on a standard viewing window.

56. a. Solve the equation $x^4 - 2x^2 + 1 = 0$.

    b. How many solutions are real and how many solutions are imaginary?

    c. How many x-intercepts do you anticipate for the function defined by $y = x^4 - 2x^2 + 1$?

    d. Graph $Y_1 = x^4 - 2x^2 + 1$ on a standard viewing window.

57. a. Solve the equation $x^4 - x^3 - 6x^2 = 0$.

    b. How many solutions are real and how many solutions are imaginary?

    c. How many x-intercepts do you anticipate for the function defined by $y = x^4 - x^3 - 6x^2$?

    d. Graph $Y_1 = x^4 - x^3 - 6x^2$ on a standard viewing window.

58. a. Solve the equation $x^4 - 10x^2 + 9 = 0$.

    b. How many solutions are real and how many solutions are imaginary?

    c. How many x-intercepts do you anticipate for the function defined by $y = x^4 - 10x^2 + 9$?

    d. Graph $Y_1 = x^4 - 10x^2 + 9$ on a standard viewing window.

Chapter 7   SUMMARY

SECTION 7.1—GREATEST COMMON FACTOR AND FACTORING BY GROUPING

KEY CONCEPTS:

The greatest common factor (GCF) is the largest factor common to all terms of a polynomial. To factor out the GCF from a polynomial, use the distributive property.

A four-term polynomial may be factorable by grouping.

Steps to Factor by Grouping:

1. Identify and factor out the GCF from all four terms.
2. Factor out the GCF from the first pair of terms. Factor out the GCF from the second pair of terms. (Sometimes it is necessary to factor out the *opposite* of the GCF.)
3. If the two pairs of terms share a common binomial factor, factor out the binomial factor.

KEY TERMS:

factoring by grouping
greatest common factor (GCF)

EXAMPLES:

Factor out the GCF:

$$3x^2(a + b) - 6x(a + b)$$
$$= 3x(a + b)x - 3x(a + b)(2)$$
$$= 3x(a + b)(x - 2)$$

Factor by grouping:

$$60xa - 30xb - 80ya + 40yb$$
$$= 10[6xa - 3xb - 8ya + 4yb]$$
$$= 10[3x(2a - b) - 4y(2a - b)]$$
$$= 10[(2a - b)(3x - 4y)]$$

SECTION 7.2—FACTORING TRINOMIALS

KEY CONCEPTS:

Grouping Method

To factor trinomials of the form: $ax^2 + bx + c$

1. Factor out the GCF.
2. Find the product ac.
3. Find two integers whose product is ac and whose sum is b. (If no pair of numbers can be found, then the trinomial is prime.)
4. Rewrite the middle term (bx) as the sum of two terms whose coefficients are the numbers found in step 3.
5. Factor the polynomial by grouping.

EXAMPLES:

Factor:

$$10y^2 + 35y - 20$$
$$= 5(2y^2 + 7y - 4)$$

$$ac = (2)(-4) = -8$$

Find two integers whose product is -8 and whose sum is 7. The numbers are 8 and -1.

$$5[2y^2 + 8y - 1y - 4]$$
$$= 5[2y(y + 4) - 1(y + 4)]$$
$$= 5(y + 4)(2y - 1)$$

Trial-and-Error Method

To factor trinomials in the form: $ax^2 + bx + c$

1. Factor out the GCF.
2. List the pairs of factors of a and the pairs of factors of c. Consider the reverse order in either list.
3. Construct two binomials of the form:

4. Test each combination of factors until the product of the outer terms and the product of inner terms add up to the middle term.
5. If no combination of factors work, the polynomial is prime.

The factored form of a perfect square trinomial is the square of a binomial:

$$a^2 + 2ab + b^2 = (a + b)^2$$
$$a^2 - 2ab + b^2 = (a - b)^2$$

KEY TERMS:

perfect square trinomial

Factor:

$$10y^2 + 35y - 20 = 5(2y^2 + 7y - 4)$$

The pairs of factors of 2 are: $2 \cdot 1$
The pairs of factors of -4 are:

$$-1 \cdot 4 \qquad 1 \cdot (-4)$$
$$-2 \cdot 2 \qquad 2 \cdot (-2)$$
$$-4 \cdot 1 \qquad 4 \cdot (-1)$$

$(2y - 1)(y + 4) = 2y^2 + 7y - 4$	Yes
$(2y - 2)(y + 2) = 2y^2 + 2y - 4$	No
$(2y - 4)(y + 1) = 2y^2 - 2y - 4$	No
$(2y + 1)(y - 4) = 2y^2 - 7y - 4$	No
$(2y + 2)(y - 2) = 2y^2 - 2y - 4$	No
$(2y + 4)(y - 1) = 2y^2 + 2y - 4$	No

Factor:

$$9w^2 - 30wz + 25z^2$$
$$= (3w)^2 - 2(15wz) + (5z)^2$$

$$= (3w - 5z)^2$$

SECTION 7.3—FACTORING BINOMIALS

KEY CONCEPTS:

Factoring Binomials: Summary

Difference of Squares:

$$a^2 - b^2 = (a + b)(a - b)$$

Difference of Cubes:

$$a^3 - b^3 = (a - b)(a^2 + ab + b^2)$$

Sum of Cubes:

$$a^3 + b^3 = (a + b)(a^2 - ab + b^2)$$

KEY TERMS:

difference of cubes
difference of squares
sum of cubes

EXAMPLES:

Factor:

1. $25u^2 - 9v^4 = (5u + 3v^2)(5u - 3v^2)$

2. $8c^3 - d^6 = (2c - d^2)(4c^2 + 2cd^2 + d^4)$

3. $27w^9 + 64x^3$
   $= (3w^3 + 4x)(9w^6 - 12w^3x + 16x^2)$

Section 7.4—Zero Product Rule

Key Concepts:

An equation of the form: $ax^2 + bx + c = 0$, where $a \neq 0$ is a quadratic equation.

The zero product rule states that if $a \cdot b = 0$, then either $a = 0$ or $b = 0$. The zero product rule can be used to solve a quadratic equation or higher degree polynomial equation that is factored and equal to zero.

$f(x) = ax^2 + bx + c \ (a \neq 0)$ defines a **quadratic function**. The x-intercepts of a function defined by $y = f(x)$ are determined by finding the real solutions to the equation $f(x) = 0$. The y-intercept of a function $y = f(x)$ is at $f(0)$.

Key Terms:

parabola
quadratic equation
quadratic function
zero product rule

Examples:

Solve:

$$0 = x(2x - 3)(x + 4)$$

$$x = 0 \quad \text{or} \quad 2x - 3 = 0 \quad \text{or} \quad x + 4 = 0$$

$$x = 0 \quad \text{or} \quad x = \frac{3}{2} \quad \text{or} \quad x = -4$$

Find the x-intercepts:

$$f(x) = 3x^2 - 8x + 5$$

$$0 = 3x^2 - 8x + 5$$

$$0 = (3x - 5)(x - 1)$$

$$3x - 5 = 0 \quad \text{or} \quad x - 1 = 0$$

$$x = \frac{5}{3} \quad \text{or} \quad x = 1$$

The x-intercepts are $\left(\frac{5}{3}, 0\right)$ and $(1, 0)$.

Find the y-intercept:

$$f(x) = 3x^2 - 8x + 5$$

$$f(0) = 3(0)^2 - 8(0) + 5$$

$$f(0) = 5$$

The y-intercept is $(0, 5)$.

Section 7.5—Completing the Square and the Square Root Property

Key Concepts:

The square root property states that if

$$x^2 = k, \text{ then } x = \pm\sqrt{k}.$$

The square root property can be used to solve quadratic equations in the form:

$$(x + h)^2 = k$$

Examples:

Solve:

$$(x - 5)^2 = -13$$

$$x - 5 = \pm\sqrt{-13} \quad \text{(square root property)}$$

$$x = 5 \pm i\sqrt{13}$$

Steps to solve a quadratic equation in the form $ax^2 + bx + c = 0 \, (a \neq 0)$ by completing the square and applying the square root property:

1. Divide both sides by a to make the leading coefficient 1.
2. Isolate the variable terms on one side of the equation.
3. Complete the square: Add the square of one-half the linear term coefficient to both sides of the equation. Then factor the resulting perfect square trinomial.
4. Apply the square root property and solve for x.

KEY TERMS:

completing the square
square root property

Solve the equation:

$$2x^2 - 6x - 5 = 0$$

$$\frac{2x^2}{2} - \frac{6x}{2} - \frac{5}{2} = \frac{0}{2}$$

$$x^2 - 3x = \frac{5}{2}$$

$$\text{Note: } \left[\tfrac{1}{2} \cdot (-3)\right]^2 = \frac{9}{4}$$

$$x^2 - 3x + \frac{9}{4} = \frac{5}{2} + \frac{9}{4}$$

$$\left(x - \frac{3}{2}\right)^2 = \frac{19}{4}$$

$$x - \frac{3}{2} = \pm\sqrt{\frac{19}{4}}$$

$$x = \frac{3}{2} \pm \frac{\sqrt{19}}{2} \quad \text{or} \quad x = \frac{3 \pm \sqrt{19}}{2}$$

SECTION 7.6—QUADRATIC FORMULA

KEY CONCEPTS:

The solutions to a quadratic equation $ax^2 + bx + c = 0 \, (a \neq 0)$ are given by the quadratic formula:

$$x = \frac{-b \pm \sqrt{b^2 - 4ac}}{2a}$$

The discriminant of a quadratic equation $ax^2 + bx + c = 0$ is $b^2 - 4ac$. If a, b, and c are rational numbers, then:

1. If $b^2 - 4ac > 0$, then there will be two real solutions. Moreover,
   a. If $b^2 - 4ac$ is a perfect square, the solutions will be rational numbers.
   b. If $b^2 - 4ac$ is not a perfect square, the solutions will be irrational numbers.
2. If $b^2 - 4ac < 0$, then there will be two imaginary solutions.
3. If $b^2 - 4ac = 0$, then there will be one rational solution.

EXAMPLES:

Solve the equation:

$$0.03x^2 - 0.02x + 0.04 = 0$$

$$3x^2 - 2x + 4 = 0 \quad \text{(multiply by 100)}$$

$$a = 3, b = -2, c = 4$$

$$x = \frac{-(-2) \pm \sqrt{(-2)^2 - 4(3)(4)}}{2(3)}$$

$$= \frac{2 \pm \sqrt{4 - 48}}{6}$$

$$= \frac{2 \pm \sqrt{-44}}{6}$$

$$= \frac{2 \pm 2i\sqrt{11}}{6}$$

$$= \frac{1 \pm i\sqrt{11}}{3}$$

Three methods to solve a quadratic equation are:

1. Factoring
2. Completing the square and applying the square root property
3. Using the quadratic formula

KEY TERMS:

discriminant
quadratic formula

SECTION 7.7—EQUATIONS IN QUADRATIC FORM

KEY CONCEPTS:

Equations may reduce to a quadratic equation.

EXAMPLES:

Solve:

$$16y^4 - 1 = 0$$

$$(4y^2)^2 - 1^2 = 0$$

$$(4y^2 - 1)(4y^2 + 1) = 0 \quad \text{(factor)}$$

$$4y^2 - 1 = 0 \quad \text{or} \quad 4y^2 + 1 = 0 \quad \text{(zero property)}$$

$$y^2 = \frac{1}{4} \quad \text{or} \quad y^2 = -\frac{1}{4}$$

$$y = \pm\frac{1}{2} \quad \text{or} \quad y = \pm\frac{1}{2}i \quad \text{(square root property)}$$

Solve:

$$x^{2/3} - x^{1/3} - 12 = 0$$

$$\text{Let } u = x^{1/3}$$

Substitution may be used to solve equations that are in quadratic form.

$$u^2 - u - 12 = 0$$

$$(u - 4)(u + 3) = 0$$

KEY TERMS:

equations in quadratic form

$$u = 4 \quad \text{or} \quad u = -3$$

$$x^{1/3} = 4 \quad \text{or} \quad x^{1/3} = -3$$

$$x = 64 \quad \text{or} \quad x = -27 \quad \text{(cube both sides)}$$

chapter 7	REVIEW EXERCISES

Section 7.1

For Exercises 1–8, factor by removing the greatest common factor.

1. $8y^2 + 4y^4$
2. $-x^3 - 4x^2 + 11x$
3. $16m^2 - 12n + 24$
4. $21w^3 - 7w + 14$
5. $5x(x - 7) - 2(x - 7)$
6. $3t(t + 4) + 5(t + 4)$
7. $2x^2 - 26x$
8. $z^2 - \sqrt{5}z$

For Exercises 9–14, factor by grouping (remember to take out the GCF first).

9. $m^3 - 8m^2 + m - 8$
10. $24x^3 - 36x^2 + 72x - 108$
11. $4ax^2 + 2bx^2 - 6ax - 3xb$
12. $y^3 - 6y^2 + y - 6$
13. $12pq - 8q + 15p - 10$
14. $2x^2 - xy + 14xw - 7wy$

Section 7.2

15. What characteristics determine a perfect square trinomial?

For Exercises 16–27, factor the polynomials using any method.

16. $18x^2 + 27xy + 10y^2$
17. $2 + 7k + 6k^2$
18. $60a^2 + 65a^3 - 20a^4$
19. $8b^2 - 40b + 50$
20. $n^2 + 10n + 25$
21. $k^2 - 8k + 16$
22. $2x^2 + 5x + 12$
23. $x^2 + 2x - 15$
24. $y^3 - y(10 - 3y)$
25. $m + 18 - m(m - 2)$
26. $9x^2 - 12x + 4$
27. $25q^2 + 30q + 9$

Section 7.3

For Exercises 28–37, factor the binomials.

28. $25 - y^2$
29. $x^3 - \dfrac{1}{27}$
30. $b^2 + 64$
31. $a^3 + 64$
32. $1 - 8t^3$
33. $h^3 + 9h$
34. $c^6 - 729$
35. $k^4 - 16$
36. $25k^2 - 49$
37. $9y^3 - 4y$

For Exercises 38–41, factor by grouping and using the difference of squares.

38. $9p^2 - 49q^2 + 3p + 7q$
39. $u^2 - 100v^2 + u - 10v$
40. $x^2 - 8xy + 16y^2 - 9$ (*Hint*: Group three terms that constitute a perfect square trinomial, then factor as a difference of squares.)
41. $a^2 + 12a + 36 - b^2$

Section 7.4

42. How do you determine if an equation is quadratic?

43. What shape is the graph of a quadratic function?

For Exercises 44–47, label the equation as quadratic or linear.

44. $x^2 + 6x = 7$
45. $(x - 3)(x + 4) = 9$
46. $2x - 5 = 3$
47. $x + 3 = 5x^2$

48. Explain the zero product rule.

For Exercises 49–52, use the zero product rule to solve the equations.

49. $(x + 3)(x - 5) = 0$
50. $(8x - 3)(x - 7) = 0$
51. $\left(x - \dfrac{3}{2}\right)(x + \sqrt{7}) = 0$
52. $(x - 1)(x + 5)(2x - 9) = 0$

For Exercises 53–56, find the *x*- and *y*-intercepts of the function. Then match the function with its graph.

53. $f(x) = -4x^2 + 4$ 54. $g(x) = 2x^2 - 2$

55. $h(x) = 5x^3 - 10x^2 - 20x + 40$

56. $k(x) = -\dfrac{1}{8}x^2 + \dfrac{1}{2}$

a.

b.

c.

d.
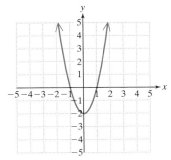

57. A moving van has the capacity to hold 1200 ft³ in volume. If the van is 10 ft high and the length is 1 ft less than twice the width, find the dimensions of the van.

Figure for Exercise 57

58. A missile is shot upward from a submarine 1280 ft below sea level. The initial velocity of the missile is 672 ft/s. A function that approximates the height of the missile (relative to sea level) is given by

$$h(t) = -16t^2 + 672t - 1280, \text{ where } h(t) \text{ is the}$$
height in feet and t is the time in seconds.

a. Complete the table to determine the height of the missile for the given values of t.

Time, t (seconds)	Height, $h(t)$ (feet)
0	
1	
3	
10	
20	
30	
40	
42	

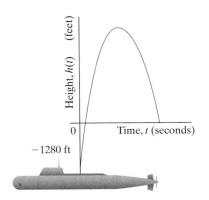

Figure for Exercise 58

b. Interpret the meaning of a negative value of $h(t)$.

c. Factor the function to find the time required for the missile to emerge from the water and the time required for the missile to reenter the water. (*Hint*: The height of the missile will be zero at sea level.)

Section 7.5

For Exercises 59–66, solve the equations using the square root property.

59. $x^2 = 5$

60. $2y^2 = -8$

61. $a^2 = 81$

62. $3b^2 = -19$

63. $(x - 2)^2 = 72$

64. $(2x - 5)^2 = -9$

65. $(3y - 1)^2 = 3$

66. $3(m - 4)^2 = 15$

67. The length of each side of an equilateral triangle is 10 in. Find the height of the triangle. Round the answer to the nearest tenth of an inch.

Figure for Exercise 67

68. Use the square root property to find the length of the sides of a square whose area is 81 in.²

69. Use the square root property to find the length of the sides of a square whose area is 150 in.² Round the answer to the nearest tenth of an inch.

For Exercises 70–73, find the value of k so that the expression is a perfect square trinomial. Then factor the trinomial.

70. $x^2 + 16x + k$

71. $x^2 - 9x + k$

72. $y^2 + \dfrac{1}{2}y + k$

73. $z^2 - \dfrac{2}{5}z + k$

For Exercises 74–79, solve the equation by completing the square and applying the square root property.

74. $w^2 + 4w + 13 = 0$

75. $4y^2 - 12y + 13 = 0$

76. $3x^2 + 2x = 1$

77. $b^2 + \dfrac{7}{2}b = 2$

78. $2x^2 = 12x + 6$

79. $-t^2 + 8t - 25 = 0$

Section 7.6

80. Explain how the discriminant can determine the type and number of solutions to a quadratic equation with rational coefficients.

For Exercises 81–86, determine the type (rational, irrational, or imaginary) and number of solutions for the equations using the discriminant.

81. $x^2 - 5x = -6$

82. $2y^2 = -3y$

83. $z^2 + 23 = 17z$

84. $a^2 + a + 1 = 0$

85. $10b + 1 = -25b^2$

86. $3x^2 + 15 = 0$

For Exercises 87–96, solve the equations by using the quadratic formula.

87. $y^2 - 4y + 1 = 0$

88. $m^2 - 5m + 25 = 0$

89. $6a^2 - 7a - 10 = 0$

90. $3x^2 - 10x + 8 = 0$

91. $b^2 - \dfrac{4}{25} = \dfrac{3}{5}b$

92. $k^2 + 0.4k = 0.05$

93. $32 + 4x - x^2 = 0$

94. $8y - y^2 = 0$

95. $5x^2 - 20 = 0$

96. $14 = a(a - 5)$

97. The landing distance that a certain plane will travel on a runway is determined by the initial landing speed at the instant the plane touches down. The function D relates landing distance in feet to initial landing speed, s:

$$D(s) = \frac{1}{10}s^2 - 3s + 22, \text{ where } s \text{ is in feet per second.}$$

a. Find the landing distance for a plane traveling 150 ft/s at touchdown.

b. If the landing speed is too fast, the pilot may run out of runway. If the speed is too slow, the plane may stall. Find the maximum initial landing speed of a plane for a runway that is 1000 ft long. Round to one decimal place.

c. Convert the landing speed you found in part (b), into miles per hour. Note that 1 mile = 5280 feet, and 1 hour = 3600 seconds. Round to the nearest mile per hour.

98. The recent population, P (in thousands), of Kenya can be approximated by: $P(t) = 4.62t^2 + 564.6t + 13{,}128$, where t is the number of years since 1974.

a. Approximate the number of people in Kenya in the year 1990.

b. If this trend continues, approximate the number of people in Kenya in the year 2025.

c. What is the y-intercept of this function and what does it mean in the context of this problem?

d. In what year after 1974 will the population of Kenya reach 50 million? (*Hint*: 50 million equals 50,000 thousands)

Section 7.7

For Exercises 99–106, solve the equations using substitution, if necessary.

99. $x - 4\sqrt{x} - 21 = 0$

100. $n - 6\sqrt{n} + 8 = 0$

101. $y^4 - 11y^2 + 18 = 0$

102. $2m^4 - m^2 - 3 = 0$

103. $t^{2/5} + t^{1/5} - 6 = 0$

104. $p^{2/5} - 3p^{1/5} + 2 = 0$

105. $\sqrt{4a - 3} - \sqrt{8a + 1} = -2$

106. $\sqrt{2b - 5} - \sqrt{b - 2} = 2$

---

chapter 7   TEST

1. Explain the strategy for factoring a polynomial expression.

2. Explain the process to solve a polynomial equation by the zero product rule.

3. Solve: $4x - 64x^3 = 0$

4. Factor: $3y^2 + 23y - 8$

5. Solve: $(x - \sqrt{7})(10x + 1) = 0$

6. Solve: $(y - 2)^2 = 2y + 1$

7. Factor: $a^3 - 6a^2 - a + 6$

8. Solve: $x^2 + \dfrac{1}{2}x + \dfrac{1}{16} = 0$

9. Solve: $(3a - 5)^2 = -7$

10. Factor: $3x^3 + 24$

For Exercises 11–12: (a) Write the equation in standard form, $ax^2 + bx + c = 0$. (b) Identify a, b, and c. (c) Find the discriminant. (d) Determine the number and type (rational, irrational, or imaginary) of solutions.

11. $x^2 - 3x = -12$

12. $y(y - 2) = -1$

13. Find the value of k so that the expression is a perfect square trinomial. Then factor the trinomial: $d^2 + 7d + k$.

14. Solve the equation by completing the square and applying the square root property: $2x^2 = 3x - 7$.

15. The base of a triangle is 3 ft less than twice the height. The area of the triangle is 14 ft^2. Find the base and the height. Round to the nearest tenth of a foot.

16. A circular garden has an area of approximately 450 ft^2. Find the radius. Round the answer to the nearest tenth of a foot.

For Exercises 17–20, find the x- and y-intercepts of the function. Then match the function with its graph.

17. $f(x) = x^2 - 6x + 8$

18. $k(x) = x^3 + 4x^2 - 9x - 36$

19. $p(x) = -2x^2 - 8x - 6$

20. $q(x) = x^3 - x^2 - 12x$

a.

b.

c.

d.

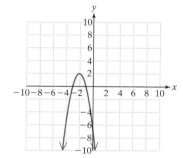

21. A child launches a toy rocket from the ground. The height of the rocket, h, can be determined by its horizontal distance from the launchpad, x, by:

$h(x) = -\dfrac{x^2}{256} + x$, where x and h are in feet and $x \geq 0$ and $h \geq 0$.

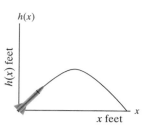

Figure for Exercise 21

How many feet from the launchpad will the rocket hit the ground?

22. The recent population, P (in millions), of India can be approximated by: $P(t) = 0.136t^2 + 12.6t + 607.7$, where $t = 0$ corresponds to the year 1974.

a. Approximate the number of people in India in the year 1978. (Round to the nearest million.)

b. If this trend continues approximate the number of people in India in the year 2010.

c. In what year after 1974 did the population of India reach 700 million? (Round to the nearest year.)

d. If this trend continues, approximate the year in which the population of India will have reached 1 billion (1000 million). (Round to the nearest year.)

CUMULATIVE REVIEW EXERCISES, CHAPTERS 1–7

1. Given $A = \{2, 4, 6, 8, 10\}$ and $B = \{2, 8, 12, 16\}$
   a. Find $A \cup B$
   b. $A \cap B$

2. Perform the indicated operations and simplify:
   $(2x^2 - 5) - (x + 3)(5x - 2)$

3. Simplify completely: $4^0 - \left(\dfrac{1}{2}\right)^{-3} - 81^{1/2}$

4. Perform the indicated operations. Leave the answer in scientific notation:
   $$\frac{(3.0 \times 10^{12})(6.0 \times 10^{-3})}{(2.5 \times 10^{-4})}$$

5. a. Factor completely: $x^3 + 2x^2 - 9x - 18$
   b. Divide by using either long division or synthetic division. Identify the quotient and remainder.
   $$(x^3 + 2x^2 - 9x - 18) \div (x - 3)$$

6. Multiply: $(\sqrt[3]{x} + \sqrt[3]{2})(\sqrt[3]{x^2} - \sqrt[3]{2x} + \sqrt[3]{4})$

7. Simplify: $\dfrac{4}{\sqrt{2x}}$

8. Jacques invests a total of $10,000 in two mutual funds. After 1 year, one fund produced 12% growth, and the other lost 3%. Find the amount invested in each fund if the total investment grew by $900.

9. Solve the system of equations:
   $$\frac{1}{9}x - \frac{1}{3}y = -\frac{13}{9}$$
   $$x - \frac{1}{2}y = \frac{9}{2}$$

10. An object is fired straight up into the air from an initial height of 384 ft with an initial velocity of 160 ft/s. The height, h, in feet is given by:
    $h(t) = -16t^2 + 160t + 384$, where t is the time in seconds.
    a. Find the height of the object after 3 s.
    b. Find the height of the object after 7 s.
    c. Find the time required for the object to hit the ground.

11. Solve the equation: $(x - 3)^2 + 16 = 0$.

12. Solve the equation: $2x^2 + 5x - 1 = 0$.

13. What number would have to be added to the quantity $x^2 + 10x$ to make it a perfect square trinomial?

14. Factor completely: $2x^3 + 250$.

15. Graph the line $3x - 5y = 10$.

16. a. Find the x-intercepts of the function defined by $g(x) = 2x^2 - 9x + 10$.
    b. What is the y-intercept of $y = g(x)$?

17. The poverty threshold for four-person families in 1960 was $3022. The poverty threshold for four-person families in 1990 was $13,359. Let y represent the poverty threshold, and let x represent the year, where $x = 0$ corresponds to 1960. (Source: U.S. Bureau of the Census)
    a. Plot the ordered pairs $(0, 3022)$ and $(30, 13,359)$.
    b. Find a linear model that represents the poverty threshold y, as a function of the year, x. Round the slope to the nearest whole number.
    c. Use the model you found in part (b) to estimate the poverty level in 1980.

18. Michael Jordan was the NBA leading scorer for 10 of 12 seasons between 1987 and 1998. In his last season, he scored a total of 2357 points consisting of 1-point free throws, 2-point field goals, and 3-point field goals. He scored 286 more 2-point shots than he did free throws. The number of 3-point shots was 821 less than the number of 2-point shots. Determine the number of free throws, 2-point shots, and 3-point shots scored by Michael Jordan during his last season.

19. Explain why this relation is *not* a function.

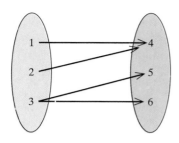

20. Graph the function defined by

$$f(x) = \begin{cases} \dfrac{1}{x} & \text{if } x < 0 \\ 3 & \text{if } x \geq 0 \end{cases}$$

21. The quantity y varies directly as x and inversely as z. If $y = 15$ when $x = 50$ and $z = 10$, find y when $x = 65$ and $z = 5$.

22. The total number of flights, F, (including passenger flights and cargo flights) at a large airport can be approximated by $F(x) = 300{,}000 + 0.008x$, where x is the number of passengers.

    a. Is this function linear, quadratic, constant, or other?

    b. What is the y-intercept and interpret its meaning in the context of this problem.

    c. What is the slope of the function and what does the slope mean in the context of this problem?

23. Given the function defined by $g(x) = \sqrt{2 - x}$, find the function values (if they exist) over the set of real numbers:

    a. $g(-7)$ b. $g(0)$ c. $g(3)$

24. Let $m(x) = \sqrt{x + 4}$, and $n(x) = x^2 + 2$, find:

    a. $(m \circ n)(x)$ b. $(n \circ m)(x)$

25. Consider the function $y = f(x)$ graphed here. Find:

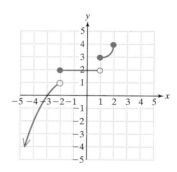

    a. The domain   b. The range

    c. The open interval(s) where $f(x)$ is increasing

    d. The open interval(s) where $f(x)$ is decreasing

    e. The open interval(s) where $f(x)$ is constant

    f. $f(-2)$ g. $f(1)$ h. $f(0)$

    i. For what value(s) of x is $f(x) = 0$?

    j. For what interval(s) is $f(x) < 0$?

RATIONAL EXPRESSIONS

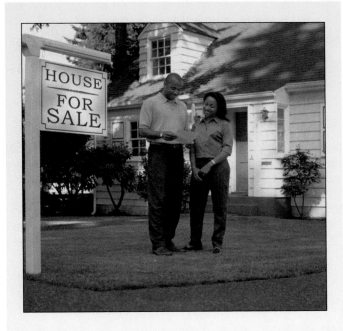

When purchasing a new home, most people make a down payment and then take out a mortgage for the remaining balance on the house. After acquiring the mortgage, the homeowner usually makes monthly payments over the course of 15–30 years.

For more information visit monthlypayment at

www.mhhe.com/miller_oneill

The monthly payment, P, is based on the original amount of the mortgage, A, the interest rate, r, and the term of the loan, t, in years.

A formula to calculate the monthly payment for a loan is given by the complex fraction:

$$P = \frac{\dfrac{Ar}{12}}{1 - \dfrac{1}{\left(1 + \dfrac{r}{12}\right)^{12t}}}$$

section

8.1   INTRODUCTION TO RATIONAL FUNCTIONS

1.   Definition of a Rational Function

Thus far in the text, we have introduced several types of functions including constant, linear, and quadratic functions. In this chapter, we will study another category of functions called rational functions.

Definition of a Rational Function

A function, f, is a **rational function** if it can be written in the form $f(x) = p(x)/q(x)$, where p and q are polynomial functions and $q(x) \neq 0$.

The definition indicates that a rational function is a quotient of two polynomials. For example, the functions f, g, h, and k are rational functions.

$$f(x) = \frac{1}{x}, \qquad g(x) = \frac{2}{x - 3}, \qquad h(a) = \frac{a + 6}{a^2 - 5}, \qquad k(x) = \frac{x + 4}{2x^2 - 11x + 5}$$

In Section 4.3, we introduced the rational function defined by $f(x) = \frac{1}{x}$. Recall that $f(x) = \frac{1}{x}$ has a restriction on its domain that $x \neq 0$ and the graph of $f(x) = \frac{1}{x}$ has a vertical asymptote at $x = 0$ (Figure 8-1).

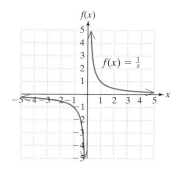

Figure 8-1

2.   Evaluating Rational Functions

example 1

Evaluating a Rational Function

Given $g(x) = \dfrac{2}{x - 3}$

a. Find the function values (if they exist): $g(0)$, $g(1)$, $g(2)$, $g(2.5)$, $g(2.9)$, $g(3)$, $g(3.1)$, $g(3.5)$, $g(4)$, and $g(5)$.

b. Sketch the function.

Solution:

$$g(0) = \frac{2}{(0) - 3} = -\frac{2}{3} \qquad\qquad g(3) = \frac{2}{(3) - 3} = \frac{2}{0} \text{ (undefined)}$$

$$g(1) = \frac{2}{(1) - 3} = -1 \qquad\qquad g(3.1) = \frac{2}{(3.1) - 3} = \frac{2}{0.1} = 20$$

$$g(2) = \frac{2}{(2) - 3} = -2 \qquad\qquad g(3.5) = \frac{2}{(3.5) - 3} = \frac{2}{0.5} = 4$$

$$g(2.5) = \frac{2}{(2.5) - 3} = \frac{2}{-0.5} = -4 \qquad g(4) = \frac{2}{(4) - 3} = 2$$

$$g(2.9) = \frac{2}{(2.9) - 3} = \frac{2}{-0.1} = -20 \qquad g(5) = \frac{2}{(5) - 3} = 1$$

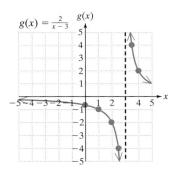

$g(x) = \frac{2}{x-3}$

Figure 8-2

b. $g(x) = 2/(x - 3)$ is undefined for $x = 3$.
Furthermore, the function values decrease for values of x taken close to 3 on the left. The function values increase for values of x taken close to 3 on the right. In this case, g has a vertical asymptote at $x = 3$ (Figure 8-2).

Graphing Calculator Box

A *Table* feature can be used to check the function values in Example 1.

The graph of a rational function may be misleading on a graphing calculator. For example, $g(x) = 2/(x - 3)$ has a vertical asymptote at $x = 3$, but the vertical asymptote is *not* part of the graph (Figure 8-3). A graphing calculator may try to "connect the dots" between two consecutive points, one to the left of $x = 3$ and one to the right of $x = 3$. This creates a line that is nearly vertical and appears to be part of the graph.

Figure 8-3

To show that this line is not part of the graph, we can graph the function in a *Dot Mode* (see the owner's manual for your calculator). The graph of $g(x) = 2/(x - 3)$ in dot mode indicates that the line $x = 3$ is not part of the function (Figure 8-4).

Figure 8-4

---

3.   Domain of Rational Functions

Recall that if a function is defined by an equation $y = f(x)$, the domain is the set of x-values that when substituted into the function make the function a real number. Therefore, the **domain of a rational function** must exclude values that make the denominator zero. For example:

Given $f(x) = \dfrac{1}{x}$, the domain of f is $\{x \mid x \neq 0\}$ The set of all real numbers, x, excluding $x = 0$

Given $g(x) = \dfrac{2}{x - 3}$, the domain of g is $\{x \mid x \neq 3\}$ The set of all real numbers, x, excluding $x = 3$

Steps to Find the Domain of a Rational Expression

1. Set the denominator equal to zero and solve the resulting equation.
2. The domain is the set of all real numbers *excluding* the values found in Step 1.

---

example 2

Finding the Domain of a Rational Function

Find the domain of the functions defined here. Write the domain in set-builder notation and in interval notation.

a. $g(t) = \dfrac{5}{4t - 1}$

b. $k(x) = \dfrac{x + 4}{2x^2 - 11x + 5}$

c. $h(a) = \dfrac{a + 6}{a^2 - 5}$

d. $w(x) = \dfrac{x}{x^2 + 4}$

Solution:

a. $g(t) = \dfrac{5}{4t - 1}$ The function will not be a real number when the denominator is zero.

$4t - 1 = 0$ Set the denominator equal to zero and solve for t.

$4t = 1$

$t = \frac{1}{4}$ The value $t = \frac{1}{4}$ must be excluded from the domain.

Domain: $\{t \mid t \neq \frac{1}{4}\}$

Interval notation: $(-\infty, \frac{1}{4}) \cup (\frac{1}{4}, \infty)$

b. $k(x) = \dfrac{x + 4}{2x^2 - 11x + 5}$

$2x^2 - 11x + 5 = 0$ Set the denominator equal to zero and solve for x.

$(2x - 1)(x - 5) = 0$ This is a factorable quadratic equation.

$2x - 1 = 0$ or $x - 5 = 0$

$x = \frac{1}{2}$ or $x = 5$

Domain: $\{x \mid x \neq \frac{1}{2}, x \neq 5\}$

Interval notation: $(-\infty, \frac{1}{2}) \cup (\frac{1}{2}, 5) \cup (5, \infty)$

Tip: The domain of a rational function excludes values for which the denominator is zero. The values for which the numerator is zero *do not affect* the domain of the function.

c. $h(a) = \dfrac{a + 6}{a^2 - 5}$

$a^2 - 5 = 0$ Set the denominator equal to zero and solve for a.

$a^2 = 5$ Isolate a^2 and apply the square root property.

$a = \pm\sqrt{5}$ The values $a = \sqrt{5}$ and $a = -\sqrt{5}$ must be excluded from the domain.

Domain: $\{a \mid a \neq \sqrt{5}, a \neq -\sqrt{5}\}$

Interval notation:
$(-\infty, -\sqrt{5}) \cup (-\sqrt{5}, \sqrt{5}) \cup (\sqrt{5}, \infty)$

d. $w(x) = \dfrac{x}{x^2 + 4}$

Because the quantity x^2 cannot be negative for any real number, x, the denominator $x^2 + 4$ cannot equal zero; therefore, no real numbers are excluded from the domain.

Domain: Set of all real numbers

Interval notation: $(-\infty, \infty)$

4.   Reducing Rational Expressions

A rational expression is an expression in the form $\frac{p}{q}$, where p and q are polynomials and $q \neq 0$. Like fractions, it is often advantageous to reduce rational expressions to lowest terms.

The method for **reducing rational expressions** mirrors the process to reduce fractions. In each case, factor the numerator and denominator. Common factors in the numerator and denominator form a ratio of 1 and can be reduced.

Reducing a fraction: $\dfrac{15}{35} \xrightarrow{\text{factor}} \dfrac{3 \cdot \cancel{5}}{7 \cdot \cancel{5}} = \dfrac{3}{7}(1) = \dfrac{3}{7}$

Reducing a rational expression: $\dfrac{x^2 - x - 12}{x^2 - 16} \xrightarrow{\text{factor}} \dfrac{(x + 3)(\cancel{x - 4})}{(x + 4)(\cancel{x - 4})} = \dfrac{(x + 3)}{(x + 4)}(1) = \dfrac{x + 3}{x + 4}$

This process is stated formally as the fundamental principle of rational expressions.

Fundamental Principle of Rational Expressions

Let p, q, and r represent polynomials. Then

$$\frac{pr}{qr} = \frac{p}{q} \quad \text{for } q \neq 0 \text{ and } r \neq 0$$

example 3   **Reducing Rational Functions**

Given $f(x) = \dfrac{2x^3 + 12x^2 + 16x}{6x + 24}$

a.   Factor the numerator and denominator.
b.   Determine the domain and write the domain in set-builder notation.
c.   Reduce the expression.

Solution:

a. $f(x) = \dfrac{2x^3 + 12x^2 + 16x}{6x + 24}$

      $= \dfrac{2x(x^2 + 6x + 8)}{6(x + 4)}$ Factor the numerator and denominator.

      $= \dfrac{2x(x + 2)(x + 4)}{6(x + 4)}$

⬢ **Avoiding Mistakes**

The domain of a rational function is always determined *before* reducing the function.

b.   To determine the domain, set the denominator equal to zero and solve for x.

      $6(x + 4) = 0$

           $x = -4$

The domain of the function is $\{x \mid x \neq -4\}$.

c. $f(x) = \dfrac{\overset{1}{2x}(\overset{}{x+4})(x + 2)}{\underset{}{2} \cdot 3(\overset{1}{x+4})}$ Reduce the ratio of common factors to 1.

      $= \dfrac{x(x + 2)}{3}$ (provided $x \neq -4$)

It is important to note that the expressions

$$\frac{2x^3 + 12x^2 + 16x}{6x + 24} \quad \text{and} \quad \frac{x(x + 2)}{3}$$

are equal for all values of x that make each expression a real number. Therefore,

$$\frac{2x^3 + 12x^2 + 16x}{6x + 24} = \frac{x(x + 2)}{3}$$

for all values of x *except* $x = -4$. (At $x = -4$, the original expression is undefined.) This is why the *domain of a rational function is always determined before the expression is reduced.*

     The objective to reducing a rational function or rational expression is to create an equivalent function that is simpler to evaluate. Consider the function from Example 3 in its original form and in its reduced form. If we substitute an arbitrary value of x into the function (such as $x = 3$), we see that the reduced form is easier to evaluate.

Original Function	**Simplified Form**
$f(x) = \dfrac{2x^3 + 12x^2 + 16x}{6x + 24}$	$f(x) = \dfrac{x(x + 2)}{3}$

Substitute $x = 3$ ⟶ $f(3) = \dfrac{2(3)^3 + 12(3)^2 + 16(3)}{6(3) + 24}$ $f(3) = \dfrac{(3)((3) + 2)}{3}$

$\qquad\qquad\qquad = \dfrac{2(27) + 12(9) + 48}{18 + 24}$ $= \dfrac{3(5)}{3}$

$\qquad\qquad\qquad = \dfrac{54 + 108 + 48}{42}$ $= 5$

$\qquad\qquad\qquad = \dfrac{210}{42}$

$\qquad\qquad\qquad = 5$

---

example 4   **Reducing a Rational Function**

Reduce $p(t) = \dfrac{t^3 + 8}{t^2 + 6t + 8}$

Solution:

$p(t) = \dfrac{t^3 + 8}{t^2 + 6t + 8}$ Factor the numerator and denominator. The restrictions on the domain are $t \neq -2$ and $t \neq -4$.

$= \dfrac{(t + 2)(t^2 - 2t + 4)}{(t + 2)(t + 4)}$

> **Tip:** $t^3 + 8$ is a sum of cubes.
>
> Recall: $a^3 + b^3 = (a + b)(a^2 - ab + b^2)$
>
> $t^3 + 8 = (t + 2)(t^2 - 2t + 4)$

$= \dfrac{\overset{1}{\cancel{(t + 2)}}(t^2 - 2t + 4)}{\cancel{(t + 2)}(t + 4)}$ Reduce common factors whose ratio is 1.

$= \dfrac{t^2 - 2t + 4}{t + 4}$ (provided $t \neq -2, t \neq -4$)

Graphing Calculator Box

Try using a *Table* feature to evaluate the functions Y_1 and Y_2 for several values of x:

$$Y_1 = (x^3 + 8)/(x^2 + 6x + 8) \qquad \text{and}$$

$$Y_2 = (x^2 - 2x + 4)/(x + 4)$$

The function values are the same for all values of x in the table except at $x = -4$ and $x = -2$. This is consistent with the solution to Example 4.

X	Y₁	Y₂
-5	-39	-39
-4	ERROR	ERROR
-3	19	19
-2	ERROR	6
-1	2.3333	2.3333
0	1	1
1	.6	.6

X= -5

⬡ Avoiding Mistakes

The fundamental principle of rational expressions indicates that common *factors* in the numerator and denominator may be reduced.

$$\frac{pr}{qr} = \frac{p}{q} \cdot \frac{r}{r} = \frac{p}{q} \cdot (1) = \frac{p}{q}$$

Because this property is based on the identity property of multiplication, reducing or canceling applies only to factors (remember that factors are multiplied). Therefore, terms that are added or subtracted cannot be reduced or canceled. For example:

$$\frac{3x}{3y} = \frac{\overset{1}{\cancel{3}}x}{\cancel{3}y} = (1) \cdot \frac{x}{y} = \frac{x}{y} \qquad \text{however, } \frac{x + 3}{y + 3} \text{ cannot be reduced}$$

      ↑   ↑

   reduce   cannot reduce

common factor   common terms

---

example 5

Reducing a Rational Expression

Reduce the rational expression. $\dfrac{2x^2y^5}{8x^4y^3}$

Solution:

$$\frac{2x^2y^5}{8x^4y^3}$$

This expression has the restriction that $x \neq 0$ and $y \neq 0$.

$$= \frac{2x^2y^5}{2^3x^4y^3}$$

Factor the denominator.

$$= 2^{1-3}x^{2-4}y^{5-3}$$

This expression can be simplified using the properties of exponents.

$$= 2^{-2}x^{-2}y^2$$

$$= \frac{y^2}{4x^2} \quad \text{(provided } x \neq 0 \text{ and } y \neq 0)$$

Remove negative exponents.
Include the restrictions on x and y.

5. Reducing a Ratio of −1

When two factors are identical in the numerator and denominator, they form a ratio of 1 and can be reduced. Sometimes we encounter two factors that are *opposites* and form a ratio of −1. For example:

Reduced Form	Details/Notes
$\dfrac{-5}{5} = -1$	The ratio of a number and its opposite is −1.
$\dfrac{100}{-100} = -1$	The ratio of a number and its opposite is −1.
$\dfrac{x+7}{-x-7} = -1$	$\dfrac{x+7}{-x-7} = \dfrac{x+7}{-1(x+7)} = \dfrac{\overset{1}{\cancel{x+7}}}{-1(\cancel{x+7})} = \dfrac{1}{-1} = -1$

factor out −1

| $\dfrac{2-x}{x-2} = -1$ | $\dfrac{2-x}{x-2} = \dfrac{-1(-2+x)}{x-2} = \dfrac{-1(\cancel{x-2})}{\cancel{x-2}} = \dfrac{-1}{1} = -1$ |

Graphing Calculator Box

The graph of $Y_1 = \dfrac{x+7}{-x-7}$

equals 1 for all real numbers except −7.

The graph of $Y_2 = \dfrac{x-2}{2-x}$

equals −1 for all real numbers except 2.

Recognizing factors that are opposites is useful when reducing rational expressions.

example 6   **Reducing Rational Functions**

Reduce the rational functions.

a. $f(x) = \dfrac{x-5}{25-x^2}$ b. $g(x) = \dfrac{2x-6}{15-5x}$

Solution:

a. $f(x) = \dfrac{x-5}{25-x^2}$

$= \dfrac{x-5}{(5-x)(5+x)}$ Factor. The restrictions on x are $x \ne 5$ and $x \ne -5$.

Notice that $x - 5$ and $5 - x$ are opposites and form a ratio of -1.

$= \dfrac{\overset{-1}{\cancel{x-5}}}{(\cancel{5-x})(5+x)}$ Details: $\dfrac{(x-5)}{(5-x)(5+x)} = \dfrac{x-5}{-1(-5+x)(5+x)}$
$= \dfrac{x-5}{-1(x-5)(5+x)} = \dfrac{1}{-1(5+x)}$

$= (-1)\left(\dfrac{1}{5+x}\right)$

$= -1 \cdot \dfrac{1}{x+5}$ (provided $x \ne 5, x \ne -5$)

Tip: The factor of -1 may be applied in front of the rational expression, or it may be applied to the numerator or to the denominator. Therefore, the final answer may be written in several forms. For $x \ne 5$ and $x \ne -5$ we have

$f(x) = -\dfrac{1}{x+5}$ or $f(x) = \dfrac{-1}{x+5}$ or $f(x) = \dfrac{1}{-(x+5)}$

---

b. $g(x) = \dfrac{2x-6}{15-5x}$

$= \dfrac{2(x-3)}{5(3-x)}$ Factor. The restriction on x is $x \ne 3$.

$= \dfrac{2(\overset{-1}{\cancel{x-3}})}{5(\cancel{3-x})}$ Details: $\dfrac{2(x-3)}{5(3-x)} = \dfrac{2(x-3)}{5(-1)(-3+x)} = \dfrac{2(x-3)}{-5(x-3)} = \dfrac{2}{-5}$

$= -\dfrac{2}{5}$ (provided $x \ne 3$)

section 8.1   PRACTICE EXERCISES

1. Let $h(x) = -3/(x - 1)$. Find the function values $h(0), h(1), h(-3), h(-1), h(\frac{1}{2})$.

2. Explain the concept of domain as it applies to Exercise 1.

3. Let $k(x) = 2/(x + 1)$. Find the function values $k(0), k(1), k(-3), k(-1), k(\frac{1}{2})$.

4. Explain the concept of domain as it applies to Exercise 3.

For Exercises 5–8, find the domain of each function and use that information to match the function with its graph.

5. $m(x) = \dfrac{1}{x + 4}$

6. $n(x) = \dfrac{1}{x + 1}$

7. $q(x) = \dfrac{1}{x - 4}$

8. $p(x) = \dfrac{1}{x - 1}$

a.

b.

c.

d.

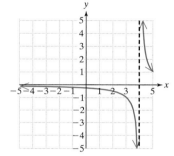

For Exercises 9–22, write the domain of the function in interval notation.

9. $f(x) = \dfrac{1}{3x - 1}$

10. $r(t) = \dfrac{1}{2t - 1}$

11. $q(t) = \dfrac{t + 5}{t - 1}$

12. $p(x) = \dfrac{3x - 4}{x + 4}$

13. $g(y) = \dfrac{y + 1}{(y - 3)(y - 9)}$

14. $f(y) = \dfrac{4y - 1}{(y + 8)(y + 10)}$

15. $w(x) = \dfrac{(x - 4)(x + 2)}{(x - 3)(2x + 5)}$

16. $s(t) = \dfrac{(t - 5)(t - 8)}{(t + 4)(3t - 5)}$

17. $m(x) = \dfrac{3}{6x^2 - 7x - 10}$

18. $n(x) = \dfrac{1}{2x^2 + 11x + 12}$

19. $f(a) = \dfrac{a^2 + 10a + 25}{9a^2 - 25}$

20. $g(x) = \dfrac{x^2 - 6x + 9}{x^2 - 11x + 28}$

21. $r(x) = \dfrac{x + 1}{6x^3 - x^2 - 15x}$

22. $s(t) = \dfrac{t + 5}{t^3 - 8t^2 + 16t}$

23. Given $g(x) = \dfrac{x^2 + 6x + 8}{x^2 + 3x - 4}$

   a. Factor the numerator and denominator.

   b. Determine the domain and write the domain in set-builder notation.

   c. Reduce the expression.

24. Given $f(x) = \dfrac{x^2 - 6x}{2x^2 - 11x - 6}$

   a. Factor the numerator and denominator.

   b. Determine the domain and write the domain in set-builder notation.

   c. Reduce the expression.

25. Given $p(x) = \dfrac{x^2 - 18x + 81}{x^2 - 81}$

   a. Factor the numerator and denominator.

   b. Determine the domain and write the domain in set-builder notation.

   c. Reduce the expression.

26. Given

$$q(x) = \dfrac{x^2 + 14x + 49}{x^2 - 49}$$

   a. Factor the numerator and denominator.

   b. Determine the domain and write the domain in set-builder notation.

   c. Reduce the expression.

For Exercises 27–60, reduce the rational expressions.

27. $\dfrac{100x^3y^5}{36xy^8}$

28. $\dfrac{48ab^3c^2}{6a^7bc^0}$

29. $\dfrac{7w^{11}z^6}{14w^3z^3}$

30. $\dfrac{12r^9s^3}{24r^8s^4}$

31. $\dfrac{8a^5b^9}{4a^6b^2}$

32. $\dfrac{16u^7v}{24u^3v^4}$

33. $\dfrac{6a + 18}{9a + 27}$

34. $\dfrac{5y - 15}{3y - 9}$

35. $\dfrac{b^2 - 9}{b^2 - b - 6}$

36. $\dfrac{3z - 6}{z^2 - 4}$

37. $\dfrac{21c^2 - 35c}{-7c}$

38. $\dfrac{30x^2 - 25x}{45x}$

39. $\dfrac{r + 6}{6 + r}$

40. $\dfrac{a + 2}{2 + a}$

41. $\dfrac{b + 8}{-b - 8}$

42. $\dfrac{7 + w}{-7 - w}$

43. $\dfrac{10 - x}{x - 10}$

44. $\dfrac{y - 14}{14 - y}$

45. $\dfrac{2t - 2}{1 - t}$

46. $\dfrac{5p - 10}{2 - p}$

47. $\dfrac{c + 4}{c - 4}$

48. $\dfrac{b + 2}{b - 2}$

49. $\dfrac{2t^2 + 7t - 4}{-2t^2 - 5t + 3}$

50. $\dfrac{y^2 + 8y - 9}{y^2 - 5y + 4}$

51. $\dfrac{b^2 - 25}{3b^2 - 13b - 10}$

52. $\dfrac{2x^2 - x - 15}{x^2 - 9}$

53. $\dfrac{9 - z^2}{2z^2 + z - 15}$

54. $\dfrac{2c^2 + 2c - 12}{8 - 2c - c^2}$

55. $\dfrac{4x - 2x^2}{5x - 10}$

56. $\dfrac{2y - 6}{3y^2 - y^3}$

57. $\dfrac{2z^3 + 16}{10 + 3z - z^2}$

58. $\dfrac{5p^2 - p - 4}{p^3 - 1}$

59. $\dfrac{10x^3 - 25x^2 + 4x - 10}{-4 - 10x^2}$

60. $\dfrac{8x^3 - 12x^2 + 6x - 9}{16x^4 - 9}$

▦ GRAPHING CALCULATOR EXERCISES

For Exercises 61–66, use a *Table* feature of a graphing calculator to find the values of the function from $x = -8$ to 8 in increments of 1. Then match each function with the appropriate graph.

61. $m(x) = \dfrac{2x + 1}{(x - 1)(x - 5)}$

62. $n(x) = \dfrac{x + 6}{(x + 1)(x + 5)}$

63. $p(x) = \dfrac{x - 2}{(x - 2)(x + 1)}$

64. $q(x) = \dfrac{x + 4}{(x + 4)(x - 3)}$

65. $r(x) = \dfrac{1}{(x - 2)(x + 1)}$

66. $s(x) = \dfrac{3}{(x + 4)(x - 3)}$

a.

b.

c.

d.

e.

f.

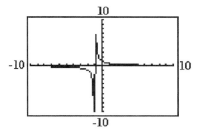

8.2   MULTIPLICATION AND DIVISION OF RATIONAL EXPRESSIONS

1. Multiplication of Rational Expressions

Recall that to multiply fractions, we multiply the numerators and multiply the denominators. The same is true for **multiplying rational expressions**.

Multiplication of Rational Expressions

Let p, q, r, and s represent polynomials, such that $q \neq 0$, $s \neq 0$. Then,

$$\frac{p}{q} \cdot \frac{r}{s} = \frac{pr}{qs}$$

For example:

Multiply the fractions	**Multiply the rational expressions**
$\dfrac{2}{3} \cdot \dfrac{5}{7} = \dfrac{10}{21}$	$\dfrac{2x}{3y} \cdot \dfrac{5z}{7} = \dfrac{10xz}{21y}$

Sometimes it is possible to reduce a ratio of common factors to 1 *before* multiplying. To do so, we must first factor the numerators and denominators of each fraction.

$$\frac{7}{10} \cdot \frac{15}{21} \xrightarrow{\text{factor}} \frac{\overset{1}{\cancel{7}}}{2 \cdot \underset{}{\cancel{5}}} \frac{\overset{1}{\cancel{5}} \cdot \overset{1}{\cancel{3}}}{\cancel{3} \cdot \cancel{7}} = \frac{1}{2}$$

The same process is also used to multiply rational expressions.

Multiplying Rational Expressions

1. Factor the numerators and denominators of all rational expressions.
2. Reduce the ratios of common factors to 1.
3. Multiply the remaining factors in the numerator and multiply the remaining factors in the denominator.

---

example 1   **Multiplying Rational Expressions**

Multiply:

a. $\dfrac{5a - 5b}{10} \cdot \dfrac{2}{a^2 - b^2}$

b. $\dfrac{4w - 20p}{2w^2 - 50p^2} \cdot \dfrac{2w^2 + 7wp - 15p^2}{3w + 9p}$

Solution:

a. $\dfrac{5a - 5b}{10} \cdot \dfrac{2}{a^2 - b^2}$

$= \dfrac{5(a - b)}{5 \cdot 2} \cdot \dfrac{2}{(a - b)(a + b)}$ Factor numerator and denominator.

$= \dfrac{\overset{1}{\cancel{5}}\overset{1}{\cancel{(a - b)}}}{\cancel{5} \cdot \cancel{2}} \cdot \dfrac{\overset{1}{\cancel{2}}}{\cancel{(a - b)}(a + b)}$ Reduce common factors.

$= \dfrac{1}{a + b}$

> ⬢ **Avoiding Mistakes**
>
> If all factors in the numerator reduce to a ratio of 1, do not forget to write the factor of 1 in the numerator.

b. $\dfrac{4w - 20p}{2w^2 - 50p^2} \cdot \dfrac{2w^2 + 7wp - 15p^2}{3w + 9p}$

$= \dfrac{4(w - 5p)}{2(w^2 - 25p^2)} \cdot \dfrac{(2w - 3p)(w + 5p)}{3(w + 3p)}$ Factor numerator and denominator.

$= \dfrac{2 \cdot 2(w - 5p)}{2(w - 5p)(w + 5p)} \cdot \dfrac{(2w - 3p)(w + 5p)}{3(w + 3p)}$ Factor further.

$= \dfrac{\overset{1}{\cancel{2}} \cdot 2\overset{1}{\cancel{(w - 5p)}}}{\cancel{2}\cancel{(w - 5p)}(w + 5p)} \cdot \dfrac{(2w - 3p)\overset{1}{\cancel{(w + 5p)}}}{3(w + 3p)}$ Reduce common factors.

$= \dfrac{2(2w - 3p)}{3(w + 3p)}$

Notice that the expression is left in factored form to show that it has been reduced to lowest terms.

■━━━━━━━━━━━━━━━━━━

2. Division of Rational Expressions

Recall that to divide fractions, multiply the first fraction by the reciprocal of the second fraction.

$$\text{Divide: } \dfrac{15}{14} \div \dfrac{10}{49} \xrightarrow[\text{of the second fraction}]{\text{Multiply by the reciprocal}} \dfrac{15}{14} \cdot \dfrac{49}{10} = \dfrac{3 \cdot \overset{1}{\cancel{5}}}{2 \cdot \cancel{7}} \cdot \dfrac{\overset{1}{\cancel{7}} \cdot 7}{2 \cdot \cancel{5}} = \dfrac{21}{4}$$

The same process is used for **dividing rational expressions**.

Division of Rational Expressions

Let p, q, r, and s represent polynomials, such that $q \neq 0, r \neq 0, s \neq 0$. Then,

$$\dfrac{p}{q} \div \dfrac{r}{s} = \dfrac{p}{q} \cdot \dfrac{s}{r} = \dfrac{ps}{qr}$$

example 2

Dividing Rational Expressions

Divide. a. $\dfrac{8t^3 + 27}{9 - 4t^2} \div \dfrac{4t^2 - 6t + 9}{2t^2 - t - 3}$ b. $\dfrac{\frac{5c}{6d}}{\frac{10}{d^2}}$

Solution:

a. $\dfrac{8t^3 + 27}{9 - 4t^2} \div \dfrac{4t^2 - 6t + 9}{2t^2 - t - 3}$

$= \dfrac{8t^3 + 27}{9 - 4t^2} \cdot \dfrac{2t^2 - t - 3}{4t^2 - 6t + 9}$ Multiply the first fraction by the reciprocal of the second.

$= \dfrac{(2t + 3)(4t^2 - 6t + 9)}{(3 - 2t)(3 + 2t)} \cdot \dfrac{(2t - 3)(t + 1)}{4t^2 - 6t + 9}$ Factor numerator and denominator. Notice $8t^3 + 27$ is a sum of cubes. Furthermore, $4t^2 - 6t + 9$ does not factor over the real numbers.

Tip: In Example 2(a), the factors $(2t - 3)$ and $(3 - 2t)$ are opposites and form a ratio of -1.

$$\dfrac{2t - 3}{3 - 2t} = -1$$

The factors $(2 + 3t)$ and $(3t + 2)$ are equal and form a ratio of 1.

$$\dfrac{2 + 3t}{3t + 2} = 1$$

$= \dfrac{\overset{1}{(2t + 3)}\,\overset{1}{(4t^2 - 6t + 9)}}{(3 - 2t)(3 + 2t)} \cdot \dfrac{\overset{-1}{(2t - 3)}(t + 1)}{4t^2 - 6t + 9}$ Reduce common factors.

$= (-1)\dfrac{(t + 1)}{1}$

$= -(t + 1)$ or $-t - 1$

b. $\dfrac{\frac{5c}{6d}}{\frac{10}{d^2}}$ ⟵——————— This fraction bar denotes division ($\div$).

$= \dfrac{5c}{6d} \div \dfrac{10}{d^2}$

$= \dfrac{5c}{6d} \cdot \dfrac{d^2}{10}$ Multiply the first fraction by the reciprocal of the second.

$= \dfrac{\overset{1}{5c}}{\overset{}{6d}} \cdot \dfrac{\overset{1}{d} \cdot d}{2 \cdot \overset{}{5}}$

$= \dfrac{cd}{12}$

In Section 4.2, we learned that a function can be defined in terms of the sum, difference, product, or quotient of two or more functions. Recall that for all values of x for which both f and g are defined, we can define $(fg)(x)$ and $\left(\frac{f}{g}\right)(x)$ as follows:

$$(fg)(x) = f(x)g(x)$$

$$\left(\frac{f}{g}\right)(x) = \frac{f(x)}{g(x)}; \quad g(x) \neq 0$$

3. Multiplication and Division of Rational Functions

example 3

Multiplying and Dividing Rational Functions

Given.

$$f(x) = \frac{x^2 + 10x + 25}{2x^2 + 3x - 5}, \quad g(x) = \frac{-x^2 - x + 2}{x^3 + 5x^2 - 4x - 20}, \quad h(x) = \frac{-3x - 15}{2 - x}$$

Find $(fg/h)(x)$ and simplify the result.

Solution:

$$\left(\frac{fg}{h}\right)(x) = \frac{f(x)g(x)}{h(x)} = [f(x)g(x)] \div h(x)$$

$$= \left(\frac{x^2 + 10x + 25}{2x^2 + 3x - 5} \cdot \frac{-x^2 - x + 2}{x^3 + 5x^2 - 4x - 20}\right) \div \frac{-3x - 15}{2 - x}$$

Multiply the expression in parentheses by the reciprocal of $(-3x - 15)/(2 - x)$

$$= \frac{x^2 + 10x + 25}{2x^2 + 3x - 5} \cdot \frac{-x^2 - x + 2}{x^3 + 5x^2 - 4x - 20} \cdot \frac{2 - x}{-3x - 15}$$

Factor the numerator and denominator of all rational expressions.

$$x^2 + 10x + 25 = (x + 5)^2$$

$$-x^2 - x + 2 = -1(x^2 + x - 2) = -1(x + 2)(x - 1)$$

$$= \frac{(x + 5)^2}{(2x + 5)(x - 1)} \cdot \frac{-1(x + 2)(x - 1)}{(x + 5)(x + 2)(x - 2)} \cdot \frac{2 - x}{-3(x + 5)}$$

$$-3x - 15 = -3(x + 5)$$

$$x^3 + 5x^2 - 4x - 20 = x^2(x + 5) - 4(x + 5) = (x + 5)(x^2 - 4) = (x + 5)(x + 2)(x - 2)$$

$$2x^2 + 3x - 5 = (2x + 5)(x - 1)$$

$$= \frac{(\cancel{x+5})^{\overset{1}{}}}{(2x+5)(\cancel{x-1})} \cdot \frac{-1(\cancel{x+2})(\cancel{x-1})}{(\cancel{x+5})(\cancel{x+2})(\cancel{x-2})} \cdot \frac{\overset{1}{\cancel{2}} \cdot x}{-3(\cancel{x+5})^{-1}}$$ Reduce common factors.

$$= \frac{1}{(2x+5)} \cdot \frac{-1}{1} \cdot \frac{-1}{-3}$$

Hence,

$$\left(\frac{fg}{h}\right)(x) = -\frac{1}{3(2x+5)} \quad \text{or} \quad \frac{-1}{3(2x+5)} \quad \text{or} \quad \frac{1}{-3(2x+5)}$$

---

section 8.2   PRACTICE EXERCISES

1. Write a rational function whose domain is $(-\infty, 4) \cup (4, \infty)$. (Answers may vary.)

2. Write a rational function whose domain is $(-\infty, 3) \cup (3, \infty)$. (Answers may vary.)

3. Write a rational function whose domain is $(-\infty, -5) \cup (-5, \infty)$. (Answers may vary.)

4. Write a rational function whose domain is $(-\infty, -6) \cup (-6, \infty)$. (Answers may vary.)

For Exercises 5–8, reduce the rational expressions.

5. $\dfrac{5x^2yz^3}{20xyz}$

6. $\dfrac{7x + 14}{7x^2 - 7x - 42}$

7. $\dfrac{25 - x^2}{x^2 - 10x + 25}$

8. $\dfrac{a^3b^2c^5}{2a^3bc^2}$

For Exercises 9–20, multiply the rational expressions.

9. $\dfrac{8w^2}{9} \cdot \dfrac{3}{2w^4}$

10. $\dfrac{16}{z^7} \cdot \dfrac{z^4}{8}$

11. $\dfrac{5p^2q^4}{12pq^3} \cdot \dfrac{6p^2}{20q^2}$

12. $\dfrac{27r^5}{7s} \cdot \dfrac{28rs^3}{9r^3s^2}$

13. $\dfrac{3z + 12}{8z^3} \cdot \dfrac{16z^3}{9z + 36}$

14. $\dfrac{x^2y}{x^2 - 4x - 5} \cdot \dfrac{2x^2 - 13x + 15}{xy^3}$

15. $\dfrac{2y^2 + 16y - 18}{y + 1} \cdot \dfrac{y - 9}{y^2 - 81}$

16. $\dfrac{2w - 6}{w + 2} \cdot \dfrac{3w^2 - w - 14}{w^2 - 9}$

17. $\dfrac{x - 5y}{x^2 + xy} \cdot \dfrac{y^2 - x^2}{10y - 2x}$

18. $\dfrac{3x - 15}{4x^2 - 2x} \cdot \dfrac{10x - 20x^2}{5 - x}$

19. $x(x + 5)^2\left(\dfrac{2}{x^2 - 25}\right)$

20. $y(y^2 - 4)\left(\dfrac{y}{y + 2}\right)$

For Exercises 21–32, divide the rational expressions.

21. $\dfrac{6x^2y^2}{(x - 2)} \div \dfrac{3xy^2}{(x - 2)^2}$

22. $\dfrac{(r + 3)^2}{4r^3s} \div \dfrac{r + 3}{rs}$

23. $\dfrac{t^2 + 5t}{t + 1} \div (t + 5)$

24. $\dfrac{w + 3}{w + 2} \div (w^2 - 9)$

25. $\dfrac{a}{a - 3} \div \dfrac{a^3 - a^2 - 12a}{a^2 - 9}$

26. $\dfrac{b^2 - 6b + 9}{b^2 - b - 6} \div \dfrac{b^2 - 9}{4}$

27. $\dfrac{2x^2 + 5xy + 2y^2}{4x^2 - y^2} \div \dfrac{x^2 + xy - 2y^2}{2x^2 + xy - y^2}$

28. $\dfrac{6s^2 + st - 2t^2}{6s^2 - 5st + t^2} \div \dfrac{3s^2 + 17st + 10t^2}{6s^2 + 13st - 5t^2}$

29. $\dfrac{x^4 - x^3 + x^2 - x}{2x^3 + 2x^2 + x + 1} \div \dfrac{x^3 - 4x^2 + x - 4}{2x^3 - 8x^2 + x - 4}$

30. $\dfrac{a^3 + a + a^2 + 1}{a^3 + a^2 + ab^2 + b^2} \div \dfrac{a^3 + a + a^2b + b}{2a^2 + 2ab + ab^2 + b^3}$

31. $\dfrac{3y - y^2}{y^3 - 27} \div \dfrac{y}{y^2 + 3y + 9}$

32. $\dfrac{8x - 4x^2}{xy - 2y + 3x - 6} \div \dfrac{3x + 6}{y + 3}$

For Exercises 33–38, perform the indicated operations.

33. $\dfrac{2}{25x^2} \cdot \dfrac{5x}{12} \div \dfrac{2}{15x}$

34. $\dfrac{4y}{7} \div \dfrac{y^2}{14} \cdot \dfrac{3}{y}$

35. $\dfrac{(a + b)^2}{a - b} \cdot \dfrac{a^3 - b^3}{a^2 - b^2} \div \dfrac{a^2 + ab + b^2}{(a - b)^2}$

36. $\dfrac{m^2 - n^2}{(m - n)^2} \div \dfrac{m^2 - 2mn + n^2}{m^2 - mn + n^2} \cdot \dfrac{(m - n)^4}{m^3 + n^3}$

37. $\dfrac{x^2 - 4y^2}{x + 2y} \div (x + 2y) \cdot \dfrac{2y}{x - 2y}$

38. $\dfrac{x^2 - 6xy + 9y^2}{x^2 - 4y^2} \cdot \dfrac{x^2 - 5xy + 6y^2}{3y - x} \div \dfrac{x^2 - 9y^2}{x + 2y}$

■ EXPANDING YOUR SKILLS

39. Let $m(x) = \dfrac{2x + 10}{x}, n(x) = \dfrac{15}{x^2 - 1},$

and $p(x) = \dfrac{10x^2}{x^2 + 6x + 5}.$
Find $(m \div np)(x).$

40. Let $f(w) = \dfrac{w^2 - w}{w^2 - 6w + 8}, g(w) = w - 2,$

and $h(w) = \dfrac{5w}{w^2 - 9w + 20}.$
Find $(fg \div h)(w).$

41. Let $p(z) = \dfrac{z^2 + z - 6}{3z^2 + 5z - 12},$

$q(z) = \dfrac{2z^2 - 14z}{16z^2 - 4z}, r(z) = \dfrac{z - 7}{z + 7},$

and $s(z) = \dfrac{12z^2 - 19z + 4}{z^2 + 5z - 14}.$
Find $(pq \div rs)(z).$

42. Let $f(y) = \dfrac{y + 2}{y - 2},$

$g(y) = \dfrac{y - 4}{5y^2 - 10y}, h(y) = \dfrac{y + 6}{10y^2},$

and $k(y) = \dfrac{y^2 - y - 6}{y^2 - 7y + 12}.$
Find $(f \div gh \div k)(y).$

For Exercises 43–46, write an expression for the area of the figure and simplify.

43.

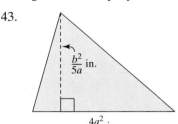

$\dfrac{b^2}{5a}$ in.

$\dfrac{4a^2}{b}$ in.

44.

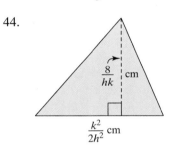

$\dfrac{8}{hk}$ cm

$\dfrac{k^2}{2h^2}$ cm

45.

$\dfrac{12x}{x^2 - 4}$ m

$\dfrac{x + 2}{6}$ m

46.

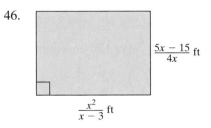

$\dfrac{5x - 15}{4x}$ ft

$\dfrac{x^2}{x - 3}$ ft

47. Graph $Y_1 = (x^2 - 49)[2/(2x - 14)]$ and $Y_2 = x + 7$ on a standard viewing window. Does it appear that $Y_1 = Y_2$ on the standard viewing window?

48. Graph $Y_1 = (x^2 - 81)[4/(4x - 36)]$ and $Y_2 = x + 9$ on a standard viewing window. Does it appear that $Y_1 = Y_2$ on the standard viewing window?

49. Graph $Y_1 = (3x - 6) \div [(x - 2)/x]$ and $Y_2 = 3x$ on a standard viewing window. Does it appear that $Y_1 = Y_2$ on the standard viewing window?

50. Graph $Y_1 = (4x + 8) \div [(x + 2)/x]$ and $Y_2 = 4x$ on a standard viewing window. Does it appear that $Y_1 = Y_2$ on the standard viewing window?

---

section

Concepts

1. Addition and Subtraction of Rational Expressions with *Like* Denominators

2. Identifying the Least Common Denominator

3. Addition and Subtraction of Rational Expressions with Un*like* Denominators

4. Addition and Subtraction of Rational Functions

5. Applying the Order of Operations

8.3   ADDITION AND SUBTRACTION OF RATIONAL EXPRESSIONS

1. Addition and Subtraction of Rational Expressions with *Like* Denominators

To add or subtract rational expressions the expressions must have the same denominator. As with fractions, we add or subtract rational expressions with the same denominator by combining the terms in the numerator and then writing the result over the common denominator. Then, if possible, we reduce the expression to lowest terms.

Addition and Subtraction of Rational Expressions

Let p, q, and r represent polynomials where $q \neq 0$. Then,

1. $\dfrac{p}{q} + \dfrac{r}{q} = \dfrac{p + r}{q}$

2. $\dfrac{p}{q} - \dfrac{r}{q} = \dfrac{p - r}{q}$

---

example 1   **Adding and Subtracting Rational Expressions with *Like* Denominators**

Add or subtract as indicated.

a. $\dfrac{1}{8} + \dfrac{3}{8}$

b. $\dfrac{5x}{2x - 1} + \dfrac{3}{2x - 1}$

c. $\dfrac{x^2}{x - 4} - \dfrac{x + 12}{x - 4}$

Solution:

a. $\dfrac{1}{8} + \dfrac{3}{8} = \dfrac{1+3}{8}$ Add the terms in the numerator.

$ = \dfrac{4}{8}$

$ = \dfrac{1}{2}$ Reduce the fraction.

b. $\dfrac{5x}{2x-1} + \dfrac{3}{2x-1} = \dfrac{5x+3}{2x-1}$ Add the terms in the numerator. The answer is already in lowest terms.

c. $\dfrac{x^2}{x-4} - \dfrac{x+12}{x-4}$

$ = \dfrac{x^2 - (x+12)}{x-4}$ Combine the terms in the numerator.

$ = \dfrac{x^2 - x - 12}{x-4}$ Apply the distributive property.

$ = \dfrac{(x-4)(x+3)}{(x-4)}$ Factor the numerator and denominator.

$ = \dfrac{\overset{1}{(\cancel{x-4})}(x+3)}{(\cancel{x-4})}$ Reduce the rational expression.

$ = x + 3$

◆ Avoiding Mistakes

When subtracting rational expressions, use parentheses to group the terms in the numerator that follow the subtraction sign. This will help you remember to apply the distributive property.

2.   Identifying the Least Common Denominator

If two rational expressions have different denominators, each expression must be rewritten with a common denominator before adding or subtracting the expressions. The **least common denominator (LCD)** of two or more rational expressions is defined as the least common multiple of the denominators.

For example, consider the fractions $\frac{1}{20}$ and $\frac{1}{8}$. By inspection, you can probably see that the least common denominator is 40. To understand why, find the prime factorization of both denominators.

$$20 = 2^2 \cdot 5 \qquad \text{and} \qquad 8 = 2^3$$

A common multiple of 20 and 8 must be a multiple of 5, a multiple of 2^2, and a multiple of 2^3. However, any number that is a multiple of $2^3 = 8$ is automatically a multiple of $2^2 = 4$. Therefore, it is sufficient to construct the least common denominator as the product of unique prime factors, where each factor is raised to its highest power.

$$\text{The LCD of } \dfrac{1}{2^2 \cdot 5} \text{ and } \dfrac{1}{2^3} \text{ is } 2^3 \cdot 5 = 40.$$

> ### Steps to Find the LCD of Two or More Rational Expressions
>
> 1. Factor all denominators completely.
> 2. The LCD is the product of unique factors from the denominators, where each factor is raised to the highest power to which it appears in any denominator.

example 2

Finding the LCD of Rational Expressions

Find the LCD of the following sets of rational expressions.

a. $\dfrac{1}{12}; \dfrac{5}{18}; \dfrac{7}{30}$

b. $\dfrac{1}{2x^3y}; \dfrac{5}{16xy^2z}$

c. $\dfrac{x+2}{2x-10}; \dfrac{x^2+3}{x^2-25}; \dfrac{6}{x^2+8x+16}$

d. $\dfrac{x+4}{2(x-3)}; \dfrac{1}{3-x}$

Solution:

a. $\dfrac{1}{12}; \dfrac{5}{18}; \dfrac{7}{30}$

$\dfrac{1}{2^2 \cdot 3}; \dfrac{5}{2 \cdot 3^2}; \dfrac{7}{2 \cdot 3 \cdot 5}$ Factor the denominators completely.

The LCD is $2^2 \cdot 3^2 \cdot 5 = 180$ The LCD is the product of the factors 2, 3, and 5. Each factor is raised to its highest power.

b. $\dfrac{1}{2x^3y}; \dfrac{5}{16xy^2z}$

$\dfrac{1}{2x^3y}; \dfrac{5}{2^4xy^2z}$ Factor the denominators completely.

$\text{LCD} = 2^4 x^3 y^2 z$ The LCD is the product of the factors 2, x, y, and z. Each factor is raised to its highest power.

c. $\dfrac{x+2}{2x-10}; \dfrac{x^2+3}{x^2-25}; \dfrac{6}{x^2+8x+16}$

$\dfrac{x+2}{2(x-5)}; \dfrac{x^2+3}{(x-5)(x+5)}; \dfrac{6}{(x+4)^2}$ Factor the denominators completely.

$\text{LCD} = 2(x-5)(x+5)(x+4)^2$ The LCD is the product of the factors 2, $(x-5)$, $(x+5)$, and $(x+4)$. Each factor is raised to its highest power.

d. $\dfrac{x+4}{2(x-3)}; \dfrac{1}{3-x}$ The denominators are already factored.

Notice that $x - 3$ and $3 - x$ are opposite factors. If -1 is factored from either expression, the binomial factors will be the same.

$$\frac{x + 4}{2(x - 3)}, \frac{1}{-1(-3 + x)} \qquad \frac{x + 4}{2[-1(-x + 3)]}, \frac{1}{3 - x}$$

factor out -1

same binomial factors

factor out -1

same binomial factors

$$\text{LCD} = 2(x - 3)(-1) \qquad \text{LCD} = 2(-1)(3 - x)$$
$$= -2(x - 3) \qquad = -2(3 - x)$$

The LCD can be taken as either $\quad -2(x - 3) \quad$ [equivalently $2(3 - x)$]
$$\text{or} \quad -2(3 - x) \quad \text{[equivalently } 2(x - 3)]$$

3. Addition and Subtraction of Rational Expressions with Un*like* Denominators

To add or subtract rational expressions with un*like* denominators, we must convert each expression to an equivalent expression with the same denominator. For example, consider adding the expressions $3/(x - 2) + 5/(x + 1)$. The LCD is $(x - 2)(x + 1)$. For each expression, identify the factors from the LCD that are missing in the denominator. Then multiply the numerator and denominator of the expression by the missing factor(s):

$$\frac{(3)}{(x - 2)} \cdot \frac{(x + 1)}{(x + 1)} + \frac{(5)}{(x + 1)} \cdot \frac{(x - 2)}{(x - 2)} \qquad \begin{array}{l}\text{The rational expressions now} \\ \text{have the same denominator and} \\ \text{can be added.}\end{array}$$

$$= \frac{3(x + 1) + 5(x - 2)}{(x - 2)(x + 1)} \qquad \text{Combine terms in the numerator.}$$

$$= \frac{3x + 3 + 5x - 10}{(x - 2)(x + 1)} \qquad \text{Clear parentheses and simplify.}$$

$$= \frac{8x - 7}{(x - 2)(x + 1)}$$

Graphing Calculator Box

The graphs of

$$Y_1 = \frac{3}{x - 2} + \frac{5}{x + 1}$$

and

$$Y_2 = \frac{8x - 7}{(x - 2)(x + 1)}$$

are the same in the standard viewing window.

Steps to Add or Subtract Rational Expressions

1. Factor the denominators of each rational expression.
2. Identify the LCD.
3. Rewrite each rational expression as an equivalent expression with the LCD as its denominator.
4. Add or subtract the numerators and write the result over the common denominator.
5. Simplify and reduce.
---

example 3 **Adding and Subtracting Rational Expressions with Un*like* Denominators**

Add or subtract as indicated.

a. $\dfrac{3}{8b} + \dfrac{5}{4b^2}$ b. $\dfrac{3t - 2}{t^2 + 4t - 12} - \dfrac{5}{2t + 12}$ c. $\dfrac{-w^2 - w - 6}{w^3 - 8} - \dfrac{1}{w - 2}$

Solution:

a. $\dfrac{3}{8b} + \dfrac{5}{4b^2}$

$= \dfrac{3}{2^3 b} + \dfrac{5}{2^2 b^2}$ **Step 1:** Factor the denominators.

Step 2: The LCD is $2^3 b^2$.

$= \dfrac{3}{2^3 b} \cdot \dfrac{b}{b} + \dfrac{5}{2^2 b^2} \cdot \dfrac{2}{2}$ **Step 3:** Write each expression with the LCD.

$= \dfrac{3b + 10}{2^3 b^2}$ **Step 4:** Add the numerators and write the result over the LCD.

$= \dfrac{3b + 10}{8b^2}$ **Step 5:** Simplify.

b. $\dfrac{3t - 2}{t^2 + 4t - 12} - \dfrac{5}{2t + 12}$

$= \dfrac{3t - 2}{(t + 6)(t - 2)} - \dfrac{5}{2(t + 6)}$ **Step 1:** Factor the denominators.

Step 2: The LCD is $2(t + 6)(t - 2)$.

$$= \frac{(2)}{(2)} \cdot \frac{(3t - 2)}{(t + 6)(t - 2)} - \frac{5}{2(t + 6)} \cdot \frac{(t - 2)}{(t - 2)}$$

Step 3: Write each expression with the LCD.

$$= \frac{2(3t - 2) - 5(t - 2)}{2(t + 6)(t - 2)}$$

Step 4: Add the numerators and write the result over the LCD.

$$= \frac{6t - 4 - 5t + 10}{2(t + 6)(t - 2)}$$

Step 5: Simplify.

$$= \frac{t + 6}{2(t + 6)(t - 2)}$$

Combine *like* terms.

$$= \frac{t \cancel{+ 6}^{1}}{2(t \cancel{+ 6})(t - 2)}$$

Reduce.

$$= \frac{1}{2(t - 2)}$$

c. $\dfrac{-w^2 - w - 6}{w^3 - 8} - \dfrac{1}{w - 2}$

$$= \frac{-w^2 - w - 6}{(w - 2)(w^2 + 2w + 4)} - \frac{1}{w - 2}$$

Step 1: Factor the denominators.

Step 2: The LCD is $(w - 2)$ $(w^2 + 2w + 4)$.

Tip: $w^3 - 8$ is a difference of cubes.

Recall: $a^3 - b^3 = (a - b)(a^2 + ab + b^2)$

$w^3 - 8 = (w - 2)(w^2 + 2w + 4)$

$$= \frac{-w^2 - w - 6}{(w - 2)(w^2 + 2w + 4)} - \frac{1}{w - 2} \cdot \frac{(w^2 + 2w + 4)}{(w^2 + 2w + 4)}$$

Step 3: Write each expression with the LCD.

$$= \frac{-w^2 - w - 6 - 1(w^2 + 2w + 4)}{(w - 2)(w^2 + 2w + 4)}$$

Step 4: Combine terms in the numerator and write the result over the LCD.

$$= \frac{-w^2 - w - 6 - w^2 - 2w - 4}{(w - 2)(w^2 + 2w + 4)}$$

Step 5: Apply the distributive property.

$$= \frac{-2w^2 - 3w - 10}{(w - 2)(w^2 + 2w + 4)}$$

Combine *like* terms.

$$= \frac{-(2w^2 + 3w + 10)}{(w - 2)(w^2 + 2w + 4)}$$

Factor the numerator to verify that the expression is reduced.

4. Addition and Subtraction of Rational Functions

example 4

Adding and Subtracting Rational Functions

Given $f(x) = \dfrac{x}{x^2 - 6x + 9}$; $g(x) = \dfrac{5}{3 - x}$; $h(x) = \dfrac{3}{x + 1}$

Find $(f - g - h)(x)$ and simplify.

Solution:

$$(f - g - h)(x) = f(x) - g(x) - h(x)$$

$$= \frac{x}{x^2 - 6x + 9} - \frac{5}{3 - x} - \frac{3}{x + 1}$$

$$= \frac{x}{(x-3)^2} - \frac{5}{3-x} - \frac{3}{x+1}$$

Step 1: Factor the denominators.

$$= \frac{x}{(x-3)^2} - \frac{(-1)\cdot 5}{(-1)(3-x)} - \frac{3}{x+1}$$

$x - 3$ and $3 - x$ are opposites and differ by a factor of -1. Multiply the numerator and denominator of the second expression by -1.

$$= \frac{x}{(x-3)^2} - \frac{-5}{x-3} - \frac{3}{x+1}$$

Step 2: The LCD is $(x-3)^2(x+1)$.

Step 3: Write each expression with the LCD.

$$= \frac{x}{(x-3)^2}\cdot\frac{(x+1)}{(x+1)} - \frac{-5}{(x-3)}\cdot\frac{(x-3)(x+1)}{(x-3)(x+1)} - \frac{3}{(x+1)}\cdot\frac{(x-3)^2}{(x-3)^2}$$

$$= \frac{x(x+1) + 5(x-3)(x+1) - 3(x-3)^2}{(x-3)^2(x+1)}$$

Step 4: Combine the numerators and write the result over the LCD.

$$= \frac{x^2 + x + 5(x^2 - 2x - 3) - 3(x^2 - 6x + 9)}{(x-3)^2(x+1)}$$

$$= \frac{x^2 + x + 5x^2 - 10x - 15 - 3x^2 + 18x - 27}{(x-3)^2(x+1)}$$

Clear parentheses.

$$= \frac{3x^2 + 9x - 42}{(x-3)^2(x+1)}$$

Add *like* terms.

$$= \frac{3(x^2 + 3x - 14)}{(x-3)^2(x+1)}$$

Step 5: The function cannot be reduced further.

5. Applying the Order of Operations

example 5

Applying the Order of Operations

Simplify.

$$\frac{x^2 - 3x - 4}{x^2 + 5x} \cdot \frac{x}{8 - 2x} - \frac{x + 7}{x + 5}$$

Solution:

$$\left(\frac{x^2 - 3x - 4}{x^2 + 5x} \cdot \frac{x}{8 - 2x}\right) - \frac{x + 7}{x + 5}$$

The order of operations dictates that we must multiply expressions first.

$$= \left[\frac{(x - 4)(x + 1)}{x(x + 5)} \cdot \frac{x}{2(4 - x)}\right] - \frac{x + 7}{x + 5}$$

Factor the first two expressions.

$$= \left[\frac{\overset{-1}{(x - 4)}(x + 1)}{x(x + 5)} \cdot \frac{\overset{1}{x}}{2(4 - x)}\right] - \frac{x + 7}{x + 5}$$

Reduce common factors.

$$= \frac{(-1)(x + 1)}{2(x + 5)} - \frac{x + 7}{x + 5}$$

Simplify.

$$= \frac{-x - 1}{2(x + 5)} - \frac{x + 7}{x + 5}$$

Now subtract the rational expressions.

$$= \frac{-x - 1}{2(x + 5)} - \frac{(2)(x + 7)}{(2)(x + 5)}$$

Write each expression with the LCD.

$$= \frac{-x - 1 - 2(x + 7)}{2(x + 5)}$$

Subtract the numerators and write the result over the LCD.

$$= \frac{-x - 1 - 2x - 14}{2(x + 5)}$$

Clear parentheses.

$$= \frac{-3x - 15}{2(x + 5)}$$

Combine *like* terms.

$$= \frac{-3(x + 5)}{2(x + 5)}$$

Factor.

$$= \frac{-3(x + \overset{1}{5})}{2(x + 5)}$$

$$= -\frac{3}{2}$$

Reduce.

section 8.3 PRACTICE EXERCISES

For Exercises 1–2, reduce the expression.

1. $\dfrac{27 - 3a^2}{27 - a^3}$

2. $\dfrac{8x^3 - 27}{4x^2 + 6x + 9}$

For Exercises 3–8, perform the indicated operation.

3. $\dfrac{x}{x - y} \div \dfrac{x^2}{y - x}$

4. $\dfrac{9b + 9}{4b + 8} \cdot \dfrac{2b + 4}{3b - 3}$

5. $\dfrac{(5 - a)^2}{10a - 2} \cdot \dfrac{25a^2 - 1}{a^2 - 10a + 25}$

6. $\dfrac{x^2 - z^2}{14x^2 z^4} \div \dfrac{x^2 + 2xz + z^2}{3xz^3}$

7. $\dfrac{25y^3}{y^3 + 3y^2 - 10y} \div \dfrac{30y^2}{y^2 - 7y + 10} \cdot \dfrac{3y^2 + 3y - 60}{2y - 8}$

8. $\dfrac{c^2 - 1}{2c^2} \cdot \dfrac{c^3 - 25c}{c^2 - 6c + 5} \div \dfrac{c^2 + 5c}{6c + 6}$

9. For $f(x) = \dfrac{4x + 4}{x^2 - 1}$

   a. Factor the numerator and denominator completely.

   b. Identify the domain.

10. For $g(x) = \dfrac{3x + 6}{x^2 - 3x - 10}$

    a. Factor numerator and denominator completely.

    b. Identify the domain.

For Exercises 11–20, add or subtract as indicated. Be sure to reduce your answer.

11. $\dfrac{3}{5x} + \dfrac{7}{5x}$

12. $\dfrac{1}{2x^2} - \dfrac{5}{2x^2}$

13. $\dfrac{x}{x^2 - 2x - 3} - \dfrac{3}{x^2 - 2x - 3}$

14. $\dfrac{x}{x^2 + 4x - 12} + \dfrac{6}{x^2 + 4x - 12}$

15. $\dfrac{5x - 1}{(2x + 9)(x - 6)} - \dfrac{3x - 6}{(2x + 9)(x - 6)}$

16. $\dfrac{4 - x}{8x + 1} - \dfrac{5x - 6}{8x + 1}$

17. $\dfrac{6}{x - 5} + \dfrac{3}{5 - x}$

18. $\dfrac{8}{2 - x} + \dfrac{7}{x - 2}$

19. $\dfrac{x - 2}{x - 6} - \dfrac{x + 2}{6 - x}$

20. $\dfrac{x - 10}{x - 8} - \dfrac{x + 10}{8 - x}$

For Exercises 21–30, find the least common denominator (LCD).

21. $\dfrac{x}{8}, \dfrac{-5}{20}$

22. $\dfrac{y}{15}, \dfrac{y^2}{35}$

23. $\dfrac{-7}{24x}, \dfrac{5}{75x^2}$

24. $\dfrac{2}{7y^3}, \dfrac{-13}{5y^2}$

25. $\dfrac{6}{(x - 4)(x + 2)}, \dfrac{-8}{(x - 4)(x - 6)}$

26. $\dfrac{x}{(2x - 1)(x - 7)}, \dfrac{2}{(2x - 1)(x + 1)}$

27. $\dfrac{3}{x(x - 1)(x + 7)^2}, \dfrac{-1}{x^2(x + 7)}$

28. $\dfrac{14}{(x - 2)^2(x + 9)}, \dfrac{41}{x(x - 2)(x + 9)}$

29. $\dfrac{5}{x - 6}, \dfrac{x - 5}{x^2 - 8x + 12}$

30. $\dfrac{7a}{a + 4}, \dfrac{a + 12}{a^2 - 16}$

For Exercises 31–36, write an equivalent fraction with the given denominator.

31. $\dfrac{5}{3x} = \dfrac{}{9x^2 y}$

32. $\dfrac{-5}{xy} = \dfrac{}{4x^2 y^3}$

33. $\dfrac{2x}{x - 1} = \dfrac{}{x(x - 1)(x + 2)}$

34. $\dfrac{5x}{2x - 5} = \dfrac{}{(2x - 5)(x + 8)}$

35. $\dfrac{y}{y + 6} = \dfrac{}{y^2 + 5y - 6}$

36. $\dfrac{t^2}{t - 8} = \dfrac{}{t^2 - 6t - 16}$

For Exercises 37–58, add or subtract as indicated.

37. $\dfrac{x+3}{x^2} + \dfrac{x+5}{2x}$

38. $\dfrac{x+2}{5x^2} + \dfrac{x+4}{15x}$

39. $\dfrac{s-1}{s} - \dfrac{t+1}{t}$

40. $\dfrac{x+2}{x} - \dfrac{y-2}{y}$

41. $\dfrac{4a-2}{3a+12} - \dfrac{a-2}{a+4}$

42. $\dfrac{10}{b(b+5)} + \dfrac{2}{b}$

43. $\dfrac{6}{w(w-2)} + \dfrac{3}{w}$

44. $\dfrac{6y+5}{5y-25} - \dfrac{y+2}{y-5}$

45. $w+2+\dfrac{1}{w-2}$

46. $h-3+\dfrac{1}{h+3}$

47. $\dfrac{6b}{b-4} - \dfrac{1}{b+1}$

48. $\dfrac{a}{a-3} - \dfrac{5}{a+6}$

49. $\dfrac{t+5}{t-5} - \dfrac{10t-5}{t^2-25}$

50. $\dfrac{s+8}{s-8} - \dfrac{16s+64}{s^2-64}$

51. $\dfrac{x+2}{x^2-36} - \dfrac{x}{x^2+9x+18}$

52. $\dfrac{7}{x^2-x-2} + \dfrac{x}{x^2+4x+3}$

53. $\dfrac{2}{3x-15} + \dfrac{x}{25-x^2}$

54. $\dfrac{5}{9-x^2} - \dfrac{4}{x^2+4x+3}$

55. $\dfrac{k}{k+7} - \dfrac{2}{k^2+6k-7} + \dfrac{4k}{k-1}$

56. $\dfrac{t}{t-2} - \dfrac{1}{t^2-t-2} + \dfrac{3t}{t+1}$

57. $\dfrac{2x}{x^2-y^2} - \dfrac{1}{x-y} + \dfrac{1}{y-x}$

58. $\dfrac{3w-1}{2w^2+w-3} - \dfrac{2-w}{w-1} - \dfrac{w}{1-w}$

59. Given $f(x) = \dfrac{x-11}{x^2-22x+121}$ and $g(x) = \dfrac{x+11}{x^2-121}$, find $(f-g)(x)$. (*Hint*: Reduce f and g before subtracting.)

60. Given $h(t) = \dfrac{t-12}{t^2-24t+144}$ and $k(t) = \dfrac{1}{t^2-144}$, find $(h-k)(t)$. (*Hint*: Reduce h before subtracting.)

61. Let $a(x) = \dfrac{2}{3x}$, $b(x) = \dfrac{x-2}{3x(x+1)}$, and $c(x) = \dfrac{x}{x+1}$.

    a. Find $(a+b-c)(x)$.

    b. Find $(a-b+c)(x)$.

62. Let $f(t) = \dfrac{t}{t+2}$, $g(t) = \dfrac{2}{(t+2)^2}$, and $h(t) = \dfrac{8}{t^2-4}$.

    a. Find $(f+g-h)(t)$.

    b. Find $(f-g+h)(t)$.

EXPANDING YOUR SKILLS

For Exercises 63–66, write an expression that represents the perimeter of the figure and simplify.

63.

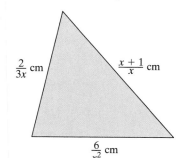

$\frac{2}{3x}$ cm

$\frac{x+1}{x}$ cm

$\frac{6}{x^2}$ cm

64.

65.

66.

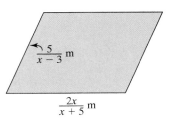

---

chapter 8   MIDCHAPTER REVIEW

1. Explain the process to reduce a rational expression.

2. Explain the process to multiply two rational expressions.

3. Explain the process to divide two rational expressions.

4. Explain the process to add and subtract rational expressions.

For Exercises 5–14, perform the indicated operations.

5. $\dfrac{2}{2y-3} - \dfrac{3}{2y} + 1$

6. $(x+5) + \left(\dfrac{7}{x-4}\right)$

7. $\dfrac{5x^2 - 6x + 1}{x^2 - 1} \div \dfrac{16x^2 - 9}{4x^2 + 7x + 3}$

8. $\dfrac{a^2 - 25}{3a^2 + 3ab} \cdot \dfrac{a^2 + 4a + ab + 4b}{a^2 + 9a + 20}$

9. $\dfrac{4}{y+1} + \dfrac{y+2}{y^2 - 1} - \dfrac{3}{y-1}$

10. $\dfrac{8w^2}{w^3 - 16w} - \dfrac{4w}{w^2 - 4w}$

11. $\dfrac{a^2 - 16}{2x + 6} \cdot \dfrac{x + 3}{a - 4}$

12. $\dfrac{t^2 - 9}{t} \div \dfrac{t + 3}{t + 2}$

13. $\dfrac{6xy}{x^2 - y^2} + \dfrac{x + y}{y - x}$

14. $(x^2 - 6x + 8)\left(\dfrac{3}{x - 2}\right)$

For Exercises 15–16, reduce the expressions.

15. $\dfrac{x - 3 - bx + 3b}{bx + 3b - x - 3}$

16. $\dfrac{m^2 - n^2}{n - m}$

17. Let $h(t) = t + 3$ and $k(t) = \dfrac{2}{3t - 5}$. Find $(h - k)(t)$.

18. Let $f(x) = \dfrac{4}{x - 5}$ and $g(x) = \dfrac{x + 5}{x^2 - 25}$. Find $(f + g)(x)$.

19. Let $f(x) = \dfrac{4}{x - 3}$, $g(x) = \dfrac{x + 2}{2x^2 - 11x + 15}$, and $h(x) = \dfrac{2x - 5}{x - 2}$. Find $(f + g \cdot h)(x)$.

section

8.4   COMPLEX FRACTIONS

1. Simplifying Complex Fractions (Method I)

A **complex fraction** is a fraction whose numerator or denominator contains one or more fractions. For example,

$$\frac{\frac{5x^2}{y}}{\frac{10x}{y^2}} \quad \text{and} \quad \frac{2 + \frac{1}{2} - \frac{1}{3}}{\frac{3}{4} + \frac{1}{6}}$$

are complex fractions.

Two methods will be presented to simplify complex fractions. The first method (method I) follows the order of operations to simplify the numerator and denominator separately before dividing. The process is summarized as follows.

Steps to Simplify a Complex Fraction (Method I)

1. Add or subtract expressions in the numerator to form a single fraction. Add or subtract expressions in the denominator to form a single fraction.
2. Divide the rational expressions from step 1 by multiplying the numerator of the complex fraction by the reciprocal of the denominator of the complex fraction.
3. Simplify and reduce if possible.

example 1   **Simplifying a Complex Fraction (Method I)**

Simplify the expression. $\dfrac{\frac{5x^2}{y}}{\frac{10x}{y^2}}$

Solution:

$\dfrac{\frac{5x^2}{y}}{\frac{10x}{y^2}}$

Step 1: The numerator and denominator of the complex fraction are already single fractions.

$= \dfrac{5x^2}{y} \cdot \dfrac{y^2}{10x}$

Step 2: Multiply the numerator of the complex fraction by the reciprocal of the denominator.

$= \dfrac{5 \cdot x \cdot x}{y} \cdot \dfrac{y \cdot y}{2 \cdot 5 \cdot x}$

Factor the numerators and denominators.

$$= \frac{\overset{1}{\cancel{5}} \cdot \overset{1}{x} \cdot x}{\cancel{y}} \cdot \frac{\overset{1}{\cancel{y}} \cdot y}{2 \cdot \cancel{5} \cdot \cancel{x}}$$ **Step 3:**   Reduce common factors and simplify.

$$= \frac{xy}{2}$$

Sometimes it is necessary to simplify the numerator and denominator of a complex fraction before the division is performed. This is illustrated in the next example.

example 2   **Simplifying a Complex Fraction (Method I)**

Simplify the expression. $\dfrac{2 + \dfrac{1}{2} - \dfrac{1}{3}}{\dfrac{3}{4} + \dfrac{1}{6}}$

Solution:

$\dfrac{2 + \dfrac{1}{2} - \dfrac{1}{3}}{\dfrac{3}{4} + \dfrac{1}{6}}$ **Step 1:**   Combine fractions in numerator and denominator separately.

$= \dfrac{\dfrac{12}{6} + \dfrac{3}{6} - \dfrac{2}{6}}{\dfrac{9}{12} + \dfrac{2}{12}}$ The LCD in the numerator is 6. The LCD in the denominator is 12.

$= \dfrac{\dfrac{13}{6}}{\dfrac{11}{12}}$ Form single fractions in the numerator and denominator.

$= \dfrac{13}{6} \cdot \dfrac{12}{11}$ **Step 2:**   Multiply by the reciprocal of $\frac{11}{12}$ which is $\frac{12}{11}$.

$= \dfrac{13}{\cancel{6}} \cdot \dfrac{\overset{2}{\cancel{12}}}{11}$

$= \dfrac{26}{11}$ **Step 3:**   Simplify.

example 3   **Simplifying Complex Fractions (Method I)**

Simplify the expression. $\dfrac{a - a^{-1}b^2}{a^{-1} - b^{-1}}$

Solution:

$$\frac{a - a^{-1}b^2}{a^{-1} - b^{-1}}$$

$$= \frac{a - \dfrac{b^2}{a}}{\dfrac{1}{a} - \dfrac{1}{b}}$$

Rewrite the expression with positive exponents.

$$= \frac{\dfrac{a}{1} \cdot \dfrac{a}{a} - \dfrac{b^2}{a}}{\dfrac{1}{a} \cdot \dfrac{b}{b} - \dfrac{1}{b} \cdot \dfrac{a}{a}}$$

Step 1: Simplify numerator and denominator separately. Numerator LCD = a. Denominator LCD = ab.

$$= \frac{\dfrac{a^2}{a} - \dfrac{b^2}{a}}{\dfrac{b}{ab} - \dfrac{a}{ab}}$$

$$= \frac{\dfrac{a^2 - b^2}{a}}{\dfrac{b - a}{ab}}$$

Form single fractions in the numerator and denominator.

$$= \frac{a^2 - b^2}{a} \cdot \frac{ab}{b - a}$$

Step 2: Multiply the numerator of the complex fraction by the reciprocal of the denominator.

$$= \frac{\overset{-1}{\cancel{(a - b)}}(a + b)}{\cancel{a}} \cdot \frac{\cancel{a}b}{\cancel{b - a}}$$

Step 3: Factor. Reduce common factors. Recall: $(a - b)/(b - a) = -1$.

$$= \frac{(-1)(a + b)}{1} \cdot \frac{b}{1}$$

$$= -b(a + b)$$

Simplify.

2. Simplifying Complex Fractions (Method II)

We will now simplify the expressions from Examples 2 and 3 again using a second method to simplify complex fractions (method II). Recall that multiplying the numerator and denominator of a rational expression by the same quantity does not change the value of the expression. This is the basis for method II.

Steps to Simplify a Complex Fraction (Method II)

1. Multiply the numerator and denominator of the complex fraction by the LCD of *all* individual fractions within the expression.
2. Apply the distributive property and simplify the numerator and denominator.
3. Reduce if necessary.

example 4   **Simplifying Complex Fractions (Method II)**

Simplify the expression by method II. $\dfrac{2 + \dfrac{1}{2} - \dfrac{1}{3}}{\dfrac{3}{4} + \dfrac{1}{6}}$

Solution:

$\dfrac{2 + \dfrac{1}{2} - \dfrac{1}{3}}{\dfrac{3}{4} + \dfrac{1}{6}}$

The LCD of the expressions, $\dfrac{2}{1}, \dfrac{1}{2}, \dfrac{1}{3}, \dfrac{3}{4}$, and $\dfrac{1}{6}$ is 12.

$= \dfrac{12\left(2 + \dfrac{1}{2} - \dfrac{1}{3}\right)}{12\left(\dfrac{3}{4} + \dfrac{1}{6}\right)}$

Step 1: Multiply the numerator and denominator of the complex fraction by the LCD, 12.

$= \dfrac{12(2) + 12\left(\dfrac{1}{2}\right) - 12\left(\dfrac{1}{3}\right)}{12\left(\dfrac{3}{4}\right) + 12\left(\dfrac{1}{6}\right)}$

Step 2: Apply the distributive property.

$= \dfrac{24 + 6 - 4}{9 + 2}$

Step 3: Simplify numerator and denominator.

$= \dfrac{26}{11}$

---

example 5   **Simplifying Complex Fractions (Method II)**

Simplify the expression by method II. $\dfrac{a - a^{-1}b^2}{a^{-1} - b^{-1}}$

Solution:

$\dfrac{a - a^{-1}b^2}{a^{-1} - b^{-1}}$

$= \dfrac{a - \dfrac{b^2}{a}}{\dfrac{1}{a} - \dfrac{1}{b}}$

Rewrite the expressions with positive exponents.

The LCD of $a, \dfrac{b^2}{a}, \dfrac{1}{a}$, and $\dfrac{1}{b}$ is ab.

$$= \frac{ab\left(a - \dfrac{b^2}{a}\right)}{ab\left(\dfrac{1}{a} - \dfrac{1}{b}\right)}$$ **Step 1:** Multiply numerator and denominator of the complex fraction by ab.

$$= \frac{ab(a) - ab\left(\dfrac{b^2}{a}\right)}{ab\left(\dfrac{1}{a}\right) - ab\left(\dfrac{1}{b}\right)}$$ **Step 2:** Apply the distributive property.

$$= \frac{a^2 b - b^3}{b - a}$$ Simplify numerator and denominator.

$$= \frac{b(a^2 - b^2)}{b - a}$$ **Step 3:** Factor and reduce.

$$= \frac{b(a - b)(a + b)}{b - a}$$

$$= \frac{b(\overset{-1}{\cancel{a - b}})(a + b)}{\cancel{b - a}}$$ Reduce common factors. Recall: $(a - b)/(b - a) = -1$.

$$= -b(a + b)$$ Simplify.

---

example 6

Simplifying Complex Fractions (Method II)

Simplify the expression by method II. $\dfrac{\dfrac{1}{w + 3} - \dfrac{1}{w - 3}}{1 + \dfrac{9}{w^2 - 9}}$

Solution:

$$\frac{\dfrac{1}{w + 3} - \dfrac{1}{w - 3}}{1 + \dfrac{9}{w^2 - 9}}$$

$$= \frac{\dfrac{1}{w + 3} - \dfrac{1}{w - 3}}{1 + \dfrac{9}{(w + 3)(w - 3)}}$$ Factor all denominators to find the LCD.

The LCD of $\dfrac{1}{1}, \dfrac{1}{w + 3}, \dfrac{1}{w - 3},$ and $\dfrac{9}{(w + 3)(w - 3)}$ is $(w + 3)(w - 3)$.

$$= \frac{(w + 3)(w - 3)\left(\dfrac{1}{w + 3} - \dfrac{1}{w - 3}\right)}{(w + 3)(w - 3)\left(1 + \dfrac{9}{(w + 3)(w - 3)}\right)}$$ **Step 1:** Multiply numerator and denominator of the complex fraction by $(w + 3)(w - 3)$.

$$= \frac{(w+3)(w-3)\left(\frac{1}{w+3}\right) - (w+3)(w-3)\left(\frac{1}{w-3}\right)}{(w+3)(w-3)1 + (w+3)(w-3)\left(\frac{9}{(w+3)(w-3)}\right)}$$

Step 2:
Distributive property.

$$= \frac{(w-3) - (w+3)}{(w+3)(w-3) + 9}$$

Step 3:
Simplify.

$$= \frac{w-3-w-3}{w^2-9+9}$$

Apply the distributive property.

$$= \frac{-6}{w^2}$$

3.   Finding the Midpoint of a Line Segment

example 7

Finding the Midpoint of a Line Segment

Find the midpoint of the line segment containing the points

$$\left(\frac{5}{6}, \frac{13}{4}\right) \qquad \text{and} \qquad \left(-\frac{9}{4}, \frac{3}{2}\right)$$

Solution:

$$\text{Let } (x_1, y_1) = \left(\frac{5}{6}, \frac{13}{4}\right) \text{ and } (x_2, y_2) = \left(-\frac{9}{4}, \frac{3}{2}\right) \qquad \text{Label the points.}$$

$$M = \left(\frac{x_1 + x_2}{2}, \frac{y_1 + y_2}{2}\right)$$

$$= \left(\frac{\frac{5}{6} + \frac{-9}{4}}{2}, \frac{\frac{13}{4} + \frac{3}{2}}{2}\right) \qquad \text{Apply the midpoint formula.}$$

Using method I, to simplify the complex fractions, we have

$$M = \left(\frac{\frac{10}{12} + \frac{-27}{12}}{2}, \frac{\frac{13}{4} + \frac{6}{4}}{2}\right) \qquad \text{Obtain a common denominator for each pair of fractions.}$$

$$= \left(\frac{-\frac{17}{12}}{\frac{2}{1}}, \frac{\frac{19}{4}}{\frac{2}{1}}\right) \qquad \text{Simplify.}$$

$$= \left(-\frac{17}{12} \cdot \frac{1}{2}, \frac{19}{4} \cdot \frac{1}{2}\right) \qquad \begin{array}{l}\text{Multiply by the reciprocal}\\ \text{of the denominators of}\\ \text{the complex fractions.}\end{array}$$

$$= \left(-\frac{17}{24}, \frac{19}{8}\right) \qquad \text{See Figure 8-5.}$$

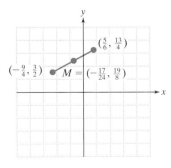

Figure 8-5

4. Simplifying Complex Fractions in a Formula

example 8   **Simplifying a Complex Fraction in a Formula**

In a circuit, if two resistors R_1 and R_2 are connected in parallel, the total resistance is given by

$$R_T = \cfrac{1}{\dfrac{1}{R_1} + \dfrac{1}{R_2}}$$

a.   Simplify the expression for R_T by simplifying the complex fraction.
b.   Use the simplified form of R_T to determine the total resistance if $R_1 = 4\,\Omega$ (ohms) and $R_2 = 6\,\Omega$.

Solution:

We will simplify the expression using method II.

a. $R_T = \cfrac{1}{\dfrac{1}{R_1} + \dfrac{1}{R_2}}$ The LCD of $\dfrac{1}{1}$; $\dfrac{1}{R_1}$; and $\dfrac{1}{R_2}$ is R_1R_2.

$= \cfrac{(R_1R_2)}{(R_1R_2)} \cdot \cfrac{(1)}{\left(\dfrac{1}{R_1} + \dfrac{1}{R_2}\right)}$ **Step 1:**   Multiply by the LCD $= R_1R_2$.

$= \cfrac{R_1R_2(1)}{R_1R_2\left(\dfrac{1}{R_1}\right) + R_1R_2\left(\dfrac{1}{R_2}\right)}$ **Step 2:**   Apply the distributive property.

$= \cfrac{R_1R_2(1)}{\cancel{R_1}R_2\left(\dfrac{1}{\cancel{R_1}}\right) + R_1\cancel{R_2}\left(\dfrac{1}{\cancel{R_2}}\right)}$ **Step 3:**   Simplify and reduce.

$= \cfrac{R_1R_2}{R_2 + R_1}$

b. $R_T = \cfrac{R_1R_2}{R_2 + R_1}$

$= \cfrac{(4)(6)}{(6) + (4)}$ Substitute $R_1 = 4$ and $R_2 = 6$.

$= \dfrac{24}{10}$ or $\dfrac{12}{5}$

The total resistance is $\dfrac{12}{5}\,\Omega$.

section 8.4 PRACTICE EXERCISES

1. Let $m(x) = \dfrac{(x+2)(x-1)}{x+3}$ and $n(x) = \dfrac{x-1}{x+2}$.

   a. Find $(mn)(x)$.

   b. Find $\left(\dfrac{m}{n}\right)(x)$.

2. Let $p(x) = \dfrac{x(x-5)}{x+4}$ and $q(x) = \dfrac{x}{x-5}$.

   a. Find $(pq)(x)$.

   b. Find $\left(\dfrac{p}{q}\right)(x)$.

3. Let $f(x) = \dfrac{1}{x^2-1}$, $g(x) = \dfrac{5}{x^2-5x+4}$,

   and $h(x) = \dfrac{2}{x^2+3x+2}$.

   a. Find $(f+g)(x)$.

   b. Find $(f-h)(x)$.

   c. Find $\dfrac{(f+g)(x)}{(f-h)(x)}$ by dividing the answer in part (a) by the answer in part (b).

4. Let $f(t) = \dfrac{6}{t^2-4}$, $g(t) = \dfrac{5}{t+2}$, $h(t) = \dfrac{7}{t^2-4}$,

   and $k(t) = \dfrac{4}{t-2}$.

   a. Find $(f-g)(t)$.

   b. Find $(h+k)(t)$.

   c. Find $\dfrac{(f-g)(t)}{(h+k)(t)}$ by dividing the answer in part (a) by the answer in part (b).

For Exercises 5–34, simplify the complex fractions using either method presented in the text.

5. $\dfrac{\frac{5x^2}{9y^2}}{\frac{3x}{y^2x}}$

6. $\dfrac{\frac{3w^2}{4rs}}{\frac{15wr}{s^2}}$

7. $\dfrac{\frac{x-6}{3x}}{\frac{3x-18}{9}}$

8. $\dfrac{\frac{a+4}{6}}{\frac{16-a^2}{3}}$

9. $\dfrac{\frac{7y}{y+3}}{\frac{1}{4y+12}}$

10. $\dfrac{\frac{6x}{x-5}}{\frac{1}{4x-20}}$

11. $\dfrac{1+\frac{1}{3}}{\frac{5}{6}-1}$

12. $\dfrac{2+\frac{4}{5}}{-1+\frac{3}{10}}$

13. $\dfrac{\frac{2}{3}+\frac{1}{6}}{\frac{1}{2}-\frac{1}{4}}$

14. $\dfrac{\frac{7}{8}+\frac{3}{4}}{\frac{1}{3}-\frac{5}{6}}$

15. $\dfrac{2-\frac{1}{y}}{4+\frac{1}{y}}$

16. $\dfrac{\frac{1}{x}-3}{\frac{1}{x}+3}$

17. $\dfrac{\frac{3q}{p}-q}{q-\frac{q}{p}}$

18. $\dfrac{\frac{b}{a}+3b}{b+\frac{2b}{a}}$

19. $\dfrac{\frac{2}{a}+\frac{3}{a^2}}{\frac{4}{a^2}-\frac{9}{a}}$

20. $\dfrac{\frac{2}{y^2}+\frac{1}{y}}{\frac{4}{y^2}-\frac{1}{y}}$

21. $\dfrac{-8}{\frac{6w}{w-1}-4}$

22. $\dfrac{6}{2z-\frac{10}{z-4}}$

23. $\dfrac{\frac{y}{y+3}}{\frac{y}{y+3}+y}$

24. $\dfrac{\frac{4}{w-4}}{\frac{4}{w-4}-1}$

25. $\dfrac{1-\frac{1}{x}-\frac{6}{x^2}}{1-\frac{4}{x}+\frac{3}{x^2}}$

26. $\dfrac{1+\frac{1}{x}-\frac{12}{x^2}}{\frac{9}{x^2}+\frac{3}{x}-2}$

27. $\dfrac{2-\frac{2}{t+1}}{2+\frac{2}{t}}$

28. $\dfrac{3+\frac{3}{p-1}}{3-\frac{3}{p}}$

29. $\dfrac{\dfrac{2}{a} - \dfrac{3}{a+1}}{\dfrac{2}{a+1} - \dfrac{3}{a}}$

30. $\dfrac{\dfrac{5}{b} + \dfrac{4}{b+1}}{\dfrac{4}{b} - \dfrac{5}{b+1}}$

31. $\dfrac{\dfrac{1}{y+2} + \dfrac{4}{y-3}}{\dfrac{2}{y-3} - \dfrac{7}{y+2}}$

32. $\dfrac{\dfrac{1}{t-4} + \dfrac{1}{t+5}}{\dfrac{6}{t+5} + \dfrac{2}{t-4}}$

33. $\dfrac{\dfrac{x+1}{x-1} + \dfrac{x-1}{x+1}}{\dfrac{x+1}{x-1} - \dfrac{x-1}{x+1}}$

34. $\dfrac{\dfrac{t-1}{t+1} - \dfrac{t+1}{t-1}}{\dfrac{t-1}{t+1} + \dfrac{t+1}{t-1}}$

35. Show that $(x + x^{-1})^{-1} = x/(x^2 + 1)$ by writing the expression on the left without negative exponents and simplifying.

36. Show that $(x^{-1} + y^{-1})^{-1} = xy/(x + y)$ by writing the expression on the left without negative exponents and simplifying.

For Exercises 37–42, first write the expression with positive exponents, then simplify.

37. $\dfrac{x^{-2}}{x + 3x^{-1}}$

38. $\dfrac{x^{-1} + x^{-2}}{5x^{-2}}$

39. $\dfrac{2a^{-1} + 3b^{-2}}{a^{-1} - b^{-1}}$

40. $\dfrac{2m^{-1} + n^{-1}}{m^{-2} - 4n^{-1}}$

41. $\dfrac{x}{1 - \left(1 + \dfrac{1}{x}\right)^{-1}}$

42. $\dfrac{x}{1 - \left(1 - \dfrac{1}{x}\right)^{-1}}$

EXPANDING YOUR SKILLS

43. The midpoint formula is used to find the midpoint of the line segment between the points (x_1, y_1) and (x_2, y_2). Write the midpoint formula from memory.

For Exercises 44–49, find the midpoint of the line segment with the given endpoints.

44. $\left(\dfrac{2}{3}, -\dfrac{1}{2}\right), \left(\dfrac{8}{3}, \dfrac{1}{4}\right)$

45. $\left(-\dfrac{5}{6}, -\dfrac{1}{5}\right), \left(\dfrac{1}{3}, \dfrac{3}{10}\right)$

46. $\left(\dfrac{8}{9}, 3\right), \left(\dfrac{1}{2}, -\dfrac{1}{7}\right)$

47. $\left(0, \dfrac{2}{7}\right), \left(-\dfrac{1}{9}, -\dfrac{2}{3}\right)$

48. $\left(2, -\dfrac{1}{33}\right), \left(\dfrac{1}{6}, -\dfrac{10}{11}\right)$

49. $(1, -3), \left(\dfrac{3}{8}, -\dfrac{1}{8}\right)$

50. The slope formula is used to find the slope of the line passing through the points (x_1, y_1) and (x_2, y_2). Write the slope formula from memory.

For Exercises 51–56, find the slope of the line that passes through the given points.

51. $\left(1\dfrac{1}{2}, \dfrac{2}{5}\right), \left(\dfrac{1}{4}, -2\right)$

52. $\left(-\dfrac{3}{7}, \dfrac{3}{5}\right), (-1, -3)$

53. $\left(\dfrac{5}{8}, \dfrac{9}{10}\right), \left(-\dfrac{1}{16}, -\dfrac{1}{5}\right)$

54. $\left(\dfrac{1}{4}, \dfrac{1}{3}\right), \left(\dfrac{1}{8}, \dfrac{1}{6}\right)$

55. $\left(\dfrac{2}{7}, -\dfrac{5}{6}\right), (1, 2)$

56. $\left(-\dfrac{6}{11}, \dfrac{11}{12}\right), (0, 0)$

GRAPHING CALCULATOR EXERCISES

57. a.   Enter $Y_1 = \dfrac{x}{2} + \dfrac{x}{3}$, $Y_2 = \dfrac{x}{4} + \dfrac{7x}{12}$, and

$$Y_3 = Y_1 \div Y_2$$

Graph Y_3 only.

b.   Simplify the complex fraction

$$\dfrac{\dfrac{x}{2} + \dfrac{x}{3}}{\dfrac{x}{4} + \dfrac{7x}{12}}$$

c.   Does the graph of Y_3 describe the result found in part (b)?

(*Hint*: Enter Y_1 as $(x/2) + (x/3)$ and Y_2 as $(x/4) + (7x/12)$.)

58. a. Enter $Y_1 = \dfrac{x}{5} - \dfrac{x}{10}$, $Y_2 = \dfrac{x}{6} - \dfrac{x}{5}$, and

    $Y_3 = Y_1 \div Y_2$

    Graph Y_3 only.

b. Simplify the complex fraction

$$\frac{\dfrac{x}{5} - \dfrac{x}{10}}{\dfrac{x}{6} - \dfrac{x}{5}}$$

c. Does the graph of Y_3 describe the result found in part (b)?

Concepts

1. Definition of a Rational Equation

2. Solving Rational Equations

3. Formulas Involving Rational Equations

section

8.5   RATIONAL EQUATIONS

1. Definition of a Rational Equation

Thus far we have studied several types of equations in one variable: linear equations, radical equations, and quadratic equations. In this section, we will study another type of equation called a rational equation.

Definition of a Rational Equation

An equation with one or more rational expressions is called a **rational equation**.

The following equations are rational equations:

$$\frac{1}{2}x + \frac{1}{3} = \frac{1}{4}x, \qquad \frac{3}{5} + \frac{1}{x} = \frac{2}{3}, \qquad 3 - \frac{6w}{w+1} = \frac{6}{w+1}$$

2. Solving Rational Equations

To understand the process of solving a rational equation, first review the process of clearing fractions from Section 1.4.

example 1   **Solving a Rational Equation**

Solve the equation. $\dfrac{1}{2}x + \dfrac{1}{3} = \dfrac{1}{4}x$

Solution:

$$\frac{1}{2}x + \frac{1}{3} = \frac{1}{4}x \qquad \text{The LCD of all terms in the equation is 12.}$$

$$12\left(\frac{1}{2}x + \frac{1}{3}\right) = 12\left(\frac{1}{4}x\right) \qquad \text{Multiply both sides by 12 to clear fractions.}$$

$$12 \cdot \frac{1}{2}x + 12 \cdot \frac{1}{3} = 12 \cdot \frac{1}{4}x \qquad \text{Apply the distributive property.}$$

$$6x + 4 = 3x \qquad \text{Solve the resulting equation.}$$

$$3x = -4$$

$$x = -\frac{4}{3}$$

Check:
$$\frac{1}{2}x + \frac{1}{3} = \frac{1}{4}x$$

$$\frac{1}{2}\left(-\frac{4}{3}\right) + \frac{1}{3} \stackrel{?}{=} \frac{1}{4}\left(-\frac{4}{3}\right)$$

$$-\frac{2}{3} + \frac{1}{3} \stackrel{?}{=} -\frac{1}{3}$$

$$-\frac{1}{3} = -\frac{1}{3} \checkmark$$

The same process of clearing fractions is used to solve rational equations when variables are present in the denominator.

---

example 2

Solving a Rational Equation

Solve the equation. $\dfrac{3}{5} + \dfrac{1}{x} = \dfrac{2}{3}$

Solution:

$$\frac{3}{5} + \frac{1}{x} = \frac{2}{3} \qquad \text{The LCD of all terms in the equation is } 15x.$$

$$15x\left(\frac{3}{5} + \frac{1}{x}\right) = 15x\left(\frac{2}{3}\right) \qquad \text{Multiply by } 15x \text{ to clear fractions.}$$

$$15x \cdot \frac{3}{5} + 15x \cdot \frac{1}{x} = 15x \cdot \frac{2}{3} \qquad \text{Apply the distributive property.}$$

$$9x + 15 = 10x \qquad \text{Solve the resulting equation.}$$

$$15 = x$$

Check: $x = 15$

$$\frac{3}{5} + \frac{1}{x} = \frac{2}{3}$$

$$\frac{3}{5} + \frac{1}{(15)} \stackrel{?}{=} \frac{2}{3}$$

$$\frac{9}{15} + \frac{1}{15} \stackrel{?}{=} \frac{2}{3}$$

$$\frac{10}{15} = \frac{2}{3} \checkmark$$

---

example 3

Solving a Rational Equation

Solve the equation. $3 - \dfrac{6w}{w + 1} = \dfrac{6}{w + 1}$

Solution:

$$3 - \frac{6w}{w + 1} = \frac{6}{w + 1}$$

The LCD of all terms in the equation is $w + 1$.

$$(w + 1)(3) - (w + 1)\left(\frac{6w}{w + 1}\right) = (w + 1)\left(\frac{6}{w + 1}\right)$$

Multiply by $(w + 1)$ on both sides to clear fractions.

$$(w + 1)(3) - (\cancel{w + 1})\left(\frac{6w}{\cancel{w + 1}}\right) = (\cancel{w + 1})\left(\frac{6}{\cancel{w + 1}}\right)$$

Apply the distributive property.

$$3w + 3 - 6w = 6$$

$$3w = -3$$

$$w = -1$$

Solve the resulting equation.

Check:

$$3 - \frac{6w}{w + 1} = \frac{6}{w + 1}$$

$$3 - \frac{6(-1)}{(-1) + 1} \stackrel{?}{=} \frac{6}{(-1) + 1}$$

the denominator is 0 for the value of $w = -1$

Because the value $w = -1$ makes the denominator zero in one (or more) of the rational expressions within the equation, the equation is *undefined* for $w = -1$. No other potential solutions exist, so the equation $3 - 6w/(w + 1) = 6/(w + 1)$ has no solution.

Examples 1–3 show that the steps for solving a rational equation mirror the process of clearing fractions from Section 1.4. However, there is one significant difference. The solutions of a rational equation must be defined in each rational expression in the equation. When $w = -1$ is substituted into the expression $6w/(w + 1)$ or $6/(w + 1)$ the denominator is zero and the expression is undefined. Hence $w = -1$ cannot be a solution to the equation

$$3 - 6w/(w + 1) = 6/(w + 1).$$

The steps for solving a rational equation are summarized as follows.

Steps for Solving a Rational Equation

1. Factor the denominators of all rational expressions.
2. Identify the LCD of all expressions in the equation.
3. Multiply both sides of the equation by the LCD.
4. Solve the resulting equation.
5. Check the potential solutions in the original equation.

example 4   **Solving Rational Equations**

Solve the equations.

a. $1 + \dfrac{3}{x} = \dfrac{28}{x^2}$ b. $\dfrac{36}{p^2 - 9} = \dfrac{2p}{p + 3} - 1$

Solution:

a. $\qquad 1 + \dfrac{3}{x} = \dfrac{28}{x^2}$ The LCD of all terms in the equation is x^2.

$x^2\left(1 + \dfrac{3}{x}\right) = x^2\left(\dfrac{28}{x^2}\right)$ Multiply both sides by x^2 to clear fractions.

$x^2 \cdot 1 + x^2 \cdot \dfrac{3}{x} = x^2 \cdot \dfrac{28}{x^2}$ Apply the distributive property.

$x^2 + 3x = 28$ The resulting equation is quadratic.

$x^2 + 3x - 28 = 0$ Set the equation equal to zero and factor.

$(x + 7)(x - 4) = 0$

$x = -7 \quad$ or $\quad x = 4$

Check: $x = -7$ $\qquad$ Check: $x = 4$

$1 + \dfrac{3}{x} = \dfrac{28}{x^2}$ $\qquad$ $1 + \dfrac{3}{x} = \dfrac{28}{x^2}$

$1 + \dfrac{3}{-7} \overset{?}{=} \dfrac{28}{(-7)^2}$ $\qquad$ $1 + \dfrac{3}{4} \overset{?}{=} \dfrac{28}{(4)^2}$

$\dfrac{49}{49} - \dfrac{21}{49} \overset{?}{=} \dfrac{28}{49}$ $\qquad$ $\dfrac{16}{16} + \dfrac{12}{16} \overset{?}{=} \dfrac{28}{16}$

$\dfrac{28}{49} = \dfrac{28}{49} \checkmark$ $\qquad$ $\dfrac{28}{16} = \dfrac{28}{16} \checkmark$ $\quad$ Both solutions check.

b. $\dfrac{36}{p^2 - 9} = \dfrac{2p}{p + 3} - 1$

$\dfrac{36}{(p + 3)(p - 3)} = \dfrac{2p}{p + 3} - 1$ The LCD is $(p + 3)(p - 3)$.

Multiply both sides by the LCD to clear fractions.

$(p + 3)(p - 3)\left[\dfrac{36}{(p + 3)(p - 3)}\right] = (p + 3)(p - 3)\left(\dfrac{2p}{p + 3}\right) - (p + 3)(p - 3)1$

$\cancel{(p + 3)}\cancel{(p - 3)}\left[\dfrac{36}{\cancel{(p + 3)}\cancel{(p - 3)}}\right] = \cancel{(p + 3)}(p - 3)\left(\dfrac{2p}{\cancel{p + 3}}\right) - (p + 3)(p - 3)1$

$36 = 2p(p - 3) - (p + 3)(p - 3)$ Solve the resulting equation.

$36 = 2p^2 - 6p - (p^2 - 9)$ The equation is quadratic.

$36 = 2p^2 - 6p - p^2 + 9$

$36 = p^2 - 6p + 9$

$0 = p^2 - 6p - 27$ Set the equation equal to zero and factor.

$0 = (p - 9)(p + 3)$

$p = 9$ or $p = -3$

Check: $p = 9$ Check: $p = -3$

$\dfrac{36}{p^2 - 9} = \dfrac{2p}{p + 3} - 1$ $\dfrac{36}{p^2 - 9} = \dfrac{2p}{p + 3} - 1$

$\dfrac{36}{(9)^2 - 9} \overset{?}{=} \dfrac{2p}{(9) + 3} - 1$ $\dfrac{36}{(-3)^2 - 9} \overset{?}{=} \dfrac{2p}{(-3) + 3} - 1$

$\dfrac{36}{72} \overset{?}{=} \dfrac{18}{12} - 1$ denominator is zero

$\dfrac{1}{2} \overset{?}{=} \dfrac{3}{2} - 1$

$\dfrac{1}{2} = \dfrac{1}{2}$ ✓

$p = -3$ is *not* a solution to the original equation because it is undefined in the original equation. However, $p = 9$ checks in the original equation.

The solution is $p = 9$.

3. Formulas Involving Rational Equations

example 5	**Solving Literal Equations Involving Rational Expressions**

Solve for the indicated variable.

a. $P = \dfrac{A}{1 + rt}$; for r 　　　　b. $V = \dfrac{mv}{m + M}$; for m

Solution:

a.　　　　$P = \dfrac{A}{1 + rt}$; for r

$(1 + rt)P = (1 + rt)\left(\dfrac{A}{1 + rt}\right)$ 　　Multiply both sides by the LCD $= (1 + rt)$.

$(1 + rt)P = (1 + rt)\left(\dfrac{A}{1 + rt}\right)$ 　　Clear fractions.

$P + Prt = A$ 　　Apply the distributive property to clear parentheses.

$Prt = A - P$ 　　Isolate the r-term on one side.

$\dfrac{Prt}{Pt} = \dfrac{A - P}{Pt}$

$r = \dfrac{A - P}{Pt}$

◆ **Avoiding Mistakes**

Variables in algebra are case-sensitive. Therefore, V and v are different variables.

b.　　　　$V = \dfrac{mv}{m + M}$; for m

$V(m + M) = \left(\dfrac{mv}{m + M}\right)(m + M)$ 　　Multiply by the LCD and clear fractions.

$V(m + M) = mv$

$Vm + VM = mv$ 　　Use the distributive property to clear parentheses.

$Vm - mv = -VM$ 　　Collect all m terms on one side.

$m(V - v) = -VM$ 　　Factor out m.

$\dfrac{m(V - v)}{(V - v)} = \dfrac{-VM}{(V - v)}$ 　　Divide by $(V - v)$.

$m = \dfrac{-VM}{V - v}$

Tip: The factor of -1 that appears in the numerator may be written in the denominator or out in front of the expression. The following expressions are therefore equivalent:

$$m = \frac{-VM}{V - v}$$

$$= \frac{VM}{-(V - v)} \quad \text{or} \quad \frac{VM}{v - V}$$

$$= -\frac{VM}{V - v}$$

---

section 8.5   PRACTICE EXERCISES

For Exercises 1–8, perform the indicated operations.

1. $\dfrac{1}{x^2 - 16} + \dfrac{1}{x^2 + 8x + 16}$

2. $\dfrac{3}{y^2 - 1} - \dfrac{2}{y^2 - 2y + 1}$

3. $\dfrac{m^2 - 9}{m^2 - 3m} \div (m^2 - m - 12)$

4. $\dfrac{2t^2 + 7t + 3}{4t^2 - 1} \div (t + 3)$

5. $\dfrac{1 + x^{-1}}{1 - x^{-2}}$

6. $\dfrac{x + y}{x^{-1} + y^{-1}}$

7. $\left(\dfrac{y - 2}{y + 4}\right)\left(\dfrac{3}{y - 2} - \dfrac{1}{y + 1}\right)$

8. $\left(\dfrac{p + 4}{4}\right)\left(\dfrac{p}{p^2 - 16} - \dfrac{1}{p + 4}\right)$

9. a. Explain the first step to clear fractions.

$$\frac{x + 2}{3} - \frac{x - 4}{4} = \frac{1}{2}$$

  b. Solve the equation.

  c. Check the answer in the original equation.

10. a. Explain the first step to clear fractions.

$$\frac{x + 6}{3} - \frac{x + 8}{5} = 0$$

  b. Solve the equation.

  c. Check the answer in the original equation.

11. a. Explain the first step to clear fractions.

$$\frac{1}{x - 1} + \frac{2}{3x - 3} = -\frac{5}{12}$$

  b. Solve the equation.

  c. Check the answer in the original equation.

12. a. Explain the first step to clear fractions.

$$\frac{2}{y - 5} + \frac{1}{y + 5} = \frac{11}{y^2 - 25}$$

  b. Solve the equation.

  c. Check the answer in the original equation.

13. a. Explain the first step to solve this equation.

$$\frac{x}{x - 5} + \frac{1}{5} = \frac{5}{x - 5}$$

  b. Solve the equation.

  c. Check the answer in the original equation.

14. a. Explain the first step to solve this equation.

$$\frac{x}{x - 2} + \frac{2}{3} = \frac{2}{x - 2}$$

  b. Solve the equation.

  c. Check the answer in the original equation.

15. If five is added to the reciprocal of a number, the result is $\frac{16}{3}$. Find the number.

16. If $\frac{2}{3}$ is added to the reciprocal of a number the result is $\frac{17}{3}$. Find the number.

17. If 7 is decreased by the reciprocal of a number the result is $\frac{9}{2}$. Find the number.

18. If a number is added to its reciprocal, the result is $\frac{13}{6}$. Find the number.

For Exercises 19–40, solve the rational equations.

19. $\dfrac{3y}{4} - 6 = \dfrac{y}{4}$

20. $\dfrac{2w}{5} - 8 = \dfrac{4w}{5}$

21. $\dfrac{1}{2} - \dfrac{3}{2x} = \dfrac{4}{x} - \dfrac{5}{12}$

22. $\dfrac{2}{3x} + \dfrac{1}{4} = \dfrac{11}{6x} - \dfrac{1}{3}$

23. $\dfrac{3}{x - 4} + 2 = \dfrac{5}{x - 4}$

24. $\dfrac{5}{x + 3} - 2 = \dfrac{7}{x + 3}$

25. $\dfrac{1}{3} + \dfrac{2}{w - 3} = 1$

26. $\dfrac{3}{5} + \dfrac{7}{p + 2} = 2$

27. $\dfrac{12}{x} - \dfrac{12}{x - 5} = \dfrac{2}{x}$

28. $\dfrac{25}{y} - \dfrac{25}{y - 2} = \dfrac{2}{y}$

29. $\dfrac{1}{4}a - 4a^{-1} = 0$

30. $\dfrac{1}{3}t - 12t^{-1} = 0$

31. $3a^{-2} - 4a^{-1} = -1$

32. $-3w^{-1} = 2 + w^{-1}$

33. $8t^{-1} + 2 = 3t^{-1}$

34. $6z^{-2} - 5z^{-1} = 0$

35. $\dfrac{6}{x^2 - 4x + 3} - \dfrac{1}{x - 3} = \dfrac{1}{4x - 4}$

36. $\dfrac{1}{4x^2 - 36} + \dfrac{2}{x - 3} = \dfrac{5}{x + 3}$

37. $\dfrac{3}{k - 2} + \dfrac{2k}{4 - k^2} = \dfrac{5}{k + 2}$

38. $\dfrac{h}{2} + \dfrac{4}{h - 4} = \dfrac{h}{h - 4}$

39. $\dfrac{5}{x^2 - 7x + 12} = \dfrac{2}{x - 3} + \dfrac{5}{x - 4}$

40. $\dfrac{9}{x^2 + 7x + 10} = \dfrac{5}{x + 2} - \dfrac{3}{x + 5}$

41. Solve for r^2: $F = \dfrac{Gm_1m_2}{r^2}$

42. Solve for n: $P = \dfrac{R - C}{n}$

43. Solve for a: $\dfrac{1}{f} = \dfrac{1}{a} + \dfrac{1}{b}$

44. Solve for R_1: $\dfrac{1}{R} = \dfrac{1}{R_1} + \dfrac{1}{R_2}$

For Exercises 45–54, perform the indicated operation and simplify, or solve the equation for the variable.

45. $\dfrac{2}{a^2 + 4a + 3} + \dfrac{1}{a + 3}$

46. $\dfrac{1}{c + 6} + \dfrac{4}{c^2 + 8c + 12}$

47. $\dfrac{7}{y^2 - y - 2} + \dfrac{1}{y + 1} = \dfrac{3}{y - 2}$

48. $\dfrac{-5}{b^2 + b - 2} + \dfrac{3}{b + 2} = \dfrac{1}{b - 1}$

49. $\dfrac{x}{x - 1} - \dfrac{12}{x^2 - x}$

50. $\dfrac{3}{5t - 20} + \dfrac{4}{t - 4}$

51. $\dfrac{3}{w} - 5 = \dfrac{7}{w} - 1$

52. $\dfrac{-3}{y^2} - \dfrac{1}{y} = -2$

53. $\dfrac{4p + 1}{8p - 12} + \dfrac{p - 3}{2p - 3}$

54. $\dfrac{x + 1}{2x + 4} - \dfrac{x^2}{x + 2}$

GRAPHING CALCULATOR EXERCISES

For Exercises 55–58, enter the left side of the equation as Y_1 and the right side of the equation as Y_2. Then graph Y_1 and Y_2 on a graphing calculator and use the *Intersect* feature or *Zoom* and *Trace* to approximate the point(s) intersection.

55. $\dfrac{3}{x - 4} + 2 = \dfrac{5}{x - 4}$ (Exercise 23)

56. $\dfrac{5}{x + 3} - 2 = \dfrac{7}{x + 3}$ (Exercise 24)

57. $\dfrac{6}{x^2 - 4x + 3} - \dfrac{1}{x - 3} = \dfrac{1}{4x - 4}$ (Exercise 35)

58. $\dfrac{x}{2} + \dfrac{4}{x - 4} = \dfrac{x}{x - 4}$ (Exercise 38)

section

8.6   APPLICATIONS OF RATIONAL EQUATIONS AND PROPORTIONS

1. Definition of Ratio and Proportion

A proportion is a rational equation that equates two ratios. The process for solving rational equations can be used to solve proportions.

Definition of Ratio and Proportion

1. The **ratio** of a to b is $\dfrac{a}{b}$ $(b \neq 0)$ and can also be expressed as $a:b$ or $a \div b$.

2. An equation that equates two ratios is called a **proportion**. Therefore, if $b \neq 0$ and $d \neq 0$, then $\dfrac{a}{b} = \dfrac{c}{d}$ is a proportion.

---

2. Solving Proportions

example 1

Solving a Proportion

Solve the proportion. $\dfrac{5}{19} = \dfrac{95}{y}$

Solution:

$$\frac{5}{19} = \frac{95}{y} \qquad \text{The LCD is } 19y. \text{ Note that } y \neq 0.$$

$$19y\left(\frac{5}{19}\right) = 19y\left(\frac{95}{y}\right) \qquad \text{Multiply both sides by the LCD.}$$

$$\cancel{19}y\left(\frac{5}{\cancel{19}}\right) = 19\cancel{y}\left(\frac{95}{\cancel{y}}\right) \qquad \text{Clear fractions.}$$

$$5y = 1805 \qquad \text{Solve the resulting equation.}$$

$$\frac{5y}{5} = \frac{1805}{5}$$

$$y = 361 \qquad \text{The solution checks in the original equation.}$$

Tip: For any proportion

$$\frac{a}{b} = \frac{c}{d} \quad (b \neq 0, d \neq 0)$$

the cross products of terms are equal. Hence, $ad = bc$. Finding the cross product is a quick way to clear fractions in a proportion.* Consider Example 1:

$$\frac{5}{19} \diagdown\!\!\!\!\diagup \frac{95}{y}$$

$$5y = (19)(95) \qquad \text{Equate the cross products.}$$

$$5y = 1805$$

$$y = 361$$

*It is important to realize that this method is only valid for proportions.

3. Applications of Proportions

example 2

Solving a Proportion

In the 1996 presidential election, the number of popular votes for Bill Clinton exceeded those of Bob Dole by a ratio of 54.7 to 45.3. If Bill Clinton received approximately 47.4 million votes, then approximately how many votes (to the nearest tenth of a million) did Bob Dole receive?

Solution:

One method of solving this problem is to set up a proportion. Write two equivalent ratios depicting the number of votes of the winner to the loser.

$$\boxed{\begin{array}{c}\text{Winning}\\\text{ratio}\end{array}} \longrightarrow \frac{54.7}{45.3} = \frac{47.4}{x} \longleftarrow \boxed{\begin{array}{c}\text{Winner's votes}\\\text{Loser's votes}\end{array}}$$

$$45.3x\left(\frac{54.7}{45.3}\right) = 45.3x\left(\frac{47.4}{x}\right) \qquad \begin{array}{l}\text{Multiply both sides by } 45.3x \text{ to}\\\text{clear fractions.}\end{array}$$

$$54.7x = (45.3)(47.4)$$

$$54.7x = 2147.22$$

$$x = \frac{2147.22}{54.7}$$

$$x \approx 39.3$$

Bob Dole received approximately 39.3 million votes.

example 3

Solving a Proportion

The ratio of male-to-female police officers in a certain town is 11:3. If the total number of officers is 112, how many are men and how many are women?

Solution:

Let x represent the number of male police officers.

Then, $112 - x$ represents the number of female police officers.

Male	$\rightarrow$	11	$=$	x	$\leftarrow$	Number of males
Female	$\rightarrow$	3		$112 - x$	$\leftarrow$	Number of females

$$3(112 - x)\left(\frac{11}{3}\right) = 3(112 - x)\left(\frac{x}{112 - x}\right) \qquad \text{Multiply both sides by } 3(112 - x).$$

$$11(112 - x) = 3x \qquad \text{The resulting equation is linear.}$$

$$1232 - 11x = 3x$$

$$1232 = 14x$$

$$\frac{1232}{14} = \frac{14x}{14}$$

$$x = 88$$

The number of male police officers is $x = 88$.

The number of female officers is $112 - x = 112 - 88 = 24$.

4.   Rational Equations—Business Applications

example 4

Solving an Application of Rational Expressions

To produce a certain mountain bike, the manufacturer has a fixed cost of $56,000, plus a variable cost of $140 per bike. The cost in dollars to produce x bikes is given by $C(x) = 56,000 + 140x$. The average cost per bike, $\overline{C}(x)$, is defined as $\overline{C}(x) = C(x)/x$ or

$$\overline{C}(x) = \frac{56,000 + 140x}{x}$$

Find the number of bikes the manufacturer must produce so that the average cost per bike is $180.

Solution:

Given

$$\overline{C}(x) = \frac{56,000 + 140x}{x} \qquad \text{Replace } \overline{C}(x) \text{ by } 180 \text{ and solve for } x.$$

$$180 = \frac{56{,}000 + 140x}{x}$$

$$x180 = \cancel{x} \cdot \frac{56{,}000 + 140x}{\cancel{x}} \qquad \text{Multiply by the LCD} = x.$$

$$180x = 56{,}000 + 140x \qquad \text{The resulting equation is linear.}$$

$$40x = 56{,}000 \qquad \text{Solve for } x.$$

$$x = \frac{56{,}000}{40}$$

$$= 1400$$

The manufacturer must produce 1400 bikes for the average cost to be \$180.

5. Rational Equations—Distance, Rate, Time Applications

example 5

Solving an Application Involving a Rational Equation

An athlete's average speed on her bike is 14 mph faster than her average speed running. She can bike 31.5 miles in the same amount of time that it takes her to run 10.5 miles. Find her average speed running and her average speed biking.

Solution:

Because the average speed biking is given in terms of the average speed running, let x represent the running speed.

Let x represent the average speed running.

Then $x + 14$ represents the average speed biking.

Organize the given information in a chart.

	Distance	Rate	Time
Running	10.5	x	$\dfrac{10.5}{x}$
Biking	31.5	$x + 14$	$\dfrac{31.5}{x + 14}$

Because $d = rt$, then $t = \dfrac{d}{r}$

The time required to run 10.5 miles is the same as the time required to bike 31.5 miles, so we can equate the two expressions for time:

$$\frac{10.5}{x} = \frac{31.5}{x + 14} \qquad \text{The LCD is } x(x + 14).$$

$$x(x + 14)\left(\frac{10.5}{x}\right) = x(x + 14)\left(\frac{31.5}{x + 14}\right) \qquad \begin{array}{l}\text{Multiply by } x(x + 14) \text{ to}\\ \text{clear fractions.}\end{array}$$

$$10.5(x + 14) = 31.5x$$ The resulting equation is linear.

$$10.5x + 147 = 31.5x$$ Solve for x.

$$-21x = -147$$

$$x = 7$$

The athlete's average speed running is 7 mph.

The average speed biking is $x + 14$ or $7 + 14 = 21$ mph.

6.   Rational Equations—"Work" Applications

example 6

Solving an Application Involving a Rational Expression

JoAn can wallpaper a bathroom in 3 hours. Bonnie can wallpaper the same bathroom in 5 hours. How long would it take them if they worked together?

Solution:

Let x represent the time required for both people working together to complete the job.

One method of approaching this problem is to determine the portion of the job that each person can complete in 1 h and extend that rate to the portion of the job completed in x hours.

- JoAn can perform the job in 3 h. Therefore, she completes $\frac{1}{3}$ of the job in 1 h and $\frac{1}{3}x$ jobs in x hours.
- Bonnie can perform the job in 5 h. Therefore, she completes $\frac{1}{5}$ of the job in 1 h and $\frac{1}{5}x$ jobs in x hours.

	Work Rate	Time	Portion of Job Completed
JoAn	$\frac{1}{3}$ job/h	x hours	$\frac{1}{3}x$ jobs
Bonnie	$\frac{1}{5}$ job/h	x hours	$\frac{1}{5}x$ jobs

The sum of the portions of the job completed by each person must equal one whole job:

$$\begin{pmatrix} \text{Portion of job} \\ \text{completed} \\ \text{by JoAn} \end{pmatrix} + \begin{pmatrix} \text{Portion of job} \\ \text{completed} \\ \text{by Bonnie} \end{pmatrix} = \begin{pmatrix} 1 \\ \text{whole} \\ \text{job} \end{pmatrix}$$

$$\frac{1}{3}x + \frac{1}{5}x = 1 \qquad \text{The LCD is 15.}$$

$$15\left(\frac{1}{3}x + \frac{1}{5}x\right) = 15(1)$$ Multiply by the LCD.

$$15 \cdot \frac{1}{3}x + 15 \cdot \frac{1}{5}x = 15 \cdot 1$$ Apply the distributive property.

$$5x + 3x = 15$$ Solve the resulting linear equation.

$$8x = 15$$

$$x = \frac{15}{8} \quad \text{or} \quad x = 1\frac{7}{8}$$

Together JoAn and Bonnie can wallpaper the bathroom in $1\frac{7}{8}$ h.

---

section 8.6 PRACTICE EXERCISES

For Exercises 1–10, perform the indicated operation and simplify, or solve the equation for the variable.

1. $3 - \dfrac{6}{x} = x + 8$

2. $2 + \dfrac{6}{x} = x + 7$

3. $\dfrac{5}{3x - 6} - \dfrac{3}{4x - 8}$

4. $\dfrac{4}{5t - 1} + \dfrac{1}{10t - 2}$

5. $\dfrac{2}{y - 1} - \dfrac{5}{4} = \dfrac{-1}{y + 1}$

6. $\dfrac{5}{w - 2} = 7 - \dfrac{10}{w + 2}$

7. $\dfrac{5}{x^2 - y^2} + \dfrac{3x}{x^3 + x^2 y}$

8. $\dfrac{7a}{a^2 + 2ab + b^2} + \dfrac{4}{a^2 + ab}$

9. $\dfrac{3}{t - 2} + \dfrac{1}{t - 1} = \dfrac{7}{t^2 - 3t + 2}$

10. $\dfrac{2}{m^2 - 2m - 3} = \dfrac{3}{m - 3} + \dfrac{2}{m + 1}$

For Exercises 11–22, solve the proportions.

11. $\dfrac{y}{6} = \dfrac{20}{15}$

12. $\dfrac{12}{18} = \dfrac{14}{x}$

13. $\dfrac{9}{75} = \dfrac{m}{50}$

14. $\dfrac{n}{15} = \dfrac{12}{45}$

15. $\dfrac{p - 1}{4} = \dfrac{p + 3}{3}$

16. $\dfrac{q - 5}{2} = \dfrac{q + 2}{3}$

17. $\dfrac{x + 1}{5} = \dfrac{4}{15}$

18. $\dfrac{t - 1}{7} = \dfrac{2}{21}$

19. $\dfrac{5 - 2x}{x} = \dfrac{1}{4}$

20. $\dfrac{2y + 3}{y} = \dfrac{3}{2}$

21. $\dfrac{p + 2}{p + 8} = \dfrac{2}{5}$

22. $\dfrac{q - 3}{q + 1} = \dfrac{9}{7}$

23. A preschool advertises that it has a 3 to 1 ratio of children to adults. If 18 children are enrolled, how many adults must be on the staff?

24. An after-school care facility tries to maintain a 4 to 1 ratio of children to adults. If the facility hired five adults, what is the maximum number of children that can enroll?

25. A 3.5-oz box of candy has a total of 21.0 g of fat. How many grams of fat would a 14-oz box of candy contain?

26. A 6-oz box of candy has 350 Calories. How many calories would a 10-oz box contain?

27. A fisherman in the North Atlantic catches eight swordfish for a total of 1840 lb. Approximately how many swordfish were caught if a commercial fishing boat arrives in port with 230,000 lb of swordfish?

28. If a 64-oz bottle of laundry detergent costs $4.00, how much would an 80-oz bottle cost?

Two triangles are said to be similar if the corresponding sides are proportional. Use this fact to solve Exercises 29–32.

29. The triangles shown here are similar. Find the lengths of the missing sides.

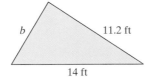

30. The triangles shown here are similar. Find the lengths of the missing sides.

31. The triangles shown here are similar. Find the lengths of the missing sides. Round to two decimal places.

32. The triangles shown here are similar. Find the lengths of the missing sides.

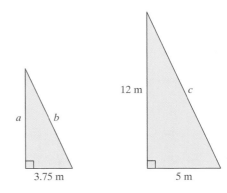

33. The profit in dollars for selling x mountain bikes is given by $P(x) = 360x - 56,000$. The average profit per bike is defined as:

$$\overline{P}(x) = \frac{P(x)}{x} \qquad \text{or} \qquad \overline{P}(x) = \frac{360x - 56,000}{x}$$

Find the number of bikes the manufacturer must produce so that the average profit per bike is $110.

34. The profit in dollars when x ballpoint pens are sold is given by $P(x) = 0.47x - 100$. The average profit per unit is defined as:

$$\overline{P}(x) = \frac{P(x)}{x} \qquad \text{or} \qquad \overline{P}(x) = \frac{0.47x - 100}{x}$$

Find the number of pens that need to be produced so that the average profit per pen is $0.27.

35. The current in a stream is 2 mph. Find the speed of a boat in still water if it goes 26 miles downstream (with the current) in the same amount of time it takes to go 18 miles upstream (against the current).

36. A bus leaves a terminal at 9:00. A car leaves 3 h later and averages a speed 21 mph faster than the bus. If the car overtakes the bus after 196 miles, find the average speed of the bus and the average speed of the car.

37. A bicyclist rides 24 miles against a wind and returns 24 miles with the wind. His average speed for the return trip is 8 mph faster. If x represents the bicyclist's speed going out against the wind, then the total time required for the round trip is given by:

$$t(x) = \frac{24}{x} + \frac{24}{x + 8}, \text{ where } x > 0$$

How fast did the cyclist ride against the wind if the total time of the trip was 3.2 h?

38. A boat travels 45 miles to an island and 45 miles back again. Changes in the wind and tide made

the average speed on the return trip 3 mph slower than the speed on the way out. If the total time of the trip took 6 h and 45 min (6.75 h), find the average speed going to the island. What was the average speed of the return trip?

39. One carpenter can complete a kitchen in 8 days. With the help of another carpenter, they can do the job together in 4 days. How long would it take the second carpenter if she worked alone?

40. One painter can paint a room in 6 h. Another painter can paint the same room in 8 h. How long would it take them working together?

41. Gus works twice as fast as Sid. Together they can dig a garden in 4 h. How long would it take each person working alone?

42. It takes a child three times longer to vacuum a house than an adult. If it takes 1 h for one adult and one child working together to vacuum a house, how long would it take each person working alone?

43. Find the value of y so that the slope of the line between the points $(3, 1)$ and $(11, y)$ is $\frac{1}{2}$.

44. Find the value of x so that the slope of the line between the points $(-2, -5)$ and $(x, 10)$ is 3.

45. Find the value of x so that the slope of the line between the points $(4, -2)$ and $(x, 2)$ is 4.

46. Find the value of y so that the slope of the line between the points $(3, 2)$ and $(-1, y)$ is $-\frac{3}{4}$.

chapter 8   SUMMARY

SECTION 8.1—INTRODUCTION TO RATIONAL FUNCTIONS

KEY CONCEPTS:

A rational function is in the form

$$f(x) = \frac{p(x)}{q(x)}$$

where $p(x)$ and $q(x)$ are polynomial functions and $q(x) \neq 0$.

The domain of a rational function excludes the values for which the denominator is zero.

To reduce a rational function, factor the numerator and denominator completely and reduce factors whose ratio is equal to 1 or to -1. A rational function written in lowest terms will still have the same restrictions on the domain as the original function.

KEY TERMS:

domain of a rational function
rational functional
reducing rational expressions

EXAMPLES:

Find the domain of f:

$$f(x) = \frac{x + 2}{(x + 2)(x - 7)}$$

Domain: $\{x \mid x \neq -2, x \neq 7\}$

$$(-\infty, -2) \cup (-2, 7) \cup (7, \infty)$$

Reduce:

$$g(x) = \frac{25x - x^3}{x^3 - 4x^2 - 5x}$$

$$= \frac{x(25 - x^2)}{x(x^2 - 4x - 5)} = \frac{x\overset{1}{(5 - x)}(5 + x)}{x\underset{}{(x - 5)}(x + 1)}^{-1}$$

$$= -\frac{(x + 5)}{(x + 1)}; \qquad x \neq 0, x \neq 5, x \neq -1$$

SECTION 8.2—MULTIPLICATION AND DIVISION OF RATIONAL EXPRESSIONS

KEY CONCEPTS:

To multiply rational expressions, factor the numerators and denominators completely. Then reduce factors whose ratio is 1 or -1.

EXAMPLES:

Multiply:

$$\frac{b^2 - a^2}{a^2 - 2ab + b^2} \cdot \frac{a^2 - 3ab + 2b^2}{2a + 2b}$$

$$= \frac{\overset{-1}{(b - a)}\overset{1}{(b - a)}}{(a - b)^2} \cdot \frac{(a - 2b)\overset{1}{(a - b)}}{2(a + b)}$$

$$= -\frac{a - 2b}{2} \text{ or } \frac{2b - a}{2}$$

To divide rational expressions, multiply by the reciprocal of the divisor.

KEY TERMS:

dividing rational expressions
multiplying rational expressions

Divide:

$$\frac{2c^2d^5}{15e^4} \div \frac{6c^4d^3}{20e}$$

$$= \frac{2c^2d^5}{15e^4} \cdot \frac{20e}{6c^4d^3}$$

$$= \frac{2c^2d^5}{3 \cdot 5e^4} \cdot \frac{2 \cdot 2 \cdot 5e}{2 \cdot 3c^4d^3}$$

$$= \frac{4d^2}{9c^2e^3}$$

SECTION 8.3—ADDITION AND SUBTRACTION OF RATIONAL EXPRESSIONS

KEY CONCEPTS:

To add or subtract rational expressions, the expressions must have the same denominator.

The least common denominator (LCD) is the product of unique factors from the denominators, in which each factor is raised to its highest power.

Steps to Add or Subtract Rational Expressions:

1. Factor the denominators of each rational expression.
2. Identify the LCD.
3. Rewrite each rational expression as an equivalent expression with the LCD as its denominator. (This is accomplished by multiplying the numerator and denominator of each rational expression by the missing factor(s) from the LCD.)
4. Add or subtract the numerators and write the result over the common denominator.
5. Simplify and reduce.

KEY TERMS:

least common denominator (LCD)

EXAMPLES:

Find the LCD:

$$\frac{1}{3(x-1)^3(x+2)}, \frac{-5}{6(x-1)(x+7)^2}$$

$$\text{LCD} = 6(x-1)^3(x+2)(x+7)^2$$

Subtract:

$$\frac{c}{c^2-c-12} - \frac{1}{2c-8}$$

$$= \frac{c}{(c-4)(c+3)} - \frac{1}{2(c-4)}$$

The LCD is $2(c-4)(c+3)$

$$\frac{2}{2} \cdot \frac{c}{(c-4)(c+3)} - \frac{1}{2(c-4)} \cdot \frac{(c+3)}{(c+3)}$$

$$= \frac{2c-(c+3)}{2(c-4)(c+3)}$$

$$= \frac{2c-c-3}{2(c-4)(c+3)}$$

$$= \frac{c-3}{2(c-4)(c+3)}$$

SECTION 8.4—COMPLEX FRACTIONS

KEY CONCEPTS:

Complex fractions can be simplified by using method I or method II.

Method I uses the order of operations to simplify the numerator and denominator separately before multiplying by the reciprocal of the denominator of the complex fraction.

EXAMPLES:

Simplify Using Method I:

$$\frac{1 - \dfrac{4}{w^2}}{1 - \dfrac{1}{w} - \dfrac{6}{w^2}}$$

$$\frac{1 - \dfrac{4}{w^2}}{1 - \dfrac{1}{w} - \dfrac{6}{w^2}} = \frac{\dfrac{w^2}{w^2} - \dfrac{4}{w^2}}{\dfrac{w^2}{w^2} - \dfrac{w}{w^2} - \dfrac{6}{w^2}}$$

$$= \frac{\dfrac{w^2 - 4}{w^2}}{\dfrac{w^2 - w - 6}{w^2}} = \frac{w^2 - 4}{w^2} \cdot \frac{w^2}{w^2 - w - 6}$$

$$= \frac{(w - 2)(w + 2)}{w^2} \cdot \frac{w^2}{(w - 3)(w + 2)}$$

$$= \frac{w - 2}{w - 3}$$

To use method II, multiply the numerator and denominator of the complex fraction by the LCD of all the individual fractions. Then simplify the result.

Simplify Using Method II:

$$\frac{1 - \dfrac{4}{w^2}}{1 - \dfrac{1}{w} - \dfrac{6}{w^2}}$$

KEY TERMS:

complex fractions

$$= \frac{w^2\left(1 - \dfrac{4}{w^2}\right)}{w^2\left(1 - \dfrac{1}{w} - \dfrac{6}{w^2}\right)} = \frac{w^2 - 4}{w^2 - w - 6}$$

$$= \frac{(w - 2)(w + 2)}{(w - 3)(w + 2)} = \frac{w - 2}{w - 3}$$

SECTION 8.5—RATIONAL EQUATIONS

KEY CONCEPTS:

Steps to Solve a Rational Equation

1. Factor the denominators of all rational expressions. Identify any restrictions on the variable.
2. Identify the LCD of all expressions in the equation.
3. Multiply both sides of the equation by the LCD.
4. Solve the resulting equation.
5. Check each potential solution.

KEY TERMS:

rational equation

EXAMPLES:

Solve:

$$\frac{1}{w} - \frac{1}{2w - 1} = \frac{-2w}{2w - 1}$$

The LCD is $w(2w - 1)$.

$$w(2w - 1)\frac{1}{w} - w(2w - 1) \cdot \frac{1}{2w - 1}$$

$$= w(2w - 1) \cdot \frac{-2w}{2w - 1}$$

$$(2w - 1)1 - w(1) = w(-2w)$$

$$2w - 1 - w = -2w^2 \quad \text{(quadratic equation)}$$

$$2w^2 + w - 1 = 0$$

$$(2w - 1)(w + 1) = 0$$

$$w = \frac{1}{2} \quad \text{or} \quad w = -1$$

(does not check)   (checks)

SECTION 8.6—APPLICATIONS OF RATIONAL EQUATIONS AND PROPORTIONS

KEY CONCEPTS:

An equation that equates two ratios is called a proportion:

$$\frac{a}{b} = \frac{c}{d} \quad (b \neq 0, d \neq 0)$$

The cross products of terms in a proportion are equal: $ad = bc$.

KEY TERMS:

proportion
ratio

EXAMPLES:

A sample of 85 g of a particular ice cream contains 17 g of fat. How much fat does 324 g of the same ice cream contain?

$$\frac{17 \text{ g fat}}{85 \text{ g ice cream}} = \frac{x \text{ grams fat}}{324 \text{ g ice cream}}$$

$$\frac{17}{85} = \frac{x}{324} \quad \text{Multiply by the LCD.}$$

$$(85 \cdot 324) \cdot \frac{17}{85} = (85 \cdot 324) \cdot \frac{x}{324}$$

$$5508 = 85x$$

$$x = 64.8 \text{ g}$$

chapter 8   REVIEW EXERCISES

Section 8.1

1. Let $g(x) = \dfrac{(x-1)(2x+3)}{(x+6)(x-1)}$.

   a. Find the function values (if they exist): $g(2)$, $g(0)$, $g\left(-\frac{3}{2}\right)$, $g(1)$, $g(-6)$.

   b. Identify the domain for g. Write the answer in interval notation.

2. Let $f(t) = \dfrac{t-10}{t^2 - 9t - 10}$.

   a. Find the function values (if they exist): $f(3)$, $f(0)$, $f(10)$, $f(-1)$, $f(1)$.

   b. Identify the domain for f. Write the answer in interval notation.

3. Let $k(y) = \dfrac{y}{y^2 - 1}$.

   a. Find the function values (if they exist): $k(2)$, $k(0)$, $k(1)$, $k(-1)$, $k\left(\dfrac{1}{2}\right)$.

   b. Identify the domain for k. Write the answer in interval notation.

4. Let $h(x) = \dfrac{x}{x^2 + 1}$.

   a. Find the function values (if they exist): $h(1)$, $h(0)$, $h(-1)$, $h(-3)$, $h\left(\dfrac{1}{2}\right)$.

   b. Identify the domain for h. Write the answer in interval notation.

For Exercises 5–12, reduce the rational expressions.

5. $\dfrac{28a^3b^3}{14a^2b^3}$

6. $\dfrac{25x^2yz^3}{125xyz}$

7. $\dfrac{x^2 - 4x + 3}{x - 3}$

8. $\dfrac{k^2 + 3k - 10}{k^2 - 5k + 6}$

9. $\dfrac{x^3 - 27}{9 - x^2}$

10. $\dfrac{a^4 - 81}{3 - a}$

11. $\dfrac{2t^2 + 3t - 5}{7 - 6t - t^2}$

12. $\dfrac{y^3 - 4y}{y^2 - 5y + 6}$

For Exercises 13–16, find the domain of each function and use that information to match the function with its graph.

13. $f(x) = \dfrac{1}{x - 3}$

14. $m(x) = \dfrac{1}{x + 2}$

15. $k(x) = \dfrac{6}{x^2 - 3x}$

16. $p(x) = \dfrac{-2}{x^2 + 4}$

a.

b.

c.

d.

Section 8.2

For Exercises 17–28, multiply or divide as indicated.

17. $\dfrac{3a + 9}{a^2} \cdot \dfrac{a^3}{6a + 18}$

18. $\dfrac{4 - y}{5} \div \dfrac{2y - 8}{15}$

19. $\dfrac{x - 4y}{x^2 + xy} \div \dfrac{20y - 5x}{x^2 - y^2}$

20. $(x^2 + 5x - 24)\left(\dfrac{x + 8}{x - 3}\right)$

21. $\dfrac{7k + 28}{2k + 4} \cdot \dfrac{k^2 - 2k - 8}{k^2 + 2k - 8}$

22. $\dfrac{ab + 2a + b + 2}{ab - 3b + 2a - 6} \cdot \dfrac{ab - 3b + 4a - 12}{ab - b + 4a - 4}$

23. $\dfrac{x^2 + 8x - 20}{x^2 + 6x - 16} \div \dfrac{x^2 + 6x - 40}{x^2 + 3x - 40}$

24. $\dfrac{2b - b^2}{b^3 - 8} \cdot \dfrac{b^2 + 2b + 4}{b^2}$

25. $\dfrac{2w}{21} \div \dfrac{3w^2}{7} \cdot \dfrac{4}{w}$

26. $\dfrac{5y^2 - 20}{y^3 + 2y^2 + y + 2} \div \dfrac{7y}{y^3 + y}$

27. $\dfrac{x^2 + x - 20}{x^2 - 4x + 4} \cdot \dfrac{x^2 + x - 6}{12 + x - x^2} \div \dfrac{2x + 10}{10 - 5x}$

28. $(9k^2 - 25) \cdot \left(\dfrac{k + 5}{3k - 5}\right)$

Section 8.3

For Exercises 29–40, add or subtract as indicated.

29. $\dfrac{1}{x} + \dfrac{1}{x^2} - \dfrac{1}{x^3}$

30. $\dfrac{1}{x + 2} + \dfrac{5}{x - 2}$

31. $\dfrac{y}{2y - 1} + \dfrac{3}{1 - 2y}$

32. $\dfrac{a + 2}{2a + 6} - \dfrac{3}{a + 3}$

33. $\dfrac{4k}{k^2 + 2k + 1} + \dfrac{3}{k^2 - 1}$

34. $4x + 3 - \dfrac{2x + 1}{x + 4}$

35. $\dfrac{2}{a + 3} + \dfrac{2a^2 - 2a}{a^2 - 2a - 15}$

36. $\dfrac{6}{x^2 + 4x + 3} + \dfrac{7}{x^2 + 5x + 6}$

37. $\dfrac{2}{3x - 5} - 8$

38. $\dfrac{7}{4k^2 - k - 3} + \dfrac{1}{4k^2 - 7k + 3}$

39. $\dfrac{6a}{3a^2 - 7a + 2} - \dfrac{2}{3a - 1} + \dfrac{3a}{a - 2}$

40. $\dfrac{y}{y - 3} - \dfrac{2y - 5}{y + 2} - 4$

Section 8.4

For Exercises 41–50, simplify the complex fraction.

41. $\dfrac{\dfrac{4}{y} - 1}{\dfrac{1}{y} - \dfrac{4}{y^2}}$

42. $\dfrac{\dfrac{k + 2}{3}}{\dfrac{5}{k - 2}}$

43. $\dfrac{\dfrac{2}{x} + \dfrac{1}{xy}}{\dfrac{4}{x^2}}$

44. $\dfrac{\dfrac{2x}{3x^2 - 3}}{\dfrac{4x}{6x - 6}}$

45. $\dfrac{\dfrac{1}{a - 1} + 1}{\dfrac{1}{a + 1} - 1}$

46. $\dfrac{\dfrac{3}{x - 1} - \dfrac{1}{1 - x}}{\dfrac{2}{x - 1} - \dfrac{2}{x}}$

47. $\dfrac{1 - 16y^{-2}}{1 - 4y^{-1} - 32y^{-2}}$

48. $\dfrac{(w + 6)^{-1} + 3}{(w + 6)^{-1} + 2}$

49. $\dfrac{1 + xy^{-1}}{x^2 y^{-2} - 1}$

50. $\dfrac{5a^{-1} + (ab)^{-1}}{3a^{-2}}$

In Exercises 51–54 the endpoints of a line segment are given. Find (a) the midpoint of the line segment, (b) the slope of the line segment if it exists.

51. $\left(\dfrac{5}{4}, -1\right), \left(-\dfrac{1}{2}, \dfrac{1}{8}\right)$

52. $\left(-\dfrac{1}{3}, -\dfrac{3}{2}\right), \left(0, \dfrac{5}{2}\right)$

53. $\left(\dfrac{1}{3}, \dfrac{5}{2}\right), \left(\dfrac{1}{3}, \dfrac{3}{2}\right)$ 54. $\left(\dfrac{1}{4}, \dfrac{12}{7}\right), \left(\dfrac{3}{4}, \dfrac{12}{7}\right)$

Section 8.5

For Exercises 55–60, solve the equation.

55. $\dfrac{x + 3}{x^2 - x} - \dfrac{8}{x^2 - 1} = 0$

56. $\dfrac{y}{y + 3} + \dfrac{3}{y - 3} = \dfrac{18}{y^2 - 9}$

57. $x - 9 = \dfrac{72}{x - 8}$

58. $\dfrac{3x + 1}{x + 5} = \dfrac{x - 1}{x + 1} + 2$

59. $5y^{-2} + 1 = 6y^{-1}$

60. $1 + \dfrac{7}{6}m^{-1} = \dfrac{13}{6}m^{-1}$

61. Solve for t_2: $V = \dfrac{d_2 - d_1}{t_2 - t_1}$

62. Solve for R: $I = \dfrac{2V}{R + 2r}$

Section 8.6

For Exercises 63–66, solve the proportions.

63. $\dfrac{5}{4} = \dfrac{x}{6}$

64. $\dfrac{x}{36} = \dfrac{6}{7}$

65. $\dfrac{x + 2}{3} = \dfrac{5(x + 1)}{4}$

66. $\dfrac{x}{x + 2} = \dfrac{-3}{5}$

67. Twelve peaches sell for $4.50. How much would 50 peaches cost?

68. The force to compress a spring is proportional to the distance the spring is compressed. A force of 5 lb compresses a spring 7 in. How much force would it take to compress the spring 10 in.?

69. The average cost to produce x units is given by

$$\overline{C}(x) = \dfrac{1.5x + 4200}{x}$$

How many units need to be produced to have an average cost per unit of $54?

70. Stephen drove in his car for 45 miles. He ran out of gas and had to walk 3 miles to a gas station. His speed driving is 15 times his speed walking. If the total time for the drive and walk was $1\frac{1}{2}$ h, what was his speed driving?

71. Two pipes can fill a tank in 6 h. The larger pipe works twice as fast as the smaller pipe. How long would it take each pipe to fill the tank if they worked separately?

---

chapter 8   TEST

1. Let $f(x) = \dfrac{2x - 14}{x^2 - 6x - 7}$

   a. Find the function values if they exist: $f(0)$, $f(1)$, $f(7)$.

   b. Identify the domain of f. Write the answer in interval notation.

   c. Factor $f(x)$ and reduce.

2. Reduce: $\dfrac{9x^2 - 9}{x^2 + 4x + 3}$ 3. Reduce: $\dfrac{4 - a^2}{a^3 + 8}$

For Exercises 4–7, let

$$f(x) = \dfrac{x - 3}{x^2 + 6x + 9} \text{ and } g(x) = \dfrac{5}{x^2 - 9}$$

4. Find $(fg)(x)$.

5. Find $(f \div g)(x)$.

6. Find $(f + g)(x)$.

7. Find $(f - g)(x)$.

8. a. The endpoints of a line segment are $\left(-\frac{7}{2}, \frac{3}{4}\right)$ and $\left(\frac{17}{4}, -\frac{7}{8}\right)$. Draw the line segment.

    b. Approximate location of the midpoint based on your graph. Then use the midpoint formula to find the exact coordinates.

    c. Find the slope of the line segment.

For Exercises 9–14, simplify.

9. $\dfrac{3x}{5}\left(\dfrac{5}{x} - \dfrac{2}{5x}\right)$

10. $\dfrac{4x}{x + 1} + x + \dfrac{2}{x + 1}$

11. $\dfrac{3 + \dfrac{3}{k}}{4 + \dfrac{4}{k}}$

12. $\dfrac{2u^{-1} + 2v^{-1}}{4u^{-3} + 4v^{-3}}$

13. $\dfrac{ax + bx + 2a + 2b}{ax - 3a + bx - 3b} \cdot \dfrac{x - 3}{x - 5} \div \dfrac{x + 2}{ax - 5a}$

14. $\dfrac{3}{x^2 + 8x + 15} - \dfrac{1}{x^2 + 7x + 12} - \dfrac{1}{x^2 + 9x + 20}$

For Exercises 15–16, solve the equation.

15. $\dfrac{7}{z + 1} - \dfrac{z - 5}{z^2 - 1} = \dfrac{6}{z}$

16. $\dfrac{3}{y^2 - 9} + \dfrac{4}{y + 3} = 1$

17. Solve for T: $\dfrac{PV}{T} = \dfrac{pv}{t}$

18. Solve for m_1: $F = \dfrac{Gm_1m_2}{r^2}$

19. If the reciprocal of a number is added to 3 times the number, the result is $\frac{13}{2}$. Find the number.

20. The following figures are similar. Find the lengths of the missing sides.

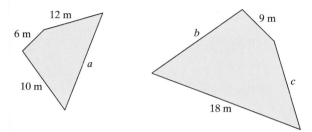

21. On a certain map, the distance between New York and Los Angeles is 8.2 in. and the actual distance is 2820 miles. What is the distance between two cities that are 5.7 in. apart on the same map? Round to the nearest mile.

22. The average profit per unit for a manufacturer to sell x units is given by

$$\overline{P}(x) = \dfrac{1.75x - 1500}{x}$$

    How many units must be sold to obtain an average profit of $0.25 per unit?

23. Lance rode 80 miles on his bike. If he had increased his speed by 4 mph, the trip would have taken 1 h less time. What was his original speed and what would his speed be 4 mph faster?

24. Gail can type a chapter in a book in 4 h. Jack can type a chapter in a book in 10 h. How long would it take them to type a chapter if they worked together?

CUMULATIVE REVIEW EXERCISES, CHAPTERS 1–8

1. Check the sets to which each number belongs.

Set \ Number	-22	$3 - 4i$	π	6	$-\sqrt{2}$
Imaginary numbers					
Real numbers					
Irrational numbers					
Rational numbers					
Integers					
Whole numbers					
Natural numbers					

2. At the age of 30, tennis player, Steffi Graf announced her retirement from tennis. After 17 years on the tour, her total prize money amounted to $\$2.1839777 \times 10^7$.

   a. Write the amount of prize money in expanded form.

   b. What was Steffi Graf's average winnings per year? Round to the nearest dollar.

3. Perform the indicated operations:
   $(2x - 3)(x - 4) - (x - 5)^2$

4. Express each factor in terms of i and simplify:
   $\sqrt{-4}\sqrt{-9}$

5. Simplify: $(\frac{1}{2} + \frac{1}{3}i)(\frac{3}{2} - \frac{5}{3}i)$. Write your answer in standard form, $a + bi$.

6. a. Find the perimeter of the rectangle.

   b. Find the area of the rectangle.

$\sqrt{3}$ in.

$\sqrt{12}$ in.

Figure for Exercise 6

7. Rationalize the denominator: $4/(\sqrt{5} - \sqrt{3})$

8. Simplify the radical: $1/\sqrt[3]{x^2}$. (Assume that x is a positive real number)

9. Simplify the radical: $\sqrt{\dfrac{50ab^4}{2a^2}}$. (Assume that a and b represent positive real numbers)

10. The area of a trapezoid is given by $A = \frac{1}{2}h(b_1 + b_2)$.

    a. Solve for b_1.

    b. Find b_1 when $h = 4$ cm, $b_2 = 6$ cm, and $A = 32$ cm^2.

11. The dimensions of a rectangular swimming pool are such that the length is 10 m less than twice the width. If the total perimeter is 160 m, find the length and width.

12. Solve the system of equations.
$$x - 3y + z = 1$$
$$2x - y - 2z = 2$$
$$x + 2y - 3z = -1$$

13. Find an equation of the line through $(-3, 5)$ that is perpendicular to the line $y = 3x$. Write the answer in slope-intercept form.

14. The value, $V(x)$, of a car (in dollars) decreases with age according to $V(x) = 15{,}000 - 1250x$; $0 \le x \le 12$, where x represents the age of the car in years.

    a. Is this function constant, linear, quadratic, or other?

    b. Sketch the function over its domain.

    c. What is the y-intercept? What does the y-intercept mean in the context of this problem?

    d. What is the x-intercept? What does the x-intercept mean in the context of this problem?

    e. What is the slope? Interpret the slope in the context of this problem.

    f. What is the value of $V(5)$? Interpret the value of $V(5)$ in the context of the problem.

    g. After how many years will the car be worth $\$5625$?

15. The speed of a car varies inversely as the time to travel a fixed distance. A car traveling the speed limit, 60 mph, travels between two points in 10 s. How fast is a car moving if it takes only 8 s to cover the same distance?

16. a. Solve by completing the square:
$2x^2 - 12x = 20$

b. Verify the answer in part (a) using the quadratic formula.

17. Find the x-intercepts: $f(x) = -12x^3 + 17x^2 - 6x$

18. Factor completely: $64y^3 - 8z^6$ over the real numbers.

19. Write the additive inverse of the matrix **A**:

$$\mathbf{A} = \begin{bmatrix} 3 & -4 & 2 \\ 4 & 1 & 0 \\ 11 & 3 & 18 \end{bmatrix}$$

20. Explain how to solve the following system for z using Cramer's rule.

$$x + 2y - 6z = 9$$
$$y - 5z = 0$$
$$3x - y + 2z = -7$$

21. Find the domain of the functions f and g.

a. $f(x) = \dfrac{x + 7}{2x - 3}$ b. $g(x) = \dfrac{x + 3}{x^2 - x - 12}$

22. Perform the indicated operations.

$$\frac{2x^2 + 11x - 21}{4x^2 - 10x + 6} \div \frac{2x^2 - 98}{x^2 - x + xa - a}$$

23. Reduce to lowest terms.

$$\frac{x^2 - 6x + 8}{20 - 5x}$$

24. Perform the indicated operations.

$$\frac{x}{x^2 + 5x - 50} - \frac{1}{x^2 - 7x + 10} + \frac{1}{x^2 + 8x - 20}$$

25. Simplify the complex fraction.

$$\frac{1 - \dfrac{49}{c^2}}{\dfrac{7}{c} + 1}$$

26. Solve the equation.

$$\frac{4y}{y + 2} - \frac{y}{y - 1} = \frac{9}{y^2 + y - 2}$$

27. Max knows that the distance between Roanoke, Virginia, and Washington, D.C., is 195 miles. On a certain map, the distance between the two cities is 6.5 in. On the same map, the distance between Roanoke and Cincinnati, Ohio, is 9.25 in. Find the distance in miles between Roanoke and Cincinnati. Round to the nearest mile.

28. Find the values of x and y so that the point $(3, 1)$ is the midpoint of the line segment with endpoints $(x, -1)$ and $(5, y)$.

29. In 1960, the number of registered vehicles in the United States was approximately 7.4×10^7 (to the nearest million). In 1996, the number of registered vehicles was 2.10×10^8 (to the nearest million). What percent increase does this represent? Round to the nearest percent.

30. Let $p(x) = 4x - 2$ and $q(x) = x^2 - x + 3$, find

a. $(p - q)(x)$ b. $(p - q)(-2)$

MORE EQUATIONS AND INEQUALITIES

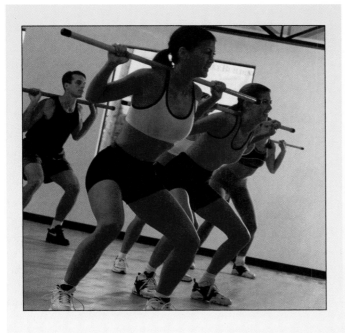

In the spring of 1998, the National Institutes of Health (NIH) issued new guidelines for determining whether an individual is overweight. The standard of measure is called the body mass index (BMI). Body mass index is a measure of an individual's weight in relation to the person's height according to the formula:

$$\text{BMI} = \frac{703W}{h^2}$$

where W is weight in pounds and h is height in inches. (Source: National Institutes of Health)

For more information visit BMIcalc at

www.mhhe.com/miller_oneill

The NIH categorizes body mass indices according to the following intervals:

Body Mass Index (BMI)	Weight Status
19.5–24.9	ideal
25.0–29.9	overweight
30.0 or above	obese

Inequalities and interval notation are studied in detail in this chapter.

section

9.1   COMPOUND INEQUALITIES

1.   Union and Intersection of Sets

In Chapter 1 we graphed simple inequalities and expressed the solution set in in-terval notation and in set-builder notation. In this chapter, we will solve **compound inequalities** that involve the union or intersection of two or more inequalities. The solution to two inequalities joined by the word **And** is the **intersection** of the two inequalities (Figure 9-1). The solution to two inequalities joined by the word **Or** is the **union** of the two inequalities (Figure 9-2).

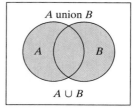

Figure 9-1   **Figure 9-2**

2.   Solving Compound Inequalities

Steps to Solve a Compound Inequality

1.   Solve and graph each inequality separately.
2.   • If the inequalities are joined by the word *and*, find the intersection of the two solution sets.
      • If the inequalities are joined by the word *or*, find the union of the two solution sets.
3.   Express the solution set in interval notation or in set-builder notation.

3.   Solving Compound Inequalities (And)

example 1

Solving Compound Inequalities (And)

Solve the inequalities. Write the solution set in set-builder notation and in interval notation.

a. $-2x < 6$ and $x + 5 \leq 7$
b. $4.4a + 3.1 < -12.3$ and $-2.8a + 9.1 < -6.3$

Solution:

a. $-2x < 6$ and $x + 5 \leq 7$ Solve each equation separately.

$$\frac{-2x}{-2} > \frac{6}{-2} \quad \text{and} \quad x \leq 2$$

Reverse the first inequality sign.

$$x > -3 \quad \text{and} \quad x \leq 2$$

$$\{x \,|\, x > -3\}$$

$$\{x \,|\, x \leq 2\}$$

Take the intersection of the solution sets: $\{x \,|\, -3 < x \leq 2\}$.

The solution is $\{x \,|\, -3 < x \leq 2\}$ or equivalently in interval notation, $(-3, 2]$.

b. $4.4a + 3.1 < -12.3 \quad \text{and} \quad -2.8a + 9.1 < -6.3$

$\quad\quad 4.4a < -15.4 \quad \text{and} \quad -2.8a < -15.4$

Solve each inequality separately.

$$\frac{4.4a}{4.4} < \frac{-15.4}{4.4} \quad \text{and} \quad \frac{-2.8a}{-2.8} > \frac{-15.4}{-2.8}$$

Reverse the second inequality sign.

$$a < -3.5 \quad \text{and} \quad a > 5.5$$

$$\{a \,|\, a < -3.5\}$$

$$\{a \,|\, a > 5.5\}$$

The intersection of the solution sets is the empty set: { }.

There are no real numbers that are simultaneously less than -3.5 and greater than 5.5. Hence, there is no solution.

In Section 1.7, we learned that the inequality $a < x < b$ is the intersection of two simultaneous conditions implied on x.

$$a < x < b$$

is equivalent to

$$a < x \quad \text{and} \quad x < b$$

example 2

Solving Compound Inequalities (And)

Solve the inequality: $-2 \leq -3x + 1 < 5$

Solution:

$$-2 \leq \overbrace{-3x + 1} < 5$$

$-2 \leq -3x + 1$	and	$-3x + 1 < 5$	Set up the intersection of two inequalities.
$-3 \leq -3x$	and	$-3x < 4$	Solve each inequality.
$\dfrac{-3}{-3} \geq \dfrac{-3x}{-3}$	and	$\dfrac{-3x}{-3} > \dfrac{4}{-3}$	Reverse the direction of the inequality signs.
$1 \geq x$	and	$x > -\dfrac{4}{3}$	
$x \leq 1$	and	$x > -\dfrac{4}{3}$	Rewrite the inequalities.

$$-\frac{4}{3} < x \leq 1 \qquad \text{Take the intersection of the solution sets.}$$

Tip: As an alternative approach to Example 1(c), we can isolate the variable, x, in the "middle" portion of the inequality. Recall that the operations performed on the middle part of the inequality must also be performed on the left- and right-hand sides.

$-2 \leq -3x + 1 < 5$	
$-2 - 1 \leq -3x + 1 - 1 < 5 - 1$	Subtract 1 from all three parts of the inequality.
$-3 \leq -3x < 4$	Simplify.
$\dfrac{-3}{-3} \geq \dfrac{-3x}{-3} > \dfrac{4}{-3}$	Divide by -3 in all three parts of the inequality. (Remember to reverse inequality signs.)
$1 \geq x > -\dfrac{4}{3}$	Simplify.
$-\dfrac{4}{3} < x \leq 1$	Rewrite the inequality.

The solution is: $\{x \mid -\frac{4}{3} < x \leq 1\}$ or equivalently in interval notation, $(-\frac{4}{3}, 1]$.

4. Solving Compound Inequalities (Or)

example 3

Solving Compound Inequalities (Or)

Solve the inequalities. Write the solution set in set-builder notation and in interval notation.

a. $-3y - 5 > 4$ or $4 - y < 6$
b. $4x + 3 < 16$ or $-2x < 3$

Solution:

a. $-3y - 5 > 4$ or $4 - y < 6$

$\qquad -3y > 9$ or $-y < 2$ Solve each inequality separately.

$\qquad \dfrac{-3y}{-3} < \dfrac{9}{-3}$ or $\dfrac{-y}{-1} > \dfrac{2}{-1}$ Reverse the inequality signs.

$\qquad y < -3$ or $y > -2$

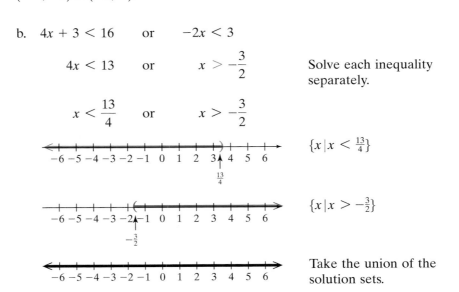

$\{y \mid y < -3\}$

$\{y \mid y > -2\}$

Take the union of the solution sets $\{y \mid y < -3 \text{ or } y > -2\}$.

The solution is $\{y \mid y < -3 \text{ or } y > -2\}$ or equivalently in interval notation, $(-\infty, -3) \cup (-2, \infty)$.

b. $4x + 3 < 16$ or $-2x < 3$

$\qquad 4x < 13$ or $x > -\dfrac{3}{2}$ Solve each inequality separately.

$\qquad x < \dfrac{13}{4}$ or $x > -\dfrac{3}{2}$

$\{x \mid x < \frac{13}{4}\}$

$\{x \mid x > -\frac{3}{2}\}$

Take the union of the solution sets.

The union of the solution sets is all real numbers, $(-\infty, \infty)$.

5. Applications of Compound Inequalities

---

example 4 | **Translating Compound Inequalities**

The normal level of thyroid-stimulating hormone (TSH) for adults ranges from 0.4 μU/mL (microunits per milliliter) to 4.8 μU/mL. Let x represent the amount of TSH measured in microunits per milliliter.

a.   Write an inequality representing the normal range of TSH.
b.   Write a compound inequality representing abnormal TSH levels.

Solution:

a. $0.4 \leq x \leq 4.8$
b. $x < 0.4$ or $x > 4.8$

---

example 5 | **Translating and Solving a Compound Inequality**

The sum of a number and 4 is between -5 and 12. Find all such numbers.

Solution:

Let x represent a number.

$-5 < x + 4 < 8$	Translate the inequality.
$-5 - 4 < x + 4 - 4 < 12 - 4$	Subtract 4 from all three parts of the inequality.
$-9 < x < 8$	

Tip: By convention for $a < b$, we will interpret the statement "x is between a and b" to exclude the endpoints a and b:

$a < x < b$ (not $a \leq x \leq b$)

The number may be any real number between -9 and 8: $\{x \mid -9 < x < 8\}$.

---

section 9.1   PRACTICE EXERCISES

For Exercises 1–6, review solving linear inequalities from Section 1.7. Write the answer in interval notation.

1. $6u + 5 > 2$

2. $-2 + 3z \leq 4$

3. $-\dfrac{3}{4}p \leq 12$

4. $-6q > -\dfrac{1}{3}$

5. $-1.5 < 0.1x - 8.1$

6. $4 \geq 2.6 + 7t$

For Exercises 7–8, review intersection and union of sets from Section 1.1. Write the answer in set notation.

7.   Let $A = \{10, 20, 30, 40, 50\}$ and $B = \{5, 10, 15, 20, 25, 30, 35\}$

a.   Find $A \cap B$ (A and B)
b.   Find $A \cup B$ (A or B)

8.   Let $C = \{a, b, c, d, e, f, g, h\}$ and $D = \{a, e, i, o, u\}$

a.   Find $C \cup D$ (C or D)
b.   Find $C \cap D$ (C and D)

9.   a.   Solve the inequality and graph the solution: $4x > 8$.

b.   Solve the inequality and graph the solution: $2 + x < 6$.

c.   Solve the compound inequality and graph the solution: $4x > 8$ and $2 + x < 6$.

10. a. Solve the inequality and graph the solution: $3x - 11 < 4$.

    b. Solve the inequality and graph the solution: $4x + 9 > 1$.

    c. Solve the compound inequality and graph the solution: $3x - 11 < 4$ and $4x + 9 > 1$.

11. a. Solve the inequality and graph the solution: $-5 \leq 3x - 4$.

    b. Solve the inequality and graph the solution: $3x - 4 \leq 8$.

    c. Solve the compound inequality and graph the solution: $-5 \leq 3x - 4 \leq 8$.

12. a. Solve the inequality and graph the solution: $-10 \leq 3x + 2$.

    b. Solve the inequality and graph the solution: $3x + 2 \leq 17$.

    c. Solve the compound inequality and graph the solution: $-10 \leq 3x + 2 \leq 17$.

13. a. Solve the inequality and graph the solution: $4x - 7 < 1$.

    b. Solve the inequality and graph the solution: $-3x + 7 > -8$.

    c. Solve the compound inequality and graph the solution: $4x - 7 < 1$ and $-3x + 7 > -8$.

14. a. Solve the inequality and graph the solution: $5 - 7x < 19$.

    b. Solve the inequality and graph the solution: $2 - 3x < -4$.

    c. Solve the compound inequality and graph the solution: $5 - 7x < 19$ and $2 - 3x < -4$.

For Exercises 15–28, solve the inequality and graph the solution. Write the answer in interval notation.

15. $y - 7 \geq -9$ and $y + 2 \leq 5$

16. $a + 6 > -2$ and $5a < 30$

17. $2t + 7 < 19$ and $5t + 13 > 28$

18. $5p + 2p \geq -21$ and $-9p + 3p \geq -24$

19. $0 \leq 2b - 5 < 9$

20. $-6 < 3k - 9 \leq 0$

21. $21k - 11 \leq 6k + 19$ and $3k - 11 < -k + 7$

22. $6w - 1 > 3w - 11$ and $-3w + 7 \leq 8w - 13$

23. $-1 < \dfrac{a}{6} \leq 1$ 24. $-3 \leq \dfrac{1}{2}x < 0$

25. $-\dfrac{2}{3} < \dfrac{y - 4}{-6} < \dfrac{1}{3}$

26. $\dfrac{1}{3} > \dfrac{t - 4}{-3} > -2$

27. $\dfrac{2}{3}(2p - 1) \geq 10$ and $\dfrac{4}{5}(3p + 4) \geq 20$

28. $5(a + 3) + 9 < 2$ and $3(a - 2) + 6 < 10$

29. a. Solve the inequality and graph the solution: $-2x + 7 > 9$.

    b. Solve the inequality and graph the solution: $3x + 1 < -14$.

    c. Solve the compound inequality and graph the solution: $-2x + 7 > 9$ or $3x + 1 < -14$.

30. a. Solve the inequality and graph the solution: $5 - 7x < 19$.

    b. Solve the inequality and graph the solution: $2 - 3x < -4$.

    c. Solve the compound inequality and graph the solution: $5 - 7x < 19$ or $2 - 3x < -4$.

31. a. Solve the inequality and graph the solution: $5x + 8 \leq 23$.

    b. Solve the inequality and graph the solution: $2x - 15 \geq 1$.

    c. Solve the compound inequality and graph the solution: $5x + 8 \leq 23$ or $2x - 15 \geq 1$.

32. a. Solve the inequality and graph the solution: $4x - 7 < 1$.

    b. Solve the inequality and graph the solution: $-3x + 7 < -8$.

    c. Solve the compound inequality and graph the solution: $4x - 7 < 1$ or $-3x + 7 > -8$.

33. a. Solve the inequality and graph the solution: $-3x - 5 \leq -11$.

    b. Solve the inequality and graph the solution: $-7 \geq 5x - 2$.

    c. Solve the compound inequality and graph the solution: $-3x - 5 \leq -11$ or $-7 \geq 5x - 2$.

34. a. Solve the inequality and graph the solution: $2x - 2 \geq 6$.

    b. Solve the inequality and graph the solution: $3x - 5 \leq 10$.

    c. Solve the compound inequality and graph the solution: $2x - 2 \geq 6$ or $3x - 5 \leq 10$.

For Exercises 35–46, solve the inequality and graph the solution. Write the answer in interval notation.

35. $h + 4 < 0$ or $6h > -12$

36. $5y > 12$ or $y - 3 < -2$

37. $2y - 1 \geq 3$ or $y < -2$

38. $x < 0$ or $3x + 1 \geq 7$

39. $\dfrac{5}{3}v \geq 5$ or $-v - 6 > 1$

40. $\dfrac{3}{8}u + 1 < 0$ or $-2u \leq -4$

41. $5(x - 1) \geq -5$ or $5 - x \leq 11$

42. $-p + 7 \geq 10$ or $3(p - 1) \leq 12$

43. $\dfrac{3t - 1}{10} > \dfrac{1}{2}$ or $\dfrac{3t - 1}{10} < -\dfrac{1}{2}$

44. $\dfrac{6 - x}{12} > \dfrac{1}{4}$ or $\dfrac{6 - x}{12} < -\dfrac{1}{6}$

45. $0.5w + 5 < 2.5w - 4$ or $0.3w \leq -0.1w - 1.6$

46. $1.25a + 3 \leq 0.5a - 6$ or $2.5a - 1 \geq 9 - 1.5a$

47. a. Solve the compound inequality and graph the solution:

    $3x - 5 < 19$ and $-2x + 3 < 23$

    b. Solve the compound inequality and graph the solution:

    $3x - 5 < 19$ or $-2x + 3 < 23$

48. a. Solve the compound inequality and graph the solution:

    $0.5(6x + 8) > 0.8x - 7$ and $4(x + 1) < 7.2$

    b. Solve the compound inequality and graph the solution:

    $0.5(6x + 8) > 0.8x - 7$ or $4(x + 1) < 7.2$

49. a. Solve the compound inequality and graph the solution:

    $8x - 4 \geq 6.4$ or $0.3(x + 6) \leq -0.6$

    b. Solve the compound inequality and graph the solution:

    $8x - 4 \geq 6.4$ and $0.3(x + 6) \leq -0.6$

50. a. Solve the compound inequality and graph the solution:

    $-2r + 4 \leq -8$ or $3r + 5 \leq 8$

    b. Solve the compound inequality and graph the solution:

    $-2r + 4 \leq -8$ and $3r + 5 \leq 8$

51. The normal number of white blood cells for human blood is between 4800 and 10,800 cells per cubic millimeter, inclusive. Let x represent the number of white blood cells per cubic millimeter (mm^3).

    a. Write an inequality representing the normal range of white blood cells per cubic millimeter.

    b. Write a compound inequality representing abnormal levels of white blood cells per cubic millimeter.

52. The normal number of platelets in human blood is between 2.0×10^5 and 3.5×10^5 platelets per cubic millimeter, inclusive. Let x represent the number of platelets per cubic millimeter.

    a. Write an inequality representing a normal platelet count per cubic millimeter.

    b. Write a compound inequality representing abnormal platelet counts per cubic millimeter.

53. Normal hemoglobin levels in human blood for adult males is between 13 and 16 g/dL (grams per deciliter), inclusive. Let x represent the level of hemoglobin measured in grams per deciliter.

a. Write an inequality representing normal hemoglobin levels for adult males.

b. Write a compound inequality representing abnormal levels of hemoglobin for adult males.

54. Normal hemoglobin levels in human blood for adult females is between 12 and 15 g/dL, inclusive. Let x represent the level of hemoglobin measured in grams per deciliter.

    a. Write an inequality representing normal hemoglobin levels for adult females.

b. Write a compound inequality representing abnormal levels of hemoglobin for adult females.

55. Twice a number is between -3 and 12. Find all such numbers.

56. The difference of a number and 6 is between 0 and 8. Find all such numbers.

57. One plus twice a number is either greater than 5 or less than -1. Find all such numbers.

58. One third of a number is either less than -2 or greater than 5. Find all such numbers.

Concepts

1. Solving Inequalities Graphically

2. Test Point Method

3. Solving Polynomial Inequalities Using the Test Point Method

4. Solving Rational Inequalities Using the Test Point Method

5. Inequalities with "Special Case" Solution Sets

section

9.2   POLYNOMIAL AND RATIONAL INEQUALITIES

1.   Solving Inequalities Graphically

In Sections 1.7 and 9.1, we solved simple and compound linear inequalities. In this section we will solve polynomial and rational inequalities. We begin by defining a quadratic inequality.

Quadratic inequalities are inequalities that can be written in any of the following forms:

$$ax^2 + bx + c \geq 0 \qquad ax^2 + bx + c \leq 0$$
$$ax^2 + bx + c > 0 \qquad ax^2 + bx + c < 0 \quad \text{where } (a \neq 0)$$

A quadratic function defined by $f(x) = ax^2 + bx + c\,(a \neq 0)$ is a parabola that opens up or down. The quadratic inequality $f(x) > 0$ or equivalently $ax^2 + bx + c > 0$ is asking the question "For what values of x is the function positive (above the x-axis)?" The inequality $f(x) < 0$ or equivalently $ax^2 + bx + c < 0$ is asking "For what values of x is the function negative (below the x-axis)?" The graph of a quadratic function can be used to answer these questions.

---

example 1

Solving a Quadratic Inequality by Graphing

Use the graph of $f(x) = x^2 - 6x + 8$ to solve the inequalities:

a. $x^2 - 6x + 8 < 0$ b. $x^2 - 6x + 8 > 0$

Solution:

From Figure 9-3, we see that the graph of $f(x) = x^2 - 6x + 8$ is a parabola opening upward. The function factors as $f(x) = (x - 2)(x - 4)$. The x-intercepts are at $x = 2$ and $x = 4$, and the y-intercept is $(0, 8)$. Because the function opens up, the vertex is below the x-axis.

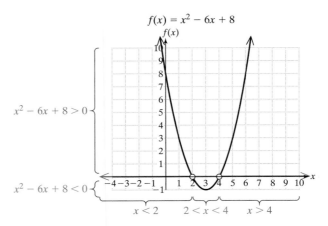

Figure 9-3

a. The solution to $x^2 - 6x + 8 < 0$ is the set of all real numbers x for which $f(x) < 0$. Graphically, this is the set of all x-values corresponding to the points where the parabola is below the x-axis (shown in red).

Hence $x^2 - 6x + 8 < 0$ for $\{x \mid 2 < x < 4\}$

b. The solution to $x^2 - 6x + 8 > 0$ is the set of x-values for which $f(x) > 0$. This is the set of x-values where the parabola is above the x-axis (shown in blue).

Hence $x^2 - 6x + 8 > 0$ for $\{x \mid x < 2$ or $x > 4\}$

Notice that the points $x = 2$ and $x = 4$ define the boundaries of the solution sets to the inequalities in Example 1. These values are the solutions to the related equation, $x^2 - 6x + 8 = 0$.

Tip: The inequalities in Example 1 are strict inequalities. Therefore, the points $x = 2$ and $x = 4$ (where $f(x) = 0$) are not included in the solution set. However, the corresponding inequalities using the symbols $\leq$ and $\geq$ do include the points where $f(x) = 0$. Hence,

The solution to $x^2 - 6x + 8 \leq 0$ is $\{x \mid 2 \leq x \leq 4\}$.

The solution to $x^2 - 6x + 8 \geq 0$ is $\{x \mid x \leq 2$ or $x \geq 4\}$.

example 2   **Solving a Rational Inequality by Graphing**

Use the graph of $g(x) = \dfrac{1}{x + 1}$ to solve the inequalities:

a. $\dfrac{1}{x + 1} < 0$
b. $\dfrac{1}{x + 1} > 0$

Solution:

a. The graph of $g(x) = 1/(x + 1)$ shown in Figure 9-4 indicates that $1/(x + 1) < 0$ for $\{x \mid x < -1\}$ (shown in red).
b. Furthermore, $1/(x + 1)$ for $\{x \mid x > -1\}$ (shown in blue).

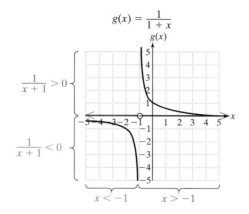

Figure 9-4

Notice that the point $x = -1$ defines the boundary of the solution sets to the inequalities in Example 2. The point $x = -1$ is a point where the inequality is undefined.

2.   Test Point Method

The **boundary points** of an inequality consist of the real solutions to the related equation and the points where the inequality is undefined. Examples 1 and 2 demonstrate that the boundary points of an inequality provide the boundaries of the solution set. This is the basis of the test point method to solve inequalities.

Solving Inequalities Using the Test Point Method

1. Find the boundary points of the inequality.
2. Plot the boundary points on the number line. This divides the number line into regions.
3. Select a test point from each region and substitute it into the original inequality.
    *   If a test point makes the original inequality true, then that region is part of the solution set.
4. Test the boundary points in the original inequality.
    *   If a boundary point makes the original inequality true, then that point is part of the solution set.

3. Solving Polynomial Inequalities Using the Test Point Method

example 3   **Solving Polynomial Inequalities Using the Test Point Method**

Solve the inequalities using the test point method.

a. $2x^2 + 5x < 12$ b. $2x + 1 \geq 3x - 2$ c. $x(x - 2)(x + 4)^2(x - 4) > 0$

Solution:

a. $2x^2 + 5x < 12$

$2x^2 + 5x = 12$

$2x^2 + 5x - 12 = 0$

$(2x - 3)(x + 4) = 0$

$x = \frac{3}{2}, \; x = -4$

Step 1: Find the boundary points. Because polynomials are defined for all values of x, the only boundary points are the real solutions to the related equation.

Solve the related equation.

The boundary points are $\frac{3}{2}$ and -4.

Step 2: Plot the boundary points.

Step 3: Select a test point from each region.

Test $x = -5$

$2x^2 + 5x < 12$

$2(-5)^2 + 5(-5) \overset{?}{<} 12$

$50 - 25 \overset{?}{<} 12$

$25 \overset{?}{<} 12$ False

Test $x = 0$

$2x^2 + 5x < 12$

$2(0)^2 + 5(0) \overset{?}{<} 12$

$0 \overset{?}{<} 12$

$0 \overset{?}{<} 12$ True

Test $x = 2$

$2x^2 + 5x < 12$

$2(2)^2 + 5(2) \overset{?}{<} 12$

$8 + 10 \overset{?}{<} 12$

$18 \overset{?}{<} 12$ False

Test $x = -4$

$$2x^2 + 5x < 12$$

$$2(-4)^2 + 5(-4) \overset{?}{<} 12$$

$$32 - 20 \overset{?}{<} 12$$

$$12 \overset{?}{<} 12 \quad \text{False}$$

Test $x = \frac{3}{2}$

$$2x^2 + 5x < 12$$

$$2\left(\frac{3}{2}\right)^2 + 5\left(\frac{3}{2}\right) \overset{?}{<} 12$$

$$2\left(\frac{9}{4}\right) + \frac{15}{2} \overset{?}{<} 12$$

$$\frac{9}{2} + \frac{15}{2} \overset{?}{<} 12$$

$$\frac{24}{2} \overset{?}{<} 12 \quad \text{False}$$

Step 4: Test the boundary points.

Tip: The strict inequality, $<$, excludes values of x for which $2x^2 + 5x = 12$. This implies that the boundary points are not included in the solution set.

Neither boundary point makes the inequality true. Therefore, the boundary points are not included in the solution set.

```
   False          True          False
 +--+--(--+--+--+--+--)+--+--+--+--+-->
 -6 -5 -4 -3 -2 -1  0  1  2  3  4  5  6
                       ↑
                      3/2
```

The solution is $\{x \mid -4 < x < \frac{3}{2}\}$ or equivalently in interval notation: $\left(-4, \frac{3}{2}\right)$.

Graphing Calculator Box

Graph $Y_1 = 2x^2 + 5x$ and $Y_2 = 12$. Notice that $Y_1 < Y_2$ for $\{x \mid -4 < x < \frac{3}{2}\}$.

b. $2x + 1 \geq 3x - 2$

$$2x + 1 = 3x - 2$$

$$-x = -3$$

$$x = 3$$

The only boundary point is $x = 3$.

Step 1: Solve the related equation.

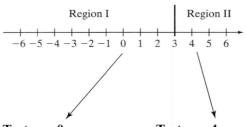

Step 2: Plot the boundary point.

Step 3: Select a test point from each region.

Test x = 0

$2x + 1 \geq 3x - 2$

$2(0) + 1 \overset{?}{\geq} 3(0) - 2$

$1 \overset{?}{\geq} -2$ True

Test x = 4

$2x + 1 \geq 3x - 2$

$2(4) + 1 \overset{?}{\geq} 3(4) - 2$

$9 \overset{?}{\geq} 10$ False

Tip: The inequality $2x + 1 \geq 3x - 2$ is linear, so we could have solved for x directly.

$2x + 1 \geq 3x - 2$

$-x \geq -3$

$x \leq 3$ Reverse the inequality sign.

Test x = 3

$2x + 1 \geq 3x - 2$

$2(3) + 1 \overset{?}{\geq} 3(3) - 2$

$7 \overset{?}{\geq} 7$ True

Step 4: Test the boundary point.

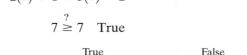

The solution is $\{x \mid x \leq 3\}$ or equivalently in interval notation: $(-\infty, 3]$.

Graphing Calculator Box

Graph $Y_1 = 2x + 1$ and $Y_2 = 3x - 2$. The point of intersection of the two lines is $x = 3$. Hence $Y_1 = Y_2$ for $x = 3$. Furthermore, $Y_1 = Y_2$ for $x \leq 3$.

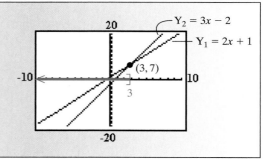

---

c. $x(x - 2)(x + 4)^2(x - 4) > 0$

$x(x - 2)(x + 4)^2(x - 4) = 0$

$x = 0, x = 2, x = -4, x = 4$

Step 1: Find the boundary points.

Step 2: Plot the boundary points.

Step 3: Select a test point from each region.

Test $x = -5$: $-5(-5-2)(-5+4)^2(-5-4) \overset{?}{>} 0$ $-315 \overset{?}{>} 0$ False

Test $x = -1$: $-1(-1-2)(-1+4)^2(-1-4) \overset{?}{>} 0$ $-135 \overset{?}{>} 0$ False

Test $x = 1$: $1(1-2)(1+4)^2(1-4) \overset{?}{>} 0$ $75 \overset{?}{>} 0$ True

Test $x = 3$: $3(3-2)(3+4)^2(3-4) \overset{?}{>} 0$ $-147 \overset{?}{>} 0$ False

Test $x = 5$: $5(5-2)(5+4)^2(5-4) \overset{?}{>} 0$ $1216 \overset{?}{>} 0$ True

False   False   True   False   True

$-6\ -5\ -4\ -3\ -2\ -1\ \ 0\ \ 1\ \ 2\ \ 3\ \ 4\ \ 5\ \ 6$

Step 4: The boundary points are not included because the inequality, $>$, is strict.

The solution is $\{x \mid 0 < x < 2 \text{ or } x > 4\}$, or equivalently in interval notation: $(0, 2) \cup (4, \infty)$.

Graphing Calculator Box

Graph $Y_1 = x(x-2)(x+4)^2(x-4)$. Y_1 is positive (above the x-axis) for $\{x \mid 0 < x < 2 \text{ or } x > 4\}$ or equivalently $(0, 2) \cup (4, \infty)$.

$Y_1 = x(x-2)(x+4)^2(x-4)$

---

4. Solving Rational Inequalities Using the Test Point Method

The test point method can be used to solve rational inequalities. However, the solution set to a rational inequality must exclude all values of the variable that make the inequality undefined. That is, exclude all values that make the denominator equal to zero for any rational expression in the inequality.

example 4

Solving a Rational Inequality Using the Test Point Method

Solve the inequality using the test point method.

$$\frac{x+2}{x-4} \le 3$$

Solution:

$$\frac{x + 2}{x - 4} \leq 3$$

Step 1: Find the boundary points. Note that the inequality is undefined for $x = 4$. Hence $x = 4$ is automatically a boundary point. To find any other boundary points, solve the related equation.

$$\frac{x + 2}{x - 4} = 3 \quad \text{(related equation)}$$

Clear fractions.

$$x + 2 = 3(x - 4) \qquad \text{Solve for } x.$$

$$x + 2 = 3x - 12$$

$$-2x = -14$$

$$x = 7$$

The solution to the related equation is $x = 7$, and the inequality is undefined for $x = 4$. Therefore, the boundary points are $x = 4$ and $x = 7$.

Region I | Region II | Region III

$$\begin{array}{ccccccccccccc} & & & & & & & | & & & | & \\ -3 & -2 & -1 & 0 & 1 & 2 & 3 & 4 & 5 & 6 & 7 & 8 \end{array}$$

Step 2: Plot boundary points.

Step 3: Select test points.

Test $x = 0$

$$\frac{x + 2}{x - 4} \leq 3$$

$$\frac{0 + 2}{0 - 4} \overset{?}{\leq} 3$$

$$-\frac{1}{2} \overset{?}{\leq} 3 \quad \text{True}$$

Test $x = 5$

$$\frac{x + 2}{x - 4} \leq 3$$

$$\frac{5 + 2}{5 - 4} \overset{?}{\leq} 3$$

$$\frac{7}{1} \overset{?}{\leq} 3 \quad \text{False}$$

Test $x = 8$

$$\frac{x + 2}{x - 4} \leq 3$$

$$\frac{8 + 2}{8 - 4} \overset{?}{\leq} 3$$

$$\frac{10}{4} \overset{?}{\leq} 3$$

$$\frac{5}{2} \overset{?}{\leq} 3 \quad \text{or} \quad 2\frac{1}{2} \overset{?}{\leq} 3 \quad \text{True}$$

Step 4: Test the boundary points.

Test $x = 4$

$$\frac{x + 2}{x - 4} \leq 3$$

$$\frac{4 + 2}{4 - 4} \overset{?}{\leq} 3$$

$$\frac{6}{0} \overset{?}{\leq} 3 \quad \text{Undefined}$$

Test $x = 7$

$$\frac{x + 2}{x - 4} \leq 3$$

$$\frac{7 + 2}{7 - 4} \overset{?}{\leq} 3$$

$$\frac{9}{3} \overset{?}{\leq} 3 \quad \text{True}$$

The boundary point $x = 4$ cannot be included in the solution set, because it is undefined in the inequality. The boundary point $x = 7$ makes the original inequality true and must be included in the solution set.

The solution is $\{x \mid x < 4 \text{ or } x \geq 7\}$ or equivalently in interval notation: $(\infty, 4) \cup [7, \infty)$.

Graphing Calculator Box

Graph $Y_1 = \dfrac{x + 2}{x - 4}$ and $Y_2 = 3$.

Y_1 has a vertical asymptote at $x = 4$. Furthermore, $Y_1 = Y_2$ at $x = 7$. $Y_1 \leq Y_2$ (that is, Y_1 is below Y_2) for $x < 4$ and for $x \geq 7$.

---

5.   Inequalities with "Special Case" Solution Sets

The solution to an inequality is often one or more regions on the real number line. Sometimes, however, the solution to an inequality may be a single point on the number line, the empty set, or the set of all real numbers.

example 5

Solving Inequalities

Solve the inequalities.

a. $-\dfrac{16}{x^2 + 2} < 0$

b. $-\dfrac{16}{x^2 + 2} > 0$

Solution:

a. Since the expressions 16 and $x^2 + 2$ are greater than zero for all real numbers, x, then their ratio is positive for all real numbers, x. The opposite of their ratio, $-16/(x^2 + 2)$ will be negative for all values of x. That is, $-16/(x^2 + 2) < 0$ for all real numbers, x.

The solution is all real numbers.

The test point method can also be used to determine the solution set.

$$-\frac{16}{x^2 + 2} < 0 \qquad \text{Find the boundary points.}$$

The denominator $x^2 + 2$ will be positive for all real numbers, x. Because the denominator will never be zero, there are no points for which the inequality is undefined.

> **Tip:** A fraction will equal zero only if its numerator equals zero. Hence $-16/(x^2 + 2) = 0$ has no solution.

$$-\frac{16}{x^2 + 2} = 0 \qquad \text{Solve the related equation.}$$

$$(x^2 + 2)\left(-\frac{16}{x^2 + 2}\right) = (x^2 + 2)(0) \qquad \text{Clear fractions.}$$

$$-16 = 0 \quad \text{Contradiction}$$

Because there is no solution to the related equation and no points for which the inequality is undefined, there are no boundary points. Therefore, there is only one test region, the whole real number line.

Region I

$$\text{Test } x = 0: \qquad \text{Test any point on the number line such as } x = 0.$$

$$-\frac{16}{(0)^2 + 2} \overset{?}{<} 0$$

$$-\frac{16}{2} \overset{?}{<} 0 \quad \text{True} \qquad \text{The test point is true in the inequality, so include that region in the solution set. The solution is all real numbers, } (-\infty, \infty).$$

b. Because $-16/(x^2 + 2) < 0$ for all real numbers, x, then there are no values of x for which $-16/(x^2 + 2) > 0$.

The inequality $-16/(x^2 + 2) > 0$ has no solution.

Graphing Calculator Box

The graph of

$$Y_1 = -\frac{16}{x^2 + 2}$$

is below the x-axis for all x-values on the viewing window. Therefore

$$-\frac{16}{x^2 + 2} < 0$$

for all x on the display window. Furthermore, there are no values of x for which

$$-\frac{16}{x^2 + 2} \geq 0$$

---

example 6

Solving Inequalities

Solve the inequalities.

a. $x^2 + 6x + 9 \geq 0$ b. $x^2 + 6x + 9 > 0$
c. $x^2 + 6x + 9 \leq 0$ d. $x^2 + 6x + 9 < 0$

Solution:

a. $x^2 + 6x + 9 \geq 0$ Notice that $x^2 + 6x + 9$ is a perfect square trinomial.

$(x + 3)^2 \geq 0$ Factor: $x^2 + 6x + 9 = (x + 3)^2$.

The quantity $(x + 3)^2$ is a perfect square and is greater than or equal to zero for all real numbers, x. The solution is all real numbers, $(-\infty, \infty)$.

b. $x^2 + 6x + 9 > 0$

$(x + 3)^2 > 0$ This is the same inequality as in part (a) with the exception that the inequality is strict. The solution set does not include the point where $x^2 + 6x + 9 = 0$. Therefore, the boundary point $x = -3$ is *not* included in the solution set.

The solution set is $\{x \mid x < -3 \text{ or } x > -3\}$ or equivalently $(-\infty, -3) \cup (-3, \infty)$.

c. $x^2 + 6x + 9 \leq 0$

$(x + 3)^2 \leq 0$

A perfect square cannot be less than zero. However, $(x + 3)^2$ is equal to zero at $x = -3$. Therefore, the solution set is $\{-3\}$.

False   False

−6 −5 −4 −3 −2 −1 0 1 2 3 4

True

d. $x^2 + 6x + 9 < 0$

$(x + 3)^2 < 0$

A perfect square cannot be negative; therefore, there are no real numbers, x, such that $(x + 3)^2 < 0$. There is no solution.

Tip: The graph of $f(x) = x^2 + 6x + 9$ or equivalently, $f(x) = (x + 3)^2$ is equal to zero at $x = 3$ and positive (above the x-axis) for all other values of x on its domain.

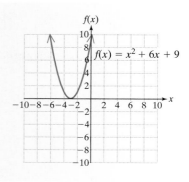

$f(x) = x^2 + 6x + 9$

---

section 9.2   PRACTICE EXERCISES

For Exercises 1–8, solve the compound inequalities. Write the solutions in interval notation.

1. $6x - 10 > 8$ or $8x + 2 < 5$

2. $3(a - 1) + 2 > 0$ or $2a > 5a + 12$

3. $5(k - 2) > -25$ and $7(1 - k) > 7$

4. $2y + 4 \geq 10$ and $5y - 3 \leq 13$

5. $2t - 7 > 3$ and $-3t < 4$

6. $2.7c - 1.1 \leq 7$ or $9 \geq 4c$

7. $\dfrac{3}{2}h - 1 < 0$ or $h + 2 > \dfrac{7}{4}$

8. $\dfrac{1}{3}p + 1 \geq p$ and $p - \dfrac{3}{4} \geq 5$

For Exercises 9–12, determine from the graph the intervals for which the inequality is true.

9.

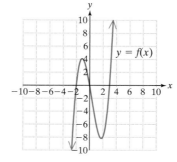

$y = f(x)$

a. $f(x) > 0$ b. $f(x) < 0$

c. $f(x) \leq 0$ d. $f(x) \geq 0$

10.

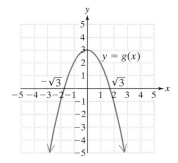

a. $g(x) < 0$ b. $g(x) > 0$
c. $g(x) \geq 0$ d. $g(x) \leq 0$

11.

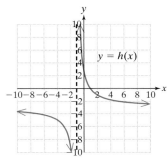

a. $h(x) \geq 0$ b. $h(x) \leq 0$
c. $h(x) < 0$ d. $h(x) > 0$

12.

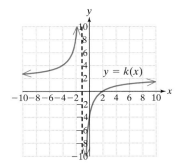

a. $k(x) \leq 0$ b. $k(x) \geq 0$
c. $k(x) > 0$ d. $k(x) < 0$

For Exercises 13–20, solve the equation and related inequalities.

13. a. $3(2b - 4) - b = 5 - b$
     b. $3(2b - 4) - b < 5 - b$
     c. $3(2b - 4) - b > 5 - b$

14. a. $(a - 6) - (3a + 2) = a + 10$
     b. $(a - 6) - (3a + 2) < a + 10$
     c. $(a - 6) - (3a + 2) > a + 10$

15. a. $\frac{1}{2}y + 3 = \frac{2}{3}y$

     b. $\frac{1}{2}y + 3 \leq \frac{2}{3}y$

     c. $\frac{1}{2}y + 3 \geq \frac{2}{3}y$

16. a. $-\frac{3}{2}t = \frac{1}{2}t - \frac{15}{8}$

     b. $-\frac{3}{2}t \leq \frac{1}{2}t - \frac{15}{8}$

     c. $-\frac{3}{2}t \geq \frac{1}{2}t - \frac{15}{8}$

17. a. $3w(w + 4) = 10 - w$
     b. $3w(w + 4) < 10 - w$
     c. $3w(w + 4) > 10 - w$

18. a. $x^2 + 7x = 30$ 19. a. $q^2 - 4q = 5$
     b. $x^2 + 7x < 30$ b. $q^2 - 4q \leq 5$
     c. $x^2 + 7x > 30$ c. $q^2 - 4q \geq 5$

20. a. $2p(p - 2) = p + 3$
     b. $2p(p - 2) \leq p + 3$
     c. $2p(p - 2) \geq p + 3$

For Exercises 21–36, solve the polynomial inequality. Write the answer in interval notation.

21. $(t - 7)(t + 1) < 0$

22. $(p - 4)(p + 2) > 0$

23. $(5y - 3)(y - 8) > 0$

24. $(2t + 5)(t - 6) < 0$

25. $a^2 - 12a \leq -32$ 26. $w^2 + 20w \geq -64$

27. $b^2 - 121 < 0$ 28. $c^2 - 25 < 0$

29. $3p^2 - 8p - 3 \geq 0$ 30. $2t^2 + 5t - 12 \leq 0$

31. $2x(x - 4)(3x + 1) > 0$

32. $-y(2y - 3)(y + 3) < 0$

33. $x^3 - x^2 \leq 12x$

34. $x^3 + 36 > 4x^2 + 9x$

35. $w^3 + w^2 > 4w + 4$

36. $2p^3 - 5p^2 \leq 3p$

For Exercises 37–40, solve the equation and related inequalities.

37. a. $\dfrac{1}{x-5} = 5$

    b. $\dfrac{1}{x-5} < 5$

    c. $\dfrac{1}{x-5} > 5$

38. a. $\dfrac{1}{a+1} = 4$

    b. $\dfrac{1}{a+1} > 4$

    c. $\dfrac{1}{a+1} < 4$

39. a. $\dfrac{z+2}{z-6} = -3$

    b. $\dfrac{z+2}{z-6} \leq -3$

    c. $\dfrac{z+2}{z-6} \geq -3$

40. a. $\dfrac{w-8}{w+6} = 2$

    b. $\dfrac{w-8}{w+6} \leq 2$

    c. $\dfrac{w-8}{w+6} \geq 2$

For Exercises 41–52, solve the rational inequalities. Write the answer in interval notation.

41. $\dfrac{2}{x-1} \geq 0$

42. $\dfrac{-3}{x+2} \leq 0$

43. $\dfrac{a+1}{a-3} < 0$

44. $\dfrac{b+4}{b-4} > 0$

45. $\dfrac{3}{2x-7} < -1$

46. $\dfrac{8}{4x+9} > 1$

47. $\dfrac{x+1}{x-5} \geq 4$

48. $\dfrac{x-2}{x+6} \leq 5$

49. $\dfrac{1}{x} \leq 2$

50. $\dfrac{1}{x} \geq 3$

51. $\dfrac{(x+2)^2}{x} > 0$

52. $\dfrac{(x-3)^2}{x} < 0$

For Exercises 53–60, solve the inequalities.

53. $x^2 + 6x + 9 \geq 0$

54. $x^2 + 6x + 9 < 0$

55. $x^2 + 2x + 1 < 0$

56. $x^2 + 8x + 16 \geq 0$

57. $\dfrac{x^2}{x^2+4} < 0$

58. $\dfrac{x^2}{x^2+4} \geq 0$

59. $x^4 + 3x^2 \leq 0$

60. $x^4 + 2x^2 \leq 0$

EXPANDING YOUR SKILLS

For Exercises 61–64, solve the polynomial inequality. Use the quadratic formula to find the boundary points. Write the answer in interval notation.

61. $-t^2 - 4t + 8 \geq 0$

62. $p^2 - 2p - 10 \leq 0$

63. $a^2 + 6a - 22 < 0$

64. $-b^2 + 4b + 6 < 0$

GRAPHING CALCULATOR EXERCISES

65. To solve the inequality

$$\frac{x}{x-2} > 0$$

enter Y_1 as $x/(x-2)$ and determine where the graph is above the x-axis. Write the solution in interval notation.

66. To solve the inequality

$$\frac{x}{x-2} < 0$$

enter Y_1 as $x/(x-2)$ and determine where the graph is below the x-axis. Write the solution in interval notation.

67. To solve the inequality $x^2 - 1 < 0$, enter Y_1 as $x^2 - 1$ and determine where the graph is below the x-axis. Write the solution in interval notation.

68. To solve the inequality $x^2 - 1 > 0$, enter Y_1 as $x^2 - 1$ and determine where the graph is above the x-axis. Write the solution in interval notation.

For Exercises 69–72, determine the solution by graphing the inequalities.

69. $x^2 + 10x + 25 \leq 0$

70. $-x^2 + 10x - 25 \geq 0$

71. $\dfrac{8}{x^2+2} < 0$

72. $\dfrac{-6}{x^2+3} > 0$

---

chapter 9   MIDCHAPTER REVIEW

Solve the inequalities. Write the answers in interval notation.

1. $\frac{1}{3}x + 5 < 2$ or $\frac{2}{5}x \geq 4$

2. $3a^2 - 4a > 7$

3. $2 \geq t - 3$ and $-5t + 8 < t$

4. $\frac{4}{y^2} > 0$

5. $y^2 - y - 12 < 0$

6. $10k - 3 > 7$ and $-k + 6 > 8$

7. $w^3 + 2w^2 - w - 2 \geq 0$

8. $\frac{t + 1}{t - 2} \leq 0$

9. $\frac{y}{y - 5} > \frac{1}{5}$

10. $p + 1.8 > 7.9$ and $5p - 0.4 \geq 0.6$

11. $n^2 + 2n + 1 > 0$

12. $\frac{x + 1}{2x + 3} > \frac{2}{3}$

13. $x^2 + 22x < -121$

14. $(m - 3)^2 < 4m$

15. $0.4k - 3 \geq 0.25k^2 - 0.2$

16. $\frac{1}{2}p - \frac{2}{3} < \frac{1}{6}p - 4$

17. $\frac{a + 2}{a - 5} \geq 0$

18. $(x + 3)^2(x - 1) \leq 0$

---

section

Concepts

1. **Definition of an Absolute Value Equation**

2. **Solving Absolute Value Equations**

3. **Solving Equations Having Two Absolute Values**

4 units   4 units

$-4 \ -3 \ -2 \ -1 \ \ 0 \ \ 1 \ \ 2 \ \ 3 \ \ 4$

Figure 9-5

9.3   ABSOLUTE VALUE EQUATIONS

1.   Definition of an Absolute Value Equation

An equation of the form $|x| = a$ is called an **absolute value equation**. The solution includes all real numbers whose absolute value equals a. For example, the solutions to the equation, $|x| = 4$ are $x = 4$ and $x = -4$, because $|4| = 4$ and $|-4| = 4$. In Chapter 1, we introduced a geometric interpretation of $|x|$. The absolute value of a number is its distance from zero on the number line (Figure 9-5). Therefore, the solutions to the equation $|x| = 4$ are the values of x that are 4 units away from zero:

$|x| = 4$

$x = -4$ or $x = 4$

2.   Solving Absolute Value Equations

Solutions to Absolute Value Equations of the Form $|x| = a$

If a is a real number, then

1.   If $a \geq 0$, the solutions to the equation $|x| = a$ are $x = a$ and $x = -a$.
2.   If $a < 0$, there is no solution to the equation $|x| = a$.

To solve an absolute value equation of the form, $|x| = a \ (a \geq 0)$, rewrite the equation as the union of the equations $x = a$ or $x = -a$.

---

example 1

Solving Absolute Value Equations

Solve the absolute value equations.

a. $|x| = 5$ b. $|w| - 2 = 12$ c. $|p| = 0$ d. $|x| = -6$

Solution:

a.

$$|x| = 5$$

$x = 5$ or $x = -5$

The equation is in the form $|x| = a$, where $a = 5$.

Rewrite as the union of the equations $x = a$ or $x = -a$.

b. $|w| - 2 = 12$

Isolate the absolute value to write the equation in the form $|w| = a$.

$$|w| = 14$$

$w = 14$ or $w = -14$

Rewrite as the union of the equations $w = a$ or $w = -a$.

c.

$$|p| = 0$$

$p = 0$ or $p = -0$

Rewrite as the union of two equations. Notice that the second equation $p = -0$ is the same as the first equation. Intuitively, $p = 0$ is the only number whose absolute value equals 0.

d. $|x| = -6$

No solution

This equation is of the form $|x| = a$, but a is negative. There is no number whose absolute value is negative.

We have solved absolute value equations of the form $|x| = a$. Notice that x can represent any algebraic quantity. For example to solve the equation $|2w - 3| = 5$, we still rewrite the absolute value equation as the union of two equations. In this case, we set the quantity $2w - 3$ equal to 5 and to -5, respectively.

$$|2w - 3| = 5$$

$2w - 3 = 5$ or $2w - 3 = -5$

Steps to Solve an Absolute Value Equation

1. Isolate the absolute value. That is, write the equation in the form $|x| = a$, where a is a constant real number.
2. If $a < 0$, there is no solution.
3. Otherwise, if $a \geq 0$, rewrite the absolute value equation as the union of the equations $x = a$ or $x = -a$.
4. Solve the individual equations from Step 3.
5. Check the answers in the original absolute value equation.

example 2   **Solving Absolute Value Equations**

Solve the absolute value equations:

a. $|2w - 3| = 5$ b. $|2c - 5| + 6 = 2$

Solution:

a. $|2w - 3| = 5$ The equation is already in the form $|x| = a$, where $x = 2w - 3$.

   $2w - 3 = 5$ or $2w - 3 = -5$ Rewrite as the union of two equations.

   $2w = 8$ or $2w = -2$ Solve each equation.

   $w = 4$ or $w = -1$

The solutions are 4 and -1.

<u>Check</u>: $x = 4$ <u>Check</u>: $x = -1$ Check the solutions in the original equation.
$|2w - 3| = 5$ $|2w - 3| = 5$
$|2(4) - 3| \overset{?}{=} 5$ $|2(-1) - 3| \overset{?}{=} 5$
$|8 - 3| \overset{?}{=} 5$ $|-2 - 3| \overset{?}{=} 5$
$|5| \overset{?}{=} 5 \checkmark$ $|-5| \overset{?}{=} 5 \checkmark$

Graphing Calculator Box

To confirm the answers to Example 2(a), graph $Y_1 = \text{abs}(2x - 3)$ and $Y_2 = 5$. The solutions to the equation $|2w - 3| = 5$ are the x-coordinates of the points of intersection $(4, 5)$ and $(-1, 5)$.

Avoiding Mistakes

Always isolate the absolute value *before* rewriting the problem as the union of two equations. In Example 2(b), if we had forgotten to isolate the absolute value first, we would have found two answers that do not check.

b. $|2c - 5| + 6 = 2$

$$|2c - 5| = -4$$ Isolate the absolute value. The equation is in the form $|x| = a$, where $x = 2c - 5$ and $a = -4$. Because $a < 0$, there is no solution.

No solution

There are no numbers, x, that will make an absolute value equal to a negative number.

Graphing Calculator Box

The graphs of $Y_1 = \text{abs}(2x - 5) + 6$ and $Y_2 = 2$ do not intersect.

Therefore, there is no solution to the equation $|2x - 5| + 6 = 2$.

---

example 3

Solving Absolute Value Equations

Solve the absolute value equations.

a. $-2\left|\dfrac{2}{5}p + 3\right| - 7 = -19$ b. $|4.1 - p| + 6.9 = 6.9$

Solution:

a. $-2\left|\dfrac{2}{5}p + 3\right| - 7 = -19$

$$-2\left|\dfrac{2}{5}p + 3\right| = -12$$ Isolate the absolute value.

$$\dfrac{-2\left|\dfrac{2}{5}p + 3\right|}{-2} = \dfrac{-12}{-2}$$

$$\left|\dfrac{2}{5}p + 3\right| = 6$$

$\dfrac{2}{5}p + 3 = 6$ or $\dfrac{2}{5}p + 3 = -6$ Rewrite as the union of two equations.

$2p + 15 = 30$ or $2p + 15 = -30$ Multiply by 5 to clear fractions.

$$2p = 15 \quad \text{or} \quad 2p = -45$$

$$p = \frac{15}{2} \quad \text{or} \quad p = -\frac{45}{2}$$

The solutions are $\frac{15}{2}$ and $-\frac{45}{2}$.   Both solutions check in the original equation.

b. $|4.1 - p| + 6.9 = 6.9$

$\qquad |4.1 - p| = 0$ Isolate the absolute value.

$4.1 - p = 0 \quad \text{or} \quad 4.1 - p = -0$ Rewrite as the union of two equations. Notice that the equations are the same.

$\qquad -p = -4.1$ Subtract 4.1 from both sides.

$\qquad p = 4.1$ $\underline{\text{Check}}: p = 4.1$

$\qquad\qquad |4.1 - p| + 6.9 = 6.9$

$\qquad\qquad |4.1 - 4.1| + 6.9 \overset{?}{=} 6.9$

$\qquad\qquad |0| + 6.9 \overset{?}{=} 6.9$

The solution is 4.1. $6.9 \overset{?}{=} 6.9 \checkmark$

3. Solving Equations Having Two Absolute Values

Some equations have two absolute values. The solutions to the equation $|x| = |y|$ are $x = y$ or $x = -y$. That is, if two quantities have the same absolute value, then the quantities are equal or the quantities are opposites.

Equality of Absolute Values

$$|x| = |y| \text{ implies that } x = y \text{ or } x = -y.$$

example 4   Solving an Equation Having Two Absolute Values

Solve the equations.

a. $|2w - 3| = |5w + 1|$ b. $|x - 4| = |x + 8|$

Solution:

a. $\qquad\qquad |2w - 3| = |5w + 1|$

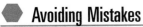 **Avoiding Mistakes**

To take the opposite of the quantity, $5w + 1$, use parentheses and apply the distributive property.

$2w - 3 = 5w + 1 \quad \text{or} \quad 2w - 3 = -(5w + 1)$ Rewrite as the union two equations, $x = y$ or $x = -y$.

$$2w - 3 = 5w + 1 \quad \text{or} \quad 2w - 3 = -5w - 1$$

Apply the distributive property.

$$-3w - 3 = 1 \quad \text{or} \quad 7w - 3 = -1$$

Solve for w.

$$-3w = 4 \quad \text{or} \quad 7w = 2$$

$$w = -\frac{4}{3} \quad \text{or} \quad w = \frac{2}{7}$$

The solutions are $-\dfrac{4}{3}$ and $\dfrac{2}{7}$.

Both values check in the original equation.

b. $|x - 4| = |x + 8|$

$$x - 4 = x + 8 \quad \text{or} \quad x - 4 = -(x + 8)$$

Rewrite as the union of two equations
$x = y$ or $x = -y$

$$-4 = 8 \quad \text{or} \quad x - 4 = -x - 8$$

contradiction

$$2x - 4 = -8$$

$$2x = -4$$

$$x = -2$$

Apply the distributive property.

The only solution is -2.

$x = -2$ checks in the original equation.

Graphing Calculator Box

Graph $Y_1 = \text{abs}(x - 4)$ and $Y_2 = \text{abs}(x + 8)$. There is one point of intersection at $(-2, 6)$. Therefore, the solution to $|x - 4| = |x + 8|$ is $x = -2$.

section 9.3 PRACTICE EXERCISES

For Exercises 1–8, solve the inequalities. Write the answers in interval notation.

1. $3(a + 2) - 6 > 2$ and $-2(a - 3) + 14 > -3$

2. $3x - 5 \geq 7x + 3$ or $2x - 1 \leq 4x - 5$

3. $\dfrac{4}{y - 4} \geq 3$

4. $\dfrac{3}{t + 1} \leq 2$

5. The sum of a number and 6 is between -1 and 13. Find all such numbers.

6. The difference of 12 and a number is between -3 and -1. Find all such numbers.

7. $3(x - 2)(x + 4)(2x - 1) < 0$

8. $x^3 - 7x^2 - 8x > 0$

For Exercises 9–50, solve the absolute value equations.

9. $|p| = 7$

10. $|q| = 10$

11. $|x| + 5 = 11$

12. $|x| - 3 = 20$

13. $|y| = \sqrt{2}$

14. $|y| = \dfrac{5}{8}$

15. $|w| - 3 = -5$

16. $|w| + 4 = -8$

17. $|3q| = 0$

18. $|4p| = 0$

19. $\left|3x - \dfrac{1}{2}\right| = \dfrac{1}{2}$

20. $|4x + 1| = 6$

21. $|4x - 2| = |-8|$

22. $|3x + 5| = |-5|$

23. $\left|\dfrac{7z}{3} - \dfrac{1}{3}\right| + 3 = 6$

24. $\left|\dfrac{w}{2} + \dfrac{3}{2}\right| - 2 = 7$

25. $\left|\dfrac{5y + 2}{2}\right| = 6$

26. $\left|\dfrac{2t - 1}{3}\right| = 5$

27. $|0.2x - 3.5| = -5.6$

28. $|1.81 + 2x| = -2.2$

29. $|4w + 3| = |2w - 5|$

30. $|3y + 1| = |2y - 7|$

31. $|2y + 5| = |7 - 2y|$

32. $|9a + 5| = |9a - 1|$

33. $1 = -4 + \left|2 - \dfrac{1}{4}w\right|$

34. $-12 + |6 - 2x| = -6$

35. $10 = 4 + |2y + 1|$

36. $-1 = -|5x + 7|$

37. $|3b - 7| - 9 = -9$

38. $|3x - 7| = 0$

39. $|4w - 1| = |2w + 3|$

40. $|3p + 2| = |p - 4|$

41. $-2|x + 3| = 5$

42. $-3|x - 5| = 7$

43. $|6x - 9| = 0$

44. $|4k - 6| + 7 = 7$

45. $|2h - 6| = |2h + 5|$

46. $|6n - 7| = |4 - 6n|$

47. $\left|-\dfrac{1}{5} - \dfrac{1}{2}k\right| = \dfrac{9}{5}$

48. $\left|-\dfrac{1}{6} - \dfrac{2}{9}h\right| = \dfrac{1}{2}$

49. $|3.5m - 1.2| = |8.5m + 6|$

50. $|11.2n + 9| = |7.2n - 2.1|$

51. Write an absolute value equation whose solution is the set of real numbers 6 units from zero on the number line.

52. Write an absolute value equation whose solution is the set of real numbers $\frac{7}{2}$ units from zero on the number line.

53. Write an absolute value equation whose solution is the set of real numbers $\frac{4}{3}$ units from zero on the number line.

54. Write an absolute value equation whose solution is the set of real numbers 9 units from zero on the number line.

▪ EXPANDING YOUR SKILLS

For Exercises 55–60, solve the absolute value equations.

55. $|5y - 3| + \sqrt{5} = 1 + \sqrt{5}$

56. $|2x - \sqrt{3}| + 4 = 4 + \sqrt{3}$

57. $|\sqrt{3} + x| = 7$

58. $\sqrt{2} + |w - 8| = 3 + 4\sqrt{2}$

59. $|w - \sqrt{6}| = |3w + \sqrt{6}|$

60. $\left|\frac{\sqrt{5}}{2}x - 4\right| = 6$

🔢 GRAPHING CALCULATOR EXERCISES

For Exercises 61–68, enter the left side of the equation as Y_1 and enter the right side of the equation as Y_2. Then use the *Intersect* feature or *Zoom* and *Trace* to approximate the x-values where the two graphs intersect (if they intersect).

61. $|4x - 3| = 5$

62. $|x - 4| = 3$

63. $|8x + 1| + 8 = 1$

64. $|3x - 2| + 4 = 2$

65. $|x - 3| = |x + 2|$

66. $|x + 4| = |x - 2|$

67. $|2x - 1| = |-x + 3|$

68. $|3x| = |2x - 5|$

Concepts

1. **Solving Absolute Value Inequalities**

2. **Absolute Value Inequalities with "Special Case" Solution Sets**

3. **Translations Involving Absolute Value**

4. **Solving Absolute Value Inequalities Using the Test Point Method**

section

9.4   ABSOLUTE VALUE INEQUALITIES

1.   Solving Absolute Value Inequalities

In Section 9.3, we studied absolute value equations in the form $|x| = a$. In this section we will solve absolute value *inequalities*. An inequality in any of the forms $|x| < a$, $|x| \le a$, $|x| > a$, or $|x| \ge a$ is called an **absolute value inequality**.

Recall that an absolute value represents distance from zero on the real number line. Consider the following absolute value equation and inequalities.

1. $|x| = 3$

    Solution:

    The set of all points 3 units from zero on the number line.

    $x = 3$ or $x = -3$

2. $|x| > 3$

    Solution:

    The set of all points more than 3 units from zero.

    $x < -3$ or $x > 3$

3. $|x| < 3$

Solution:

The set of all points less than 3 units from zero.

$-3 < x < 3$

Solutions to Absolute Value Equations and Inequalities

Let a be a real number such that $a > 0$. Then,

Equation/ Inequality	Solution (equivalent form)	Graph
$|x| = a$	$x = -a$ or $x = a$	•$-a$ •a
$|x| > a$	$x < -a$ or $x > a$	$\longleftarrow$)$-a$ (a $\longrightarrow$
$|x| < a$	$-a < x < a$	($-a$)a

To solve an absolute value inequality, first isolate the absolute value and then rewrite the absolute value inequality in its equivalent form.

---

example 1

Solving Absolute Value Inequalities

Solve the inequalities.

a. $|3w + 1| - 4 < 7$ 　　　　b. $\left|\dfrac{1}{2}t - 5\right| + 1 \geq 3$

Solution:

a. $|3w + 1| - 4 < 7$

$\quad |3w + 1| < 11$ ←— Isolate the absolute value first.

The inequality is in the form $|x| < a$, where $x = 3w + 1$.

$-11 < 3w + 1 < 11$　　Rewrite in the equivalent form, $-a < x < a$.

$-12 < 3w < 10$　　Solve for w.

$-4 < w < \dfrac{10}{3}$

The solution is $\{w \mid -4 < w < \frac{10}{3}\}$ or equivalently in interval notation, $(-4, \frac{10}{3})$.

Graphing Calculator Box

Graph $Y_1 = \text{abs}(3w + 1) - 4$ and $Y_2 = 7$. On the given display window, $Y_1 < Y_2$ (Y_1 is below Y_2) for $4 < x < \frac{10}{3}$.

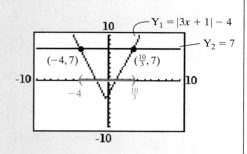

b. $\left|\dfrac{1}{2}t - 5\right| + 1 \geq 3$

$\left|\dfrac{1}{2}t - 5\right| \geq 2$ Isolate the absolute value.

The inequality is in the form $|x| \geq a$, where $x = \frac{1}{2}t - 5$.

$\dfrac{1}{2}t - 5 \leq -2$ or $\dfrac{1}{2}t - 5 \geq 2$ Rewrite in the equivalent form $x \leq -a$ or $x \geq a$.

$\dfrac{1}{2}t \leq 3$ or $\dfrac{1}{2}t \geq 7$ Solve the compound inequality.

$2\left(\dfrac{1}{2}t\right) \leq 2(3)$ or $2\left(\dfrac{1}{2}t\right) \geq 2(7)$ Clear fractions.

$t \leq 6$ or $t \geq 14$ 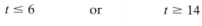

The solution is $\{t \mid t \leq 6 \text{ or } t \geq 14\}$ or equivalently in interval notation, $(-\infty, 6] \cup [14, \infty)$.

Graphing Calculator Box

Graph $Y_1 = \text{abs}(\frac{1}{2}x - 5) + 1$ and $Y_2 = 3$. On the given display window, $Y_1 \geq Y_2$ for $x \leq 6$ or $x \geq 14$.

2. Absolute Value Inequalities with "Special Case" Solution Sets

Tip: By definition, the absolute value of a real number will always be nonnegative. Therefore, the absolute value of any expression will always be greater than a negative number. Similarly, an absolute value can never be less than a negative number. Let a represent a positive real number. Then,

1. The solution to the inequality $|x| > -a$ is all real numbers, $(-\infty, \infty)$.
2. There is no solution to the inequality $|x| < -a$.

---

example 2

Solving Absolute Value Inequalities

Solve the inequalities.

a. $|3d - 5| + 7 < 4$ b. $|3d - 5| + 7 > 4$

Solution:

a. $|3d - 5| + 7 < 4$

   $|3d - 5| < -3$ Isolate the absolute value. An absolute value expression cannot be less than a negative number. Therefore, there is no solution.

   No solution

b. $|3d - 5| + 7 > 4$

   $|3d - 5| > -3$ Isolate the absolute value. The inequality is in the form $|x| > a$, where a is negative. An absolute value of any real number is greater than a negative number. Therefore, the solution is all real numbers.

   All real numbers, $(-\infty, \infty)$

Graphing Calculator Box

By graphing $Y_1 = \text{abs}(3x - 5) + 7$ and $Y_2 = 4$, we see that $Y_1 > Y_2$ (Y_1 is above Y_2) for all real numbers, x, on the given display window.

example 3

Solving Absolute Value Inequalities

Solve the inequalities.

a. $|4x + 2| \geq 0$ b. $|4x + 2| > 0$

Solution:

a. $|4x + 2| \geq 0$ ◄—— The absolute value is already isolated.

The absolute value of any real number is nonnegative. Therefore, the solution is all real numbers, $(-\infty, \infty)$.

b. $|4x + 2| > 0$

An absolute value will be greater than zero at all points *except where it is equal to zero*. That is, the point(s) for which $|4x + 2| = 0$ must be excluded from the solution set.

$$|4x + 2| = 0$$

$4x + 2 = 0$ or $4x + 2 = -0$ The second equation is the same as the first.

$$4x = -2$$

$$x = -\frac{1}{2}$$ Therefore, exclude $x = -\frac{1}{2}$ from the solution.

The solution is $\{x \,|\, x \neq -\frac{1}{2}\}$ or equivalently in interval notation, $(-\infty, -\frac{1}{2}) \cup (-\frac{1}{2}, \infty)$.

Graphing Calculator Box

Graph $Y_1 = \text{abs}(4x + 2)$. From the graph, $Y_1 = 0$ at $x = -\frac{1}{2}$ (the x-intercept). On the given display window, $Y_1 > 0$ for $x < -\frac{1}{2}$ or $x > -\frac{1}{2}$.

---

3. Translations Involving Absolute Value

Absolute value expressions can be used to describe distances. The distance between c and d is given by $|c - d|$. For example, the distance between -2 and 3 on the number line is $|(-2) - 3| = 5$ as expected.

example 4

Translations Involving Distances

Write an absolute value inequality to represent the following phrases.

a. All real numbers, x, whose distance from zero is greater than 5 units
b. All real numbers, x, whose distance from -7 is less than 3 units

Solution:

a. All real numbers, x, whose distance from zero is greater than 5 units

$|x - 0| > 5$ or simply: $|x| > 5$

b. All real numbers, x, whose distance from -7 is less than 3 units

$|x - (-7)| < 3$ or simply: $|x + 7| < 3$

Absolute value expressions can also be used to describe boundaries for measurement error.

example 5

Translations Involving Measurement Error

Latoya measured a certain compound on a scale in the chemistry lab at school. She measured 8 g of the compound, but the scale is only accurate to the nearest tenth of a gram. Write an absolute value inequality to express an interval for the true mass, x, of the compound she measured.

Solution:

Because the scale is only accurate to the nearest tenth of a gram, the true mass, x, of the compound may deviate by as much as 0.1 g above or below 8 g. This may be expressed as an absolute value inequality:

$|x - 8.0| \leq 0.1$ or equivalently, $7.9 \leq x \leq 8.1$

4.   Solving Absolute Value Inequalities Using the Test Point Method

For each problem in Example 1, the absolute value inequality was converted to an equivalent compound inequality. However, sometimes students have difficulty setting up the appropriate compound inequality. To avoid this problem, you may want to use the test point method to solve absolute value inequalities.

Solving Inequalities Using the Test Point Method

1. Find the boundary points of the inequality. (Boundary points are the real solutions to the related equation and points where the inequality is undefined.)
2. Plot the boundary points on the number line. This divides the number line into regions.
3. Select a test point from each region and substitute it into the original inequality.
   - If a test point makes the original inequality true, then that region is part of the solution set.
4. Test the boundary points in the original inequality.
   - If a boundary point makes the original inequality true, then that point is part of the solution set.

To demonstrate the use of the test point method, we will repeat the absolute value inequalities from Example 1. Notice that regardless of the method used, the absolute value is always isolated *first* before any further action is taken.

---

example 6

Solving Absolute Value Inequalities with the Test Point Method

Solve the inequalities using the test point method.

a. $|3w + 1| - 4 < 7$

b. $\left|\frac{1}{2}t - 5\right| + 1 \geq 3$

Solution:

a.

$$|3w + 1| - 4 < 7$$

$$|3w + 1| < 11 \longleftarrow \qquad \text{Isolate the absolute value first.}$$

$$|3w + 1| = 11 \qquad \qquad \textbf{Step 1:} \quad \text{Solve the related equation.}$$

$$3w + 1 = 11 \quad \text{or} \quad 3w + 1 = -11 \qquad \text{Write as an equivalent system of two equations.}$$

$$3w = 10 \quad \text{or} \quad 3w = -12$$

$$w = \frac{10}{3} \quad \text{or} \quad w = -4 \qquad \text{These are the only boundary points.}$$

Step 2: Plot the boundary points.

Step 3: Select a test point from each region.

Test $w = -5$:

$|3(-5) + 1| - 4 \overset{?}{<} 7$

$|-14| - 4 \overset{?}{<} 7$

$14 - 4 \overset{?}{<} 7$

$10 \overset{?}{<} 7$ False

Test $w = 0$:

$|3(0) + 1| - 4 \overset{?}{<} 7$

$|1| - 4 \overset{?}{<} 7$

$-3 \overset{?}{<} 7$ True

Test $w = 4$:

$|3(4) + 1| - 4 \overset{?}{<} 7$

$|13| - 4 \overset{?}{<} 7$

$13 - 4 \overset{?}{<} 7$

$9 \overset{?}{<} 7$ False

Step 4: The last step in the test point method is to determine whether the boundary points are part of the solution set. Because the original inequality is a strict inequality, the boundary points (where equality occurs) are not included.

The solution is $\{w \mid -4 < w < \frac{10}{3}\}$ or equivalently in interval notation, $(-4, \frac{10}{3})$.

b. $\left|\frac{1}{2}t - 5\right| + 1 \ge 3$

$\left|\frac{1}{2}t - 5\right| \ge 2 \longleftarrow$ ————— Isolate the absolute value first.

$\left|\frac{1}{2}t - 5\right| = 2$ **Step 1:** Solve the related equation.

$\frac{1}{2}t - 5 = 2$ or $\frac{1}{2}t - 5 = -2$ Write the union of two equations.

$\frac{1}{2}t = 7$ or $\frac{1}{2}t = 3$

$t = 14$ or $t = 6$ These are the boundary points.

Region I	Region II	Region III

6   14

Step 2: Plot the boundary points.

Step 3: Select a test point from each region.

Test $t = 0$:

$$\left|\frac{1}{2}(0) - 5\right| + 1 \overset{?}{\geq} 3$$

$$|0 - 5| + 1 \overset{?}{\geq} 3$$

$$|-5| + 1 \overset{?}{\geq} 3$$

$$5 + 1 \overset{?}{\geq} 3 \quad \text{True}$$

Test $t = 10$:

$$\left|\frac{1}{2}(10) - 5\right| + 1 \overset{?}{\geq} 3$$

$$|5 - 5| + 1 \overset{?}{\geq} 3$$

$$|0| + 1 \overset{?}{\geq} 3$$

$$1 \overset{?}{\geq} 3 \quad \text{False}$$

Test $t = 16$:

$$\left|\frac{1}{2}(16) - 5\right| + 1 \overset{?}{\geq} 3$$

$$|8 - 5| + 1 \overset{?}{\geq} 3$$

$$|3| + 1 \overset{?}{\geq} 3$$

$$4 \overset{?}{\geq} 3 \quad \text{True}$$

True ——— False ——— True, boundary points at 6 and 14

Step 4: The original inequality uses the sign $\geq$. Therefore, the boundary points (where equality occurs) must be part of the solution set.

The solution is $\{x \mid x \leq 6 \text{ or } x \geq 14\}$ or equivalently in interval notation, $(-\infty, 6] \cup [14, \infty)$.

---

example 7

Solving Absolute Value Inequalities

Solve the inequalities.

a. $\left|\frac{1}{3}x + 4\right| < 0$ b. $\left|\frac{1}{3}x + 4\right| \leq 0$

Solution:

a. $\left|\frac{1}{3}x + 4\right| < 0$ ←——— The absolute value is already isolated.

No solution   Because the absolute value of any real number is non-negative, an absolute value cannot be strictly less than zero. Therefore, there is no solution to this inequality.

b. $\left|\frac{1}{3}x + 4\right| \leq 0$ ←——— The absolute value is already isolated.

An absolute value will never be less than zero. However, an absolute value may be equal to zero. Therefore, the only solutions to this inequality are the solutions to the related equation.

$\left|\frac{1}{3}x + 4\right| = 0$ Set up the related equation.

$\frac{1}{3}x + 4 = 0$

$$\frac{1}{3}x = -4$$

$$x = -12 \qquad \text{This is the only boundary point.}$$

The solution set is $\{-12\}$.

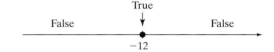

Graphing Calculator Box

Graph $Y_1 = |\frac{1}{3}x + 4|$. Notice that on the given viewing window the graph of Y_1 does not extend below the x-axis. Therefore, there is no solution to the inequality $Y_1 < 0$.
   Because $Y_1 = 0$ at $x = -12$, the inequality $Y_1 \le 0$ has a solution at $x = -12$.

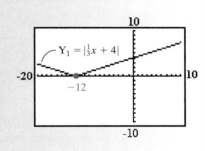

---

section 9.4   PRACTICE EXERCISES

For Exercises 1–6, solve the equations.

1. $10x - 6 = -5$

2. $7x - 6 + x = 8x - 2$

3. $|10x - 6| = -5$

4. $2 = |5 - 7x| + 1$

5. $|6x| = |9x + 5|$

6. $|3y - 1| = |3y + 4|$

For Exercises 7–12, solve the inequalities and graph the solution set. Write the solution in interval notation.

7. $0.73 > -0.22 + 0.5x$

8. $-3(x - 6) \ge 2x - 5$

9. $-15 < 3w - 6 \le -9$

10. $5 - 2y \le 1 \qquad$ and $\qquad 3y + 2 \ge 14$

11. $m - 7 \le -5 \qquad$ or $\qquad m - 7 \ge -10$

12. $3b - 2 < 7 \qquad$ or $\qquad b - 2 > 4$

For Exercises 13–20, solve the equations and inequalities. For each inequality, graph the solution set and express the solution in interval notation.

13. a. $|x| = 5$
     b. $|x| > 5$
     c. $|x| < 5$

14. a. $|a| = 4$
     b. $|a| > 4$
     c. $|a| < 4$

15. a. $|p| = -2$
     b. $|p| > -2$
     c. $|p| < -2$

16. a. $|x| = -14$
     b. $|x| > -14$
     c. $|x| < -14$

17. a. $|x - 3| = 7$
     b. $|x - 3| > 7$
     c. $|x - 3| < 7$

18. a. $|w + 2| = 6$
     b. $|w + 2| > 6$
     c. $|w + 2| < 6$

19. a. $|y + 1| = -6$
     b. $|y + 1| > -6$
     c. $|y + 1| < -6$

20. a. $|z - 4| = -3$

b. $|z - 4| > -3$

c. $|z - 4| < -3$

For Exercises 21–24, match the graph with the inequality:

21.

22.

23.

24.

a. $|x - 2| < 4$ b. $|x - 1| > 4$

c. $|x - 3| < 2$ d. $|x - 5| > 1$

For Exercises 25–48, solve the absolute value inequalities. Graph the solution set and write the solution in interval notation.

25. $|x| > 6$

26. $|x| \le 6$

27. $|t| \le 3$

28. $|p| > 3$

29. $|y + 2| \ge 0$

30. $0 \le |7n + 2|$

31. $5 \le |2x - 1|$

32. $|x - 2| \ge 7$

33. $|k - 7| < -3$

34. $|h + 2| < -9$

35. $\left|\dfrac{w - 2}{3}\right| - 3 \le 1$

36. $\left|\dfrac{x + 3}{2}\right| - 2 \ge 4$

37. $|9 - 4y| \ge 14$

38. $1 > |2m - 7|$

39. $\left|\dfrac{2x + 1}{4}\right| < 5$

40. $\left|\dfrac{x - 4}{5}\right| \le 7$

41. $8 < |4 - 3x| + 12$

42. $-16 < |5x - 1| - 1$

43. $5 - |2m + 1| > 5$

44. $3 - |5x + 3| > 3$

45. $|p + 5| \le 0$

46. $|y + 1| - 4 \le -4$

47. $|z - 6| + 5 \ge 5$

48. $|2c - 1| \ge 0$

For Exercises 49–52, write an absolute value inequality equivalent to the expression given.

49. All real numbers whose distance from 0 is greater than 7.

50. All real numbers whose distance from -3 is less than 4.

51. All real numbers whose distance from 2 is at most 13.

52. All real numbers whose distance from 0 is at least 6.

53. A 32-oz jug of orange juice may not contain exactly 32 oz of juice. The possibility of measurement error exists when the jug is filled in the factory. If there is a ± 0.05-oz measurement error, write an absolute value inequality representing the range of volumes, x, in which the orange juice jug may be filled.

54. The length of a board is measured to be 32.3 in. There is a ± 0.2 in. measurement error. Write an absolute value inequality that represents the range for the length of the board.

55. A bag of potato chips states that its weight is $6\frac{3}{4}$ oz. There is a $\pm\frac{1}{8}$-oz measurement error. Write an absolute value inequality that represents the range for the weight, x, of the bag of chips.

56. A $\frac{7}{8}$-in. bolt varies in length by $\pm\frac{1}{16}$ in. Write an absolute value inequality that represents the range for the length of the bolt.

GRAPHING CALCULATOR EXERCISES

To solve an absolute value inequality using a graphing calculator, let Y_1 equal the right side of the inequality and let Y_2 equal the left side of the inequality. Graph both Y_1 and Y_2 on a standard viewing window and use an *Intersect* feature or *Zoom* and *Trace* to approximate the intersection of the graphs. To solve $Y_1 > Y_2$, determine all x-values where the graph of Y_1 is above the graph of Y_2. To solve $Y_1 < Y_2$, determine all x-values where the graph of Y_1 is below the graph of Y_2.

For Exercises 57–66, solve the inequalities using a graphing calculator.

57. $|x + 2| > 4$

58. $|3 - x| > 6$

59. $\left|\dfrac{x + 1}{3}\right| < 2$

60. $\left|\dfrac{x - 1}{4}\right| < 1$

61. $|x - 5| < -3$

62. $|x + 2| < -2$

63. $|2x + 5| > -4$

64. $|1 - 2x| > -4$

65. $|6x + 1| \le 0$

66. $|3x - 4| \le 0$

---

section

9.5   LINEAR INEQUALITIES IN TWO VARIABLES

Concepts

1. **Introduction to Linear Inequalities in Two Variables**
2. **Graphing Linear Inequalities in Two Variables**
3. **Compound Linear Inequalities in Two Variables**
4. **Graphing a Feasible Region**

1. Introduction to Linear Inequalities in Two Variables

A **linear inequality in two variables** x and y is an inequality that can be written in one of the following forms: $ax + by < c, ax + by > c, ax + by \le c,$ or $ax + by \ge c$.

A solution to a linear inequality in two variables is an ordered pair that makes the inequality true. For example, solutions to the inequality $x + y < 6$ are ordered pairs (x, y) such that the sum of the x- and y-coordinates is less than 6. This inequality has an infinite number of solutions, and therefore it is convenient to express the solution set as a graph.

2. Graphing Linear Inequalities in Two Variables

To graph a linear inequality in two variables, we will use the test point method. The first step is to graph the related equation. This will be a line that separates the xy-plane into three regions: (1) the region below the line, (2) the region above the line, and (3) the line itself. Then, by selecting a test point (ordered pair) from each region and substituting it into the inequality, we can determine which region(s) represents the solution set.

Test Point Method—Summary

1. Graph the related equation. The equation will be a boundary line in the xy-plane.
   - If the original inequality is a strict inequality, $<$ or $>$, then the line is not part of the solution set. Graph the boundary as a *dashed line*.
   - If the original inequality uses $\le$ or $\ge$ then the line is part of the solution set. Graph the boundary as a *solid line*.
2. From each region above and below the line, select an ordered pair as a test point and substitute it into the original inequality.
   - If a test point makes the inequality true, then that region is part of the solution set.

example 1

Graphing a Linear Inequality in Two Variables

Graph the solution set of the inequality $x + y < 6$.

Solution:

Step 1: Graph the related equation $x + y = 6$ using a dashed line (Figure 9-6).

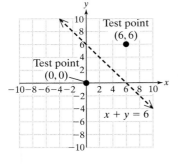

Figure 9-6

Tip: To graph the related equation, you may either create a table of points, or you may use the slope-intercept form of the line.

table of points   slope-intercept form

x	y
0	6
6	0
4	2

$x + y = 6 \longrightarrow y = -x + 6$

Step 2: Choose test points (ordered pairs) above and below the line and substitute the points into the original inequality.

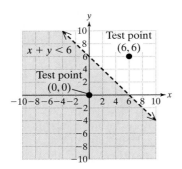

Figure 9-7

Test Point Above: (6, 6)

$$x + y < 6$$

$$(6) + (6) \overset{?}{<} 6$$

$$12 \overset{?}{<} 6 \quad \text{False}$$

The test point $(6, 6)$ *is not a* solution to the original inequality.

Test Point Below: (0, 0)

$$x + y < 6$$

$$(0) + (0) \overset{?}{<} 6$$

$$0 \overset{?}{<} 6 \quad \text{True}$$

The test point $(0, 0)$ *is* a solution to the original inequality. Shade the region below the boundary. See Figure 9-7.

example 2

Graphing a Linear Inequality in Two Variables

Graph the solution set of the inequality $3x - 5y \leq 10$.

Solution:

$$3x - 5y \leq 10$$

$$3x - 5y = 10$$

$$y = \frac{3}{5}x - 2$$

Step 1: Graph the related equation to form the boundary of the solution set. (Here we use the slope-intercept form to graph the line.)

Step 2: Choose test points above and below the line.

Test Point Above: (0, 0)

$$3x - 5y \leq 10$$

$$3(0) - 5(0) \overset{?}{\leq} 10$$

$$0 \overset{?}{\leq} 10 \quad \text{True}$$

Test Point Below: (4, −5)

$$3x - 5y \leq 10$$

$$3(4) - 5(-5) \overset{?}{\leq} 10$$

$$12 + 25 \overset{?}{\leq} 10$$

$$37 \overset{?}{\leq} 10 \quad \text{False}$$

Because the test point $(0, 0)$ above the boundary is true in the original inequality, shade the region above the line (Figure 9-8).

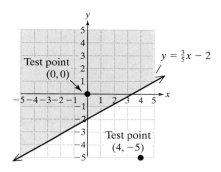

Figure 9-8

Tip: An inequality can also be graphed by first solving the inequality for y. Then,

- Shade below the line if the inequality is of the form $y < mx + b$ or $y \leq mx + b$.
- Shade above the line if the inequality is of the form $y > mx + b$ or $y \geq mx + b$.

From Example 2, we have:

$$3x - 5y \leq 10$$

$$-5y \leq -3x + 10$$

$$\frac{-5y}{-5} \geq \frac{-3x}{-5} + \frac{10}{-5} \qquad \text{Reverse the inequality sign.}$$

$$y \geq \frac{3}{5}x - 2 \qquad \text{Shade } above \text{ the line.}$$

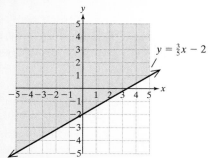

Graphing Calculator Box

Some graphing calculators can shade a region above or below a line. Consider the inequality $y \geq \frac{3}{5}x - 2$.

3. Compound Linear Inequalities in Two Variables

Some applications require us to find of the union or intersection of two or more linear inequalities.

example 3

Graphing a Compound Linear Inequality in Two Variables

Graph the solution set of the system of inequalities: $2x + y < 1$ and $2y \geq x - 4$.

Solution:

First Inequality		**Second Inequality**	
$2x + y < 1$		$2y \geq x - 4$	
$2x + y = 1$	Related equation	$2y = x - 4$	Related equation
$y = -2x + 1$	Slope-intercept form	$y = \dfrac{1}{2}x - 2$	Slope-intercept form

For each inequality, draw the boundary line. Then, pick test points above and below the line to determine the appropriate region to shade.

$2x + y < 1$	**Test Point Above: (1, 1)**	**Test Point Below: (0, 0)**
	$2(1) + (1) \overset{?}{<} 1$	$2(0) + (0) \overset{?}{<} 1$
	$3 \overset{?}{<} 1$ False	$0 \overset{?}{<} 1$ True (Figure 9-9)

Figure 9-9

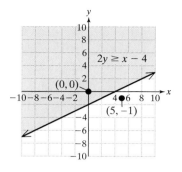

Figure 9-10

$2y \geq x - 4$ **Test Point Above: (0, 0)**   **Test Point Below: (5, −1)**

$$2(0) \stackrel{?}{\geq} (0) - 4 \qquad\qquad 2(-1) \stackrel{?}{\geq} (5) - 4$$

$$0 \stackrel{?}{\geq} -4 \;\; \text{True} \qquad\qquad -2 \stackrel{?}{\geq} 1 \;\; \text{False}$$

(Figure 9-10)

The solution to the compound inequality $2x + y < 1$ and $2y \geq x - 4$ is the intersection of the two individual solution sets. Therefore, the solution is the region of the plane below the line $y = -2x + 1$ and above the line $y = \frac{1}{2}x - 2$. See Figure 9-11.

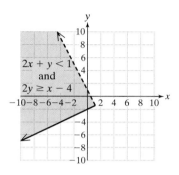

Figure 9-11

---

example 4

Graphing a Compound Linear Inequality in Two Variables

Graph the solution set of the inequality: $3y \geq 6$ or $y - x < 0$.

Solution:

First Inequality	**Second Inequality**
$3y \geq 6$	$y - x < 0$
$3y = 6$ Related equation	$y - x = 0$ Related equation
$y = 2$	$y = x$

For each inequality, draw the boundary line. Then, pick test points above and below the line to determine the appropriate region to shade:

$3y \geq 6$ **Test Point Above: (0, 3)**   **Test Point Below: (0, 1)**

$$3(3) \stackrel{?}{\geq} 6 \qquad\qquad 3(1) \stackrel{?}{\geq} 6$$

$$9 \stackrel{?}{\geq} 6 \;\; \text{True (Figure 9-12)} \qquad\qquad 3 \stackrel{?}{\geq} 6 \;\; \text{False}$$

Figure 9-12

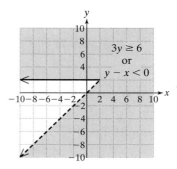

Figure 9-13

$$y - x < 0$$ **Test Point Above: (1, 2)**

$$(2) - (1) \overset{?}{<} 0$$

$$1 \overset{?}{<} 0 \quad \text{False}$$

Test Point Below: (1, −2)

$$(-2) - (1) \overset{?}{<} 0$$

$$-3 \overset{?}{<} 0 \quad \text{True}$$

(Figure 9-13)

The solution to the compound inequality
$3y \geq 6$ or $y - x < 0$ is the union of
the two solution sets (Figure 9-14).

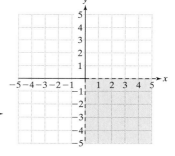

Figure 9-14

---

example 5

Translating Compound Linear Inequalities

Describe the region of the plane defined by the following systems of inequalities.

a. $x > 0$ and $y < 0$ b. $x \leq 0$ and $y \geq 0$ c. $|x| \leq 4$ and $|y| \geq 4$

Solution:

a. $x > 0$ $x > 0$ in the first and fourth
quadrants.

$y < 0$ $y < 0$ in the third and fourth
quadrants.

The intersection of these
inequalities is the set of
points in the fourth quadrant
(with the boundary excluded).

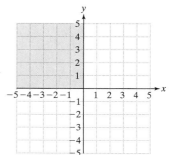

b. $x \leq 0$ $x \leq 0$ in the second and third
quadrants.

$y \geq 0$ $y \geq 0$ in the first and second
quadrants.

The intersection of these regions
is the set of points in the second
quadrant (with the boundary
included).

c. $|x| \le 4$ and $|y| \le 4$

$|x| \le 4$ represents the set of points whose x-coordinates are between 4 and -4, inclusive.

$|y| \le 4$ represents the set of points whose y-coordinates are between 4 and -4, inclusive.

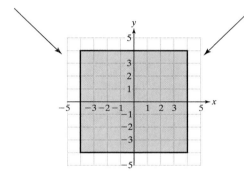

The intersection of the two inequalities represents a square.

4.   Graphing a Feasible Region

When two variables are related under certain constraints, a system of linear inequalities can be used to show a region of feasible values for the variables.

example 6

Graphing a Feasible Region

Susan has two tests on Friday: one in chemistry and one in psychology. Because the two classes meet in consecutive hours, she has no study time between tests. Susan estimates that she has a maximum of 12 h of study time to prepare for the tests, and she must divide her time between chemistry and psychology.

Let x represent the number of hours Susan spends studying chemistry.

Let y represent the number of hours Susan spends studying psychology.

a.   Find a set of inequalities to describe the constraints on Susan's study time.
b.   Graph the constraints to find the feasible region defining Susan's study time.

Solution:

a. Because Susan cannot study chemistry or psychology for a negative period of time, we have: $x \geq 0$ and $y \geq 0$.

Furthermore, her total time studying cannot exceed 12 h: $x + y \leq 12$.

A system of inequalities that defines the constraints on Susan's study time is

$$x \geq 0$$

$$y \geq 0$$

$$x + y \leq 12$$

b. The first two conditions $x \geq 0$ and $y \geq 0$ represent the set of points in the first quadrant. The third condition, $x + y \leq 12$ represents the set of points below and including the line $x + y = 12$ (Figure 9-15).

Figure 9-15

Discussion:

1. Refer to the feasible region drawn in Example 6(b). Is the ordered pair $(8, 5)$ part of the feasible region?

No. The ordered pair $(8, 5)$ indicates that Susan spent 8 h studying chemistry and 5 h studying psychology. This is a total of 13 h, which exceeds the constraint that Susan only had 12 h to study. The point $(8, 5)$ lies outside the feasible region, above the line $x + y = 12$ (Figure 9-16).

2. Is the ordered pair $(7, 3)$ part of the feasible region?

Yes. The ordered pair $(7, 3)$ indicates that Susan spent 7 h studying chemistry and 3 studying psychology.

This point lies within the feasible region and satisfies all three constraints.

$$x \geq 0 \longrightarrow \quad 7 \geq 0 \quad \text{True}$$

$$y \geq 0 \longrightarrow \quad 3 \geq 0 \quad \text{True}$$

$$x + y \leq 12 \longrightarrow (7) + (3) \leq 12 \quad \text{True}$$

Notice that the ordered pair $(7, 3)$ corresponds to a point where Susan is not making full use of the 12 h of study time.

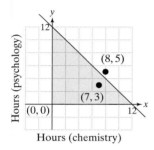

Figure 9-16

3. Suppose there was one additional constraint imposed on Susan's study time. She knows she needs to spend at least twice as much time studying chemistry as she does studying psychology. Graph the feasible region with this additional constraint.

Because the time studying chemistry must be at least twice the time studying psychology, we have: $x \geq 2y$.

This inequality may also be written as: $y \leq x/2$

Figure 9-17 shows the feasible region with the additional constraint $y \leq x/2$.

4. At what point in the feasible region is Susan making the most efficient use of her time for both classes?

First and foremost, Susan must make use of *all* 12 h. This occurs for points along the line $x + y = 12$. Susan will also want to study for both classes with approximately twice as much time devoted to chemistry. Therefore,

Figure 9-17

Susan will be deriving the maximum benefit at the point of intersection of the line $x + y = 12$ and the line $y = x/2$.

Using the substitution method, replace $y = x/2$ into the equation $x + y = 12$.

$$x + \frac{x}{2} = 12$$

$2x + x = 24$ Clear fractions.

$3x = 24$

$x = 8$ Solve for x.

$$y = \frac{(8)}{2}$$ To solve for y, substitute $x = 8$ into the equation $y = x/2$.

$$y = 4$$

Therefore Susan should spend 8 hours studying chemistry and 4 hours studying psychology.

---

section 9.5   PRACTICE EXERCISES

1. Explain how you would solve the inequality $|x + 3| > 4$.

2. Explain how you would solve the inequality $|2x - 1| < 6$.

For Exercises 3–8, solve the inequalities.

3. $-3 < 2k - 5 < 3$

4. $\dfrac{1}{2} < \dfrac{3}{4}y < \dfrac{3}{5}$

5. $|6a - 1| - 4 \le 2$

6. $|3b + 5| - 8 \le 5$

7. $|2t + 1| + 4 \ge 7$

8. $|2h - 6| - 1 \ge 3$

For Exercises 9–12, decide if the following points are solutions to the inequality.

9. $2x - y > 8$
   a. $(3, -5)$
   b. $(-1, -10)$
   c. $(4, -2)$
   d. $(0, 0)$

10. $3y + x < 5$
    a. $(-1, 7)$
    b. $(5, 0)$
    c. $(0, 0)$
    d. $(2, -3)$

11. $y \le -2$
    a. $(5, -3)$
    b. $(-4, -2)$
    c. $(0, 0)$
    d. $(3, 2)$

12. $x \ge 5$
    a. $(4, 5)$
    b. $(5, -1)$
    c. $(8, 8)$
    d. $(0, 0)$

For Exercises 13–18, decide which inequality symbol should be used. $(<, >, \ge, \le)$ by looking at the graph.

13.

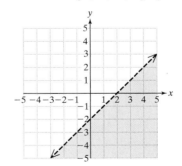

$x - y$ _____ 2

14.

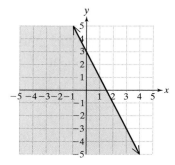

y _____ $-2x + 3$

15.

y _____ -4

16.

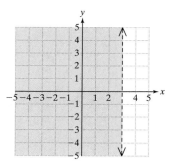

$x =$ _____ 3

17.

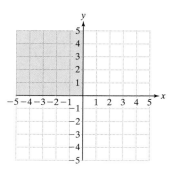

x _____ 0 and y _____ 0

18.

x _____ 0 and y _____ 0

For Exercises 19–38, solve the inequalities using the test point method.

19. $x - 2y > 4$

20. $x - 3y > 6$

21. $5x - 2y < 10$

22. $x - 3y < 8$

23. $2x + 6y \leq 12$

24. $4x - 3y \leq 12$

25. $y \geq -2$

26. $y \geq 5$

27. $4x < 5$

28. $x + 6 < 7$

29. $y \geq \dfrac{2}{5}x - 4$

30. $y \geq -\dfrac{5}{2}x - 4$

31. $y \leq \dfrac{1}{3}x + 6$

32. $y \leq -\dfrac{1}{4}x + 2$

33. $y > 5x$

34. $y > \dfrac{1}{2}x$

35. $\dfrac{x}{5} + \dfrac{y}{4} < 1$

36. $x + \dfrac{y}{2} \geq 2$

37. $0.1x + 0.2y \leq 0.6$

38. $0.3x - 0.2y < 0.6$

For Exercises 39–54, graph the union or intersection of inequalities.

39. $y \leq 4$ and $y \geq -x + 2$

40. $y < 3$ and $x + 2y < 6$

41. $2x + y < 5$ or $x > 3$

42. $x + 3y \geq 7$ or $x \leq -2$

43. $x + y \le 3$ and $4x + y < 6$

44. $x + y < 4$ and $3x + y \le 9$

45. $2x - y \le 2$ or $2x + 3y > 6$

46. $3x + 2y > 4$ or $x - y \le 3$

47. $x \ge 4$ and $y \le 2$

48. $x \le 3$ and $y \ge 4$

49. $x \le -2$ or $y \le 0$

50. $x \ge 0$ or $y \ge -3$

51. $x \ge 0$ and $x + y < 6$

52. $x \le 0$ and $x + y < 2$

53. $y \le 0$ or $x - y < -4$

54. $y \ge 0$ or $x - y > -3$

For Exercises 55–60, graph the feasible regions.

55. $x + y \le 3$ and

    $x \ge 0, y \ge 0$

56. $x - y \le 2$ and

    $x \ge 0, y \ge 0$

57. $y < \dfrac{1}{2}x - 3$ and

    $x \le 0, y \ge -4$

58. $y > \dfrac{1}{2}x - 3$ and

    $x \ge -2, y \le 0$

59. $x \ge 0, y \ge 0$

    $x + y \le 8$ and

    $3x + 5y \le 30$

60. $x \ge 0, y \ge 0$

    $x + y \le 5$ and

    $x + 2y \le 6$

61. In scheduling two drivers for delivering pizza, James needs to have at least 65 hours scheduled this week. His two drivers, Karen and Todd, are not allowed to get overtime, so each one can work at most 40 hours. Let x represent the number of hours that Karen can be scheduled and let y represent the number of hours Todd can be scheduled.

    a. Write two inequalities that express the fact that Karen and Todd cannot work a negative number of hours.

    b. Write two inequalities that express the fact that neither Karen nor Todd are allowed overtime (i.e., must have at most 40 h).

    c. Write an inequality that expresses the fact that the total number of hours from both Karen and Todd needs to be at least 65.

    d. Graph the feasible region formed by graphing the inequalities.

62. A manufacturer produces two models of desks. Model A requires $1\frac{1}{2}$ h to stain and finish and $1\frac{1}{4}$ h to assemble. Model B requires 2 h to stain and finish and $\frac{3}{4}$ h to assemble. The total amount of time available for staining and finishing is 12 h and for assembling is 6 h. Let x represent the number of Model A desks, and let y represent the number of Model B desks.

    a. Write two inequalities that express the fact that the number of desks to be produced cannot be negative.

    b. Write an inequality in terms of the number of Model A and Model B desks that can be produced if the total time for staining and finishing is at most 12 h.

    c. Write an inequality in terms of the number of Model A and Model B desks that can be produced if the total time for assembly is no more than 6 h.

    d. Identify the feasible region formed by graphing the preceding inequalities.

GRAPHING CALCULATOR EXERCISES

To solve a two variable inequality using a graphing calculator, first solve the inequality for y. Be careful to change the direction of the inequality when multiplying or dividing by a negative. Let Y_1 equal the related equation. Shade the region above the line if the inequality is $>$ and shade below the line if the inequality is $<$.

For Exercises 63–68, solve the inequality using a graphing calculator.

63. $2x + 3y < 12$

64. $2x - 3y > 6$

65. $2y - x > 4$

66. $2x - y > -2$

67. $4x - 3y < 0$

68. $5x + 2y < 0$

chapter 9   SUMMARY

SECTION 9.1—COMPOUND INEQUALITIES

KEY CONCEPTS:

Solve two or more inequalities joined by *and* by finding the intersection of the inequalities. Solve two or more inequalities joined by *or* by finding the union of the solution sets.

KEY TERMS:

and (intersection)
compound inequality
or (union)

EXAMPLES:

Solve:

$$-7x + 3 \geq -11 \quad \text{and} \quad 1 - x < 4.5$$

Solution:

$$-7x \geq -14 \quad \text{and} \quad -x < 3.5$$
$$x \leq 2 \quad \text{and} \quad x > -3.5$$

$x \leq 2$

$x > -3.5$

$x \leq 2$ and $x > -3.5$ or equivalently $(-3.5, 2]$

Solve:

$$5y + 1 \geq 6 \quad \text{or} \quad 2y - 5 \leq -11$$

Solution:

$$5y \geq 5 \quad \text{or} \quad 2y \leq -6$$
$$y \geq 1 \quad \text{or} \quad y \leq -3$$

$y \geq 1$

$y \leq -3$

$y \geq 1$ or $y \leq -3$ or equivalently $(-\infty, -3] \cup [1, \infty)$

Solve: $-6 < \frac{3}{4}(x - 1) < 6$

Solution: $\frac{4}{3} \cdot -6 < \frac{4}{3} \cdot \frac{3}{4}(x - 1) < \frac{4}{3} \cdot 6$

$$-8 < x - 1 < 8$$

$$-7 < x < 9$$

$$(-7, 9)$$

SECTION 9.2—POLYNOMIAL AND RATIONAL INEQUALITIES

KEY CONCEPTS:

The Test Point Method to Solve Polynomial and Rational Inequalities

1. Find the boundary points of the inequality. (Boundary points are the real solutions to the related equation and points where the inequality is undefined.)
2. Plot the boundary points on the number line. This divides the number line into regions.
3. Select a test point from each region and substitute it into the original inequality.

   • If a test point makes the original inequality true, then that region is part of the solution set.

4. Test the boundary points in the original inequality.

   • If a boundary point makes the original inequality true, then that point is part of the solution set.

EXAMPLE:

Solve: $\dfrac{28}{2x - 3} \leq 4$

$$\frac{28}{2x - 3} = 4 \qquad \text{Related equation}$$

$$(2x - 3) \cdot \frac{28}{2x - 3} = (2x - 3) \cdot 4$$

$$28 = 8x - 12$$

$$40 = 8x$$

$$x = 5$$

The expression $28/(2x - 3)$ is undefined for $x = \frac{3}{2}$.

Region I:

Test $x = 1$: $\dfrac{28}{2(1) - 3} \overset{?}{\leq} 4$ True

Region II:

Test $x = 2$: $\dfrac{28}{2(2) - 3} \overset{?}{\leq} 4$ False

KEY TERMS:

boundary points
quadratic inequality
test point method

Region III:

Test $x = 6$: $\dfrac{28}{2(6) - 3} \overset{?}{\leq} 4$ True

The boundary point $x = \frac{3}{2}$ is not included because $28/(2x - 3)$ is undefined there. The boundary $x = 5$ does check in the original inequality.

Interval notation: $(-\infty, \frac{3}{2}) \cup [5, \infty)$

SECTION 9.3—ABSOLUTE VALUE EQUATIONS

KEY CONCEPTS:

The equation $|x| = a$ is an absolute value equation. For $a \geq 0$, the solution to the equation $|x| = a$ is: $x = a$ or $x = -a$.

Steps to solve an absolute value equation

1. Isolate the absolute value to write the equation in the form $|x| = a$.
2. If $a < 0$, there is no solution.

3. Otherwise, rewrite the equation $|x| = a$ as $x = a$ or $x = -a$.
4. Solve the equations from step 3.
5. Check answers in the original equation.

The solution to the equation $|x| = |y|$ is $x = y$ or $x = -y$.

KEY TERMS:

absolute value equation

EXAMPLES:

Solve:

$$|2x - 3| + 5 = 10$$
$$|2x - 3| = 5$$

$$2x - 3 = 5 \quad \text{or} \quad 2x - 3 = -5$$
$$2x = 8 \quad \text{or} \quad 2x = -2$$
$$x = 4 \quad \text{or} \quad x = -1$$

Solve:

$$|x + 2| + 5 = 1$$
$$|x + 2| = -4 \quad \text{No solution}$$

Solve:

$$|2x - 1| = |x + 4|$$

$$2x - 1 = x + 4 \quad \text{or} \quad 2x - 1 = -(x + 4)$$
$$x = 5 \quad \text{or} \quad 2x - 1 = -x - 4$$
$$\text{or} \quad 3x = -3$$
$$\text{or} \quad x = -1$$

SECTION 9.4—ABSOLUTE VALUE INEQUALITIES

KEY CONCEPTS:

Solutions to absolute value inequalities:

$$|x| > a \Rightarrow x < -a \quad \text{or} \quad x > a$$
$$|x| < a \Rightarrow -a < x < a$$

EXAMPLES:

Solve:

$$|5x - 2| < 12$$

Solution: $-12 < 5x - 2 < 12$

$$-10 < 5x < 14$$

$$-2 < x < \frac{14}{5}$$

$$\left(-2, \frac{14}{5}\right)$$

Solve: $|x - 3| + 2 \geq 7$

Solution: $|x - 3| \geq 5$ Isolate the absolute value.

$|x - 3| = 5$ Related equation

$x - 3 = 5$ or $x - 3 = -5$

$x = 8$ or $x = -2$ Boundary points

Test point method to solve inequalities

1. Find the boundary points of the inequality. (Boundary points are the real solutions to the related equation and points where the inequality is undefined.)

I | II | III
         -2 8

2. Plot the boundary points on the number line. This divides the number line into regions.

Region I:

     Test $x = -3$: $|(-3) - 3| + 2 \overset{?}{\geq} 7$ True

3. Select a test point from each region and substitute it into the original inequality.

   - If a test point makes the original inequality true, then that region is part of the solution set.

Region II:

     Test $x = 0$: $|(0) - 3| + 2 \overset{?}{\geq} 7$ False

Region III:

4. Test the boundary points in the original inequality.

   - If a boundary point makes the original inequality true, then that point is part of the solution set.

     Test $x = 9$: $|(9) - 3| + 2 \overset{?}{\geq} 7$ True

$$(-\infty, -2] \cup [8, \infty)$$

True   False   True
      -2 8

If *a* is *negative* (*a* < 0), then:

1. $|x| < a$ has no solution.
2. $|x| > a$ is true for all real numbers.

Solve: $|x + 5| > -2$

Solution: The solution is all real numbers because an absolute value will always be greater than a negative number.

KEY TERMS:

absolute value inequality

$$(-\infty, \infty)$$

SECTION 9.5—LINEAR INEQUALITIES IN TWO VARIABLES

KEY CONCEPTS:

A linear inequality in two variables is an inequality of the form: $ax + by < c, ax + by > c, ax + by \leq c$, or $ax + by \geq c$.

Use the test point method to solve a linear inequality in two variables. That is, graph the related equation and shade above or below the line.

If an inequality is strict $(<, >)$ then a dashed line is used for the boundary. If the inequality contains $\leq$ or $\geq$, then a solid line is drawn.

The union or intersection of two or more linear inequalities is the union or intersection of the solution sets.

KEY TERMS:

compound linear inequality in two variables
linear inequality in two variables

EXAMPLES:

Solve the inequality: $2x - y < 4$

Test Points: $(0, 0)$ and $(4, -4)$

$2(0) - (0) \overset{?}{<} 4$ True;   Shade above.

$2(4) - (-4) \overset{?}{<} 4$ False;   Do not shade below.

Solve: $x < 0$ and $y \geq 2$

Solve: $x < 0$ or $y \geq 2$

---

chapter 9   REVIEW EXERCISES

Section 9.1

For Exercises 1–10, solve the compound inequalities. Write the solutions in interval notation.

1. $4m > -11$ and $4m - 3 \leq 13$

2. $4n - 7 < 1$ and $7 + 3n \geq -8$

3. $-3y + 1 \geq 10$ and $-2y - 5 \leq 15$

4. $\dfrac{1}{2} - \dfrac{h}{12} \leq \dfrac{7}{12}$ and $\dfrac{1}{2} - \dfrac{h}{10} > -\dfrac{1}{5}$

5. $\dfrac{2}{3}t - 3 \leq 1$ or $\dfrac{3}{4}t - 2 > 7$

6. $2(3x + 1) < -10$ or $3(2x - 4) \geq 0$

7. $-7 < -7(2w + 3)$ or $-2 < -4(3w - 1)$

8. $5(p + 3) + 4 > p - 1$ or $4(p - 1) + 2 > p + 8$

9. $2 \geq -(b - 2) - 5b \geq -6$

10. $-4 \leq \dfrac{1}{2}(x - 1) < -\dfrac{3}{2}$

11. The product of $\frac{1}{3}$ and the sum of a number and 3 is between -1 and 5. Find all such numbers.

12. Normal levels of total cholesterol vary according to age. For adults between 25 and 40 years old, the normal range is generally accepted to be between 140 and 225 mg/dL (milligrams per deciliter), inclusive.

    a. Write an inequality representing the normal range for total cholesterol for adults between 25 and 40 years old.

    b. Write a compound inequality representing abnormal ranges for total cholesterol for adults between 25 and 40 years old.

13. Normal levels of total cholesterol vary according to age. For adults younger than 25 years old, the normal range is generally accepted to be between 125 and 200 mg/dL, inclusive.

    a. Write an inequality representing the normal range for total cholesterol for adults younger than 25 years old.

    b. Write a compound inequality representing abnormal ranges for total cholesterol for adults younger than 25 years old.

14. In certain applications in statistics, a data value that is more than 3 standard deviations from the mean is said to be an "outlier" (a value unusually far from the average). If μ represents the mean of population, and σ represents the population standard deviation, then the inequality $|x - \mu| > 3\sigma$ can be used to test whether a data value, x, is an outlier.

    The mean height, μ, of adult men is 69.0 in. (5′9″) and the standard deviation, σ, of the height of adult men is 3.0. Determine whether the heights of the following men are outliers:

    a. Shaquille O'Neal, 7′1″ = 85 in.

    b. Charlie Ward, 6′3″ = 75 in.

    c. Elmer Fudd, 4′5″ = 53 in.

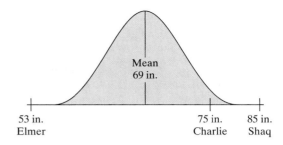

Figure for Exercise 14

15. Explain the difference between the solution sets of the following compound inequalities.

    a. $x \leq 5$ and $x \geq -2$

    b. $x \leq 5$ or $x \geq -2$

Section 9.2

16. Solve the equation and inequalities. How do your answers to parts (a), (b), and (c) relate to the graph of $f(x) = -\frac{1}{2}x - 3$?

    a. $-\dfrac{1}{2}x - 3 = 0$

    b. $-\dfrac{1}{2}x - 3 < 0$

    c. $-\dfrac{1}{2}x - 3 > 0$

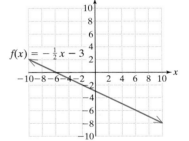

Figure for Exercise 16

17. Solve the equation and inequalities. How do your answers to parts (a), (b), and (c) relate to the graph of $g(x) = x^2 - 4$?

    a. $x^2 - 4 = 0$

    b. $x^2 - 4 < 0$

    c. $x^2 - 4 > 0$

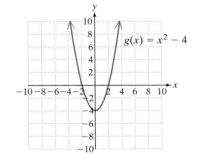

Figure for Exercise 17

18. Solve the equation and inequalities. How do your answers to parts (a), (b), (c), and (d) relate to the graph of $k(x) = 4x/(x - 2)$?

a. $\dfrac{4x}{x - 2} = 0$

b. For which values is $k(x)$ undefined?

c. $\dfrac{4x}{x - 2} \geq 0$

d. $\dfrac{4x}{x - 2} \leq 0$

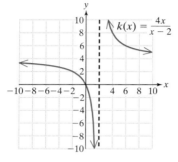

Figure for Exercise 18

For Exercises 19–30, solve the inequalities. Write the answers in interval notation.

19. $w^2 - 4w - 12 < 0$

20. $t^2 + 6t + 9 \geq 0$

21. $\dfrac{12}{x + 2} \geq 6$

22. $\dfrac{8}{p - 1} \leq -4$

23. $3y(y - 5)(y + 2) > 0$

24. $-3c(c + 2)(2c - 5) < 0$

25. $-x^2 - 4x \geq 4$

26. $y^2 + 4y > 5$

27. $\dfrac{w + 1}{w - 3} > 1$

28. $\dfrac{2a}{a + 3} < 2$

29. $t^2 + 10t + 25 \leq 0$

30. $-x^2 - 4x < 4$

Section 9.3

For Exercises 31–44, solve the absolute value equations.

31. $|x| = 10$

32. $|x| = 17$

33. $|y + 6| = \dfrac{1}{2}$

34. $|y - 3| = \dfrac{3}{4}$

35. $|8.7 - 2x| = 6.1$

36. $|5.25 - 5x| = 7.45$

37. $16 = |x + 2| + 9$

38. $5 = |x - 2| + 4$

39. $|4x - 1| + 6 = 4$

40. $|3x - 1| + 7 = 3$

41. $|7x - 3| = 0$

42. $|4x + 5| = 0$

43. $|3x - 5| = |2x + 1|$

44. $|8x + 9| = |8x - 1|$

45. Which absolute value expression represents the distance between 3 and -2 on the number line? Explain your answer.

$$|3 - (-2)|, \qquad |-2 - 3|$$

Section 9.4

46. Write the compound inequality $x < -5$ or $x > 5$ as an absolute value inequality.

47. Write the compound inequality $-4 < x < 4$ as an absolute value inequality.

48. Write an absolute value inequality that represents the solution sets graphed here:

a.

b.

For Exercises 49–62, solve the absolute value inequalities. Graph the solution set and write the solution in interval notation.

49. $|x + 6| \geq 8$

50. $|x + 8| \leq 3$

51. $|7x - 1| > 0$

52. $|5x + 1| > 0$

53. $|3x + 4| - 6 \leq -4$

54. $|5x - 3| + 3 \leq 6$

55. $\left|\dfrac{x}{2} - 6\right| < 5$

56. $\left|\dfrac{x}{3} + 2\right| < 2$

57. $|2x - 4| + 2 > 8$

58. $|3x + 9| - 1 > 5$

59. $|5.2x - 7.8| < 13$

60. $|2.5x + 1.5| < 7$

61. $|3x - 8| < -1$

62. $|x + 5| < -4$

63. State one possible situation when an absolute value inequality will have no solution.

64. State one possible situation when an absolute value inequality will have a solution of all real numbers.

Section 9.5

For Exercises 65–74, solve the inequalities by graphing.

65. $2x + y < 5$

66. $2x + 3y \leq -8$

67. $y \geq -\dfrac{2}{3}x + 3$

68. $y > \dfrac{3}{4}x - 2$

69. $x > -3$

70. $x \leq 2$

71. $y < 4\frac{1}{3}$

72. $y \geq -2\frac{1}{2}$

73. $y \leq 2x$

74. $y > \dfrac{5}{2}x$

For Exercises 75–78, solve the system of inequalities.

75. $2x - y > -2$ and $2x - y \leq 2$

76. $3x + y \geq 6$ or $3x + y < -6$

77. $x \geq 0, y \geq 0$, and $y \geq -\dfrac{3}{2}x + 4$

78. $x \geq 0, y \geq 0$, and $y \leq -\dfrac{2}{3}x + 4$

79. A pirate's treasure is buried on a small, uninhabited island in the eastern Caribbean. A shipwrecked sailor finds a treasure map at the base of a coconut palm tree. The treasure is buried within the intersection of three linear inequalities. The palm tree is located at the origin, and the positive y-axis is oriented due north. The scaling on the map is in 1-yd increments. Find the region where the sailor should dig for the treasure.

$$-2x + y \leq 4$$
$$y \leq -x + 6$$
$$y \geq 0$$

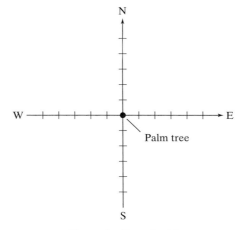

Figure for Exercise 79

80. Suppose a farmer has 100 acres of land on which to grow oranges and grapefruit. Furthermore, because of demand from his customers, he wants to plant at least four times as many acres of orange trees as grapefruit trees.

Let x represent the number of acres of orange trees.

Let y represent the number of acres of grapefruit trees.

a. Write two inequalities that express the fact that the farmer cannot use a negative number of acres to plant orange and grapefruit trees.

b. Write an inequality that expresses the fact that the total number of acres used for growing orange and grapefruit trees is at most 100.

c. Write an inequality that expresses the fact that the farmer wants to plant at least four times as many orange trees as grapefruit trees.

d. Sketch the inequalities in parts (a)–(c) to find the feasible region for the farmer's distribution of orange and grapefruit trees.

chapter 9   TEST

1. Solve the compound inequalities:

   a. $-2 \le 3x - 1 \le 5$

   b. $-\dfrac{3}{5}x - 1 \le 8$ or $-\dfrac{2}{3}x \ge 16$

2. The normal range in humans of the enzyme adenosine deaminase, ADA, is between 9 and 33 IU (international units), inclusive. Let x represent the ADA level in international units.

   a. Write an inequality representing the normal range for ADA.

   b. Write a compound inequality representing abnormal ranges for ADA.

   c. Patients with tuberculosis have unusually high levels of adenosine deaminase and physicians strongly suspect tuberculosis if a patient's ADA level is greater than 40 IU. Write an inequality representing ADA levels at which tuberculosis is suspected.

For Exercises 3–8, solve the polynomial and rational inequalities.

3. $\dfrac{2x - 1}{x - 6} \le 0$

4. $50 - 2a^2 > 0$

5. $y^3 + 3y^2 - 4y - 12 < 0$

6. $\dfrac{3}{w + 3} > 2$

7. $\dfrac{p^2}{2 + p^2} < 0$

8. $t^2 + 22t + 121 \le 0$

9. Solve the absolute value equations.

   a. $\left| \dfrac{1}{2}x + 3 \right| = 8$

   b. $|3x + 4| = |x - 12|$

10. Solve the following equation and inequalities. How do your answers to parts (a)–(c) relate to the graph of $f(x) = |x - 3| - 4$?

    a. $|x - 3| - 4 = 0$

    b. $|x - 3| - 4 < 0$

    c. $|x - 3| - 4 > 0$

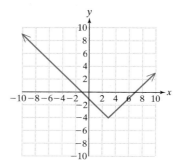

Figure for Exercise 10

For Exercises 11–14, solve the absolute value inequalities. Write the answers in interval notation.

11. $|3 - 2x| + 6 < 2$

12. $|3x - 8| > 9$

13. $|0.4x + 0.3| - 0.2 < 7$

14. $|7 - 3x| + 1 > -3$

15. The mass of a small piece of metal is measured to be 15.41 g. If the measurement error is ± 0.01 g, write an absolute value inequality that represents the possible mass, x, of the piece of metal.

16. Solve the system of inequalities by graphing. $x + y < 3$ and $3x - 2y \ge -6$

17. After menopause, women are at higher risk for hip fractures as a result of low calcium. As early as their teen years, women need at least 1000 mg of calcium per day (the USDA recommended daily allowance). One 8-oz glass of skim milk contains 300 mg of calcium, and one Tums (regular strength) contains 400 mg of calcium. Let x represent the number of 8-oz glasses of milk that a woman drinks per day. Let y represent the number of Tums tablets (regular strength) that a woman takes per day.

    a. Write two inequalities that express the fact that the number of glasses of milk and the number of Tums taken each day cannot be negative.

    b. Write a linear inequality in terms of x and y for which the daily calcium intake is at least 1000 mg.

    c. Graph the inequalities.

CUMULATIVE REVIEW EXERCISES, CHAPTERS 1–9

1. Solve the equation: $5x - 4\sqrt{7} = 5 - \sqrt{7}$

2. Solve the equation: $-3 - 4m = 2m(m - 4)$

For Exercises 3–4, solve the equation and inequalities. Write the solution to the inequalities in interval notation.

3. a. $2|3 - p| - 4 = 2$

   b. $2|3 - p| - 4 < 2$

   c. $2|3 - p| - 4 > 2$

4. a. $\left|\dfrac{y - 2}{4}\right| - 6 = -3$

   b. $\left|\dfrac{y - 2}{4}\right| - 6 < -3$

   c. $\left|\dfrac{y - 2}{4}\right| - 6 > -3$

5. Graph the inequality: $4x - y > 12$

6. The time, t, in minutes required for a rat to run through a maze depends on the number of trials, n, that the rat has practiced.

$$t(n) = \frac{3n + 15}{n + 1}; \quad n \geq 1$$

   a. Find $t(1)$, $t(50)$, and $t(500)$, and interpret the results in the context of this problem. Round to two decimal places, if necessary.

   b. Does there appear to be a limiting time in which the rat can complete the maze?

   c. How many trials are required so that the rat is able to finish the maze in under 5 min?

7. a. Solve the inequality: $2x^2 + x - 10 \geq 0$

   b. How does the answer in part (a) relate to the graph of the function $f(x) = 2x^2 + x - 10$?

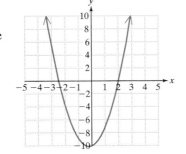

Figure for Exercise 7

8. Shade the region defined by the compound inequality: $3x + y < -2$ or $y \geq 1$.

9. Match the expression on the left with the appropriate property of real numbers.

   a. $\dfrac{2}{7} \cdot \dfrac{7}{2} = 1$

   b. $17 \cdot 1 = 17$

   c. $-\dfrac{2}{3} + 0 = -\dfrac{2}{3}$

   d. $5(2 + 10)$ $= 5 \cdot 2 + 5 \cdot 10$

   e. $10 \cdot 2 = 2 \cdot 10$

   f. $(2 + 3) + (4 + 5)$ $= (4 + 5) + (2 + 3)$

   g. $(2 + 7) + 8$ $= 2 + (7 + 8)$

   h. $\dfrac{3}{5} + \left(-\dfrac{3}{5}\right) = 0$

   i. $2 \cdot (3 \cdot 4) =$ $(2 \cdot 3) \cdot 4$

   i. Commutative property of addition

   ii. Commutative property of multiplication

   iii. Associative property of multiplication

   iv. Associative property of addition

   v. Distributive property of multiplication over addition

   vi. Identity property of addition

   vii. Identity property of multiplication

   viii. Inverse property of addition

   ix. Inverse property of multiplication

10. McDonald's corporation is the world's largest food service retailer. At the end of 1996, McDonald's operated 2.1×10^4 restaurants in over 100 countries. Worldwide sales in 1996 were nearly 3.18×10^{10}. Find the average sales per restaurant in 1996. Write the answer in scientific notation.

11. a. Divide the polynomials: $(2x^4 - x^3 + 5x - 7) \div (x^2 + 2x - 1)$. Identify the quotient and remainder.

   b. Check your answer by multiplying.

   c. Based on the value of the remainder, is $x^2 + 2x - 1$ a factor of $2x^4 - x^3 + 5x - 7$?

12. Perform the indicated operations.

$$\sqrt{72a^3b} - a\sqrt{8ab} + \sqrt{\frac{2a^5b^2}{a^2b}}$$

   Assume a and b are positive real numbers.

13. Perform the indicated operations:
   $(\sqrt{x} - \sqrt{y})(\sqrt{x} + \sqrt{y})$

14. Two angles are supplementary. One angle is $9°$ more than twice the other angle. Find the angles.

15. Chemique invests $3000 less in an account bearing 5% simple interest than she does in an account bearing 6.5% simple interest. At the end of one year, she earns a total $770 in interest. Find the amount invested in each account.

16. Determine algebraically whether the lines are parallel, perpendicular, or neither:

$$4x - 2y = 5$$
$$-3x + 6y = 10$$

17. Find the x- and y-intercepts and slope (if they exist) of the lines. Then graph the lines.

   a. $3x + 5 = 8$ b. $\frac{1}{2}x + y = 4$

18. Find an equation of the line with slope $-\frac{2}{3}$ passing through the point $(4, -7)$. Write the final answer in slope-intercept form.

19. Solve the system of equations.

$$3x + y = z + 2$$
$$y = 1 - 2x$$
$$3z = -2y$$

20. Identify the order of the matrices:

   a. $\begin{bmatrix} 2 & 4 & 5 \\ -1 & 0 & 1 \\ 9 & 2 & 3 \\ 3 & 0 & 1 \end{bmatrix}$ b. $\begin{bmatrix} 5 & 6 & 3 \\ 6 & 0 & -1 \\ 0 & 1 & -2 \end{bmatrix}$

21. Against a head wind, a plane can travel 6240 miles in 13 hours. The return trip flying with the same wind, the plane can fly 6240 miles in 12 hours. Find the wind speed and the speed of the plane in still air.

22. The profit that a company makes manufacturing computer desks is given by: $P(x) = -\frac{1}{5}(x - 20)(x - 650);$ $x \geq 0$, where x is the number of desks produced and $P(x)$ is the profit in dollars.

   a. Is this function constant, linear, or quadratic?

   b. Find $P(0)$ and interpret the result in the context of this problem.

   c. Find the values of x, where $P(x) = 0$. Interpret the results in the context of this problem.

   d. Find the vertex of the function. Interpret the meaning of the vertex in the context of this problem.

23. Given $h(x) = \sqrt{50 - x}$

   a. Find the domain of h.

   b. Find $h(2)$ and simplify the result.

24. a. Graph $k(x) = \begin{cases} -x + 3 & x < 0 \\ x^2 & x > 0 \end{cases}$

   b. From the graph, determine the domain of k.

   c. From the graph, determine the range of k.

   d. Find the open interval(s) on which k is increasing.

   e. Find the open interval(s) on which k is decreasing.

   f. Find the value of $k(3)$.

25. Simplify completely.

$$\frac{x^{-1} - y^{-1}}{y^{-2} - x^{-2}}$$

26. Divide.

$$\frac{a^3 + 64}{16 - a^2} \div \frac{a^3 - 4a^2 + 16a}{a^2 - 3a - 4}$$

27. Find the determinant of matrix $\mathbf{X}$:

$$\mathbf{X} = \begin{bmatrix} 4 & 0 & 9 \\ -1 & 2 & -3 \\ 5 & 0 & 1 \end{bmatrix}$$

EXPONENTIAL AND LOGARITHMIC FUNCTIONS

In the year 1999, the population of Mexico was approximately 100 million and the population of Japan was 126 million. Although the population of Mexico was less than that of Japan in 1999, its growth rate is higher. The population of Mexico is growing at a rate of 2.02% per year, whereas the population of Japan is growing at a rate of 0.24% per year.

For t representing the number of years since 1999, the population (in millions) of each country can be modeled by an exponential function:

Mexico: $M(t) = 100(1.0202)^t$

Japan: $J(t) = 126(1.0024)^t$

For more information about population statistics visit popUS and popCANADA at

www.mhhe.com/miller_oneill

Projected Population of Mexico and Japan

$M(t) = 100(1.0202)^t$

$J(t) = 126(1.0024)^t$

Year ($t = 0$ corresponds to 1999)

Number of People (millions)

From the graphs of $M(t) = 100(1.0202)^t$ and $J(t) = 126(1.0024)^t$, we see that after approximately 14 years, the population of Mexico will overtake the population of Japan.

Avoiding Mistakes

f^{-1} denotes the inverse of a function. The "−1" does not represent an exponent.

section

10.1 INVERSE FUNCTIONS

1. Definition of the Inverse of a Function

Recall from Section 4.2 that a function is a set of ordered pairs (x, y), such that for every element x in the domain, there corresponds exactly one element y in the range. For example, the function, f, relates the weight of a package of deli meat, x, to its cost, y.

$$f = \{(1, 2.99), (1.5, 4.49), (4, 11.96)\}$$

That is, 1 lb of meat sells for $2.99, 1.5 lb sells for $4.49, and 4 lb sells for $11.96. Now suppose we create a new function in which the values of x and y are interchanged. The new function, called the **inverse of f** (denoted f^{-1}) relates the price of meat, x, to its weight, y.

$$f^{-1} = \{(2.99, 1), (4.49, 1.5), (11.96, 4)\}$$

Notice that interchanging the x- and y-values has the following outcome. The domain of f is the same as the range of f^{-1}, and the range of f is the domain of f^{-1}.

2. Definition of a One-to-One Function

A necessary condition for a function f to have an inverse function is that no two ordered pairs in f may have different x-coordinates and the same y-coordinate. A function that satisfies this condition is called a **one-to-one function**. The function relating the weight of a package of meat to its price is a one-to-one function. However, consider the function g defined by

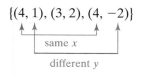

This function is not one-to-one because the range element 4 has two different x-coordinates, 1 and −2. Interchanging the x- and y-values produces a relation that violates the definition of a function.

$\{(4, 1), (3, 2), (4, -2)\}$ This relation is not a function because for $x = 4$ there are two different y-values, $y = 1$ and $y = -2$.

same x

different y

3. Horizontal Line Test

In Section 4.2, you learned the vertical line test to determine visually if a graph represents a function. Similarly, we use a **horizontal line test** to determine whether a function is one-to-one.

Horizontal Line Test

Consider a function defined by a set of points (x, y) in a rectangular coordinate system. The graph of the ordered pairs defines y as a *one-to-one* function of x if no horizontal line intersects the graph in more than one point.

To understand the horizontal line test, consider the functions f and g.

$$f = \{(1, 2.99), (1.5, 4.49), (4, 11.96)\} \qquad g = \{(1, 4), (2, 3), (-2, 4)\}$$

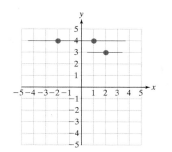

This function is one-to-one. No horizontal line intersects more than once.

This function is *not* one-to-one. A horizontal line intersects more than once.

example 1

Identifying One-to-One Functions

Determine whether the function is one-to-one.

a.

b.

c.

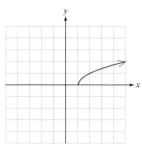

Solution:

a. Function is not one-to-one.
    A horizontal line intersects
    in more than one point.

b. Function is one-to-one.
    No horizontal line intersects more
    than once.

c. Function is one-to-one.
    No horizontal line intersects
    more than once.

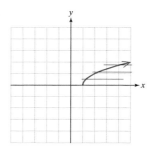

4.   Finding an Equation of the Inverse of a Function

Another way to view the construction of the inverse of a function is to find a function that performs the inverse operations in the reverse order. For example, the function defined by $f(x) = 2x + 1$ multiplies x by 2 and then adds 1. Therefore, the inverse function must *subtract* 1 from x and *divide* by 2. We have

$$f^{-1}(x) = \frac{x - 1}{2}$$

To facilitate the process of finding an equation of the inverse of a one-to-one function, we offer the following steps.

Finding an Equation of an Inverse of a Function

For a one-to-one function defined by $y = f(x)$, the equation of the inverse can be found as follows:
1. Replace $f(x)$ by y.
2. Interchange x and y.
3. Solve for y.
4. Replace y by $f^{-1}(x)$.

example 2

Finding an Equation of the Inverse of a Function

Find the inverse: $f(x) = 2x + 1$

Solution:

Foremost, we know the graph of f is a nonvertical line. Therefore, $f(x) = 2x + 1$ defines a one-to-one function. To find the inverse we have

$y = 2x + 1$	**Step 1:** Replace $f(x)$ by y.
$x = 2y + 1$	**Step 2:** Interchange x and y.
$x - 1 = 2y$	**Step 3:** Solve for y. Subtract 1 from both sides.
$\dfrac{x - 1}{2} = y$	Divide both sides by 2.
$f^{-1}(x) = \dfrac{x - 1}{2}$	**Step 4:** Replace y by $f^{-1}(x)$.

The key step in determining the equation of the inverse of a function is interchanging x and y. By so doing, a point (a, b) on f corresponds to a point (b, a) on f^{-1}. For this reason, the graph of f and f^{-1} are symmetric with respect to the line $y = x$ (Figure 10-1).

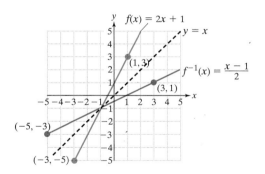

Figure 10-1

example 3

Finding an Equation of the Inverse of a Function

Find the inverse of the one-to-one function: $g(x) = \sqrt[3]{5x} - 4$.

Solution:

$y = \sqrt[3]{5x} - 4$	**Step 1:**	Replace $g(x)$ by y.
$x = \sqrt[3]{5y} - 4$	**Step 2:**	Interchange x and y.
$x + 4 = \sqrt[3]{5y}$	**Step 3:**	Solve for y. Add 4 to both sides.
$(x + 4)^3 = (\sqrt[3]{5y})^3$		To eliminate the cube root, cube both sides.
$(x + 4)^3 = 5y$		Simplify the right side.
$\dfrac{(x + 4)^3}{5} = y$		Divide both sides by 5.
$g^{-1}(x) = \dfrac{(x + 4)^3}{5}$	**Step 4:**	Replace y by $g^{-1}(x)$.

The graphs of g and g^{-1} are shown in Figure 10-2. Once again we see that the graphs of a function and its inverse are symmetric with respect to the line $y = x$.

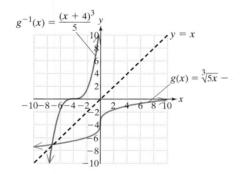

Figure 10-2

5.   Composition of a Function and Its Inverse

An important relationship between a function and its inverse is shown in Figure 10-3.

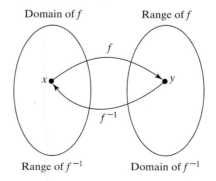

Figure 10-3

Recall that the domain of f is the range of f^{-1} and the range of f is the domain of f^{-1}. The operations performed by f are reversed by f^{-1}. This leads to a formal definition of an inverse of a function.

Definition of the Inverse of a Function

If f is a one-to-one function, then g is the inverse of f if and only if

$$(f \circ g)(x) = x \quad \text{for all } x \text{ in the domain of } g$$

and

$$(g \circ f)(x) = x \quad \text{for all } x \text{ in the domain of } f$$

Recall that function composition was first introduced in Section 4.2.

example 4

Composing a Function with Its Inverse

Show that the functions defined by

$$h(x) = 2x + 1 \quad \text{and} \quad k(x) = \frac{x - 1}{2}$$

are inverses.

Solution:

To show that the functions h and k are inverses we need to confirm that $(h \circ k)(x) = x$ and $(k \circ h)(x) = x$.

$$(h \circ k)(x) = h(k(x)) = 2(k(x)) + 1$$

$$= 2\left(\frac{x - 1}{2}\right) + 1$$

$$= x - 1 + 1$$

$$= x \checkmark \qquad (h \circ k)(x) = x \text{ as desired.}$$

$$(k \circ h)(x) = k(h(x)) = \frac{(h(x)) - 1}{2}$$

$$= \frac{(2x + 1) - 1}{2}$$

$$= \frac{2x + \cancel{1} - \cancel{1}}{2}$$

$$= \frac{2x}{2}$$

$$= x \checkmark \qquad (k \circ h)(x) = x \text{ as desired.}$$

The functions h and k are inverses because $(h \circ k)(x) = x$ and $(k \circ h)(x) = x$, for all real numbers, x.

example 5

Determining Whether Two Functions Are Inverses

Determine whether the functions are inverses: $f(x) = 3x - 6$ and $g(x) = \frac{1}{3}x - 6$

Solution:

To show that the functions f and g are inverses we need to confirm that $(f \circ g)(x) = x$ and $(g \circ f)(x) = x$.

$$(f \circ g)(x) = f(g(x)) = 3(g(x)) - 6$$

$$= 3\left(\frac{1}{3}x - 6\right) - 6$$

$$= x - 18 - 6$$

$$= x - 24$$

Notice that $(f \circ g)(x) \neq x$. Therefore, the functions f and g are not inverses.

6. Restricting the Domain of a Function

For a function that is not one-to-one, sometimes we can restrict its domain to create a new function that is one-to-one. This is demonstrated in the next example.

example 6

Finding the Equation of an Inverse of a Function with a Restricted Domain

Given the function defined by $m(x) = x^2 + 4$ for $x \geq 0$, find an equation defining m^{-1}.

Solution:

From Section 7.4, we know that $y = x^2 + 4$ is a parabola with the y-intercept at $(0, 4)$ (Figure 10-4). The graph represents a function that is not one-to-one. However, with the restriction on the domain $x \geq 0$, the graph of $m(x) = x^2 + 4$, $x \geq 0$ consists of only the "right" branch of the parabola (Figure 10-5). This *is* a one-to-one function.

Figure 10-4

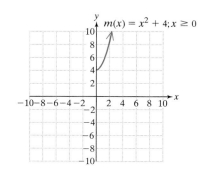

Figure 10-5

To find the inverse, we have

$$y = x^2 + 4; \quad x \geq 0$$ **Step 1:** Replace $m(x)$ by y.

$$x = y^2 + 4; \quad y \geq 0$$ **Step 2:** Interchange x and y. Notice that the restriction $x \geq 0$ becomes $y \geq 0$.

$$x - 4 = y^2; \quad y \geq 0$$ **Step 3:** Solve for y. Subtract 4 from both sides.

$$\sqrt{x - 4} = y; \quad y \geq 0$$ Apply the square root property. Notice that we obtain the *positive* square root of $x - 4$ because of the restriction $y \geq 0$.

$$m^{-1}(x) = \sqrt{x - 4}; \quad x \geq 4$$ **Step 4:** Replace y by $m^{-1}(x)$. Notice that the domain of m^{-1} is the range of m.

Figure 10-6 shows the graphs of m and m^{-1}.

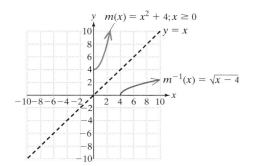

Figure 10-6

---

section 10.1   PRACTICE EXERCISES

For Exercises 1–6, determine if the relation is a function by using the vertical line test. (See Section 4.2.)

1.

2.

3.

4.

5.

6.

For Exercises 7–12, determine if the function is one-to-one by using the horizontal line test.

7.

8.

 9.

10.

11.

12.

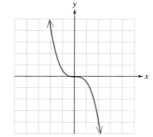

For Exercises 13–16, write the inverse function for each function as defined.

13. $g = \{(3, 5), (8, 1), (-3, 9), (0, 2)\}$

14. $f = \{(-6, 2), (-9, 0), (-2, -1), (3, 4)\}$

15. $r = \{(a, 3), (b, 6), (c, 9)\}$

16. $s = \{(-1, x), (-2, y), (-3, z)\}$

17.   The table relates a state (x) to the number of representatives in the House of Representatives (y) in the year 2000. Does this relation define a one-to-one function? If so, write a function defining the inverse as a set of ordered pairs.

State (x)	Number of Representatives (y)
Colorado	6
California	52
Texas	30
Connecticut	6
Pennsylvania	21

Table for Exercise 17

Age (x)	Maximum Recommended Heart Rate (y)
20	200
60	160
36	184
25	195
44	176

Table for Exercise 20

18. The table relates a city, (x) to its average January temperature (y). Does this relation define a one-to-one function? If so, write a function defining the inverse as a set of ordered pairs.

City (x)	Temperature (°C) (y)
Gainesville, FL	13.6
Keene, NH	−6.0
Wooster, OH	−4.0
Rock Springs, WY	−6.0
Lafayette, LA	10.9

Table for Exercise 18

19. The table relates the name of a building (x) to its height (y). Does this relation define a one-to-one function? If so, write a function defining the inverse as a set of ordered pairs.

Building (x)	Height (meters) (y)
John Hancock Tower, Boston	240
IDS Center, Minneapolis	236
Opera City Tower, Tokyo	234
Society Tower, Cleveland	290

Table for Exercise 19

20. The table relates the age of an individual and the individual's maximum recommended heart rate. Does this relation define a one-to-one function? If so, write a function defining the inverse as a set of ordered pairs.

For Exercises 21–28, write an equation of the inverse for each one-to-one function as defined.

21. $h(x) = x + 4$

22. $k(x) = x - 3$

23. $m(x) = \frac{1}{3}x - 2$

24. $n(x) = 4x + 2$

25. $p(x) = -x + 10$

26. $q(x) = -x - \frac{2}{3}$

27. $f(x) = x^3$

28. $g(x) = \sqrt[3]{x}$

29. The function defined by $f(x) = 0.3048x$ converts a length of x feet into $f(x)$ meters.

    a. Find the equivalent length in meters for a 4-ft board and a 50-ft wire.

    b. Find an equation defining $y = f^{-1}(x)$.

    c. Use the inverse function from part (b) to find the equivalent length in feet for a 1500-m race in track and field. Round to the nearest tenth of a foot.

30. The function defined by $s(x) = 1.47x$ converts a speed of x miles per hour to $s(x)$ feet per second.

    a. Find the equivalent speed in feet per second for a car traveling 60 mph.

    b. Find an equation defining $y = s^{-1}(x)$.

    c. Use the inverse function from part (b) to find the equivalent speed in miles per hour for a train traveling 132 ft/s. Round to the nearest tenth.

For Exercises 31–37, answer true or false.

31. The function defined by $y = 2$ has an inverse function defined by $x = 2$.

32. The domain of any one-to-one function is the same as the domain of its inverse.

33. All linear functions have an inverse function.

34. The function defined by $g(x) = |x|$ is one-to-one.

35. The function defined by $k(x) = x^2$ is one-to-one.

36. The function defined by $h(x) = |x|$ for $x \geq 0$ is one-to-one.

37. The function defined by $L(x) = x^2$ for $x \geq 0$ is one-to-one.

38. Explain how the domain and range of a one-to-one function and its inverse are related.

39. If $(0, b)$ is the y-intercept of a one-to-one function, what is the x-intercept of its inverse?

40. If $(a, 0)$ is the x-intercept of a one-to-one function, what is the y-intercept of its inverse?

41. Can you think of any function that is its own inverse?

42. a. What are the domain and range of the function defined by $f(x) = \sqrt{x - 1}$?

    b. What are the domain and range of the function defined by $f^{-1}(x) = x^2 + 1; x \geq 0$?

43. a. What are the domain and range of the function defined by $g(x) = x^2 - 4; x \leq 0$?

    b. What are the domain and range of the function defined by $g^{-1}(x) = -\sqrt{x + 4}$?

For Exercises 44–47, given the graph of $y = f(x)$,

    a. State the domain of f.

    b. State the range of f.

    c. State the domain of f^{-1}.

    d. State the range of f^{-1}.

    e. Graph the function defined by $y = f^{-1}(x)$. The line $y = x$ is provided for your reference.

44.

45.

46.

47.

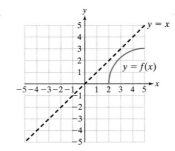

EXPANDING YOUR SKILLS

For Exercises 48–59, write an equation of the inverse of the one-to-one function.

48. $f(x) = \dfrac{x - 1}{x + 1}, \quad x \neq -1$

49. $p(x) = \dfrac{3 - x}{x + 3}, \quad x \neq -3$

50. $t(x) = \dfrac{2}{x - 1}, \quad x \neq 1$

51. $w(x) = \dfrac{4}{x + 2}, \quad x \neq -2$

52. $g(x) = x^2 + 9, \quad x \geq 0$

53. $m(x) = x^2 - 1, \quad x \geq 0$

54. $n(x) = x^2 + 9, \quad x \leq 0$

55. $g(x) = x^2 - 1, \quad x \leq 0$

56. $q(x) = \sqrt{x + 4}$ 57. $v(x) = \sqrt{x + 16}$

58. $z(x) = -\sqrt{x + 4}$ 59. $u(x) = -\sqrt{x + 16}$

GRAPHING CALCULATOR EXERCISES

For Exercises 60–63, use a graphing calculator to graph each function on the standard viewing window defined by $-10 \leq x \leq 10$ and $-10 \leq y \leq 10$. Use the graph of the function to determine if the function is one-to-one on the interval $-10 \leq x \leq 10$. If the function is one-to-one, find its inverse and graph both functions on the standard viewing window.

60. $f(x) = \sqrt[3]{x + 5}$ 61. $k(x) = x^3 - 4$

62. $g(x) = 0.5x^3 - 2$ 63. $m(x) = 3x - 4$

---

section

10.2   EXPONENTIAL FUNCTIONS

Concepts

1. **Definition of an Exponential Function**

2. **Approximating Exponential Expressions with a Calculator**

3. **Graphs of Exponential Functions**

4. **Applications of Exponential Functions— Radioactive Decay**

5. **Applications of Exponential Functions— Population Growth**

1.   Definition of an Exponential Function

The concept of a function was first introduced in Section 4.2. Since then we have learned to recognize several categories of functions, including constant, linear, rational, and quadratic functions. In this section and the next, we will define two new types of functions called exponential and logarithmic functions.

To introduce the concept of an exponential function, consider the following salary plans for a new job. Plan A pays $1 million for a month's work. Plan B starts with a 1¢ signing bonus, and every day thereafter the salary is doubled.

At first glance, the million-dollar plan appears to be more favorable. Look, however, at Table 10-1, which shows the daily payments for 30 days under plan B.

Table 10-1					
Day	**Payment**	**Day**	**Payment**	**Day**	**Payment**
1	2¢	11	$20.48	21	$20,971.52
2	4¢	12	$40.96	22	$41,943.04
3	8¢	13	$81.92	23	$83,886.08
4	16¢	14	$163.84	24	$167,772.16
5	32¢	15	$327.68	25	$335,544.32
6	64¢	16	$655.36	26	$671,088.64
7	$1.28	17	$1310.72	27	$1,342,177.28
8	$2.56	18	$2621.44	28	$2,684,354.56
9	$5.12	19	$5242.88	29	$5,368,709.12
10	$10.24	20	$10,485.76	30	$10,737,418.24

Notice that the salary on the 30th day for plan B is over $10 million. Taking the sum of the payments, the total salary for the 30-day period is $21,474,836.46.

The daily salary for plan B can be represented by the function, $y = 2^x$, where x is the number of days on the job, and y is the salary (in cents) for that day. An interesting feature of this function is that for every positive 1-unit change in x, the y-value doubles. The function $y = 2^x$ is called an exponential function.

Definition of an Exponential Function

Let b be any real number such that $b > 0$ and $b \neq 1$. Then a function of the form $y = b^x$ is called an **exponential function**.

An exponential function is easily recognized as a function with a constant base and variable exponent. Notice that the base of an exponential function must be a positive real number not equal to 1.

2. Approximating Exponential Expressions with a Calculator

Up to this point, we have evaluated exponential expressions with integer exponents and with rational exponents. For example, $4^3 = 64$ and $4^{1/2} = \sqrt{4} = 2$. However, how do we evaluate an exponential expression with an irrational exponent such as 4^π? In such a case, the exponent is a nonterminating and nonrepeating decimal. The value of 4^π can be thought of as the limiting value of a sequence of approximations using rational exponents:

$$4^{3.14} \approx 77.7084726$$

$$4^{3.141} \approx 77.81627412$$

$$4^{3.1415} \approx 77.87023095$$

$$\cdots$$

$$4^\pi \approx 77.88023365$$

Graphing Calculator Box	
On a graphing calculator, use the $\boxed{\wedge}$ key to approximate an expression with an irrational exponent.	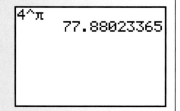

An exponential expression can be evaluated at all rational numbers and at all irrational numbers. Hence, the domain of an exponential function is all real numbers.

example 1   Approximating Exponential Expressions with a Calculator

Approximate the expressions. Round the answers to four decimal places.

a. $8^{\sqrt{3}}$ b. $5^{-\sqrt{17}}$ c. $\sqrt{10}^{\sqrt{2}}$

Solution:

a. $8^{\sqrt{3}} \approx 36.6604$
b. $5^{-\sqrt{17}} \approx 0.0013$
c. $\sqrt{10}^{\sqrt{2}} \approx 5.0946$

Graphing Calculator Box

The expressions from Example 1 can be approximated on a graphing calculator as shown.

```
8^√(3)
          36.66044576
5^-√(17)
           .00131242
(√(10))^√(2)
           5.09456117
```

---

3. Graphs of Exponential Functions

The functions defined by $f(x) = 2^x$, $g(x) = 3^x$, $h(x) = 5^x$, and $k(x) = \left(\frac{1}{2}\right)^x$ are all examples of exponential functions. Example 2 illustrates the two general shapes of exponential functions.

---

example 2

Graphing an Exponential Function

Graph the functions f and g.

a. $f(x) = 2^x$ b. $g(x) = \left(\frac{1}{2}\right)^x$

Solution:

Table 10-2 shows several function values, $f(x)$ and $g(x)$, for both positive and negative values of x. The graph is shown in Figure 10-7.

Table 10-2		
x	$f(x) = 2^x$	$g(x) = \left(\frac{1}{2}\right)^x$
-4	$\frac{1}{16}$	16
-3	$\frac{1}{8}$	8
-2	$\frac{1}{4}$	4
-1	$\frac{1}{2}$	2
0	1	1
1	2	$\frac{1}{2}$
2	4	$\frac{1}{4}$
3	8	$\frac{1}{8}$
4	16	$\frac{1}{16}$

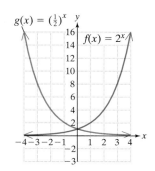

Figure 10-7

The graphs in Figure 10-7 illustrate several important features of exponential functions.

Graphs of $f(x) = b^x$

The graph of an exponential function defined by $f(x) = b^x$ ($b > 0$ and $b \neq 1$) has the following properties.

1. If $b > 1$, f is an *increasing* exponential function (sometimes called an **exponential growth function**).

    If $0 < b < 1$, f is a *decreasing* exponential function (sometimes called an **exponential decay function**).

2. The domain is the set of all real numbers.
3. The range is $(0, \infty)$.
4. The x-axis is a horizontal asymptote.
5. The function passes through the point $(0, 1)$ because $f(0) = b^0 = 1$.

These properties indicate that the graph of an exponential function is an increasing function if the base is greater than 1. Furthermore, the base affects its "steepness." Consider the graphs of $f(x) = 2^x, h(x) = 3^x$, and $k(x) = 5^x$ (Figure 10-8). For every positive 1-unit change in $x, f(x) = 2^x$ increases by 2 times, $h(x) = 3^x$ increases by 3 times, and $k(x) = 5^x$ increases by 5 times (Table 10-3).

Table 10-3

x	$f(x) = 2^x$	$h(x) = 3^x$	$k(x) = 5^x$
-3	$\frac{1}{8}$	$\frac{1}{27}$	$\frac{1}{125}$
-2	$\frac{1}{4}$	$\frac{1}{9}$	$\frac{1}{25}$
-1	$\frac{1}{2}$	$\frac{1}{3}$	$\frac{1}{5}$
0	1	1	1
1	2	3	5
2	4	9	25
3	8	27	125

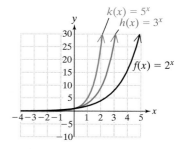

Figure 10-8

The graph of an exponential function is a *decreasing function* if the base is between 0 and 1. Consider the graphs of $g(x) = \left(\frac{1}{2}\right)^x, m(x) = \left(\frac{1}{3}\right)^x$, and $n(x) = \left(\frac{1}{5}\right)^x$ (Table 10-4 and Figure 10-9).

Table 10-4			
x	$g(x) = (\frac{1}{2})^x$	$m(x) = (\frac{1}{3})^x$	$n(x) = (\frac{1}{5})^x$
-3	8	27	125
-2	4	9	25
-1	2	3	5
0	1	1	1
1	$\frac{1}{2}$	$\frac{1}{3}$	$\frac{1}{5}$
2	$\frac{1}{4}$	$\frac{1}{9}$	$\frac{1}{25}$
3	$\frac{1}{8}$	$\frac{1}{27}$	$\frac{1}{125}$

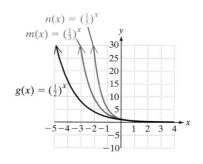

Figure 10-9

4. Applications of Exponential Functions—Radioactive Decay

Exponential growth and decay can be found in a variety of real-world phenomena. For example,

- Population growth can often be modeled by an exponential function.
- The growth of an investment under compound interest grows exponentially.
- The mass of a radioactive substance decreases exponentially with time.
- The temperature of a cup of coffee decreases exponentially as it approaches room temperature.

example 3

Applying an Exponential Function

A substance that undergoes radioactive decay is said to be radioactive. The **half-life** of a radioactive substance is the amount of time it takes for one half of the original amount of the substance to change into something else. That is, after each half-life the amount of the original substance decreases by half.

In 1898, Marie Curie discovered the highly radioactive element, radium. She shared the 1903 Nobel Prize in physics for her research on radioactivity and was awarded the 1911 Nobel Prize in chemistry for her discovery of radium and polonium. Radium-226 (an isotope of radium) has a half-life of 1620 years and decays into radon-222 (a radioactive gas).

In a sample originally having 1 g of radium-226, the amount of radium-226 present after t years is given by

$$A(t) = (\tfrac{1}{2})^{t/1620},$$ where A is the amount of radium in grams, and t is the time in years.

a. How much radium-226 will be present after 1620 years?
b. How much radium-226 will be present after 3240 years?
c. How much radium-226 will be present after 4860 years?

Marie and Pierre Curie

Solution:

a. $A(1620) = \left(\dfrac{1}{2}\right)^{1620/1620}$

$= \left(\dfrac{1}{2}\right)^1$

$= 0.5$

After 1620 years (1 half-life), 0.5 g remains.

b. $A(3240) = \left(\dfrac{1}{2}\right)^{3240/1620}$

$= \left(\dfrac{1}{2}\right)^{2}$

$= 0.25$

After 3240 years (2 half-lifes), the amount of the original substance is reduced by half, two times: 0.25 g remains.

c. $A(4860) = \left(\dfrac{1}{2}\right)^{4860/1620}$

$= \left(\dfrac{1}{2}\right)^{3}$

$= 0.125$

After 4860 years (3 half-lifes), the amount of the original substance is reduced by half, three times: 0.125 g remains.

Graphing Calculator Box

Enter $Y_1 = \left(\frac{1}{2}\right)^{t/1620}$. A *Table* feature can be used to confirm the solutions to Example 3. Here we begin the table at $x = 0$ and increment x by 1620 years.

5. Applications of Exponential Functions— Population Growth

Exponential functions are often used to model population growth. Suppose the initial value of a population at some time $t = 0$ is P_0. If the rate of increase of a population is r, then after 1, 2, and 3 years, the new population can be found as follows:

$$\text{After 1 year:} \left(\begin{matrix}\text{Total}\\\text{population}\end{matrix}\right) = \left(\begin{matrix}\text{initial}\\\text{population}\end{matrix}\right) + \left(\begin{matrix}\text{increase in}\\\text{population}\end{matrix}\right)$$

$$= P_0 + P_0 r$$

$$= P_0(1 + r) \qquad \text{Factor out } P_0.$$

After 2 years: $\left(\begin{array}{c}\text{Total}\\\text{population}\end{array}\right) = \left(\begin{array}{c}\text{population}\\\text{after 1 year}\end{array}\right) + \left(\begin{array}{c}\text{increase in}\\\text{population}\end{array}\right)$

$$= P_0(1 + r) + P_0(1 + r)r$$
$$= P_0(1 + r)1 + P_0(1 + r)r$$
$$= P_0(1 + r)(1 + r) \qquad \text{Factor out } P_0(1 + r).$$
$$= P_0(1 + r)^2$$

After 3 years: $\left(\begin{array}{c}\text{Total}\\\text{population}\end{array}\right) = \left(\begin{array}{c}\text{population}\\\text{after 2 years}\end{array}\right) + \left(\begin{array}{c}\text{increase in}\\\text{population}\end{array}\right)$

$$= P_0(1 + r)^2 + P_0(1 + r)^2 r$$
$$= P_0(1 + r)^2 1 + P_0(1 + r)^2 r$$
$$= P_0(1 + r)^2(1 + r) \qquad \text{Factor out } P_0(1 + r)^2.$$
$$= P_0(1 + r)^3$$

This pattern continues, and after t years, the population $P(t)$ is given by

$$P(t) = P_0(1 + r)^t$$

---

example 4

Applying an Exponential Function

The population of the Bahamas in 1998 was estimated at 280,000 with an annual rate of increase of 1.39%.

a. Find a mathematical model that relates the population of the Bahamas as a function of the number of years after 1998.
b. If the annual rate of increase remains the same, use this model to predict the population of the Bahamas in the year 2010. Round to the nearest thousand.
c. Graph the function.
d. Use the graph to approximate the number of years required for the population in the Bahamas to double. Round to the nearest year.

Solution:

a. The initial population is $P_0 = 280,000$ and the rate of increase is $r = 1.39\%$.

$P(t) = P_0(1 + r)^t$ Substitute $P_0 = 280,000$ and $r = 0.0139$.

$\quad = 280,000(1 + 0.0139)^t$

$\quad = 280,000(1.0139)^t$ Where $t = 0$ corresponds to the year 1998

b. Because the initial population ($t = 0$) corresponds to the year 1998, we use $t = 12$ to find the population in the year 2010.

$P(12) = 280,000(1.0139)^{12}$
$\quad\quad\quad \approx 330,000$

c.   To graph the function, we can use a table of values (Table 10-5).

Year $t = 0$ is 1998	Population $P(t) = 280{,}000(1.0139)^t$
0	280,000
10	321,000
20	369,000
30	424,000
40	486,000
50	558,000
60	641,000
70	736,000
80	845,000

Table 10-5

d.   From the graph (Figure 10-10), it will take approximately 50 years for the population of the Bahamas to reach 560,000 (two times the original population of 280,000). This corresponds to the year 2048.

Figure 10-10

To answer the question in Example 4(d), analytically, we would substitute 560,000 for $P(t)$ and solve the equation for t.

$$560{,}000 = 280{,}000(1.0139)^t$$

We can divide both sides by 280,000 to simplify the equation.

$$2 = 1.0139^t$$

However, at this point, we reach an impasse. How do we solve an equation for an unknown exponent? The functions needed to solve this type of equation are called logarithmic functions and are presented in the next section.

section 10.2 PRACTICE EXERCISES

For Exercises 1–8, evaluate the expression without the use of a calculator.

1. 5^2 2. 2^{-3} 3. 10^{-3} 4. 3^4

5. $36^{1/2}$ 6. $27^{1/3}$ 7. $16^{3/4}$ 8. $8^{2/3}$

For Exercises 9–16, evaluate the expression using a calculator. Round to four decimal places.

9. $5^{1.1}$ 10. $2^{\sqrt{3}}$ 11. 10^π

12. $3^{4.8}$ 13. $36^{-\sqrt{2}}$ 14. $27^{-0.5126}$

15. $16^{-0.04}$ 16. $8^{-0.61}$

17. Solve for x.
 a. $3^x = 9$
 b. $3^x = 27$
 c. Approximate the solution for x in $3^x = 11$.

18. Solve for x.
 a. $5^x = 125$
 b. $5^x = 625$
 c. Approximate the solution for x in $5^x = 130$.

19. Solve for x.
 a. $2^x = 16$
 b. $2^x = 32$
 c. Approximate the solution for x in $2^x = 30$.

20. Solve for x.
 a. $4^x = 16$
 b. $4^x = 64$
 c. Approximate the solution for x in $4^x = 20$.

21. For $f(x) = (\frac{1}{5})^x$ find $f(0), f(1), f(2), f(-1)$, and $f(-2)$.

22. For $g(x) = (\frac{2}{3})^x$ find $g(0), g(1), g(2), g(-1)$, and $g(-2)$.

23. For $h(x) = \pi^x$ use a calculator to find $h(0), h(1), h(-1), h(\sqrt{2})$, and $h(\pi)$. Round to two decimal places.

24. For $k(x) = (\sqrt{5})^x$ use a calculator to find $k(0), k(1), k(-1), k(\pi)$, and $k(\sqrt{2})$. Round to two decimal places.

25. For $r(x) = 3^{x+2}$ find $r(0), r(1), r(2), r(-1), r(-2)$, and $r(-3)$.

26. For $s(x) = 2^{2x-1}$ find $s(0), s(1), s(2), s(-1)$, and $s(-2)$.

27. How do you determine whether the graph of $f(x) = b^x$ is increasing or decreasing?

28. For $f(x) = b^x, (b > 0, b \neq 1)$, find $f(0)$.

Graph the functions defined in Exercises 29–36. Plot at least three points for each function.

29. $f(x) = 4^x$ 30. $g(x) = 6^x$

31. $m(x) = (\frac{1}{8})^x$ 32. $n(x) = (\frac{1}{3})^x$

33. $h(x) = 2^{x+1}$ 34. $k(x) = 5^{x-1}$

35. $g(x) = 5^{-x}$ 36. $f(x) = 2^{-x}$

37. Suppose $1000 is initially invested in an account and the value of the account grows exponentially. If the investment doubles in 7 years, then the amount in the account t years after the initial investment is given by

$$A(t) = 1000(2)^{t/7},$$ where t is expressed in years and $A(t)$ is the amount in the account.

 a. Find the amount in the account after 5 years.
 b. Find the amount in the account after 10 years.
 c. Find $A(0)$ and $A(7)$ and interpret the answers in the context of the problem.

38. Suppose $1500 is initially invested in an account and the value of the account grows exponentially. If the investment doubles in 8 years, then the amount in the account t years after the initial investment is given by

$$A(t) = 1500(2)^{t/8},$$ where t is expressed in years and $A(t)$ is the amount in the account.

 a. Find the amount in the account after 5 years.
 b. Find the amount in the account after 10 years.
 c. Find $A(0)$ and $A(8)$ and interpret the answers in the context of the problem.

39. The population of Ireland in 1998 was estimated at 3,600,000, with an annual rate of increase of 0.36%. The population of Singapore in 1998 was estimated at 3,500,000, with an annual rate of increase of 1.20%.

    a. Write a mathematical model that describes the population of Ireland, $I(t)$, as a function of the number of years, t, after 1998. (See Example 4.)

    b. Write a mathematical model that describes the population of Singapore, $S(t)$, as a function of the number of years, t, after 1998.

    c. The populations of the two countries were very nearly the same in 1998. However, Singapore has a higher rate of increase. Examine how the rate of increase affects population over time by predicting the populations of Ireland and Singapore 20, 40, and 60 years after 1998. Round to the nearest hundred thousand.

    d. Although Singapore had fewer people in 1998, it also has a higher growth rate. What is the effect of the growth rate when comparing the populations of two countries?

    e. The population of Singapore is growing more rapidly than that of Ireland. Furthermore, the land area in Singapore is only about 1/100 that of Ireland. What conclusion can you make about *population density* of the two countries?

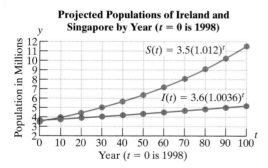

Projected Populations of Ireland and Singapore by Year ($t = 0$ is 1998)

$S(t) = 3.5(1.012)^t$

$I(t) = 3.6(1.0036)^t$

Year ($t = 0$ is 1998)

Figure for Exercise 39

40. The population of Pakistan in 1998 was estimated at 135,000,000, with an annual rate of increase of 2.20%. The population of Brazil in 1998 was estimated at 170,000,000, with an annual rate of increase of 1.24%.

    a. Write a mathematical model that describes the population of Pakistan as a function of the number of years, t, after 1998. (See Example 4.)

    b. Write a mathematical model that describes the population of Brazil as a function of the number of years, t, after 1998.

    c. Use your models from parts (a) and (b) to predict the populations of Pakistan and Brazil 10, 20, and 30 years after 1998. Round to the nearest million.

    d. Although Pakistan had approximately 35 million fewer people than Brazil in 1998, it also has a higher growth rate. What is the effect of growth rate when comparing the populations of two countries?

GRAPHING CALCULATOR EXERCISES

For Exercises 41–48, graph the functions on your calculator to support your solutions to the indicated exercises.

41. $f(x) = 4^x$ (see Exercise 29)

42. $g(x) = 6^x$ (see Exercise 30)

43. $m(x) = (\frac{1}{8})^x$ (see Exercise 31)

44. $n(x) = (\frac{1}{3})^x$ (see Exercise 32)

45. $h(x) = 2^{x+1}$ (see Exercise 33)

46. $k(x) = 5^{x-1}$ (see Exercise 34)

47. $g(x) = 5^{-x}$ (see Exercise 35)

48. $f(x) = 2^{-x}$ (see Exercise 36)

49. The function defined by $A(x) = 1000(2)^{x/7}$ represents the total amount, A, in an account x years after an initial investment of $1000.

    a. Graph $y = A(x)$ on the window where $0 \leq x \leq 25$ and $0 \leq y \leq 10{,}000$.

    b. Use *Zoom* and *Trace* to approximate the times required for the account to reach $2000, $4000, and $8000.

50. The function defined by $A(x) = 1500(2)^{x/8}$ represents the total amount, A, in an account x years after the initial investment of $1500.

    a. Graph $y = A(x)$ on the window where $0 \le x \le 40$ and $0 \le y \le 25{,}000$.

    b. Use *Zoom* and *Trace* to approximate the times required for the account to reach $3000, $6000, and $12,000.

section

10.3 LOGARITHMIC FUNCTIONS

1. Definition of a Logarithmic Function

Consider the following equations in which the variable is located in the exponent of an expression. In some cases the solution can be found by inspection because the constant on the right-hand side of the equation is a perfect power of the base.

Equation	Solution
$5^x = 5$	$x = 1$
$5^x = 20$	$x = ?$
$5^x = 25$	$x = 2$
$5^x = 60$	$x = ?$
$5^x = 125$	$x = 3$

The equation $5^x = 20$ cannot be solved by inspection. However, we might suspect that x is between 1 and 2. Similarly, the solution to the equation $5^x = 60$ is between 2 and 3. To solve an exponential equation for an unknown exponent we must use a new type of function called a logarithmic function.

Definition of a Logarithmic Function

If x and b are positive real numbers such that $b \ne 1$, then $y = \log_b(x)$ is called the **logarithmic function** with base b and

$$y = \log_b(x) \text{ is equivalent to } b^y = x.$$

Note: In the expression, $y = \log_b(x)$, y is called the **logarithm**, b is called the **base**, and x is called the **argument**.

The expression $y = \log_b(x)$ is equivalent to $b^y = x$ and indicates that *the logarithm, y, is the exponent to which b must be raised to obtain x.* The expression $y = \log_b(x)$ is called the logarithmic form of the equation, and the expression $b^y = x$ is called the exponential form of the equation.

The definition of a logarithmic function suggests a close relationship with an exponential function of the same base. In fact, a logarithmic function is the inverse of the corresponding exponential function. For example, the following steps find the inverse of the exponential function defined by $f(x) = b^x$.

$$f(x) = b^x$$
$$y = b^x \qquad \text{Replace } f(x) \text{ by } y.$$
$$x = b^y \qquad \text{Interchange } x \text{ and } y.$$
$$y = \log_b x \qquad \text{Solve for } y \text{ using the definition of a logarithmic function.}$$
$$f^{-1}(x) = \log_b x \qquad \text{Replace } y \text{ by } f^{-1}(x).$$

2. Converting Between Logarithmic Form and Exponential Form

Because the concept of a logarithm is new and unfamiliar, it may be advantageous to rewrite a logarithm in its equivalent exponential form.

---

example 1   **Converting from Logarithmic Form to Exponential Form**

Rewrite the logarithmic equations in exponential form.

a. $\log_2(32) = 5$ b. $\log_{10}\left(\dfrac{1}{1000}\right) = -3$ c. $\log_5(1) = 0$

Solution:

Logarithmic Form		**Exponential Form**
a. $\log_2(32) = 5$	$\Leftrightarrow$	$2^5 = 32$
b. $\log_{10}\left(\dfrac{1}{1000}\right) = -3$	$\Leftrightarrow$	$10^{-3} = \dfrac{1}{1000}$
c. $\log_5(1) = 0$	$\Leftrightarrow$	$5^0 = 1$

Tip: To understand the meaning of a logarithmic function intuitively, consider the function defined by $y = \log_3(x)$. If we evaluate the function at $x = 9, x = 27,$ and $x = 81$, we have

$y = \log_3(9)$ or equivalently $3^y = 9$ ← The value of the logarithm, y, is the exponent to
  $= \log_3(9) = 2$ because $3^2 = 9$ which 3 is raised to produce 9.

$y = \log_3(27)$ or equivalently $3^y = 27$ ← The value of the logarithm, y, is the exponent to
  $= \log_3(27) = 3$ because $3^3 = 27$ which 3 is raised to produce 27.

$y = \log_3(81)$ or equivalently $3^y = 81$ ← The value of the logarithm, y, is the exponent to
  $= \log_3(81) = 4$ because $3^4 = 81$ which 3 is raised to produce 81.

3.   Evaluating Logarithmic Expressions

example 2   **Evaluating Logarithmic Expressions**

Evaluate the logarithmic expressions.

a. $\log_{10}(10{,}000)$ b. $\log_5\left(\dfrac{1}{125}\right)$ c. $\log_{(1/2)}\left(\dfrac{1}{8}\right)$

d. $\log_b(b)$ e. $\log_c(c^7)$ f. $\log_3 \sqrt[4]{3}$

Solution:

a. $\log_{10}(10{,}000)$ is the exponent to which 10 must be raised to obtain 10,000.

$y = \log_{10}(10{,}000)$ Let y represent the value of the logarithm.

$10^y = 10{,}000$ Rewrite the expression in exponential form.

$y = 4$

Therefore, $\log_{10}(10{,}000) = 4$.

b. $\log_5\left(\frac{1}{125}\right)$ is the exponent to which 5 must be raised to obtain $\frac{1}{125}$.

$y = \log_5\left(\dfrac{1}{125}\right)$ Let y represent the value of the logarithm.

$5^y = \dfrac{1}{125}$ Rewrite the expression in exponential form.

$y = -3$

Therefore, $\log_5\left(\frac{1}{125}\right) = -3$.

c. $\log_{(1/2)}\left(\frac{1}{8}\right)$ is the exponent to which $\frac{1}{2}$ must be raised to obtain $\frac{1}{8}$.

$y = \log_{(1/2)}\left(\dfrac{1}{8}\right)$ Let y represent the value of the logarithm.

$\left(\dfrac{1}{2}\right)^y = \dfrac{1}{8}$ Rewrite the expression in exponential form.

$y = 3$

Therefore, $\log_{(1/2)}\left(\frac{1}{8}\right) = 3$.

d. $\log_b(b)$ is the exponent to which b must be raised to obtain b.

$y = \log_b(b)$ Let y represent the value of the logarithm.

$b^y = b$ Rewrite the expression in exponential form.

$y = 1$

Therefore, $\log_b(b) = 1$.

e. $\log_c(c^7)$ is the exponent to which c must be raised to obtain c^7.

$\quad y = \log_c(c^7)$ Let y represent the value of the logarithm.

$\quad c^y = c^7$ Rewrite the expression in exponential form.

$\quad y = 7$

Therefore, $\log_c(c^7) = 7$.

f. $\log_3 \sqrt[4]{3} = \log_3 3^{1/4}$ is the exponent to which 3 must be raised to obtain $3^{1/4}$.

$\quad y = \log_3 3^{1/4}$ Let y represent the value of the logarithm.

$\quad 3^y = 3^{1/4}$ Rewrite the expression in exponential form.

$\quad y = \dfrac{1}{4}$

Therefore, $\log_3 \sqrt[4]{3} = \frac{1}{4}$.

4. The Common Logarithmic Function

The logarithmic function with base 10 is called the **common logarithmic function** and is denoted by $y = \log(x)$. Notice that the base is not explicitly written but is understood to be 10. That is, $y = \log_{10}(x)$ is written simply as $y = \log(x)$.

Graphing Calculator Box

On most calculators, the $\boxed{\log}$ key is used to compute logarithms with base 10. For example, we know the expression $\log(1{,}000{,}000) = 6$ because $10^6 = 1{,}000{,}000$. Use the $\boxed{\log}$ key to show this result on a calculator.

```
log(1000000)
                      6
```

---

example 3

Evaluating Common Logarithms on a Calculator

Evaluate the common logarithms. Round the answers to four decimal places.

a. $\log(420)$ b. $\log(8.2 \times 10^9)$ c. $\log(0.0002)$

Solution:

a. $\log(420) \approx 2.6232$
b. $\log(8.2 \times 10^9) \approx 9.9138$
c. $\log(0.0002) \approx -3.6990$

Graphing Calculator Box

The expressions from Example 3 can be approximated on a graphing calculator as shown.

```
log(420)
          2.62324929
log(8.2E9)
          9.913813852
log(0.0002)
          -3.698970004
```

5.   Applications of the Common Logarithmic Function

example 4

Applying a Logarithmic Function to Compute pH

The pH (hydrogen potential) of a solution is defined as

$$pH = -\log[H^+], \text{ where } [H^+] \text{ represents the concentration of}$$
hydrogen ions in moles per liter (mol/L).

The pH scale ranges from 0 to 14. The midpoint of this range, 7, represents a
neutral solution. Values below 7 are progressively more acidic, and values above
7 are progressively more alkaline. Based on the equation $pH = -\log[H^+]$, a
1-unit change in pH means a 10-fold change in hydrogen ion concentration.

a.   Normal rain has a pH of 5.6. However, in some areas of the northeast United
     States the rainwater is more acidic. What is the pH of a rain sample for which
     the concentration of hydrogen ions is 0.0002 mol/L?
b.   Find the pH of household ammonia if the concentration of hydrogen ions is
     1.0×10^{-11} mol/L.

Solution:

a. $pH = -\log[H^+]$

   $= -\log(0.0002)$ Substitute $[H^+] = 0.0002$.

   ≈ 3.7 (To compare this value with a familiar substance,
                    note that the pH of orange juice is roughly 3.5.)

b. $pH = -\log[H^+]$

   $= -\log(1.0 \times 10^{-11})$ Substitute $[H^+] = 1.0 \times 10^{-11}$.

   $= 11$

The pH of household ammonia is 11.

6.   Graphs of Logarithmic Functions

In Section 10.2 we studied the graphs of exponential functions. In this section, we
will graph logarithmic functions. First, recall that $f(x) = \log_b(x)$ is the inverse of
$g(x) = b^x$. Therefore, the graph of $y = f(x)$ is symmetric to the graph of $y = g(x)$
about the line $y = x$, as shown in Figures 10-11 and 10-12.

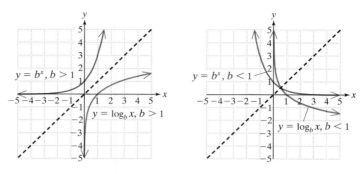

Figure 10-11   **Figure 10-12**

From Figures 10-11 and 10-12, we see that the range of $y = b^x$ is the set of positive real numbers. As expected, the domain of its inverse, the logarithmic function $y = \log_b(x)$, is also the set of positive real numbers. Therefore, the **domain of the logarithmic function** $y = \log_b(x)$ is the set of positive real numbers.

example 5

Graphing Logarithmic Functions

Graph the functions and compare the graphs to examine the effect of the base on the shape of the logarithmic function.

a. $y = \log_2(x)$ b. $y = \log(x)$

Solution:

We can write each equation in its equivalent exponential form and create a table of values (Table 10-6). To simplify the calculations, choose integer values of y and then solve for x.

$$y = \log_2(x) \text{ or } 2^y = x \qquad y = \log(x) \text{ or } 10^y = x$$

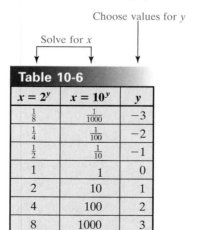

Table 10-6

$x = 2^y$	$x = 10^y$	y
$\frac{1}{8}$	$\frac{1}{1000}$	-3
$\frac{1}{4}$	$\frac{1}{100}$	-2
$\frac{1}{2}$	$\frac{1}{10}$	-1
1	1	0
2	10	1
4	100	2
8	1000	3

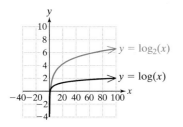

Figure 10-13

The graphs of $y = \log_2(x)$ and $y = \log(x)$ are shown in Figure 10-13. Both graphs exhibit the same general behavior, and the steepness of the curve is affected by the base. The function $y = \log(x)$ requires a 10-fold increase in x to increase the y-value by 1 unit. The function $y = \log_2(x)$ requires a two-fold increase in x to increase the y-value by 1 unit. In addition, the following characteristics are true for both graphs.

- The domain is the set of real numbers, x, such that $x > 0$.
- The range is the set of real numbers.
- The y-axis is a vertical asymptote.
- Both graphs pass through the point $(1, 0)$.

Example 5 illustrates that a logarithmic function with base, $b > 1$ is an increasing function. In the next example, we see that if the base, b, is between 0 and 1, the function decreases over its entire domain.

example 6   **Graphing a Logarithmic Function**

Graph $y = \log_{1/4}(x)$.

Solution:

$y = \log_{1/4}(x)$ can be written in exponential form as $\left(\frac{1}{4}\right)^y = x$. By choosing several values for y, we can solve for x and plot the corresponding points (Table 10-7).

Choose values for y

Solve for x

Table 10-7

$x = \left(\frac{1}{4}\right)^y$	y
64	-3
16	-2
4	-1
1	0
$\frac{1}{4}$	1
$\frac{1}{16}$	2
$\frac{1}{64}$	3

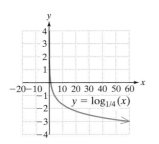

Figure 10-14

The expression $y = \log_{1/4}(x)$ defines a decreasing logarithmic function (Figure 10-14). Notice that the vertical asymptote, domain, and range are the same for both increasing and decreasing logarithmic functions.

Graphs of Exponential and Logarithmic Functions—A Summary

Exponential Functions

$y = b^x$

Domain: $(-\infty, \infty)$
Range: $(0, \infty)$
Horizontal asymptote: $y = 0$
Passes through $(0, 1)$
If $b > 1$, the function is increasing.
If $0 < b < 1$, the function is decreasing.

Logarithmic Functions

$y = \log_b(x)$

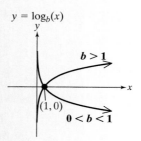

Domain: $(0, \infty)$
Range: $(-\infty, \infty)$
Vertical asymptote: $x = 0$
Passes through $(1, 0)$
If $b > 1$, the function is increasing.
If $0 < b < 1$, the function is decreasing.

Notice that the roles of x and y are interchanged for the functions $y = b^x$ and $b^y = x$. Therefore, it is not surprising that the domain and range are reversed between exponential and logarithmic functions. Moreover, an exponential function passes through $(0, 1)$, whereas a logarithmic function passes through $(1, 0)$. An exponential function has a horizontal asymptote at $y = 0$, whereas a logarithmic function has a vertical asymptote at $x = 0$. With the roles of x and y interchanged, the exponential function, base b, and the logarithmic function, base b, are said to be *inverses* of each other.

7.   Determining the Domain of Logarithmic Functions

example 7

Identifying the Domain of a Logarithmic Function

Find the domain of the functions.

a. $f(x) = \log(4 - x)$ b. $g(x) = \log(2x + 6)$

Solution:

The domain of the function $y = \log_b(x)$ is the set of all positive real numbers. That is, the argument, x, must be greater than zero: $x > 0$.

a. $f(x) = \log(4 - x)$ The argument is $4 - x$.

$\qquad 4 - x > 0$ The argument of the logarithm must be greater than zero.

$$-x > -4 \qquad \text{Solve for } x.$$

$$x < 4 \qquad \text{Divide by } -1 \text{ and reverse the inequality sign.}$$

The domain is $\{x \mid x < 4\}$.

b. $g(x) = \log(2x + 6)$ The argument is $2x + 6$.

$$2x + 6 > 0 \qquad \text{The argument of the logarithm must be greater than zero.}$$

$$2x > -6 \qquad \text{Solve for } x.$$

$$x > -3$$

The domain is $\{x \mid x > -3\}$.

Graphing Calculator Box

The graphs of $Y_1 = \log(4 - x)$ and $Y_2 = \log(2x + 6)$ are shown here and can be used to confirm the solutions to Example 7. Notice that each function has a vertical asymptote at the value of x where the argument equals zero.

---

example 8

Applying Logarithms to a Memory Model

One method of measuring a student's retention of material after taking a course is to retest the student at specified time intervals after the course has been completed. A student's score on a calculus test t months after completing a course in calculus is approximated by

$S(t) = 85 - 25 \log(t + 1)$, where t is the time in months after completing the course, and $S(t)$ is the student's score as a percent.

a.   What was the student's score at the time the course was completed ($t = 0$)?
b.   What was the student's score after 2 months?
c.   What was the student's score after 1 year?

Solution:

a. $S(t) = 85 - 25 \log(t + 1)$

$$S(0) = 85 - 25 \log(0 + 1) \qquad \text{Substitute } t = 0.$$

$$= 85 - 25 \log(1) \qquad \log(1) = 0 \text{ because } 10^0 = 1.$$

$$= 85 - 25(0)$$
$$= 85 - 0$$
$$= 85$$

The student's score at the time the course was completed was 85%.

b. $S(t) = 85 - 25 \log(t + 1)$

$S(2) = 85 - 25 \log(2 + 1)$

$\quad = 85 - 25 \log(3)$ Use a calculator to approximate $\log(3)$.

$\quad \approx 73.1$ The student's score dropped to 73.1%.

c. $S(t) = 85 - 25 \log(t + 1)$

$S(12) = 85 - 25 \log(12 + 1)$

$\quad = 85 - 25 \log(13)$ Use a calculator to approximate $\log(13)$.

$\quad \approx 57.2$ The student's score dropped to 57.2%.

---

section 10.3   PRACTICE EXERCISES

1. For which graph of $y = b^x$ is $0 < b < 1$?

   i.
   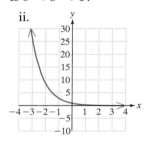

   ii.

2. Let $f(x) = 6^x$.

   a. Find $f(-2), f(-1), f(0), f(1),$ and $f(2)$.

   b. Graph $y = f(x)$ by plotting the points found in part (a).

3. Let $g(x) = 3^x$.

   a. Find $g(-2), g(-1), g(0), g(1),$ and $g(2)$.

   b. Graph $y = g(x)$ by plotting the points found in part (a).

4. Let $r(x) = \left(\frac{3}{4}\right)^x$.

   a. Find $r(-2), r(-1), r(0), r(1),$ and $r(2)$.

   b. Graph $y = r(x)$ by plotting the points found in part (a).

5. Let $s(x) = \left(\frac{2}{5}\right)^x$.

   a. Find $s(-2), s(-1), s(0), s(1),$ and $s(2)$.

   b. Graph $y = s(x)$ by plotting the points found in part (a).

6. For the expression $y = \log_b(x)$, identify the base, the argument, and the logarithm.

7. Rewrite the expression in exponential form: $y = \log_b(x)$.

For Exercises 8–19, write the expression in logarithmic form.

8. $3^x = 81$

9. $10^3 = 1000$

10. $5^2 = 25$

11. $8^{1/3} = 2$

12. $7^{-1} = \dfrac{1}{7}$

13. $8^{-2} = \dfrac{1}{64}$

14. $b^x = y$

15. $b^y = x$

16. $e^x = y$

17. $e^y = x$

18. $K^n = p$

19. $H^m = q$

For Exercises 20–31, write the expression in exponential form.

20. $\log_5 625 = 4$

21. $\log_{125} 25 = \dfrac{2}{3}$

22. $\log_{10} 0.0001 = -4$

23. $\log_{25}\left(\dfrac{1}{5}\right) = -\dfrac{1}{2}$

24. $\log_6 36 = 2$

25. $\log_2 128 = 7$

26. $\log_b 15 = x$

27. $\log_b 82 = y$

28. $\log_3 5 = x$

29. $\log_2 7 = x$

30. $\log_4 x = 10$

31. $\log_{1/2} x = 6$

For Exercises 32–52, find the logarithms without the use of a calculator.

32. $\log_7 49$

33. $\log_3 27$

34. $\log_{10} 0.1$

35. $\log_2\left(\dfrac{1}{16}\right)$

36. $\log_{16} 4$

37. $\log_8 2$

38. $\log_6 1$

39. $\log_8 8$

40. $\log_3 3^5$

41. $\log_9 9^3$

42. $\log_{10} 10$

43. $\log_7 1$

44. $\log(10)$

45. $\log(100)$

46. $\log(1000)$

47. $\log(10{,}000)$

48. $\log(1.0 \times 10^6)$

49. $\log(0.1)$

50. $\log(0.01)$

51. $\log(0.001)$

52. $\log(1.0 \times 10^{-6})$

For Exercises 53–64, use a calculator to approximate the logarithms. Round to 4 decimal places.

53. $\log 6$

54. $\log 18$

55. $\log \pi$

56. $\log \dfrac{1}{8}$

57. $\log\left(\dfrac{1}{32}\right)$

58. $\log(\sqrt{5})$

59. $\log(0.0054)$

60. $\log(0.0000062)$

61. $\log(3.4 \times 10^5)$

62. $\log(4.78 \times 10^9)$

63. $\log(3.8 \times 10^{-8})$

64. $\log(2.77 \times 10^{-4})$

65. Given that $\log 10 = 1$ and $\log 100 = 2$,
    a. Estimate $\log 93$.
    b. Estimate $\log 12$.
    c. Evaluate the logarithms in parts (a) and (b) on a calculator and compare to your estimates.

66. Given that $\log \frac{1}{10} = -1$ and $\log 1 = 0$,
    a. Estimate $\log \frac{9}{10}$.
    b. Estimate $\log \frac{1}{5}$.
    c. Evaluate the logarithms in parts (a) and (b) on a calculator and compare to your estimates.

67. Let $f(x) = \log_4 x$
    a. Find the values of $f(\frac{1}{64}), f(\frac{1}{16}), f(\frac{1}{4}), f(1), f(4),$ $f(16),$ and $f(64)$.
    b. Graph $y = f(x)$ by plotting the points found in part (a).

68. Let $g(x) = \log_2 x$
    a. Find the values of $g(\frac{1}{8}), g(\frac{1}{4}), g(\frac{1}{2}), g(1), g(2),$ $g(4),$ and $g(8)$.
    b. Graph $y = g(x)$ by plotting the points found in part (a).

Graph the logarithmic functions in Exercises 69–72 by writing the function in exponential form and making a table of points (see Examples 5 and 6).

69. $y = \log_3 x$

70. $y = \log_5 x$

71. $y = \log_{1/2} x$

72. $y = \log_{1/3} x$

73. State the domain for the function in Exercise 69.

74. State the domain for the function in Exercise 70.

75. State the domain for the function in Exercise 71.

76. State the domain for the function in Exercise 72.

For Exercises 77–82, find the domain of the function and express the domain in interval notation.

77. $y = \log_7(x - 5)$

78. $y = \log_3(2x + 1)$

79. $y = \log_3(x + 1.2)$

80. $y = \log\left(x - \dfrac{1}{2}\right)$

81. $y = \log(x^2)$ 82. $y = \log(x^2 + 1)$

83. A graduate student in education is doing research to compare the effectiveness of two different teaching techniques designed to teach vocabulary to sixth-graders. The first group of students (group 1) was taught with method I, in which the students worked individually to complete the assignments in a workbook. The second group (group 2) was taught with method II, in which the students worked cooperatively in groups of four to complete the assignments in the same workbook.

  None of the students knew any of the vocabulary words before the study began. After completing the assignments in the workbook, the students were then tested on the vocabulary at 1-month intervals to assess how much material they had retained over time. The students' average score t months after completing the assignments are given by the following functions:

Method I: $S_1(t) = 91 - 30 \log(t + 1)$, where t is the time in months and $S_1(t)$ is the average score of students in group 1.

Method II: $S_2(t) = 88 - 15 \log(t + 1)$, where t is the time in months and $S_2(t)$ is the average score of students in group 2.

a. Complete the table to find the average scores for each group of students after the indicated number of months. Round to one decimal place.

t (months)	0	1	2	6	12	24
$S_1(t)$						
$S_2(t)$						

Table for Exercise 83

b. Based on the table of values, what were the average scores for each group immediately after completion of the assigned material $(t = 0)$?

c. Based on the table of values, which teaching method helped students retain the material better for a long period of time?

84. Generally, the more money a company spends on advertising, the higher the sales. Let a represent the amount of money spent on advertising (in $100s). Then the amount of money in sales, $S(a)$, (in $1000s) is given by

  $S(a) = 10 + 20 \log(a + 1)$, where $a \geq 0$.

a. The value of $S(1) \approx 16.0$, which means that if $100 is spent on advertising, $16,000 is returned in sales. Find the values of $S(11)$, $S(21)$, and $S(31)$. Round to one decimal place. Interpret the meaning of each function value in the context of the problem.

b. The graph of $y = S(a)$ is shown here. Use the graph and your answers from part (a) to explain why the money spent in advertising becomes less "efficient" as it is used in larger amounts.

Figure for Exercise 84

GRAPHING CALCULATOR EXERCISES

For Exercises 85–90, graph the function on an appropriate viewing window. From the graph, identify the domain of the function and the location of the vertical asymptote.

85. $y = \log(x + 6)$ 86. $y = \log(2x + 4)$

87. $y = \log(0.5x - 1)$ 88. $y = \log(x + 8)$

89. $y = \log(2 - x)$ 90. $y = \log(3 - x)$

chapter 10   MIDCHAPTER REVIEW

1. Determine which of the following functions are one-to-one.

   a.

   b.

   c.

   d.
   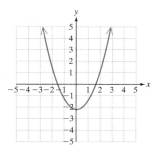

2. a. Write an equation of the inverse, f^{-1}, for the function defined by $f(x) = 3x - 5$.

   b. Graph both $y = f(x)$ and $y = f^{-1}(x)$ on the same coordinate system.

   c. Verify that the function found in part (a) is the inverse of f by showing that $(f \circ f^{-1})(x) = x$ and $(f^{-1} \circ f)(x) = x$.

3. The function defined by $g(x) = 7^x$ has the inverse defined by $g^{-1}(x) = \log_7(x)$.

   a. Graph both $y = g(x)$ and $y = g^{-1}(x)$ on the same coordinate system.

   b. Write an expression for $(g \circ g^{-1})(x) = x$.

   c. Write an expression for $(g^{-1} \circ g)(x) = x$.

4. The function defined by $h(x) = \log(x)$ has the inverse defined by $h^{-1}(x) = 10^x$.

   a. Graph both $y = h(x)$ and $y = h^{-1}(x)$ on the same coordinate system.

   b. Write an expression for $(h \circ h^{-1})(x) = x$.

   c. Write an expression for $(h^{-1} \circ h)(x) = x$.

section

10.4   PROPERTIES OF LOGARITHMS

1.   Properties of Logarithms

You have already been exposed to certain properties of logarithms that follow directly from the definition. Recall

$$y = \log_b(x) \text{ is equivalent to } b^y = x \quad \text{for } x > 0, b > 0, \text{ and } b \neq 1.$$

The following properties follow directly from the definition.

$$\log_b(1) = 0 \qquad \text{Property 1}$$

$$\log_b(b) = 1 \qquad \text{Property 2}$$

$$\log_b(b^p) = p \qquad \text{Property 3}$$

$$b^{\log_b(x)} = x \qquad \text{Property 4}$$

---

example 1   **Applying the Properties of Logarithms to Simplify Expressions**

Use the properties of logarithms to simplify the expressions. Assume that all variable expressions within the logarithms represent positive real numbers.

a. $\log_8(8) + \log_8(1)$ b. $10^{\log(x+2)}$ c. $\log_{1/2}\left(\dfrac{1}{2}\right)^x$

Solution:

a. $\log_8(8) + \log_8(1)$

$$= 1 + 0 \qquad \text{Properties 2 and 1}$$

$$= 1$$

b. $10^{\log(x+2)} = x + 2$ Property 4

c. $\log_{1/2}\left(\dfrac{1}{2}\right)^x = x$ Property 3

Three additional properties are useful when simplifying logarithmic expressions. The first is the product property for logarithms.

Product Property for Logarithms

Let b, x, and y be positive real numbers where $b \neq 1$. Then,

$$\log_b(xy) = \log_b(x) + \log_b(y)$$

The logarithm of a product equals the sum of the logarithms of the factors.

Proof:

Let $M = \log_b(x)$, which implies $b^M = x$.

Let $N = \log_b(y)$, which implies $b^N = y$.

Then $xy = b^M b^N = b^{M+N}$

Writing the expression $xy = b^{M+N}$ in logarithmic form, we have $\log_b(xy) = M + N$ or

$$\log_b(xy) = \log_b(x) + \log_b(y) \checkmark$$

To demonstrate the product property for logarithms, simplify the following expressions using the order of operations.

$$\log_3(3 \cdot 9) \overset{?}{=} \log_3(3) + \log_3(9)$$

$$\log_3(27) \overset{?}{=} 1 + 2$$

$$3 = 3 \checkmark$$

Quotient Property for Logarithms

Let b, x, and y be positive real numbers where $b \neq 1$. Then,

$$\log_b\left(\frac{x}{y}\right) = \log_b(x) - \log_b(y)$$

The logarithm of a quotient equals the difference of the logarithms of the numerator and denominator.

The proof of the quotient property for logarithms is similar to the proof of the product property and is omitted here. To demonstrate the quotient property for logarithms, simplify the following expressions using the order of operations.

$$\log\left(\frac{1,000,000}{100}\right) \overset{?}{=} \log(1,000,000) - \log(100)$$

$$\log(10,000) \overset{?}{=} 6 - 2$$

$$4 = 4 \checkmark$$

Power Property for Logarithms

Let b and x be positive real numbers where $b \neq 1$. Let p be any real number. Then,

$$\log_b(x^p) = p\log_b(x)$$

Proof:

Let $M = \log_b(x)$, which implies $b^M = x$.

Raise both sides to the p power: $(b^M)^p = (x)^p$ or equivalently $b^{Mp} = (x^p)$

Write the expression $b^{Mp} = (x^p)$ in logarithmic form: $\log_b(x^p) = Mp = pM$ or equivalently: $\log_b(x^p) = p\log_b(x)$ ✓

To demonstrate the power property for logarithms, simplify the following expressions using the order of operations.

$$\log_4(4^2) \overset{?}{=} 2\log_4(4)$$

$$2 \overset{?}{=} 2 \cdot 1$$

$$2 = 2 ✓$$

The properties of logarithms are summarized in the box.

Properties of Logarithms

Let b, x, and y be positive real numbers where $b \neq 1$, and let p be a real number. Then the following **properties of logarithms** are true.

1. $\log_b(1) = 0$ 5. $\log_b(xy) = \log_b(x) + \log_b(y)$ Product property for logarithms

2. $\log_b(b) = 1$ 6. $\log_b\left(\dfrac{x}{y}\right) = \log_b(x) - \log_b(y)$ Quotient property for logarithms

3. $\log_b(b^p) = p$ 7. $\log_b(x^p) = p\log_b(x)$ Power property for logarithms

4. $b^{\log_b(x)} = x$

---

2. Expanded Logarithmic Expressions

In many applications it is advantageous to expand a logarithm into a sum or difference of simpler logarithms.

---

example 2

Writing a Logarithmic Expression in Expanded Form

Write the expressions as the sum or difference of logarithms of x, y, and z. Assume all variable expressions within the logarithms represent positive real numbers.

a. $\log_3\left(\dfrac{xy^3}{z^2}\right)$ b. $\log\left(\dfrac{\sqrt{x+y}}{10}\right)$ c. $\log_b\sqrt[5]{\dfrac{x^4}{yz^3}}$

Solution:

a. $\log_3\left(\dfrac{xy^3}{z^2}\right)$

$= \log_3(xy^3) - \log_3(z^2)$ — Quotient property for logarithms (property 6)

$= [\log_3(x) + \log_3(y^3)] - \log_3(z^2)$ — Product property for logarithms (property 5)

$= \log_3(x) + 3\log_3(y) - 2\log_3(z)$ — Power property for logarithms (property 7)

b. $\log\left(\dfrac{\sqrt{x+y}}{10}\right)$

$= \log\sqrt{x+y} - \log(10)$ — Quotient property for logarithms (property 6)

$= \log(x+y)^{1/2} - 1$ — Write $\sqrt{x+y}$ as $(x+y)^{1/2}$ and simplify $\log(10) = 1$.

$= \dfrac{1}{2}\log(x+y) - 1$ — Power property for logarithms (property 7)

c. $\log_b \sqrt[5]{\dfrac{x^4}{yz^3}}$

$= \log_b\left(\dfrac{x^4}{yz^3}\right)^{1/5}$ — Write $\sqrt[5]{\dfrac{x^4}{yz^3}}$ as $\left(\dfrac{x^4}{yz^3}\right)^{1/5}$.

$= \dfrac{1}{5}\log_b\left(\dfrac{x^4}{yz^3}\right)$ — Power property for logarithms (property 7)

$= \dfrac{1}{5}(\log_b x^4 - \log_b(yz^3))$ — Quotient property for logarithms (property 6)

$= \dfrac{1}{5}(\log_b x^4 - [\log_b y + \log_b z^3])$ — Product property for logarithms (property 5)

$= \dfrac{1}{5}(\log_b x^4 - \log_b y - \log_b z^3)$ — Distributive property

$= \dfrac{1}{5}(4\log_b x - \log_b y - 3\log_b z)$ — Power property for logarithms (property 7)

or $\quad \dfrac{4}{5}\log_b x - \dfrac{1}{5}\log_b y - \dfrac{3}{5}\log_b z$

3. Single Logarithmic Expressions

In some applications it is necessary to write a sum or difference of logarithms as a single logarithm.

---

example 3   **Writing a Sum or Difference of Logarithms as a Single Logarithm**

Rewrite the expressions as a single logarithm, and simplify the result if possible. Assume all variable expressions within the logarithms represent positive real numbers.

a. $\log_2 560 - \log_2 7 - \log_2 5$

b. $2 \log x - \dfrac{1}{2} \log y + 3 \log z$

c. $\dfrac{1}{2}[\log_5(x^2 - y^2) - \log_5(x + y)]$

Solution:

a. $\log_2 560 - \log_2 7 - \log_2 5$

$= \log_2 560 - (\log_2 7 + \log_2 5)$	Factor out -1 from the last two terms.
$= \log_2 560 - \log_2(7 \cdot 5)$	Product property for logarithms (property 5)
$= \log_2\left(\dfrac{560}{7 \cdot 5}\right)$	Quotient property for logarithms (property 6)
$= \log_2(16)$	Simplify inside parentheses.
$= 4$	

b. $2 \log x - \dfrac{1}{2} \log y + 3 \log z$

$= \log x^2 - \log y^{1/2} + \log z^3$	Power property for logarithms (property 7)
$= \log x^2 + \log z^3 - \log y^{1/2}$	Group terms with positive coefficients.
$= \log(x^2 z^3) - \log y^{1/2}$	Product property for logarithms (property 5)
$= \log\left(\dfrac{x^2 z^3}{y^{1/2}}\right)$ or $\log\left(\dfrac{x^2 z^3}{\sqrt{y}}\right)$	Quotient property for logarithms (property 6)

c. $\dfrac{1}{2}[\log_5(x^2 - y^2) - \log_5(x + y)]$

$= \dfrac{1}{2}\log_5\left(\dfrac{x^2 - y^2}{x + y}\right)$	Quotient property for logarithms (property 6)
$= \dfrac{1}{2}\log_5\left[\dfrac{(x + y)(x - y)}{x + y}\right]$	Factor and reduce within the parentheses.

$$= \frac{1}{2}\log_5(x - y)$$

$$= \log_5(x - y)^{1/2} \text{ or } \log_5\sqrt{x - y} \qquad \text{Power property for logarithms} \\ \text{(property 7)}$$

It is important to note that the properties of logarithms may be used to write a single logarithm as a sum or difference of logarithms. Furthermore, the properties may be used to write a sum or difference of logarithms as a single logarithm. In either case, these operations may change the domain.

For example, consider the function $y = \log_b(x^2)$. Using the power property for logarithms we have $y = 2\log_b(x)$. Consider the domain of each function:

$y = \log_b(x^2)$ Domain: $\{x \mid x \neq 0\}$

$y = 2\log_b(x)$ Domain: $\{x \mid x > 0\}$

These two functions are equivalent only for values of x in the intersection of the two domains. That is for $x > 0$.

4. Applications Using the Properties of Logarithms

example 4

Applying the Properties of Logarithms

It is difficult to compare the magnitudes (brightness) and luminosities (total energy radiated) of stars because of the vast differences in their distances from the earth. Stars that are closer might appear brighter because of their proximity to the earth, not because they necessarily radiate more energy. The absolute magnitude of a star is a measure of its brightness if the star were located a distance of 10 parsecs (approximately 1.9×10^{13} miles) from the earth. The luminosity of a star, L, is related to its absolute magnitude, M, by the following formula:

$M = 4.71 + 2.5\log(3.9 \times 10^{26}) - 2.5\log(L)$, where M is the absolute magnitude of the star, and L is the luminosity of the star measured in watts (W).

a.   Show that the formula can be written as

$$M = 4.71 + 2.5\log\left(\frac{3.9 \times 10^{26}}{L}\right)$$

b.   The luminosity of the sun is 3.9×10^{26} W. Find the absolute magnitude of the sun.

c.   The luminosity of the "nearby" star, Sirius, is 8.2×10^{27} W. Find its absolute magnitude.

Solution:

a. $M = 4.71 + 2.5 \log(3.9 \times 10^{26}) - 2.5 \log(L)$

$= 4.71 + 2.5 \left[\log(3.9 \times 10^{26}) - \log(L)\right]$ Factor out 2.5 from the last two terms.

$= 4.71 + 2.5 \log\left(\dfrac{3.9 \times 10^{26}}{L}\right)$ Quotient property for logarithms (property 6)

b. $M = 4.71 + 25 \log\left(\dfrac{3.9 \times 10^{26}}{L}\right)$

$= 4.71 + 25 \log\left(\dfrac{3.9 \times 10^{26}}{3.9 \times 10^{26}}\right)$ Substitute $L = 3.9 \times 10^{26}$.

$= 4.71 + 2.5 \log(1)$
$= 4.71 + 0$

$= 4.71$ The absolute magnitude of the sun is 4.71.

c. $M = 4.71 + 2.5 \log\left(\dfrac{3.9 \times 10^{26}}{L}\right)$

$= 4.71 + 2.5 \log\left(\dfrac{3.9 \times 10^{26}}{8.2 \times 10^{27}}\right)$ Substitute $L = 8.2 \times 10^{27}$.

$\approx 4.71 + 2.5 \log(0.048)$
$\approx 4.71 + 2.5(-1.32)$

≈ 1.4 The absolute magnitude of Sirius is approximately 1.4.

---

section 10.4   PRACTICE EXERCISES

For Exercises 1–4, find the values of the logarithmic and exponential expressions without using a calculator.

1. 8^{-2}

2. $\log 10{,}000$

3. $\log_2 32$

4. 6^{-1}

For Exercises 5–8, approximate the values of the logarithmic and exponential expressions by using a calculator.

5. $(\sqrt{2})^{\pi}$

6. $\log 8$

7. $\log 27$

8. $\pi^{\sqrt{2}}$

For Exercises 9–12, match the function with the appropriate graph.

9. $f(x) = 4^x$

10. $q(x) = \left(\dfrac{1}{5}\right)^x$

11. $h(x) = \log_5 x$

12. $k(x) = \log_{1/3} x$

a.

b.

c.

d.

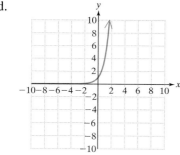

13. Property 1 of logarithms states that $\log_b 1 = 0$. Write an example of this property.

14. Property 2 of logarithms states that $\log_b b = 1$. Write an example of this property.

15. Property 3 of logarithms states that $\log_b(b^n) = n$. An example is $\log_6 6^3 = 3$. Write another example of this property.

16. Property 4 of logarithms states that $b^{\log_b(x)} = x$. An example is $10^{\log_{10} 5} = 5$. Write another example of this property.

For Exercises 17–28, evaluate each expression.

17. $\log_3 3$
18. $\log 10$
19. $\log_5 5^4$
20. $\log_4 4^5$
21. $6^{\log_6 11}$
22. $7^{\log_7 2}$
23. $\log 10^3$
24. $\log_6 6^3$
25. $\log_3 1$

26. $\log_8 1$
27. $10^{\log 9}$
28. $8^{\log_8 5}$

29. Compare the following expressions by approximating their values on a calculator. Which two expressions appear to be equivalent?

   a. $\log(3 \cdot 5)$

   b. $\log 3 \cdot \log 5$

   c. $\log 3 + \log 5$

30. Compare the following expressions by approximating their values on a calculator. Which two expressions appear to be equivalent?

   a. $\log\left(\dfrac{6}{5}\right)$

   b. $\dfrac{\log 6}{\log 5}$

   c. $\log 6 - \log 5$

31. Compare the following expressions by approximating their values on a calculator. Which two expressions appear to be equivalent?

   a. $\log(20^2)$

   b. $(\log 20)^2$

   c. $2 \log 20$

32. Compare the following expressions by approximating their values on a calculator. Which two expressions appear to be equivalent?

   a. $\log \sqrt{4}$

   b. $\dfrac{1}{2} \log 4$

   c. $\sqrt{\log 4}$

For Exercises 33–42, expand into sums and differences of logarithms.

33. $\log_3\left(\dfrac{x}{5}\right)$
34. $\log_2\left(\dfrac{y}{z}\right)$

35. $\log(2x)$
36. $\log_6(xyz)$

37. $\log_{10}(x^4)$
38. $\log_7(z^{1/3})$

39. $\log_4\left(\dfrac{ab}{c}\right)$
40. $\log_2\left(\dfrac{x}{yz}\right)$

41. $\log_b\left(\dfrac{\sqrt{xy}}{z^3 w}\right)$
42. $\log\left(\dfrac{a \cdot \sqrt[3]{b}}{cd^2}\right)$

For Exercises 43–50, write the expressions as a single logarithm.

43. $\log C + \log A + \log B + \log I + \log N$

44. $\log x + \log y - \log z$

45. $2 \log_3 x - 3 \log_3 y + \log_3 z$

46. $\log_5 a - \dfrac{1}{2} \log_5 b - 3 \log_5 c$

47. $\log_b x - 3 \log_b x + 4 \log_b x$

48. $2 \log_3 z + \log_3 z - \dfrac{1}{2} \log_3 z$

49. $5 \log_8 a - \log_8 1 + \log_8 8$

50. $\log_2 2 + 2 \log_2 b - \log_2 1$

51. The intensity of sound waves is measured in decibels and is calculated by the formula

$$B = 10 \log\!\left(\frac{I}{I_0}\right), \text{ where } I_0 \text{ is the minimum detectable decibel level.}$$

a. Expand this formula using the properties of logarithms.

b. Let $I_0 = 10^{-16}$ W/cm^2 and simplify.

52. The Richter scale is used to measure the intensity of an earthquake and is calculated by the formula

$$R = \log\!\left(\frac{I}{I_0}\right), \text{ where } I_0 \text{ is the minimum level detectable by a seismograph.}$$

a. Expand this formula using the properties of logarithms.

b. Let $I_0 = 1$ and simplify.

GRAPHING CALCULATOR EXERCISES

53. a. Graph $Y_1 = \log(x - 1)^2$ in *Dot Mode* and state its domain.

b. Graph $Y_2 = 2 \log(x - 1)$ in *Dot Mode* and state its domain.

c. For what values of x are the expressions $\log(x - 1)^2$ and $2 \log(x - 1)$ equivalent?

54. a. Graph $Y_1 = \log(x^2)$ in *Dot Mode* and state its domain.

b. Graph $Y_2 = 2 \log(x)$ in *Dot Mode* and state its domain.

c. For what values of x are the expressions $\log(x^2)$ and $2 \log(x)$ equivalent?

---

section

10.5   THE IRRATIONAL NUMBER, e

Concepts

1. Definition of the Irrational Number, e
2. Graph of $f(x) = e^x$
3. Computing Compound Interest
4. The Natural Logarithmic Function
5. Properties of the Natural Logarithmic Function
6. Simplifying Logarithmic Expressions
7. Change-of-Base Formula
8. Applications of the Natural Logarithmic Function

1. Definition of the Irrational Number, e

The exponential function base 10 is particularly easy to work with because integral powers of 10 represent different place positions in the base 10 numbering system. In this section, we introduce another important exponential function whose base is an irrational number called e.

Consider the expression $(1 + \frac{1}{x})^x$. The value of the expression for increasingly large values of x approaches a constant (Table 10-8).

Table 10-8

x	$\left(1 + \dfrac{1}{x}\right)^x$
100	2.70481382942
1000	2.71692393224
10,000	2.71814592683
100,000	2.71826823717
1,000,000	2.71828046932
1,000,000,000	2.71828182710

As x approaches infinity, the expression $(1 + \frac{1}{x})^x$ approaches a constant value that we call *e*. From Table 10-8, this value is approximately 2.718281828.

$$e \approx 2.718281828$$

The value of *e* is an irrational number (a nonterminating, nonrepeating decimal) and is a universal constant like π.

2.   **Graph of $f(x) = e^x$**

---

example 1

Graphing $f(x) = e^x$

Graph the function defined by $f(x) = e^x$.

Solution:

Because the base of the function is greater than 1 ($e \approx 2.718281828$), the graph is an increasing exponential function. We can use a calculator to evaluate $f(x) = e^x$ at several values of x.

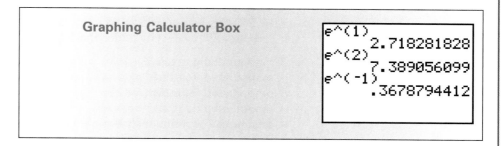

Graphing Calculator Box

Practice using your calculator by evaluating e^x for the following values of x. If you are using your calculator correctly, your answers should match those found in Table 10-9. Values are rounded to three decimal places. The corresponding graph of $f(x) = e^x$ is shown in Figure 10-15.

Table 10-9	
x	$f(x) = e^x$
-3	0.050
-2	0.135
-1	0.368
0	1.000
1	2.718
2	7.389
3	20.086

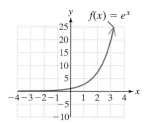

Figure 10-15

3. Computing Compound Interest

One particularly interesting application of exponential functions is in computing compound interest.

1. If the number of compounding periods per year is finite, then the amount in an account, A, is given by

    $A(t) = P\left(1 + \dfrac{r}{n}\right)^{nt}$, where P is the initial principal, r is the annual interest rate, n is the number of times compounded per year, t is the time in years that the money is invested.

2. If the number of compound periods per year is infinite, then interest is said to be **compounded continuously**. In such a case, the amount, A, in an account is given by

    $A(t) = Pe^{rt}$, where P is the initial principal, r is the annual interest rate, t is the time in years that the money is invested.

example 2   **Computing the Balance on an Account**

Suppose $5000 is invested in an account earning 6.5% interest. Find the balance in the account after 10 years under the following compounding options.

a. Compounded annually
b. Compounded quarterly
c. Compounded monthly
d. Compounded daily
e. Compounded continuously

Solution:

Compounding Option	n value	Formula	Result
annually	$n = 1$	$A(10) = 5000\left(1 + \dfrac{0.065}{1}\right)^{(1)(10)}$	$9385.69
quarterly	$n = 4$	$A(10) = 5000\left(1 + \dfrac{0.065}{4}\right)^{(4)(10)}$	$9527.79
monthly	$n = 12$	$A(10) = 5000\left(1 + \dfrac{0.065}{12}\right)^{(12)(10)}$	$9560.92
daily	$n = 365$	$A(10) = 5000\left(1 + \dfrac{0.065}{365}\right)^{(365)(10)}$	$9577.15
continuously	not applicable	$A(10) = 5000e^{(0.065)(10)}$	$9577.70

Notice that there is a $191.46 difference in the account balance between annual compounding and daily compounding. However, the difference between compounding daily and compounding continuously is small: $0.55. As n gets infinitely large, the function defined by

$$A(t) = P\left(1 + \frac{r}{n}\right)^{nt}$$

converges to $A(t) = Pe^{rt}$.

4. The Natural Logarithmic Function

Recall that the common logarithmic function $y = \log(x)$ has a base of 10. Another important logarithmic function is called the **natural logarithmic function**. The natural logarithmic function has a base of e and is written as $y = \ln(x)$. That is,

$$y = \ln(x) = \log_e(x)$$

example 3

Graphing $y = \ln(x)$

Graph $y = \ln(x)$.

Solution:

Because the base of the function $y = \ln(x)$ is base e, and $e > 1$, then the graph is an increasing logarithmic function. We can use a calculator to find specific points on the graph of $y = \ln(x)$ by using the $\boxed{\text{ln}}$ key.

Practice using your calculator by evaluating $\ln(x)$ for the following values of x. If you are using your calculator correctly, your answers should match those found in Table 10-10. Values are rounded to three decimal places. The corresponding graph of $y = \ln(x)$ is shown in Figure 10-16.

Table 10-10	
x	$\ln(x)$
1	0.000
2	0.693
3	1.099
4	1.386
5	1.609
6	1.792
7	1.946

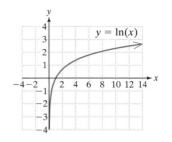

Figure 10-16

5. Properties of the Natural Logarithmic Function

The properties of logarithms stated in Section 10.4 are also true for natural logarithms.

Properties of the Natural Logarithmic Function

Let x and y be positive real numbers, and let p be a real number. Then the following properties are true.

1. $\ln(1) = 0$ 5. $\ln(xy) = \ln(x) + \ln(y)$ Product property for logarithms

2. $\ln(e) = 1$ 6. $\ln\left(\dfrac{x}{y}\right) = \ln(x) - \ln(y)$ Quotient property for logarithms

3. $\ln(e^p) = p$ 7. $\ln(x^p) = p\ln(x)$ Power property for logarithms

4. $e^{\ln(x)} = x$

6. Simplifying Logarithmic Expressions

example 4

Simplifying Expressions with Natural Logarithms

Simplify the expressions. Assume that all variable expressions within the logarithms represent positive real numbers.

a. $\ln(e)$ b. $\ln(1)$ c. $\ln e^{(x+1)}$ d. $e^{\ln(x+1)}$

Solution:

a. $\ln(e) = 1$ Property 2

b. $\ln(1) = 0$ Property 1

c. $\ln e^{(x+1)} = x + 1$ Property 3

d. $e^{\ln(x+1)} = x + 1$ Property 4

example 5

Writing a Sum or Difference of Natural Logarithms as a Single Logarithm

Write the expression as a single logarithm. Assume that all variable expressions within the logarithms represent positive real numbers.

$$\ln(x^2 - 9) - \ln(x - 3) - 2\ln(x)$$

Solution:

$$\ln(x^2 - 9) - \ln(x - 3) - 2\ln(x)$$

$$= \ln(x^2 - 9) - \ln(x - 3) - \ln(x^2) \qquad \text{Power property for logarithms (property 7)}$$

$$= \ln(x^2 - 9) - [\ln(x - 3) + \ln(x^2)] \qquad \text{Factor out } -1 \text{ from the last two terms.}$$

$$= \ln(x^2 - 9) - [\ln(x - 3)x^2] \qquad \text{Product property for logarithms (property 5)}$$

$$= \ln\left(\frac{x^2 - 9}{(x - 3)x^2}\right) \qquad \text{Quotient property for logarithms (property 6)}$$

$$= \ln\left(\frac{(x - 3)(x + 3)}{(x - 3)x^2}\right) \qquad \text{Factor.}$$

$$= \ln\left(\frac{x + 3}{x^2}\right) \quad \text{provided } x \neq 3 \qquad \text{Reduce.}$$

example 6

Writing a Logarithmic Expression in Expanded Form

Write the expression

$$\ln\left(\frac{e}{x^2\sqrt{y}}\right)$$

as a sum or difference of logarithms of x and y. Assume all variable expressions within the logarithm represents positive real numbers.

Solution:

$$\ln\left(\frac{e}{x^2\sqrt{y}}\right)$$

$$= \ln e - \ln(x^2\sqrt{y}) \qquad \text{Quotient property for logarithms (property 6)}$$

$$= \ln e - (\ln x^2 + \ln\sqrt{y}) \qquad \text{Product property for logarithms (property 5)}$$

$$= 1 - \ln x^2 - \ln y^{1/2} \qquad \text{Distributive property. Also simplify } \ln e = 1.$$

$$= 1 - 2\ln x - \frac{1}{2}\ln y \qquad \text{Power property for logarithms (property 7)}$$

7. Change-of-Base Formula

A calculator can be used to approximate the value of a logarithm with a base of 10 or a base of e by using the $\boxed{\log}$ key or the $\boxed{\ln}$ key, respectively. However, to use a calculator to evaluate a logarithmic expression with a base other than 10 or e, we must use the **change-of-base formula**.

Change-of-Base Formula

Let a and b be positive real numbers such that $a \neq 1$ and $b \neq 1$. Then for any positive real number x,

$$\log_b(x) = \frac{\log_a(x)}{\log_a(b)}$$

Proof:

Let $M = \log_b(x)$, which implies that $b^M = x$

Now, take the logarithm, base a, on both sides: $\log_a(b^M) = \log_a(x)$

Apply the power property for logarithms: $M \cdot \log_a(b) = \log_a(x)$

Divide both sides by $\log_a(b)$: $\dfrac{M \cdot \log_a(b)}{\log_a(b)} = \dfrac{\log_a(x)}{\log_a(b)}$

$$M = \frac{\log_a(x)}{\log_a(b)}$$

Because $M = \log_b(x)$, we have: $\log_b(x) = \dfrac{\log_a(x)}{\log_a(b)}$ ✓

The change-of-base formula converts a logarithm of one base to a ratio of logarithms of a different base. For the sake of using a calculator, we often apply the change-of-base formula with base 10 or base e.

---

example 7   **Using the Change-of-Base Formula**

a.   Use the change-of-base formula to evaluate $\log_4(80)$ by using base 10. (Round to three decimal places.)

b.   Use the change-of-base formula to evaluate $\log_4(80)$ by using base e. (Round to three decimal places.)

Solution:

a. $\log_4(80) = \dfrac{\log_{10}(80)}{\log_{10}(4)} = \dfrac{\log(80)}{\log(4)} \approx \dfrac{1.903089987}{0.6020599913} \approx 3.161$

b. $\log_4(80) = \dfrac{\log_e(80)}{\log_e(4)} = \dfrac{\ln(80)}{\ln(4)} \approx \dfrac{4.382026635}{1.386294361} \approx 3.161$

To check the result, we see that $4^{3.161} \approx 80$.

Graphing Calculator Box

The change-of-base formula can be used to graph logarithmic functions with bases other than 10 or *e*. For example, to graph $Y_1 = \log_2(x)$ we can enter the function as either

$$Y_1 = \frac{\log(x)}{\log(2)} \quad \text{or as} \quad Y_1 = \frac{\ln(x)}{\ln(2)}$$

8. Applications of the Natural Logarithmic Function

example 8

Applying the Natural Logarithm Function to Radioactive Decay

Plant and animal tissue contains both carbon-12 and carbon-14. Carbon-12 is a stable form of carbon, whereas carbon-14 is a radioactive isotope with a half-life of approximately 5730 years. While a plant or animal is living, it takes in carbon from the atmosphere either through photosynthesis or through its food. The ratio of carbon-14 to carbon-12 in a living organism is constant and is the same as the ratio found in the atmosphere.

When a plant or animal dies, it no longer ingests carbon from the atmosphere. The amount of stable carbon-12 remains unchanged from the time of death, but the carbon-14 begins to decay. Because the rate of decay is constant, a tissue sample can be dated by comparing the percentage of carbon-14 still present to the percentage of carbon-14 assumed to be in its original living state.

The age of a tissue sample is a function of the percentage of carbon-14 still present in the organism according to the following model:

$$A(p) = \frac{\ln(p)}{-0.000121},$$ where A is the age in years and p is the percentage (in decimal form) of carbon-14 still present.

a. Find the age of a bone that has 72% of its initial carbon-14.
b. Find the age of the Iceman, a body uncovered in the mountains of northern Italy in 1991. Samples of his hair revealed that 51.4% of the original carbon-14 was present after his death.

Solution:

a.
$$A(p) = \frac{\ln(p)}{-0.000121}$$

$$A(0.72) = \frac{\ln(0.72)}{-0.000121} \qquad \text{Substitute 0.72 for } p.$$

$$\approx 2715 \text{ years}$$

b. $\quad A(p) = \dfrac{\ln(p)}{-0.000121}$

$\quad A(0.514) = \dfrac{\ln(0.514)}{-0.000121}$ Substitute 0.514 for p.

$\quad\quad\quad\quad \approx 5500 \text{ years}$ The body of the Iceman is approximately 5500 years old.

---

section 10.5   PRACTICE EXERCISES

For Exercises 1–4, fill out the tables and graph the functions. For Exercises 3 and 4, round to two decimal places.

1. $f(x) = \left(\dfrac{3}{2}\right)^x$

x	f(x)
-3	
-2	
-1	
0	
1	
2	
3	

2. $g(x) = \left(\dfrac{1}{5}\right)^x$

x	g(x)
-3	
-2	
-1	
0	
1	
2	
3	

3. $q(x) = \log(x + 1)$

x	q(x)
-0.75	
-0.50	
-0.25	
0	
1	
2	

4. $r(x) = \log x$

x	r(x)
0.25	
0.50	
0.75	
1	
2	
3	

For Exercises 5–8, write the expression as a sum or difference of $\ln a$, $\ln b$, and $\ln c$.

5. $\ln\left(\dfrac{a^4\sqrt{b}}{c}\right)$

6. $\ln\left(\dfrac{\sqrt{ab}}{c^3}\right)$

7. $\ln\left(\dfrac{ab}{c^2}\right)^{1/5}$

8. $\ln\sqrt{2ab}$

For Exercises 9–12, write the expression as a single logarithm.

9. $2\ln a - \ln b - \dfrac{1}{3}\ln c$

10. $-\ln x + 3\ln y - \ln z$

11. $4\ln x - 3\ln y - \ln z$

12. $\dfrac{1}{2}\ln c + \ln a - 2\ln b$

13. a. Graph $f(x) = e^x$

    b. Identify the domain and range of f.

    c. Graph $g(x) = \ln x$

    d. Identify the domain and range of g.

14. a.   Graph $f(x) = 10^x$

 b.   Identify the domain and range of f.

 c.   Graph $g(x) = \log x$

 d.   Identify the domain and range of g.

15. Graph $y = e^{x+1}$ by completing the table and plotting the points. Identify the domain and range.

x	y
-4	
-3	
-2	
-1	
0	
1	
2	

16. Graph $y = e^{x+2}$ by completing the table and plotting the points. Identify the domain and range.

x	y
-5	
-4	
-3	
-2	
-1	
0	
1	

17. Graph $y = \ln(x - 2)$ by completing the table and plotting the points. Identify the domain and range.

x	y
2.25	
2.50	
2.75	
3	
4	
5	
6	

18. Graph $y = \ln(x - 1)$ by completing the table and plotting the points. Identify the domain and range.

x	y
1.25	
1.50	
1.75	
2	
3	
4	
5	

19. a.   Evaluate $\log_6(200)$ by computing $\log(200)/\log(6)$ to four decimal places.

 b.   Evaluate $\log_6(200)$ by computing $\ln(200)/\ln(6)$ to four decimal places.

 c.   How do your answers to parts (a) and (b) compare?

20. a.   Evaluate $\log_8(120)$ by computing $\log(120)/\log(8)$ to four decimal places.

 b.   Evaluate $\log_8(120)$ by computing $\ln(200)/\ln(8)$ to four decimal places.

 c.   How do your answers to parts (a) and (b) compare?

For Exercises 21–32, use the change-of-base formula to approximate the logarithms to four decimal places. Check your answers by using the exponential key on your calculator. (See Example 7.)

21. $\log_2 7$

22. $\log_3 5$

23. $\log_8 24$

24. $\log_4 17$

25. $\log_8 0.012$

26. $\log_7 0.251$

27. $\log_9 1$

28. $\log_2\left(\dfrac{1}{5}\right)$

29. $\log_4\left(\dfrac{1}{100}\right)$

30. $\log_5 0.0025$

31. $\log_7 0.0006$

32. $\log_2 0.24$

33. Given that $\log_3 9 = 2$ and $\log_3 27 = 3$,

 a.   Estimate $\log_3 15$

 b.   Estimate $\log_3 25$

c. Evaluate the logarithms in parts (a) and (b) on a calculator and compare to your estimates.

34. Given that $\log_5 1 = 0$ and $\log_5 5 = 1$,

a. Estimate $\log_5 2$

b. Estimate $\log_5 4$

c. Evaluate the logarithms in parts (a) and (b) on a calculator and compare to your estimates.

35. Given that $\log_6 6 = 1$ and $\log_6 36 = 2$,

a. Estimate $\log_6 10$

b. Estimate $\log_6 30$

c. Evaluate the logarithms in parts (a) and (b) on a calculator and compare to your estimates.

36. Given that $\log_4 4 = 1$ and $\log_4 16 = 2$,

a. Estimate $\log_4 6$

b. Estimate $\log_4 12$

c. Evaluate the logarithms in parts (a) and (b) on a calculator and compare to your estimates.

Under continuous compounding, the amount of time, t, in years required for an investment to double is a function of the interest rate, r:

$$t = \frac{\ln(2)}{r}$$

Use the formula for Exercises 37–38.

37. a. If you invest $5000, how long will it take the investment to reach $10,000 if the interest rate is 4.5%? Round to one decimal place.

b. If you invest $5000, how long will it take the investment to reach $10,000 if the interest rate is 10%? Round to one decimal place.

c. Using the doubling time found in part (b), how long would it take a $5000 investment to reach $20,000 if the interest rate is 10%?

38. a. If you invest $3000, how long will it take the investment to reach $6000 if the interest rate is 5.5%? Round to one decimal place.

b. If you invest $3000, how long will it take the investment to reach $6000 if the interest rate is 8%? Round to one decimal place.

c. Using the doubling time found in part (b), how long would it take a $3000 investment to reach $12,000 if the interest rate is 8%?

39. A certain chemotherapy drug is sometimes given to patients undergoing bone marrow transplantation. For one particular patient, the concentration of this drug in the bloodstream over time is modeled by the following piecewise-defined function:

$$C(t) = \begin{cases} -0.088 + 0.890 \ln(t + 2) & \text{for } 0 < t < 72 \\ 4.64e^{-0.003t} & \text{for } t \geq 72 \end{cases},$$

where t is the time in minutes and $C(t)$ is the drug concentration measured in micromoles per liter (μmol/L).

The graph of $y = C(t)$ is shown in the figure.

A Chemotherapy Drug Concentration Versus Time

Figure for Exercise 39

a. On what open interval is the concentration of the drug increasing? (This is called the absorption phase.)

b. On what open interval is the concentration of the drug decreasing? (This is called dissipation phase.)

c. What is the concentration of the drug after 10 min? Round to two decimal places.

d. What is the concentration of the drug after 1 h? Round to two decimal places.

e. What is the concentration of the drug after 1 day? Round to two decimal places.

f. Use the graph to estimate the time (to the nearest hundred minutes) when the drug concentration drops to 2.0 μmol/L during the dissipation phase.

40. On August 31, 1854, an epidemic of cholera was discovered in London, England, resulting from a contaminated community water pump at Broad Street. By the end of September more than 600 citizens who drank water from the pump had died.

    The cumulative number of deaths from cholera in the 1854 London epidemic can be approximated by

    $D(t) = 91 + 160 \ln(t + 1)$, where t is the number of days after the start of the epidemic ($t = 0$ corresponds to September 1, 1854).

    a. Approximate total number of deaths as of September 1 ($t = 0$).

    b. Approximate total number of deaths as of September 5, September 10, and September 20.

In Exercises 41–46 use the model

$$A(t) = P\left(1 + \frac{r}{n}\right)^{nt}$$

for interest compounded n times per year. Use the model $A(t) = Pe^{rt}$ for interest compounded continuously. **How does interest rate affect an investment?**

41. Suppose an investor deposits $10,000 in a certificate of deposit for 5 years for which the interest is compounded monthly. Find the total amount of money in the account for the following interest rates. Compare your answers and comment on the effect of interest rate on an investment.

    a. $r = 4.0\%$

    b. $r = 6.0\%$

    c. $r = 8.0\%$

    d. $r = 9.5\%$

42. Suppose an investor deposits $5000 in a certificate of deposit for 8 years for which the interest is compounded quarterly. Find the total amount of money in the account for the following interest rates. Compare your answers and comment on the effect of interest rate on an investment.

    a. $r = 4.5\%$

    b. $r = 5.5\%$

    c. $r = 7.0\%$

    d. $r = 9.0\%$

How does the number of compound periods affect an investment?

43. Suppose an investor deposits $8000 in a savings account for 10 years at 4.5% interest. Find the total amount of money in the account for the following compounding options. Compare your answers. How does the number of compound periods per year affect the total investment?

    a. Compounded annually

    b. Compounded quarterly

    c. Compounded monthly

    d. Compounded daily

    e. Compounded continuously

44. Suppose an investor deposits $15,000 in a savings account for 8 years at 5.0% interest. Find the total amount of money in the account for the following compounding options. Compare your answers. How does the number of compound periods per year affect the total investment?

    a. Compounded annually

    b. Compounded quarterly

    c. Compounded monthly

    d. Compounded daily

    e. Compounded continuously

How does the length of time money is invested affect the account value?

45. Suppose an investor deposits $5000 in an account bearing 6.5% interest compounded continuously. Find the total amount in the account for the following time periods.

    a. 5 years

    b. 10 years

    c. 15 years

    d. 20 years

    e. 30 years

46. Suppose an investor deposits $10,000 in an account bearing 6.0% interest compounded continuously. Find the total amount in the account for the following time periods.

    a. 5 years

    b. 10 years

c. 15 years

d. 20 years

e. 30 years

47. a. Graph the function defined by $f(x) = \log_3(x)$ by graphing $Y_1 = \log(x)/\log(3)$.

   b. Graph the function defined by $f(x) = \log_3(x)$ by graphing $Y_2 = \ln(x)/\ln(3)$.

   c. Does it appear that $Y_1 = Y_2$ on the standard viewing window?

48. a. Graph the function defined by $f(x) = \log_7(x)$ by graphing $Y_1 = \log(x)/\log(7)$.

   b. Graph the function defined by $f(x) = \log_7(x)$ by graphing $Y_2 = \ln(x)/\ln(7)$.

   c. Does it appear that $Y_1 = Y_2$ on the standard viewing window?

49. a. Graph the function defined by $f(x) = \log_{1/3}(x)$ by graphing $Y_1 = \log(x)/\log(\frac{1}{3})$.

   b. Graph the function defined by $f(x) = \log_{1/3}(x)$ by graphing $Y_2 = \ln(x)/\ln(\frac{1}{3})$.

   c. Does it appear that $Y_1 = Y_2$ on the standard viewing window?

50. a. Graph the function defined by $f(x) = \log_{1/7}(x)$ by graphing $Y_1 = \log(x)/\log(\frac{1}{7})$.

   b. Graph the function defined by $f(x) = \log_{1/7}(x)$ by graphing $Y_2 = \ln(x)/\ln(\frac{1}{7})$.

   c. Does it appear that $Y_1 = Y_2$ on the standard viewing window?

For Exercises 51–56, graph the functions on your calculator.

51. Graph $s(x) = \log_{1/2}(x)$

52. Graph $w(x) = \log_{1/3}(x)$

53. Graph $y = e^{x-2}$

54. Graph $y = e^{x-1}$

55. Graph $y = \ln(x + 1)$

56. Graph $y = \ln(x + 2)$

---

section

10.6   EXPONENTIAL AND LOGARITHMIC EQUATIONS

Concepts

1. Solving Logarithmic Equations

2. Solving Logarithmic Equations in Quadratic Form

3. Applications of Logarithmic Equations

4. Solving Exponential Equations

5. Applications of Exponential Equations— Population Growth

6. Applications of Exponential Equations— Radioactive Decay

1.   Solving Logarithmic Equations

Equations containing one or more logarithms are called **logarithmic equations**. For example,

$$\log_4 x = 1 - \log_4(x - 3) \qquad \text{and} \qquad \ln(x + 2) + \ln(x - 1) = \ln(9x - 17)$$

are logarithmic equations. To solve logarithmic equations of first degree, use the following guidelines.

Guidelines to Solve Logarithmic Equations

1. Isolate the logarithms on one side of the equation.
2. Write a sum or difference of logarithms as a single logarithm.
3. Rewrite the equation in step 2 in exponential form.
4. Solve the resulting equation from step 3.
5. Check all solutions to verify that they are within the domain of the logarithmic expressions in the original equation.

example 1

Solving a Logarithmic Equation

Solve the equation.

$$\log_4 x = 1 - \log_4(x - 3)$$

Solution:

$$\log_4 x = 1 - \log_4(x - 3)$$

$\log_4 x + \log_4(x - 3) = 1$	Isolate the logarithms on one side of the equation.
$\log_4[x(x - 3)] = 1$	Write as a single logarithm.
$\log_4(x^2 - 3x) = 1$	Simplify inside the parentheses.
$4^1 = x^2 - 3x$	Write the equation in exponential form.
$x^2 - 3x - 4 = 0$	The resulting equation is quadratic.
$(x - 4)(x + 1) = 0$	Factor.
$x = 4 \quad$ or $\quad x = -1$	Apply the zero product rule.

Tip: The equation from Example 1 involved the logarithmic functions $y = \log_4(x)$ and $y = \log_4(x - 3)$. The domains of these functions are $\{x \mid x > 0\}$ and $\{x \mid x > 3\}$, respectively. Therefore, the solutions to the equation are restricted to x values in the intersection of these two sets. That is, $\{x \mid x > 3\}$. The solution $x = 4$ satisfies this requirement, whereas $x = -1$ does not.

Notice that $x = -1$ is *not* a solution because $\log_4(x)$ is not defined at $x = -1$. However, $x = 4$ *is* defined in both expressions $\log_4(x)$ and $\log_4(x - 3)$. We can substitute $x = 4$ into the original equation to show that it checks.

Check: $x = 4$

$$\log_4 x = 1 - \log_4(x - 3)$$

$$\log_4(4) \overset{?}{=} 1 - \log_4(4 - 3)$$

$$1 \overset{?}{=} 1 - \log_4(1)$$

$$1 \overset{?}{=} 1 - 0 \checkmark$$

The solution is $x = -4$.

example 2

Solving Logarithmic Equations

Solve the equations.

a. $\ln(x + 2) + \ln(x - 1) = \ln(9x - 17)$

b. $\log(x + 300) = 3.7$

c. $\ln(2x + 5) = 1$

Solution:

a.
$$\ln(x + 2) + \ln(x - 1) = \ln(9x - 17)$$

$$\ln(x + 2) + \ln(x - 1) - \ln(9x - 17) = 0$$ Isolate the logarithms on one side.

$$\ln\left[\frac{(x + 2)(x - 1)}{9x - 17}\right] = 0$$ Write as a single logarithm.

$$e^0 = \frac{(x + 2)(x - 1)}{9x - 17}$$ Write the equation in exponential form.

$$1 = \frac{(x + 2)(x - 1)}{9x - 17}$$ Simplify.

$$(1) \cdot (9x - 17) = \left(\frac{(x + 2)(x - 1)}{9x - 17}\right) \cdot (9x - 17)$$ Multiply by the LCD.

$$9x - 17 = (x + 2)(x - 1)$$ The equation is quadratic.

$$9x - 17 = x^2 + x - 2$$

$$0 = x^2 - 8x + 15$$

$$0 = (x - 5)(x - 3)$$

$$x = 5 \quad \text{or} \quad x = 3$$

The solutions $x = 5$ and $x = 3$ are both within the domain of the logarithmic functions in the original equation.

<u>Check:</u> $x = 5$ <u>Check:</u> $x = 3$

$\ln(x + 2) + \ln(x - 1) = \ln(9x - 17)$ $\ln(x + 2) + \ln(x - 1) = \ln(9x - 17)$

$\ln(5 + 2) + \ln(5 - 1) \stackrel{?}{=} \ln(9(5) - 17)$ $\ln(3 + 2) + \ln(3 - 1) \stackrel{?}{=} \ln(9(3) - 17)$

$\ln(7) + \ln(4) \stackrel{?}{=} \ln(45 - 17)$ $\ln(5) + \ln(2) \stackrel{?}{=} \ln(27 - 17)$

$\ln(7 \cdot 4) \stackrel{?}{=} \ln(28)$ $\ln(5 \cdot 2) \stackrel{?}{=} \ln(10)$

$\ln(28) \stackrel{?}{=} \ln(28) \checkmark$ $\ln(10) \stackrel{?}{=} \ln(10) \checkmark$

Both solutions check.

b. $\log(x + 300) = 3.7$ The equation has a single logarithm that is already isolated.

$$10^{3.7} = x + 300$$ Write the equation in exponential form.

$$10^{3.7} - 300 = x$$ Solve for x.

$$x = 10^{3.7} - 300 \approx 4711.87$$

Check: $x = 10^{3.7} - 300$

Check the exact value of x in the original equation.

$$\log(x + 300) = 3.7$$

$$\log[(10^{3.7} - 300) + 300] \overset{?}{=} 3.7$$

$$\log(10^{3.7} - 300 + 300) \overset{?}{=} 3.7$$

$$\log(10^{3.7}) \overset{?}{=} 3.7$$

Property 3 of logarithms:
$\log_b(b^p) = p$

$$3.7 \overset{?}{=} 3.7 \checkmark$$

The solution $x = 10^{3.7} - 300$ checks.

c. $\ln(2x + 5) = 1$

The equation has a single logarithm that is already isolated.

$$e^1 = 2x + 5$$

Write the equation in exponential form.

$$2x + 5 = e$$

The resulting equation is linear.

$$2x = e - 5$$

Solve for x.

$$x = \frac{e - 5}{2} \approx -1.14$$

Check: $x = \dfrac{e - 5}{2}$

$$\ln(2x + 5) = 1$$

$$\ln\left[2\left(\frac{e - 5}{2}\right) + 5\right] \overset{?}{=} 1$$

$$\ln(e - 5 + 5) \overset{?}{=} 1$$

$$\ln(e) \overset{?}{=} 1 \checkmark$$

The solution checks.

Graphing Calculator Box

To support the solution to Example 2(c) graph $Y_1 = \ln(2x + 5)$ and $Y_2 = 1$. Use the graph to approximate the x-coordinate where $Y_1 = Y_2$.

2. Solving Logarithmic Equations in Quadratic Form

example 3

Solving a Logarithmic Equation that Is in Quadratic Form

Solve the equation.

$$(\ln x)^2 - 7 \ln x + 12 = 0$$

Solution:

$(\ln x)^2 - 7 \ln x + 12 = 0$ By letting $u = \ln x$, we see that the equation is in quadratic form.

$$u^2 - 7u + 12 = 0$$

$$(u - 4)(u - 3) = 0$$

$u = 4$ or $u = 3$ Reverse substitute.

$\ln x = 4$ or $\ln x = 3$

$x = e^4$ or $x = e^3$ Write the logarithmic equations in
$x \approx 54.6$ or $x \approx 20.1$ exponential form.

Check: $x = e^4$ Check: $x = e^3$

$(\ln x)^2 - 7 \ln x + 12 = 0$ $(\ln x)^2 - 7 \ln x + 12 = 0$

$[\ln(e^4)]^2 - 7 \ln(e^4) + 12 \overset{?}{=} 0$ $[\ln(e^3)]^2 - 7 \ln(e^3) + 12 \overset{?}{=} 0$

$(4)^2 - 7 \cdot 4 + 12 \overset{?}{=} 0$ $(3)^2 - 7 \cdot 3 + 12 \overset{?}{=} 0$

$16 - 28 + 12 \overset{?}{=} 0$ $9 - 21 + 12 \overset{?}{=} 0$

$-12 + 12 \overset{?}{=} 0 \checkmark$ $-12 + 12 \overset{?}{=} 0 \checkmark$

Both solutions check.

Graphing Calculator Box

To support the solution to Example 3 graph $Y_1 = (\ln x)^2 - 7 \ln(x) + 12$. The values of x for which $Y_1 = 0$ can be approximated by using a *Zoom* and *Trace* feature.

3. Applications of Logarithmic Equations

example 4

Applying a Logarithmic Equation to Earthquake Intensity

The magnitude of an earthquake (the amount of seismic energy released at the hypocenter of the earthquake) is measured on the Richter scale. The Richter scale value, R, is determined by the formula

$R = \log\left(\dfrac{I}{I_0}\right)$, where I is the intensity of the earthquake and I_0 is the minimum measurable intensity of an earthquake. (I_0 is a "zero level" quake—one that is barely detected by a seismograph.)

a. Compare the Richter scale values of earthquakes that are (i) 100,000 times (10^5 times) more intense than I_0 and (ii) 1,000,000 times (10^6 times) more intense than I_0.

b. On October 17, 1989, an earthquake measuring 7.1 on the Richter scale occurred in the Loma Prieta area in the Santa Cruz Mountains. The quake devastated parts of San Francisco and Oakland, California, bringing 63 deaths and over 3700 injuries. Determine how many times more intense this earthquake was than a zero-level quake.

Solution:

a. $R = \log\left(\dfrac{I}{I_0}\right)$

i. Earthquake 100,000 times I_0

$R = \log\left(\dfrac{10^5 I_0}{I_0}\right)$ Substitute $I = 10^5 I_0$

$ = \log(10^5)$

$ = 5$

ii. Earthquake 1,000,000 times I_0

$R = \log\left(\dfrac{10^6 I_0}{I_0}\right)$ Substitute $I = 10^6 I_0$

$ = \log(10^6)$

$ = 6$

Notice that the value on the Richter scale corresponds to the magnitude (power of 10) of the energy released. That is, a 1-unit increase on the Richter scale represents a 10-fold increase in the intensity of an earthquake.

b. $R = \log\left(\dfrac{I}{I_0}\right)$

$7.1 = \log\left(\dfrac{I}{I_0}\right)$ Substitute $R = 7.1$.

$\dfrac{I}{I_0} = 10^{7.1}$ Write the equation in exponential form.

$I = 10^{7.1} I_0$ Solve for I.

The Loma Prieta earthquake in 1989 was $10^{7.1}$ times ($\approx 12{,}590{,}000$ times) more intense than a zero-level earthquake.

■

4. Solving Exponential Equations

An equation with one or more exponential expressions is called an **exponential equation**. The following property is often useful in solving exponential equations.

Equivalence of Exponential Expressions

Let x, y, and b be real numbers such that $b > 0$ and $b \neq 1$. Then

$$b^x = b^y \qquad \text{implies} \qquad x = y$$

The equivalence of exponential expressions indicates that if two exponential expressions of the same base are equal, their exponents must be equal.

example 5   **Solving Exponential Equations**

Solve the equations.

a. $4^{2x-9} = 64$

b. $(2^x)^{x+3} = \dfrac{1}{4}$

Solution:

a. $4^{2x-9} = 64$

$4^{2x-9} = 4^3$ Write both sides with a common base.

$2x - 9 = 3$ If $b^x = b^y$, then $x = y$.

$2x = 12$ Solve for x.

$x = 6$

To check, substitute $x = 6$ into the original equation.

$$4^{2(6)-9} \stackrel{?}{=} 64$$

$$4^{12-9} \stackrel{?}{=} 64$$

$$4^3 = 64 \checkmark$$

b. $(2^x)^{x+3} = \dfrac{1}{4}$

   $2^{x^2+3x} = 2^{-2}$ Apply the multiplication property of exponents. Write both sides of the equation with a common base.

   $x^2 + 3x = -2$ If $b^x = b^y$, then $x = y$.

   $x^2 + 3x + 2 = 0$ The resulting equation is quadratic.

   $(x + 2)(x + 1) = 0$ Solve for x.

   $x = -2$ or $x = -1$

   <u>Check: $x = -2$</u>   <u>Check: $x = -1$</u>

   $(2^{-2})^{(-2)+3} \overset{?}{=} \dfrac{1}{4}$ $(2^{-1})^{(-1)+3} \overset{?}{=} \dfrac{1}{4}$

   $(2^{-2})^1 \overset{?}{=} \dfrac{1}{4}$ $(2^{-1})^2 \overset{?}{=} \dfrac{1}{4}$

   $2^{-2} \overset{?}{=} \dfrac{1}{4}$ ✓ $2^{-2} \overset{?}{=} \dfrac{1}{4}$ ✓

   Both solutions check.

---

example 6

Solving an Exponential Equation

Solve the equation: $4^x = 25$.

Solution:

Because 25 cannot be written as an integral power of 4, we cannot immediately use the property that if $b^x = b^y$, then $x = y$. Instead we can rewrite the equation in its corresponding logarithmic form to solve for x.

   $4^x = 25$

   $x = \log_4(25)$ Write the equation in logarithmic form.

   $= \dfrac{\ln(25)}{\ln(4)} \approx 2.322$ Change-of-base formula

---

Graphing Calculator Box

Graph $Y_1 = 4^x$ and $Y_2 = 25$.

An *Intersect* feature can be used to find the x-coordinate where $Y_1 = Y_2$.

The same result can be reached by taking a logarithm of any base on both sides of the equation. Then by applying the power property of logarithms, the unknown exponent can be written as a factor.

$$4^x = 25$$

$$\log 4^x = \log 25$$ Take the common logarithm of both sides.

$$x \log 4 = \log 25$$ Apply the power property of logarithms to express the exponent as a factor. This is now a linear equation in x.

$$\frac{x \log 4}{\log 4} = \frac{\log 25}{\log 4}$$ Solve for x.

$$x = \frac{\log(25)}{\log(4)} \approx 2.322$$

Guidelines to Solve Exponential Equations

1. Isolate one of the exponential expressions in the equation.
2. Take a logarithm on both sides of the equation. (The natural logarithm function or the common logarithm function is often used so that the final answer can be approximated with a calculator.)
3. Use the power property of logarithms (property 7) to write exponents as factors. Recall: $\log_b(M^p) = p \log_b(M)$
4. Solve the resulting equation from step 3.

---

example 7

Solving Exponential Equations by Taking a Logarithm on Both Sides

Solve the equations.

a. $2^{x+3} = 7^x$ b. $e^{-3.6x} = 9.74$

Solution:

a. $2^{x+3} = 7^x$

$$\ln 2^{(x+3)} = \ln 7^x$$ Take the natural logarithm of both sides.

$$(x + 3)\ln 2 = x \ln 7$$ Express the exponents as factors.

$$x(\ln 2) + 3(\ln 2) = x \ln 7$$ Apply the distributive property.

$$x(\ln 2) - x(\ln 7) = -3 \ln 2$$ Collect x-terms on one side.

$$x(\ln 2 - \ln 7) = -3 \ln 2$$ Factor out x.

$$\frac{x(\ln 2 - \ln 7)}{(\ln 2 - \ln 7)} = \frac{-3 \ln 2}{(\ln 2 - \ln 7)} \qquad \text{Solve for } x.$$

$$x = \frac{-3 \ln 2}{(\ln 2 - \ln 7)} \approx 1.660$$

Tip: The exponential equation $2^{x+3} = 7^x$ could have been solved by taking a logarithm of *any* base on both sides of the equation. For example, using base 10 yields:

$$\log 2^{x+3} = \log 7^x$$

$(x + 3) \log 2 = x \log 7$ Apply the power property for logarithms.

$x \log 2 + 3 \log 2 = x \log 7$ Apply the distributive property.

$x \log 2 - x \log 7 = -3 \log 2$ Collect x-terms on one side of the equation.

$x(\log 2 - \log 7) = -3 \log 2$ Factor out x.

$$x = \frac{-3 \log 2}{\log 2 - \log 7} \approx 1.660$$

b. $e^{-3.6x} = 9.74$

$\ln e^{-3.6x} = \ln 9.74$ The exponential expression has a base of e, so it is convenient to take the natural logarithm of both sides.

$(-3.6x)\ln e = \ln 9.74$ Express the exponent as a factor.

$-3.6x = \ln 9.74$ Simplify (recall that $\ln e = 1$).

$$x = \frac{\ln 9.74}{-3.6} \approx -0.632$$

5. Applications of Exponential Equations— Population Growth

example 8

Applying an Exponential Function to World Population

The population of the world was estimated to have reached 6 billion in October 1999. The population growth rate for the world is estimated to be 1.4%. (*Source: Information Please Almanac*, 1999)

$$P(t) = 6(1.014)^t$$

represents the world population in billions as a function of the number of years after October 1999 ($t = 0$ represents October 1999).

a. Use the function to estimate the world population in October of 2005 and in October of 2010.
b. Use the function to estimate the amount of time after October 1999 required for the world population to reach 12 billion.

Solution:

a. $P(t) = 6(1.014)^t$

$P(6) = 6(1.014)^6$ The year 2005 corresponds to $t = 6$.

≈ 6.5 In 2005, the world's population will be approximately 6.5 billion.

$P(11) = 6(1.014)^{11}$ The year 2010 corresponds to $t = 11$.

≈ 7.0 In 2010, the world's population will be approximately 7.0 billion.

b. $P(t) = 6(1.014)^t$

$12 = 6(1.014)^t$ Substitute $P(t) = 12$ and solve for t.

$\dfrac{12}{6} = \dfrac{\cancel{6}(1.014)^t}{\cancel{6}}$ Isolate the exponential expression on one side of the equation.

$2 = 1.014^t$

$\ln 2 = \ln 1.014^t$ Take the natural logarithm of both sides.

$\ln 2 = t \ln 1.014$ Express the exponent as a factor.

$\dfrac{\ln 2}{\ln 1.014} = \dfrac{t \cancel{\ln 1.014}}{\cancel{\ln 1.014}}$ Solve for t.

$t = \dfrac{\ln 2}{\ln 1.014} \approx 50$ The population will reach 12 billion (double the October 1999 value) approximately 50 years after 1999.

Note: It has taken thousands of years for the world's population to reach 6 billion. However, with a growth rate of 1.4%, it will take only 50 years to gain an additional 6 billion.

6. Applications of Exponential Equations— Radioactive Decay

example 9   **Applying an Exponential Equation to Radioactive Decay**

On Friday, April 25, 1986, a nuclear accident occurred at the Chernobyl nuclear reactor, resulting in radioactive contaminates being released into the atmosphere. The most hazardous isotopes released in this accident were ^{137}Cs (cesium-137), ^{131}I (iodine-131), and ^{90}Sr (strontium-90). People living close to Chernobyl (in Ukraine) were at risk of radiation exposure from inhalation, from absorption through the skin, and from food contamination. Years after the incident, scientists have seen an increase in the incidence of thyroid disease among children living in the contaminated areas. Because iodine is readily absorbed in the thyroid gland, scientists suspect that radiation from iodine-131 is the cause.

The half-life of radioactive iodine (^{131}I) is 8.04 days. If 10 g of I-131 is initially present, then the amount of radioactive iodine still present after t days is approximated by:

$$A(t) = 10e^{-0.0862t}, \text{ where } t \text{ is the time in days.}$$

a.   Use the model to approximate the amount of ^{131}I still present after 2 weeks. Round to the nearest 0.1 g.

b.   How long will it take for the amount of ^{131}I to decay to 0.5 g? Round to the nearest 0.1 year.

Solution:

a. $A(t) = 10e^{-0.0862t}$

$\quad A(14) = 10e^{-0.0862(14)}$ Substitute $t = 14$ (2 weeks).

$\quad\quad\quad\quad = 3.0 \text{ g}$

b. $\quad\quad A(t) = 10e^{-0.0862t}$

$\quad\quad\quad 0.5 = 10e^{-0.0862t}$ Substitute $A = 0.5$.

$\quad\quad \dfrac{0.5}{10} = \dfrac{\cancel{10}e^{-0.0862t}}{\cancel{10}}$ Isolate the exponential expression.

$\quad\quad 0.05 = e^{-0.0862t}$

$\quad \ln(0.05) = \ln(e^{-0.0862t})$ Take the natural logarithm of both sides.

$\quad \ln(0.05) = -0.0862t$ The resulting equation is linear.

$\quad \dfrac{\ln(0.05)}{-0.0862} = \dfrac{-0.0862t}{-0.0862}$ Solve for t.

$\quad t = \dfrac{\ln(0.05)}{-0.0862} \approx 34.8 \text{ years}$

Note: Radioactive iodine (^{131}I) is used in medicine in appropriate dosages to treat patients with hyperactive (overactive) thyroids. Because iodine is readily absorbed in the thyroid gland, the radiation is localized and will reduce the size of the thyroid while minimizing damage to surrounding tissues.

section 10.6   PRACTICE EXERCISES

1. a. Graph $f(x) = e^x$.

    b. Write the domain and range in interval notation.

2. a. Graph $g(x) = 3^x$.

    b. Write the domain and range in interval notation.

3. a. Graph $h(x) = \ln(x)$.

    b. What is the vertical asymptote?

    c. Write the domain and range in interval notation.

4. a. Graph $k(x) = \log(x)$.

    b. What is the vertical asymptote?

    c. Write the domain and range in interval notation.

For Exercises 5–8, write the expression as a single logarithm.

5. $\log_b(x - 1) + \log_b(x + 2)$

6. $\log_b(x) + \log_b(2x + 3)$

7. $\log_b(x) - \log_b(1 - x)$

8. $\log_b(x + 2) - \log_b(3x - 5)$

For Exercises 9–14, identify the location of the vertical asymptote. Determine the domain of the function and write the answer in interval notation.

9. $y = \ln(x - 5)$

10. $y = \ln(x - 10)$

11. $y = \log(x + 2)$

12. $y = \log(x + 3)$

13. $y = \log_5(2x + 1)$

14. $y = \log_3(3x - 1)$

For Exercises 15–24, solve the exponential equation using the property that $b^x = b^y$ implies $x = y$, for $b > 0$ and $b \neq 1$.

15. $5^x = 625$

16. $3^x = 81$

17. $2^{-x} = 64$

18. $6^{-x} = 216$

19. $36^x = 6$

20. $343^x = 7$

21. $4^{2x-1} = 64$

22. $5^{3x-1} = 125$

23. $81^{3x-4} = \dfrac{1}{243}$

24. $4^{2x-7} = \dfrac{1}{128}$

For Exercises 25–36, solve the exponential equations by taking a logarithm of both sides. (Round the answers to three decimal places.)

25. $8^a = 21$

26. $6^y = 39$

27. $e^x = 8.1254$

28. $e^x = 0.3151$

29. $10^t = 0.0138$

30. $10^p = 16.8125$

31. $e^{0.07h} = 15$

32. $e^{0.03k} = 4$

33. $32e^{0.04m} = 128$

34. $8e^{0.05n} = 160$

35. $3^{x+1} = 5^x$

36. $2^{x-1} = 7^x$

37. Suppose \$5000 is invested at 7% interest compounded continuously. How long will it take for the investment to grow to \$10,000? Use the model $A(t) = Pe^{rt}$ and round to the nearest tenth of a year.

38. Suppose \$2000 is invested at 10% interest compounded continuously. How long will it take for the investment to triple? Use the model $A(t) = Pe^{rt}$ and round to the nearest year.

39. Phosphorus-32 (^{32}P) has a half-life of approximately 14 days. If 10 g of ^{32}P is present initially, then the amount, A, of phosphorus-32 still present after t days is given by $A(t) = 10(0.5)^{t/14}$.

    a. Find the amount of phosphorus-32 still present after 5 days. Round to the nearest tenth of a gram.

    b. Find the amount of time necessary for the amount of ^{32}P to decay to 4 g. Round to the nearest tenth of a day.

40. Polonium-210 (^{210}Po) has a half-life of approximately 138.6 days. If 4 g of ^{210}Po is present initially, then the amount, A, of polonium-210 still present after t days is given by $A(t) = 4e^{-0.005t}$.

a. Find the amount of polonium-138 still present after 50 days. Round to the nearest tenth of a gram.

b. Find the amount of time necessary for the amount of ^{32}P to decay to 0.5 g. Round to the nearest tenth of a day.

41. Suppose you save $10,000 from working an extra job. Rather than spending the money, you decide to save the money for retirement by investing in a mutual fund that averages 12% per year. How long will it take for this money to grow to $1,000,000? Use the model $A(t) = Pe^{rt}$ and round to the nearest tenth of a year.

42. The model $A = Pe^{rt}$ is used to compute the total amount of money in an account after t years at an interest rate, r, compounded continuously. P is the initial principal. Find the amount of time required for the investment to double as a function of the interest rate. (*Hint*: Substitute $A = 2P$ and solve for t.)

Solve the logarithmic equations in Exercises 43–68.

43. $\log_3 x = 2$

44. $\log_4 x = 9$

45. $\log p = 42$

46. $\log q = \dfrac{1}{2}$

47. $\ln x = 0.08$

48. $\ln x = 19$

49. $\log_x 25 = 2 \quad (x > 0)$

50. $\log_x 100 = 2 \quad (x > 0)$

51. $\log_b 10,000 = 4 \quad (b > 0)$

52. $\log_b e^3 = 3 \quad (b > 0)$

53. $\log_y 5 = \dfrac{1}{2} \quad (y > 0)$

54. $\log_b 8 = \dfrac{1}{2} \quad (b > 0)$

55. $\log_4(c + 5) = 3$

56. $\log_5(a - 4) = 2$

57. $\log_5(4y + 1) = 1$

58. $\log_6(5t - 2) = 1$

59. $\log_3 k + \log_3(2k + 3) = 2$

60. $\log_2(h - 1) + \log_2(h + 1) = 3$

61. $\log(x + 2) = \log(3x - 6)$

62. $\log x = \log(1 - x)$

63. $\log_5(3t + 2) - \log_5 t = \log_5 4$

64. $\log(6y - 7) + \log y = \log 5$

65. $\log(4m) = \log 2 + \log(m - 3)$

66. $\log(-h) + \log 3 = \log(2h - 15)$

67. $(\log_2 x)^2 - 12 \log_2 x = -32$

68. $(\log_3 x)^2 - \log_3 x^2 = 3$

69. The isotope of plutonium of mass 238 (written ^{238}Pu) is used to make thermoelectric power sources for spacecraft. The heat and electric power derived from such units have made the Voyager, Galileo, and Cassini missions to the outer reaches of our solar system possible. The half-life of ^{238}Pu is 87.7 years.

Suppose a hypothetical space probe is launched in the year 2002 with 2.0 kg of ^{238}Pu. Then the amount of ^{238}Pu available to power the spacecraft decays over time according to

$P(t) = 2e^{-0.0079t}$, where $t \geq 0$ is the time in years, and $P(t)$ is the amount of plutonium still present (in kilograms).

a. Suppose the space probe is due to arrive at Pluto in the year 2045. How much plutonium will remain when the spacecraft reaches Pluto? Round to two decimal places.

b. If 1.5 kg of ^{238}Pu is required to power the spacecraft's data transmitter, will there be enough power in the year 2045 for us to receive close-up images of Pluto?

70. ^{99m}Tc is a radionuclide of technetium that is widely used in nuclear medicine. Although its half-life is only 6 h, the isotope is continuously produced via the decay of its longer-lived parent, ^{99}Mo (molybdenum-99) whose half-life is approximately 3 days. ^{99}Mo generators (or "cows") are sold to hospitals in which the ^{99m}Tc can be "milked" as needed over a period of a few weeks. Once separated from its parent, the ^{99m}Tc may be chemically incorporated into a variety of imaging agents, each of which is designed to be taken up by a specific target organ within the body. Special cameras, sensitive to the gamma rays emitted by the technetium, are then used to

record a "picture" (similar in appearance to an x-ray film) of the selected organ.

Suppose a technician prepares a sample of ^{99m}Tc-pyrophosphate to image the heart of a patient suspected of having had a mild heart attack. If the injection contains 10 mCi (millicuries) of ^{99m}Tc at 1:00 P.M., then the amount of technetium still present is given by

$T(t) = 10e^{-0.1155t}$, where $t > 0$ represents the time in hours after 1:00 P.M. and $T(t)$ represents the amount of ^{99m}Tc (in millicuries) still present.

a. How many millicuries of ^{99m}Tc will remain at 4:20 P.M. when the image is recorded? Round to the nearest tenth of a millicurie.

b. How long will it take for the radioactive level of the ^{99m}Tc to reach 2 mCi? Round to the nearest tenth of an hour.

GRAPHING CALCULATOR EXERCISES

71. The amount of money a company receives from sales is related to the money spent on advertising according to

$S(x) = 400 + 250 \log(x)$ $x \ge 1$, where $S(x)$ is the amount in sales (in $1000s) and x is the amount spent on advertising (in $1000s).

a. The value of $S(1) = 400$ means that if $1000 is spent on advertising, the total sales will be $400,000.

   i. Find the total sales for this company if $11,000 is spent on advertising.

   ii. Find the total sales for this company if $21,000 is spent on advertising.

   iii. Find the total sales for this company if $31,000 is spent on advertising.

b. Graph the function $y = S(x)$ on a window where $0 \le x \le 40$ and $0 \le y \le 1000$. Using the graph and your answers from part (a), describe the relationship between total sales and the money spent on advertising. As the money spent on advertising is increased what happens to the rate of increase of total sales?

c. How many advertising dollars are required for the total sales to reach $1,000,000? That is, for what value of x will $S(x) = 1000$?

72. Graph $Y_1 = 8^{\wedge}x$ and $Y_2 = 21$ on a window where $0 \le x \le 5$ and $0 \le y \le 40$. Use the graph and an *Intersect* feature or *Zoom* and *Trace* to support your answer to Exercise 25.

73. Graph $Y_1 = 6^{\wedge}x$ and $Y_2 = 39$ on a window where $0 \le x \le 5$ and $0 \le y \le 50$. Use the graph and an *Intersect* feature or *Zoom* and *Trace* to support your answer to Exercise 26.

74. Graph $Y_1 = \log_3(x)$ (use the change-of-base formula) and $Y_2 = 2$ on a window where $0 \le x \le 40$ and $-4 \le y \le 4$. Use the graph and an *Intersect* feature or *Zoom* and *Trace* to support your answer to Exercise 43.

75. Graph $Y_1 = \log_4(x)$ (use the change-of-base formula) and $Y_2 = 9$ on a window where $0 \le x \le 1,000,000$ and $-2 \le y \le 12$. Use the graph and an *Intersect* feature or *Zoom* and *Trace* to support your answer to Exercise 44.

chapter 10   SUMMARY

SECTION 10.1—INVERSE FUNCTIONS

KEY CONCEPTS:

Horizontal Line Test
Consider a function defined by a set of points (x, y) in a rectangular coordinate system. Then the graph defines y as a one-to-one function of x if no horizontal line intersects the graph in more than one point.

Finding an Equation of the Inverse of a Function
For a one-to-one function defined by $y = f(x)$, the equation of the inverse can be found as follows:

1. Replace $f(x)$ by y.
2. Interchange x and y.
3. Solve for y.
4. Replace y by $f^{-1}(x)$.

The graphs defined by $y = f(x)$ and $y = f^{-1}(x)$ are symmetric with respect to the line $y = x$.

Definition of the Inverse of a Function
If f is a one-to-one function, then g is the inverse of f if and only if $(f \circ g)(x) = x$ for all x in the domain of g, and $(g \circ f)(x) = x$ for all x in the domain of f.

KEY TERMS:

horizontal line test
inverse function
one-to-one function

EXAMPLES:

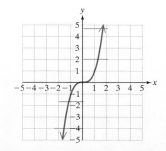

The function is one-to-one because it passes the horizontal line test.

Find the inverse of the one-to-one function defined by $f(x) = 3 - x^3$.
For $y = 3 - x^3$

1. $x = 3 - y^3$

2. $\quad x - 3 = -y^3$
   $\quad -x + 3 = y^3$
   $\quad \sqrt[3]{-x + 3} = y$

3. $f^{-1}(x) = \sqrt[3]{-x + 3}$

Verify that the functions defined by $f(x) = x - 1$ and $g(x) = x + 1$ are inverses.

$$(f \circ g)(x) = f(x + 1) = (x + 1) - 1 = x$$

$$(g \circ f)(x) = g(x - 1) = (x - 1) + 1 = x$$

SECTION 10.2—EXPONENTIAL FUNCTIONS

KEY CONCEPTS:

A function $y = b^x (b > 0, b \neq 1)$ is an exponential function.

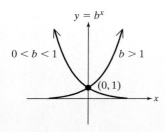

The domain is $(-\infty, \infty)$.

The range is $(0, \infty)$

The line $y = 0$ is a horizontal asymptote.

The y-intercept is $(0, 1)$.

KEY TERMS:

exponential decay function
exponential function
exponential growth function
half-life

EXAMPLES:

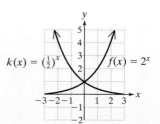

SECTION 10.3—LOGARITHMIC FUNCTIONS

KEY CONCEPTS:

The function $y = \log_b(x)$ is a logarithmic function.

$$y = \log_b(x) \Leftrightarrow b^y = x \quad (x > 0, b > 0, b \neq 1)$$

EXAMPLES:

$\log_4(64) = 3$ because $4^3 = 64$.

For $y = \log_b(x)$, the domain is $(0, \infty)$.

The range is $(-\infty, \infty)$.

The line $x = 0$ is a vertical asymptote.

The x-intercept is $(1, 0)$.

$y = \log(x)$ is the common logarithmic function (base 10).

$\log(10{,}000) = 4$ because $10^4 = 10{,}000$.

KEY TERMS:

argument
base
common logarithmic function
domain of a logarithmic function
logarithm
logarithmic function

SECTION 10.4—PROPERTIES OF LOGARITHMS

KEY CONCEPTS:

Let b, x, and y be positive real numbers where $b \neq 1$, and let p be a real number. Then the following properties are true.

1. $\log_b(1) = 0$
2. $\log_b(b) = 1$
3. $\log_b(b^p) = p$
4. $b^{\log_b(x)} = x$
5. $\log_b(xy) = \log_b(x) + \log_b(y)$
6. $\log_b\left(\dfrac{x}{y}\right) = \log_b(x) - \log_b(y)$
7. $\log_b(x^p) = p\log_b(x)$

The properties of logarithms can be used to write multiple logarithms as a single logarithm.

EXAMPLES:

1. $\log_5(1) = 0$
2. $\log_6(6) = 1$
3. $\log_4(4^7) = 7$
4. $2^{\log_2(5)} = 5$
5. $\log(5x) = \log(5) + \log(x)$
6. $\log_7\left(\dfrac{z}{10}\right) = \log_7(z) - \log_7(10)$
7. $\log x^5 = 5\log x$

Write as a single logarithm:

$$\log x - \frac{1}{2}\log y - 3\log z$$

$$= \log x - (\log y^{1/2} + \log z^3)$$

$$= \log x - \log(\sqrt{y}z^3)$$

$$= \log\left(\frac{x}{\sqrt{y}z^3}\right)$$

The properties of logarithms can be used to write a single logarithm as a sum or difference of logarithms.

KEY TERMS:

properties of logarithms

Expand into sums or differences of logarithms:

$$\log \sqrt[3]{\frac{x}{y^2}}$$

$$= \frac{1}{3}\log\left(\frac{x}{y^2}\right)$$

$$= \frac{1}{3}(\log x - \log y^2)$$

$$= \frac{1}{3}(\log x - 2\log y)$$

$$= \frac{1}{3}\log x - \frac{2}{3}\log y$$

SECTION 10.5—THE IRRATIONAL NUMBER, e

KEY CONCEPTS:

As x becomes infinitely large, the expression, $\left(1 + \frac{1}{x}\right)^x$ approaches the irrational number, e, where $e \approx 2.718281$.

The balance of an account earning compound interest, n times per year is given by

$$A(t) = P\left(1 + \frac{r}{n}\right)^{nt}$$

where P = principal, r = interest rate, t = time in years, and n = number of compound periods per year.

The balance of an account earning interest continuously is given by:

$$A(t) = Pe^{rt}$$

The function $y = e^x$ is the exponential function with base e.
The natural logarithm function, $y = \ln(x)$, is the logarithm function with base e.

EXAMPLES:

Find the account balance for $8000 invested for 10 years at 7% compounded quarterly:

$$P = 8000, t = 10, r = 0.07, n = 4$$

$$A(10) = 8000\left(1 + \frac{0.07}{4}\right)^{(4)(10)}$$

$$A(10) = \$16,012.78$$

Find the account balance for the same investment compounded continuously:

$$P = 8000, t = 10, r = 0.07$$

$$A(t) = 8000e^{(0.07)(10)}$$

$$= \$16,110.02$$

Use a calculator to approximate the value of the expressions.

$$e^{7.5} \approx 1808.04 \qquad e^{-\pi} \approx 0.0432$$

$$\ln(107) \approx 4.6728$$

$$\ln\left(\frac{1}{\sqrt{2}}\right) \approx -0.3466$$

Change-of-Base Formula:

$$\log_b(x) = \frac{\log_a(x)}{\log_a(b)} \quad a > 0, a \neq 1, b > 0, b \neq 1$$

$$\log_3(59) = \frac{\log(59)}{\log(3)} \approx 3.7115$$

KEY TERMS:

change-of-base formula
continuous compounding
e
natural logarithmic function

SECTION 10.6—EXPONENTIAL AND LOGARITHMIC EQUATIONS

KEY CONCEPTS:

Guidelines to Solve Logarithmic Equations

1. Isolate the logarithms on one side of the equation.
2. Write a sum or difference of logarithms as a single logarithm.
3. Rewrite the equation in step 2 in exponential form.
4. Solve the resulting equation from step 3.
5. Check all solutions to verify that they are within the domain of the logarithmic expressions in the equation.

The equivalence of exponential expressions can be used to solve exponential equations.

If $b^x = b^y$ then $x = y$

Guidelines to Solve Exponential Equations

1. Isolate one of the exponential expressions in the equation.
2. Take a logarithm of both sides of the equation.

EXAMPLES:

Solve:

$$\log(3x - 1) + 1 = \log(2x + 1)$$

Step 1: $\log(3x - 1) - \log(2x + 1) = -1$

Step 2: $\log\left(\dfrac{3x - 1}{2x + 1}\right) = -1$

Step 3: $\qquad 10^{-1} = \dfrac{3x - 1}{2x + 1}$

Step 4: $\qquad \dfrac{1}{10} = \dfrac{3x - 1}{2x + 1}$

$$2x + 1 = 10(3x - 1)$$

$$2x + 1 = 30x - 10$$

$$-28x = -11$$

$$x = \frac{11}{28}$$

Step 5: $x = \dfrac{11}{28}$ Checks in original equation.

Solve:

$$5^{2x} = 125$$

$$5^{2x} = 5^3 \qquad \text{implies that} \qquad 2x = 3$$

$$x = \frac{3}{2}$$

Solve:

$$4^{x+1} - 2 = 1055$$

Step 1: $\qquad 4^{x+1} = 1057$

3. Use the power property of logarithms to write exponents as factors.
4. Solve the resulting equation from step 3.

KEY TERMS:

exponential equations
logarithmic equations

Step 2: $\ln(4^{x+1}) = \ln(1057)$

Step 3: $(x + 1)\ln 4 = \ln 1057$

Step 4: $x + 1 = \dfrac{\ln 1057}{\ln 4}$

$$x = \dfrac{\ln 1057}{\ln 4} - 1 \approx 4.023$$

---

chapter 10   REVIEW EXERCISES

Section 10.1

For Exercises 1–4, determine if the function is one-to-one by using the horizontal line test.

1.

2.

3.

4.
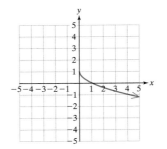

For Exercises 5–12, write the inverse for each one-to-one function.

5. $\{(3, 5), (2, 9), (0, -1), (4, 1)\}$

6. $\{(2, 0), (-1, 7), (1, 1), (0, 4)\}$

7. $p(x) = 3 - 4x$ 8. $q(x) = \dfrac{3}{4}x - 2$

9. $g(x) = \sqrt[5]{x} + 3$ 10. $f(x) = (x - 1)^3$

11. $m(x) = \dfrac{x - 2}{x + 2}$ 12. $n(x) = \dfrac{4}{x - 2}$

13. Verify that the functions defined by $f(x) = 5x - 2$ and $g(x) = \frac{1}{5}x + \frac{2}{5}$ are inverses by showing that $(f \circ g)(x) = x$ and $(g \circ f)(x) = x$.

14. Graph the functions p and p^{-1} from Exercise 7 on the same coordinate axes. What can you say about the relationship between these two graphs?

15. a. What are the domain and range of the function defined by $h(x) = \sqrt{x + 1}$?

   b. What are the domain and range of the function defined by $k(x) = x^2 - 1, x \geq 0$?

16. Determine the inverse of the function $p(x) = \sqrt{x} + 2$.

Section 10.2

For Exercises 17–24, evaluate the exponential expressions. Use a calculator and round to three decimal places, if necessary.

17. 4^5 18. 6^{-2} 19. $8^{1/3}$ 20. $\left(\dfrac{1}{100}\right)^{-1/2}$

21. 2^π 22. $5^{\sqrt{3}}$ 23. $(\sqrt{7})^{1/2}$ 24. $\left(\dfrac{3}{4}\right)^{4/3}$

For Exercises 25–28, graph the functions.

25. $f(x) = 3^x$

26. $g(x) = \left(\dfrac{1}{4}\right)^x$

27. $h(x) = 5^{-x}$

28. $k(x) = \left(\dfrac{2}{5}\right)^{-x}$

29. a. Does the graph of $y = b^x$, $b > 0$, $b \neq 1$, have a vertical or a horizontal asymptote?

    b. Write an equation of the asymptote.

30. Background radiation is radiation that we are exposed to from naturally occurring sources including the soil, the foods we eat, and the sun. Background radiation varies depending on where we live. A typical background radiation level is 150 mrem (millirems) per year. (A rem is a measure of energy produced from radiation.) Suppose a substance emits 30,000 mrem per year and has a half-life of 5 years. The function defined by

    $A(t) = 30,000\left(\dfrac{1}{2}\right)^{t/5}$ gives the radiation level (in millirems) of this substance after t years.

    a. What is the radiation level after 5 years?

    b. What is the radiation level after 15 years?

    c. Will the radiation level of this substance be below the background level of 150 mrem after 50 years?

Section 10.3

For Exercises 31–38, evaluate the logarithms without using a calculator.

31. $\log_3 \dfrac{1}{27}$

32. $\log_5 1$

33. $\log_7 7$

34. $\log_2 2^8$

35. $\log_2 16$

36. $\log_3 81$

37. $\log(100,000)$

38. $\log_8\left(\dfrac{1}{8}\right)$

For Exercises 39–40, graph the logarithmic functions.

39. $q(x) = \log_3 x$

40. $r(x) = \log_{1/2} x$

41. a. Does the graph of $y = \log_b x$ have a vertical or a horizontal asymptote?

    b. Write an equation of the asymptote.

42. Acidity of a substance is measured by its pH. The pH can be calculated by the formula $\text{pH} = -\log[H^+]$ where $[H^+]$ is the hydrogen ion concentration.

    a. What is the pH of a fruit with a hydrogen ion concentration of 0.00316 mol/L? Round to one decimal place.

    b. What is the pH of an antacid tablet with $[H^+] = 3.16 \times 10^{-10}$? Round to one decimal place.

Section 10.4

For Exercises 43–46, evaluate the logarithms without using a calculator.

43. $\log_8 8$

44. $\log_{11}(11^6)$

45. $\log_{1/2} 1$

46. $12^{\log_{12} 7}$

47. Complete the properties. Assume x, y, and b are positive real numbers such that $b \neq 1$.

    a. $\log_b(xy) =$

    b. $\log_b x - \log_b y =$

    c. $\log_b x^p =$

For Exercises 48–57, find the values of the logarithms given that $\log_b 2 \approx 0.693$, $\log_b 3 \approx 1.099$, and $\log_b 5 \approx 1.609$.

48. $\log_b 6$

49. $\log_b 4$

50. $\log_b 12$

51. $\log_b 25$

52. $\log_b 81$

53. $\log_b 30$

54. $\log_b\left(\dfrac{5}{2}\right)$

55. $\log_b\left(\dfrac{25}{3}\right)$

56. $\log_b(10^6)$

57. $\log_b(2^{12})$

For Exercises 58–61, write the logarithmic expressions as a single logarithm.

58. $\dfrac{1}{4}(\log_b y - 4 \log_b z + 3 \log_b x)$

59. $\dfrac{1}{2} \log_3 a + \dfrac{1}{2} \log_3 b - 2 \log_3 c - 4 \log_3 d$

60. $\log 540 - 3 \log 3 - 2 \log 2$

61. $-\log_4 18 + \log_4 6 + \log_4 3 - \log_4 1$

Section 10.5

For Exercises 62–73, use a calculator to approximate the expressions to four decimal places.

62. e^5

63. $e^{\sqrt{7}}$

64. $32\, e^{0.008}$

65. $58\, e^{-0.0125}$

66. $\ln 6$

67. $\ln\left(\dfrac{1}{9}\right)$

68. $\ln 1$

69. $\ln 0.0162$

70. $\log 200$

71. $\log(0.0058)$

72. $\log 22$

73. $\log e^3$

For Exercises 74–79, use the change-of-base formula to approximate the logarithms to four decimal places.

74. $\log_2 10$

75. $\log_9 80$

76. $\log_{1/2}(20)$

77. $\log_{1/3}(100)$

78. $\log_5(0.26)$

79. $\log_4(0.0062)$

80. An investor wants to deposit $20,000 in an account for 10 years at 5.25% interest. Compare the amount she would have if her money were invested with the following different compounding options. Use

$$A(t) = P\left(1 + \frac{r}{n}\right)^{nt}$$

for interest compounded n times per year and $A(t) = Pe^{rt}$ for interest compounded continuously.

   a. Compounded annually

   b. Compounded quarterly

   c. Compounded monthly

   d. Compounded continuously

81. To measure a student's retention of material at the end of a course, researchers give the student a test on the material every month for 24 months after the course is over. The student's average score t months after completing the course is given by

$S(t) = 75e^{-0.5t} + 20$, where t is the time in months, and S is the test score.

   a. Find $S(0)$ and interpret the result.

   b. Find $S(6)$ and interpret the result.

   c. Find $S(12)$ and interpret the result.

   d. The graph of $y = S(t)$ is shown here. Does it appear that the students' average score is approaching a limiting value? Explain.

Average Score Versus Time

$y = 75e^{-0.5t} + 20$

Figure for Exercise 81

82. A lake is stocked with 1000 fish and the fish population can be modeled by

$$p(t) = \frac{20{,}000}{2 + 18e^{-t/4}},$$ where p is the fish population and t is the time in months after the lake was initially stocked.

   a. Find $p(0)$ and interpret the result.

   b. Find $p(12)$ and interpret the result.

   c. The function p has a horizontal asymptote at $y = 10{,}000$. Does it appear that the fish population is approaching a limiting value? Explain.

   d. Use the graph to approximate the fish population after 8 months.

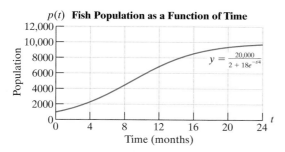

Figure for Exercise 82

Section 10.6

For Exercises 83–90, identify the domain. Write the answer in interval notation.

83. $f(x) = e^x$

84. $g(x) = e^{x+6}$

85. $h(x) = e^{x-3}$

86. $k(x) = \ln x$

87. $q(x) = \ln(x + 5)$

88. $p(x) = \ln(x - 7)$

89. $r(x) = \ln(3x - 4)$

90. $w(x) = \ln(5 - x)$

Solve the logarithmic equations in Exercises 91–98. If necessary, round to two decimal places.

91. $\log_5 x = 3$

92. $\log_7 x = -2$

93. $\log_6 y = 3$

94. $\log_3 y = \dfrac{1}{12}$

95. $\log(2w - 1) = 3$

96. $\log_2(3w + 5) = 5$

97. $\log p - 1 = -\log(p - 3)$

98. $\log_4(2 + t) - 3 = \log_4(3 - 5t)$

Solve the exponential equations in Exercises 99–106. If necessary, round to four decimal places.

99. $4^{3x+5} = 16$

100. $5^{7x} = 625$

101. $4^a = 21$

102. $5^a = 18$

103. $e^{-x} = 0.1$

104. $e^{-2x} = 0.06$

105. $10^{2n} = 1512$

106. $10^{-3m} = \dfrac{1}{821}$

107. Radioactive iodine (^{131}I) is used to treat patients with a hyperactive (overactive) thyroid. Patients with this condition may have symptoms that include rapid weight loss, heart palpitations, and high blood pressure. Because iodine is readily absorbed in the thyroid gland, the radiation is localized and will reduce the size of the thyroid while minimizing damage to surrounding tissues. The half-life of radioactive iodine is 8.04 days. If a patient is given an initial dose of 2 μg, then the amount of iodine in the body after t days is approximated by:

$A(t) = 2e^{-0.0862t}$, where t is the time in days and $A(t)$ is the amount (in micrograms) of ^{131}I remaining.

a. How much radioactive iodine is present after a week? Round to two decimal places.

b. How much radioactive iodine is present after 30 days? Round to two decimal places.

c. How long will it take for the level of radioactive iodine to reach 0.5 μg?

108. The value of a car is depreciated with time according to

$V(t) = 15{,}000e^{-0.15t}$, where $V(t)$ is the value in dollars and t is the time in years.

a. Find $V(0)$ and interpret the result in the context of the problem.

b. Find $V(10)$ and interpret the result in the context of the problem. Round to the nearest dollar.

c. Find the time required for the value of the car to drop to $5000. Round to the nearest tenth of a year.

d. The graph of $y = V(t)$ is shown here. Does it appear that the value of the car is approaching a limiting value? Explain.

Figure for Exercise 108

chapter 10   TEST

1. Explain how to determine graphically if a function is one-to-one.

2. Which of the functions is one-to-one?

a.

b.

3. Write an equation of the inverse of the one-to-one function defined by $f(x) = \frac{1}{4}x + 3$.

4. Write an equation of the inverse of the function defined by $g(x) = (x - 1)^2, x \geq 1$.

5. Given the graph of the function $y = p(x)$, graph its inverse, $p^{-1}(x)$.

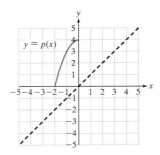

6. Use a calculator to approximate the expression to four decimal places.

a. $10^{2/3}$ b. $3^{\sqrt{10}}$ c. 8^{π}

7. Graph $f(x) = 4^{x-1}$.

8. a. Write in logarithmic form: $16^{3/4} = 8$

   b. Write in exponential form: $\log_x 31 = 5$ $(x > 0)$

9. Graph $g(x) = \log_3 x$.

10. Complete the change-of-base formula:
    $\log_b n = \underline{\hspace{1cm}}$

11. Use a calculator to approximate the expression to four decimal places:

    a. $\log 21$ b. $\log_4 13$ c. $\log_{1/2} 6$

12. Using the properties of logarithms, expand and simplify. Assume all variables represent positive real numbers.

    a. $-\log_3\left(\dfrac{3}{9x}\right)$ b. $\log\left(\dfrac{1}{10^5}\right)$

13. Write as a single logarithm. Assume all variables represent positive real numbers.

    a. $\dfrac{1}{2}\log_b x + 3\log_b y$ b. $\log a - 4\log a$

14. Use a calculator to approximate the expression to four decimal places:

    a. $e^{1/2}$ b. e^{-3} c. $\ln\left(\dfrac{1}{3}\right)$ d. $\ln e$

15. Identify the graphs as $y = e^x$ or $y = \ln x$.

    a.   b.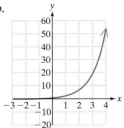

16. Researchers found that t months after taking a course, students remembered $p\%$ of the material according to

    $$p(t) = 92 - 20\ln(t + 1), \text{ where } 0 \leq t \leq 24 \text{ is the time in months.}$$

a.   Find $p(4)$ and interpret the results.

b.   Find $p(12)$ and interpret the results.

c.   Find $p(0)$ and interpret the results.

17. A certain bacterial culture grows according to

$$P(t) = \frac{1,500,000}{1 + 5000e^{-0.8t}},$$ where P is the population of the bacteria and t is the time in hours.

a.   Find $P(0)$ and interpret the result. Round to the nearest whole number.

b.   How many bacteria will be present after 6 h?

c.   How many bacteria will be present after 12 h?

d.   How many bacteria will be present after 18 h?

e.   Does it appear that the population of bacteria is reaching a limiting value? Explain.

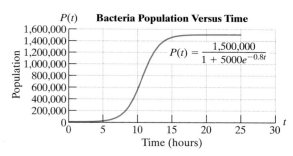

Bacteria Population Versus Time

$$P(t) = \frac{1,500,000}{1 + 5000e^{-0.8t}}$$

Figure for Exercise 17

For Exercises 18–23, solve the exponential and logarithmic equations. If necessary, round to three decimal places.

18. $\log x + \log(x - 21) = 2$

19. $\log_{1/2} x = -5$

20. $\ln(x + 7) = 2.4$ 21. $3^{x+4} = \dfrac{1}{27}$

22. $4^x = 50$ 23. $e^{2.4x} = 250$

24. Atmospheric pressure, P, decreases exponentially with altitude, x according to

$$P(x) = 760e^{-0.000122x},$$ where $P(x)$ is the pressure measured in millimeters of mercury (mm Hg) and x is the altitude measured in meters.

a.   Find $P(2500)$ and interpret the result. Round to one decimal place.

b.   Find the pressure at sea level.

c.   Find the altitude at which the pressure is 633 mm Hg.

25. Use the formula $A(t) = Pe^{rt}$ to compute the value of an investment under continuous compounding.

a.   If \$2000 is invested at 7.5% compounded continuously, find the value of the investment after 5 years.

b.   How long will it take the investment to double? Round to two decimal places.

CUMULATIVE REVIEW EXERCISES, CHAPTERS 1–10

1.   Simplify completely.

$$\frac{8 - 4 \cdot 2^2 + 15 \div 5}{|-3 + 7|}$$

2.   Divide.

$$\frac{-8p^2 + 4p^3 + 6p^5}{8p^2}$$

3.   Divide. $(t^4 - 13t^2 + 36) \div (t - 2)$. Identify the quotient and remainder. Is $(t - 2)$ a factor of $t^4 - 13t^2 + 36$?

4.   Simplify. $\sqrt{x^2 - 6x + 9}$

5.   Simplify. $\dfrac{4}{\sqrt[3]{40}}$

6.   Find the length of the missing side.

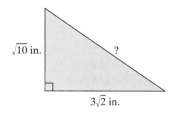

$\sqrt{10}$ in.   ?

$3\sqrt{2}$ in.

Figure for Exercise 6

7. Simplify. Write the answer with positive exponents only.

$$\frac{2^{2/5}c^{-1/4}d^{1/5}}{2^{-8/5}c^{3/4}d^{1/10}}$$

8. Find the area of the rectangle.

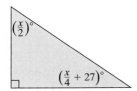

Figure for Exercise 8

9. Perform the indicated operation.

$$\frac{4 - 3i}{2 + 5i}$$

10. Find the measure of each angle in the right triangle.

Figure for Exercise 10

11. Find the positive slope of the sides of a pyramid with a square base 66 ft on a side and height of 22 ft.

Figure for Exercise 11

12. Solve for x: $2x(x - 7) = x - 18$

13. How many liters of pure alcohol must be mixed with 8 L of 20% alcohol to bring the concentration up to 50% alcohol?

14. Bank robbers leave the scene of a crime and head north through winding mountain roads to their hideaway. Their average rate of speed is 40 mph. The police leave 6 min later in pursuit. If the police car averages 50 mph traveling the same route, how long will it take the police to catch the bank robbers?

15. Solve the system using the Gauss-Jordan method:

$$5x + 10y = 25$$
$$-2x + 6y = -20$$

16. Solve for w: $-2[w - 3(w + 1)] = 4 - 7(w + 3)$

17. Solve for x: $ax - c = bx + d$

18. Solve for t: $s = \frac{1}{2}gt^2, t \geq 0$

19. Solve for T: $\sqrt{1 - kT} = \dfrac{V_0}{V}$

20. Find the x-intercepts of the function defined by $f(x) = |x - 5| - 2$.

21. Let $f(t) = 6, g(t) = -5t$, and $h(t) = 2t^2$, find
    a. $(fg)(t)$ b. $(g \circ h)(t)$ c. $(h - g)(t)$

22. Solve for q: $|2q - 5| = |2q + 5|$

23. a. Find an equation of the line parallel to the y-axis and passing through the point $(2, 6)$.

    b. Find an equation of the line perpendicular to the y-axis and passing through the point $(2, 6)$.

    c. Find an equation of the line perpendicular to the line $2x + y = 4$ and passing through the point $(2, 6)$. Write the answer in slope-intercept form.

24. The number of inmates in U.S. state and federal prisons has increased with time between 1990 and 1995. See the following table.

Year	x	Number of Inmates y
1990	0	1,148,000
1991	1	1,129,000
1992	2	1,295,000
1993	3	1,369,000
1994	4	1,478,000
1995	5	1,585,000

Source: U.S. Department of Justice

Table for Exercise 24

a. Let x represent the year, where $x = 0$ corresponds to 1990. Let y represent the number of inmates. Plot the ordered pairs.

b. Use the ordered pairs (0, 1,148,000) and (4, 1,478,000) to find a linear equation to model the number of inmates as a function of the year after 1990. Write the equation in slope-intercept form.

c. What is the slope of the line from part (b)? What does the slope mean in the context of this problem?

d. Use the equation from part (b) to estimate the prison population in the year 2000.

25. The smallest angle in a triangle is half the largest angle. The smallest angle is 20° less than the middle angle. Find the measure of all three angles.

26. Solve the system.

$$\frac{1}{2}x - \frac{1}{4}y = 1$$

$$-2x + y = -4$$

27. Match the function with the appropriate graph.

i. $f(x) = \ln(x)$ ii. $g(x) = 3^x$

iii. $h(x) = x^2$ iv. $k(x) = -2x - 3$

v. $L(x) = |x|$ vi. $m(x) = \sqrt{x}$

vii. $n(x) = \sqrt[3]{x}$ viii. $p(x) = x^3$

ix. $q(x) = \dfrac{1}{x}$ x. $r(x) = x$

a.

b.

c.

d.

e.

f.

g.

h.

i.

j.
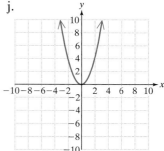

28. For

$$\mathbf{A} = \begin{bmatrix} 3 & 0 \\ 6 & -1 \end{bmatrix} \quad \text{and} \quad \mathbf{B} = \begin{bmatrix} -2 & 10 \\ 3 & 1 \end{bmatrix}$$

find

a. $\mathbf{A} + \mathbf{B}$ b. $\mathbf{AB}$

29. Find $f^{-1}(x)$ given $f(x) = 5x - \frac{2}{3}$

30. The volume of a gas varies directly as its temperature and inversely with pressure. At a temperature of 100 kelvins and a pressure of 10 N/m^2 (Newtons per square meter), the gas occupies a volume of 30 m^3. Find the volume at a temperature of 200 kelvins and pressure of 15 N/m^2.

31. Perform the indicated operations.
$$\frac{5x - 10}{x^2 - 4x + 4} \div \frac{5x^2 - 125}{15 - 3x} \cdot \frac{x^3 + 125}{6x + 3}$$

32. Perform the indicated operations.
$$\frac{x}{x - y} + \frac{y}{y - x} + x$$

33. Given the equation
$$\frac{2}{x - 4} = \frac{5}{x + 2}$$

    a. Are there any restrictions on x for which the rational expressions are undefined?

    b. Solve the equation.

    c. Solve the related inequality.
    $$\frac{2}{x - 4} \geq \frac{5}{x + 2}$$
    Write the answer in interval notation.

34. Two more than 3 times the reciprocal of a number is $\frac{4}{5}$ less than the number. Find all such numbers.

35. Solve the equation $\sqrt{-x} = x + 6$.

36. Solve the inequality: $2|x - 3| + 1 > -7$. Write the answer in interval notation.

37. Four million *Escherichia coli* (*E. coli*) bacteria are present in a laboratory culture. An antibacterial agent is introduced and the population of bacteria, P, decreases by half every 6 h according to
$$P(t) = 4,000,000\left(\frac{1}{2}\right)^{t/6} \quad t \geq 0, \text{ where } t \text{ is the time in hours.}$$

    a. Find the population of bacteria after 6, 12, 18, 24, and 30 h.

    b. Sketch a graph of $y = P(t)$ based on the function values found in part (a).

    c. Predict the time required for the population to decrease to 15,625 bacteria.

38. Evaluate the expressions without a calculator.

    a. $\log_7 49$ b. $\log_4\left(\frac{1}{64}\right)$

    c. $\log(1,000,000)$ d. $\ln(e^3)$

39. Use a calculator to approximate the expressions to four decimal places.

    a. $\pi^{4.7}$ b. e^{π}

    c. $(\sqrt{2})^{-5}$ d. $\log(5362)$

    e. $\ln(0.67)$ f. $\log_4(37)$

40. Solve the equation: $5^2 = 125^x$

41. Solve the equation: $e^x = 100$

42. Solve the equation: $\log_3(x + 6) - 3 = -\log_3(x)$

43. Write the following expression as a single logarithm: $\frac{1}{2}\log(z) - 2\log(x) - 3\log(y)$

44. Write the following expression as a sum or difference of logarithms:
$$\ln \sqrt[3]{\frac{x^2}{y}}$$

CONIC SECTIONS AND NONLINEAR SYSTEMS

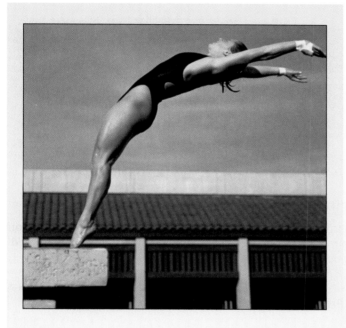

The vertical position, y, (in meters) of an object in free fall can be modeled by the *quadratic function*:

$$y(t) = \frac{1}{2}gt^2 + v_0t + y_0$$

where g is the acceleration due to gravity (on the earth, $g \approx -9.8$ m/s^2), t is the time (in seconds), v_0 is the initial velocity (in meters per second), and y_0 is the initial height (in meters).

A diver jumps off a springboard with an initial velocity of 6 m/s. The height of the diver's center of mass is given by

$$y(t) = -4.9t^2 + 6t + 3.8$$

The maximum height the diver's center of mass is approximately 5.6 m, which is the y-coordinate of the vertex of the graph.

Height of Diver's Center of Mass
$(0.61, 5.6)$　　$y(t) = -4.9t^2 + 6t + 3.8$

To graph this and other quadratic functions, visit xyplot at

www.mhhe.com/miller_oneill

Concepts

1. **Quadratic Functions of the Form** $f(x) = x^2 + k$

2. **Quadratic Functions of the Form** $f(x) = (x - h)^2$

3. **Quadratic Functions of the Form** $f(x) = ax^2$ $(a \neq 0)$

4. **Quadratic Functions of the Form** $f(x) = a(x - h)^2 + k$ $(a \neq 0)$

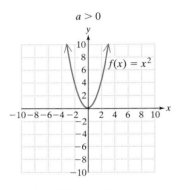

Figure 11-1

section

11.1   GRAPHS OF QUADRATIC FUNCTIONS

In Chapter 7, we defined a quadratic function as a function of the form $f(x) = ax^2 + bx + c$ $(a \neq 0)$. We also learned that the graph of a quadratic function is a parabola. The parabola opens up if $a > 0$ (Figures 11-1 and 11-2), and opens down if $a < 0$ (Figure 11-3). If a parabola opens up, the **vertex** is the lowest point on the graph. If a parabola opens down, the **vertex** is the highest point on the graph. The **axis of symmetry** is the vertical line that passes through the vertex.

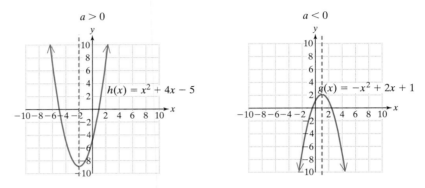

Figure 11-2   **Figure 11-3**

1.   Quadratic Functions of the Form $f(x) = x^2 + k$

One technique for graphing a function is to plot a sufficient number of points on the function until the general shape and defining characteristics can be determined. Then sketch a curve through the points.

---

example 1

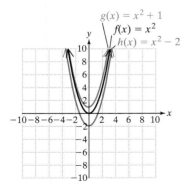

Figure 11-4

Graphing Quadratic Functions in the Form $f(x) = x^2 + k$

Graph the functions f, g, and h on the same coordinate system.

$$f(x) = x^2 \qquad g(x) = x^2 + 1 \qquad h(x) = x^2 - 2$$

Solution:

Several function values for f, g, and h are shown in Table 11-1 for selected values of x. The corresponding graphs are pictured in Figure 11-4.

Table 11-1

x	$f(x) = x^2$	$g(x) = x^2 + 1$	$h(x) = x^2 - 2$
-3	9	10	7
-2	4	5	2
-1	1	2	-1
0	0	1	-2
1	1	2	-1
2	4	5	2
3	9	10	7

Notice that the graphs of $g(x) = x^2 + 1$ and $h(x) = x^2 - 2$ take on the same shape as $f(x) = x^2$. However, the y-values of g are 1 more than the y-values of f. Hence the graph of $g(x) = x^2 + 1$ is the same as the graph of $f(x) = x^2$ shifted *up* 1 unit. Likewise the y-values of h are 2 less than those of f. The graph of $h(x) = x^2 - 2$ is the same as the graph of $f(x) = x^2$ shifted *down* 2 units.

The functions in Example 1 illustrate the following properties of quadratic functions of the form $f(x) = x^2 + k$.

Graphs of $f(x) = x^2 + k$

If $k > 0$, then the graph of $f(x) = x^2 + k$ is the same as the graph of $y = x^2$ shifted *up* k units.
If $k < 0$, then the graph of $f(x) = x^2 + k$ is the same as the graph of $y = x^2$ shifted *down* $|k|$ units.

Graphing Calculator Box

Try experimenting with a graphing calculator by graphing functions of the form $y = x^2 + k$ for several values of k.

---

example 2

Graphing Quadratic Functions of the Form $f(x) = x^2 + k$

Sketch the functions defined by.

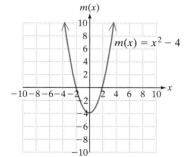

Figure 11-5

a. $m(x) = x^2 - 4$

b. $n(x) = x^2 + \dfrac{7}{2}$

Solution:

a. $m(x) = x^2 - 4$

$m(x) = x^2 + (-4)$

Because $k = -4$, the graph is obtained by shifting the graph of $y = x^2$ down $|-4|$ units (Figure 11-5).

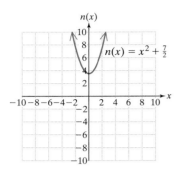

Figure 11-6

b. $n(x) = x^2 + \dfrac{7}{2}$

Because $k = \frac{7}{2}$, the graph is obtained by shifting the graph of $y = x^2$ up $\frac{7}{2}$ units (Figure 11-6).

2. Quadratic Functions of the Form $f(x) = (x - h)^2$

The graph of $f(x) = x^2 + k$ represents a vertical shift (up or down) of the function $y = x^2$. The next example shows that functions of the form $f(x) = (x - h)^2$ represent a horizontal shift (left or right) of the function $y = x^2$.

example 3

Graphing Quadratic Functions of the Form $f(x) = (x - h)^2$

Graph the functions f, g, and h on the same coordinate system.

$$f(x) = x^2 \qquad g(x) = (x + 1)^2 \qquad h(x) = (x - 2)^2$$

Solution:

Several function values for f, g, and h are shown in Table 11-2 for selected values of x. The corresponding graphs are pictured in Figure 11-7.

Table 11-2

x	$f(x) = x^2$	$g(x) = (x + 1)^2$	$h(x) = (x - 2)^2$
-4	16	9	36
-3	9	4	25
-2	4	1	16
-1	1	0	9
0	0	1	4
1	1	4	1
2	4	9	0
3	9	16	1
4	16	25	4
5	25	36	9

Figure 11-7

Example 3 illustrates the following properties of quadratic functions of the form $f(x) = (x - h)^2$.

Graphs of $f(x) = (x - h)^2$

If $h > 0$, then the graph of $f(x) = (x - h)^2$ is the same as the graph of $y = x^2$ shifted h units to the *right*.

If $h < 0$, then the graph of $f(x) = (x - h)^2$ is the same as the graph of $y = x^2$ shifted $|h|$ units to the *left*.

From Example 3 we have

$$h(x) = (x - 2)^2 \qquad \text{and} \qquad g(x) = [x - (-1)]^2$$

$y = x^2$ shifted 2 units to the right $y = x^2$ shifted $|-1|$ unit to the left

---

example 4

Graphing Functions of the Form $f(x) = (x - h)^2$

Sketch the functions p and q.

a. $p(x) = (x - 7)^2$ b. $q(x) = (x + 1.6)^2$

Solution:

a. $p(x) = (x - 7)^2$

Because $h = 7 > 0$, shift the graph of $y = x^2$ to the *right* 7 units (Figure 11-8).

b. $q(x) = (x + 1.6)^2$

$q(x) = [x - (-1.6)]^2$

Because $h = -1.6 < 0$, shift the graph of $y = x^2$ to the *left* 1.6 units (Figure 11-9).

Figure 11-8

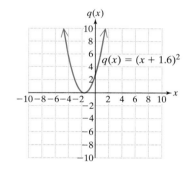

Figure 11-9

---

3.   Quadratic Functions of the Form $f(x) = ax^2$ $(a \neq 0)$

The next two examples investigate functions of the form $f(x) = ax^2$ $(a \neq 0)$.

---

example 5

Graphing Functions of the Form $f(x) = ax^2$ $(a \neq 0)$

Graph the functions $f, g,$ and h on the same coordinate system.

$$f(x) = x^2 \qquad g(x) = 2x^2 \qquad h(x) = \frac{1}{2}x^2$$

Solution:

Several function values for f, g, and h are shown in Table 11-3 for selected values of x. The corresponding graphs are pictured in Figure 11-10.

Figure 11-10

Table 11-3

x	$f(x) = x^2$	$g(x) = 2x^2$	$h(x) = \frac{1}{2}x^2$
-3	9	18	$\frac{9}{2}$
-2	4	8	2
-1	1	2	$\frac{1}{2}$
0	0	0	0
1	1	2	$\frac{1}{2}$
2	4	8	2
3	9	18	$\frac{9}{2}$

In Example 5, the function values defined by $g(x) = 2x^2$ are twice those of $f(x) = x^2$. The graph of $g(x) = 2x^2$ is the same as is the graph of $f(x) = x^2$ *stretched vertically* by a factor of 2 (the graph appears narrower than $f(x) = x^2$).

In Example 5, the function values defined by $h(x) = \frac{1}{2}x^2$ are one half those of $f(x) = x^2$. The graph of $h(x) = \frac{1}{2}x^2$ is the same as the graph of $f(x) = x^2$ *shrunk vertically* by a factor of $\frac{1}{2}$ (the graph appears wider than $f(x) = x^2$).

example 6   **Graphing Functions of the Form $f(x) = ax^2$ $(a \neq 0)$**

Graph the functions f, g, and h on the same coordinate system.

$$f(x) = -x^2 \qquad g(x) = -3x^2 \qquad h(x) = -\frac{1}{3}x^2$$

Solution:

Several function values for f, g, and h are shown in Table 11-4 for selected values of x. The corresponding graphs are pictured in Figure 11-11.

Table 11-4

x	$f(x) = -x^2$	$g(x) = -3x^2$	$h(x) = -\frac{1}{3}x^2$
-3	-9	-27	-3
-2	-4	-12	$-\frac{4}{3}$
-1	-1	-3	$-\frac{1}{3}$
0	0	0	0
1	-1	-3	$-\frac{1}{3}$
2	-4	-12	$-\frac{4}{3}$
3	-9	-27	-3

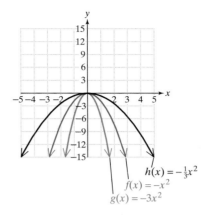

Figure 11-11

Example 6 illustrates that if the coefficient of the square term is negative, the parabola opens down. The graph of $g(x) = -3x^2$ is the same as the graph of $f(x) = -x^2$ with a *vertical stretch* by a factor of $|-3|$. The graph of $h(x) = -\frac{1}{3}x^2$ is the same as the graph of $f(x) = -x^2$ with a *vertical shrink* by a factor of $|-\frac{1}{3}|$.

Graphs of $f(x) = ax^2$ $(a \neq 0)$

1. If $a > 0$, the parabola opens up. Furthermore,
    *   If $0 < a < 1$, then the graph of $f(x) = ax^2$ is the same as the graph of $y = x^2$ with a *vertical shrink* by a factor of a.
    *   If $a > 1$, then the graph of $f(x) = ax^2$ is the same as the graph of $y = x^2$ with a *vertical stretch* by a factor of a.
2. If $a < 0$, the parabola opens down. Furthermore,
    *   If $0 < |a| < 1$, then the graph of $f(x) = ax^2$ is the same as the graph of $y = -x^2$ with a *vertical shrink* by a factor of $|a|$.
    *   If $|a| > 1$, then the graph of $f(x) = ax^2$ is the same as the graph of $y = -x^2$ with a *vertical stretch* by a factor of $|a|$.

4. Quadratic Functions of the Form $f(x) = a(x - h)^2 + k$ $(a \neq 0)$

We can summarize our findings from Examples 1–6 by graphing functions of the form $f(x) = a(x - h)^2 + k$ $(a \neq 0)$.

The graph of $y = x^2$ has its vertex at the origin, $(0, 0)$. The graph of $f(x) = a(x - h)^2 + k$ is the same as the graph of $y = x^2$ shifted to the right or left h units and shifted up or down k units. Therefore, the vertex is shifted from $(0, 0)$ to (h, k). The axis of symmetry is the vertical line through the vertex. Hence the axis of symmetry must be the line $x = h$.

Graphs of $f(x) = a(x - h)^2 + k$ $(a \neq 0)$

1. The vertex is located at (h, k).
2. The axis of symmetry is the line $x = h$.
3. If $a > 0$, the parabola opens up, and k is the **minimum value** of the function.
4. If $a < 0$, the parabola opens down, and k is the **maximum value** of the function.

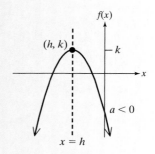

example 7

Graphing a Function of the Form $f(x) = a(x - h)^2 + k$ $(a \neq 0)$

Given the function defined by

$$f(x) = 2(x - 3)^2 + 4$$

a. Identify the vertex.
b. Sketch the function.
c. Identify the axis of symmetry.
d. Identify the maximum or minimum value of the function.

Solution:

a. $f(x) = 2(x - 3)^2 + 4$
    The function is in the form $f(x) = a(x - h)^2 + k$, where $a = 2$, $h = 3$, and $k = 4$. Therefore, the vertex is at $(3, 4)$.

b. The graph of f is the same as the graph of $y = x^2$ shifted to the right 3 units, shifted up 4 units, and stretched vertically by a factor of 2 (Figure 11-12).

c. The axis of symmetry is the line $x = 3$.

d. Because $a > 0$, the function opens up. Therefore, the minimum function value is 4. Notice that the minimum value is the minimum y-value on the graph.

Figure 11-12

example 8

Graphing a Function of the Form $f(x) = a(x - h)^2 + k$ $(a \neq 0)$

Given the function defined by

$$g(x) = -(x + 2)^2 - \frac{7}{4}$$

a.   Identify the vertex.
b.   Sketch the function.
c.   Identify the axis of symmetry.
d.   Identify the maximum or minimum value of the function.

Solution:

a. $g(x) = -(x + 2)^2 - \frac{7}{4}$

$$= -1[x - (-2)]^2 + \left(-\frac{7}{4}\right)$$

The function is in the form $g(x) = a(x - h)^2 + k$, where $a = -1$, $h = -2$, and $k = -\frac{7}{4}$. Therefore, the vertex is at $(-2, -\frac{7}{4})$.

b.   The graph of g is the same as the graph of $y = x^2$ shifted to the left 2 units, shifted down $\frac{7}{4}$ units, and opening down (Figure 11-13).

c.   The axis of symmetry is the line $x = -2$.

d.   The parabola opens down, so the maximum function value is $-\frac{7}{4}$.

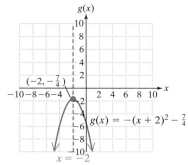

Figure 11-13

---

section 11.1   PRACTICE EXERCISES

1.   Describe the variation in the graphs of functions of the form $f(x) = x^2 + k$.

For Exercises 2–11, graph the functions.

2. $g(x) = x^2 + 1$

3. $f(x) = x^2 + 2$

4. $p(x) = x^2 - 3$

5. $q(x) = x^2 - 4$

6. $T(x) = x^2 + \frac{3}{4}$

7. $S(x) = x^2 + \frac{3}{2}$

8. $M(x) = x^2 - \frac{5}{4}$

9. $n(x) = x^2 - \frac{1}{3}$

10. $P(x) = x^2 + \frac{1}{2}$

11. $Q(x) = x^2 + \frac{1}{4}$

12. Describe the variation in the graphs of functions of the form $f(x) = (x - h)^2$.

For Exercises 13–22, graph the functions.

13. $r(x) = (x + 1)^2$

14. $h(x) = (x + 2)^2$

15. $k(x) = (x - 3)^2$

16. $L(x) = (x - 4)^2$

17. $A(x) = \left(x + \frac{3}{4}\right)^2$

18. $r(x) = \left(x + \frac{3}{2}\right)^2$

19. $W(x) = \left(x - \frac{5}{4}\right)^2$

20. $V(x) = \left(x - \frac{1}{3}\right)^2$

21. $M(x) = \left(x + \frac{1}{2}\right)^2$

22. $N(x) = \left(x + \frac{1}{4}\right)^2$

23. Describe the variation in the graphs of functions of the form $f(x) = ax^2$, where $a \neq 0$.

24. How do you determine whether the graph of a function defined by $h(x) = ax^2 + bx + c$ $(a \neq 0)$ opens up or down?

For Exercises 25–32, match the function with its graph.

25. $f(x) = -\dfrac{1}{4}x^2$

a.
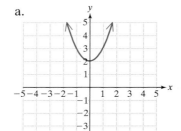

26. $g(x) = (x + 3)^2$

27. $k(x) = (x - 3)^2$

28. $h(x) = \dfrac{1}{4}x^2$

29. $t(x) = x^2 + 2$

30. $m(x) = x^2 - 4$

b.
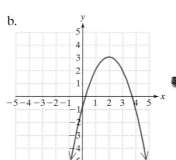

31. $n(x) = -(x - 2)^2 + 3$

32. $p(x) = (x + 1)^2 - 3$

c.

d.

e.

f.

g.

h.
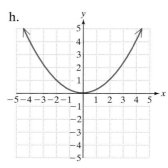

For Exercises 33–42, graph the parabola and the axis of symmetry. Label the vertex and the axis of symmetry.

33. $y = (x - 3)^2 + 2$

34. $y = (x - 2)^2 + 3$

35. $y = (x + 1)^2 - 3$

36. $y = (x + 3)^2 - 1$

37. $y = -(x - 4)^2 - 2$

38. $y = -(x - 2)^2 - 4$

39. $y = -(x + 3)^2 + 3$

40. $y = -(x + 2)^2 + 2$

41. $y = (x + 1)^2 + 1$

42. $y = (x - 4)^2 - 4$

For Exercises 43–52, without graphing the quadratic function, identify the vertex and determine if it is a maximum point or a minimum point. Then, write the maximum or minimum value.

43. $f(x) = 4(x - 6)^2 - 9$

44. $g(x) = 3(x - 4)^2 - 7$

45. $p(x) = -\dfrac{2}{5}(x - 2)^2 + 5$

46. $h(x) = -\dfrac{3}{7}(x - 5)^2 + 10$

47. $k(x) = \dfrac{1}{2}(x + 8)^2 - 3$

48. $m(x) = \dfrac{2}{9}(x + 11)^2 - 2$

49. $n(x) = -6\left(x + \dfrac{3}{4}\right)^2 + \dfrac{21}{4}$

50. $q(x) = -4\left(x + \dfrac{5}{6}\right)^2 + \dfrac{1}{6}$

51. $A(x) = 2(x - 7)^2 - \dfrac{3}{2}$

52. $B(x) = 5(x - 3)^2 - \dfrac{1}{4}$

53. True or False: The function defined by $g(x) = -5x^2$ has a maximum value but no minimum value.

54. True or False: The function defined by $f(x) = 2(x - 5)^2$ has a maximum value but no minimum value.

55. True or False: If the vertex $(-2, 8)$ represents a minimum point, then the minimum value is -2.

56. True or False: If the vertex $(-2, 8)$ represents a maximum point, then the maximum value is 8.

57. A suspension bridge is 120 ft long. Its supporting cable hangs in a shape that resembles a parabola. The function defined by $H(x) = \frac{1}{90}(x - 60)^2 + 30$ (where $0 \le x \le 120$) approximates the height of the supporting cable a distance of x feet from the end of the bridge (see figure).

   a. What is the location of the vertex of the parabolic cable?

   b. What is the minimum height of the cable?

   c. How high are the towers at either end of the supporting cable?

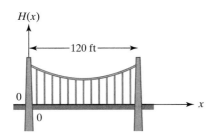

Figure for Exercise 57

58. A 50-m bridge over a crevasse is supported by a parabolic arch. The function defined by $f(x) = -0.16(x - 25)^2 + 100$ (where $0 \le x \le 50$) approximates the height of the supporting arch x meters from the end of the bridge (see figure).

   a. What is the location of the vertex of the arch?

   b. What is the maximum height of the arch?

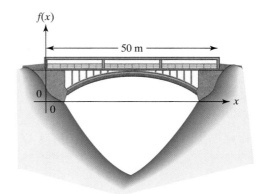

Figure for Exercise 58

GRAPHING CALCULATOR EXERCISES

For Exercises 59–66, verify the maximum and minimum points found in Exercises 43–50, by graphing each function on the calculator.

59. $Y_1 = 4(x - 6)^2 - 9$ (Exercise 43)

60. $Y_1 = 3(x - 4)^2 - 7$ (Exercise 44)

61. $Y_1 = -\dfrac{2}{5}(x - 2)^2 + 5$ (Exercise 45)

62. $Y_1 = -\dfrac{3}{7}(x - 5)^2 + 10$ (Exercise 46)

63. $Y_1 = \dfrac{1}{2}(x + 8)^2 - 3$ (Exercise 47)

64. $Y_1 = \dfrac{2}{9}(x + 11)^2 - 2$ (Exercise 48)

65. $Y_1 = -6\left(x + \dfrac{3}{4}\right)^2 + \dfrac{21}{4}$ (Exercise 49)

66. $Y_1 = -4\left(x + \dfrac{5}{6}\right)^2 + \dfrac{1}{6}$ (Exercise 50)

Concepts

1. Writing a Quadratic Function in the Form $f(x) = a(x - h)^2 + k$

2. Vertex Formula

3. Determining the Vertex and Intercepts of a Quadratic Function

4. Vertex of a Parabola—Applications

1.   Writing a Quadratic Function in the Form $f(x) = a(x - h)^2 + k$

The graph of a quadratic function is a parabola, and if the function is written in the form $f(x) = a(x - h)^2 + k$ $(a \neq 0)$, then the vertex is at (h, k). A quadratic function can be written in the form $f(x) = a(x - h)^2 + k$ $(a \neq 0)$ by completing the square. The process is similar to the steps outlined in Section 7.5 except that all algebraic manipulation is performed on the right-hand side of the function.

---

example 1   **Writing a Quadratic Function in the Form $f(x) = a(x - h)^2 + k$ $(a \neq 0)$**

Given $f(x) = x^2 + 8x + 13$

a.   Write the function in the form $f(x) = a(x - h)^2 + k$.
b.   Identify the vertex, the axis of symmetry, and the minimum function value.

Solution:

a. $f(x) = x^2 + 8x + 13$ Rather than dividing by the leading coefficient on both sides, we will factor out the leading coefficient from the variable terms on the right-hand side.

$= 1(x^2 + 8x) + 13$

$= 1(x^2 + 8x \quad) + 13$ Next, complete the square on the expression within the parentheses: $[\frac{1}{2}(8)]^2 = 16$.

$= 1(x^2 + 8x + 16 - 16) + 13$ Rather than adding 16 to both sides of the function, we will *add and subtract 16* within the parentheses on the right-hand side. This has the effect of adding 0 to the right-hand side.

$= 1(x^2 + 8x + 16) - 16 + 13$ Use the associative property of addition to regroup terms and isolate the perfect square trinomial within the parentheses.

$= (x + 4)^2 - 3$ Factor and simplify.

b. $f(x) = (x + 4)^2 - 3$

The vertex is at $(-4, -3)$.

The axis of symmetry is $x = -4$.

Because $a > 0$, the parabola opens up.

The minimum value is -3 (Figure 11-14).

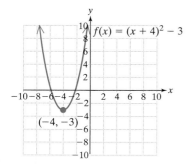

$f(x) = (x + 4)^2 - 3$

$(-4, -3)$

Figure 11-14

example 2

Analyzing a Quadratic Function

Given $f(x) = -2x^2 + 12x - 16$

a.   Write the function in the form $f(x) = a(x - h)^2 + k$.
b.   Find the vertex, axis of symmetry, and maximum function value.
c.   Find the x- and y-intercepts.
d.   Sketch the function.

Solution:

a. $f(x) = -2x^2 + 12x - 16$

To find the vertex, write the function in the form $f(x) = (x - h)^2 + k$.

$$= -2(x^2 - 6x \quad) - 16$$

Factor the leading coefficient from the variable terms.

$$= -2(x^2 - 6x + 9 - 9) - 16$$

Add and subtract the quantity $[\frac{1}{2}(-6)]^2 = 9$ within the parentheses.

$$= -2(x^2 - 6x + 9) + (-2)(-9) - 16$$

To remove the term -9 from the parentheses, we must first apply the distributive property. When -9 is removed from the parentheses, it carries with it a factor of -2.

$$= -2(x - 3)^2 + 18 - 16$$

Factor and simplify.

$$= -2(x - 3)^2 + 2$$

Avoiding Mistakes sidebar:

> ◆ **Avoiding Mistakes**
>
> Do not factor out the leading coefficient from the constant term.

b. $f(x) = -2(x - 3)^2 + 2$
The vertex is $(3, 2)$.

The line of symmetry is $x = 3$. Because $a < 0$, the parabola opens down and the maximum value is 2.

c.   The y-intercept is given by $f(0) = -2(0)^2 + 12(0) - 16 = -16$.
The y-intercept is $(0, -16)$.

To find the x-intercept(s), find the real solutions to the equation $f(x) = 0$.

$$f(x) = -2x^2 + 12x - 16$$
$$0 = -2x^2 + 12x - 16 \qquad \text{Substitute } f(x) = 0.$$
$$0 = -2(x^2 - 6x + 8) \qquad \text{Factor.}$$
$$0 = -2(x - 4)(x - 2)$$
$$x = 4 \quad \text{or} \quad x = 2$$

The x-intercepts are $(4, 0)$ and $(2, 0)$.

d.   Using the information from parts (a)–(c), sketch the graph (Figure 11-15).

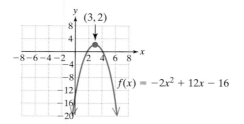

Figure 11-15

2.   Vertex Formula

Completing the square and writing a quadratic function in the form $f(x) = a(x - h)^2 + k$ $(a \neq 0)$ is one method to find the vertex of a parabola. Another method is to use the vertex formula. The **vertex formula** can be derived by completing the square on the function defined by $f(x) = ax^2 + bx + c$ $(a \neq 0)$.

$f(x) = ax^2 + bx + c$ $(a \neq 0)$

$= a\left(x^2 + \dfrac{b}{a}x \qquad\qquad \right) + c$ Factor a from the variable terms.

$= a\left(x^2 + \dfrac{b}{a}x + \dfrac{b^2}{4a^2} - \dfrac{b^2}{4a^2} \right) + c$ Add and subtract $[\frac{1}{2}(b/a)]^2 = b^2/4a^2$ within the parentheses.

$= a\left(x^2 + \dfrac{b}{a}x + \dfrac{b^2}{4a^2} \right) + (a)\left(-\dfrac{b^2}{4a^2} \right) + c$ Apply the distributive property and remove the term $b^2/4a^2$ from the parentheses.

$= a\left(x + \dfrac{b}{2a} \right)^2 - \dfrac{b^2}{4a} + c$ Factor the trinomial and simplify.

$= a\left(x + \dfrac{b}{2a} \right)^2 + c - \dfrac{b^2}{4a}$ Apply the commutative property of addition to reverse the last two terms.

$= a\left(x + \dfrac{b}{2a} \right)^2 + \dfrac{4ac}{4a} - \dfrac{b^2}{4a}$ Obtain a common denominator.

$= a\left(x + \dfrac{b}{2a} \right)^2 + \dfrac{4ac - b^2}{4a}$

$= a\left[x - \left(-\dfrac{b}{2a} \right) \right]^2 + \dfrac{4ac - b^2}{4a}$

$f(x) = a(x \quad - \quad h)^2 \quad + \quad k$

The function is in the form $f(x) = a(x - h)^2 + k$, where

$$h = \frac{-b}{2a} \quad \text{and} \quad k = \frac{4ac - b^2}{4a}$$

Hence, the vertex is at

$$\left(\frac{-b}{2a}, \frac{4ac - b^2}{4a} \right)$$

Although the y-coordinate of the vertex is given as $(4ac - b^2)/4a$, it is usually easier to determine the x-coordinate of the vertex first and then find y by evaluating the function at $x = -b/2a$.

The Vertex Formula

For $f(x) = ax^2 + bx + c$ $(a \neq 0)$, the vertex is given by

$$\left(\frac{-b}{2a}, \frac{4ac - b^2}{4a} \right) \quad \text{or} \quad \left(\frac{-b}{2a}, f\left(-\frac{b}{2a} \right) \right)$$

3. **Determining the Vertex and Intercepts of a Quadratic Function**

example 3

Determining the Vertex and Intercepts of a Quadratic Function

Given $h(x) = x^2 - 2x + 5$

a.   Use the vertex formula to find the vertex.
b.   Find the x- and y-intercepts.
c.   Sketch the function.

Solution:

a. $h(x) = x^2 - 2x + 5$

   $a = 1, b = -2, c = 5$ Identify $a, b,$ and c.

   The x-coordinate of the vertex is $\dfrac{-b}{2a} = \dfrac{-(-2)}{2(1)} = 1$.

   The y-coordinate of the vertex is $h(1) = (1)^2 - 2(1) + 5 = 4$.

   The vertex is $(1, 4)$.

b.   The y-intercept is given by $h(0) = (0)^2 - 2(0) + 5 = 5$.

   The y-intercept is $(0, 5)$.

To find the x-intercept(s), find the real solutions to the equation $h(x) = 0$.

$$h(x) = x^2 - 2x + 5$$

$$0 = x^2 - 2x + 5 \qquad \text{This quadratic equation is not factorable. Apply the quadratic formula: } a = 1, b = -2, c = 5.$$

$$x = \frac{-(-2) \pm \sqrt{(-2)^2 - 4(1)(5)}}{2(1)}$$

$$= \frac{2 \pm \sqrt{4 - 20}}{2(1)}$$

$$= \frac{2 \pm \sqrt{-16}}{2}$$

$$= \frac{2 \pm 4i}{2}$$

$$= 1 \pm 2i$$

The solutions to the equation $h(x) = 0$ are not real numbers. Therefore, there are no x-intercepts.

c.

$h(x) = x^2 - 2x + 5$

$(0, 5)$ $(1, 4)$ Because $a > 0$, the parabola opens up.

Figure 11-16

Tip: The location of the vertex and the direction that the parabola opens can be used to determine whether the function has any x-intercepts.

Given $h(x) = x^2 - 2x + 5$, the vertex $(1, 4)$ is *above* the x-axis. Furthermore, because $a > 0$, the parabola opens upward. Therefore, it is not possible for the function h to cross the x-axis (Figure 11-16).

4.   Vertex of a Parabola—Applications

example 4

Applying a Quadratic Function

The crew from Extravaganza Entertainment launches fireworks at an angle of $60°$ from the horizontal. The height, h, of one particular type of display can be approximated by the following function:

$$h(t) = -16t^2 + 128\sqrt{3}t, \text{ where } h \text{ is measured in feet and } t \text{ is measured in seconds.}$$

a.   How long will it take the fireworks to reach their maximum height? Round to the nearest second.

b.   Find the maximum height. Round to the nearest foot.

Solution:

$$h(t) = -16t^2 + 128\sqrt{3}t$$

This parabola opens downward; therefore, the maximum height of the fireworks will occur at the vertex of the parabola.

$$a = -16, b = 128\sqrt{3}, c = 0$$

Identify a, b, and c, and apply the vertex formula.

The x-coordinate of the vertex is

$$\frac{-b}{2a} = \frac{-128\sqrt{3}}{2(-16)} = \frac{-128\sqrt{3}}{-32} \approx 6.9$$

The y-coordinate of the vertex is approximately

$$h(6.9) = -16(6.9)^2 + 128\sqrt{3}(6.9) = 768$$

The vertex is $(6.9, 768)$.

a. The fireworks will reach their maximum height in 6.9 s.
b. The maximum height is 768 ft.

Graphing Calculator Box

Some graphing calculators have *Minimum* and *Maximum* features that enable the user to approximate the minimum and maximum values of a function. Otherwise, *Zoom* and *Trace* can be used.

---

example 5

Applying a Quadratic Function

In business, profit is defined as the difference of total revenue and total cost. That is,

$$P(x) = R(x) - C(x), \text{ where } x \text{ represents the number of units sold.}$$

Suppose a concession stand at the Daytona International Speedway sells a hot dog/drink combo for \$4. Then the revenue function is defined as $R(x) = 4x$. It is also known that the cost in dollars to operate the stand is $C(x) = 0.001x^2 + 1.4x + 400$.

a. Find the profit function, P, in terms of x.
b. Find the x-intercepts of the profit function (to the nearest whole unit) and interpret the meaning of the x-intercepts in the context of this problem.
c. Find the y-intercept of the profit function and interpret its meaning in the context of this problem.
d. Find the vertex of the profit function and interpret its meaning in the context of this problem.
e. Sketch the profit function.

Solution:

a. $P(x) = R(x) - C(x)$
    $= 4x - (0.001x^2 + 1.4x + 400)$
    $= 4x - 0.001x^2 - 1.4x - 400$
    $= -0.001x^2 + 2.6x - 400$

b. $P(x) = -0.001x^2 + 2.6x - 400$ The x-intercepts are the real solutions of the equation $P(x) = 0$.

    $0 = -0.001x^2 + 2.6x - 400$

    $x = \dfrac{-(2.6) \pm \sqrt{(2.6)^2 - 4(-0.001)(-400)}}{2(-0.001)}$ Use the quadratic formula.

    $= \dfrac{-2.6 \pm \sqrt{6.76 - 1.6}}{-0.002}$

    $= \dfrac{-2.6 \pm \sqrt{5.16}}{-0.002}$

    $x = \dfrac{-2.6 + \sqrt{5.16}}{-0.002} \approx 164$ or $x = \dfrac{-2.6 - \sqrt{5.16}}{-0.002} \approx 2436$

    The x-intercepts are $(164, 0)$ and $(2436, 0)$. The x-intercepts represent the breakeven points where profit is zero. At these points, the revenue and cost are in equilibrium.

c. The y-intercept is $P(0) = -0.001(0)^2 + 2.6(0) - 400 = -400$.

    The y-intercept is at the point $(0, -400)$. The y-intercept indicates that if no hot dog/drink combos are sold, the vendor has a $400 loss.

d. The x-coordinate of the vertex is

    $$\frac{-b}{2a} = \frac{-2.6}{2(-0.001)} = 1300$$

    The y-coordinate of the vertex is $P(1300) = -0.001(1300)^2 + 2.6(1300) - 400 = 1290$.

    The vertex is $(1300, 1290)$.

    A maximum profit of $1290 is obtained when the vendor sells 1300 hot dog/drink combos.

e. Using the information from parts (a)–(d), sketch the profit function (Figure 11-17).

Figure 11-17

---

example 6

Applying a Quadratic Function

The average number N, of visits to office-based physicians, is a function of the age of the patient.

$N(x) = 0.0014x^2 - 0.0658x + 2.65$, where x is a patient's age in years and $N(x)$ is the average number of doctor visits per year (Figure 11-18).

Find the age for which the number of visits to office-based physicians is a minimum.

Figure 11-18

Source: U.S. National Center for Health Statistics.

Solution:

$$N(x) = 0.0014x^2 - 0.0658x + 2.65$$

$$\frac{-b}{2a} = \frac{-(-0.0658)}{2(0.0014)} = 23.5 \qquad \text{Find the } x\text{-coordinate of the vertex.}$$

The average number of visits to office-based physicians is lowest for people approximately 23.5 years old.

section 11.2   PRACTICE EXERCISES

1. How does the graph of $f(x) = -2x^2$ compare with the graph of $y = x^2$?

2. How does the graph of $p(x) = \frac{1}{4}x^2$ compare with the graph of $y = x^2$?

3. How does the graph of $Q(x) = x^2 - \frac{8}{3}$ compare with the graph of $y = x^2$?

4. How does the graph of $r(x) = x^2 + 7$ compare with the graph of $y = x^2$?

5. How does the graph of $s(x) = (x - 4)^2$ compare with the graph of $y = x^2$?

6. How does the graph of $t(x) = (x + 10)^2$ compare with the graph of $y = x^2$?

For Exercises 7–14, find the value of k to complete the square.

7. $x^2 - 8x + k$ 8. $x^2 + 4x + k$

9. $y^2 + 7y + k$ 10. $a^2 - a + k$

11. $b^2 + \frac{2}{9}b + k$ 12. $m^2 - \frac{2}{7}m + k$

13. $t^2 - \frac{1}{3}t + k$ 14. $p^2 + \frac{1}{4}p + k$

For Exercises 15–24, write the function in the form $f(x) = a(x - h)^2 + k$ by completing the square. Then identify the vertex.

15. $g(x) = x^2 - 8x + 5$ 16. $h(x) = x^2 + 4x + 5$

17. $n(x) = 2x^2 + 12x + 13$

18. $f(x) = 4x^2 + 16x + 19$

19. $p(x) = -3x^2 + 6x - 5$

20. $q(x) = -2x^2 + 12x - 11$

21. $k(x) = x^2 + 7x - 10$ 22. $m(x) = x^2 - x - 8$

23. $f(x) = x^2 + 8x + 1$ 24. $g(x) = x^2 + 5x - 2$

For Exercises 25–34, find the vertex by using the vertex formula.

25. $Q(x) = x^2 - 4x + 7$ 26. $T(x) = x^2 - 8x + 17$

27. $r(x) = -3x^2 - 6x - 5$

28. $s(x) = -2x^2 - 12x - 19$

29. $N(x) = x^2 + 8x + 1$ 30. $M(x) = x^2 + 6x - 5$

31. $m(x) = \frac{1}{2}x^2 + x + \frac{5}{2}$ 32. $n(x) = \frac{1}{2}x^2 + 2x + 3$

33. $k(x) = -x^2 + 2x + 2$

34. $h(x) = -x^2 + 4x - 3$

For Exercises 35–40,

a. Find the vertex.

b. Find the y-intercept.

c. Find the x-intercept(s), if they exist.

d. Use this information to graph the function.

35. $y = x^2 + 9x + 8$ 36. $y = x^2 + 7x + 10$

37. $y = 2x^2 - 2x + 4$ 38. $y = 2x^2 - 12x + 19$

39. $y = -x^2 + 3x - \frac{9}{4}$ 40. $y = -x^2 - \frac{3}{2}x - \frac{9}{16}$

41. The pressure, x, in an automobile tire can affect its wear. Both overinflated and underinflated tires can lead to poor performance and poor mileage. For one particular tire, the function, P, represents the number of miles that a tire lasts (in thousands) for a given pressure, x.

$P(x) = -0.857x^2 + 56.1x - 880$, where x is the tire pressure in pounds per square inch (psi).

Mileage (thousands of miles) versus Tire Pressure (psi)

$P(x) = -0.857x^2 + 56.1x - 880$

Pressure (pounds per square inch)

Figure for Exercise 41

a. Use the function to approximate the number of miles a set of tires will get for a pressure of 28 psi. Round to one decimal place.

b. Find the tire pressure that will yield the maximum mileage. Round to the nearest pound per square inch.

42. A baseball player throws a ball and the height of the ball (in feet) can be approximated by

$y(x) = -0.011x^2 + 0.577x + 5$, where x is the horizontal position of the ball measured in feet from the origin.

a. What is the height of the ball when its horizontal position is 20 ft from the origin?

b. Where will the ball reach its highest point? Round to the nearest foot.

Figure for Exercise 42

43. For a fund-raising activity, a charitable organization produces cookbooks to sell in the community. The profit, P, (in dollars) depends on the number of cookbooks produced, x, according to

$P(x) = -\dfrac{1}{50}x^2 + 12x - 550$, where $x \geq 0$

a. How much profit is made when 100 cookbooks are produced?

b. How much profit is made when 150 cookbooks are produced?

c. How many cookbooks must be produced for the organization to break even?

d. Find the vertex.

e. Sketch the function.

f. How many cookbooks must be produced to maximize profit? What is the maximum profit?

44. A jewelry maker sells bracelets at art shows. The profit, P, (in dollars) depends on the number of bracelets produced, x, according to

$P(x) = -\dfrac{1}{10}x^2 + 42x - 1260$, where $x \geq 0$

a. How much profit does the jeweler make when 10 bracelets are produced?

b. How much profit does the jeweler make when 50 bracelets are produced?

c. How many bracelets must be produced for the jeweler to break even? Round to the nearest whole unit.

d. Find the vertex.

e. Sketch the function.

f. How many bracelets must be produced to maximize profit? What is the maximum profit?

■ EXPANDING YOUR SKILLS

45. A farmer wants to fence a rectangular corral adjacent to the side of a barn; however, she has only 200 ft of fencing and wants to enclose the largest possible area. See figure.

Figure for Exercise 45

a. If x represents the length of the corral, and y represents the width, explain why the dimensions of the corral are subject to the constraint: $2x + y = 200$.

b. The area of the corral is given by $A = xy$. Use the constraint equation from part (a) to express A as a function in terms of x, where $0 < x < 100$.

c. Use the function from part (b) to find the dimensions of the corral that will yield the maximum area. [*Hint*: Find the vertex of the function from part (b).]

46. A veterinarian wants to construct two equal-sized pens of maximum area out of 240 ft of fencing. See figure.

Figure for Exercise 46

a. If x represents the length of the pens and y represents the width of each pen, explain why the dimensions of the pens are subject to the constraint: $3x + 4y = 240$.

b. The area of each individual pen is given by $A = xy$. Use the constraint equation from part (a) to express A as a function in terms of x, where $0 < x < 80$.

c. Use the function from part (b) to find the dimensions of an individual pen that will yield the maximum area. [*Hint*: Find the vertex of the function from part (b).]

⌨ GRAPHING CALCULATOR EXERCISES

For Exercises 47–52, graph the function in Exercises 35–40 on a graphing calculator. Use the *Root* or *Zero* function to approximate the x-intercepts. Use the *Max* or *Min* feature or *Zoom* and *Trace* to approximate the vertex.

47. $Y_1 = x^2 + 9x + 8$ (Exercise 35)

48. $Y_1 = x^2 + 7x + 10$ (Exercise 36)

49. $Y_1 = 2x^2 - 2x + 4$ (Exercise 37)

50. $Y_1 = 2x^2 - 12x + 19$ (Exercise 38)

51. $Y_1 = -x^2 + 3x - \dfrac{9}{4}$ (Exercise 39)

52. $Y_1 = -x^2 - \dfrac{3}{2}x - \dfrac{9}{16}$ (Exercise 40)

section

11.3 MORE ON THE PARABOLA

1. Introduction to Conic Sections

Recall that the graph of a second-degree equation of the form $y = ax^2 + bx + c$ $(a \neq 0)$ is a parabola. In Section 11.4 we will learn that the graph of $(x - h)^2 + (y - k)^2 = r^2$ is a circle. These and two other types of figures called ellipses and hyperbolas are called **conic sections**. Conic sections derive their name because each is the intersection of a plane and a double-napped cone (Figure 11-19).

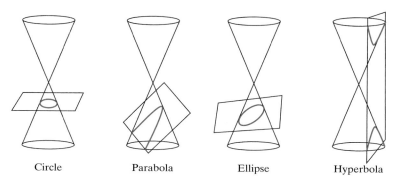

Circle   Parabola   Ellipse   Hyperbola

Figure 11-19

2. Definition of a Parabola

The points that make up the graph of a parabola may be defined by the following geometric approach.

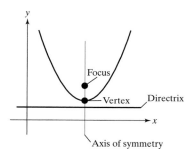

Figure 11-20

Definition of a Parabola

A **parabola** is the set of points in a plane that are equidistant (the same distance) from a fixed line (called the **directrix**) and a fixed point (called the **focus**) not on the directrix.

Note: The distance between a point and a line is taken to be the shortest distance. This is measured along a line perpendicular to the given line and through the given point.

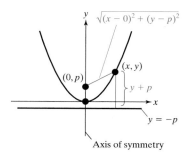

Figure 11-21

The **axis of symmetry** of the parabola passes through the focus and is perpendicular to the directrix. Furthermore, the **vertex** of the parabola is located on the axis of symmetry at the midpoint between the focus and directrix (Figure 11-20).

Suppose that the vertex of a parabola is located at $(0, 0)$ and that the axis of symmetry is the y-axis. If the focus is located at the point $(0, p)$ where $p \geq 0$, then the directrix must have the equation $y = -p$ (Figure 11-21). If the point (x, y) represents any point on the parabola, then by definition, (x, y) must be equidistant from the focus and the directrix.

Using the distance formula, the distance between (x, y) and the focus $(0, p)$ is $\sqrt{(x - 0)^2 + (y - p)^2}$.

The distance between (x, y) and the directrix is $y + p$.
Equating the distances, we have

$$\sqrt{(x - 0)^2 + (y - p)^2} = y + p$$

$$(x - 0)^2 + (y - p)^2 = (y + p)^2 \qquad \text{Square both sides.}$$

$$x^2 + y^2 - 2py + p^2 = y^2 + 2py + p^2 \qquad \text{Expand the binomials.}$$

$$x^2 - 2py = 2py \qquad \text{Subtract } y^2 \text{ and } p^2 \text{ from both sides.}$$

$$x^2 = 4py \qquad \text{Add } 2py \text{ to both sides.}$$

$$y = \frac{1}{4p}x^2 \qquad \text{Solve for } y.$$

By letting $a = \frac{1}{4p}$, we have the familiar equation $y = ax^2$. If the vertex of the parabola is located at the point (h, k), then the graph of $y = ax^2$ would be shifted $|h|$ units to the left or right and $|k|$ units up or down. The corresponding equation is

$$y = a(x - h)^2 + k, \quad \text{where } a \neq 0 \text{ and } a = \frac{1}{4p}$$

3. **Standard Form of the Equation of a Parabola (Vertical Axis of Symmetry)**

Standard Form of the Equation of a Parabola (Vertical Axis of Symmetry)

The standard form of the equation of a parabola with vertex (h, k) and vertical axis of symmetry is

$$y = a(x - h)^2 + k \quad \text{where } a \neq 0 \text{ and } a = \frac{1}{4p}$$

The focus is located at $(h, k + p)$.
The equation of the directrix is $y = k - p$.
If $a > 0$, then the parabola opens upward, and if $a < 0$, the parabola opens downward.

4. **Finding the Focus, Directrix, and Vertex of a Parabola**

example 1

Determining the Focus, Directrix, and Vertex of a Parabola

Given the equation of the parabola, $y = -\frac{1}{8}x^2$

a. Determine the coordinates of the vertex.
b. Determine the coordinates of the focus and the equation of the directrix.
c. Graph the parabola.

Solution:

a.   The equation can be written in the form

$$y = a(x - h)^2 + k$$

$$y = -\frac{1}{8}(x - 0)^2 + 0$$

Therefore, $h = 0$, $k = 0$, and $a = -\frac{1}{8}$.

The vertex is at (h, k) or $(0, 0)$.

b. $a = -\frac{1}{8} = \frac{1}{4p}$

Solving for p, we have: $-4p = 8$ or $p = -2$.

The focus is located at $(h, k + p)$: $[0, 0 + (-2)]$, or $(0, -2)$.

The directrix is $y = k - p$: $y = 0 - (-2)$, or $y = 2$.

c.

Tip: Notice that the location of the focus is "inside" the curve of the parabola and $|p|$ units from the vertex along the axis of symmetry.

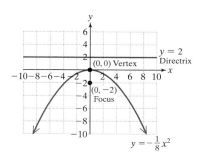

---

example 2

Determining the Focus, Directrix, and Vertex of a Parabola

Given the equation of the parabola, $y = (x + 3)^2 - 2$

a.   Determine the coordinates of the vertex.

b.   Determine the coordinates of the focus and the equation of the directrix.

c.   Graph the parabola.

Solution:

a.   The equation can be written in the form

$$y = a(x - h)^2 + k$$

$$y = 1(x + 3)^2 - 2$$

$$= 1[x - (-3)]^2 + (-2)$$

Therefore, $h = -3$, $k = -2$, and $a = 1$.
The vertex is at (h, k), or $(-3, -2)$.

b. $a = 1 = \dfrac{1}{4p}$

Solving for p, we have: $4p = 1$ or $p = \frac{1}{4}$.

The focus is located at $(h, k + p)$ or $\left[-3, -2 + \left(\frac{1}{4}\right)\right] = \left(-3, -\frac{7}{4}\right)$.

The directrix is $y = k - p$ or $y = -2 - \left(\frac{1}{4}\right)$ or equivalently, $y = -\frac{9}{4}$.

c.

5.   Completing the Square to Obtain Standard Form

To write the equation of a parabola in standard form, sometimes it is necessary to complete the square.

---

example 3

Determining the Focus, Directrix, and Vertex of a Parabola

Given the equation of the parabola, $y = -2x^2 + 4x + 1$

a.   Write the equation in standard form, $y = a(x - h)^2 + k$.

b.   Identify the vertex, focus, and directrix.

Solution:

a.   Recall from Section 11.2 that we can complete the square to write the equation in the form

$$y = a(x - h)^2 + k$$
$$= -2x^2 + 4x + 1$$
$$= -2(x^2 - 2x) + 1 \qquad \text{Factor out } -2 \text{ from the variable terms.}$$
$$= -2(x^2 - 2x + 1 - 1) + 1 \qquad \text{Add and subtract the quantity } [\tfrac{1}{2}(-2)]^2 = 1.$$
$$= -2(x^2 - 2x + 1) + (-1)(-2) + 1 \qquad \text{Remove the } -1 \text{ term from within the parentheses by first applying the distributive property. When } -1 \text{ is removed from the parentheses, it carries with it the factor of } -2 \text{ from outside the parentheses.}$$

$$= -2(x - 1)^2 + 2 + 1$$
$$= -2(x - 1)^2 + 3$$

The equation is in the form $y = a(x - h)^2 + k$, where $a = -2, h = 1$, and $k = 3$.

b. The vertex is $(1, 3)$.

Because $a = -2$, then $-2 = \frac{1}{4p}$; hence $-8p = 1$ and $p = -\frac{1}{8}$.

The focus is $(h, k + p)$: $[1, 3 + (-\frac{1}{8})]$, or $(1, \frac{23}{8})$.

The directrix is $y = k - p$: $y = 3 - (-\frac{1}{8})$, or $y = \frac{25}{8}$ (Figure 11-22).

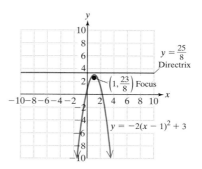

Figure 11-22

6. Standard Form of the Equation of a Parabola (Horizontal Axis of Symmetry)

We have seen that the graph of a parabola $y = a(x - h)^2 + k$ opens upward if $a > 0$ and downward if $a < 0$. A parabola can also open to the left or right. In such a case, the "roles" of x and y are essentially interchanged in the equation. Thus, the graph of $x = a(y - k)^2 + h$ opens to the right if $a > 0$ and to the left if $a < 0$.

Standard Form of the Equation of a Parabola (Horizontal Axis of Symmetry)

The standard form of the equation of a parabola with vertex (h, k) and horizontal axis of symmetry is

$$x = a(y - k)^2 + h, \text{ where } a \neq 0 \text{ and } a = \frac{1}{4p}$$

The focus is located at $(h + p, k)$.

The equation of the directrix is $x = h - p$.

If $a > 0$, then the parabola opens to the right and if $a < 0$, the parabola opens to the left.

example 4   **Determining the Focus, Directrix, and Vertex of a Parabola**

Given the equation of the parabola, $x = 4y^2$

a.   Determine the coordinates of the vertex.

b.   Determine the coordinates of the focus and the equation of the directrix.

c.   Graph the parabola.

Solution:

a.   The equation can be written in the form

$$x = a(y - k)^2 + h$$
$$x = 4(y - 0)^2 + 0$$

Therefore, $h = 0$, $k = 0$, and $a = 4$.

The vertex is at (h, k) or $(0, 0)$.

Tip: Notice that the location of the focus is "inside" the curve of the parabola and $|p|$ units from the vertex along the axis of symmetry.

b. $a = 4 = \dfrac{1}{4p}$

Solving for p, we have: $16p = 1$, or $p = \frac{1}{16}$.

The focus is located at $(h + p, k)$: $(0 + \frac{1}{16}, 0)$, or $(\frac{1}{16}, 0)$.

The directrix is $x = h - p$: $x = 0 - (\frac{1}{16})$, or $x = -\frac{1}{16}$.

c.

Graphing Calculator Box

Graphing calculators are designed to graph functions, where y is written as a function of x. The parabola from Example 4 is not a function. It can be graphed, however, as the union of two functions, one representing the top branch, and the other representing the bottom branch.

Solving for y in Example 4, we have

$$y^2 = \frac{x}{4}$$

$$y = \pm\sqrt{\frac{x}{4}}$$

$$y = \pm\frac{\sqrt{x}}{2}$$

Graph these functions as Y_1 and Y_2.

$$Y_1 = \frac{\sqrt{x}}{2} \quad \text{and} \quad Y_2 = -\frac{\sqrt{x}}{2}$$

---

example 5

Determining the Focus, Directrix, and Vertex of a Parabola

Given the equation of the parabola, $x = -\frac{1}{12}(y - 4)^2 + 2$

a.   Determine the coordinates of the vertex.

b.   Determine the coordinates of the focus and the equation of the directrix.

c.   Graph the parabola.

Solution:

a.   The equation is written in the form

$$x = a(y - k)^2 + h$$

$$x = -\frac{1}{12}(y - 4)^2 + 2$$

Therefore, $a = -\frac{1}{12}$, $h = 2$, $k = 4$.

The vertex is $(2, 4)$.

b.   Because $a = -\frac{1}{12}$, then $-\frac{1}{12} = \frac{1}{4p}$

Solving for p, we have $-4p = 12$, or $p = -3$.

The focus is $(h + p, k)$: $[2 + (-3), 4]$, or $(-1, 4)$.

The directrix is $x = h - p$: $x = 2 - (-3)$, or $x = 5$.

c.

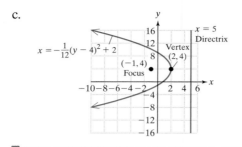

section 11.3   PRACTICE EXERCISES

1. Explain how to determine whether a parabola opens upward, downward, left, or right.

2. Explain how to determine whether a parabola has a vertical or horizontal axis of symmetry.

For Exercises 3–12, use the equation of the parabola to first determine whether the axis of symmetry is vertical or horizontal. Then determine if the parabola opens upward, downward, left, or right.

3. $y = (x - 2)^2 + 3$

4. $y = (x - 4)^2 + 2$

5. $y = -2(x + 1)^2 - 4$

6. $y = -3(x + 2)^2 - 1$

7. $x = y^2 + 4$

8. $x = y^2 - 2$

9. $x = -(y + 3)^2 + 2$

10. $x = -2(y - 1)^2 - 3$

11. $y = -2x^2 - 5$

12. $y = -x^2 + 3$

13. Explain how to determine the coordinates of the focus of a parabola whose equation is written in the form $y = a(x - h)^2 + k$.

14. Explain how to determine the equation of the directrix of a parabola whose equation is written in the form $y = a(x - h)^2 + k$.

15. Explain how to determine the equation of the directrix of a parabola whose equation is written in the form $x = a(y - k)^2 + h$.

16. Explain how to determine the coordinates of the focus of a parabola whose equation is written in the form $x = a(y - k)^2 + h$.

17. True or False: The directrix of a parabola is perpendicular to its axis of symmetry.

18. True or False: A parabola never crosses its directrix.

19. True or False: The vertex of a parabola lies on the directrix.

20. True or False: The focus of a parabola lies on the directrix.

21. True or False: The focus of a parabola lies on the axis of symmetry.

22. True or False: The vertex of a parabola lies on the axis of symmetry.

For Exercises 23–36, use the equation of the parabola to determine the coordinates of the vertex and focus and the equation of the directrix. Then use this information to graph the parabola.

23. $y = \dfrac{1}{2}x^2$

24. $y = \dfrac{1}{4}x^2$

25. $y = -4x^2$

26. $y = -2x^2$

27. $y = (x - 3)^2$

28. $y = (x + 2)^2$

29. $x = y^2$

30. $x = 3y^2$

31. $x = -2(y + 1)^2$

32. $x = -(y - 2)^2$

33. $y = \frac{1}{8}(x + 2)^2 - 5$

34. $y = \frac{1}{2}(x - 1)^2 + 1$

35. $x = -\frac{1}{12}(y - 3)^2 - 3$

36. $x = -\frac{3}{4}(y + 2)^2 + 1$

For Exercises 37–44, find the value of k to complete the square. (See Section 7.5.)

37. $x^2 - 4x + k$ 38. $x^2 + 6x + k$

39. $y^2 + 2y + k$ 40. $y^2 - 8y + k$

41. $x^2 + x + k$ 42. $x^2 - 3x + k$

43. $y^2 - 5y + k$ 44. $y^2 - y + k$

For Exercises 45–54, write the equation in standard form: $y = a(x - h)^2 + k$ or $x = a(y - k)^2 + h$. Then identify the vertex, focus, and directrix of the parabola. (See Example 3.)

45. $y = x^2 - 4x + 3$ 46. $y = x^2 + 6x - 2$

47. $x = y^2 + 2y + 6$ 48. $x = y^2 - 8y + 3$

49. $y = -2x^2 + 8x$ 50. $y = -3x^2 - 6x$

51. $y = x^2 - 3x + 2$ 52. $y = x^2 + x - 4$

53. $x = -2y^2 + 16y + 1$ 54. $x = -3y^2 - 6y + 7$

55. A reflecting telescope has a mirror with cross section in the shape of a parabola. A parabolic mirror has the property that incoming rays of light are reflected from the surface of the mirror to the focus.

    Suppose a reflecting telescope has a parabolic mirror 6 m in diameter. With the vertex of the parabola located at the origin, the mirror traces the curve defined by

    $$y = \frac{1}{50}x^2 \quad -3 \le x \le 3$$

    Find the coordinates of the focus of the mirror.

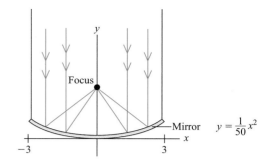

Figure for Exercise 55

56. A radio telescope has a parabolic dish 500 ft in diameter. The antenna of the telescope is located at the focus. With the vertex of the parabola located at the origin, the parabola traces the curve

    $$y = 0.0016x^2 \quad -250 \le x \le 250$$

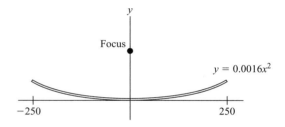

Figure for Exercise 56

Find the coordinates of the focus.

▮ EXPANDING YOUR SKILLS

For Exercises 57–68, determine if the parabola opens upward, downward, left, or right given the following information. (*Hint:* Sketch the information.)

57. Directrix is $y = 3$; focus is $(0, 0)$

58. Directrix is $y = -2$; focus is $(0, 0)$

59. Directrix is $x = -1$; focus is $(1, -2)$

60. Directrix is $x = 3$; focus is $(1, 3)$

61. Directrix is $y = 0$; vertex is $(-5, -3)$

62. Directrix is $y = -4$; vertex is $(2, -3)$

63. Directrix is $x = 0$; vertex is $(-6, 6)$

64. Directrix is $x = -2$; vertex is $(-1, 0)$

65. Vertex is $(-2, 3)$; focus is $(1, 3)$

66. Vertex is $(1, 4)$; focus is $(1, -1)$

67. Vertex is $(-3, -2)$; focus is $(-3, 2)$

68. Vertex is $(4, 1)$; focus is $(-2, 1)$

---

chapter 11   MIDCHAPTER REVIEW

1. Is it possible for the graph of a parabola to have only one x-intercept?

2. Is it possible for the graph of a quadratic function $y = f(x)$ to have two y-intercepts?

3. What two methods can be used to find the vertex of a parabola?

4. How do you find the x-intercepts of a function $y = f(x)$?

5. How do you find the y-intercept of a function $y = f(x)$?

6. How do you find the minimum or maximum value of a quadratic function?

For Exercises 7–9, answer the following questions *without* graphing the parabola.

   a. Does the parabola open up or down?

   b. What is the vertex?

   c. Does the vertex represent a maximum or a minimum point?

   d. What is the maximum or minimum value?

   e. What is the axis of symmetry?

   f. Find the x-intercepts.

   g. Find the y-intercept.

7. $y = 3x^2 - 5x + 4$

8. $y = 10x^2 - 18x - 6.3$

9. $y = -x^2 - \dfrac{1}{2}x - \dfrac{9}{16}$

For Exercises 10–12, determine the coordinates of the vertex and focus and the equation of the directrix.

10. $x = -(y - 3)^2 + 2$

11. $x = y^2 + 4y + 3$

12. $y = 2x^2 - 20x + 50$

Concepts

1. Distance Formula

2. Finding the Distance Between Two Points

3. Applying the Distance Formula

4. Circles

5. Graphing a Circle

6. Writing an Equation of a Circle

section

11.4   DISTANCE FORMULA AND CIRCLES

1. Distance Formula

Suppose we are given two points (x_1, y_1) and (x_2, y_2) in a rectangular coordinate system. The distance between the two points can be found using the Pythagorean theorem (Figure 11-23).

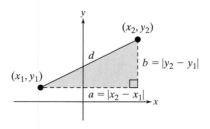

Figure 11-23

First draw a right triangle with the distance, d, as the hypotenuse. The length of the horizontal leg, a, is $|x_2 - x_1|$, and the length of the vertical leg, b, is $|y_2 - y_1|$. From the Pythagorean theorem we have

$$d^2 = a^2 + b^2 \qquad \text{Pythagorean theorem}$$
$$= (x_2 - x_1)^2 + (y_2 - y_1)^2$$
$$d = \pm\sqrt{(x_2 - x_1)^2 + (y_2 - y_1)^2}$$
$$= \sqrt{(x_2 - x_1)^2 + (y_2 - y_1)^2} \qquad \text{Because distance is positive, reject the negative solution.}$$

The Distance Formula

The distance, d, between the points (x_1, y_1) and (x_2, y_2) is

$$d = \sqrt{(x_2 - x_1)^2 + (y_2 - y_1)^2}$$

2.   Finding the Distance Between Two Points

example 1

Finding the Distance Between Two Points

Find the distance between the points $(-2, 3)$ and $(4, -1)$ (Figure 11-24).

Solution:

$$(-2, 3) \qquad \text{and} \qquad (4, -1)$$
$$(x_1, y_1) \qquad \text{and} \qquad (x_2, y_2) \qquad \text{Label the points.}$$
$$d = \sqrt{(x_2 - x_1)^2 + (y_2 - y_1)^2}$$
$$= \sqrt{[(4) - (-2)]^2 + [(-1) - (3)]^2} \qquad \text{Apply the distance formula.}$$
$$= \sqrt{(6)^2 + (-4)^2}$$
$$= \sqrt{36 + 16}$$
$$= \sqrt{52}$$
$$= \sqrt{2^2 \cdot 13}$$
$$= 2\sqrt{13}$$

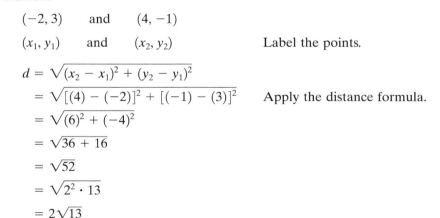

Figure 11-24

Tip: The order in which the points are labeled does not affect the result of the distance formula. For example, if the points in Example 1 had been labeled in reverse, the distance formula still yields the same result:

$(-2, 3)$ and $(4, -1)$ $d = \sqrt{(x_2 - x_1)^2 + (y_2 - y_1)^2}$

(x_2, y_2) and (x_1, y_1) $= \sqrt{[(-2) - (4)]^2 + [(3) - (-1)]^2}$

$= \sqrt{(-6)^2 + (4)^2}$

$= \sqrt{36 + 16}$

$= \sqrt{52}$

$= 2\sqrt{13}$

3. Applying the Distance Formula

example 2

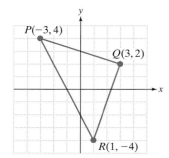

Figure 11-25

Applying the Distance Formula

Use the distance formula to determine whether the points P, Q, and R define the vertices of a right triangle (Figure 11-25).

$$P(-3, 4), Q(3, 2), \text{ and } R(1, -4)$$

Solution:

Find the lengths of the line segments $\overline{PQ}, \overline{QR},$ and $\overline{PR}$. Then determine if the three sides satisfy the Pythagorean theorem.

$(-3, 4)$ and $(3, 2)$ Find the length of the line segment $\overline{PQ}$.

(x_1, y_1) and (x_2, y_2) Label the points.

$\overline{PQ} = \sqrt{[3 - (-3)]^2 + (2 - 4)^2}$

$= \sqrt{6^2 + (-2)^2}$

$= \sqrt{40}$

$(3, 2)$ and $(1, -4)$ Find the length of the line segment $\overline{QR}$.

(x_1, y_1) and (x_2, y_2) Label the points.

$\overline{QR} = \sqrt{(1 - 3)^2 + (-4 - 2)^2}$

$= \sqrt{(-2)^2 + (-6)^2}$

$= \sqrt{40}$

Tip: The Pythagorean theorem states that, given a right triangle with legs of length a and b, and hypotenuse of length c, then $a^2 + b^2 = c^2$. It is also true that if three sides of a triangle with lengths $x, y,$ and z satisfy $x^2 + y^2 = z^2$, then the triangle is a right triangle.

$(-3, 4)$ and $(1, -4)$ Find the length of the line segment $\overline{PR}$.

(x_1, y_1) and (x_2, y_2) Label the points.

$\overline{PR} = \sqrt{[1 - (-3)]^2 + (-4 - 4)^2}$

$= \sqrt{(4)^2 + (-8)^2}$

$= \sqrt{80}$

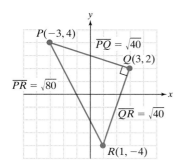

Figure 11-26

Now use the Pythagorean theorem to determine if the sides $\overline{PQ}, \overline{QR}$, and $\overline{PR}$ form a right triangle.

$$a^2 + b^2 = c^2$$

$$(\overline{PQ})^2 + (\overline{QR})^2 \overset{?}{=} (\overline{PR})^2$$

$$(\sqrt{40})^2 + (\sqrt{40})^2 \overset{?}{=} (\sqrt{80})^2$$

$$40 + 40 = 80 \checkmark$$

The three points form a right triangle (Figure 11-26).

4. Circles

A **circle** is defined as the set of all points in a plane that are equidistant from a fixed point called the **center**. The fixed distance from the center is called the **radius** and is denoted by r, where $r > 0$.

Suppose a circle is centered at the point (h, k) and has radius, r (Figure 11-27). The distance formula can be used to derive an equation of the circle.

Let (x, y) be any arbitrary point on the circle. Then by definition, the distance between (h, k) and (x, y) must be r.

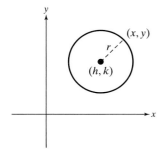

Figure 11-27

$$\sqrt{(x - h)^2 + (y - k)^2} = r$$

$$(x - h)^2 + (y - k)^2 = r^2 \qquad \text{Square both sides.}$$

Standard Form of a Circle

The **standard form of a circle**, centered at (h, k) with radius r is given by:

$$(x - h)^2 + (y - k)^2 = r^2, \text{ where } r > 0.$$

Note: For a circle centered at the origin, $(0, 0)$, then $h = 0$ and $k = 0$, and the equation simplifies to $x^2 + y^2 = r^2$.

5. Graphing a Circle

example 3

Graphing a Circle

Find the center and radius of each circle. Then graph the circle.

a. $(x - 3)^2 + (y + 4)^2 = 36$ b. $x^2 + \left(y - \dfrac{10}{3}\right)^2 = \dfrac{25}{9}$ c. $x^2 + y^2 = 10$

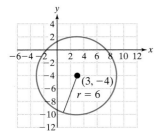

Figure 11-28

Solution:

a. $$(x - 3)^2 + (y + 4)^2 = 36$$

$$(x - 3)^2 + [y - (-4)]^2 = (6)^2$$

$$h = 3, k = -4, \text{ and } r = 6$$

The center is at $(3, -4)$ and the radius is 6 (Figure 11-28).

Graphing Calculator Box

Graphing calculators are designed to graph *functions*, in which y is written in terms of x. A circle is not a function. However, it can be graphed as the union of two functions, one representing the top semicircle, and the other representing the bottom semicircle.

Solving for y in Example 3(a), we have

$$(x - 3)^2 + (y + 4)^2 = 36$$

Graph these functions as Y_1 and Y_2 using a square viewing window.

$$(y + 4)^2 = 36 - (x - 3)^2$$

$$y + 4 = \pm\sqrt{36 - (x - 3)^2}$$

$$y = -4 \pm \sqrt{36 - (x - 3)^2}$$

$$Y_1 = -4 + \sqrt{36 - (x - 3)^2}$$

$$Y_2 = -4 - \sqrt{36 - (x - 3)^2}$$

Notice that the image from the calculator does not show the upper and lower semicircles connecting at their endpoints, when in fact the semicircles should "hook up." This is due to the calculator's limited resolution.

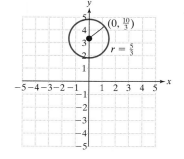

Figure 11-29

b. $x^2 + \left(y - \dfrac{10}{3}\right)^2 = \dfrac{25}{9}$

$(x - 0)^2 + \left(y - \dfrac{10}{3}\right)^2 = \left(\dfrac{5}{3}\right)^2$

The center is $\left(0, \dfrac{10}{3}\right)$ and the radius is $\dfrac{5}{3}$ (Figure 11-29).

c. $x^2 + y^2 = 10$

$(x - 0)^2 + (y - 0)^2 = (\sqrt{10})^2$

The center is $(0, 0)$ and the radius is $\sqrt{10} \approx 3.16$ (Figure 11-30).

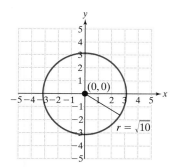

Figure 11-30

6. Writing an Equation of a Circle

example 4

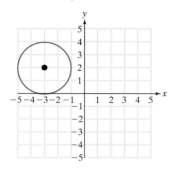

Figure 11-31

Writing an Equation of a Circle

Write an equation of the circle shown in Figure 11-31.

Solution:

The center is $(-3, 2)$; therefore, $h = -3$ and $k = 2$.
The radius is $r = 2$.

$$(x - h)^2 + (y - k)^2 = r^2$$
$$[x - (-3)]^2 + (y - 2)^2 = (2)^2$$
$$(x + 3)^2 + (y - 2)^2 = 4$$

Sometimes it is necessary to complete the square to write an equation of a circle in standard form.

example 5

Writing a Circle in the Form $(x - h)^2 + (y - k)^2 = r^2$

Identify the center and radius of the circle given by the equation:
$x^2 + y^2 + 2x - 16y + 61 = 0$.

Solution:

$$x^2 + y^2 + 2x - 16y + 61 = 0$$

To identify the center and radius, write the equation in the form $(x - h)^2 + (y - k)^2 = r^2$.

$$(x^2 + 2x \quad) + (y^2 - 16y \quad) = -61$$

Group the x-terms and group the y-terms. Move the constant to the right-hand side.

$$(x^2 + 2x + 1) + (y^2 - 16y + 64) = -61 + 1 + 64$$

- Complete the square on x. Add $\left[\frac{1}{2}(2)\right]^2 = 1$ on both sides of the equation.
- Complete the square on y. Add $\left[\frac{1}{2}(-16)\right]^2 = 64$ on both sides of the equation.

$$(x + 1)^2 + (y - 8)^2 = 4$$
$$[x - (-1)]^2 + (y - 8)^2 = 2^2$$

Factor and simplify.

The center is $(-1, 8)$ and the radius is 2.

Avoiding Mistakes

It is important to understand the difference between an equation of a circle and an equation of a parabola. A circle will have square terms for both x and y with equal coefficients. A parabola will be of second degree for one variable and first degree for the other variable. For example,

Equations of Circles

$x^2 + y^2 + 2x - 16y + 61 = 0$

$(x - 2)^2 + (y + 3)^2 = 4$

Equations of Parabolas

$x^2 + 2x + y - 3 = 0$

$y = 3(x - 2)^2 + 1$

example 6   **Writing a Circle in the Form $(x - h)^2 + (y - k)^2 = r^2$**

Identify the center and radius of the circle given by the equation: $3x^2 + 3y^2 + 9x + 6 = 0$.

Solution:

To identify the center and radius, we must write the equation in the form $(x - h)^2 + (y - k)^2 = r^2$.

$$3x^2 + 3y^2 + 9x + 6 = 0$$

$$\frac{3x^2}{3} + \frac{3y^2}{3} + \frac{9x}{3} + \frac{6}{3} = \frac{0}{3}$$ Divide both sides of the equation by the leading coefficient, 3.

$$x^2 + y^2 + 3x + 2 = 0$$

$$(x^2 + 3x \quad) + y^2 = -2$$ Group the x-terms and group the y-terms. Move the constant to the right-hand side.

$$\left(x^2 + 3x + \frac{9}{4}\right) + y^2 = -2 + \frac{9}{4}$$ • Complete the square on x. Add $[\frac{1}{2}(3)]^2 = \frac{9}{4}$ on both sides of the equation.
• Notice that the only y-term is y^2, which is already a perfect square.

$$\left(x + \frac{3}{2}\right)^2 + y^2 = -\frac{8}{4} + \frac{9}{4}$$ Factor on the left. Get a common denominator on the right.

$$\left(x + \frac{3}{2}\right)^2 + y^2 = \frac{1}{4}$$

$$\left[x - \left(-\frac{3}{2}\right)\right]^2 + (y - 0)^2 = \left(\frac{1}{2}\right)^2$$

The center is $(-\frac{3}{2}, 0)$ and the radius is $\frac{1}{2}$.

---

section 11.4   PRACTICE EXERCISES

For Exercises 1–8, graph the function by shifting the graph of $y = x^2$ to the right, left, up, or down.

1. $f(x) = x^2 - 3$
2. $g(x) = x^2 + 2$
3. $h(x) = (x - 3)^2$
4. $k(x) = (x + 2)^2$
5. $m(x) = (x + 0.5)^2$
6. $n(x) = (x - 1.5)^2$
7. $p(x) = x^2 + 0.5$
8. $q(x) = x^2 - 1.5$

For Exercises 9–20, use the distance formula to find the distance between the two points.

9. $(-2, 7)$ and $(3, -9)$
10. $(1, 10)$ and $(-2, 4)$
11. $(0, 5)$ and $(-3, 8)$
12. $(6, 7)$ and $(3, 2)$
13. $\left(\frac{2}{3}, \frac{1}{5}\right)$ and $\left(-\frac{5}{6}, \frac{3}{10}\right)$
14. $\left(-\frac{1}{2}, \frac{5}{8}\right)$ and $\left(-\frac{3}{2}, \frac{1}{4}\right)$

15. $(4, 13)$ and $(4, -6)$

16. $(-2, 5)$ and $(-2, 9)$

17. $(8, -6)$ and $(-2, -6)$

18. $(7, 2)$ and $(15, 2)$

19. $(3\sqrt{5}, 2\sqrt{7})$ and $(-\sqrt{5}, -3\sqrt{7})$

20. $(4\sqrt{6}, -2\sqrt{2})$ and $(2\sqrt{6}, \sqrt{2})$

21. Explain how to find the distance between 5 and -7 on the y-axis.

22. Explain how to find the distance between 15 and -37 on the x-axis.

23. Find a value of y such that the distance between the points $(4, 7)$ and $(-4, y)$ is 10 units.

24. Find a value of x such that the distance between the points $(-4, -2)$ and $(x, 3)$ is 13 units.

25. Find a value of x such that the distance between the points $(x, 2)$ and $(4, -1)$ is 5 units.

26. Find a value of y such that the distance between the points $(-5, 2)$ and $(3, y)$ is 10 units.

For Exercises 27–30, determine if the three points define the vertices of a right triangle. (See Example 2.)

27. $(-3, 2), (-2, -4)$, and $(3, 3)$

28. $(1, -2), (-2, 4)$, and $(7, 1)$

29. $(-3, -2), (4, -3)$, and $(1, 5)$

30. $(1, 4), (5, 3)$, and $(2, 0)$

For Exercises 31–46, identify the center and radius of the circle and then graph the circle. Complete the square if necessary.

31. $(x - 4)^2 + (y + 2)^2 = 9$

32. $(x - 3)^2 + (y + 1)^2 = 16$

33. $(x + 1)^2 + (y + 1)^2 = 1$

34. $(x - 4)^2 + (y - 4)^2 = 4$

35. $x^2 + (y - 5)^2 = 25$ 36. $(x + 1)^2 + y^2 = 1$

37. $(x - 3)^2 + y^2 = 8$ 38. $x^2 + (y + 2)^2 = 20$

39. $x^2 + y^2 = 6$ 40. $x^2 + y^2 = 15$

41. $\left(x + \dfrac{4}{5}\right)^2 + y^2 = \dfrac{64}{25}$ 42. $x^2 + \left(y - \dfrac{5}{2}\right)^2 = \dfrac{9}{4}$

43. $x^2 + y^2 - 2x - 6y - 26 = 0$

44. $x^2 + y^2 + 4x - 8y + 16 = 0$

45. $x^2 + y^2 + 6y + \dfrac{65}{9} = 0$

46. $x^2 + y^2 + 12x + \dfrac{143}{4} = 0$

For Exercises 47–52, write an equation that represents the graph of the circle.

47.

48.

49.

50.

51.

52.

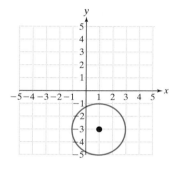

53. Write an equation of a circle centered at the origin with radius 7 m.

54. Write an equation of a circle centered at the origin with a radius of 12 m.

55. Write an equation of a circle centered at $(-3, -4)$ with a diameter of 12 ft.

56. Write an equation of a circle centered at $(5, -1)$ with a diameter of 8 ft.

EXPANDING YOUR SKILLS

57. Write an equation of a circle whose center is at $(4, 4)$ and is tangent to the x- and y-axes. (*Hint*: Sketch the circle first.)

58. Write an equation of a circle whose center is at $(-3, 3)$ and is tangent to the x- and y-axes. (*Hint*: Sketch the circle first.)

59. Write an equation of a circle whose center is at $(1, 1)$ and that passes through the point $(-4, 3)$.

60. Write an equation of a circle whose center is at $(-3, -1)$ and that passes through the point $(5, -2)$.

GRAPHING CALCULATOR EXERCISES

For Exercises 61–66, graph the circles from the indicated exercise on a square viewing window and approximate the center and the radius from the graph.

61. $(x - 4)^2 + (y + 2)^2 = 9$ (Exercise 31)

62. $(x - 3)^2 + (y + 1)^2 = 16$ (Exercise 32)

63. $x^2 + (y - 5)^2 = 25$ (Exercise 35)

64. $(x + 1)^2 + y^2 = 1$ (Exercise 36)

65. $x^2 + y^2 = 6$ (Exercise 39)

66. $x^2 + y^2 = 15$ (Exercise 40)

section

11.5 ELLIPSE AND HYPERBOLA

1. Definition of an Ellipse

In this section we will study the two remaining conic sections: the ellipse and the hyperbola. An **ellipse** is the set of all points (x, y) such that the sum of the distance between (x, y) and two distinct points is a constant (Figure 11-32). The fixed points are called the **foci** (plural of focus) of the ellipse.

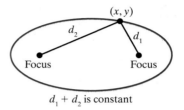

Figure 11-32

The **vertices** of the ellipse are the points where the ellipse intersects the line through the foci. The line segment connecting the vertices is called the **major axis** of the ellipse. The midpoint of the major axis is the **center** of the ellipse. The line perpendicular to the major axis and passing through the center intersects the ellipse in two points called **covertices**. The line segment defined by these points is called the **minor axis** (Figure 11-33).

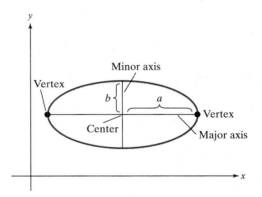

Figure 11-33

It is customary to denote the length of the major axis as $2a$ and the length of the minor axis as $2b$. The length of the major axis is longer than the length of the minor axis; therefore, $a > b$ (see Figure 11-33).

2. Standard Forms of an Equation of an Ellipse

The definition of an ellipse and the distance formula can be used to find an equation of an ellipse. The standard forms of an equation of an ellipse are shown here.

Standard Forms of an Equation of an Ellipse

Let a and b represent positive real numbers such that $a > b$.

Horizontal major axis:

The standard form of an equation of an ellipse with a *horizontal major axis* and center at (h, k) is given by

$$\frac{(x - h)^2}{a^2} + \frac{(y - k)^2}{b^2} = 1$$

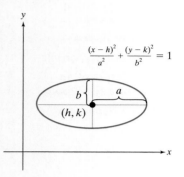

Vertical major axis:

The standard form of an equation of an ellipse with a *vertical major axis* and center at (h, k) is given by

$$\frac{(x - h)^2}{b^2} + \frac{(y - k)^2}{a^2} = 1$$

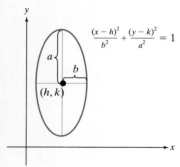

3. Graphing an Ellipse

example 1   **Graphing an Ellipse**

Given the equation of the ellipse

$$\frac{x^2}{9} + \frac{y^2}{4} = 1$$

a.   Determine the coordinates of the center.

b.   Determine whether the major axis is horizontal or vertical.

c.   Graph the ellipse.

d.   Determine the coordinates of the vertices and covertices.

Solution:

a.   The equation can be written as

$$\frac{(x - 0)^2}{(3)^2} + \frac{(y - 0)^2}{(2)^2} = 1$$

Therefore the center is $(0, 0)$.

Tip: For an ellipse written in standard form, the direction of the major axis is determined by the term that has a greater value in the denominator. In Example 1, the denominator of the x-term is 9, whereas the denominator of the y-term is 4. Therefore, the major axis is in the x-direction (horizontal).

b. $a > b$; therefore, $a = 3$ and $b = 2$.

The major axis is horizontal.

c.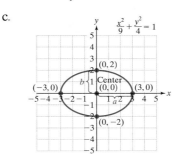

d. The vertices are located 3 units from the center and define the endpoints of the major axis. The coordinates of the vertices are $(-3, 0)$ and $(3, 0)$. The co-vertices are located 2 units from the center and define the endpoints of the minor axis. The coordinates of the covertices are $(0, -2)$ and $(0, 2)$.

Graphing Calculator Box

Graphing calculators are designed to graph *functions*, where y is written as a function of x. An ellipse is not a function; however, it can be graphed as the union of two functions: one representing the top semiellipse and the other representing the bottom semiellipse.

Solving for y in Example 1, we have

$$\frac{x^2}{9} + \frac{y^2}{4} = 1$$

$$\frac{y^2}{4} = 1 - \frac{x^2}{9}$$

$$y^2 = 4 - \frac{4x^2}{9}$$

$$y = \pm\sqrt{4 - \frac{4x^2}{9}}$$

Graph these functions as Y_1 and Y_2 on a square viewing window.

$$Y_1 = \sqrt{4 - \frac{4x^2}{9}}$$

$$Y_2 = -\sqrt{4 - \frac{4x^2}{9}}$$

---

example 2

Graphing an Ellipse

Given the equation of the ellipse,

$$x^2 + \frac{y^2}{25} = 1$$

a. Determine the coordinates of the center.

b. Determine whether the major axis is horizontal or vertical.

c. Graph the ellipse.

d. Determine the coordinates of the vertices and covertices.

Solution:

a. The equation can be written as

$$\frac{(x - 0)^2}{(1)^2} + \frac{(y - 0)^2}{(5)^2} = 1$$

Tip: For an ellipse written in standard form, the direction of the major axis is determined by the term that has a greater value in the denominator. In Example 2, the denominator of the y-term is 25, whereas the denominator of the x-term is 1. Therefore, the major axis is in the y-direction (vertical).

Therefore the center is $(0, 0)$.

b. $a > b$. Therefore, $a = 5$ and $b = 1$.

The major axis is vertical.

c.

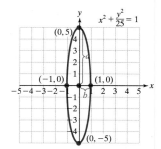

d. The vertices are located 5 units from the center and define the endpoints of the major axis. The coordinates of the vertices are $(0, -5)$ and $(0, 5)$. The covertices are located 1 unit from the center and define the endpoints of the minor axis. The coordinates of the covertices are $(-1, 0)$ and $(1, 0)$.

---

example 3 **Graphing an Ellipse**

Given the equation of the ellipse

$$\frac{(x - 3)^2}{16} + \frac{(y + 1)^2}{81} = 1$$

a. Determine the coordinates of the center.

b. Determine whether the major axis is horizontal or vertical.

c. Graph the ellipse.

d. Determine the coordinates of the vertices and covertices.

Solution:

a. The equation can be written as

$$\frac{(x - 3)^2}{(4)^2} + \frac{[y - (-1)]^2}{(9)^2} = 1$$

Therefore the center is $(3, -1)$.

b. $a > b$. Therefore, $a = 9$ and $b = 4$.

The major axis is vertical.

c.

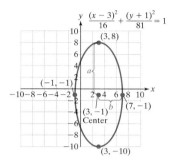

d.   The vertices are located 9 units from the center and define the endpoints of the major axis. The coordinates of the vertices are $(3, -10)$ and $(3, 8)$. The covertices are located 4 units from the center and define the endpoints of the minor axis. The coordinates of the covertices are $(-1, -1)$ and $(7, -1)$.

4.   Definition of a Hyperbola

A **hyperbola** is the set of all points (x, y) such that the *difference* of the distances between (x, y) and two distinct points is a constant (Figure 11-34). The fixed points are called the **foci** of the hyperbola.

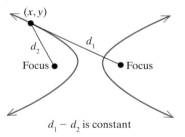

Figure 11-34

The line through the foci intersects the hyperbola at two points called the **vertices** of the hyperbola. The line segment connecting the vertices is called the **transverse axis**. The midpoint of this line segment is the **center** of the hyperbola. The **conjugate axis** passes through the center of the hyperbola and is perpendicular to the transverse axis.

A hyperbola has two branches, and each branch approaches a pair of intersecting lines called **asymptotes**. The asymptotes are not actually part of the hyperbola but may be used as an aid in sketching a hyperbola. The asymptotes of a hyperbola are the lines passing through the diagonals of a fundamental rectangle (Figure 11-35).

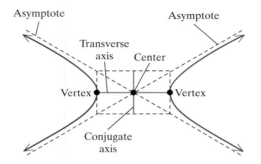

Figure 11-35

The dimensions of the fundamental rectangle are the lengths of the transverse axis and conjugate axis. Furthermore, it is customary to denote the length of the transverse axis by 2a and the length of the conjugate axis by 2b.

5.   Standard Forms of an Equation of a Hyperbola

The definition of a hyperbola and the distance formula can be used to find an equation of a hyperbola. The standard forms of an equation of a hyperbola with a horizontal or vertical transverse axis are shown here.

Standard Forms of an Equation of a Hyperbola

Let a and b represent positive real numbers.

Horizontal transverse axis:

The standard form of an equation of a hyperbola with a *horizontal transverse axis* and center at (h, k) is given by

$$\frac{(x - h)^2}{a^2} - \frac{(y - k)^2}{b^2} = 1$$

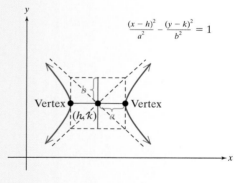

Vertical transverse axis:

The standard form of an equation of a hyperbola with a *vertical transverse axis* and center at (h, k) is given by

$$\frac{(y - k)^2}{a^2} - \frac{(x - h)^2}{b^2} = 1$$

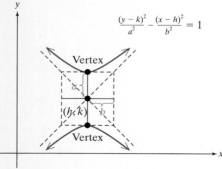

6. Graphing a Hyperbola

Given an equation of a hyperbola in standard form, the term with a positive coefficient determines the orientation of the transverse axis (either horizontal or vertical). To sketch a hyperbola, first determine the location of the center and the values of a and b. Then draw the fundamental rectangle, asymptotes, and vertices of the hyperbola. Use these features as an aid to sketch the curve. This is demonstrated in Examples 4 and 5.

---

example 4

Graphing a Hyperbola

Given the equation of the hyperbola

$$\frac{x^2}{36} - \frac{y^2}{9} = 1$$

a. Determine the coordinates of the center.

b. Determine whether the transverse axis is horizontal or vertical.

c. Graph the hyperbola.

d. Determine the coordinates of the vertices.

e. Determine the equations of the asymptotes.

Solution:

a. The equation can be written as

$$\frac{(x - 0)^2}{(6)^2} - \frac{(y - 0)^2}{(3)^2} = 1$$

Therefore the center is $(0, 0)$.

b. $a = 6$ and $b = 3$. Because the positive coefficient is on the x-term, the transverse axis is horizontal.

c.

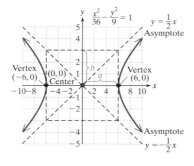

d. The vertices are located 6 units from the center and define the endpoints of the transverse axis. The coordinates of the vertices are $(-6, 0)$ and $(6, 0)$.

e. The asymptotes must pass through the diagonals of the box; therefore, one asymptote must pass through $(-6, -3)$ and $(6, 3)$. The other must pass through $(-6, 3)$ and $(6, -3)$. Finding the slope of each line and applying the point-slope formula, we have

Tip: The slopes of the asymptotes of a hyperbola are opposites of each other.

Line through $(-6, -3)$ and $(6, 3)$

$$m = \frac{3 - (-3)}{6 - (-6)} = \frac{6}{12} = \frac{1}{2}$$

$$y - y_1 = m(x - x_1)$$

$$y - (-3) = \frac{1}{2}(x - (-6))$$

$$y + 3 = \frac{1}{2}x + 3$$

$$y = \frac{1}{2}x$$

Line through $(-6, 3)$ and $(6, -3)$

$$m = \frac{-3 - (3)}{6 - (-6)} = \frac{-6}{12} = -\frac{1}{2}$$

$$y - y_1 = m(x - x_1)$$

$$y - 3 = -\frac{1}{2}(x - (-6))$$

$$y - 3 = -\frac{1}{2}x - 3$$

$$y = -\frac{1}{2}x$$

---

example 5   **Graphing a Hyperbola**

Given the equation of the hyperbola

$$\frac{(y - 2)^2}{16} - \frac{(x + 4)^2}{4} = 1$$

a. Determine the coordinates of the center.

b. Determine whether the transverse axis is horizontal or vertical.

c. Graph the hyperbola.

d. Determine the coordinates of the vertices.

Solution:

a. The equation can be written as

$$\frac{(y - 2)^2}{(4)^2} - \frac{[x - (-4)]^2}{(2)^2} = 1$$

Therefore the center is $(-4, 2)$.

b. $a = 4$ and $b = 2$. Because the positive coefficient is on the y-term, the transverse axis is vertical.

c.

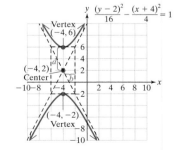

d. The vertices are located 4 units from the center and define the endpoints of the transverse axis. The coordinates of the vertices are $(-4, 6)$ and $(-4, -2)$.

section 11.5   PRACTICE EXERCISES

1. Draw an ellipse with a vertical major axis and label the following:

   a. The center

   b. The vertices

   c. The covertices

   d. The major axis

   e. The minor axis

2. Draw an ellipse with a horizontal major axis and label the following:

   a. The center

   b. The vertices

   c. The covertices

   d. The major axis

   e. The minor axis

For Exercises 3–10, use the equation of the ellipse to identify the center and determine whether the major axis is horizontal or vertical.

3. $\dfrac{x^2}{4} + \dfrac{y^2}{12} = 1$

4. $\dfrac{x^2}{9} + \dfrac{y^2}{14} = 1$

5. $\dfrac{(x - 2)^2}{9} + \dfrac{(y - 5)^2}{4} = 1$

6. $\dfrac{(x - 6)^2}{16} + \dfrac{(y - 2)^2}{4} = 1$

7. $\dfrac{(x + 2)^2}{2} + \dfrac{(y + 4)^2}{10} = 1$

8. $\dfrac{(x + 1)^2}{5} + \dfrac{(y + 8)^2}{8} = 1$

9. $\dfrac{(x + 4)^2}{7} + \dfrac{(y - 1)^2}{1} = 1$

10. $\dfrac{(x - 4)^2}{9} + \dfrac{(y + 4)^2}{3} = 1$

For Exercises 11–20, graph the ellipse and identify the center, vertices, and covertices.

11. $\dfrac{x^2}{4} + \dfrac{y^2}{9} = 1$

12. $\dfrac{x^2}{16} + \dfrac{y^2}{25} = 1$

13. $\dfrac{x^2}{25} + \dfrac{y^2}{16} = 1$

14. $\dfrac{x^2}{81} + \dfrac{y^2}{36} = 1$

15. $\dfrac{x^2}{16} + \dfrac{(y - 2)^2}{4} = 1$

16. $\dfrac{(x - 2)^2}{9} + \dfrac{y^2}{4} = 1$

17. $\dfrac{(x + 1)^2}{1} + \dfrac{(y + 3)^2}{36} = 1$

18. $\dfrac{(x + 4)^2}{16} + \dfrac{(y + 2)^2}{25} = 1$

19. $\dfrac{(x - 3)^2}{49} + \dfrac{(y + 1)^2}{25} = 1$

20. $\dfrac{(x + 3)^2}{4} + \dfrac{(y - 1)^2}{1} = 1$

21. Sonya wants to cut an elliptical rug from a rectangular rug to avoid a stain made by the family dog. She places two tacks along the center horizontal line. Then she ties the ends of a slack piece of rope to each tack. With the rope pulled tight, she traces out a curve. Use the definition of an ellipse to explain why this method will produce an elliptical shape curve.

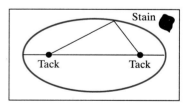

Figure for Exercise 21

22. An arch for a tunnel is in the shape of a semi-ellipse. The distance between vertices is 120 ft, and the height to the top of the arch is 50 ft. Find the height of the arch 10 ft from the center. Round to the nearest foot.

Figure for Exercise 22

23. A bridge over a gorge is supported by an arch in the shape of a semiellipse. The length of the bridge is 400 ft, and the height is 100 ft. Find the height of the arch 50 ft from the center. Round to the nearest foot.

Figure for Exercise 23

24. Draw a hyperbola with a vertical transverse axis and label the following:
    a. The center
    b. The vertices
    c. The asymptotes
    d. The transverse axis
    e. The conjugate axis

25. Draw a hyperbola with a horizontal transverse axis and label the following:
    a. The center
    b. The vertices
    c. The asymptotes
    d. The transverse axis
    e. The conjugate axis

For Exercises 26–33, identify the center of the hyperbola and determine whether the transverse axis is horizontal or vertical.

26. $\dfrac{x^2}{14} - \dfrac{y^2}{8} = 1$

27. $\dfrac{x^2}{10} - \dfrac{y^2}{4} = 1$

28. $\dfrac{y^2}{6} - \dfrac{x^2}{16} = 1$

29. $\dfrac{y^2}{9} - \dfrac{x^2}{25} = 1$

30. $\dfrac{(x - 2)^2}{12} - \dfrac{(y + 4)^2}{9} = 1$

31. $\dfrac{(x + 1)^2}{24} - \dfrac{(y + 8)^2}{4} = 1$

32. $\dfrac{(y - 5)^2}{9} - \dfrac{(x - 2)^2}{9} = 1$

33. $\dfrac{(y + 4)^2}{12} - \dfrac{(x + 1)^2}{12} = 1$

For Exercises 34–43, graph the hyperbola and identify the center and vertices.

34. $\dfrac{x^2}{25} - \dfrac{y^2}{16} = 1$

35. $\dfrac{x^2}{9} - \dfrac{y^2}{36} = 1$

36. $\dfrac{y^2}{4} - \dfrac{x^2}{4} = 1$

37. $\dfrac{y^2}{9} - \dfrac{x^2}{9} = 1$

38. $\dfrac{(x - 1)^2}{25} - \dfrac{(y - 1)^2}{4} = 1$

39. $\dfrac{(x - 2)^2}{36} - \dfrac{(y - 2)^2}{25} = 1$

40. $\dfrac{(y + 3)^2}{1} - \dfrac{x^2}{16} = 1$

41. $\dfrac{y^2}{4} - \dfrac{(x + 4)^2}{9} = 1$

42. $\dfrac{(x + 5)^2}{49} - \dfrac{(y + 1)^2}{9} = 1$

43. $\dfrac{(x + 6)^2}{25} - \dfrac{(y + 2)^2}{1} = 1$

44. Explain how to find the equations of the asymptotes of a hyperbola written in the form
$$\frac{(x - h)^2}{a^2} - \frac{(y - k)^2}{b^2} = 1$$

For Exercises 45–48, find the equations of the asymptotes of the hyperbola.

45. $\dfrac{x^2}{16} - \dfrac{y^2}{16} = 1$

46. $\dfrac{x^2}{9} - \dfrac{y^2}{1} = 1$

47. $\dfrac{(x - 2)^2}{36} - \dfrac{(y + 4)^2}{9} = 1$

48. $\dfrac{(x-1)^2}{25} - \dfrac{(y-1)^2}{4} = 1$

49. Explain how to tell the difference between the equations of a hyperbola and an ellipse.

For Exercises 50–57, determine if the equation represents an ellipse or a hyperbola.

50. $\dfrac{x^2}{6} - \dfrac{y^2}{10} = 1$

51. $\dfrac{x^2}{14} + \dfrac{y^2}{2} = 1$

52. $\dfrac{(y-4)^2}{4} + \dfrac{(x+3)^2}{16} = 1$

53. $-\dfrac{(x+1)^2}{5} + \dfrac{y^2}{5} = 1$

54. $4x^2 + y^2 = 16$

55. $-3x^2 - 4y^2 = -36$

56. $-y^2 + 2x^2 = -10$

57. $x^2 - y^2 = -1$

■ **EXPANDING YOUR SKILLS**

The foci of an ellipse are located $|c|$ units from the center along the major axis, where $c^2 = a^2 - b^2$.

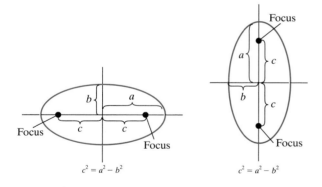

For Exercises 58–61, find the coordinates of the foci of the ellipse.

58. $\dfrac{x^2}{25} + \dfrac{y^2}{16} = 1$

59. $\dfrac{x^2}{9} + \dfrac{y^2}{25} = 1$

60. $\dfrac{x^2}{64} + \dfrac{y^2}{100} = 1$

61. $\dfrac{x^2}{100} + \dfrac{y^2}{36} = 1$

62. The orbit of Venus around the sun can be approximated by an ellipse with an equation

$$\dfrac{x^2}{(113.93)^2} + \dfrac{y^2}{(113.34)^2} = 1$$

where the sun is located at one of the foci and all distances are in millions of kilometers.

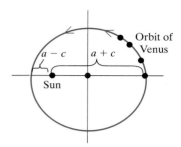

Figure for Exercise 62

a. Find the coordinates of the foci. Round to the nearest hundredth.

b. Find the greatest distance from Venus to the sun (this distance is called the apogee).

c. Find the least distance from Venus to the sun (this distance is called the perigee).

The foci of a hyperbola are located $|c|$ units from the center along the line defined by the transverse axis where $c^2 = a^2 + b^2$.

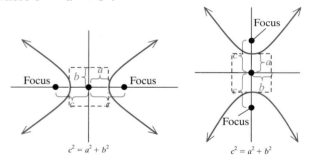

For Exercises 63–66, find the coordinates of the foci of the hyperbola.

63. $\dfrac{x^2}{16} - \dfrac{y^2}{9} = 1$

64. $\dfrac{y^2}{36} - \dfrac{x^2}{64} = 1$

65. $\dfrac{y^2}{144} - \dfrac{x^2}{25} = 1$

66. $\dfrac{x^2}{64} - \dfrac{y^2}{36} = 1$

■ **GRAPHING CALCULATOR EXERCISES**

For Exercises 67–70, solve the equation for y. Graph both functions on a calculator. Confirm your answers to the indicated problem.

67. $\dfrac{x^2}{6} - \dfrac{y^2}{10} = 1$ (Exercise 50)

69. $\dfrac{(y-4)^2}{4} + \dfrac{(x+3)^2}{16} = 1$ (Exercise 52)

68. $\dfrac{x^2}{14} + \dfrac{y^2}{2} = 1$ (Exercise 51)

70. $-\dfrac{(x+1)^2}{5} + \dfrac{y^2}{5} = 1$ (Exercise 53)

11.6   Nonlinear Systems of Equations in Two Variables

Concepts

1. **Solving Nonlinear Systems of Equations by the Substitution Method**

2. **Solving Nonlinear Systems of Equations by the Addition Method**

1. Solving Nonlinear Systems of Equations by the Substitution Method

Recall that a linear equation in two variables x and y is an equation that can be written in the form $ax + by = c$, where a and b are not both zero. In Section 3.1, we solved systems of linear equations in two variables using the graphing method, the substitution method, and the addition method. In this section, we will solve *nonlinear* systems of equations using the same methods. A **nonlinear system of equations** is a system in which at least one of the equations is nonlinear.

Graphing the equations in a nonlinear system helps to determine the number of solutions and to approximate the coordinates of the solutions. The substitution method is used most often to solve a nonlinear system of equations analytically.

example 1   **Solving a Nonlinear System of Equations by the Substitution Method**

Given the system

$$x - 7y = -25$$
$$x^2 + y^2 = 25$$

a. Solve the system by graphing.
b. Solve the system by the substitution method.

Solution:

a. $x - 7y = -25$ is a line (the slope-intercept form is $y = \frac{1}{7}x + \frac{25}{7}$).

$\quad\quad x^2 + y^2 = 25$ is a circle centered at the origin with radius 5.

From Figure 11-36, we appear to have two solutions at $(-4, 3)$ and $(3, 4)$.

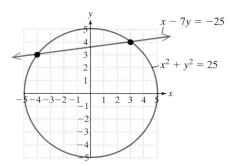

Figure 11-36

b.   To use the substitution method, isolate one of the variables from one of the equations. We will solve for x in the first equation.

$\boxed{A}$ $x - 7y = -25 \xrightarrow{\text{solve for } x} x = 7y - 25$

$\boxed{B}$ $x^2 + y^2 = 25$

$\boxed{B}$ $(7y - 25)^2 + y^2 = 25$ Substitute $(7y - 25)$ for x in the second equation.

$49y^2 - 350y + 625 + y^2 = 25$ The resulting equation is quadratic in y.

$50y^2 - 350y + 600 = 0$ Set the equation equal to zero.

$50(y^2 - 7y + 12) = 0$ Factor.

$50(y - 3)(y - 4) = 0$

$y = 3$ or $y = 4$

For each value of y, find the corresponding x value from the equation $x = 7y - 25$.

$y = 3$: $x = 7(3) - 25 = -4$ The solution point is $(-4, 3)$.

$y = 4$: $x = 7(4) - 25 = 3$ The solution point is $(3, 4)$.   (See Figure 11-37.)

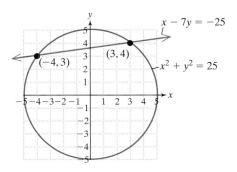

Figure 11-37

example 2

Solving a Nonlinear System by the Substitution Method

Given the system

$$y = \sqrt{x}$$
$$x^2 + y^2 = 20$$

a. Sketch the equations.
b. Solve the system by the substitution method.

Solution:

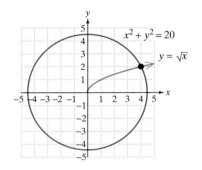

Figure 11-38

a. $y = \sqrt{x}$ is one of the six basic functions graphed in Section 4.3.

$x^2 + y^2 = 20$ is a circle centered at the origin with radius $\sqrt{20} \approx 4.5$.

From Figure 11-38, we find one solution.

b. To use the substitution method, we will substitute $y = \sqrt{x}$ into equation $\boxed{B}$.

$\boxed{A}$ $y = \sqrt{x}$

$\boxed{B}$ $x^2 + y^2 = 20$

$\boxed{B}$ $x^2 + (\sqrt{x})^2 = 20$ Substitute $y = \sqrt{x}$ into the second equation.

$x^2 + x = 20$

$x^2 + x - 20 = 0$ Set the second equation equal to zero.

$(x + 5)(x - 4) = 0$ Factor.

$x \neq -5$ or $x = 4$ Reject $x = -5$ because it is not in the domain of the equation, $y = \sqrt{x}$.

Substitute $x = 4$ into the equation $y = \sqrt{x}$.

If $x = 4$, then $y = \sqrt{4} = 2$ The solution point is $(4, 2)$.

Graphing Calculator Box

Graph the equations from Example 2 to confirm your solution to the system of equations. Use an *Intersect* feature or *Zoom* and *Trace* to approximate the point of intersection. Recall that the circle must be entered into the calculator as two functions:

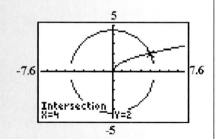

$$Y_1 = \sqrt{20 - x^2}$$
$$Y_2 = -\sqrt{20 - x^2}$$
$$Y_3 = \sqrt{x}$$

example 3

Solving a Nonlinear System Using the Substitution Method

Solve the system using the substitution method.

$$y = \sqrt[3]{x}$$

$$y = x$$

Solution:

$\boxed{A}$ $y = \sqrt[3]{x}$

$\boxed{B}$ $y = x$

$\sqrt[3]{x} = x$	Because y is isolated in both equations, we can equate the expressions for y.
$(\sqrt[3]{x})^3 = (x)^3$	To solve the radical equation, raise both sides to the third power.
$x = x^3$	This is a third-degree polynomial equation.
$0 = x^3 - x$	Set the equation equal to zero.
$0 = x(x^2 - 1)$	Factor out the GCF.
$0 = x(x + 1)(x - 1)$	Factor completely.

$x = 0$ or $x = -1$ or $x = 1$

For each value of x, find the corresponding y-value from either original equation. We will use equation $\boxed{B}$: $y = x$.

If $x = 0$, then $y = 0$ The solution point is $(0, 0)$.

If $x = -1$, then $y = -1$ The solution point is $(-1, -1)$.

If $x = 1$, then $y = 1$ The solution point is $(1, 1)$.

Graphing Calculator Box

Graph the equations $y = \sqrt[3]{x}$ and $y = x$ to support the solutions to Example 3.

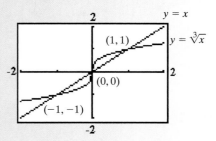

2. Solving Nonlinear Systems of Equations by the Addition Method

The substitution method is used most often to solve a system of nonlinear equations. In some situations, however, the addition method offers an efficient means of finding a solution. The next example demonstrates that we can eliminate a variable from both equations provided the terms containing that variable are *like* terms.

example 4

Solving a Nonlinear System of Equations by the Addition Method

Solve the system

$$2x^2 + y^2 = 17$$

$$x^2 + 2y^2 = 22$$

Solution:

$\boxed{A}$ $2x^2 + y^2 = 17$ Notice that the y^2 terms are *like* in each equation.

$\boxed{B}$ $x^2 + 2y^2 = 22$ To eliminate the y^2 terms, multiply the first equation by -2.

$\boxed{A}$ $2x^2 + y^2 = 17$ $\xrightarrow{\text{multiply by } -2}$ $-4x^2 - 2y^2 = -34$

$\boxed{B}$ $x^2 + 2y^2 = 22$ $\xrightarrow{\hspace{2cm}}$ $\underline{x^2 + 2y^2 = 22}$

$\qquad\qquad\qquad\qquad\qquad\qquad -3x^2 \qquad\quad = -12$ Eliminate the y^2 term.

Tip: In Example 4, the x^2 terms are also *like* in both equations. We could have eliminated the x^2 terms by multiplying equation $\boxed{B}$ by -2.

$$\frac{-3x^2}{-3} = \frac{-12}{-3}$$

$$x^2 = 4$$

$$x = \pm 2$$

Substitute each value of x into one of the original equations to solve for y. We will use equation $\boxed{A}$: $2x^2 + y^2 = 17$.

$x = 2$: $\boxed{A}$ $2(2)^2 + y^2 = 17$

$\qquad\qquad\qquad\quad 8 + y^2 = 17$

$\qquad\qquad\qquad\qquad y^2 = 9$

$\qquad\qquad\qquad\qquad y = \pm 3$ The solution points are $(2, 3)$ and $(2, -3)$.

$x = -2$: $\boxed{A}$ $2(-2)^2 + y^2 = 17$

$\qquad\qquad\qquad\quad 8 + y^2 = 17$

$\qquad\qquad\qquad\qquad y^2 = 9$

$\qquad\qquad\qquad\qquad y = \pm 3$ The solution points are $(-2, 3)$ and $(-2, -3)$.

Graphing Calculator Box

The solutions to Example 4 can be checked from the graphs of the equations.

For the equation $2x^2 + y^2 = 17$, we have: $Y = \pm\sqrt{17 - 2x^2}$

For the equation $x^2 + 2y^2 = 22$, we have: $Y = \pm\sqrt{(22 - x^2)/2}$

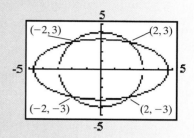

Tip: It is important to note that the addition method can only be used if two equations share a pair of *like* terms. The substitution method is effective in solving a wider range of systems of equations. The system in Example 4 could also have been solved using substitution.

$\boxed{A}$ $\qquad$ $2x^2 + y^2 = 17 \xrightarrow{\text{solve for } y^2} y^2 = 17 - 2x^2$

$\boxed{B}$ $\qquad$ $x^2 + 2y^2 = 22$

$\boxed{B}$ $x^2 + 2(17 - 2x^2) = 22$ $\qquad\qquad$ $x = 2:$ $y^2 = 17 - 2(2)^2$

$\qquad\quad x^2 + 34 - 4x^2 = 22$ $\qquad\qquad\qquad\qquad$ $y^2 = 9$

$\qquad\qquad\qquad -3x^2 = -12$ $\qquad\qquad\qquad\qquad$ $y = \pm 3$ The solutions are $(2, 3)$
$\qquad\qquad\qquad\qquad\qquad\qquad\qquad\qquad\qquad\qquad\qquad\qquad\qquad$ and $(2, -3)$.

$\qquad\qquad\qquad\qquad x^2 = 4$

$\qquad\qquad\qquad x = \pm 2$ $\qquad\qquad\qquad$ $x = -2:$ $y^2 = 17 - 2(-2)^2$

$\qquad\qquad\qquad\qquad\qquad\qquad\qquad\qquad\qquad\qquad$ $y^2 = 9$

$\qquad\qquad\qquad\qquad\qquad\qquad\qquad\qquad\qquad\qquad$ $y = \pm 3$ The solutions are $(-2, 3)$
$\qquad\qquad\qquad\qquad\qquad\qquad\qquad\qquad\qquad\qquad\qquad\qquad\qquad\qquad$ and $(-2, -3)$.

---

section 11.6   PRACTICE EXERCISES

1. Write the distance formula between two points (x_1, y_1) and (x_2, y_2) from memory.

2. Find the distance between the two points $(8, -1)$ and $(1, -8)$.

3. Find the distance between the two points $(2.7, -5.9)$ and $(4.6, -2.1)$. (Round the answer to one decimal place.)

4. Find the distance between the two points $(6\frac{1}{8}, 3\frac{1}{4})$ and $(6\frac{3}{8}, 2\frac{1}{2})$.

5. Write an equation representing the set of all points 2 units from the point $(-1, 1)$.

6. Write an equation representing the set of all points 8 units from the point $(-5, 3)$.

7. Write an equation representing the set of all points $\sqrt{11}$ units from the point $(8, -2)$.

8. Write an equation representing the set of all points $\sqrt{15}$ units from the origin.

For Exercises 9–16, determine if the equation represents a parabola, circle, ellipse, or hyperbola.

9. $x^2 + y^2 = 15$

10. $\dfrac{x^2}{4} - \dfrac{y^2}{2} = 1$

11. $y = (x - 6)^2 + 4$

12. $\dfrac{(x + 1)^2}{2} + \dfrac{(y + 1)^2}{5} = 1$

13. $\dfrac{(y - 1)^2}{3} - \dfrac{(x + 2)^2}{3} = 1$

14. $3x^2 + 3y^2 = 1$

15. $\dfrac{x^2}{9} + \dfrac{y^2}{12} = 1$

16. $x = (y + 2)^2 - 5$

For Exercises 17–26, match the equations with their graphs.

17. $y = x + 3$

18. $y = -x^2 + 4$

19. $\dfrac{x^2}{4} + y^2 = 1$

20. $x^2 - \dfrac{y^2}{4} = 1$

21. $x^2 + y^2 = 6$

22. $y = 2x$

23. $\dfrac{y^2}{9} - \dfrac{x^2}{9} = 1$

24. $\dfrac{(x - 1)^2}{9} + \dfrac{(y - 1)^2}{16} = 1$

25. $y = x^2$

26. $x^2 + y^2 = 20$

a.

b.

c.

d.

e.

i.

f.

j.

g.

h.

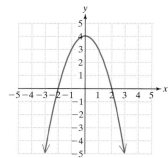

For Exercises 27–34, use sketches to explain.

27. How many points of intersection are possible between a line and a parabola?

28. How many points of intersection are possible between a line and a circle?

29. How many points of intersection are possible between two distinct circles?

30. How many points of intersection are possible between two distinct parabolas of the form $y = ax^2 + bx + c, a \neq 0$?

31. How many points of intersection are possible between a circle and a parabola?

32. How many points of intersection are possible between two distinct lines?

33. How many points of intersection are possible with an ellipse and a hyperbola?

34. How many points of intersection are possible with an ellipse and a parabola?

For Exercises 35–46, sketch each system of equations. Then solve the system by the substitution method.

35. $y = x + 3$ 36. $y = x - 2$
$x^2 + y = 9$ $x^2 + y = 4$

37. $x^2 + y^2 = 1$ 38. $x^2 + y^2 = 25$
$y = x + 1$ $y = 2x$

39. $x^2 + y^2 = 6$ 40. $x^2 + y^2 = 12$
$y = x^2$ $y = x^2$

41. $x^2 + y^2 = 20$ 42. $x^2 + y^2 = 30$
$y = \sqrt{x}$ $y = \sqrt{x}$

43. $y = x^2$ 44. $y = -x^2$
$y = -\sqrt{x}$ $y = -\sqrt{x}$

45. $y = x^2$ 46. $y = (x + 4)^2$
$y = (x - 3)^2$ $y = x^2$

For Exercises 47–56, solve the system of nonlinear equations by the addition method.

47. $x^2 + y^2 = 13$ 48. $4x^2 - y^2 = 4$
$x^2 - y^2 = 5$ $4x^2 + y^2 = 4$

49. $9x^2 + 4y^2 = 36$ 50. $x^2 + y^2 = 4$
$x^2 + y^2 = 9$ $2x^2 + y^2 = 8$

51. $3x^2 + 4y^2 = 16$ 52. $2x^2 - 5y^2 = -2$
$2x^2 - 3y^2 = 5$ $3x^2 + 2y^2 = 35$

53. $y = x^2 - 2$ 54. $y = x^2$
$y = -x^2 + 2$ $y = -x^2 + 8$

55. $\dfrac{x^2}{4} + \dfrac{y^2}{9} = 1$ 56. $\dfrac{x^2}{16} + \dfrac{y^2}{4} = 1$
$x^2 + y^2 = 4$ $x^2 + y^2 = 4$

EXPANDING YOUR SKILLS

57. The sum of two numbers is 7. The sum of the squares of the numbers is 25. Find the numbers.

58. The sum of the squares of two numbers is 100. The sum of the numbers is 2. Find the numbers.

59. The sum of the squares of two numbers is 32. The difference of the squares of the numbers is 18. Find the numbers.

60. The sum of the squares of two numbers is 24. The difference of the squares of the numbers is 8. Find the numbers.

GRAPHING CALCULATOR EXERCISES

For Exercises 61–64, use the *Intersect* feature or *Zoom* and *Trace* to approximate the solutions to the system.

61. $y = x + 3$ (Exercise 35)
$x^2 + y = 9$

62. $y = x - 2$ (Exercise 36)
$x^2 + y = 4$

63. $y = x^2$ (Exercise 43)
$y = -\sqrt{x}$

64. $y = -x^2$ (Exercise 44)
$y = -\sqrt{x}$

For Exercises 65–66, graph the system on a standard viewing window. What can be said about the solution to the system?

65. $x^2 + y^2 = 4$ 66. $x^2 + y^2 = 16$
$y = x^2 + 3$ $y = -x^2 - 5$

chapter 11   SUMMARY

SECTION 11.1—GRAPHS OF QUADRATIC FUNCTIONS

KEY CONCEPTS:

A quadratic function of the form $f(x) = x^2 + k$ shifts the graph of $y = x^2$ up k units if $k > 0$, and down $|k|$ units if $k < 0$.

A quadratic function of the form $f(x) = (x - h)^2$ shifts the graph of $y = x^2$ right h units if $h > 0$, and left $|h|$ units if $h < 0$.

A quadratic function of the form $f(x) = ax^2$ is a parabola that opens up when $a > 0$ and opens down when $a < 0$. If $|a| > 1$ the graph of $y = x^2$ is stretched vertically by a factor of $|a|$. If $0 < |a| < 1$ the graph of $y = x^2$ is shrunk vertically by a factor of $|a|$.

EXAMPLES:

A quadratic function of the form $f(x) = a(x - h)^2 + k$ has vertex (h, k). If $a > 0$ the vertex represents the minimum point. If $a < 0$ the vertex represents the maximum point.

KEY TERMS:

axis of symmetry
maximum value
minimum value
vertex

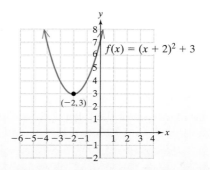

$f(x) = (x + 2)^2 + 3$

$(-2, 3)$

SECTION 11.2—APPLICATIONS OF QUADRATIC FUNCTIONS

KEY CONCEPTS:

Completing the square is used to write a quadratic function $f(x) = ax^2 + bx + c$ $(a \neq 0)$ in the form $f(x) = a(x - h)^2 + k$ for the purpose of identifying the vertex, (h, k).

EXAMPLES:

Find the vertex:

$$
\begin{aligned}
f(x) &= 3x^2 + 6x + 11 \\
&= 3(x^2 + 2x \qquad\quad) + 11 \\
&= 3(x^2 + 2x + 1 - 1) + 11 \\
&= 3(x^2 + 2x + 1) - 3 + 11 \\
&= 3(x + 1)^2 + 8 \\
&= 3[x - (-1)]^2 + 8
\end{aligned}
$$

The vertex is $(-1, 8)$. Because $a = 3 > 0$, $(-1, 8)$ is a minimum point.

The vertex formula finds the vertex of a quadratic function $f(x) = ax^2 + bx + c$ $(a \neq 0)$. The vertex is

$$\left(\frac{-b}{2a}, \frac{4ac - b^2}{4a}\right) \quad \text{or} \quad \left(\frac{-b}{2a}, f\left(\frac{-b}{2a}\right)\right)$$

KEY TERMS:

vertex formula

Find the vertex:

$$f(x) = -5x^2 + 4x - 1 \qquad a = -5, b = 4, c = -1$$

$$x = \frac{-4}{2(-5)} = \frac{2}{5}$$

$$f\left(\frac{2}{5}\right) = -5\left(\frac{2}{5}\right)^2 + 4\left(\frac{2}{5}\right) - 1 = -\frac{1}{5}$$

The vertex is $\left(\frac{2}{5}, -\frac{1}{5}\right)$. Because $a = -5 < 0$, $\left(\frac{2}{5}, -\frac{1}{5}\right)$ is a maximum point.

SECTION 11.3—MORE ON THE PARABOLA

KEY CONCEPTS:

A parabola is the set of points in a plane that are equidistant (the same distance) from a fixed line (called the directrix) and a fixed point (called the focus) not on the directrix.

The standard form of an equation of a parabola with vertex (h, k) and vertical axis of symmetry is

$$y = a(x - h)^2 + k, \text{ where } a = \frac{1}{4p}$$

The focus is located at $(h, k + p)$.

The equation of the directrix is $y = k - p$.

If $a > 0$, then the parabola opens upward, and if $a < 0$, the parabola opens downward.

The standard form of an equation of a parabola with vertex (h, k) and horizontal axis of symmetry is

$$x = a(y - k)^2 + h, \text{ where } a = \frac{1}{4p}$$

The focus is located at $(h + p, k)$.

The equation of the directrix is $x = h - p$.

If $a > 0$, then the parabola opens to the right, and if $a < 0$, the parabola opens to the left.

KEY TERMS:

axis of symmetry
conic sections
directrix
focus
parabola
standard form of a parabola (horizontal axis)
standard form of a parabola (vertical axis)
vertex

EXAMPLES:

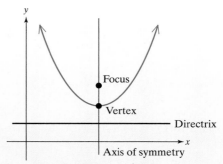

Given the parabola, $x = -\frac{1}{4}y^2 + 1$.

Determine the coordinates of the vertex and the focus and write an equation of the directrix.

$$x = -\frac{1}{4}(y - 0)^2 + 1$$

The vertex is $(1, 0)$.

$-\frac{1}{4} = \frac{1}{4p}$, therefore $p = -1$.

The focus is $(0, 0)$.

The directrix is $x = 2$.

SECTION 11.4—DISTANCE FORMULA AND CIRCLES

KEY CONCEPTS:

The distance between two points (x_1, y_1) and (x_2, y_2) is

$$d = \sqrt{(x_2 - x_1)^2 + (y_2 - y_1)^2}$$

The standard form of a circle with center (h, k) and radius r is

$$(x - h)^2 + (y - k)^2 = r^2$$

KEY TERMS:

center of a circle
circle
distance formula
radius
standard form of a circle

EXAMPLES:

Find the distance between two points:

$$(5, -2) \quad \text{and} \quad (-1, -6)$$

$$\begin{aligned} d &= \sqrt{(-1 - 5)^2 + [-6 - (-2)]^2} \\ &= \sqrt{(-6)^2 + (-4)^2} \\ &= \sqrt{36 + 16} \\ &= \sqrt{52} = 2\sqrt{13} \end{aligned}$$

Find the center and radius of the circle:

$$x^2 + y^2 - 8x + 6y = 0$$

$$(x^2 - 8x + 16) + (y^2 + 6y + 9) = 16 + 9$$

$$(x - 4)^2 + (y + 3)^2 = 25$$

The center is $(4, -3)$ and the radius is 5.

SECTION 11.5—ELLIPSE AND HYPERBOLA

KEY CONCEPTS:

An ellipse is the set of all points (x, y) such that the sum of the distances between (x, y) and two distinct points is a constant. The fixed points are called the foci of the ellipse.

Standard Forms of an Equation of an Ellipse
Let a and b represent positive real numbers such that $a > b$.

Horizontal Major Axis:
The standard form of an equation of an ellipse with a horizontal major axis and center at (h, k) is given by

$$\frac{(x - h)^2}{a^2} + \frac{(y - k)^2}{b^2} = 1$$

EXAMPLES:

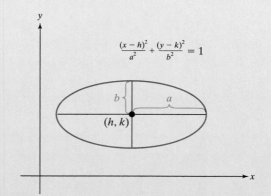

Vertical Major Axis:
The standard form of an equation of an ellipse with a vertical major axis and center at (h, k) is given by

$$\frac{(x - h)^2}{b^2} + \frac{(y - k)^2}{a^2} = 1$$

A hyperbola is the set of all points (x, y) such that the difference of the distances between (x, y) and two distinct points is a constant. The fixed points are called the foci of the hyperbola.

Standard Forms of an Equation of a Hyperbola

Let a and b represent positive real numbers.

Horizontal Transverse Axis:
The standard form of an equation of a hyperbola with a horizontal transverse axis and center at (h, k) is given by

$$\frac{(x - h)^2}{a^2} - \frac{(y - k)^2}{b^2} = 1$$

Vertical Transverse Axis:
The standard form of an equation of a hyperbola with a vertical transverse axis and center at (h, k) is given by

$$\frac{(y - k)^2}{a^2} - \frac{(x - h)^2}{b^2} = 1$$

KEY TERMS:

asymptotes
center
conjugate axis
covertices
ellipse
foci
hyperbola
major axis
minor axis
standard forms of an equation of an ellipse
standard forms of an equation of a hyperbola
transverse axis
vertices

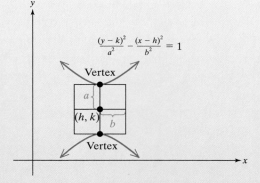

Section 11.6—Nonlinear Systems of Equations in Two Variables

Key Concepts:

A nonlinear system of equations can be solved by graphing or by the substitution method.

$$2x^2 + y^2 = 15$$
$$x^2 - y = 0$$

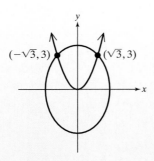

A nonlinear system may also be solved using the addition method when the equations share *like* terms.

Key Terms:

nonlinear system of equations

Examples:

Solve the nonlinear system:

$$\boxed{A} \qquad 2x^2 + y^2 = 15$$
$$\boxed{B} \qquad x^2 - y = 0 \qquad \text{Solve for } y: y = x^2$$

$$\boxed{A} \quad 2x^2 + (x^2)^2 = 15 \qquad \text{Substitute in first equation.}$$

$$2x^2 + x^4 = 15$$

$$x^4 + 2x^2 - 15 = 0$$

$$(x^2 + 5)(x^2 - 3) = 0$$

$$x^2 + 5 = 0 \qquad \text{or} \qquad x^2 - 3 = 0$$
$$\cancel{x^2 = -5} \qquad \text{or} \qquad x^2 = 3$$
$$x = \pm\sqrt{3}$$
$$\Rightarrow y = (\pm\sqrt{3})^2 = 3$$

Points of intersection are: $(\sqrt{3}, 3)$ and $(-\sqrt{3}, 3)$.

Solve the nonlinear system:

$$2x^2 + y^2 = 4 \longrightarrow -10x^2 - 5y^2 = -20$$
$$3x^2 + 5y^2 = 13 \longrightarrow \underline{3x^2 + 5y^2 = 13}$$
$$-7x^2 \qquad = -7$$

$$\frac{-7x^2}{-7} = \frac{-7}{-7}$$

$$x^2 = 1 \longrightarrow x = \pm 1$$

If $x = 1$, $\qquad 2(1)^2 + y^2 = 4.$
$$y^2 = 2$$
$$y = \pm\sqrt{2}$$

If $x = -1$, $\qquad 2(-1)^2 + y^2 = 4.$
$$y^2 = 2$$
$$y = \pm\sqrt{2}$$

The points of intersection are

$$(1, \sqrt{2}), (1, -\sqrt{2}), (-1, \sqrt{2}), \text{ and } (-1, -\sqrt{2})$$

chapter 11   REVIEW EXERCISES

Section 11.1

For Exercises 1–8, graph the functions.

1. $g(x) = x^2 - 5$

2. $f(x) = x^2 + 3$

3. $h(x) = (x - 5)^2$

4. $k(x) = (x + 3)^2$

5. $m(x) = -2x^2$

6. $n(x) = -4x^2$

7. $p(x) = -2(x - 5)^2 - 5$

8. $q(x) = -4(x + 3)^2 + 3$

For Exercises 9–10, identify the vertex of the parabola and determine if it is a maximum or a minimum point. Then write the maximum or the minimum value.

9. $t(x) = \dfrac{1}{3}(x - 4)^2 + \dfrac{5}{3}$

10. $s(x) = -\dfrac{5}{7}(x - 1)^2 - \dfrac{1}{7}$

For Exercises 11–12, identify the axis of symmetry.

11. $a(x) = -\dfrac{3}{2}\left(x + \dfrac{2}{11}\right)^2 - \dfrac{4}{13}$

12. $w(x) = -\dfrac{4}{3}\left(x - \dfrac{3}{16}\right)^2 + \dfrac{2}{9}$

Section 11.2

For Exercises 13–16, write the function in the form $f(x) = a(x - h)^2 + k$ by completing the square. Then identify the vertex.

13. $z(x) = x^2 - 6x + 7$

14. $b(x) = x^2 - 4x - 44$

15. $p(x) = -5x^2 - 10x - 13$

16. $q(x) = -3x^2 - 24x - 54$

For Exercises 17–20, find the vertex of each function by using the vertex formula.

17. $f(x) = -2x^2 + 4x - 17$

18. $g(x) = -4x^2 - 8x + 3$

19. $m(x) = 3x^2 - 3x + 11$

20. $n(x) = 3x^2 + 2x - 7$

21. The number of tourists (in thousands) who visited the Philippines each year between 1987 and 1991 can be approximated by $V(x) = -68.3x^2 + 302.5x + 805$, where x is the number of years after 1987 and $0 \le x \le 4$.

   a. Use the function to approximate the number of tourists who visited the Philippines in the year 1990.

   b. Find the maximum number of tourists who visited the Philippines in any one year between 1987 and 1991.

Number of Visitors (in thousands) to the Philippines, 1987–1991

$V(x) = -68.3x^2 + 302.5x + 805$

Year ($x = 0$ corresponds to 1987)

Source: Statistical Abstract of the World.

Figure for Exercise 21

22. The number of tourists (in thousands) who visited Norway each year between 1987 and 1991 can be approximated by $T(x) = 38x^2 - 64x + 1777$, where x is the number of years after 1987 and $0 \le x \le 4$.

   a. Use the function to approximate the number of tourists who visited Norway in the year 1988.

   b. Find the minimum number of tourists who visited Norway in any one year between 1987 and 1991.

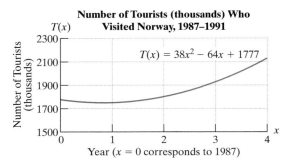

Source: Statistical Abstract of the World.

Figure for Exercise 22

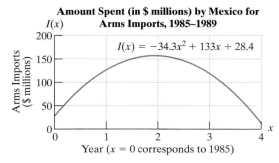

Source: Statistical Abstract of the World.

Figure for Exercise 24

23. The amount spent (in millions of dollars) by Nicaragua on arms imports each year between 1985 and 1989 can be approximated by $A(x) = -52.1x^2 + 233.6x + 317.7$, where x is the number of years after 1985 and $0 \le x \le 4$.

    a. Use the function to approximate the amount spent by Nicaragua on arms imports in the year 1986.

    b. Find the maximum amount spent on arms imports in any one year between 1985 and 1989.

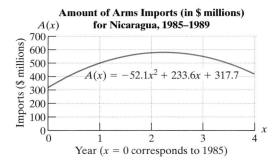

Source: Statistical Abstract of the World.

Figure for Exercise 23

24. The amount spent (in millions of dollars) by Mexico on arms imports each year between 1985 and 1989 can be approximated by $I(x) = -34.3x^2 + 133x + 28.4$, where x is the number of years after 1985 and $0 \le x \le 4$.

    a. Use the function to approximate the amount spent by Mexico on arms imports in the year 1986.

    b. Find the maximum amount spent on arms imports in any one year between 1985 and 1989.

Section 11.3

For Exercises 25–28, determine whether the axis of symmetry is vertical or horizontal and if the parabola opens upward, downward, left, or right.

25. $y = -2(x - 3)^2 + 2$

26. $x = 3(y - 9)^2 + 1$

27. $x = -(y + 4)^2 - 8$

28. $y = (x + 3)^2 - 10$

For Exercises 29–32, determine the coordinates of the vertex and focus and the equation of the directrix. Then use this information to graph the parabola.

29. $x = \dfrac{1}{8}(y - 1)^2$ 30. $y = (x + 2)^2$

31. $y = -\dfrac{1}{4}x^2$ 32. $x = 2y^2 - 1$

For Exercises 33–36, write the equation in standard form: $y = a(x - h)^2 + k$ or $x = a(y - k)^2 + h$. Then identify the vertex, focus, and directrix.

33. $y = x^2 - 6x + 5$ 34. $x = y^2 + 4y + 2$

35. $x = -4y^2 + 4y$ 36. $y = -2x^2 - 2x$

Section 11.4

For Exercises 37–38, find the distance between the two points using the distance formula.

37. $(-6, 3)$ and $(0, 1)$

38. $(4, 13)$ and $(-1, 5)$

39. Find x such that $(x, 5)$ is 5 units from $(2, 9)$.

40. Find x such that $(-3, 4)$ is 3 units from $(x, 1)$.

Points are said to be collinear if they all lie on the same line. If three points are collinear then the distance between the outer most points will equal the sum of the distances between the middle point and each of the outer points. For Exercises 41–42, determine if the three points are collinear.

41. $(-2, -3), (1, 3),$ and $(5, 11)$

42. $(-2, 11), (0, 5),$ and $(4, -7)$

For Exercises 43–46, find the center and the radius of the circle.

43. $(x - 12)^2 + (y - 3)^2 = 16$

44. $(x + 7)^2 + (y - 5)^2 = 81$

45. $(x + 3)^2 + (y + 8)^2 = 20$

46. $(x - 1)^2 + (y + 6)^2 = 32$

47. A stained glass window is in the shape of a circle with a 16-in. diameter. Find an equation of the circle relative to the origin for each of the following graphs.

a.

b.
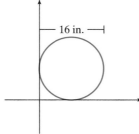

For Exercises 48–51, write the equation of the circle in standard form by completing the square.

48. $x^2 + y^2 + 12x - 10y + 51 = 0$

49. $x^2 + y^2 + 4x + 16y + 60 = 0$

50. $x^2 + y^2 - x - 4y + \dfrac{1}{4} = 0$

51. $x^2 + y^2 - 6x - \dfrac{2}{3}y + \dfrac{1}{9} = 0$

52. Write an equation of a circle with center at the origin and a diameter of 7 m.

53. Write an equation of a circle with center at $(0, 2)$ and a diameter of 6 m.

Section 11.5

54. For the ellipse shown in the graph, label the center, foci, vertices, covertices, major axis, and minor axis.

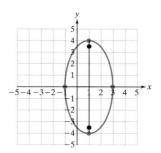

Figure for Exercise 54

For Exercises 55–58, identify the center of the ellipse and determine whether the major axis is horizontal or vertical.

55. $\dfrac{x^2}{9} + \dfrac{y^2}{25} = 1$

56. $\dfrac{x^2}{12} + \dfrac{y^2}{8} = 1$

57. $\dfrac{(x - 1)^2}{36} + \dfrac{y^2}{9} = 1$

58. $\dfrac{x^2}{1} + \dfrac{(y + 2)^2}{6} = 1$

59. For the hyperbola pictured, label the center, foci, vertices, transverse axis, and conjugate axis. Draw the asymptotes.

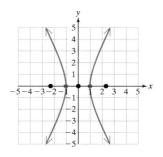

Figure for Exercise 59

For Exercises 60–63, identify the center of the hyperbola and determine whether the transverse axis is horizontal or vertical.

60. $\dfrac{x^2}{12} - \dfrac{y^2}{16} = 1$

61. $\dfrac{y^2}{9} - \dfrac{x^2}{9} = 1$

62. $\dfrac{(y-3)^2}{24} - \dfrac{(x+2)^2}{10} = 1$

63. $\dfrac{(x+1)^2}{6} - \dfrac{y^2}{16} = 1$

For Exercises 64–67, identify as an ellipse or a hyperbola. Then graph, labeling the center and the vertices.

64. $\dfrac{x^2}{4} - \dfrac{y^2}{9} = 1$ 65. $\dfrac{x^2}{16} + \dfrac{y^2}{9} = 1$

66. $\dfrac{x^2}{4} + \dfrac{(y+2)^2}{1} = 1$ 67. $\dfrac{(y-1)^2}{1} - \dfrac{(x-1)^2}{16} = 1$

Section 11.6

68. Given the nonlinear system

$$3x + 2y = 10$$
$$y = x^2 - 5$$

   a. Identify each equation as a line, a parabola, a circle, an ellipse, or a hyperbola.

   b. Graph both equations on the same coordinate axes.

   c. Solve the system and verify the answers from the graph.

69. Given the nonlinear system

$$4x + 2y = 10$$
$$y = x^2 - 10$$

   a. Identify each equation as a line, a parabola, a circle, an ellipse, or a hyperbola.

   b. Graph both equations on the same coordinate axes.

   c. Solve the system and verify the answers from the graph.

70. Given the nonlinear system

$$\dfrac{x^2}{9} + \dfrac{y^2}{9} = 1$$
$$2x + y = 3$$

   a. Identify each equation as a line, a parabola, a circle, an ellipse, or a hyperbola.

   b. Graph both equations on the same coordinate axes.

   c. Solve the system and verify the answers from the graph.

71. Given the nonlinear system

$$x^2 + y^2 = 16$$
$$x - 2y = 8$$

   a. Identify each equation as a line, a parabola, a circle, an ellipse, or a hyperbola.

   b. Graph both equations on the same coordinate axes.

   c. Solve the system and verify the answers from the graph.

For Exercises 72–77, solve the system of nonlinear equations using either the substitution method or the addition method.

72. $x^2 + 2y^2 = 8$ 73. $x^2 + 4y^2 = 29$
    $2x - y = 2$ $x - y = -4$

74. $x - y = 4$ 75. $\quad\quad y = x^2$
    $y^2 = 2x$ $6x^2 - y^2 = 8$

76. $x^2 + y^2 = 10$ 77. $x^2 + y^2 = 61$
    $x^2 + 9y^2 = 18$ $x^2 - y^2 = 11$

chapter 11   TEST

1. Explain the relationship between the graphs of $y = x^2$ and $y = x^2 - 2$.

2. Explain the relationship between the graphs of $y = x^2$ and $y = (x + 3)^2$.

3. Explain the relationship between the graphs of $y = 4x^2$ and $y = -4x^2$.

4. Given the function defined by $f(x) = -(x - 4)^2 + 2$.

   a. Identify the vertex of the parabola.

   b. Does this parabola open up or down?

   c. Does the vertex represent the maximum or minimum point of the function?

   d. What is the maximum or minimum value of the function f?

   e. What is the axis of symmetry for this parabola?

5. For the function defined by $g(x) = 2x^2 - 20x + 51$, find the vertex using two methods:

   a. Complete the square to write g in the form $g(x) = a(x - h)^2 + k$. Identify the vertex.

   b. Use the vertex formula to find the vertex.

6. The exchange rate that measures the number of Canadian dollars equivalent to $1 (U.S.) fluctuates daily. The average exchange rate in January for the years 1988 through 1993 can be approximated by

   $C(x) = 0.016x^2 - 0.072x + 1.2354$ where $C(x)$ represents the number of Canadian dollars equivalent to $1 U.S. and x is the number of years after 1988 ($0 \le x \le 5$).

   a. Use the function to approximate the exchange rate for January, 1992.

   b. Use the exchange rate found in part (a) to determine how many Canadian dollars could be exchanged for $50 U.S. in January of 1992.

   c. Use the exchange rate in part (a) to determine how many U.S. dollars could be exchanged for $100 Canadian in January of 1992.

d. Use the function to determine the minimum exchange rate between 1988 and 1993. (Round to two decimal places.)

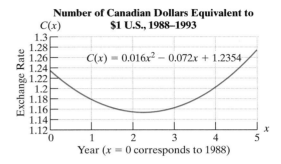

Number of Canadian Dollars Equivalent to $1 U.S., 1988–1993

Figure for Exercise 6

7. Determine the coordinates of the vertex and focus and write an equation of the directrix.

   $$x = -(y + 6)^2 + 3$$

8. Write the equation in standard form, $y = a(x - h)^2 + k$, and graph.

   $$y = x^2 - 4x + 5$$

9. Use the distance formula to find the distance between the two points $(5, 19)$ and $(-2, 13)$.

10. Determine if the three points, $(3, 4)$, $(-1, 1)$, and $(6, 0)$ are vertices of a right triangle.

11. Determine the center and radius of the circle.

    $$\left(x - \frac{5}{6}\right)^2 + \left(y + \frac{1}{3}\right)^2 = \frac{25}{49}$$

12. Determine the center and radius of the circle. $x^2 + y^2 - 4y - 5 = 0$.

13. Let $(0, 4)$ be the center of a circle that passes through the point $(-2, 5)$.

    a. What is the radius of the circle?

    b. Write an equation of the circle in standard form.

14. Identify the center of the ellipse and determine whether the major axis is horizontal or vertical.

    $$\frac{(x - 3)^2}{8} + \frac{y^2}{14} = 1$$

15. Graph the hyperbola and identify the center and vertices.

$$\frac{y^2}{1} - \frac{x^2}{4} = 1$$

16. Solve the systems and identify the correct graph of the equations:

 a. $16x^2 + 9y^2 = 144$

  $4x - 3y = -12$

 b. $x^2 + 4y^2 = 4$

  $4x - 3y = -12$

17. Describe the circumstances in which a nonlinear system of equations can be solved using the addition method.

18. Solve the system using either the substitution method or the addition method.

$$25x^2 + 4y^2 = 100$$
$$25x^2 - 4y^2 = 100$$

i.

ii.

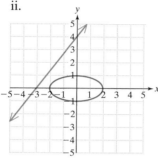

CUMULATIVE REVIEW EXERCISES, CHAPTERS 1–11

1. Solve the equation:
 $5(2y - 1) = 2y - 4 + 8y - 1$

2. Solve the inequality. Graph the solution and write the solution in interval notation.

$$4(x - 1) + 2 > 3x + 8 - 2x$$

3. The product of two integers is 150. If one integer is 5 less than twice the other, find the integers.

4. For $5y - 3x - 15 = 0$:

 a. Find the x- and y-intercepts.

 b. Find the slope.

 c. Graph the line.

5. The amount spent by the Philippines on arms imports each year between 1985 and 1989 is linear as shown in the graph (see figure). Let x represent the year, where $x = 0$ corresponds to 1985. Let y represent the amount spent on arms imports (in millions of dollars).

 a. Use any two data points to find the slope of the line.

 b. Find an equation of the line. Write the answer in slope-intercept form.

 c. Use the linear model found in part (b) to approximate the amount spent on arms imports by the Philippines in the year 1990.

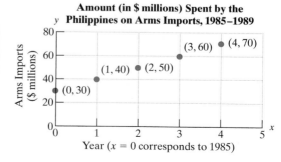

Source: Statistical Abstract of the World.

Figure for Exercise 5

6. A collection of dimes and quarters has a total value of \$2.45. If there are 17 coins, how many of each type are there?

7. Solve the system.

$$x + y = -1$$
$$2x - z = 3$$
$$ y + 2z = -1$$

8. a. Given the matrix $\mathbf{A} = \begin{bmatrix} 1 & -2 & | & -8 \\ 0 & 3 & | & 6 \end{bmatrix}$, write the matrix obtained by multiplying the elements in the second row by $\frac{1}{3}$.

   b. Using the matrix obtained from part (a), write the matrix obtained by multiplying the second row by 2 and adding the result to the first row.

9. Solve the following system using Cramer's rule.

$$4x - 2y = 7$$
$$-3x + 5y = 0$$

10. For $f(x) = 3x - x^2 - 12$, find the function values: $f(0), f(-1), f(2),$ and $f(4)$.

11. For $g = \{(2, 5), (8, -1), (3, 0), (-5, 5)\}$ find the function values: $g(2), g(8), g(3),$ and $g(-5)$.

12. The quantity z varies jointly as y and as the square of x. If z is 80 when x is 5 and y is 2, find z when $x = 2$ and $y = 5$.

13. a. Find the value of the expression
    $x^3 + x^2 + x + 1$ for $x = -2$.

    b. Factor the expression $x^3 + x^2 + x + 1$ and find the value when x is -2.

    c. Compare the values for parts (a) and (b).

14. Solve the radical equations.

    a. $\sqrt{2x - 5} = -3$

    b. $\sqrt[3]{2x - 5} = -3$

15. Perform the indicated operations with complex numbers.

    a. $6i(4 + 5i)$ b. $\dfrac{3}{4 - 5i}$

16. An automobile starts from rest and accelerates at a constant rate for 10 s. The distance, $d(t)$, in feet traveled by the car is given by

$$d(t) = 4.4t^2 \quad \text{where } 0 \le t \le 10 \text{ is the time in}$$
seconds.

    a. How far has the car traveled after 2, 3, and 4 s, respectively?

    b. How long will it take for the car to travel 281.6 ft?

17. Solve the equation $125w^3 + 1 = 0$ by factoring and using the quadratic formula. (*Hint:* You will find one real solution and two imaginary solutions.)

18. Solve the rational equation.

$$\frac{x}{x + 2} - \frac{3}{x - 1} = \frac{1}{x^2 + x - 2}$$

19. Solve the inequality and write the answer in interval notation.

$$|x - 9| - 3 < 7$$

20. Write the expression in logarithmic form:
    $8^{5/3} = 32$.

21. Find the vertex of $f(x) = x^2 + 10x - 11$ by completing the square.

22. Graph the quadratic function defined by $g(x) = -x^2 - 2x + 3$.

    a. Label the x-intercepts.

    b. Label the y-intercept.

    c. Label the vertex.

23. Write an equation representing the set of all points 4 units from the point $(0, 5)$.

24. Can a circle and a parabola intersect in only one point? Explain.

25. Solve the system of nonlinear equations.

$$x^2 + y^2 = 16$$
$$y = -x^2 - 4$$

POLYNOMIAL AND RATIONAL FUNCTIONS

12

Polynomial functions can often be used to model physical phenomena that occur in nature. For example, consider the average monthly low temperatures for Fairbanks, Alaska shown in the table.

Month	Month Number, x	Temperature (°F), y
January	0	−19
February	1	−15
March	2	−3
April	3	20
May	4	37
June	5	49
July	6	52
August	7	46
September	8	40
October	9	16
November	10	2
December	11	−6

The function defined by

$$T(x) = 0.078x^4 - 1.808x^3 + 11.2x^2 - 6.93x - 18.7,$$
$$\text{for } 0 \le x \le 11$$

can be used to approximate the temperature as a function of the month number (with January corresponding to month 0). In this chapter we will develop tools to analyze polynomial functions and construct their graphs.

Average Low Temperature, Fairbanks, AK

$T(x) = 0.078x^4 - 1.808x^3 + 11.2x^2 - 6.93x - 18.7$

Months ($x = 0$ corresponds to January)

For more information about modeling temperatures, visit <u>weather</u> at

www.mhhe.com/miller_oneill

section

12.1 REMAINDER THEOREM AND FACTOR THEOREM

1. Zeros of a Polynomial

Recall from Section 4.3 that we can find the x-intercepts of a function defined by $y = f(x)$ by finding the real solutions to the equation $f(x) = 0$. In this chapter we will be interested in finding all solutions (both real and imaginary) to the equation $P(x) = 0$, where P is a polynomial function. A solution or **root** of a polynomial equation $P(x) = 0$ is a value $x = c$ such that $P(c) = 0$. In such a case, $x = c$ is called a **zero** of the polynomial.

It is particularly easy to solve a polynomial equation $P(x) = 0$ if the polynomial is expressed as a product of linear factors. For example,

$$P(x) = x^4 - 3x^3 - 12x - 16$$

can be factored as

$$P(x) = (x - 4)(x + 1)(x - 2i)(x + 2i)$$

Therefore, to find the solutions to $P(x) = 0$, we have

$$(x - 4)(x + 1)(x - 2i)(x + 2i) = 0$$

$x - 4 = 0$ or	$x + 1 = 0$ or	$x - 2i = 0$ or	$x + 2i = 0$
$x = 4$ or	$x = -1$ or	$x = 2i$ or	$x = -2i$

The values $x = 4$, $x = -1$, $x = 2i$, and $x = -2i$ when substituted into the function make the function equal to 0. Therefore, we say 4, -1, $2i$, and $-2i$ are zeros of the polynomial.

2. Division Algorithm for Polynomials

In this section, we will investigate the connection between the factored form of a polynomial and the zeros of the polynomial.

For a simple division problem in arithmetic, we can easily identify the dividend, divisor, quotient, and remainder.

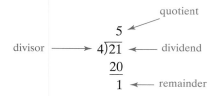

We also know that dividend = (divisor)(quotient) + remainder. The same logic can be applied to polynomials.

Division Algorithm for Polynomials

Let $P(x)$ and $d(x)$ be polynomials of degree 1 or more. If the degree of $d(x)$ is less than the degree of $P(x)$, then there exists unique polynomials $q(x)$ and $r(x)$ such that

$$P(x) = d(x)q(x) + r(x)$$

where either $r(x) = 0$ or $r(x)$ has degree less than $d(x)$.

example 1

Dividing Polynomials

Divide the polynomials and use the division algorithm to check the answer.

$$(2x^3 - 3x + 1) \div (x - 2)$$

Solution:

We can use long division, or because the divisor is of the form $(x - c)$, we can use synthetic division.

$$
\begin{array}{r}
2x^2 + 4x + 5 \\
x - 2\overline{)2x^3 + 0x^2 - 3x + 1} \\
-(2x^3 - 4x^2) \\
\hline
4x^2 - 3x \\
-(4x^2 - 8x) \\
\hline
5x + 1 \\
-(5x - 10) \\
\hline
11
\end{array}
$$

$$
\begin{array}{r|rrrr}
2 & 2 & 0 & -3 & 1 \\
  &   & 4 & 8 & 10 \\
\hline
  & 2 & 4 & 5 & \underline{11}
\end{array}
$$

The quotient is $2x^2 + 4x + 5$ and the remainder is 11.

Checking by the division algorithm for polynomials, we have

$$P(x) = d(x)q(x) + r(x)$$
$$2x^3 - 3x + 1 \overset{?}{=} (x - 2)(2x^2 + 4x + 5) + 11$$
$$\overset{?}{=} 2x^3 + 4x^2 + 5x - 4x^2 - 8x - 10 + 11$$
$$= 2x^3 - 3x + 1 \checkmark$$

3. Remainder Theorem

Example 1 illustrates polynomial division by a linear divisor of the form $(x - c)$. When the divisor is of the form $(x - c)$, then the division algorithm can be written as

$$P(x) = (x - c)q(x) + r$$

In this case, the remainder is a constant because it must be a polynomial of degree less than that of the divisor. Furthermore, because the equality is true for all complex values of x, we can evaluate P at $x = c$ to get

$$P(c) = (c - c)q(c) + r$$
$$= 0 \cdot q(c) + r$$
$$= r$$

This important result proves the **remainder theorem**, which provides a new method to evaluate a polynomial function at $x = c$.

Remainder Theorem

If the polynomial $P(x)$ is divided by $(x - c)$, the remainder is $P(c)$.

To illustrate this theorem, consider the function defined by $P(x) = 2x^3 - 3x + 1$. In Example 1, we divided $P(x)$ by $(x - 2)$ and found a remainder of 11. Evaluating $P(2)$ yields the same result.

$$P(2) = 2(2)^3 - 3(2) + 1$$
$$= 2(8) - 6 + 1$$
$$= 16 - 6 + 1$$
$$= 11$$

4. Evaluating a Polynomial Using the Remainder Theorem

Often it is convenient to evaluate a polynomial by using synthetic division and finding the remainder as shown in the next example.

---

example 2

Evaluating a Polynomial Using the Remainder Theorem

Given the polynomial $P(x) = 3x^5 - 2x^3 - 7x^2 + 5x + 1$, evaluate $P(1)$ and $P(-2)$.

Solution:

The value of $P(1)$ is equal to the remainder found by dividing $P(x)$ by $(x - 1)$. Using synthetic division, we have

$$
\begin{array}{r|rrrrrr}
1 & 3 & 0 & -2 & -7 & 5 & 1 \\
  &   & 3 & 3 & 1 & -6 & -1 \\
\hline
  & 3 & 3 & 1 & -6 & -1 & \underline{0} \\
\end{array}
$$
hence, $P(1) = 0$

Similarly, $P(-2)$ is equal to the remainder found by dividing $P(x)$ by $(x - (-2))$.

$$
\begin{array}{r|rrrrrr}
-2 & 3 & 0 & -2 & -7 & 5 & 1 \\
   &   & -6 & 12 & -20 & 54 & -118 \\
\hline
   & 3 & -6 & 10 & -27 & 59 & \underline{-117} \\
\end{array}
$$
hence, $P(-2) = -117$

Tip: To check the validity of the remainder theorem, we can evaluate $P(1)$ and $P(-2)$ by direct substitution.

$$P(1) = 3(1)^5 - 2(1)^3 - 7(1)^2 + 5(1) + 1$$
$$= 3 - 2 - 7 + 5 + 1$$
$$= 0$$

$$P(-2) = 3(-2)^5 - 2(-2)^3 - 7(-2)^2 + 5(-2) + 1$$
$$= 3(-32) - 2(-8) - 7(4) - 10 + 1$$
$$= -96 + 16 - 28 - 10 + 1$$
$$= -117$$

5. Determining Whether a Value Is a Zero of a Polynomial

example 3

Determining Whether a Value Is a Zero of a Polynomial

Determine whether the values of x are zeros of the polynomial, $P(x) = x^3 - 5x^2 + 9x - 45$.

a. $x = 5$ b. $x = -2$ c. $x = 3i$

Solution:

a. To determine if $x = 5$ is a zero of the polynomial, we must determine if $P(5) = 0$. Using the remainder theorem, we have

$$\begin{array}{r|rrrr} 5 & 1 & -5 & 9 & -45 \\ & & 5 & 0 & 45 \\ \hline & 1 & 0 & 9 & \underline{|0} \end{array}$$

The remainder is 0 indicating that $P(5) = 0$; hence 5 is a zero of the polynomial.

b.
$$\begin{array}{r|rrrr} -2 & 1 & -5 & 9 & -45 \\ & & -2 & 14 & -46 \\ \hline & 1 & -7 & 23 & \underline{|-91} \end{array}$$

The remainder is not 0; therefore, -2 is not a zero of the polynomial.

c.
$$\begin{array}{r|rrrr} 3i & 1 & -5 & 9 & -45 \\ & & 3i & -9 - 15i & 45 \\ \hline & 1 & -5 + 3i & -15i & \underline{|0} \end{array}$$

The remainder is 0 indicating that $P(3i) = 0$; hence $3i$ is a zero of the polynomial.

6. Factor Theorem

By the remainder theorem, if $P(c) = 0$, then the remainder is 0 when $P(x)$ is divided by $(x - c)$. This means that $(x - c)$ is a factor of $P(x)$. Conversely, if $(x - c)$ is a factor of $P(x)$, then the remainder is 0 for $P(x) \div (x - c)$. Hence, $P(c)$ must equal 0. This result is stated formally in the **factor theorem**.

Factor Theorem

The polynomial $(x - c)$ is a factor of the polynomial $P(x)$ if and only if $P(c) = 0$.

Tip: In the division of real numbers, if the remainder is 0, then the divisor and quotient are factors of the dividend. For example,

$$\begin{array}{r} 5 \\ 3\overline{)15} \\ \underline{15} \\ 0 \end{array}$$

remainder is zero

factors of 15

$$15 = 3 \cdot 5$$

example 4

Testing for Factors of a Polynomial

Determine whether the following polynomials are factors of $P(x) = x^4 - 5x^3 + 3x^2 + 19x - 30$.

a. $x - 3$ b. $x - (2 - i)$ c. $x + 5$

Solution:

a.   The expression $x - 3$ is a factor of $P(x)$ if $x = 3$ is a zero of $P(x)$.

$$\begin{array}{r|rrrrr} 3 & 1 & -5 & 3 & 19 & -30 \\ & & 3 & -6 & -9 & 30 \\ \hline & 1 & -2 & -3 & 10 & \underline{|\,0} \end{array}$$

The remainder is 0, indicating that $P(3) = 0$. It follows from the factor theorem that $(x - 3)$ is a factor of $P(x)$.

Tip: Because the divisor $(x - 3)$ is a factor of $P(x)$, the quotient is also a factor of $P(x)$. The result of the synthetic division indicates that the quotient is $x^3 - 2x^2 - 3x + 10$; hence,

$$x^4 - 5x^3 + 3x^2 + 19x - 30 = (x - 3)(x^3 - 2x^2 - 3x + 10)$$

b.   The expression $(x - (2 - i))$ is a factor of $P(x)$ if $x = 2 - i$ is a zero of $P(x)$.

$$\begin{array}{r|rrrrr} 2-i & 1 & -5 & 3 & 19 & -30 \\ & & 2-i & -7+i & -7+6i & 30 \\ \hline & 1 & -3-i & -4+i & 12+6i & \underline{|\,0} \end{array}$$

The remainder is 0, indicating that $P(2 - i) = 0$. It follows from the factor theorem that $(x - (2 - i))$ or equivalently $(x - 2 + i)$ is a factor of $P(x)$.

c.

$$\begin{array}{r|rrrrr} -5 & 1 & -5 & 3 & 19 & -30 \\ & & -5 & 50 & -265 & 1230 \\ \hline & 1 & -10 & 53 & -246 & \underline{|\,1200} \end{array}$$

The remainder is not equal to 0, which implies that $(x + 5)$ is not a factor of $P(x)$.

example 5

Finding a Polynomial Given Its Zeros

Find a polynomial of degree 3 whose zeros are 4, -1, and $\frac{3}{2}$.

Solution:

Because $x = 4$ is a zero of the polynomial, then $(x - 4)$ is a factor. Similarly, $(x + 1)$ and $(x - \frac{3}{2})$ are factors of the polynomial. Therefore, one possible polynomial is,

$$P(x) = (x - 4)(x + 1)\left(x - \frac{3}{2}\right)$$

$$= (x^2 - 3x - 4)\left(x - \frac{3}{2}\right) \qquad \text{Multiply first two factors.}$$

$$= x^3 - \frac{9}{2}x^2 + \frac{1}{2}x + 6 \qquad \text{Multiply polynomials.}$$

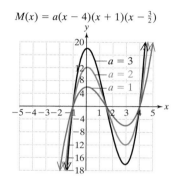

$M(x) = a(x - 4)(x + 1)(x - \frac{3}{2})$

$a = 3$
$a = 2$
$a = 1$

Figure 12-1

The polynomial $P(x) = x^3 - \frac{9}{2}x^2 + \frac{1}{2}x + 6$ from Example 5 is not the only third-degree polynomial having zeros of 4, -1, and $\frac{3}{2}$. Any polynomial of the form $M(x) = a(x - 4)(x + 1)(x - \frac{3}{2})$, where a is any nonzero number, has zeros of 4, -1, and $\frac{3}{2}$. There are infinitely many such polynomials. Figure 12-1 gives three polynomials corresponding to $a = 1$, $a = 2$, and $a = 3$, respectively.

section 12.1   Practice Exercises

For Exercises 1–12, find the zeros of the polynomial by solving the equation $P(x) = 0$.

1. $P(x) = (2x + 3)(x - 4)$

2. $P(x) = (x + 5)(3x - 1)$

3. $P(x) = (x - 2i)(x + 2i)$

4. $P(x) = (x - 5i)(x + 5i)$

5. $P(x) = 3x(x + 2)(4x + 5)$

6. $P(x) = x(5x - 1)(x - 12)$

7. $P(x) = 2x^2 - 5x - 42$

8. $P(x) = 3x^2 - 5x + 2$

9. $P(x) = 2x^2 - 18$

10. $P(x) = x^2 - 16$

11. $P(x) = x^2 + 21x$

12. $P(x) = x^2 + 11x$

For Exercises 13–18, use synthetic division to divide $P(x)$ by $(x - c)$ to find the quotient, $q(x)$, and remainder, r. Then express the results as $P(x) = (x - c)q(x) + r$.

13. $P(x) = x^3 - 7x^2 + 13x + 3$; $(x - 2)$

14. $P(x) = 2x^3 + 7x^2 + x - 12$; $(x + 3)$

15. $P(x) = 2x^4 + 3x^2 - 5x + 7$; $(x + 1)$

16. $P(x) = x^4 - 3x^3 - 3x + 4$; $(x - 1)$

17. $P(x) = x^4 - 8x^2 + 15$; $(x + 2)$

18. $P(x) = x^4 - 18x^2 + 83$; $(x - 3)$

19. Find $f(3)$ for $f(x) = x^3 + 2x^2 - 17x - 10$ using the remainder theorem and synthetic division. Then check the answer by evaluating $f(3)$ by direct substitution.

20. Find $g(-2)$ for $g(x) = 3x^3 + 11x^2 + 20x + 3$ using the remainder theorem and synthetic division. Then check the answer by evaluating $g(-2)$ by direct substitution.

21. Find $k(-3)$ for $k(x) = 2x^3 - 3x^2 - 5x + 4$ using the remainder theorem and synthetic division. Then check the answer by evaluating $k(-3)$ by direct substitution.

22. Find $h(2)$ for $h(x) = 5x^3 + 2x^2 - x + 5$ using the remainder theorem and synthetic division. Then check the answer by evaluating $h(2)$ by direct substitution.

For Exercises 23–26, find the indicated function value for the given polynomial functions.

23. $F(x) = -x^4 + 2x^3 + 10x^2 - 10x - 9$

    a. $F(2)$ b. $F(-3)$ c. $F(5)$ d. $F(-4)$

24. $W(x) = -x^4 - 5x^3 + x^2 + 20x + 5$

    a. $W(-3)$ b. $W(2)$ c. $W(-4)$ d. $W(-5)$

25. $Q(t) = 2t^3 + 3t^2 - 3t + 2$

    a. $Q(4)$ b. $Q(-5)$ c. $Q\left(\dfrac{1}{2}\right)$ d. $Q\left(\dfrac{3}{2}\right)$

26. $R(t) = 3t^3 + t^2 - 4t + 6$

    a. $R(-3)$ b. $R(4)$ c. $R\left(-\dfrac{1}{3}\right)$ d. $R\left(\dfrac{2}{3}\right)$

For Exercises 27–38, determine if the value given is zero of the polynomial.

27. $P(x) = x^3 - x^2 - 13x - 3; x = -3$

28. $P(x) = x^3 - 4x^2 + 2x + 4; x = 2$

29. $P(x) = 2x^3 - 7x^2 + 2x + 3; x = 3$

30. $P(x) = 2x^3 - 7x^2 - 6x + 3; x = -1$

31. $P(x) = x^4 + 9x^3 + 23x^2 + 8x - 16; x = -4$

32. $P(x) = x^4 - 2x^3 - 14x^2 + 30x + 9; x = 3$

33. $P(x) = 4x^3 - x^2 - 6x + 16; x = 2$

34. $P(x) = 3x^3 + 7x^2 + 3x - 2; x = -2$

35. $P(x) = x^3 + x^2 + 16x + 16; x = 4i$

36. $P(x) = x^3 - 2x^2 + 16x - 32; x = -4i$

37. $P(x) = x^3 - 5x^2 + 17x - 13; x = 2 - 3i$

38. $P(x) = 3x^3 - 28x^2 + 58x + 52; x = 5 + i$

For Exercises 39–50, determine if the second polynomial is a factor of the first.

39. $x^3 - x^2 - 21x + 45; (x - 3)$

40. $x^3 - x^2 - 21x + 45; (x + 5)$

41. $x^3 + 7x^2 + 8x - 16; (x + 4)$

42. $x^3 + 7x^2 + 8x - 16; (x - 1)$

43. $x^3 + 3x^2 - 8x + 10; (x - (1 - i))$

44. $x^3 + 3x^2 - 8x + 10; (x - (1 + i))$

45. $x^4 + 6x^3 + 5x^2 - 24x - 36; (x - 4)$

46. $x^4 + 6x^3 + 5x^2 - 24x - 36; (x + 3)$

47. $2x^4 + 11x^3 + 21x^2 + 17x + 5; (x + 1)$

48. $2x^4 + 11x^3 + 21x^2 + 17x + 5; (x - 2)$

49. $x^5 - x^4 - 7x^3 + 7x^2 - 12x - 12; (x - 3)$

50. $x^5 - x^4 - 7x^3 + 7x^2 - 12x - 24; (x + 1)$

For Exercises 51–56, find a polynomial with the given zeros. (Answers may vary.)

51. $x = 4, x = -1$

52. $x = -2, x = 5$

53. $x = 0, x = 1, x = 3$

54. $x = 0, x = 2, x = -1$

55. $x = -i, x = i, x = 5$

56. $x = 3i, x = -3i, x = -1$

EXPANDING YOUR SKILLS

57. The polynomial $P(x) = (x - 4)(x + 1) = x^2 - 3x - 4$ has zeros $x = 4$ and $x = -1$. Which of the following polynomials also have $x = 4$ and $x = -1$ as zeros?

    a. $6(x - 4)(x + 1) = 6x^2 - 18x - 24$

    b. $(x - 4)^2(x + 1) = x^3 - 7x^2 + 8x + 16$

58. The polynomial $P(x) = (x + 2)(x - 5) = x^2 - 3x - 10$ has zeros $x = -2$ and $x = 5$. Which of the following polynomials also have $x = -2$ and $x = 5$ as zeros?

    a. $3(x + 2)(x - 5) = 3x^2 - 9x - 30$

    b. $(x + 2)(x - 5)^2 = x^3 - 8x^2 + 5x + 50$

In general, if the zeros of a polynomial are $x = p$ and $x = q$, then polynomials of the form $a(x - p)^m(x - q)^n$ (where a is a real number and m and n are positive integers) also have $x = p$ and $x = q$ as zeros. Use this fact to answer Exercises 59 and 60.

59. Find a polynomial with zeros $x = 0$, $x = 1$, and $x = 3$ that is different from the polynomial found in Exercise 53. (Answers may vary.)

60. Find a polynomial with zeros $x = 0$, $x = 2$, and $x = -1$ that is different from the polynomial found in Exercise 54. (Answers may vary.)

61. Find the remainder for $(5x^{87} - 6x^{43} + 4x^2 - 3) \div (x - 1)$.

62. Find the remainder for $(-3x^{59} + 7x^{46} + 2) \div (x + 1)$.

---

section

12.2 ZEROS OF POLYNOMIALS

1. Fundamental Theorem of Algebra

A polynomial function of degree 1 is a linear function of the form $P(x) = ax + b$, where a and b are complex numbers and $a \neq 0$. This function has 1 zero of the form $x = -b/a$. This value may either be a real number or an imaginary number depending on the values of the coefficients a and b. In this section we will determine the number of zeros and the type (real or imaginary) of zeros for a given polynomial.

In his 1799 doctoral dissertation, the German mathematician Carl Friedrich Gauss proved an important theorem whose proof had eluded great mathematicians for many years. Gauss proved that every polynomial of degree 1 or more has at least one zero. This further implies that every such polynomial can be factored. This important theorem is so basic to the study of algebra that it is called the **fundamental theorem of algebra**.

Fundamental Theorem of Algebra

Every polynomial of degree 1 or more has at least one complex zero.

By the fundamental theorem of algebra, it follows that if $P(x)$ is a polynomial of degree 1 or more, then there is some number c_1, such that $P(c_1) = 0$. By the factor theorem, there exists some polynomial $q_1(x)$ such that

$$P(x) = (x - c_1)q_1(x)$$

In a similar way, if $q_1(x)$ is of degree 1 or more, the fundamental theorem of algebra and the factor theorem can be applied to $q_1(x)$. That is, there is some number c_2 such that $q_1(c_2) = 0$, and by the factor theorem, there exists a polynomial $q_2(x)$ such that

$$P(x) = (x - c_1)(x - c_2)q_2(x)$$

If $P(x)$ is a degree n polynomial, we can repeat this process n times to obtain

$$P(x) = a(x - c_1)(x - c_2)(x - c_3) \ldots (x - c_n)$$

where a is the leading coefficient of $P(x)$. Each factor corresponds to a zero of $P(x)$. Consequently, $P(x)$ has n zeros $c_1, c_2, c_3, \ldots c_n$ that are not necessarily distinct. This implies that an nth-degree polynomial can be factored into n linear factors.

2. Determining the Number of Zeros of a Polynomial

Number of Zeros of a Polynomial

A polynomial of degree n has at most n distinct zeros.

It is important to note that the theorem says there exists *at most n* distinct zeros. It may be the case that some of the zeros of a polynomial are "repeated" as a result of repeated linear factors. For example, consider the following third-degree polynomials and their factored forms.

$$f(x) = x^3 - 2x^2 - 5x + 6$$
$$= (x - 1)(x + 2)(x - 3) \qquad f(x) \text{ has three zeros: } 1, -2, \text{ and } 3.$$

$$g(x) = x^3 + 2x^2 - 7x + 4$$
$$= (x - 1)^2(x + 4) \qquad g(x) \text{ has two zeros: } 1 \text{ and } -4.$$

Because the factor $(x - 1)$ appears twice, the value, $x = 1$ is a "repeated" zero. We say that the zero, $x = 1$, has a **multiplicity** of 2.

$$h(x) = x^3 + 3x^2 + 3x + 1$$
$$= (x + 1)^3 \qquad h(x) \text{ has one zero: } -1.$$

The factor $(x + 1)$ appears three times. In this case, we say that the zero, $x = -1$, has a multiplicity of 3.

In general, an nth-degree polynomial can be factored into n linear factors. Therefore, the number of zeros (counting multiplicities) is also n.

example 1   **Finding a Polynomial Given Its Zeros**

Find a polynomial $f(x)$ that satisfies the following conditions.

a. Degree 3, has zeros of 4, -1, and 2, and $f(1) = 18$
b. Degree 3 where 3 is a zero of multiplicity 2 and 1 is a zero of multiplicity 1. The function passes through the point $(0, 1)$.

Solution:

a.
$$f(x) = a(x - c_1)(x - c_2)(x - c_3)$$
$$= a(x - 4)(x - (-1))(x - 2)$$
$$= a(x - 4)(x + 1)(x - 2)$$
$$= a(x^3 - 5x^2 + 2x + 8)$$

The zeros of a polynomial do not give sufficient information to identify the polynomial uniquely. To find the value of the leading coefficient, a, we can use the fact that $f(1) = 18$.

$$f(1) = a((1)^3 - 5(1)^2 + 2(1) + 8) = 18$$
$$a(6) = 18$$
$$a = 3$$

Hence,
$$f(x) = 3(x^3 - 5x^2 + 2x + 8)$$
$$= 3x^3 - 15x^2 + 6x + 24$$

The real zeros of $f(x)$ are the x-intercepts of the graph of $f(x) = 3x^3 - 15x^2 + 6x + 24$ as shown in Figure 12-2.

$f(x) = 3x^3 - 15x^2 + 6x + 24$

Figure 12-2

b. $f(x) = a(x - 3)^2(x - 1)$ The zero $x = 3$ has multiplicity 2.
$$= a(x^2 - 6x + 9)(x - 1)$$
$$= a(x^3 - 7x^2 + 15x - 9)$$

To find the value of a, we can use the fact that the function passes through $(0, 1)$.

$$1 = a((0)^3 - 7(0)^2 + 15(0) - 9)$$
$$1 = a(-9)$$
$$-\frac{1}{9} = a$$

Hence,
$$f(x) = -\frac{1}{9}(x^3 - 7x^2 + 15x - 9)$$
$$= -\frac{1}{9}x^3 + \frac{7}{9}x^2 - \frac{5}{3}x + 1$$

Graphing Calculator Box

A graphing calculator can be used to support the results of Example 1(b).

3. Rational Zero Theorem

The zeros of a polynomial may either be real or imaginary numbers. Furthermore, the real zeros of a function may either be rational or irrational numbers. The following theorem provides a method to determine all possible candidates for the rational zeros of a polynomial with integer coefficients.

Rational Zero Theorem

Let $P(x) = a_n x^n + a_{n-1}x^{n-1} + \cdots + a_1 x + a_0$, where $a_n \neq 0$, be a polynomial function with integer coefficients. If $\frac{c}{d}$ is a rational number written in lowest terms, and if $\frac{c}{d}$ is a zero of $P(x)$, then c is a factor of a_0 and d is a factor of a_n.

---

example 2

Applying the Rational Zero Theorem

Given $P(x) = 2x^4 - 9x^3 + 11x^2 - 4x - 6$

a.   List the possible rational zeros of $P(x)$.
b.   Find the rational zeros of $P(x)$ and if possible all the zeros of $P(x)$.

Solution:

Tip: When constructing the values of $\frac{c}{d}$, do not list redundant values. For example,

$$\frac{\pm 2}{\pm 2} = \pm 1$$

is already listed.

a. $2x^4 - 9x^3 + 11x^2 - 4x - 6$
     $\quad\uparrow\qquad\qquad\qquad\qquad\quad\uparrow$
     $\quad a_n\qquad\qquad\qquad\qquad\quad a_0$

The term c must be a factor of -6 and d must be a factor of 2. Therefore, the values of c and d are taken from

$$c: \ \pm 1, \pm 2, \pm 3, \pm 6$$

$$d: \ \pm 1, \pm 2$$

The possible rational zeros, $\frac{c}{d}$, are $\pm 1, \pm 2, \pm 3, \pm 6, \pm\frac{1}{2}, \pm\frac{3}{2}$.

b.   Using synthetic division, we can test each value of $\frac{c}{d}$ in the list until a remainder of 0 is found. For example, test $x = 3$.

$$
\begin{array}{r|rrrrr}
3 & 2 & -9 & 11 & -4 & -6 \\
  &   & 6 & -9 & 6 & 6 \\
\hline
  & 2 & -3 & 2 & 2 & \underline{0}
\end{array}
$$

Synthetic division indicates that $x = 3$ is a zero of $P(x)$. Consequently, $(x - 3)$ is a factor of $P(x)$ and the quotient $2x^3 - 3x^2 + 2x + 2$ is also a factor of $P(x)$. Hence,

$$P(x) = (x - 3)(2x^3 - 3x^2 + 2x + 2)$$
$$\qquad\qquad\qquad\quad\uparrow\qquad\qquad\qquad\uparrow$$
$$\qquad\qquad\qquad\quad a_n\qquad\qquad\qquad a_0$$

Finding the remaining zeros of $P(x)$ is equivalent to finding the zeros of $2x^3 - 3x^2 + 2x + 2$. Using the "new" values of a_n and a_0, the list of rational zeros, $\frac{c}{d}$, can be shortened to ± 1, ± 2, $\pm\frac{1}{2}$. Using synthetic division, we find that $-\frac{1}{2}$ is a zero of $2x^3 - 3x^2 + 2x + 2$.

$$
\begin{array}{r|rrrr}
-\frac{1}{2} & 2 & -3 & 2 & 2 \\
 & & -1 & 2 & -2 \\
\hline
 & 2 & -4 & 4 & \underline{|\,0}
\end{array}
$$

Because $x = -\frac{1}{2}$ is a zero of $2x^3 - 3x^2 + 2x + 2$, then $(x + \frac{1}{2})$ is a factor. $P(x)$ factors as

$$P(x) = (x - 3)(x + \tfrac{1}{2})(2x^2 - 4x + 4)$$

The values $x = 3$ and $x = -\frac{1}{2}$ are zeros of $P(x)$. The remaining zeros of $P(x)$ can be found by finding the zeros of $2x^2 - 4x + 4$. That is, we can solve the equation $2x^2 - 4x + 4 = 0$. Using the quadratic formula, we have

$$
\begin{aligned}
x &= \frac{-(-4) \pm \sqrt{(-4)^2 - 4(2)(4)}}{2(2)} \\
&= \frac{4 \pm \sqrt{-16}}{4} \\
&= \frac{4 \pm 4i}{4} \\
&= 1 \pm i
\end{aligned}
$$

In summary, $P(x)$ has rational zeros of 3 and $-\frac{1}{2}$, and imaginary zeros of $1 \pm i$.

■

Tip: It is important to note that the rational zero theorem does not guarantee the existence of rational zeros. Instead, if a polynomial has rational zeros, the rational zero theorem provides a finite list of possibilities telling us where to look.

4. Imaginary Zero Theorem

The polynomial $P(x) = 2x^4 - 9x^3 + 11x^2 - 4x - 6$ from Example 2 has both real-valued and imaginary numbers as its zeros. Notice that both $1 + i$ and its conjugate $1 - i$ are zeros of $P(x)$. The following theorem indicates that for a polynomial with real coefficients, imaginary zeros come in conjugate pairs.

Conjugate Zero Theorem

If an imaginary number $a + bi$ is a zero of a polynomial $P(x)$, where $P(x)$ has real coefficients, then the conjugate, $a - bi$, is also a zero of the polynomial.

---

example 3

Finding a Polynomial Given Its Zeros

Find a polynomial with real coefficients of lowest degree that has zeros of $3i$ and $4 - i$.

Solution:

If the polynomial has real coefficients, then imaginary zeros must appear in conjugate pairs. Therefore, if $3i$ is a zero, then $-3i$ must also be a zero. Similarly, if

$4 - i$ is a zero, then $4 + i$ is a zero. Using the zeros, we can construct a product of factors that defines a polynomial.

$$P(x) = (x - 3i)(x - (-3i))(x - (4 - i))(x - (4 + i))$$
$$= (x - 3i)(x + 3i)(x - 4 + i)(x - 4 - i)$$
$$= (x^2 + 9)(x^2 - 8x + 17) \qquad \text{Multiply each pair of conjugate factors.}$$
$$= x^4 - 8x^3 + 26x^2 - 72x + 153 \qquad \text{Multiply.}$$

Tip: Recall that there are actually an infinite number of polynomials having zeros of $\pm 3i$ and $4 \pm i$. By varying the leading coefficient or the multiplicities of the zeros, then any polynomial of the form

$$P(x) = a(x - 3i)^n(x - (-3i))^m(x - (4 - i))^r(x - (4 + i))^t$$

will work.

---

example 4

Finding Zeros of a Polynomial, Given One Zero

Find all zeros of $P(x) = x^4 - 10x^3 + 20x^2 + 90x - 261$ given that $5 - 2i$ is a zero of $P(x)$.

Solution:

$P(x)$ is a fourth-degree polynomial and consequently must have four zeros (including multiplicities). Because $5 - 2i$ is a zero of $P(x)$, then $P(x) = (x - (5 - 2i))q_1(x)$ for some polynomial $q_1(x)$. Furthermore, because $P(x)$ has real coefficients, then $5 + 2i$ must also be a zero. By the factor theorem, there exists a polynomial $q_2(x)$ such that,

$$P(x) = (x - (5 - 2i))(x - (5 + 2i))q_2(x)$$

Successive synthetic divisions can be used to find $q_2(x)$.

$$
\begin{array}{r|rrrrr}
5 - 2i & 1 & -10 & 20 & 90 & -261 \\
       &   & 5 - 2i & -29 & -45 + 18i & 261 \\
\hline
5 + 2i & 1 & -5 - 2i & -9 & 45 + 18i & \underline{0} \\
       &   & 5 + 2i & 0 & -45 - 18i & \\
\hline
       & 1 & 0 & -9 & \underline{0} &
\end{array}
$$

Thus, $P(x) = (x - (5 - 2i))(x - (5 + 2i))(x^2 - 9)$

The remaining zeros of $P(x)$ are the zeros of the factor $(x^2 - 9)$. But $x^2 - 9 = 0$ for $x = \pm 3$. Hence, the zeros of $P(x)$ are $5 - 2i$, $5 + 2i$, 3, and -3.

5.   Descartes' Rule of Signs

The rational zero theorem gives us a list of potential rational zeros of a polynomial. However, sometimes the list can be very long and the process of checking all possible cases is tedious. The next two theorems provide insight regarding the number and location of real-valued zeros.

First consider $P(x) = x^5 + 2x^3 + 4x^2 + 7x + 18$. Because each term has a positive coefficient, no positive values of x will produce a function value of 0. (We cannot add five positive values and produce a sum of 0.) Therefore, any real-valued zero of this function must be negative. This result could also have been found by applying a more general rule called Descartes' rule of signs.

Descartes' Rule of Signs
_____

Let $P(x)$ be a polynomial with real coefficients and a nonzero constant term.

The number of positive real zeros of $P(x)$ is either:

    1. The same as the number of sign changes in $P(x)$

       or

    2. Less than the number of sign changes in $P(x)$ by a positive even integer.

The number of negative real zeros of $P(x)$ is either

    3. The same as the number of sign changes in $P(-x)$

       or

    4. Less than the number of sign changes in $P(-x)$ by a positive even integer.

Note: A zero of multiplicity m must be counted m times.

---

example 5

Applying Descartes' Rule of Signs

Use Descartes' rule of signs to determine the number of possible positive real zeros and the number of possible negative real zeros of the polynomial. Also comment on the number of imaginary zeros in each case.

a. $P(x) = 2x^5 + 2x^4 - 2x^3 + 14x^2 - 40x + 24$

b. $Q(x) = -x^4 - 3x^2 - 6$

Solution:

a. Because $P(x)$ is a fifth-degree polynomial, the number of zeros (including multiplicities) must be 5.

$$P(x) = 2x^5 + 2x^4 - 2x^3 + 14x^2 - 40x + 24$$

$$\underset{\text{4 sign changes}}{\underbrace{+ \quad + \quad - \quad + \quad - \quad +}}$$

The number of sign changes in $P(x)$ is 4. According to Descartes' rule of signs, the number of possible positive real zeros must be 4, 2, or 0.

The number of sign changes in $P(-x)$ is 1.

$$P(-x) = 2(-x)^5 + 2(-x)^4 - 2(-x)^3 + 14(-x)^2 - 40(-x) + 24$$

$$= -2x^5 + 2x^4 + 2x^3 + 14x^2 + 40x + 24$$

$$\underbrace{-\quad +}_{\text{1 sign change}} \quad + \quad + \quad + \quad +$$

According to Descartes' rule of signs, the number of negative real zeros must be 1. We also know that $P(x)$ has real coefficients, therefore, all imaginary zeros must come in conjugate pairs. In summary, we have the following possibilities.

Number of Positive Real Zeros	Number of Negative Real Zeros	Number of Imaginary Zeros	Total, Including Multiplicities
4	1	0	5
2	1	2	5
0	1	4	5

b. $Q(x)$ is a fourth-degree polynomial, which implies that it must have four zeros (including multiplicities). Furthermore,

$$Q(x) = -x^4 - 3x^2 - 6 \qquad \text{Has 0 sign changes}$$

$$Q(-x) = -(-x)^4 - 3(-x)^2 - 6$$

$$= -x^4 - 3x^2 - 6 \qquad \text{Has 0 sign changes}$$

Because neither $Q(x)$ nor $Q(-x)$ has any sign changes, there are no positive real zeros and no negative real zeros. Therefore, $Q(x)$ must have four imaginary zeros.

6. Upper and Lower Bounds for the Real Zeros of a Polynomial

The next theorem helps us limit our search for the location of the real zeros of a polynomial. A real number b is called an **upper bound** of the zeros of $P(x)$ if all real zeros of $P(x)$ are less than or equal to b. A real number a is called a **lower bound** of the zeros of $P(x)$ if all real zeros of $P(x)$ are greater than or equal to a. It is important to note that upper and lower bounds are not unique because any number greater than b is also an upper bound and any number less than a is also a lower bound. An upper and lower bound of the zeros of a polynomial $P(x)$ define an interval $[a, b]$ that contains the real zeros of the polynomial.

The following theorem helps us find upper and lower bounds for the zeros of a polynomial.

Upper and Lower Bounds for Real Zeros of Polynomials

Let $P(x)$ be a polynomial of degree $n \geq 1$ with real coefficients and a positive leading coefficient. Furthermore, suppose that $P(x)$ is divided by $(x - c)$.

1. If $c > 0$ and all coefficients of the quotient are nonnegative, and the remainder is nonnegative, then c is an upper bound to the zeros of $P(x)$.
2. If $c < 0$ and the coefficients of the quotient and remainder are alternatively positive and negative (with 0 being considered either positive or negative), then c is a lower bound to the zeros of $P(x)$.

The rules for finding upper and lower bounds were stated for a polynomial having a positive leading coefficient. However, $P(x) = 0$ and $-P(x) = 0$ are equivalent equations. If a polynomial $P(x)$ has a negative leading coefficient, then we can factor -1 from $P(x)$ and apply the upper and lower bound theorem accordingly.

example 6

Applying the Upper and Lower Bound Theorem

Given $P(x) = 2x^5 + 2x^4 - 2x^3 + 14x^2 - 40x + 24$,

a. Determine whether $x = 2$ is an upper bound of the zeros of $P(x)$.
b. Determine whether $x = -1$ is a lower bound of the zeros of $P(x)$.

Solution:

a.
$$
\begin{array}{r|rrrrrr}
2 & 2 & 2 & -2 & 14 & -40 & 24 \\
  &   & 4 & 12 & 20 & 68 & 56 \\
\hline
  & 2 & 6 & 10 & 34 & 28 & \lfloor 80 \\
\end{array}
$$

First note that $2 > 0$. Then, because the remainder and all coefficients in the quotient are positive, we know that $x = 2$ is an upper bound to the zeros of $P(x)$. Any real zeros of $P(x)$ must be less than or equal to 2.

b.
$$
\begin{array}{r|rrrrrr}
-1 & 2 & 2 & -2 & 14 & -40 & 24 \\
   &   & -2 & 0 & 2 & -16 & 56 \\
\hline
   & 2 & 0 & -2 & 16 & -56 & \lfloor 80 \\
\end{array}
\qquad
\begin{array}{r|rrrrrr}
-1 & 2 & 2 & -2 & 14 & -40 & 24 \\
   &   & -2 & 0 & 2 & -16 & 56 \\
\hline
   & 2 & 0 & -2 & 16 & -56 & \lfloor 80 \\
\end{array}
$$

taking the 0 coefficient as negative

$+$ $-$ $-$ $+$ $-$ $+$
no sign change here

taking the 0 coefficient as positive

$+$ $+$ $-$ $+$ $-$ $+$
no sign change here

The signs of the quotient do not alternate, therefore we cannot conclude that $x = -1$ is a lower bound of the zeros of $P(x)$.

Tip: Although $x = -1$ is not necessarily a lower bound for the real zeros of $P(x)$, we can try other negative real numbers. For example $x = -4$ is a lower bound as shown here:

$$
\begin{array}{r|rrrrrr}
-4 & 2 & 2 & -2 & 14 & -40 & 24 \\
   &   & -8 & 24 & -88 & 296 & -1024 \\
\hline
   & 2 & -6 & 22 & -74 & 256 & \underline{|-1000} \\
\end{array}
$$

The signs change between the remainder and each coefficient of the quotient.

7. Finding the Zeros of a Polynomial: A Summary

example 7

Finding the Zeros of a Polynomial

Find the zeros of the polynomial and state the multiplicity of each.

$$P(x) = 2x^5 + 2x^4 - 2x^3 + 14x^2 - 40x + 24$$

Solution:

$P(x)$ is a fifth-degree polynomial and must have five zeros (including multiplicities). We can begin by finding the rational zeros (if any exist). By the rational zero theorem, we know that the possible rational zeros are

$$\frac{c}{d} = \pm1, \pm2, \pm3, \pm4, \pm6, \pm8, \pm12, \pm24, \pm\tfrac{1}{2}, \text{ and } \pm\tfrac{3}{2}.$$

However, we also know from Example 6 that although $x = 2$ is not a zero of $P(x)$, it is an upper bound. From the Tip accompanying Example 6 we see that although $x = -4$ is not a zero of $P(x)$, it is a lower bound. Therefore, we can restrict our list of rational zeros to

$$\frac{c}{d} = -3, -2, \pm1, \pm\tfrac{1}{2}, \pm\tfrac{3}{2}$$

We can apply synthetic division to test each possible rational zero. We first try $x = 1$.

$$
\begin{array}{r|rrrrrr}
1 & 2 & 2 & -2 & 14 & -40 & 24 \\
  &   & 2 & 4 & 2 & 16 & -24 \\
\hline
  & 2 & 4 & 2 & 16 & -24 & \underline{|0} \\
\end{array}
$$
$x = 1$ is a zero.

We have $P(x) = (x - 1)(2x^4 + 4x^3 + 2x^2 + 16x - 24)$. Try $x = 1$ again because it may be a repeated zero.

$$
\begin{array}{r|rrrrr}
1 & 2 & 4 & 2 & 16 & -24 \\
  &   & 2 & 6 & 8 & 24 \\
\hline
  & 2 & 6 & 8 & 24 & \underline{|0} \\
\end{array}
$$
$x = 1$ is a repeated zero.

We have, $P(x) = (x - 1)^2(2x^3 + 6x^2 + 8x + 24)$.

Because the polynomial $2x^3 + 6x^2 + 8x + 24$ has no sign changes, Descartes' rule of signs indicates that there are no additional positive real zeros. Now we can try the possible negative values from our list, $\frac{c}{d}$. We find that $x = -3$ works.

$$
\begin{array}{r|rrrr}
-3 & 2 & 6 & 8 & 24 \\
   &   & -6 & 0 & -24 \\
\hline
   & 2 & 0 & 8 & \underline{|\,0}
\end{array}
$$

Thus, $P(x) = (x - 1)^2(x + 3)(2x^2 + 8)$.

The remaining two zeros of $P(x)$ are found by solving the equation $2x^2 + 8 = 0$.

$$2x^2 + 8 = 0$$
$$2x^2 = -8$$
$$x^2 = -4$$
$$x = \pm 2i \qquad \text{Note that the imaginary zeros appear as conjugates.}$$

In summary, the zeros are

$$x = 1 \text{ (multiplicity of 2)}$$
$$x = -3 \text{ (multiplicity of 1)}$$
$$x = 2i \text{ (multiplicity of 1)}$$
$$x = -2i \text{ (multiplicity of 1)}$$

section 12.2   PRACTICE EXERCISES

For Exercises 1–4, find $P(c)$ using the remainder theorem.

1. $P(x) = x^3 - 19x - 30; c = 2$

2. $P(x) = x^3 + 3x^2 - 6x - 8; c = -2$

3. $P(x) = x^3 + 2x^2 - 3x - 10; c = -3$

4. $P(x) = x^3 + x + 10; c = 3$

For Exercises 5–8, determine if $x = c$ is a zero of $Q(x)$.

5. $Q(x) = x^4 + 2x^3 - 10x^2 - 18x + 9; \ c = 3$

6. $Q(x) = x^4 - 2x^3 + 9x^2 + 2x - 40; c = 2$

7. $Q(x) = 2x^5 + 3x^2 + 1; c = -1$

8. $Q(x) = 3x^5 - 2x^4 - 16x^3 + x - 6; c = -2$

For Exercises 9–12, determine if the second polynomial is a factor of the first polynomial.

9. $x^3 - 3x^2 - x + 3; (x - 1)$

10. $2x^3 + x^2 - 13x + 6; (x + 3)$

11. $x^3 + 4x^2 + 9x + 36; (x + 3i)$

12. $x^3 - 5x^2 + 4x - 20; (x - 2i)$

For Exercises 13–16, state the zeros and their multiplicity for each polynomial.

13. $f(x) = (x - 3)(x + 5)(2x - 3)^3$

14. $f(x) = (3x + 5)(x - 7)^2(x + 1)^4$

15. $f(x) = 5(x - 9)^4(x + 12)^2$

16. $f(x) = 8(3 - x)^3(x + 6)$

For Exercises 17–22, find a polynomial of lowest degree that has the given zeros. Answers may vary.

17. $2, -2, 1$

18. $1, -3, 5$

19. $-6, i, -i$

20. $5, 4i, -4i$

21. $0, 3 + 2i, 3 - 2i$

22. $0, 4 + 6i, 4 - 6i$

For Exercises 23–30, find a polynomial, $F(x)$, with real coefficients that satisfies the following conditions.

23. Degree 3
Zero of 6 (multiplicity 1)
Zero of -2 (multiplicity 2)
$F(-1) = 21$

24. Degree 3
Zero of -1 (multiplicity 2)
Zero of 7 (multiplicity 1)
$F(-2) = -18$

25. Degree 3
Zeros 4, -4, and 2
Function passes through $(1, -15)$

26. Degree 3
Zeros 3, -3, and -5
Function passes through $(0, 45)$

27. Lowest degree
Zeros 1 and $5i$
$F(0) = -75$
(Recall that imaginary zeros come in conjugate pairs.)

28. Lowest degree
Zeros -4 and $3i$
$F(-1) = -60$

29. Lowest degree
Zeros $1 - i$ and $2i$
Function passes through $(0, 8)$

30. Lowest degree
Zeros $2 + i$ and $4i$
Function passes through $(0, 80)$

For Exercises 31–38, use the rational zero theorem to list all possible rational zeros for each polynomial.

31. $p(x) = 4x^3 + 3x^2 - x + 5$

32. $p(x) = 3x^3 - 4x^2 + 2x - 6$

33. $p(x) = 2x^4 + 2x^2 - 8x + 8$

34. $p(x) = 6x^4 - 3x^2 - 9$

35. $p(x) = 12x^3 - x^2 - 3x + 4$

36. $p(x) = 9x^3 + 4x^2 + 5x + 3$

37. $p(x) = 10x^5 - 3x^4 + x - 1$

38. $p(x) = 8x^5 + 4x^3 - x + 1$

39. Explain why the rational zero theorem cannot be applied to the polynomial

$$N(x) = \sqrt{2}x^3 + \pi x^2 + 3$$

40. Explain why the rational zero theorem cannot be applied to the polynomial

$$M(x) = 4ix^2 + 2ix + 3$$

For Exercises 41–50, use Descartes' rule of signs to determine the possible number of positive and negative zeros of the function.

41. $P(x) = -4x^3 + 15x^2 + 8x - 3$

42. $P(x) = 10x^4 - 3x^2 + 8$

43. $P(x) = 3x^3 + 2x^2 + 6x - 1$

44. $P(x) = 8x^5 - 13x^2 - 6$

45. $P(x) = 6x^4 + 10$

46. $P(x) = x^3 + x^2 + 1$

47. $P(x) = -4x^3 - x - 10$

48. $P(x) = -x^4 - 3x - 4$

49. $P(x) = 7x^5 - x^4 + 2x^3 - 1$

50. $P(x) = -3x^3 + 8x^2 - x + 13$

51. Explain why $f(x) = x^3 + 2x^2 + 5x + 7$ cannot have any positive real zeros.

52. Explain why $g(x) = -x^4 - 2x^2 - 6$ cannot have any negative real zeros.

For Exercises 53–60, determine if the given number represents an upper or a lower bound for the zeros of the function.

53. $P(x) = 6x^3 - 5x^2 + x + 2; x = 3$

54. $P(x) = 2x^3 - 4x^2 + x + 4; x = 3$

55. $P(x) = -2x^3 + 5x^2 + x + 3; x = -1$

56. $P(x) = -3x^3 + 2x^2 - x - 14; x = -2$

57. $P(x) = 2x^5 - 4x^4 + 4x^3 + 2x^2 - 2; x = 2$

58. $P(x) = 3x^5 - 2x^4 - x^3 + 5x - 2; x = 1$

59. $P(x) = x^4 + 4x^3 + 2x^2 - 2x - 20; x = -4$

60. $P(x) = 2x^4 + 3x^3 - 7x^2 + 6x + 1; x = -3$

For Exercises 61–74, find all of the zeros of the polynomial. State the multiplicity of the zero if it is greater than 1.

61. $F(x) = x^3 - 6x^2 + 3x + 10$

62. $F(x) = x^3 + 4x^2 + x - 6$

63. $F(x) = 6x^3 + 19x^2 + 11x - 6$

64. $F(x) = 6x^3 - 11x^2 - 4x + 4$

65. $F(x) = x^4 - x^3 - 19x^2 + 49x - 30$

66. $F(x) = x^4 + 11x^3 + 41x^2 + 61x + 30$

67. $F(x) = 4x^4 - 4x^3 - 19x^2 + 16x + 12$

68. $F(x) = 4x^4 + 16x^3 + 7x^2 - 18x - 9$

69. $F(x) = x^3 + x^2 - 7x - 7$

70. $F(x) = x^3 - 2x^2 - 6x + 12$

71. $F(x) = 2x^3 - 5x^2 + 6x - 2$

72. $F(x) = x^3 + 3x^2 + x + 3$

73. $F(x) = x^5 - 15x^3 - 10x^2 + 60x + 72$

74. $F(x) = x^5 + 7x^4 - 2x^3 - 46x^2 + 65x - 25$

■ EXPANDING YOUR SKILLS

For Exercises 75–78, use the given zero to find the remaining zeros of each polynomial.

75. $Q(x) = x^3 - x^2 + 8x + 60; 2 + 4i$

76. $Q(x) = x^3 - 10x^2 + 33x - 34; 4 + i$

77. $Q(x) = x^4 - 8x^3 + 24x^2 - 20x - 13; 3 - 2i$

78. $Q(x) = x^4 - 6x^3 + 19x^2 - 42x + 10; 1 - 3i$

79. Use Descartes' rule of signs to prove that for every positive even integer, n, $x^n - 1$ has only two real zeros.

80. Use Descartes' rule of signs to prove that for every positive odd integer, n, $x^n - 1$ has only one real zero.

---

chapter 12   MIDCHAPTER REVIEW

For Exercises 1–8, let $P(x) = 2x^3 - 5x^2 - x + 6$. Use synthetic division to perform the operations.

1. Identify the quotient and remainder of $P(x) \div (x - 3)$.

2. Identify the quotient and remainder of $P(x) \div (x - 1)$.

3. Find $P(5)$ using the remainder theorem.

4. Find $P(-6)$ using the remainder theorem.

5. Use synthetic division to decide if -1 is a zero of $P(x)$.

6. Use synthetic division to decide if $\frac{3}{2}$ is a zero of $P(x)$.

7. Use synthetic division to decide if $(x - 2)$ is a factor of $P(x)$.

8. Use synthetic division to decide if $(x + 1)$ is a factor of $P(x)$.

For Exercises 9–16, let $Q(x) = 3x^3 - 11x^2 + 5x + 3$. Use synthetic division to perform the operations.

9. Identify the quotient and remainder of $Q(x) \div (x - 2)$.

10. Identify the quotient and remainder of $Q(x) \div (x + 1)$.

11. Find $Q(4)$ using the remainder theorem.

12. Find $Q(-5)$ using the remainder theorem.

13. Use synthetic division to decide if $-\frac{1}{3}$ is a zero of $Q(x)$.

14. Use synthetic division to decide if -3 is a zero of $Q(x)$.

15. Use synthetic division to decide if $(x - 2)$ is a factor of $Q(x)$.

16. Use synthetic division to decide if $(x - 3)$ is a factor of $Q(x)$.

Concepts

1. Graphing Functions of the Form $y = x^n$

2. End Behavior

3. Continuity of Polynomial Functions

4. Graphing Polynomial Functions

5. Finding Zeros and Graphing Polynomial Functions

6. Zero Location Theorem

7. Applications of Polynomial Functions

section

12.3 GRAPHS OF POLYNOMIAL FUNCTIONS

1. Graphing Functions of the Form $y = x^n$

In Section 4.3 we became familiar with the graphs of several basic functions. Among these were the graphs of $y = x$, $y = x^2$, and $y = x^3$, shown in Figures 12-3 through 12-5.

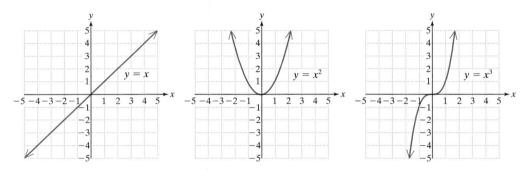

Figure 12-3   **Figure 12-4**   **Figure 12-5**

Now suppose we wanted to know the basic shape of a function of the form $y = x^n$, where n is a positive integer. We might begin by graphing several more functions such as $y = x^4$, $y = x^5$, and $y = x^6$ to see if a pattern emerges (Figures 12-6 through 12-8).

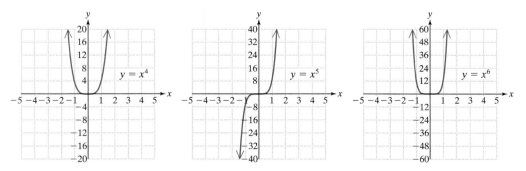

Figure 12-6   **Figure 12-7**   **Figure 12-8**

Notice that the graphs of functions of the form $y = x^n$, where n is a positive *even* integer resemble the graph of $y = x^2$. The graphs are symmetric with respect to the y-axis with variations in the "steepness" in the y-direction (Figure 12-9).

The graphs of the functions of the form $y = x^n$, where n is a positive *odd* integer ($n > 1$) resemble the graph of $y = x^3$ (Figure 12-10).

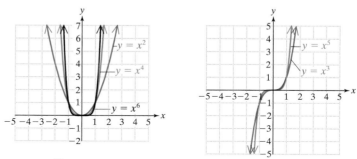

Figure 12-9

Figure 12-10

2.   End Behavior

Recall from Section 11.1 that the graph of $f(x) = ax^2$ is a parabola opening upward if $a > 0$. If $a < 0$, then the graph is reflected across the x-axis (Figure 12-11). The value of a will have the same effect on the graph of $f(x) = ax^n$, where n is a positive integer. Therefore, the graph of $f(x) = ax^n$, where $a \neq 0$ and n is a positive integer will have one of the following general shapes (Figure 12-12).

Figure 12-11

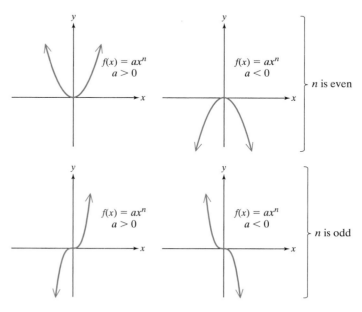

Figure 12-12

For a general polynomial function defined by $P(x) = a_n x^n + a_{n-1}x^{n-1} + \cdots + a_1 x + a_0$, the domain is all real numbers. For large values of $|x|$ (i.e., for x values far to the right or far to the left), the leading term is said to "dominate" the polynomial. This means that as $|x|$ becomes large, the value of $a_n x^n$ is larger than the sum of the other terms combined. For this reason the graph of $P(x) = a_n x^n + a_{n-1}x^{n-1} + \cdots + a_1 x + a_0$ will follow the same far-right and far-left behavior as $y = a_n x^n$.

Far-Right and Far-Left Behavior of a Polynomial Function

The graph of a polynomial function defined by $P(x) = a_n x^n + a_{n-1}x^{n-1} + \cdots + a_1 x + a_0$ has the following far-right and far-left behavior.

	n is even	*n* is odd
$a_n > 0$	Up to the left and up to the right	Down to the left and up to the right
$a_n < 0$	Down to the left and down to the right	Up to the left and down to the right

---

example 1

Determining Far-Right and Far-Left Behavior

Examine the leading term of the polynomial to determine the far-left and far-right behavior of the graph.

a. $P(x) = -2x^3 + 14x^2 - 14x - 30$

b. $Q(x) = \dfrac{1}{2}x^2 - 2x$

c. $M(x) = -(2x - 5)^2(3x + 2)(x - 4)$

d. $N(x) = 0.1(x - 2)(x - 4)(3x + 7)$

Solution:

a. $P(x) = -2x^3 + 14x^2 - 14x - 30$. The leading coefficient is negative and the polynomial is of odd degree. The end behavior of the graph of $y = P(x)$ is up to the left and down to the right.

Graphing Calculator Box

Graph the function from Example 1(a) on a graphing calculator to verify the end behavior. The window parameters must be sufficiently large to capture the end behavior.

b. $Q(x) = \frac{1}{2}x^2 - 2x$. The leading coefficient is positive and the polynomial is of even degree. The end behavior of the graph of $y = Q(x)$ is up to the left and up to the right.

Tip: Notice that the factor

$(2x - 5)^2 = (2x - 5)(2x - 5)$

Therefore, when multiplying leading terms of these factors, we have $(2x)(2x) = (2x)^2$.

c. $M(x) = -(2x - 5)^2(3x + 2)(x - 4)$. To identify the leading term, we can multiply factors and expand the polynomial. However, because we are interested only in the leading term of the polynomial, we can simply multiply the leading terms of each factor. Thus,

$$a_n x^n = -1(2x)^2(3x)(x) = -12x^4$$

The leading coefficient is negative and the polynomial is of even degree. The end behavior of the graph of $y = M(x)$ is down to the left and down to the right.

d. $N(x) = 0.1(x - 2)(x - 4)(3x + 7)$. The leading term is given by $a_n x^n = 0.1(x)(x)(3x) = 0.3x^3$. The leading coefficient is positive and the polynomial is of odd degree. The end behavior of the graph of $y = N(x)$ is down to the left and up to the right.

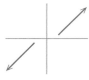

3. Continuity of Polynomial Functions

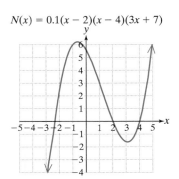

$N(x) = 0.1(x - 2)(x - 4)(3x + 7)$

Figure 12-13

The graph of the function given in Example 1(d) is shown in Figure 12-13. One notable feature illustrated in this graph and in the graphs of all polynomial functions is that there are no "breaks" or "holes." Based on this informal observation, we say that polynomial functions are **continuous**. The function, f, in Figure 12-14 is continuous, and the function g in Figure 12-15 is **discontinuous** at $x = -1$ and at $x = 2$.

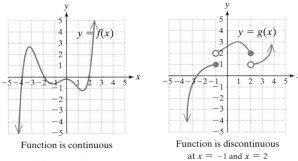

Function is continuous

Figure 12-14

Function is discontinuous
at $x = -1$ and $x = 2$

Figure 12-15

The continuity of a function implies that function values between two successive zeros must either be all positive (above the x-axis) or all negative (below the x-axis). That is, the function values will not change sign between two successive zeros. The graph of $N(x) = 0.1(x - 2)(x - 4)(3x + 7)$ in Figure 12-13 shows that between $x = -\frac{7}{3}$ and $x = 2$, the function values are all positive. Between $x = 2$ and $x = 4$, the function values are all negative. Furthermore, between two successive zeros of a polynomial function, at least one **turning point** must exist where the function changes from increasing to decreasing or from decreasing to increasing.

4. Graphing Polynomial Functions

To sketch the graph of a polynomial function, we can first determine its far-right and far-left behavior. Then we can use skills already mastered such as finding the x- and y-intercepts and plotting points. The x-intercepts of a function are its real zeros. To determine the sign of the function values between two successive x-intercepts, we can use test points. This process is demonstrated in the next example.

example 2

Sketching the Graph of a Polynomial Function

Sketch the functions.

a. $F(x) = x^3 - 4x$

b. $P(x) = \dfrac{1}{12}(x - 4)^2(x + 1)(2x + 9)$

Solution:

a. $F(x) = x^3 - 4x$. The leading coefficient is positive and the polynomial is of odd degree. The end behavior of the graph of the polynomial is down to the left and up to the right.

Because $F(0) = (0)^3 - 4(0) = 0$, the y-intercept is $(0, 0)$. The x-intercepts are the real zeros of the function. Factoring yields

$$F(x) = x^3 - 4x$$

$$= x(x^2 - 4)$$

$$= x(x + 2)(x - 2) \qquad \text{The real zeros of the function are } 0, -2, \text{ and } 2.$$

Using the intercepts and far-left and far-right behavior, the graph takes the following form.

To determine the sign of the function on the intervals $(-2, 0)$ and $(0, 2)$ we can use test points. Synthetic division and the remainder theorem provides one method to find the corresponding function values.

Interval $(-2, 0)$, test $x = -1$ Interval $(0, 2)$, test $x = 1$

$$\underline{-1|} \quad 1 \quad\quad 0 \quad -4 \quad\quad 0 \qquad\qquad \underline{1|} \quad 1 \quad\quad 0 \quad -4 \quad\quad 0$$
$$\qquad\qquad -1 \quad\quad 1 \quad\quad 3 \qquad\qquad\qquad\qquad 1 \quad\quad 1 \quad -3$$
$$\overline{\quad 1 \quad -1 \quad -3 \quad \lfloor 3} = f(-1) \qquad\quad \overline{1 \quad\quad 1 \quad -3 \quad \lfloor -3} = f(1)$$

Because $f(-1) = 3$, the function is positive on the interval $(-2, 0)$. The function must also have a turning point somewhere between $x = -2$ and $x = 0$. Similarly, because $f(1) = -3$, the function is negative on the interval $(0, 2)$. The function must have a turning point somewhere between $x = 0$ and $x = 2$. To sketch the function, we can plot the test points and the x- and y-intercepts and then join the points with a smooth curve (Figure 12-16).

b. $P(x) = \dfrac{1}{12}(x - 4)^2(x + 1)(2x + 9)$

The leading term, $a_n x^n = \frac{1}{12}(x)^2(x)(2x) = \frac{1}{6}x^4$. Therefore, the far-left and far-right behavior is up to the left and up to the right.

The real zeros of the polynomial are $4, -1$, and $-\frac{9}{2}$. Therefore, the x-intercepts are $(4, 0)$, $(-1, 0)$, and $(-\frac{9}{2}, 0)$.

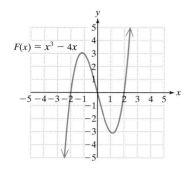

$F(x) = x^3 - 4x$

Figure 12-16

Tip: The exact location and height of the turning points can be found using techniques of calculus. For now, we will simply sketch the curve to determine general behavior.

To find the y-intercept, evaluate $P(0)$.

$$P(0) = \frac{1}{12}((0) - 4)^2((0) + 1)(2(0) + 9) = 12. \quad \text{The } y\text{-intercept is } (0, 12).$$

Using the intercepts and far-left and far-right behavior, the graph takes the following form.

The far-left behavior tells us that the function is positive on the interval $(-\infty, -\frac{9}{2})$, and the far-right behavior tells us that the function is positive on the interval $(4, \infty)$. The y-intercept tells us that the function is positive on the interval $(-1, 4)$. To determine the sign of the function on the interval $(-\frac{9}{2}, -1)$, we can use a test point. The function is written in factored form rather than expanded form. Therefore, it is easier to evaluate the function at the test point by using direct substitution.

Interval $(-\frac{9}{2}, -1)$, test $x = -3$

$$P(-3) = \frac{1}{12}((-3) - 4)^2((-3) + 1)(2(-3) + 9)$$

$$= \frac{1}{12}(-7)^2(-2)(3)$$

$$= -\frac{49}{2}, \text{ or } -24.5$$

Because $P(-3) = -24.5$, the function is negative on the interval $(-\frac{9}{2}, -1)$. To sketch the function, plot the test point and intercepts, and sketch a smooth curve through the points (Figure 12-17).

Once again, to find the exact location of the turning points would require advanced techniques.

$y = \frac{1}{12}(x - 4)^2(x + 1)(2x + 9)$

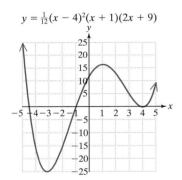

Figure 12-17

Notice that the graph of $P(x) = \frac{1}{12}(x - 4)^2(x + 1)(2x + 9)$ crosses the x-axis at points corresponding to the real zeros having odd multiplicity. The graph touches but does not cross the x-axis (does not change sign) at points corresponding to the real zeros having even multiplicity. This is true in general.

- The graph of a polynomial function crosses the x-axis at real zeros of odd multiplicity.
- The graph of a polynomial function touches (but does not cross) the x-axis at real zeros of even multiplicity.

This convention will be used in the next example.

5.   Finding Zeros and Graphing Polynomial Functions

example 3

Finding Zeros and Graphing a Polynomial Function

Given $P(x) = -x^5 - 4x^4 - 5x^3 - 4x^2 - 4x$

a.   Find the zeros of $P(x)$
b.   Sketch $y = P(x)$

Solution:

a. $P(x)$ is a fifth-degree polynomial, which implies that there must be five zeros (including multiplicities). A common factor of $-x$ can be removed from $P(x)$ so that

$$P(x) = -x(x^4 + 4x^3 + 5x^2 + 4x + 4)$$

Hence $P(x)$ has a zero at the origin with multiplicity of 1. The remaining zeros of $P(x)$ are zeros of $x^4 + 4x^3 + 5x^2 + 4x + 4$. The possible rational zeros, $\frac{c}{d}$, are $\pm 1, \pm 2, \pm 4$. However, because the terms in the polynomial $x^4 + 4x^3 + 5x^2 + 4x + 4$ are all positive, any real-valued zero must be negative. We can use synthetic division to determine if $x = -1$, $x = -2$, or $x = -4$ are zeros.

$$
\begin{array}{r|rrrrr}
-1 & 1 & 4 & 5 & 4 & 4 \\
   &   & -1 & -3 & -2 & -2 \\
\hline
   & 1 & 3 & 2 & 2 & \lfloor 2 \\
\end{array}
\qquad
\begin{array}{r|rrrrr}
-4 & 1 & 4 & 5 & 4 & 4 \\
   &   & -4 & 0 & -20 & 64 \\
\hline
   & 1 & 0 & 5 & -16 & \lfloor 68 \\
\end{array}
$$

$$
\begin{array}{r|rrrrr}
-2 & 1 & 4 & 5 & 4 & 4 \\
   &   & -2 & -4 & -2 & -4 \\
\hline
   & 1 & 2 & 1 & 2 & \lfloor 0 \\
\end{array}
\qquad x = -2 \text{ is a zero of } P(x).
$$

$$
\begin{array}{r|rrrr}
-2 & 1 & 2 & 1 & 2 \\
   &   & -2 & 0 & -2 \\
\hline
   & 1 & 0 & 1 & \lfloor 0 \\
\end{array}
\qquad x = -2 \text{ is a repeated zero of } P(x).
$$

$P(x)$ factors as: $P(x) = -x(x + 2)^2(x^2 + 1)$. The remaining zeros of the function are the zeros of the factor $x^2 + 1$.

$$x^2 + 1 = 0$$
$$x^2 = -1$$
$$x = \pm i$$

The zeros of $P(x)$ are
$$x = 0 \text{ (multiplicity 1)}$$
$$x = -2 \text{ (multiplicity 2)}$$
$$x = i \text{ (multiplicity 1)}$$
$$x = -i \text{ (multiplicity 1)}$$

b. $P(x) = -x^5 - 4x^4 - 5x^3 - 4x^2 - 4x$ factors as $P(x) = -x(x + 2)^2(x - i)(x + i)$.

The leading term of the polynomial is $-x^5$, indicating that the far-left and far-right behavior is up to the left and down to the right.

The function has x-intercepts at $(0, 0)$ and $(-2, 0)$. The y-intercept is $(0, 0)$.

Because $x = 0$ is a zero of odd multiplicity, the function will cross the x-axis at $(0, 0)$.

Because $x = -2$ is a zero of even multiplicity, the function will touch but not cross the x-axis at $(-2, 0)$.

$P(x) = -x(x + 2)^2(x - i)(x + i)$

Figure 12-18

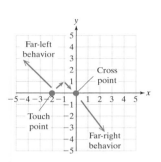

Using this information, the graph has the shape shown in Figure 12-18.

6. Zero Location Theorem

In Sections 12.1 and 12.2, we learned several techniques to find the zeros of a polynomial. If a polynomial has rational zeros, we can locate the zeros with the rational zero theorem. Irrational zeros can sometimes be found by inspection, but in most cases, we need to use advanced techniques or approximation methods. For example, $f(x) = x^2 - 7$ has zeros of $x = \pm\sqrt{7}$. However, the irrational zeros of $g(x) = x^4 - 2x^3 + 2x^2 - 6x - 3$ cannot be found by inspection.

Recall that a polynomial function is continuous. One important result, known as the intermediate value theorem, follows from the continuity of a function. The **intermediate value theorem** indicates that for any real numbers a and b in the domain of a continuous function, f, the function can be drawn between $(a, f(a))$ and $(b, f(b))$ without lifting the pencil from the paper. Hence, f must assume all real values between $f(a)$ and $f(b)$. Further suppose that $f(a)$ and $f(b)$ have opposite signs, then f must attain a value of 0 somewhere on the interval $[a, b]$. This is stated formally in the **zero location theorem**.

Zero Location Theorem for Polynomial Functions

Let f be a polynomial function with real coefficients. For real numbers a and b, if $f(a)$ and $f(b)$ have opposite signs, then there exists at least one real zero of f between a and b.

The zero location theorem is illustrated in Figures 12-19 and 12-20.

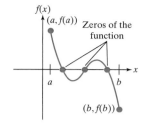

Figure 12-19   **Figure 12-20**

example 4

Applying the Zero Location Theorem

On which of the following intervals does the zero location theorem guarantee the existence of a zero for $g(x) = x^4 - 2x^3 + 2x^2 - 6x - 3$?

a. $[-1, 0]$ b. $[0, 1]$ c. $[1, 2]$ d. $[2, 3]$

Solution:

a. By inspection $g(0) = -3$. To find $g(-1)$ we can use synthetic division.

$$
\begin{array}{r|rrrrr}
-1 & 1 & -2 & 2 & -6 & -3 \\
   &   & -1 & 3 & -5 & 11 \\
\hline
   & 1 & -3 & 5 & -11 & \boxed{8} = g(-1)
\end{array}
$$

Because $g(-1)$ and $g(0)$ have opposite signs and because g is a polynomial, the function must have at least one zero on the interval $[-1, 0]$.

b. From part (a), we know that $g(0) = -3$. To find $g(1)$, use synthetic division.

$$
\begin{array}{r|rrrrr}
1 & 1 & -2 & 2 & -6 & -3 \\
  &   & 1 & -1 & 1 & -5 \\
\hline
  & 1 & -1 & 1 & -5 & \boxed{-8} = g(1)
\end{array}
$$

Because $g(0)$ and $g(1)$ have the same sign (both negative), the zero location theorem cannot be applied. We do not have sufficient information to determine whether a zero exists on the interval $[0, 1]$.

⬢ Avoiding Mistakes

In Example 4(b), the conditions of the zero location theorem are not met. Therefore, no conclusion can be drawn. There may or may not be a zero on the interval $[0, 1]$ as illustrated here.

c.   Using a similar strategy, we have $g(1) = -8$ and $g(2) = -7$. Once again, the conditions of the zero location theorem are not met. We cannot determine whether a zero exists on the interval $[1, 2]$.

d.   We have $g(2) = -7$ and $g(3) = 24$. Because the function values have opposite signs, there exists at least one zero on the interval $[2, 3]$.

Graphing Calculator Box

From Example 4, we have, $Y1 = x^4 - 2x^3 + 2x^2 - 6x - 3$. There are two real zeros: $x = 1 + \sqrt{2}$ and $x = 1 - \sqrt{2}$; and two imaginary zeros: $x = \sqrt{3}i$ and $x = -\sqrt{3}i$. A *Root* or *Zero* feature on a graphing calculator can be used to graph the function and approximate its real zeros.

---

7.   Applications of Polynomial Functions

example 5

Interpreting a Polynomial Function in an Application

The average temperature for Aspen, Colorado, can be approximated by

$$T(x) = 0.0194x^4 - 0.4963x^3 + 3.3708x^2 - 2.9313x - 5.7439$$

where T is the temperature in degrees Celsius, and x is the number of months after Jan. 1, and $0 \le x \le 12$.

a.   Explain what the zeros of the function represent in the context of the problem.

b.   Explain what the turning points represent in the context of the problem.

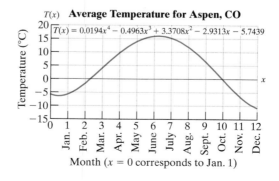

Average Temperature for Aspen, CO

Solution:

a. The zeros of the polynomial represent the number of months after January 1 that the average temperature changes from being below zero to being above zero or vice versa. In Aspen, Colorado, approximately $2\frac{1}{2}$ months after the first of the year (mid-March), the average temperatures rise to positive values. Approximately 10 months after the first of the year (November), the average temperatures drop below 0°C.

b. The turning points represent the number of months after the first of the year that the trend in temperature changes from either decreasing to increasing or from increasing to decreasing. In this case, winter temperatures begin to rise approximately 1 month after the beginning of the year (beginning of February). Summer temperatures begin to fall approximately $6\frac{1}{2}$ months into the year (mid-July).

---

section 12.3   PRACTICE EXERCISES

For Exercises 1–10, find the zeros of the polynomial. Use the result to identify the x-intercepts of the function.

1. $y = (x + 10)(x - 3)$

2. $y = (x - 2)(x + 11)$

3. $y = 4x(2x + 5)(x^2 + 3)$

4. $y = -3x(6x - 5)(x^2 + 4)$

5. $y = x^2 + 9x + 14$

6. $y = x^2 - 13x - 30$

7. $y = x^3 - x^2 - 64x + 64$

8. $y = x^3 + 6x^2 - 100x - 600$

9. $y = x^2 - 7x + 2$

10. $y = x^2 + 5x + 3$

For Exercises 11–18, sketch a graph of the equation from memory without plotting points.

11. $y = -x^2$

12. $y = x^2$

13. $y = x^3$

14. $y = -x^3$

15. $y = x^4$

16. $y = -x^4$

17. $y = -x^5$

18. $y = x^5$

For Exercises 19–22, use the far-left and far-right behavior to match the function with a graph.

19. $f(x) = 0.03x^5 + 0.03x^4 - 0.42x^3 - 0.18x^2 - 2.16$

20. $h(x) = -x^3 + x + 1$

21. $g(x) = -0.2(x + 1)^2(x - 2)(x - 4)$

22. $k(x) = \dfrac{1}{200}(2x + 9)(x - 2)^2(x + 1)^3$

a.

b.

c.

d.

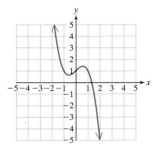

For Exercises 23–32, identify the leading term and determine the far-right and far-left behavior for the polynomial.

23. $f(x) = 6x^3 + 4x^2 - 9x + 11$

24. $g(x) = 3x^3 - 8x^2 + x - 2$

25. $h(x) = 5 + x^2 + 3x^3 - 7x^4$

26. $k(x) = 1 - 2x + 4x^2 - x^3 - 8x^4$

27. $m(x) = \dfrac{1}{3}x^2 - \dfrac{4}{5}x - \dfrac{7}{3}$

28. $n(x) = \dfrac{2}{3}x^2 + \dfrac{6}{7}x - \dfrac{1}{2}$

29. $p(x) = (2x - 3)(x + 4)(x - 5)$

30. $q(x) = 2x^2(3x - 2)(x + 7)$

31. $r(x) = (x + 8)(3x - 1)(4 - x)$

32. $s(x) = (2x - 9)(3 - x)(x + 10)$

For Exercises 33–40, determine if the graph is continuous or discontinuous.

33.

34.

35.

36.

37.

38.

39.

40.

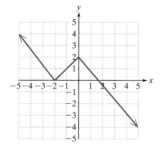

41. Explain how to find the y-intercept of a function, f.

42. Explain how to find the x-intercepts of a function, f (if any exist).

For Exercises 43–60,

a.   Determine the far-right and far-left behavior.

b.   Find the x- and y-intercepts.

c.   Sketch the function.

43. $p(x) = -x^2(x - 3)^2$

44. $f(x) = -\dfrac{1}{6}x^2(x + 4)^2$

45. $q(x) = -x(x - 1)(x + 3)$

46. $m(x) = -2x(x + 2)(x + 4)$

47. $f(x) = \dfrac{1}{60}(x - 4)(x + 3)^3(x - 2)^2$

48. $g(x) = \dfrac{1}{30}(x - 5)^2(x + 3)^2$

49. $h(x) = \dfrac{1}{150}(2x - 3)^2(3x + 10)^2$

50. $z(x) = 0.025(x + 1)^3(x - 4)$

51. $r(x) = x^4 - 5x^2 + 4$

52. $n(x) = 3x^4 + 3x^3 + 3x^2$

53. $g(x) = -2x^5 - x^4 + 3x^3$

54. $s(x) = x^5 - x^4 - 6x^3$

55. $h(x) = 4x^4 - 9x^2 + 2$

56. $k(x) = 2x^4 - 5x^3 + 3x^2 + x - 1$

57. $P(x) = x^3 + 3x^2 - 6x - 8$

58. $Q(x) = x^3 - 2x^2 - 5x + 6$

59. $a(x) = -4x^2 - 12x - 9$

60. $b(x) = 9x^2 - 30x + 25$

For Exercises 61–64, answer true or false.

61. If f is a polynomial function such that $f(2) = -1.6$ and $f(4) = 3.8$, then there exists at least one zero between 2 and 4.

62. If P is a polynomial function such that $P(6) = 0$ and $P(8) = 0$, then there must be a real zero between 6 and 8.

63. If g is a polynomial function such that $g(-1) = 5$ and $g(3) = 2$, then there cannot be a real zero of g on the interval $[-1, 3]$.

64. If Q is a polynomial function such that $Q(3) = -5$ and $Q(6) = 7$, then there can only exist exactly 1 real zero on the interval $[3, 6]$.

For Exercises 65–70, determine the intervals on which the zero location theorem guarantees the existence of a zero.

65. $P(x) = x^3 - 27x - 90$
    a. $[-1, 4]$ b. $[6, 7]$ c. $[3, 5]$

66. $P(x) = 3x^4 - 6x^2 + 8x - 3$
    a. $[-2, -1]$ b. $[0, 1]$ c. $[3, 5]$

67. $P(x) = x^4 - 8x^3 + 25x^2 - 36x + 8$
    a. $[0, 1]$ b. $[-3, -1]$ c. $[3, 4]$

68. $P(x) = x^3 + 18x - 30$
    a. $[-2, 0]$ b. $[4, 6]$ c. $[1, 2]$

69. $P(x) = x^5 - 4x^3 - 5$
    a. $[1, 3]$ b. $[-1, 0]$ c. $[0, 1]$

70. $P(x) = x^5 + x^2 + 1$
    a. $[-2, 0]$ b. $[0, 1]$ c. $[2, 4]$

71. The average temperature for Cedar Rapids, Iowa, can be approximated by

    $$T(x) = -0.0568x^3 - 0.0073x^2 + 7.284x - 9.766$$

    where T is the temperature in degrees Celsius, and x is the number of months after January 1, and $0 \le x \le 12$.

    a. Explain what the zeros of the function represent in the context of the problem.

    b. Explain what the turning points represent in the context of the problem.

    Average Temperature in Cedar Rapids, IA

    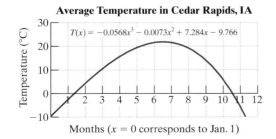

    Months ($x = 0$ corresponds to Jan. 1)

    Figure for Exercise 71

72. The average temperature for Kalamazoo, Michigan, can be approximated by

    $$T(x) = 0.0219x^4 - 0.545x^3 + 3.512x^2$$
    $$- 1.619x - 4.555$$

    where T is the temperature in degrees Celsius, and x is the number of months after January 1, and $0 \le x \le 12$.

    a. Explain what the zeros of the function represent in the context of the problem.

    b. Explain what the turning points represent in the context of the problem.

    Average Temperature for Kalamazoo, MI

    Months ($x = 0$ corresponds to Jan. 1)

    Figure for Exercise 72

73. The profit for a company can be approximated by $P(x) = -0.05x^2 + 20x - 100$, where x is the number of units produced and P is the profit in dollars.

    a. Explain what the zeros of the function represent in the context of the problem.

    b. Explain what the turning point represents in the context of the problem.

    Number of Units Produced

    Figure for Exercise 73

74. The profit for a company can be approximated by $P(x) = -0.2x^2 + 40x - 250$, where x is the number of units produced and P is the profit in dollars.

a. Explain what the zeros of the function represent in the context of the problem.

b. Explain what the turning point represents in the context of the problem.

Figure for Exercise 74

■ EXPANDING YOUR SKILLS

Recall from Section 11.1 that the graph of $y = a(x - h)^2 + k$, $(a \neq 0)$ is the graph of $y = x^2$ shifted $|h|$ units left or right, shifted $|k|$ units up or down, and stretched or shrunk vertically by a factor of $|a|$. Furthermore, the sign of a determines whether the parabola opens upward or downward. These same phenomena affect the graph of $y = a(x - h)^n + k$ where $a \neq 0$ and n is a positive integer. Use this fact to answer Exercises 75–78.

75. a. Sketch $f(x) = (x - 2)^2$

   b. Sketch $g(x) = (x - 2)^4$

76. a. Sketch $f(x) = -x^2 + 1$

   b. Sketch $g(x) = -x^3 + 1$

77. a. Sketch $f(x) = -(x + 3)^2 + 1$

   b. Sketch $g(x) = -(x + 3)^5 + 1$

78. a. Sketch $f(x) = \frac{1}{4}x^2$

   b. Sketch $g(x) = \frac{1}{4}x^6$

■ GRAPHING CALCULATOR EXERCISES

For Exercises 79–82,

   a. Show that the polynomial has a zero on the given interval.

   b. Use a graphing calculator to approximate the real zeros on the given interval. Round the answer to 4 decimal places.

79. $f(x) = 0.125x^3 + 2x + 4$ $[-2, -1]$

80. $g(x) = -x^5 + x^3 - 2$ $[-2, -1]$

81. $h(x) = -x^4 + 3x^3 - 4$ $[1, 2]$ and $[2, 3]$

82. $k(x) = x^4 + x^3 - 2x - 6$ $[-2, -1]$ and $[1, 2]$

For Exercises 83–86, use the table to determine the interval or intervals in which a zero of the polynomial $Y1 = f(x)$ is guaranteed.

83.

X	Y1
-2	17
-1	1.5
0	-5
1	-8.5
2	-3
3	29.5
4	119

X=-2

84.

X	Y1
-5	77
-4	17.2
-3	-5.8
-2	-8.8
-1	-3.8
0	2
1	6.2

X=-5

85.

X	Y1
-5	1
-4	-2.2
-3	-2.6
-2	-1.4
-1	.2
0	1
1	-.2

X=-5

86.

X	Y1
-4	-4.2
-3	-.1
-2	.6
-1	-.3
0	-1
1	.3
2	5.4

X=-4

section
12.4   GRAPHS OF RATIONAL FUNCTIONS

1.   Introduction to Horizontal, Vertical, and Slant Asymptotes

In Chapter 8, we were first introduced to rational functions and operations on rational expressions. In this section, the focus will be on graphing rational functions. The graph of $f(x) = \frac{1}{x}$, first introduced in Section 4.3, is shown in Figure 12-21.

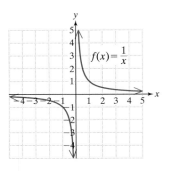

Figure 12-21

Notice that for values of x far to the right and far to the left, the function approaches the horizontal line $y = 0$. Mathematically, this may be written as follows:

Tip: In mathematics, the arrow $\rightarrow$ is translated as "approaches."

$f(x) \rightarrow 0$ as $x \rightarrow \infty$, which is read as "$f(x)$ approaches 0 as x approaches infinity."

$f(x) \rightarrow 0$ as $x \rightarrow -\infty$, read as "$f(x)$ approaches 0 as x approaches negative infinity."

If the far-left or far-right behavior of a function approaches a finite real number, a, as x approaches ∞ or $-\infty$, we say that the line $y = a$ is a **horizontal asymptote** of the function.

Notice that $f(x) = \frac{1}{x}$ also has interesting behavior for x values near 0. The function approaches infinity as x approaches 0 from the right-hand side. We may write this mathematically as

$$f(x) \rightarrow \infty \text{ as } x \rightarrow 0^{+}$$

Similarly, the function approaches negative infinity as x approaches 0 from the left-hand side. That is,

Tip: The notation $x \rightarrow c^{+}$ indicates that x approaches c from the *positive* direction. Thus x approaches c from the right-hand side. The notation $x \rightarrow c^{-}$ indicates that x approaches c from the *negative* direction. Thus, x approaches c from the left-hand side.

$$f(x) \rightarrow -\infty \text{ as } x \rightarrow 0^{-}$$

As a result of this behavior, we say that $f(x) = \frac{1}{x}$ has a vertical asymptote at $x = 0$.

In general, if a function approaches ∞ or $-\infty$ as x approaches a value c from either the left- or right-hand side, then the line $x = c$ is a **vertical asymptote** of the function (Figure 12-22).

Figure 12-22

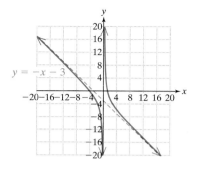

Figure 12-23

The last type of asymptote presented here is the slant asymptote. Loosely speaking, a **slant asymptote** is a line $y = mx + b$ ($m \neq 0$) that the function approaches as $x \to \infty$ or $x \to -\infty$ (Figure 12-23 and Figure 12-24).

2. Identifying the Horizontal Asymptote of a Rational Function

To find the horizontal asymptotes of a rational function, we must ask how the function behaves for large values of $|x|$. This can be accomplished by examining the degree of the numerator and degree of the denominator. As with polynomial functions, the leading terms of the numerator and denominator of a rational function define the far-left and far-right behavior.

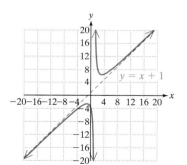

Figure 12-24

Determining the Horizontal Asymptotes of a Rational Function

Let

$$f(x) = \frac{a_n x^n + a_{n-1}x^{n-1} + \cdots + a_1 x + a_0}{b_m x^m + b_{m-1}x^{m-1} + \cdots + b_1 x + b_0}$$

define a rational function. Then,

1. If $n < m$ (i.e., if the degree of the numerator is less than the degree of the denominator), then the line $y = 0$ (the x-axis) is a horizontal asymptote of f.
2. If $n = m$ (i.e., if the degree of the numerator equals the degree of the denominator), then the line $y = \frac{a_n}{b_m}$ is a horizontal asymptote of f.
3. If $n > m$ (i.e., if the degree of the numerator is greater than the degree of the denominator), then f has no horizontal asymptote.

example 1

Finding the Horizontal Asymptotes of a Rational Function

Find the horizontal asymptotes of each function.

a. $f(x) = \dfrac{2x + 4}{x^2 + 1}$ b. $g(x) = \dfrac{3x^2 + 1}{2x^2}$ c. $h(x) = \dfrac{x^2 - 3x + 6}{x - 2}$

Figure 12-25

Figure 12-26

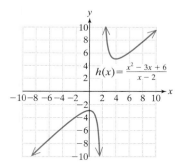

Figure 12-27

Solution:

a. $f(x) = \dfrac{2x + 4}{x^2 + 1}$

The degree of the numerator is 1, and the degree of the denominator is 2. Because the degree of the numerator is less than the degree of the denominator, the line $y = 0$ is a horizontal asymptote of the function (Figure 12-25).

b. $g(x) = \dfrac{3x^2 + 1}{2x^2}$

The degree of the numerator and the degree of the denominator are both equal to 2. Because the degrees are the same, the line $y = \frac{3}{2}$ is a horizontal asymptote of the function (Figure 12-26).

c. $h(x) = \dfrac{x^2 - 3x + 6}{x - 2}$

The degree of the numerator is 2, and the degree of the denominator is 1. Because the degree of the numerator is greater than the degree of the denominator, the function has no horizontal asymptote (Figure 12-27).

■

3. Identifying the Slant Asymptote of a Rational Function

From Figure 12-27 we might suspect that the graph of

$$h(x) = \frac{x^2 - 3x + 6}{x - 2}$$

has a slant asymptote. We offer the following rule to determine whether a rational function has a slant asymptote.

Slant Asymptotes

Consider a rational function defined by

$$f(x) = \frac{p(x)}{q(x)}$$

where $p(x)$ and $q(x)$ have no common factors other than 1 or -1. The function has a **slant asymptote** if the degree of $p(x)$ is one greater than the degree of $q(x)$.

To find the slant asymptote of a function, use division to express

$$f(x) = \frac{p(x)}{q(x)} \text{ in the form } f(x) = mx + b + \frac{r(x)}{q(x)}$$

where the degree of $r(x)$ is less than the degree of $q(x)$.

The expression

$$\frac{r(x)}{q(x)} \rightarrow 0 \text{ as } |x| \rightarrow \infty$$

because the degree of $q(x)$ is greater than the degree of $r(x)$. Hence, $f(x) \rightarrow mx + b$ as $|x| \rightarrow \infty$. The line $y = mx + b$ is called the **slant asymptote** of f.

example 2

Finding the Slant Asymptote of a Rational Function

Given

$$h(x) = \frac{x^2 - 3x + 6}{x - 2}$$

find the equation of the slant asymptote.

Solution:

The degree of the numerator is 2 and is exactly one greater than the degree of the denominator. Therefore, we know that the function has a slant asymptote. Using long division, we see that

$$\frac{x^2 - 3x + 6}{x - 2} = x - 1 + \frac{4}{x - 2}$$

$$\begin{array}{r} x - 1 \\ x - 2 \overline{)\ x^2 - 3x + 6} \\ \underline{-(x^2 - 2x)} \\ -x + 6 \\ \underline{-(-x + 2)} \\ 4 \end{array}$$

slant asymptote is
$y = x - 1$

Figure 12-28

The equation of the slant asymptote is $y = x - 1$ (Figure 12-28).

---

4. Identifying the Vertical Asymptotes of a Rational Function

To find the location of the vertical asymptotes of a rational function, reduce the function and then determine the values for which the denominator is zero.

Determining the Vertical Asymptotes of a Rational Function

Let

$$f(x) = \frac{p(x)}{q(x)}$$

define a rational function written in lowest terms. If the real number c is a zero of the denominator of f, then $x = c$ is a **vertical asymptote** of f.

example 3

Finding the Vertical Asymptotes of a Rational Function

Find the vertical asymptotes of

$$f(x) = \frac{x}{x^2 - 2x - 3}$$

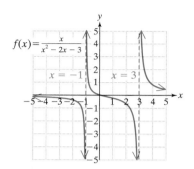

$f(x) = \frac{x}{x^2 - 2x - 3}$

Figure 12-29

Solution:

$$f(x) = \frac{x}{x^2 - 2x - 3}$$

$$= \frac{x}{(x - 3)(x + 1)} \qquad \text{The function is already written in lowest terms.}$$

The reduced function has vertical asymptotes where the denominator is zero. Therefore, the vertical asymptotes are $x = 3$ and $x = -1$ (Figure 12-29).

---

example 4

Finding the Vertical Asymptotes of a Rational Function

Find the vertical asymptotes of

$$g(x) = \frac{x + 3}{x^2 - 9}$$

Solution:

$$g(x) = \frac{x + 3}{x^2 - 9}$$

$$= \frac{x + 3}{(x + 3)(x - 3)} \qquad \text{Factor the function.}$$

$$= \frac{1}{x - 3}; (x \neq -3) \qquad \text{The function can be reduced.}$$

The function has a vertical asymptote at $x = 3$ (Figure 12-30).

Tip:

$$g(x) = \frac{x + 3}{(x + 3)(x - 3)}$$

is not defined for $x = 3$ or for $x = -3$. However, from the reduced form of the function, we see that the only vertical asymptote is $x = 3$. At $x = -3$, there is a "hole" in the graph because the function is still undefined at that point.

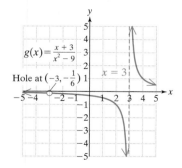

$g(x) = \frac{x + 3}{x^2 - 9}$

Hole at $\left(-3, -\frac{1}{6}\right)$

$x = 3$

Figure 12-30

example 5

Finding the Vertical Asymptotes of a Rational Function

Find the vertical asymptotes of

$$h(x) = \frac{-3}{x^2 + 1}$$

Solution:

Because $x^2 \geq 0$ for all real numbers, x, then $x^2 + 1 > 0$. Because the denominator is never equal to zero, this function has no vertical asymptotes (Figure 12-31).

■

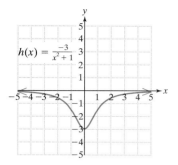

$h(x) = \frac{-3}{x^2 + 1}$

Figure 12-31

5. Graphing Rational Functions

Identifying the horizontal, vertical, and slant asymptotes of a rational function is one of the key steps in graphing a rational function. We will also identify the x- and y-intercepts of the function and the points (if any) where a function intersects its horizontal asymptote. The following guidelines are helpful in graphing a rational function.

Graphing a Rational Function

Let $f(x) = \frac{p(x)}{q(x)}$ define a rational function in lowest terms. To sketch its graph, use the following steps.

1. Find any vertical asymptotes.
2. Find any horizontal or slant asymptotes.
3. Find any x-intercepts.
4. Find the y-intercept.
5. Determine if the function intersects its horizontal asymptote, $y = a$, by solving the equation $f(x) = a$.
6. Sketch the features found in steps 1–5. Draw the asymptotes as dashed lines.
7. Evaluate the function at test points to the left and right of the vertical asymptotes, x-intercepts, and points where the function intersects the horizontal asymptote.
8. Complete the sketch.

example 6

Graphing a Rational Function

Graph

$$f(x) = \frac{x + 4}{2x^2 + x - 6}$$

Solution:

$$f(x) = \frac{x + 4}{2x^2 + x - 6} = \frac{x + 4}{(2x - 3)(x + 2)} \qquad \text{Factor the function.}$$

Step 1: The vertical asymptotes are $x = \frac{3}{2}$ and $x = -2$.

Step 2: Because the degree of the numerator is less than the degree of the denominator, the function has a horizontal asymptote at $y = 0$.

Step 3: The x-intercepts are the real solutions to

$$\frac{x + 4}{(2x - 3)(x + 2)} = 0$$

or equivalently $x + 4 = 0$.
The x-intercept is $(-4, 0)$.

Step 4: The y-intercept is given by

$$f(0) = \frac{(0) + 4}{2(0)^2 + (0) - 6} = -\frac{2}{3}$$

The y-intercept is $(0, -\frac{2}{3})$.

Step 5: The function crosses its horizontal asymptote at the x-intercept $(-4, 0)$.

Step 6: The function has the following features.

Step 7: Select test points to the left and right of the x-intercept, and vertical asymptotes to determine the behavior of the function on the intervals $(-\infty, -4)$, $(-4, -2)$, $(-2, \frac{3}{2})$, and $(\frac{3}{2}, \infty)$.

Test: $x = -5$

$$f(-5) = \frac{-5 + 4}{2(-5)^2 + (-5) - 6}$$

$$= -\frac{1}{39}$$

Test: $x = -3$

$$f(-3) = \frac{-3 + 4}{2(-3)^2 + (-3) - 6}$$

$$= \frac{1}{9}$$

Test: $x = 0$

From the y-intercept, we know $f(0) = -\frac{2}{3}$

Test: $x = 2$

$$f(2) = \frac{2 + 4}{2(2)^2 + (2) - 6} = \frac{3}{2}$$

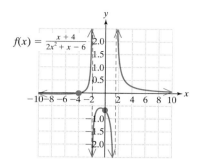

$$f(x) = \frac{x+4}{2x^2+x-6}$$

Figure 12-32

Step 8:   Complete the sketch (Figure 12-32).

On the interval $(-\infty, -4)$ the function is negative (below the x-axis). However, we know the function must approach its horizontal asymptote as $x \to -\infty$.

On the interval $(-4, -2)$, the function is positive and as $x \to -2^-$, the function must approach positive infinity.

On the interval $(-2, \frac{3}{2})$, the function is negative. Therefore, as $x \to -2^+$ the function must approach negative infinity. As $x \to \frac{3}{2}^-$, the function must approach negative infinity.

On the interval $(\frac{3}{2}, \infty)$, the function is positive. Therefore, as $x \to \frac{3}{2}^+$, the function must approach positive infinity. As $x \to \infty$, the function must approach its horizontal asymptote.

example 7

Graphing a Rational Function

Graph

$$g(x) = \frac{3x^2 - 3}{x^2 + 4x + 4}$$

Solution:

$$g(x) = \frac{3x^2 - 3}{x^2 + 4x + 4} = \frac{3(x-1)(x+1)}{(x+2)^2} \qquad \text{Factor the function.}$$

Step 1:   The vertical asymptote is $x = -2$.

Step 2:   The numerator and denominator have the same degree. The horizontal asymptote is $y = 3$.

Step 3:   The x-intercepts are the real solutions to

$$\frac{3(x-1)(x+1)}{(x+2)^2} = 0$$

or equivalently, $3(x-1)(x+1) = 0$. The x-intercepts are $(1, 0)$ and $(-1, 0)$.

Step 4:   The y-intercept is given by

$$g(0) = \frac{3(0)^2 - 3}{(0)^2 + 4(0) + 4} = -\frac{3}{4}$$

The y-intercept is $(0, -\frac{3}{4})$.

Step 5:   The values of x for which the function intersects its horizontal asymptote are the real solutions to the equation

$$\frac{3x^2 - 3}{x^2 + 4x + 4} = 3$$

$$3x^2 - 3 = 3(x^2 + 4x + 4)$$

$$x^2 - 1 = x^2 + 4x + 4 \qquad \text{Divide both sides by 3.}$$

$$-1 = 4x + 4 \qquad \text{Subtract } x^2 \text{ from both sides.}$$

$$-5 = 4x \qquad \text{Subtract 4 from both sides.}$$

$$x = -\frac{5}{4}, \text{ or } -1.25 \qquad \text{Divide by 4 on both sides.}$$

The function intersects its horizontal asymptote at $(-\frac{5}{4}, 3)$.

Step 6:   The graph has the following features.

Step 7:   Use test points to determine the behavior of the function on the intervals $(-\infty, -2)$, $(-2, -1.25)$, $(-1.25, -1)$, $(-1, 1)$, and $(1, \infty)$.

$g(-3) = 24$ The function is above its horizontal asymptote on the interval $(-\infty, -2)$.

$g(-1.5) = 15$ The function is above its horizontal asymptote on the interval $(-2, -1.25)$.

$g(-1.1) = \dfrac{7}{9}$ The function is between its horizontal asymptote and the x-axis on the interval $(-1.25, -1)$.

$g(0) = -\dfrac{3}{4}$ The function is below the x-axis on the interval $(-1, 1)$.

$g(2) = \dfrac{9}{16}$ The function is between the x-axis and the horizontal asymptote on the interval $(1, \infty)$.

Figure 12-33

Step 8:   Complete the graph (Figure 12-33).

---

example 8   **Graphing a Rational Function**

Graph

$$h(x) = \frac{x^2 - 3x + 6}{x - 2}$$

Solution:

Step 1: $h(x) = \dfrac{x^2 - 3x + 6}{x - 2}$

has a vertical asymptote of $x = 2$.

Step 2: Because the degree of the numerator is exactly 1 greater than the degree of the denominator, there is a slant asymptote. From Example 2, the equation of the slant asymptote is $y = x - 1$.

Step 3: The x-intercepts are the real solutions to the equation

$$\frac{x^2 - 3x + 6}{x - 2} = 0$$

or equivalently, $x^2 - 3x + 6 = 0$. Using the quadratic formula, we have,

$$x = \frac{-(-3) \pm \sqrt{(-3)^2 - 4(1)(6)}}{2(1)} = \frac{3 \pm i\sqrt{15}}{2}$$

The values of x are imaginary indicating that there are no x-intercepts for this function.

Step 4: The y-intercept is given by

$$h(0) = \frac{(0)^2 - 3(0) + 6}{(0) - 2} = -3$$

The y-intercept is $(0, -3)$.

Step 5: The function has no horizontal asymptotes to intersect.

Step 6: The function has the following characteristics.

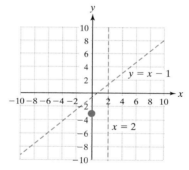

Step 7: Use test points to determine the behavior of the function on the intervals $(-\infty, 2)$ and $(2, \infty)$.

$h(0) = -3$ The function is below its slant asymptote on the interval $(-\infty, 2)$. As $x \rightarrow 2^-$, the function must approach $-\infty$.

$h(3) = 6$ The function is above its slant asymptote on the interval $(2, \infty)$. As $x \rightarrow 2^+$, the function must approach ∞.

Step 8: Complete the graph (Figure 12-34).

$h(x) = \dfrac{x^2 - 3x + 6}{x - 2}$

Figure 12-34

---

section 12.4   PRACTICE EXERCISES

For Exercises 1–12, find the x- and y-intercepts (if they exist).

1. $y = x^3 + 3x^2 - 2x - 6$

2. $y = x^3 - x^2 - 4x + 4$

3. $y = 3x^4 - 4x^3 + x^2 + 6x - 2$

4. $y = x^4 - 3x^3 + 4x^2 - 6x + 4$

5. $y = x^2 + 6x + 10$

6. $y = -x^2 + 8x - 20$

7. $y = \dfrac{2x - 6}{x^2 + x + 3}$

8. $y = \dfrac{x - 4}{x^2 + 2x - 8}$

9. $y = \dfrac{3x}{x^2 - 4x + 2}$

10. $y = \dfrac{-2x}{x^3 + x - 4}$

11. $y = \dfrac{1}{2x - 7}$

12. $y = \dfrac{3}{x - 10}$

13. Translate the expression $g(x) \to 0$ as $x \to \infty$. What type of asymptote does this define (vertical or horizontal)?

14. Translate the expression $f(x) \to 5$ as $x \to \infty$. What type of asymptote does this define (vertical or horizontal)?

15. Translate the expression $h(x) \to \infty$ as $x \to 3^+$. What type of asymptote does this define (vertical or horizontal)?

16. Translate the expression $k(x) \to \infty$ as $x \to 2^+$. What type of asymptote does this define (vertical or horizontal)?

For Exercises 17–20, find the horizontal asymptote and match the equation with one of the following graphs.

17. $f(x) = \dfrac{x + 1}{x - 2}$

18. $P(x) = \dfrac{3x - 2}{x + 1}$

19. $q(x) = \dfrac{-2x - 1}{x + 1}$

20. $h(x) = \dfrac{-4x + 1}{x}$

a.

b.

c.

d.

For Exercises 21–24, find the slant asymptote and match the equation with one of the following graphs.

21. $T(x) = \dfrac{3x^2 + 1}{x}$

22. $g(x) = \dfrac{x^2 - 3x - 4}{x - 2}$

23. $w(x) = \dfrac{-x^2 + 5}{x + 1}$

24. $M(x) = \dfrac{-x^2 + 3}{x}$

a.

b.

c.

d.

For Exercises 25–34, determine the horizontal or slant asymptote for each function.

25. $f(x) = \dfrac{1}{x^2 - 3}$

26. $f(x) = \dfrac{2}{x^2 + x + 1}$

27. $f(x) = \dfrac{-3x}{x + 6}$

28. $f(x) = \dfrac{2x}{x - 5}$

29. $f(x) = \dfrac{1 - x}{2x + 3}$

30. $f(x) = \dfrac{3 - x}{x + 4}$

31. $f(x) = \dfrac{x^3 + 3}{x^2}$

32. $f(x) = \dfrac{3x^2 + x + 1}{x}$

33. $f(x) = \dfrac{3x^2 - 4x + 1}{4x^2 + 2x - 5}$

34. $f(x) = \dfrac{x^2 - 2x - 3}{2x^2 - x + 9}$

For Exercises 35–38, find the vertical asymptote(s) and match the equation with one of the following graphs.

35. $g(x) = \dfrac{1}{x^2 + 2x + 1}$

36. $h(x) = \dfrac{3}{x^2 - 4x + 4}$

37. $k(x) = \dfrac{-5}{x^2 - 4}$

38. $p(x) = \dfrac{-1}{x^2 - 1}$

a.

b.

c.

d.

For Exercises 39–48, determine the vertical asymptote(s) associated with each function.

39. $f(x) = \dfrac{x}{x + 4}$

40. $f(x) = \dfrac{x}{x - 2}$

41. $f(x) = \dfrac{x - 2}{(x - 1)(x + 5)}$

42. $f(x) = \dfrac{x + 4}{(x + 7)(x - 3)}$

43. $f(x) = \dfrac{x + 3}{(x - 2)(x + 3)}$

44. $f(x) = \dfrac{x - 4}{(x - 4)(x + 1)}$

45. $f(x) = \dfrac{x^2 + x + 4}{x^2 + 16}$

46. $f(x) = \dfrac{x^2 + 7}{x^2 + 4}$

47. $f(x) = \dfrac{x^2 - x - 2}{x^2 - 5x + 6}$

48. $f(x) = \dfrac{2x^2 - 3x - 2}{x^2 + 2x - 8}$

49. List the steps for graphing a rational function.

50. Do all graphs of rational functions have a horizontal asymptote? Explain why or why not.

For Exercises 51–66, graph the function using the steps provided on page 863 of the text.

51. $f(x) = \dfrac{1}{x + 2}$

52. $f(x) = \dfrac{1}{x - 2}$

53. $g(x) = \dfrac{x}{x - 1}$

54. $h(x) = \dfrac{x}{x + 1}$

55. $p(x) = \dfrac{3}{x}$

56. $q(x) = -\dfrac{3}{x}$

57. $b(x) = \dfrac{2}{x^2 - 9}$

58. $d(x) = \dfrac{1}{x^2 - 4}$

59. $m(x) = \dfrac{x + 3}{2x - 2}$

60. $n(x) = \dfrac{-x + 2}{2x + 1}$

61. $f(x) = \dfrac{x^3 - 1}{x^2}$

62. $g(x) = \dfrac{x^3 + 1}{x^2}$

63. $k(x) = \dfrac{x^2 - 2x - 3}{x^2 - 2x + 1}$

64. $L(x) = \dfrac{x^2 + x - 6}{x^2 + 3x - 4}$

65. $P(x) = \dfrac{-1}{x^2 + x - 6}$

66. $Q(x) = \dfrac{1}{x^2 - x - 2}$

EXPANDING YOUR SKILLS

For Exercises 67–70, graph the rational functions.

67. $h(x) = \dfrac{x^2 - 9}{x - 3}$

68. $M(x) = \dfrac{2x^2 - 8}{x + 2}$

69. $k(x) = \dfrac{x^3 + x^2}{x + 1}$

70. $N(x) = \dfrac{2x^3 + 8x^2}{x + 4}$

chapter 12 SUMMARY

SECTION 12.1—REMAINDER THEOREM AND FACTOR THEOREM

KEY CONCEPTS:

A zero of a polynomial is a value, c, such that $P(c) = 0$.

The Remainder Theorem
If the polynomial $P(x)$ is divided by $(x - c)$, the remainder is $P(c)$.

The Factor Theorem
The polynomial $(x - c)$ is a factor of the polynomial $P(x)$ if and only if $P(c) = 0$.

KEY TERMS:

factor theorem
remainder theorem
root of a polynomial
zero of a polynomial

EXAMPLES:

Find the zeros of the polynomial
$P(x) = x(3x + 2)(x - 9)(x + 2)$

$$x = 0, \quad 3x + 2 = 0, \quad x - 9 = 0, \quad x + 2 = 0$$

$$\text{Zeros are } x = 0, x = -\frac{2}{3}, x = 9, x = -2$$

For $P(x) = x^3 - 4x^2 + x - 5$, find $P(6)$ using the remainder theorem.

$$
\begin{array}{r|rrrr}
6 & 1 & -4 & 1 & -5 \\
  &   & 6 & 12 & 78 \\
\hline
  & 1 & 2 & 13 & \underline{|73} \\
\end{array}
$$

$P(6) = 73$

Is $(x - 2)$ a factor of
$P(x) = 2x^3 + x^2 - 13x + 6$?

$$
\begin{array}{r|rrrr}
2 & 2 & 1 & -13 & 6 \\
  &   & 4 & 10 & -6 \\
\hline
  & 2 & 5 & -3 & \underline{|0} \\
\end{array}
$$

Because $P(2) = 0$, $(x - 2)$ is a factor of $P(x)$.

SECTION 12.2—ZEROS OF POLYNOMIALS

KEY CONCEPTS:

The Fundamental Theorem of Algebra
Every polynomial of degree 1 or more has at least one complex zero.

Number of Zeros of a Polynomial
A polynomial of degree n has at most n distinct zeros.
    If a factor $(x - c)$ is repeated m times in a polynomial, then the zero, c, has a multiplicity of m.

EXAMPLE:

Find the zeros of $P(x) = x^2(x - 3)(x + 5)^3$ and state their multiplicities.

Zeros are   0 of multiplicity 2,

3 of multiplicity 1,

−5 of multiplicity 3.

The Rational Zero Theorem

Let $P(x) = a_n x^n + a_{n-1} x^{n-1} + \cdots + a_1 x + a_0$

($a_n \neq 0$) be a polynomial function with integer coefficients. If $\frac{c}{d}$ is a rational number written in lowest terms, and if $\frac{c}{d}$ is a zero of $P(x)$, then c is a factor of a_0 and d is a factor of a_n.

The Conjugate Zero Theorem

If an imaginary number $a + bi$ is a zero of a polynomial, $P(x)$, where $P(x)$ has real coefficients, then the conjugate, $a - bi$, is also a zero of the polynomial.

List all possible rational zeros of
$$f(x) = 3x^4 - 2x^3 + 8x^2 + 3x - 4$$

$c = \pm 1, \pm 2, \pm 4$ and $d = \pm 1, \pm 3$, therefore,

$$\frac{c}{d} = \pm 1, \pm\frac{1}{3}, \pm 2, \pm\frac{2}{3}, \pm 4, \pm\frac{4}{3}$$

Find all zeros of $h(x) = 2x^3 - 3x^2 + 8x - 12$
given that $x = 2i$ **is a zero.**

$$
\begin{array}{r|rrrr}
2i & 2 & -3 & 8 & -12 \\
   &   & 4i & -8-6i & 12 \\
\hline
   & 2 & -3+4i & -6i & \underline{|0}
\end{array}
$$

$$
\begin{array}{r|rrr}
-2i & 2 & -3+4i & -6i \\
    &   & -4i & 6i \\
\hline
    & 2 & -3 & \underline{|0}
\end{array}
$$

$$2x - 3 = 0$$
$$x = \frac{3}{2}$$

The zeros are $2i$, $-2i$, and $\frac{3}{2}$.

Descartes' Rule of Signs

Let $P(x)$ be a polynomial with real coefficients and a nonzero constant term.

The number of positive real zeros of $P(x)$ is either:

1. The same as the number of sign changes in $P(x)$ or
2. Less than the number of sign changes in $P(x)$ by a positive even integer.

The number of negative real zeros of $P(x)$ is either:

3. The same as the number of sign changes in $P(-x)$ or
4. Less than the number of sign changes in $P(-x)$ by a positive even integer.

A zero of multiplicity m must be counted m times.

Upper and Lower Bounds for Real Zeros of Polynomials

Let $P(x)$ be a polynomial of degree $n \geq 1$ with real coefficients and a positive leading coefficient. Further suppose that $P(x)$ is divided by $(x - c)$.
1. If $c > 0$ and all coefficients of the quotient are nonnegative, and the remainder is nonnegative, then c is an upper bound to the zeros of $P(x)$.

Determine the possible number of positive and negative zeros for

$$P(x) = 3x^4 - 5x^3 - x^2 + 2x - 5$$

The number of sign changes in $P(x)$ is 3. Therefore, there are 3 or 1 positive real zeros.

$$P(-x) = 3x^4 + 5x^3 - x^2 - 2x - 5$$

The number of sign changes of $P(-x)$ is 1. Therefore, there is one negative zero.

Find all the zeros of
$$P(x) = 4x^5 - 18x^4 + 24x^3 - 7x^2 - 4x + 4$$
The possible rational zeros are

$$\pm 1, \pm\frac{1}{2}, \pm\frac{1}{4}, \pm 2, \pm 4$$

$$
\begin{array}{r|rrrrrr}
-\frac{1}{2} & 4 & -18 & 24 & -7 & -4 & 4 \\
             &   & -2 & 10 & -17 & 12 & -4 \\
\hline
             & 4 & -20 & 34 & -24 & 8 & \underline{|0}
\end{array}
$$

2. If $c < 0$ and the coefficients of the quotient and remainder are alternately positive and negative (with 0 being considered either positive or negative), then c is a lower bound to the zeros of $P(x)$.

KEY TERMS:

conjugate zero theorem
Descartes' rule of signs
fundamental theorem of algebra
lower bound
multiplicity
rational zero theorem
upper bound

Alternate signs indicate that $-\frac{1}{2}$ is a lower bound.

$$
\begin{array}{r|rrrrr}
2 & 4 & -20 & 34 & -24 & 8 \\
  &   & 8 & -24 & 20 & -8 \\
\hline
  & 4 & -12 & 10 & -4 & \underline{|0}
\end{array}
$$

$$
\begin{array}{r|rrrr}
2 & 4 & -12 & 10 & -4 \\
  &   & 8 & -8 & 4 \\
\hline
  & 4 & -4 & 2 & \underline{|0}
\end{array}
$$

To find the remaining zeros, solve $4x^2 - 4x + 2 = 0$. The quadratic formula gives $x = \frac{1}{2} \pm \frac{1}{2}i$.

Therefore, the zeros are $-\frac{1}{2}, 2$ (of multiplicity 2), and $\frac{1}{2} \pm \frac{1}{2}i$.

SECTION 12.3—GRAPHS OF POLYNOMIAL FUNCTIONS

KEY CONCEPTS:

The graph of a polynomial function defined by

$$P(x) = a_n x^n + a_{n-1} x^{n-1} + \cdots + a_1 x + a_0$$

has the following far-right and far-left behavior:

1. If n is even and a_n is positive, then $y = P(x)$ is up to the left and up to the right.
2. If n is even and a_n is negative, then $y = P(x)$ is down to the left and down to the right.
3. If n is odd and a_n is positive, then $y = P(x)$ is down to the left and up to the right.
4. If n is odd and a_n is negative, then $y = P(x)$ is up to the left and down to the right.

Graph a polynomial function by determining the far-left and far-right behavior and locating zeros of the function.

EXAMPLES:

Determine the far-right and far-left behavior of the graphs of the following polynomials:

$$P(x) = -3x^4 + 4x^2 - 9$$

n is even and a_n is negative. Therefore, $P(x)$ is down to the left and down to the right.

$$Q(x) = -x^5 - 2x^4 + 6x^3 + x^2 - 1$$

n is odd and a_n is negative. Therefore, $Q(x)$ is up to the left and down to the right.

Sketch $P(x) = x^3 - x^2 - 3x + 3$

Factoring by grouping yields:

$$P(x) = (x - 1)(x^2 - 3)$$

Zeros are 1 and $\pm\sqrt{3}$.

Graph is down to the left and up to the right.

Now sketch the graph.

$$P(x) = x^3 - x^2 - 3x + 3$$

The Zero Location Theorem
Let f be a polynomial function with real coefficients. For real numbers a and b, if $f(a)$ and $f(b)$ have opposite signs, then there exists at least one real zero of f between a and b.

KEY TERMS:

continuous
discontinuous
far-left behavior
far-right behavior
intermediate value theorem
turning point
zero location theorem

Determine the interval(s) on which the zero location theorem guarantees the existence of a zero.

$$f(x) = 2x^3 - 7x^2 - 8$$

a. $[-2, 0]$ b. $[0, 5]$

$$f(-2) = -52$$

$$f(0) = -8$$

$$f(5) = 67$$

Because $f(0)$ and $f(5)$ have opposite signs, there exists at least one zero on the interval $[0, 5]$.

SECTION 12.4—GRAPHS OF RATIONAL FUNCTIONS

KEY CONCEPTS:

The line $y = a$ is a horizontal asymptote of a function f, if $f(x) \rightarrow a$ as $x \rightarrow \pm\infty$.

Use the following steps to determine the horizontal asymptote of a rational function defined by,

$$f(x) = \frac{a_n x^n + a_{n-1} x^{n-1} + \cdots + a_1 x + a_0}{b_m x^m + b_{m-1} x^{m-1} + \cdots + b_1 x + b_0}$$

1. If $n < m$, then the line $y = 0$ (the x-axis) is a horizontal asymptote of f.
2. If $n = m$, then the line

$$y = \frac{a_n}{b_m}$$

is a horizontal asymptote of f.
3. If $n > m$, then f has no horizontal asymptotes.

EXAMPLES:

Find the horizontal asymptote of

$$f(x) = \frac{4x + 1}{2x - 2}$$

Because $n = m$ the horizontal asymptote is

$$y = \frac{a_n}{b_m} = \frac{4}{2} = 2$$

The line $x = c$ is a vertical asymptote of f if $f(x) \to \pm\infty$ as $x \to c^+$ or if $f(x) \to \pm\infty$ as $x \to c^-$.

To find the vertical asymptotes of a rational function, first write the function in lowest terms

$$f(x) = \frac{p(x)}{q(x)}$$

If the real number c is a zero of the denominator of f, then $x = c$ is a vertical asymptote of f.

A rational function defined by $f(x) = \dfrac{p(x)}{q(x)}$, where $p(x)$ and $q(x)$ have no common factors other than 1 or -1, has a slant asymptote if the degree of $p(x)$ is one greater than the degree of $q(x)$.

To find the slant asymptote of f, use division to express

$$f(x) = \frac{p(x)}{q(x)} \quad \text{in the form}$$

$$f(x) = mx + b + \frac{r(x)}{q(x)}$$

where the degree of $r(x)$ is less than the degree of $q(x)$. Then the line $y = mx + b$ is the slant asymptote.

Sketching a Rational Function

Let

$$f(x) = \frac{p(x)}{q(x)}$$

define a rational function in lowest terms. To sketch its graph, use the following steps.

1. Find any vertical asymptotes.
2. Find any horizontal or slant asymptotes.
3. Find any x-intercepts.
4. Find the y-intercept.
5. Determine if the function intersects its horizontal asymptote, $y = a$, by solving the equation $f(x) = a$.
6. Sketch the features found in steps 1–5. Draw the asymptotes as dashed lines.

Find the vertical asymptote(s) of

$$f(x) = \frac{x + 1}{(x - 2)(x + 2)}$$

$(x - 2)(x + 2) = 0$ when $x = 2$ or $x = -2$

Therefore the vertical asymptotes are $x = 2$ and $x = -2$.

Find the slant asymptote of

$$f(x) = \frac{x^2 - 2x + 3}{x - 1}$$

$$\begin{array}{r} 1| \quad 1 \quad -2 \quad \quad 3 \\ \quad \quad \quad \quad 1 \quad -1 \\ \hline 1 \quad -1 \quad |\underline{2} \\ \end{array}$$

$$f(x) = x - 1 + \frac{2}{x - 1}$$

therefore, the slant asymptote is $y = x - 1$.

Graph $f(x) = \dfrac{-3x}{4x + 4}$

1. $x = -1$ Vertical asymptote

2. $y = -\dfrac{3}{4}$ Horizontal asymptote

7. Evaluate the function at test points to the left and right of the vertical asymptotes, x-intercepts, and points where the function intersects the horizontal asymptote.

8. Complete the sketch.

KEY TERMS:

horizontal asymptote
slant asymptote
vertical asymptote

3. $x = 0$ $(0, 0)$ x-intercept

4. $y = 0$ $(0, 0)$ y-intercept

5. $\dfrac{-3x}{4x + 4} = -\dfrac{3}{4}$

$$-12x = -12x - 12$$

$$0 = -12$$ The graph of f does not cross the horizontal asymptote.

6.

7. Test points are $(-4, -1)$, $(-\frac{1}{2}, \frac{3}{4})$, and $(2, -\frac{1}{2})$.

---

chapter 12   REVIEW EXERCISES

Section 12.1

For Exercises 1–6, find the zeros of the polynomial by solving the equation $P(x) = 0$.

1. $P(x) = (x - 9)(x + 2)$

2. $P(x) = (4x - 1)(x - 11)$

3. $P(x) = x^2 - 2x - 35$

4. $P(x) = 3x^2 + 18x$

5. $P(x) = (x - (4 + i))(x + (4 - i))$

6. $P(x) = (x - 9i)(x + 9i)$

7. Explain the remainder theorem.

8. How can you check your results from using the remainder theorem?

For Exercises 9–10, find the indicated function value for the given polynomial functions using the remainder theorem.

9. $k(x) = x^4 - 7x^3 - 4x^2 + 52x + 48$
   a. $k(-3)$ b. $k(2)$ c. $k(4)$ d. $k(5)$

10. $h(t) = -3t^3 - 7t^2 + 22t + 8$
    a. $h(3)$ b. $h(-4)$ c. $h\left(-\dfrac{1}{3}\right)$ d. $h(-5)$

11. Explain how the use of synthetic division can determine if a value of c is a zero of a polynomial, $P(x)$.

For Exercises 12–15, determine if the given value is a zero of the polynomial.

12. $P(x) = x^3 - 2x^2 - 7x + 12$; $x = 3$

13. $P(x) = 2x^4 + 7x^3 - 4x^2 - 27x - 18$; $x = -3$

14. $P(x) = x^5 + 2x^4 - 37x^3 - 74x^2 + 36x + 72$; $x = 6$

15. $P(x) = 5x^3 - 16x^2 + 8; \ x = 4$

16. Explain how the use of synthetic division can determine if a polynomial of the form $(x - c)$ is a factor of another polynomial, $P(x)$.

For Exercises 17–20, determine if the second polynomial is a factor of the first.

17. $x^4 + 5x^3 + 6x^2 - x - 2; (x + 2)$

18. $x^3 - 13x^2 + 52x - 70; (x - (3 - i))$

19. $4x^4 - 9x^2 + 8x - 18; (x - 2)$

20. $3x^3 - 5x^2 - x + 2; \left(x - \dfrac{2}{3}\right)$

For Exercises 21–24, find a polynomial with the given zeros. (Answers may vary.)

21. $x = 3, x = 9$

22. $x = \sqrt{5}, x = -\sqrt{5}$

23. $x = 5i, x = -5i, x = 0$

24. $x = 2, x = -4, x = 0$

Section 12.2

For Exercises 25–26, state the zeros and their multiplicities for each polynomial.

25. $P(x) = 6(x - 8)^3(2x + 5)^2$

26. $P(x) = x^4(3x - 2)(x + 4)^3$

For Exercises 27–30, find a polynomial, $F(x)$, with real coefficients that satisfies the following conditions.

27. Degree 3
Zero of 2 (multiplicity 1)
Zero of -3 (multiplicity 2)
$F(-2) = 24$

28. Degree 3
Zeros 1, -1, and 6
Function passes through $(2, -24)$

29. Lowest degree
Zeros 3 and $-i$
Function passes through $(0, 16)$

30. Lowest degree
Zeros $1 + 2i$ and $3i$
$F(0) = -45$

31. Explain how to use the rational zero theorem and synthetic division to find the rational zeros of a polynomial with rational coefficients.

For Exercises 32–33, use the rational zero theorem to list all possible rational zeros.

32. $Q(x) = 8x^3 + 7x^2 - 2x + 6$

33. $Q(x) = 15x^4 - 12x^3 + 8x^2 + 2x - 5$

34. Explain how Descartes' rule of signs can determine the possible number of positive zeros of a polynomial with real coefficients and a nonzero constant term.

For Exercises 35–36, use Descartes' rule of signs to determine the possible number of positive and negative zeros of the function.

35. $f(x) = x^5 - 7x^4 + x^3 + 2x^2 - 5$

36. $f(x) = 12x^4 + 3x^3 + x^2 + 10$

For Exercises 37–42, determine if the given number represents an upper bound or lower bound.

37. $P(x) = x^3 - 2x^2 + 3x - 8; \ x = 3$

38. $P(x) = x^3 - 3x^2 - 4x + 1; \ x = 4$

39. $P(x) = x^3 - 2x^2 + 3x - 8; \ x = -1$

40. $P(x) = x^3 - 3x^2 - 4x + 1; \ x = -2$

41. $P(x) = x^4 - 5x^2 + 7x - 22; \ x = 2$

42. $P(x) = x^4 - 5x^2 + 7x - 22; \ x = -1$

For Exercises 43–48, find all of the zeros of the polynomial. State the multiplicity of the zero if it is greater than 1.

43. $F(x) = 6x^3 + 19x^2 + 11x - 6$

44. $F(x) = x^3 - 4x^2 + 2x + 4$

45. $F(x) = x^4 - 2x^3 - 11x^2 + 12x + 36$

46. $F(x) = x^4 + 2x^3 - 10x^2 - 18x + 9$

47. $F(x) = x^4 - 11x^2 + 12x + 4$

48. $F(x) = 2x^4 - 7x^3 + 14x^2 - 63x - 36$

Section 12.3

For Exercises 49–56, determine the far-right and far-left behavior for the graph of the polynomial.

49. $P(x) = x^3 - 3x + 2$

50. $P(x) = -2x^3 + 7x^2 + x - 9$

51. $P(x) = -4x^4 + 3x^3 - x^2 + 10x - 3$

52. $P(x) = x^4 - 9x^3 + x + 11$

53. $P(x) = 3 + 8x^2 - 2x^4 + 6x^6$

54. $P(x) = -9 + 3x + 2x^2 - 3x^4$

55. $P(x) = 3x(8 - x)(4x + 3)$

56. $P(x) = x^2(5x - 8)$

For Exercises 57–60, determine if the graph is continuous or discontinuous.

57.

58.

59.

60.

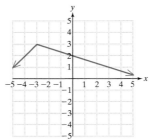

For Exercises 61–66, sketch the function by finding the x- and y-intercepts and determining the far-right and far-left behavior.

61. $k(x) = \dfrac{1}{2}x(x + 3)(x - 2)$

62. $f(x) = -x^2(x - 3)$

63. $g(x) = x^4 + 3x^2 + 2$

64. $h(x) = -x^4 + 2x^2 - 1$

65. $p(x) = x^3 + 9x^2 + 24x + 16$

66. $q(x) = x^3 - 3x^2 + 4$

For Exercises 67–70, use the zero location theorem to verify the existence of a zero on the given interval.

67. $f(x) = x^4 - 8x^3 + 25x^2 - 36x + 8; [0, 1]$

68. $g(x) = x^3 - 27x - 90; [6, 7]$

69. $q(x) = x^3 - 2x - 20; [2, 3]$

70. $p(x) = 3x^4 - 6x^2 + 8x - 3; [-2, -1]$

71. The average temperature for Grand Forks, North Dakota, can be approximated by $T(x) = 0.0207x^4 - 0.5137x^3 + 2.978x^2 + 2.368x - 17.0325$ where T is the temperature in degrees Celsius, and x is the number of months after January 1, and $0 \le x \le 12$.

a. Explain what the zeros of the function represent in the context of the problem.

b. Explain what the turning points represent in the context of the problem.

Average Temperature in Grand Forks, ND

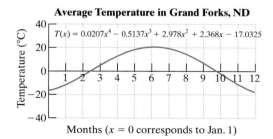

$T(x) = 0.0207x^4 - 0.5137x^3 + 2.978x^2 + 2.368x - 17.0325$

Months ($x = 0$ corresponds to Jan. 1)

Figure for Exercise 71

Section 12.4

72. Explain how to find the horizontal asymptote of a rational function.

For Exercises 73–78, find the horizontal asymptotes.

73. $f(x) = \dfrac{2x^2 + 6x}{-2x^3 + 6}$

74. $f(x) = \dfrac{5x^2 + 4x + 9}{x^4 - x^2 + 1}$

75. $f(x) = \dfrac{3x + 5}{6x - 8}$

76. $f(x) = \dfrac{2x^2 - 7}{-3x^2 + x}$

77. $f(x) = \dfrac{1 + x - 3x^3}{3x^3 + 4x - 2}$

78. $f(x) = \dfrac{-4 + x + 2x^2}{2x^2 + 7x - 13}$

79. Explain how to determine if a rational function has a horizontal or slant asymptote.

For Exercises 80–83, determine the slant asymptote for each function.

80. $g(x) = \dfrac{4x^2 - 9}{x + 3}$

81. $g(x) = \dfrac{x^3 - 1}{x^2}$

82. $g(x) = \dfrac{x^3 - 4x - 5}{x^2 - 1}$

83. $g(x) = \dfrac{2x^2 + 5x + 3}{x - 4}$

84. Explain how to find vertical asymptotes of a rational function.

For Exercises 85–90, determine the vertical asymptotes.

85. $p(x) = \dfrac{x}{x^2 - 16}$

86. $p(x) = \dfrac{x - 3}{x^2 + 4x + 4}$

87. $p(x) = \dfrac{3x^2}{x^2 + 6x + 9}$

88. $p(x) = \dfrac{x^2 + x + 1}{x^2 - 2x - 3}$

89. $p(x) = \dfrac{x^2 + 2x + 1}{x^2 - 1}$

90. $p(x) = \dfrac{x^2 - 16}{x^2 - 8x + 16}$

For Exercises 91–96, sketch the graph of the rational function. Label all asymptotes and intercepts.

91. $f(x) = \dfrac{x^2}{x^2 - 1}$

92. $f(x) = \dfrac{-1}{x^2 - 4}$

93. $f(x) = \dfrac{x}{x^2 - x - 2}$

94. $f(x) = \dfrac{4x^2}{3x^2 + 1}$

95. $f(x) = \dfrac{x^2 - 6x + 9}{x^2 + x - 2}$

96. $f(x) = \dfrac{x^2 - 6x + 8}{x^2 - x - 2}$

chapter 12   TEST

1. Find the zeros of the polynomial $P(x) = x^3 + 3x^2 - 18x$ by solving the equation $P(x) = 0$.

2. Use synthetic division to divide $P(x) = x^3 + 2x^2 - 13x + 14$ by $(x - 2)$ to find the quotient $q(x)$ and the remainder, r. Express the result in the form $P(x) = (x - c)q(x) + r$.

3. Use the remainder theorem to find the following function values given the function defined by $G(x) = 3x^4 - 5x^3 - 3x^2 - x + 2$:
   a. $G(2)$ b. $G(-2)$ c. $G(3)$

4. Determine if $x = 5$ is a zero of the polynomial $F(x) = -6x^4 + 45x^3 - 84x^2 + 45x$.

5. Explain how to determine if a polynomial of the form $(x - c)$ is a factor of a polynomial, $P(x)$, without using long division.

6. Is $(x - 3)$ a factor of $P(x) = 3x^3 + 14x^2 - 77x + 24$?

7. True or False: Given that $(x - 2)$ is a factor of $f(x) = x^5 - 2x^4 + 3x^2 - 12x + 12$, then $f(2) = 0$.

8. True or False: Given that $(x + 3)$ is a factor of $f(x) = -x^4 - 8x^3 + 7x^2 + 50x - 48$, then $f(3) = 0$.

9. State the zeros and their multiplicities for the polynomial $x^3(x + 1)(x - 9)^3$.

10. Find a polynomial, $p(x)$, with real coefficients of degree 4 that has zeros 2 and -4, each of multiplicity 2. Answers will vary.

11. For $f(x) = 6x^4 - 23x^3 - 22x^2 + 105x + 18$,
    a. Use the rational zero theorem to list all possible rational zeros.
    b. Use Descartes' rule of signs to determine the possible number of positive and negative real zeros.
    c. Find all of the zeros of f and state their multiplicities.

12. For $M(x) = 3x^6 + 12x^4 - 2x^2 + 18$
    a. Identify the leading term of the polynomial.
    b. Determine the far-right and the far-left behavior of the polynomial.

13. a. Draw a graph of a function that is continuous over the interval $[-3, 3]$. Answers will vary.
    b. Draw a graph of a function that is not continuous over the interval $[-3, 3]$. Answers will vary.

14. For the polynomial $P(x) = -2x^3 + 7x^2 - 2x - 3$,
    a. Determine the far-right and far-left behavior.
    b. Find the x- and y-intercepts.
    c. Sketch a graph of the function.

15. Use the zero location theorem to prove that there is a zero of the polynomial $g(x) = 6x^4 - 2x^3 + x - 12$ between $x = -1$ and $x = 2$.

16. For $f(x) = \dfrac{2x^2}{x^2 - 2x + 1}$
    a. Find any vertical and horizontal asymptotes.
    b. Find the x- and y-intercepts.
    c. Determine if the function intersects its horizontal asymptote, $y = a$, by solving the equation $f(x) = a$.
    d. Complete the sketch.

CUMULATIVE REVIEW EXERCISES, CHAPTERS 1–12

1. Evaluate the expression $-b^2 - a$ when $a = -2$ and $b = 3$.

2. Simplify the expression: $\frac{1}{2}(x - 20) - \frac{1}{5}(x + 15)$

3. Solve the equation: $-3 - 4(t - 5) = -2(t + 3) + 11$

4. True or False:
   a. The slope of any line perpendicular to the line $y = 4x - 2$ is $-\frac{1}{4}$.
   b. The slope of the line $3x + 2y = 6$ is 3.
   c. The lines $2x + y = 1$ and $y = -2x + 9$ are parallel.

5. Given

$$A = \begin{bmatrix} 3 & 6 \\ -8 & 3 \end{bmatrix}$$

and

$$B = \begin{bmatrix} -2 & 7 \\ 9 & 4 \\ 1 & 0 \end{bmatrix}$$

perform the matrix operations if possible.

a. $A + B$ b. $A \cdot B$ c. $B \cdot A$

6. Solve the system of equations using Cramer's rule.

$$x - 2y = -7$$
$$3x + 2y = -5$$

7. Find the following function values for $p(x) = |x - 3| + 2$: $p(0), p(2), p(3), p(-3)$

8. Multiply the following polynomials:

a. $(x - 5)^2$

b. $(x - 5)(x + 5)$

c. $(x - 5)^3$

9. Divide and leave your answer in scientific notation.

$$\frac{120,000,000,000}{(800,000)(0.0002)}$$

10. Simplify: $27^{1/6} \cdot 27^{1/2}$

11. Subtract: $\sqrt[3]{3x^5y^7} - xy^2\sqrt[3]{24x^2y}$

12. The diagonal of a square is 2 ft longer than a side. Find the length of a side.

13. Find the vertex of the parabola and determine if the parabola opens upward, downward, left, or right. Then sketch the parabola.

$$y = x^2 + 6x + 2$$

14. Graph the ellipse:

$$\frac{x^2}{4} + \frac{(y - 1)^2}{9} = 1$$

15. Solve this system using substitution.

$$x^2 + 9y^2 = 9$$
$$y = x^2 - 1$$

16. Solve the equation:

$$\frac{2x}{x^2 - 9} + \frac{3x}{x^2 + 4x + 3} = 0$$

17. Express the perimeter of the triangle as a rational expression.

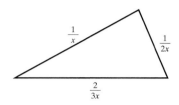

18. Solve the inequality. Write the answer in interval notation: $|2x - 3| < 5$

19. Write $y = \log_2 x$ in exponential form.

20. Write the expression as a single logarithm:

$$\ln(x + 2) + \ln(x - 2) - 3 \ln x$$

21. True or False: Given a function defined by $y = f(x)$. If $f(0) = 0$, then x must be a factor of $f(x)$.

22. Find all of the zeros of $f(x) = x^3 - 4x^2 - 4x + 16$.

23. Find the vertical and horizontal asymptotes of

$$g(x) = \frac{x^2 - 6x + 9}{x^2 + x - 2}$$

SEQUENCES, SERIES, COUNTING, AND PROBABILITY

To supplement their revenue income, many states have instituted games of chance called lotteries. In Pennsylvania for example, in 2002, the game Super 6 Lotto calls for the player to select a group of 6 numbers taken from 1–63. If a person matches three, four, five, or all six numbers, the player wins a cash prize. The amount of the prize depends on the number of numbers matched, the amount of money collected by the state in ticket sales, and the number of other players who also won.

The state makes money regardless of the number of winners. The payoffs are computed so that the total revenue from ticket sales exceeds the total payout in cash prizes.

In this chapter, we will learn how to compute the number of possible outcomes in such a game of chance and the probability of winning. For more information about lotteries and expected payoffs, visit lottery at

www.mhhe.com/miller_oneill

section

13.1   SEQUENCES AND SERIES

1.   Definition of Finite and Infinite Sequences

In everyday life we think of a sequence as a set of events or items with some order or pattern. In mathematics, a sequence is a list of terms that correspond with the set of positive integers. For example, the sequence

$$1, 4, 9, 16, 25$$

represents the squares of the first five positive integers. This sequence has a finite number of terms and is called a **finite sequence**. The sequence

$$1, 4, 9, 16, 25, \ldots$$

represents the squares of *all* positive integers. This sequence continues indefinitely and is called an **infinite sequence**.

Because the terms in a sequence are related to the set of positive integers, we give a formal definition of finite and infinite sequences using the language of functions.

Definition of Finite and Infinite Sequences

An **infinite sequence** is a function whose domain is the set of positive integers. A **finite sequence** is a function whose domain is the set of the first n positive integers.

For any positive integer n (the independent variable), the value of the sequence (the dependent variable) is denoted by a_n (read as "a sub-n"). The values a_1, a_2, a_3, . . . are called the **terms of the sequence**. The expression a_n defines the **nth term** (or general term) of the sequence.

2.   Listing the Terms of a Sequence

example 1   **Listing the Terms of a Sequence**

List the terms of the following sequences:

a. $a_n = 3n^2 - 4;\quad 1 \le n \le 4$ b. $a_n = 3 \cdot 2^n$

Solution:

a.   The domain is restricted to the first four positive integers, indicating that the sequence is finite.

n	a_n
1	$3(1)^2 - 4 = -1$
2	$3(2)^2 - 4 = \ 8$
3	$3(3)^2 - 4 = 23$
4	$3(4)^2 - 4 = 44$

The sequence is $-1, 8, 23, 44$.

b. The sequence $a_n = 3 \cdot 2^n$ has no restrictions on its domain; therefore, it is an infinite sequence.

n	a_n
1	$3 \cdot 2^1 = \ \ 6$
2	$3 \cdot 2^2 = 12$
3	$3 \cdot 2^3 = 24$
4	$3 \cdot 2^4 = 48$

The sequence is $6, 12, 24, 48, \ldots$

$\ldots$

Graphing Calculator Box

If the nth term of a sequence is known, a *Seq* function on a graphing calculator can quickly display a list of terms. It is necessary to enter the following: the formula for the nth term, the independent variable, the starting value for n, the ending value for n, and the increment for n.

$$\text{Seq}(a_n, n, \text{begin}, \text{end}, \text{increment})$$

The first four terms of the sequence $a_n = 3 \cdot 2^n$ from Example 1(b) are given by:

```
seq(3*2^n,n,1,4,
1)
          {6 12 24 48}
```

Sometimes the terms of a sequence may have alternating signs. Such a sequence is called an **alternating sequence**.

example 2

Listing the Terms of an Alternating Sequence

List the first four terms of the alternating sequence.

a. $a_n = (-1)^n \cdot \dfrac{1}{n}$

b. $a_n = (-1)^{n+1} \cdot \left(\dfrac{2}{3}\right)^n$

Solution:

a.

n	a_n
1	$(-1)^1 \cdot \dfrac{1}{1} = -1$
2	$(-1)^2 \cdot \dfrac{1}{2} = \dfrac{1}{2}$
3	$(-1)^3 \cdot \dfrac{1}{3} = -\dfrac{1}{3}$
4	$(-1)^4 \cdot \dfrac{1}{4} = \dfrac{1}{4}$

The first four terms are $-1, \frac{1}{2}, -\frac{1}{3}, \frac{1}{4}$.

> **Tip:** Notice that the factor $(-1)^n$ makes the even-numbered terms positive and the odd-numbered terms negative.

b.

n	a_n
1	$(-1)^{1+1} \cdot \left(\dfrac{2}{3}\right)^1 = (-1)^2 \cdot \left(\dfrac{2}{3}\right) = \dfrac{2}{3}$
2	$(-1)^{2+1} \cdot \left(\dfrac{2}{3}\right)^2 = (-1)^3 \cdot \left(\dfrac{4}{9}\right) = -\dfrac{4}{9}$
3	$(-1)^{3+1} \cdot \left(\dfrac{2}{3}\right)^3 = (-1)^4 \cdot \left(\dfrac{8}{27}\right) = \dfrac{8}{27}$
4	$(-1)^{4+1} \cdot \left(\dfrac{2}{3}\right)^4 = (-1)^5 \cdot \left(\dfrac{16}{81}\right) = -\dfrac{16}{81}$

> **Tip:** Notice that the factor $(-1)^{n+1}$ makes the odd-numbered terms positive and the even-numbered terms negative.

The first four terms are $\frac{2}{3}, -\frac{4}{9}, \frac{8}{27}, -\frac{16}{81}$.

■

3. Finding a Formula for the nth Term of a Sequence

In Examples 1 and 2, we were given the formula for the nth term of a sequence and asked to list several terms of the sequence. We now consider the reverse process. Given several terms of the sequence, we will find a formula for the nth term. To do so, look for a pattern that establishes each term as a function of the term number.

example 3

Finding the nth Term of a Sequence

Find a formula for the nth term of the sequence:

a. $\dfrac{1}{2}, \dfrac{2}{3}, \dfrac{3}{4}, \dfrac{4}{5}, \ldots$ b. $-2, 4, -6, 8, -10, \ldots$ c. $\dfrac{1}{2}, \dfrac{1}{4}, \dfrac{1}{8}, \dfrac{1}{16}, \ldots$

Solution:

a. For each term in the sequence, the numerator is equal to the term number, and the denominator is equal to one more than the term number. Therefore, the nth term may be given by

$$a_n = \frac{n}{n+1}$$

b.   The odd-numbered terms are negative and the even-numbered terms are positive. The factor $(-1)^n$ will produce the required alternation of signs. The numbers $2, 4, 6, 8, 10, \ldots$ are equal to $2(1), 2(2), 2(3), 2(4), 2(5), \ldots$ Therefore, the nth term may be given by

$$a_n = (-1)^n \cdot 2n$$

c.   The denominators are consecutive powers of 2. The sequence can be written as

$$\frac{1}{2^1}, \frac{1}{2^2}, \frac{1}{2^3}, \frac{1}{2^4}, \ldots$$

Therefore, the nth term may be given by

$$a_n = \frac{1}{2^n}$$

 Avoiding Mistakes

The first few terms of a sequence are not sufficient to define the sequence uniquely. For example, consider the sequence:

$$\frac{1}{2}, \frac{1}{4}, \frac{1}{8}, \ldots$$

The following formulas both produce the first three terms, but differ at the fourth term:

$$a_n = \frac{1}{2^n} \quad \text{and} \quad b_n = \frac{1}{n^2 - n + 2}$$

$$a_4 = \frac{1}{16} \quad \text{whereas} \quad b_4 = \frac{1}{14}$$

To define a sequence uniquely, the nth term must be provided.

4.   Applications of Sequences

example 4

Using a Sequence in an Application

A child drops a ball from a height of 4 ft. With each bounce, the ball rebounds to 50% of its height. Write a sequence whose terms represent the heights from which the ball falls (begin with the initial height from which the ball was dropped).

Solution:

The ball first drops 4 ft and then rebounds to a new height of $0.50(4 \text{ ft}) = 2$ ft. Similarly, it falls from 2 ft and rebounds $0.50(2 \text{ ft}) = 1$ ft. Repeating this process, we have

$$4, 2, 1, \frac{1}{2}, \frac{1}{4}, \frac{1}{8}, \ldots$$

The nth term can be represented by $a_n = 4 \cdot (0.50)^{n-1}$.

Graphing Calculator Box

A graphing calculator may be used to visualize the values and graph of a sequence. To enter a sequence in graphing mode, first change the mode to *Seq* and select *Dot*. Then in the graphing editor, enter the minimum *n* value (*nMin*) and the function under *u*(*n*). A *Table* feature can be used to view several selected terms.

To graph the sequence, set the window parameters defining the minimum and maximum *n* values, and the range values for *x* and *y*.

5. Definition of a Series

In many mathematical applications it is important to find the sum of the terms of a sequence. For example, suppose that the yearly interest earned in an account over a 4-year period is given by the sequence

$$\$250, \quad \$265, \quad \$278.25, \quad \$292.16$$

The sum of the terms gives the total interest earned

$$\$250 + \$265 + \$278.25 + \$292.16 = \$1085.41$$

By adding the terms of a sequence, we obtain a series.

Definition of a Series

The indicated sum of the terms of a sequence is called a **series**.

As with a sequence, a series may be a finite or infinite sum of terms.

6. Summation Notation

A convenient notation used to denote the sum of a set of terms is called **sigma notation**. The Greek letter Σ (sigma) is used to indicate sums. For example, the first four terms of the sequence defined by $a_n = n^3$ is denoted by

$$\sum_{n=1}^{4} n^3$$

This is read as "the sum from n equals 1 to 4 of n^3," and is simplified as

$$\sum_{n=1}^{4} n^3 = (1)^3 + (2)^3 + (3)^3 + (4)^3$$
$$= 1 + 8 + 27 + 64$$
$$= 100$$

In this example, the letter n is called the **index of summation**. Many times, the letters $i, j,$ and k are also used for the index of summation.

Graphing Calculator Box

The sum of a finite series may be found on a graphing calculator if the nth term of the corresponding sequence is known. The calculator takes the sum of a sequence by using the *Sum* and *Seq* functions.

```
sum(seq(n^3,n,1,
4,1)
            100
```

---

example 5

Finding a Sum from Sigma Notation

Find the sum

$$\sum_{i=1}^{3} (-1)^{i+1} \cdot (3i + 4)$$

Avoiding Mistakes

The letter i is used as a variable for the index of summation. In this context, it does not represent an imaginary number.

Solution:

$$\sum_{i=1}^{3} (-1)^{i+1} \cdot (3i + 4) = (-1)^{1+1} \cdot [3(1) + 4] + (-1)^{2+1} \cdot [3(2) + 4]$$

$$+ (-1)^{3+1} \cdot [3(3) + 4]$$

$$= (-1)^2 \cdot (7) + (-1)^3 \cdot (10) + (-1)^4 \cdot (13)$$

$$= 7 - 10 + 13$$

$$= 10$$

7. Writing a Sum Using Sigma Notation

example 6

Converting to Summation Notation

Write the series in summation notation.

a. $\dfrac{2}{3} + \dfrac{4}{9} + \dfrac{8}{27} + \dfrac{16}{81}$ (Use n as the index of summation.)

b. $1 - \dfrac{1}{2} + \dfrac{1}{3} - \dfrac{1}{4} + \dfrac{1}{5} - \dfrac{1}{6}$ (Use j as the index of summation.)

Solution:

a. The sum can be written as

$$\left(\frac{2}{3}\right)^1 + \left(\frac{2}{3}\right)^2 + \left(\frac{2}{3}\right)^3 + \left(\frac{2}{3}\right)^4$$

Taking n from 1 to 4, we have

$$\sum_{n=1}^{4} \left(\frac{2}{3}\right)^n$$

b. The even-numbered terms are negative. Therefore, the factor $(-1)^{j+1}$ is negative for even values of j. The series can be written as

$$\sum_{j=1}^{6} (-1)^{j+1} \cdot \frac{1}{j}$$

section 13.1 PRACTICE EXERCISES

For Exercises 1–16, list the terms of each sequence.

1. $a_n = 3n + 1, \quad 1 \le n \le 4$

2. $a_n = -2n + 3, \quad 1 \le n \le 4$

3. $a_n = \sqrt{n + 2}, \quad 1 \le n \le 4$

4. $a_n = \sqrt{n - 1}, \quad 1 \le n \le 4$

5. $a_n = \dfrac{3}{n}, \quad 1 \le n \le 5$

6. $a_n = \dfrac{n}{n + 2}, \quad 1 \le n \le 5$

7. $a_n = (-1)^n \dfrac{n + 1}{n + 2}, \quad 1 \le n \le 4$

8. $a_n = (-1)^n \dfrac{n - 1}{n + 2}, \quad 1 \le n \le 4$

9. $a_n = (-1)^{n+1} (n^2 - 1), \quad 1 \le n \le 4$

10. $a_n = (-1)^{n+1} (n^2), \quad 1 \le n \le 4$

11. $a_n = 3 - \dfrac{1}{n}, \quad 2 \le n \le 5$

12. $a_n = 2 - \dfrac{1}{n + 1}, \quad 2 \le n \le 5$

13. $a_n = n^2 - n, \quad 1 \le n \le 4$

14. $a_n = n(n^2 - 1), \quad 1 \le n \le 4$

15. $a_n = (-1)^n 3^n, \quad 1 \le n \le 4$

16. $a_n = (-1)^n n, \quad 1 \le n \le 4$

17. If the nth term of a sequence is $a_n = (-1)^n \cdot n^2$, which terms are positive and which are negative?

18. If the nth term of a sequence is $a_n = (-1)^{n-1} \cdot \frac{1}{n}$, which terms are positive and which are negative?

19. Edmond borrowed $500. To pay off the loan, he agreed to pay 2% of the balance plus $50 each month. Write a sequence representing the amount Edmond will pay each month for the next 6 months. Round each term to the nearest cent.

20. Janice deposited $1000 in a savings account that pays 3% interest compounded annually. Write a sequence representing the amount Janice receives in interest each year for the first 4 years. Round each term to the nearest cent.

21. A certain bacteria culture doubles its size each day. If there are 25,000 bacteria on the first day, write a sequence representing the population each day for the first week (7 days).

22. A radioactive chemical decays by half of its amount each week. If there is 16 g of the chemical in week 1, write a sequence representing the amount present each week for 2 months (8 weeks).

For Exercises 23–34, find a formula for the nth term of the sequence. Answers may vary.

23. $2, 4, 6, 8, \ldots$

24. $3, 6, 9, 12, \ldots$

25. $1, 3, 5, 7, \ldots$

26. $3, 5, 7, 9, \ldots$

27. $1, \dfrac{1}{4}, \dfrac{1}{9}, \dfrac{1}{16}, \ldots$

28. $\dfrac{1}{2}, \dfrac{2}{3}, \dfrac{3}{4}, \dfrac{4}{5}, \ldots$

29. $1, -1, 1, -1, \ldots$

30. $-1, 1 -1, 1, \ldots$

31. $-2, 4, -8, 16, \ldots$

32. $3, -9, 27, -81, \ldots$

33. $\dfrac{3}{5}, \dfrac{3}{25}, \dfrac{3}{125}, \dfrac{3}{625}, \ldots$

34. $\dfrac{1}{4}, \dfrac{1}{16}, \dfrac{1}{64}, \dfrac{1}{256}, \ldots$

35. What is the difference between a sequence and a series?

36. What is the index of a summation?

For Exercises 37–52, find the sums.

37. $\displaystyle\sum_{i=1}^{4} (3i^2)$

38. $\displaystyle\sum_{i=1}^{4} (2i^2)$

39. $\displaystyle\sum_{j=0}^{4} \left(\dfrac{1}{2}\right)^j$

40. $\displaystyle\sum_{j=0}^{4} \left(\dfrac{1}{3}\right)^j$

41. $\displaystyle\sum_{i=1}^{6} 5$

42. $\displaystyle\sum_{i=1}^{7} 3$

43. $\displaystyle\sum_{j=1}^{4} (-1)^j (5j)$

44. $\displaystyle\sum_{j=1}^{4} (-1)^j (4j)$

45. $\sum_{i=1}^{4} \dfrac{i+1}{i}$

46. $\sum_{i=2}^{5} \dfrac{i-1}{i}$

47. $\sum_{j=1}^{3} (j+1)(j+2)$

48. $\sum_{j=1}^{3} j(j+2)$

49. $\sum_{k=1}^{7} (-1)^k$

50. $\sum_{k=0}^{5} (-1)^{k+1}$

51. $\sum_{k=1}^{5} k^2$

52. $\sum_{k=1}^{5} 2^k$

For Exercises 53–62, write the series in summation notation.

53. $1 + 2 + 3 + 4 + 5 + 6$

54. $1 - 2 + 3 - 4 + 5 - 6$

55. $4 + 4 + 4 + 4 + 4$

56. $8 + 8 + 8 + 8 + 8$

57. $4 + 8 + 12 + 16 + 20$

58. $3 + 6 + 9 + 12 + 15$

59. $\dfrac{1}{3} - \dfrac{1}{9} + \dfrac{1}{27} - \dfrac{1}{81}$

60. $\dfrac{1}{2} - \dfrac{1}{4} + \dfrac{1}{8} - \dfrac{1}{16}$

61. $x + x^2 + x^3 + x^4 + x^5$

62. $y^2 + y^4 + y^6 + y^8 + y^{10}$

63. A certain plant will grow $1\frac{1}{2}$ in. each day for 1 week (7 days). If the plant begins with a height of 1 in., the height of the plant can be represented as a series. For example, after 1 day the plant will be $1 + 1\frac{1}{2}$ in. tall. Write out a series to represent the height of the plant each day for 1 week (7 days). Then write the series in summation notation. Finally, determine the height after 1 week.

64. A company produces a product and sells 5000 units. The company's research department found that for each year, 10% of the units cease to operate.

   a. Write out a sum representing how many units will become inoperative in the first 3 years.

b. How many of the original 5000 units will still be operational at the end of the 3 years?

Summation notation is used extensively in statistics. The sample mean, $\bar{x}$, of a set of values $x_1, x_2, x_3, \ldots, x_n$ is given by

$$\bar{x} = \dfrac{1}{n} \sum_{i=1}^{n} x_i$$

Use this formula for Exercises 65–66.

65. Find the mean number of grams of protein for a sample of five energy bars: 10, 15, 12, 18, 22

66. Find the mean age of a sample of viewers who regularly watch CNN on television: 29, 56, 62, 39, 58, 74.

The sample standard deviation, s, of a set of values x_1, $x_2, x_3, \ldots, x_n$ is given by:

$$s = \sqrt{\dfrac{n \cdot \sum_{i=1}^{n} (x_i)^2 - \left(\sum_{i=1}^{n} x_i \right)^2}{n(n-1)}}$$

Use this formula for Exercises 67–68.

67. Find the standard deviation for the number of grams of protein for a sample of five energy bars: 10, 15, 12, 18, 22. Round to one decimal place.

68. Find the standard deviation of a sample of viewers who regularly watch CNN on television: 29, 56, 62, 39, 58, 74. Round to one decimal place.

■ EXPANDING YOUR SKILLS

Some sequences are defined by a recursion formula, which defines each term of a sequence in terms of one or more of its preceding terms. For example, if $a_1 = 5$ and $a_n = 2a_{n-1} + 1$ for $n > 1$, then the terms of the sequence are $5, 11, 23, 47, \ldots$ In this case, each term after the first is one more than twice the term before it.

   For Exercises 69–72, list the first five terms of the sequence.

69. $a_1 = -3, a_n = a_{n-1} + 5$ for $n > 1$

70. $a_1 = 10, a_n = a_{n-1} - 3$ for $n > 1$

71. $a_1 = 5, a_n = 4a_{n-1} + 1$ for $n > 1$

72. $a_1 = -2, a_n = -3a_{n-1} + 4$ for $n > 1$

73. A famous sequence in mathematics is called the Fibonacci sequence, named after the Italian mathematician Leonardo Fibonacci of the 13th century. The Fibonacci sequence is defined by

$$a_1 = 1$$
$$a_2 = 1$$
$$a_n = a_{n-1} + a_{n-2} \quad \text{for } n > 2$$

This definition implies that beginning with the third term, each term is the sum of the preceding two terms. Write out the first 10 terms of the Fibonacci sequence.

GRAPHING CALCULATOR EXERCISES

For Exercises 74–77, use a graphing calculator to list the first five terms of the sequence. Then graph the sequence.

74. $a_n = 1 + 3n$

75. $a_n = \dfrac{8}{n}$

76. $a_n = (-1)^n \left(\dfrac{7}{8}\right)^n$

77. $a_n = (-1)^n (n^2)$

For Exercises 78–81, use the *Sum* and *Seq* functions on a graphing calculator to find the sum.

78. $\displaystyle\sum_{n=1}^{20} (1 + 3n)$

79. $\displaystyle\sum_{n=1}^{4} \dfrac{8}{n}$

80. $\displaystyle\sum_{n=1}^{6} (-1)^n \left(\dfrac{1}{2}\right)^n$

81. $\displaystyle\sum_{n=1}^{100} (-1)^n (n^2)$

---

section

13.2 ARITHMETIC AND GEOMETRIC SEQUENCES AND SERIES

Concepts

1. Definition of an Arithmetic Sequence
2. Writing the *n*th Term of an Arithmetic Sequence
3. Finding a Specific Term of an Arithmetic Sequence
4. Definition of an Arithmetic Series
5. Definition of a Geometric Sequence
6. Definition of a Geometric Series
7. Infinite Geometric Series

1. Definition of an Arithmetic Sequence

In this section we will study two special types of sequences and series. The first is called an arithmetic sequence. For example:

$$4, 7, 10, 13, 16, \ldots$$

This sequence is an arithmetic sequence. Note the characteristic that each successive term after the first is a fixed value more than the previous term (in this case the terms differ by 3).

Definition of an Arithmetic Sequence

An **arithmetic sequence** is a sequence in which the difference between consecutive terms is constant.

The fixed difference between a term and its predecessor is called the **common difference** and is denoted by the letter d. The common difference is found by subtracting a term by the preceding term. That is,

$$d = a_{n+1} - a_n$$

Furthermore, if a_1 is the first term then

$$a_2 = a_1 + d \quad \text{is the second term,}$$

$$a_3 = a_1 + 2d \quad \text{is the third term,}$$

$$a_4 = a_1 + 3d \quad \text{is the fourth term and so on.}$$

$$\cdots$$

In general, $a_n = a_1 + (n - 1)d$

nth Term of an Arithmetic Sequence

The nth term of an arithmetic sequence is given by

$$a_n = a_1 + (n - 1)d$$

where a_1 is the first term of the sequence and d is the common difference.

2.   Writing the nth Term of an Arithmetic Sequence

example 1

Writing the nth Term of an Arithmetic Sequence

Write the nth term of the sequence: $9, 2, -5, -12, \ldots$

Solution:

$$9, \quad 2, \quad -5, \quad -12, \ldots$$

$$-7 \quad -7 \quad -7$$

The common difference can be found by subtracting a term by its predecessor: $2 - 9 = -7$

With $a_1 = 9$ and $d = -7$, we have

$$a_n = 9 + (n - 1)(-7)$$

$$= 9 - 7n + 7$$

$$= -7n + 16$$

In Example 1, the common difference between terms is -7. Accordingly, each term of the sequence *decreases* by 7.

3. Finding a Specific Term of an Arithmetic Sequence

The formula $a_n = a_1 + (n - 1)d$ contains four variables: $a_n, a_1, n,$ and d. Consequently, if we know the value of three of the four variables, we can solve for the fourth.

---

example 2

Finding a Specified Term of an Arithmetic Sequence

Find the ninth term of the arithmetic sequence in which $a_1 = -4$ and $a_{22} = 164$.

Solution:

To find the value of the ninth term, a_9, we need to determine the value of d. To find d, substitute $a_1 = -4$, $n = 22$, and $a_{22} = 164$ into the formula $a_n = a_1 + (n - 1)d$.

$$a_n = a_1 + (n - 1)d$$
$$164 = -4 + (22 - 1)d$$
$$164 = -4 + 21d$$
$$168 = 21d$$
$$d = 8$$

Therefore,

$$a_9 = -4 + (9 - 1)(8)$$
$$= -4 + (8)(8)$$
$$= 60$$

---

example 3

Finding the Number of Terms in an Arithmetic Sequence

Find the number of terms of the sequence $7, 3, -1, -5, \ldots, -113$.

Solution:

To find the number of terms, n, we can substitute $a_1 = 7, d = -4$, and $a_n = -113$ into the formula for the nth term.

$$a_n = a_1 + (n - 1)d$$
$$-113 = 7 + (n - 1)(-4)$$
$$-113 = 7 - 4n + 4$$
$$-113 = 11 - 4n$$
$$-124 = -4n$$
$$n = 31$$

4.   Definition of an Arithmetic Series

The indicated sum of an arithmetic sequence is called an **arithmetic series**. For example, the series

$$3 + 7 + 11 + 15 + 19 + 23$$

is an arithmetic series because the common difference between terms is constant (4). Adding the terms in a lengthy sum is cumbersome, so we offer the following "short-cut," which is developed here. Let S represent the sum of the terms in the series.

$S = \ \ 3 + \ \ 7 + 11 + 15 + 19 + 23$	Add the terms in ascending order.
$S = 23 + 19 + 15 + 11 + \ \ 7 + \ \ 3$	Add the terms in descending order.
$2S = 26 + 26 + 26 + 26 + 26 + 26$	Adding the two series produces 6 terms of 26.
$2S = 6 \cdot 26$	
$S = \dfrac{6 \cdot 26}{2}$	
$\ \ \ = 78$	

By adding the terms in ascending and descending order, we double the sum, but create a pattern that is easily added. This is true in general. To find the sum, S_n, of the first n terms of the arithmetic series $a_1 + a_2 + a_3, + \cdots + a_n$, we have

$S_n = a_1 \qquad\quad + (a_1 + d) + (a_1 + 2d) + \cdots + a_n$	Ascending order
$S_n = a_n \qquad\quad + (a_n - d) + (a_n - 2d) + \cdots + a_1$	Descending order
$2S_n = (a_1 + a_n) + (a_1 + a_n) + (a_1 + a_n) + \cdots + (a_1 + a_n)$	
$2S_n = n(a_1 + a_n)$	
$S_n = \dfrac{n}{2}(a_1 + a_n)$	

Sum of an Arithmetic Series

The sum, S_n, of the first n terms of an arithmetic series is given by

$$S_n = \frac{n}{2}(a_1 + a_n)$$

where a_1 is the first term of the series and a_n is the nth term of the series.

example 4

Finding the Sum of an Arithmetic Series

Find the sum of the series

$$\sum_{i=1}^{25} (2i + 3)$$

Solution:

In this series, $n = 25$. Furthermore, $a_1 = 2(1) + 3 = 5$ and $a_{25} = 2(25) + 3 = 53$. Therefore,

$$S_{25} = \frac{25}{2}(5 + 53) \qquad \text{Apply the formula } S_n = \frac{n}{2}(a_1 + a_n).$$

$$= \frac{25}{2}(58) \qquad \text{Simplify.}$$

$$= 725$$

⬡ **Avoiding Mistakes**

When applying the sum formula $S_n = \frac{n}{2}(a_1 + a_n)$ to find the sum $\sum_{i=1}^{n} a_n$, the index of summation, i, must begin at 1.

example 5

Finding the Sum of an Arithmetic Series

Find the sum of the series: $-3 + (-5) + (-7) + \cdots + (-127)$

Solution:

For this series, $a_1 = -3$ and $a_n = -127$. However, to determine the sum we first need to find the value of n. The common difference between the second term and its predecessor is $-5 - (-3) = -2$. We have

$$-127 = -3 + (n - 1)(-2) \qquad \text{Apply the formula } a_n = a_1 + (n - 1)d.$$

$$-127 = -3 - 2n + 2 \qquad \text{Apply the distributive property.}$$

$$-127 = -1 - 2n \qquad \text{Combine } like \text{ terms.}$$

$$-126 = -2n \qquad \text{Solve for } n.$$

$$n = 63$$

Using $n = 63$, $a_1 = -3$ and $a_{63} = -127$, we have

$$S_n = \frac{n}{2}(a_1 + a_n) = \frac{63}{2}[-3 + (-127)] = \frac{63}{2}(-130) = -4095$$

5. Definition of a Geometric Sequence

The sequence $2, 4, 8, 16, 32, \ldots$ is not an arithmetic sequence because the difference between terms is not constant. However, a different pattern exists. Notice that each term after the first is 2 times the preceding term. This sequence is called a **geometric sequence**.

Definition of a Geometric Sequence

A **geometric sequence** is a sequence in which each term after the first term is a constant multiple of the preceding term.

The constant multiple between a term and its predecessor is called the **common ratio** and is denoted by r. The common ratio is found by dividing a term by the preceding term. That is,

$$r = \frac{a_{n+1}}{a_n}$$

For the sequence $2, 4, 8, 16, 32, \ldots$ we have $r = \frac{4}{2} = \frac{8}{4} = \frac{16}{8} = \frac{32}{16} = 2$.

If a_1 denotes the first term of a geometric sequence, then

$$a_2 = a_1 r \qquad \text{is the second term.}$$
$$a_3 = a_1 r^2 \qquad \text{is the third term.}$$
$$a_4 = a_1 r^3 \qquad \text{is the fourth term, and so on.}$$
$$\ldots$$

This pattern gives $a_n = a_1 r^{n-1}$

nth Term of a Geometric Sequence

The nth term of a geometric sequence is given by

$$a_n = a_1 r^{n-1}$$

where a_1 is the first term and r is the common ratio.

---

example 6

Finding the nth Term of a Geometric Sequence

Find the nth term of the sequence.

a. $-1, 4, -16, 64, \ldots$ b. $12, 8, \dfrac{16}{3}, \dfrac{32}{9}, \ldots$

Solution:

a.   The common ratio is found by dividing any term (after the first) by its predecessor.

$$r = \frac{4}{-1} = -4$$

With $r = -4$ and $a_1 = -1$, we have $a_n = -1(-4)^{n-1}$.

b.   The common ratio is $r = \frac{8}{12} = \frac{2}{3}$. With $a_1 = 12$ and $r = \frac{2}{3}$, we have

$$a_n = 12 \left(\frac{2}{3} \right)^{n-1}$$

The formula $a_n = a_1 r^{n-1}$ contains the variables $a_n, a_1, n,$ and r. If we know the value of three of the four variables, we can find the fourth.

example 7

Finding a Specified Term of a Geometric Sequence

Given $a_n = 6 \left(\frac{1}{2} \right)^{n-1}$ find a_5.

Solution:

$$a_n = 6 \left(\frac{1}{2} \right)^{n-1}$$

$$a_5 = 6 \left(\frac{1}{2} \right)^{5-1} = 6 \left(\frac{1}{2} \right)^4 = 6 \left(\frac{1}{16} \right) = \frac{3}{8}$$

example 8

Finding a Specified Term of a Geometric Sequence

Find the first term of the geometric sequence where $a_5 = -162$ and $r = 3$.

Solution:

$-162 = a_1 (3)^{5-1}$ Substitute $a_5 = -162$ and $r = 3$ into the formula $a_n = a_1 r^{n-1}$.

$-162 = a_1 (3)^4$ Simplify and solve for a_1.

$-162 = a_1 (81)$

$a_1 = -2$

6. Definition of a Geometric Series

The indicated sum of a geometric sequence is called a **geometric series**. For example

$$1 + 3 + 9 + 27 + 81 + 243$$

is a geometric series. To find the sum, consider the following procedure. Let S represent the sum

$$S = 1 + 3 + 9 + 27 + 81 + 243$$

Now multiply S by the common ratio, which in this case is 3.

$$3S = 3 + 9 + 27 + 81 + 243 + 729$$

Then

$$3S - S = (3 + 9 + 27 + 81 + 243 + 729) - (1 + 3 + 9 + 27 + 81 + 243)$$

$$2S = 3 + 9 + 27 + 81 + 243 + 729 - 1 - 3 - 9 - 27 - 81 - 243$$

$$2S = 729 - 1 \qquad \text{The terms in red form a sum of zero.}$$

$$2S = 728$$

$$S = 364$$

This same procedure can be used to find the sum S_n of the first n terms of any geometric series. Subtract rS_n from S_n.

$$S_n = a_1 \qquad + a_1 r \qquad + a_1 r^2 \qquad + a_1 r^3 \qquad + \cdots + a_1 r^{n-1}$$

$$rS_n = a_1 r \qquad + a_1 r^2 \qquad + a_1 r^3 \qquad + a_1 r^4 \qquad + \cdots + a_1 r^n$$

$$S_n - rS_n = (a_1 - a_1 r) + (a_1 r - a_1 r^2) + (a_1 r^2 - a_1 r^3) + (a_1 r^3 - a_1 r^4) + \cdots + (a_1 r^{n-1} - a_1 r^n).$$

$$S_n - rS_n = a_1 - a_1 r^n \qquad \text{The terms in red form a sum of zero.}$$

$$S_n(1 - r) = a_1(1 - r^n) \qquad \text{Factor each side of the equation.}$$

$$S_n = \frac{a_1(1 - r^n)}{1 - r} \qquad \text{Divide by } (1 - r).$$

Sum of a Geometric Series

The sum, S_n, of the first n terms of a geometric series, $\sum\limits_{i=1}^{n} (a_1 r^{i-1})$, is given by

$$S_n = \frac{a_1(1 - r^n)}{1 - r}$$

where a_1 is the first term of the series and r is the common ratio and $r \neq 1$.

example 9

Finding the Sum of a Geometric Series

Find the sum of the series

$$4 + 2 + 1 + \frac{1}{2} + \frac{1}{4} + \frac{1}{8}$$

Solution:

$$a_1 = 4, \quad r = \frac{1}{2}, \text{ and } n = 6$$

$$S_n = \frac{a_1(1 - r^n)}{1 - r} = \frac{4\left[1 - \left(\frac{1}{2}\right)^6\right]}{1 - \frac{1}{2}} = \frac{4\left(1 - \frac{1}{64}\right)}{\frac{1}{2}} = 8\left(\frac{63}{64}\right) = \frac{63}{8}$$

example 10

Finding the Sum of a Geometric Series

Find the sum of the series: $5 + 10 + 20 + \cdots + 5120$.

Solution:

The common ratio is 2, and $a_1 = 5$. The nth term of the sequence can be written as $a_n = 5(2)^{n-1}$. To find the value of n, substitute 5120 for a_n.

$5120 = 5(2)^{n-1}$

$\dfrac{5120}{5} = \dfrac{5(2)^{n-1}}{5}$ Divide both sides by 5.

$1024 = 2^{n-1}$ To solve the exponential equation, write each side as a power

$2^{10} = 2^{n-1}$ of 2.

$10 = n - 1$ From Section 10.6, we know that if $b^x = b^y$, then $x = y$.

$n = 11$

With $a_1 = 5$, $r = 2$, and $n = 11$, we have

$$S_n = \frac{a_1(1 - r^n)}{1 - r} = \frac{5(1 - 2^{11})}{1 - 2} = \frac{5(1 - 2048)}{-1} = \frac{5(-2047)}{-1} = 10{,}235$$

7. Infinite Geometric Series

Consider a geometric series where $|r| < 1$. For increasing values of n, r^n decreases. For example,

$$\left(\frac{1}{2}\right)^5 = 0.03125, \qquad \left(\frac{1}{2}\right)^{10} \approx 0.00097656, \qquad \left(\frac{1}{2}\right)^{15} \approx 0.00003052$$

For $|r| < 1$, r^n approaches 0 as n gets larger and larger. As n approaches infinity, the sum

$$S = \frac{a_1(1 - r^n)}{1 - r} \qquad \text{approaches} \qquad \frac{a_1(1 - 0)}{1 - r} = \frac{a_1}{1 - r}$$

Sum of an Infinite Geometric Series

Given an infinite geometric series $a_1 + a_1 r + a_1 r^2 + \ldots$, with $|r| < 1$, the sum S of all terms in the series is given by

$$S = \frac{a_1}{1 - r}$$

Note: If $|r| \geq 1$, then the sum does not exist.

example 11

Finding the Sum of an Infinite Geometric Series

Find the sum of the series

$$1 + \frac{1}{3} + \frac{1}{9} + \frac{1}{27} + \frac{1}{81} + \cdots$$

Solution:

This is a geometric series with $a_1 = 1$ and $r = \frac{1}{3}$. Because $|r| = |\frac{1}{3}| < 1$, we have

$$S = \frac{a_1}{1 - r} = \frac{1}{1 - \frac{1}{3}} = \frac{1}{\frac{2}{3}} = \frac{3}{2}$$

The sum is $\frac{3}{2}$.

---

example 12

Using Geometric Series in a Physics Application

A child drops a ball from a height of 4 ft. With each bounce, the ball rebounds to 50% of its original height. Determine the total distance traveled by the ball.

Solution:

The heights from which the ball drops are given by the sequence

$$4, 2, 1, \frac{1}{2}, \frac{1}{4}, \cdots$$

After the ball falls from its initial height of 4 ft, the distance traveled for every bounce thereafter is doubled (the ball travels up and down). Therefore, the total distance traveled is given by the series

$$4 + 2 \cdot 2 + 2 \cdot 1 + 2 \cdot \frac{1}{2} + 2 \cdot \frac{1}{4} + \cdots \quad \text{or equivalently}$$

$$4 + 4 + 2 + 1 + \frac{1}{2} + \cdots$$

The sum of terms beginning with the second term represents an infinite geometric series with $a_1 = 4$ and $r = \frac{1}{2}$.

Initial height from which the ball was dropped   Infinite geometric series

$$4 \quad + 4 + 2 + 1 + \frac{1}{2} + \cdots$$

$$= 4 + \frac{4}{1 - \frac{1}{2}} = 4 + \frac{4}{\frac{1}{2}} = 4 + 8 = 12$$

The ball traveled a total of 12 ft.

section 13.2 PRACTICE EXERCISES

1. Explain how to determine if a sequence is arithmetic.

For Exercises 2–7, find the common difference, d, for each arithmetic sequence.

2. $1, 3, 5, 7, 9, \ldots$

3. $2, 8, 14, 20, 26, \ldots$

4. $6, 3, 0, -3, -6, \ldots$

5. $8, 3, -2, -7, -12, \ldots$

6. $-7, -9, -11, -13, -15, \ldots$

7. $-15, -11, -7, -3, 1, \ldots$

For Exercises 8–13, write the first five terms of the arithmetic sequence.

8. $a_1 = 3, d = 5$

9. $a_1 = -3, d = 2$

10. $a_1 = 2, d = \dfrac{1}{2}$

11. $a_1 = 0, d = \dfrac{1}{3}$

12. $a_1 = 2, d = -4$

13. $a_1 = 10, d = -6$

For Exercises 14–23, write the nth term of the sequence.

14. $0, 5, 10, 15, 20, \ldots$

15. $7, 12, 17, 22, 27, \ldots$

16. $-2, -4, -6, -8, -10, \ldots$

17. $1, -3, -7, -11, -15, \ldots$

18. $2, \dfrac{5}{2}, 3, \dfrac{7}{2}, 4, \ldots$

19. $1, \dfrac{4}{3}, \dfrac{5}{3}, 2, \dfrac{7}{3}, \ldots$

20. $21, 17, 13, 9, 5, \ldots$

21. $9, 6, 3, 0, -3, \ldots$

22. $-8, -2, 4, 10, 16, \ldots$

23. $-9, -1, 7, 15, 23, \ldots$

For Exercises 24–31, find the indicated term of each sequence.

24. Find the eighth term given $a_1 = -6$ and $d = -3$.

25. Find the sixth term given $a_1 = -3$ and $d = 4$.

26. Find the 12th term given $a_1 = -8$ and $d = -2$.

27. Find the ninth term given $a_1 = -1$ and $d = 6$.

28. Find the seventh term given $a_1 = 0$ and $d = -5$.

29. Find the 10th term given $a_1 = 1$ and $d = 5$.

30. Find the sixth term given $a_1 = 3$ and $d = 3$.

31. Find the 11th term given $a_1 = 12$ and $d = -6$.

For Exercises 32–39, find the number of terms, n, of each sequence.

32. $2, 0, -2, \ldots, -56$

33. $8, 13, 18, \ldots, 98$

34. $1, -3, -7, \ldots, -67$

35. $1, 5, 9, \ldots, 85$

36. $1, \dfrac{3}{4}, \dfrac{1}{2}, \ldots, -4$

37. $2, \dfrac{5}{2}, 3, \ldots, 13$

38. $-\dfrac{5}{3}, -1, -\dfrac{1}{3}, \ldots, 12\dfrac{1}{3}$

39. $\dfrac{13}{3}, \dfrac{19}{3}, \dfrac{25}{3}, \ldots, \dfrac{73}{3}$

40. If the third and fourth terms of an arithmetic sequence are 18 and 21, what are the first and second terms?

41. If the third and fourth terms of an arithmetic sequence are -8 and -11, what are the first and second terms?

42. Explain the difference between an arithmetic sequence and an arithmetic series.

For Exercises 43–56, find the sum of the arithmetic series.

43. $\displaystyle\sum_{i=1}^{20} (3i + 2)$

44. $\displaystyle\sum_{i=1}^{15} (2i - 3)$

45. $\displaystyle\sum_{i=1}^{20} (i + 4)$

46. $\displaystyle\sum_{i=1}^{25} (i - 3)$

47. $\sum_{j=1}^{10} (4 - j)$ 48. $\sum_{j=1}^{10} (6 - j)$

49. $\sum_{j=1}^{15} \left(\frac{2}{3}j + 1\right)$ 50. $\sum_{j=1}^{15} \left(\frac{1}{2}j - 2\right)$

51. $4 + 8 + 12 + \cdots + 84$

52. $4 + 9 + 14 + \cdots + 49$

53. $6 + 8 + 10 + \cdots + 34$

54. $-4 + (-3) + (-2) + \cdots + 12$

55. $-3 + (-7) + (-11) + \cdots + (-39)$

56. $2 + 5 + 8 + \cdots + 53$

57. Find the sum of the first 100 positive integers.

58. Find the sum of the first 50 positive even integers.

59. Find the sum of the first 50 positive odd integers.

60. Find the sum of the first 20 positive multiples of 5.

61. The seating in a certain theater is arranged so that there are 30 seats in row 1, 32 in row 2, 34 in row 3, and so on. If there are 20 rows, how many total seats are there? What is the total revenue if the average ticket price is $15 per seat and the theater is sold out?

62. A triangular array of dominos has one domino in the first row, two dominos in the second row, three dominos in the third row and so on. If there are 15 rows, how many dominos are in the array?

Figure for Exercise 62

63. Explain how to determine if a sequence is geometric.

For Exercises 64–69, determine the common ratio, r, for the geometric sequence.

64. $5, 10, 20, 40, \ldots$ 65. $-2, -1, -\frac{1}{2}, -\frac{1}{4}, \ldots$

66. $8, -2, \frac{1}{2}, -\frac{1}{8}, \ldots$ 67. $4, -12, 36, -108, \ldots$

68. $3, -6, 12, -24, \ldots$ 69. $1, 4, 16, 64, \ldots$

For Exercises 70–75, write the first five terms of the geometric sequence.

70. $a_1 = -3, r = -2$ 71. $a_1 = -4, r = -1$

72. $a_1 = 6, r = \frac{1}{2}$ 73. $a_1 = 8, r = \frac{1}{4}$

74. $a_1 = -1, r = 6$ 75. $a_1 = 2, r = -3$

For Exercises 76–81, find the nth term of each geometric sequence.

76. $3, 12, 48, 192, \ldots$

77. $2, 6, 18, 36, \ldots$

78. $-5, 15, -45, 135, \ldots$

79. $-6, 12, -24, 48, \ldots$

80. $\frac{1}{2}, 2, 8, 32, \ldots$

81. $\frac{16}{3}, 4, 3, \frac{9}{4}, \ldots$

For Exercises 82–91, find the indicated term of each sequence.

82. Given $a_n = 2(\frac{1}{2})^{n-1}$, find a_8.

83. Given $a_n = -3(\frac{1}{2})^{n-1}$, find a_8.

84. Given $a_n = 4(-\frac{3}{2})^{n-1}$, find a_6.

85. Given $a_n = 6(-\frac{1}{3})^{n-1}$, find a_6.

86. Given $a_n = -3(2)^{n-1}$, find a_5.

87. Given $a_n = 5(3)^{n-1}$, find a_4.

88. Given $a_5 = -\frac{16}{9}$ and $r = -\frac{2}{3}$, find a_1.

89. Given $a_6 = \frac{5}{16}$ and $r = -\frac{1}{2}$, find a_1.

90. Given $a_7 = 8$ and $r = 2$, find a_1.

91. Given $a_6 = 27$ and $r = 3$, find a_1.

92. If the second and third terms of a geometric sequence are 16 and 64, what is the first term?

93. If the second and third terms of a geometric sequence are $\frac{1}{3}$ and $\frac{1}{9}$, what is the first term?

94. Explain the difference between a geometric sequence and a geometric series.

For Exercises 95–104, find the sum of the geometric series.

95. $10 + 2 + \dfrac{2}{5} + \dfrac{2}{25} + \dfrac{2}{125}$

96. $1 + 3 + 9 + 27 + 81 + 243$

97. $-2 + 1 + \left(-\dfrac{1}{2}\right) + \dfrac{1}{4} + \left(-\dfrac{1}{8}\right)$

98. $\dfrac{1}{4} + (-1) + 4 + (-16) + 64$

99. $12 + 16 + \dfrac{64}{3} + \dfrac{256}{9} + \dfrac{1024}{27}$

100. $9 + 6 + 4 + \dfrac{8}{3} + \dfrac{16}{9}$

101. $1 + \dfrac{2}{3} + \dfrac{4}{9} + \cdots + \dfrac{64}{729}$

102. $\dfrac{8}{3} + 2 + \dfrac{3}{2} + \cdots + \dfrac{243}{512}$

103. $-4 + 8 + (-16) + \cdots + (-256)$

104. $-\dfrac{7}{3} + 7 + (-21) + \cdots + (-1701)$

105. A deposit of $1000 is made in an account that earns 5% interest compounded annually. The balance in the account after n years is given by

$$a_n = 1000(1.05)^n \quad \text{for } n \geq 1$$

  a. List the first four terms of the sequence. Round to the nearest cent.

  b. Find the balance after 10 years, 20 years, and 40 years by computing a_{10}, a_{20}, and a_{40}. Round to the nearest cent.

106. A home purchased for $125,000 increases by 4% of its value each year. The value of the home after n years is given by

$$a_n = 125{,}000(1.04)^n \quad \text{for } n \geq 1$$

  a. List the first four terms of the sequence. Round to the nearest dollar.

  b. Find the value of the home after 5 years, 10 years, and 20 years by computing a_5, a_{10}, and a_{20}. Round to the nearest dollar.

For Exercises 107–112, first find the common ratio, r. Then determine the sum of the infinite series if it exists.

107. $1 + \dfrac{1}{6} + \dfrac{1}{36} + \dfrac{1}{216} + \cdots$

108. $-2 + \left(-\dfrac{1}{2}\right) + \left(-\dfrac{1}{8}\right) + \left(-\dfrac{1}{32}\right) + \cdots$

109. $-3 + 1 + \left(-\dfrac{1}{3}\right) + \dfrac{1}{9} + \cdots$

110. $\dfrac{1}{2} + \left(-\dfrac{1}{10}\right) + \dfrac{1}{50} + \left(-\dfrac{1}{250}\right) + \cdots$

111. $\dfrac{2}{3} + (-1) + \dfrac{3}{2} + \left(-\dfrac{9}{4}\right) + \cdots$

112. $3 + 5 + \dfrac{25}{3} + \dfrac{125}{9} + \cdots$

113. Suppose $200 million is spent by tourists at a certain resort town. Further suppose that 75% of the revenue is respent in the community, and then respent over and over again, each time at a rate of 75%. The series

$$200 + 200(0.75) + 200(0.75)^2 + 200(0.75)^3 + \cdots$$

gives the total amount spent (and respent) in the community. Find the sum of the infinite series.

114. A bungee jumper jumps off a platform and stretches the cord 80 ft before rebounding upward. Each successive bounce stretches the cord 60% of its previous length. The total vertical distance traveled is given by

$$80 + 2(0.60)(80) + 2(0.60)^2(80) + 2(0.60)^3(80) + \cdots$$

Ignoring the first term, the series is an infinite geometric series. Compute the total vertical distance traveled. See Example 12.

115. A ball drops from a height of 4 ft. With each bounce, the ball rebounds to $\frac{3}{4}$ of its height. The total vertical distance traveled is given by

$$4 + 2\left(\frac{3}{4}\right)(4) + 2\left(\frac{3}{4}\right)^2(4) + 2\left(\frac{3}{4}\right)^3(4) + \cdots$$

Ignoring the first term, the series is an infinite geometric series. Compute the total vertical distance traveled. See Example 12.

116. The repeating decimal number $0.\overline{2}$ can be written as an infinite geometric series by:

$$\frac{2}{10} + \frac{2}{100} + \frac{2}{1000} + \cdots$$

   a.   What is a_1?

   b.   What is r?

   c.   Find the sum of the series.

117. The repeating decimal number $0.\overline{7}$ can be written as an infinite geometric series by

$$\frac{7}{10} + \frac{7}{100} + \frac{7}{1000} + \cdots$$

   a.   What is a_1?

   b.   What is r?

   c.   Find the sum of the series.

For Exercises 118–121, match the sequence with its graph.

118. $a_n = \left(\frac{1}{2}\right)^n$

119. $a_n = 2^n$

120. $a_n = 2n$

121. $a_n = \frac{1}{2}n$

a.

b.

c.

d.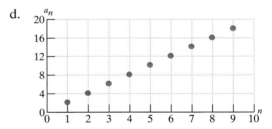

For Exercises 122–135, determine if the sequence is arithmetic, geometric, or neither.

122. $5, -\dfrac{5}{2}, \dfrac{5}{4}, -\dfrac{5}{8}, \ldots$

123. $1, -\dfrac{3}{2}, \dfrac{9}{4}, -\dfrac{27}{8}, \ldots$

124. $\dfrac{1}{2}, 1, \dfrac{3}{2}, 2, \dfrac{5}{2}, \ldots$

125. $-\dfrac{1}{3}, \dfrac{1}{3}, 1, \dfrac{5}{3}, \ldots$

126. $-2, -4, -8, -16, -32, \ldots$

127. $2, 6, 18, 54, 162, \ldots$

128. $-2, -4, -6, -8, -10, \ldots$

129. $2, 6, 10, 14, 18, 22, \ldots$

130. $-2, -4, -7, -11, -16, \ldots$

131. $2, 6, 11, 17, 24, \ldots$

132. $1, 3, 1, 3, 1, \ldots$

133. $0, 1, 0, 1, 0, 1, \ldots$

134. $2, -2, 2, -2, 2, \ldots$

135. $-1, 1, -1, 1, -1, \ldots$

■ EXPANDING YOUR SKILLS

136. The yearly salary for job A is $30,000 initially with an annual raise of $2000 per year. The yearly salary for job B is $29,000 initially with an annual raise of 6% per year.

    a. Find the total earnings for job A over 20 years (there will be 19 raises). Is this an arithmetic or geometric series?

    b. For job B, what is the amount of the raise after 1 year?

    c. Find the total earnings for job B over 20 years. Round to the nearest dollar. Is this an arithmetic or geometric series?

    d. What is the difference in total salary earned over 20 years between job A and job B?

137. a. Brook has a job that pays $40,000 the first year. She receives a 4% raise each year. Find the sum of her yearly salaries over a 20-year period. Round to the nearest dollar.

    b. Chamille has a job that pays $40,000 the first year. She receives a 4.5% raise each year. Find the sum of her yearly salaries over a 20-year period. Round to the nearest dollar.

    c. Chamille's raise each year was 0.5% higher than Brook's raise. How much more total income did Chamille receive than Brook over 20 years?

■ GRAPHING CALCULATOR EXERCISES

138. Use the *Seq* function on a graphing calculator to list the first four terms of the sequence $a_n = 1000(1.05)^n$. Verify your answer to Exercise 105(a).

139. Use the *Seq* function on a graphing calculator to list the first four terms of the sequence $a_n = 125{,}000(1.04)^n$. Verify your answer to Exercise 106(a).

140. Use the *Sum* and *Seq* functions on a graphing calculator to confirm your answer to Exercise 61.

141. Use the *Sum* and *Seq* functions on a graphing calculator to confirm your answer to Exercise 62.

142. Use the *Sum* and *Seq* functions on a graphing calculator to find the sum of the first 10 terms and the first 20 terms of the series given below. Then compute the exact value of the infinite geometric series.

    $$10 + 10(0.6) + 10(0.6)^2 + 10(0.6)^3 + \cdots$$

143. Use the *Sum* and *Seq* functions on a graphing calculator to find the sum of the first 10 terms and the first 20 terms of the series given below. Then compute the exact value of the infinite geometric series.

    $$4 + 2 + 1 + \frac{1}{2} + \cdots$$

chapter 13   MIDCHAPTER REVIEW

For Exercises 1–3,

   a. Determine whether the sequence is arithmetic, geometric, or neither.

   b. Find a formula for the nth term of the sequence.

1. $\dfrac{3}{4}, \dfrac{1}{2}, \dfrac{1}{3}, \dfrac{2}{9}, \ldots$

2. $\dfrac{1}{2}, \dfrac{4}{3}, \dfrac{9}{4}, \dfrac{16}{5}, \dfrac{25}{6}, \ldots$

3. $-\dfrac{3}{4}, -\dfrac{1}{4}, \dfrac{1}{4}, \dfrac{3}{4}, \ldots$

For Exercises 4–7,

   a. Identify whether the series is arithmetic, geometric, or neither.

   b. Find the sum of the series.

4. $\displaystyle\sum_{i=1}^{15} -6i + 17$ 5. $\displaystyle\sum_{i=1}^{5} 15\left(\dfrac{2}{5}\right)^{i-1}$

6. $\displaystyle\sum_{k=1}^{4} (k^2 + k)$ 7. $\displaystyle\sum_{n=1}^{7} (-1)^{n+1}$

For Exercises 8–9, find the 10th term of the sequence.

8. $a_n = -4 + (-3n)$ 9. $a_n = (-1)^{n+1}(6n)$

For Exercises 10–11, determine the number of terms in the sequence.

10. $8, 4, 0, -4, \ldots, -68$ 11. $15, 9, \dfrac{27}{5}, \ldots, \dfrac{729}{625}$

For Exercises 12–13, determine the sum of the series.

12. $8 + 4 + 0 + (-4) + \cdots + (-68)$

13. $15 + 9 + \dfrac{27}{5} + \cdots + \dfrac{729}{625}$

14. Study the following figures and the corresponding expression for the area of each region. Write the nth term of a sequence representing the area of the region.

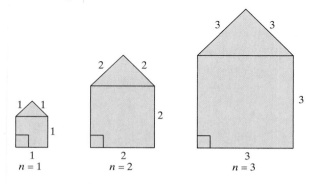

$$A = 1 + \dfrac{1\sqrt{3}}{4} \qquad A = 4 + \dfrac{4\sqrt{3}}{4} \qquad A = 9 + \dfrac{9\sqrt{3}}{4}$$

15. Find the sum of the infinite series if possible.

$$15 + 10 + \dfrac{20}{3} + \dfrac{40}{9} + \cdots$$

section

13.3   BINOMIAL EXPANSIONS

1.   Introduction to Binomial Expansions

In Section 5.4 we learned how to square a binomial.

$$(a + b)^2 = a^2 + 2ab + b^2$$

The expression $a^2 + 2ab + b^2$ is called the **binomial expansion** of $(a + b)^2$. To expand $(a + b)^3$, we can find the product $(a + b)(a + b)^2$.

$$(a + b)(a + b)^2 = (a + b)(a^2 + 2ab + b^2)$$

$$= a^3 + 2a^2b + ab^2 + a^2b + 2ab^2 + b^3$$

$$= a^3 + 3a^2b + 3ab^2 + b^3$$

Similarly, to expand $(a + b)^4$, we can multiply $(a + b)$ by $(a + b)^3$. Using this method, we can expand several powers of $(a + b)$ to find the following pattern:

$$(a + b)^0 = 1$$

$$(a + b)^1 = a + b$$

$$(a + b)^2 = a^2 + 2ab + b^2$$

$$(a + b)^3 = a^3 + 3a^2b + 3ab^2 + b^3$$

$$(a + b)^4 = a^4 + 4a^3b + 6a^2b^2 + 4ab^3 + b^4$$

$$(a + b)^5 = a^5 + 5a^4b + 10a^3b^2 + 10a^2b^3 + 5ab^4 + b^5$$

Notice that the exponent on a decreases from left to right while the exponents on b increase from left to right. Also observe that for each term, the sum of the exponents is equal to the exponent to which $(a + b)$ is raised. Finally, notice that the number of terms in the expansion is exactly one more than the power to which $(a + b)$ is raised. For example, the expansion of $(a + b)^4$ has five terms and the expansion of $(a + b)^5$ has six terms.

With these guidelines in mind, we know that $(a + b)^6$ will contain seven terms involving

$$a^6, \quad a^5b, \quad a^4b^2, \quad a^3b^3, \quad a^2b^4, \quad ab^5, \quad b^6$$

We can complete the expansion of $(a + b)^6$ if we can determine the correct coefficients of each term.

2.   Determining the Coefficients of a Binomial Expansion Using Pascal's Triangle

If we write the coefficients for several expansions of $(a + b)^n$, where $n \geq 0$, we have a triangular array of numbers.

$(a + b)^0$

$(a + b)^1 = 1a + 1b$

$(a + b)^2 = 1a^2 + 2ab + 1b^2$

$(a + b)^3 = 1a^3 + 3a^2b + 3ab^2 + 1b^3$

$(a + b)^4 = 1a^4 + 4a^3b + 6a^2b^2 + 4ab^3 + 1b^4$

$(a + b)^5 = 1a^5 + 5a^4b + 10a^3b^2 + 10a^2b^3 + 5ab^4 + 1b^5$

```
          1
        1   1
      1   2   1
    1   3   3   1
  1   4   6   4   1
1   5   10   10   5   1
```

Each row begins and ends with a 1 and each entry in between is the sum of the two entries from the line above. For example, in the last row, $5 = 1 + 4$, $10 = 4 + 6$, and so on. This triangular array of coefficients for a binomial expansion is called **Pascal's triangle**, named after French mathematician Blaise Pascal (1623–1662).

```
              1
            1   1
          1   2   1
        1   3   3   1
      1   4   6   4   1
    1   5   10   10   5   1
  1   6   15   20   15   6   1
```

Using the pattern shown in Pascal's triangle, the coefficients corresponding to $(a + b)^6$ would be 1, 6, 15, 20, 15, 6, 1. Inserting the coefficients, the sum becomes

$$(a + b)^6 = 1a^6 + 6a^5b + 15a^4b^2 + 20a^3b^3 + 15a^2b^4 + 6ab^5 + 1b^6$$

3. Determining the Coefficients of a Binomial Expansion Using Factorial Notation

Although Pascal's triangle provides an easy method to find the coefficients of $(a + b)^n$, it is impractical for large values of n. A more efficient method to find the coefficients of a binomial expansion involves **factorial notation**.

Definition of n!

Let n be a positive integer. Then $n!$ (read as "n factorial") is defined as the product of integers from 1 through n. That is,

$$n! = n(n - 1)(n - 2) \cdots (2)(1)$$

Note: For $n = 0$, then $n! = 0! = 1$.

example 1

Evaluating Factorial Notation

Evaluate the expressions.

a. 4!   b. 10!   c. 0!

Solution:

a. $4! = 4 \cdot 3 \cdot 2 \cdot 1 = 24$
b. $10! = 10 \cdot 9 \cdot 8 \cdot 7 \cdot 6 \cdot 5 \cdot 4 \cdot 3 \cdot 2 \cdot 1 = 3,628,800$
c. $0! = 1$ by definition

Graphing Calculator Box

Most calculators have a ▢! key. Try evaluating the expressions from Example 1 on a calculator:

```
4!
                    24
10!
              3628800
0!
                     1
```

Sometimes factorial notation is used with other operations such as multiplication and division.

example 2

Operations with Factorials

Evaluate the expressions.

a. $\dfrac{4!}{4! \cdot 0!}$ b. $\dfrac{4!}{3! \cdot 1!}$ c. $\dfrac{4!}{2! \cdot 2!}$ d. $\dfrac{4!}{1! \cdot 3!}$ e. $\dfrac{4!}{0! \cdot 4!}$

Solution:

a. $\dfrac{4!}{4! \cdot 0!} = \dfrac{(4 \cdot 3 \cdot 2 \cdot 1)}{(4 \cdot 3 \cdot 2 \cdot 1) \cdot (1)} = \dfrac{4 \cdot 3 \cdot 2 \cdot 1}{4 \cdot 3 \cdot 2 \cdot 1 \cdot 1} = 1$

b. $\dfrac{4!}{3! \cdot 1!} = \dfrac{(4 \cdot 3 \cdot 2 \cdot 1)}{(3 \cdot 2 \cdot 1) \cdot (1)} = \dfrac{4 \cdot 3 \cdot 2 \cdot 1}{3 \cdot 2 \cdot 1 \cdot 1} = 4$

c. $\dfrac{4!}{2! \cdot 2!} = \dfrac{(4 \cdot 3 \cdot 2 \cdot 1)}{(2 \cdot 1) \cdot (2 \cdot 1)} = \dfrac{4 \cdot 3 \cdot 2 \cdot 1}{2 \cdot 1 \cdot 2 \cdot 1} = 6$

d. $\dfrac{4!}{1! \cdot 3!} = \dfrac{(4 \cdot 3 \cdot 2 \cdot 1)}{(1) \cdot (3 \cdot 2 \cdot 1)} = \dfrac{4 \cdot \cancel{3 \cdot 2 \cdot 1}}{1 \cdot \cancel{3 \cdot 2 \cdot 1}} = 4$

e. $\dfrac{4!}{0! \cdot 4!} = \dfrac{(4 \cdot 3 \cdot 2 \cdot 1)}{(1) \cdot (4 \cdot 3 \cdot 2 \cdot 1)} = \dfrac{\cancel{4 \cdot 3 \cdot 2 \cdot 1}}{1 \cdot \cancel{4 \cdot 3 \cdot 2 \cdot 1}} = 1$

Graphing Calculator Box

To evaluate the expressions from Example 2 on a calculator, use parentheses around the factors in the denominator:

```
4!/(4!*0!)
                    1
4!/(3!*1!)
                    4
4!/(2!*2!)
                    6
```

---

4. The Binomial Theorem

Notice from Example 2 that the values of

$$\dfrac{4!}{4! \cdot 0!}, \quad \dfrac{4!}{3! \cdot 1!}, \quad \dfrac{4!}{2! \cdot 2!}, \quad \dfrac{4!}{1! \cdot 3!}, \quad \text{and} \quad \dfrac{4!}{0! \cdot 4!}$$

correspond to the values $1, 4, 6, 4, 1$, which are the coefficients for the expansion of $(a + b)^4$. Generalizing this pattern, the coefficients for the terms in the expansion of $(a + b)^n$ are given by

$$\dfrac{n!}{r! \cdot (n - r)!}$$

where r corresponds to the exponent on the factor of a and $(n - r)$ corresponds to the exponent on the factor of b.

Using this formula for the coefficients in a binomial expansion, we have the **binomial theorem**.

The Binomial Theorem

For any positive integer, n,

$$(a + b)^n = \dfrac{n!}{n! \cdot 0!}\,a^n + \dfrac{n!}{(n - 1)! \cdot 1!}\,a^{(n-1)}b + \dfrac{n!}{(n - 2)! \cdot 2!}\,a^{(n-2)}b^2$$

$$+ \cdots + \dfrac{n!}{0! \cdot n!}\,b^n$$

---

example 3 **Applying the Binomial Theorem**

Write out the first three terms of the expansion of $(a + b)^{10}$.

Solution:

$$(a + b)^{10} = \frac{10!}{10! \cdot 0!} a^{10} + \frac{10!}{9! \cdot 1!} a^9 b + \frac{10!}{8! \cdot 2!} a^8 b^2$$

$$= \frac{10!}{10! \cdot 1} a^{10} + \frac{10 \cdot 9!}{9! \cdot 1!} a^9 b + \frac{10 \cdot 9 \cdot 8!}{8! \cdot 2 \cdot 1} a^8 b^2$$

$$= a^{10} + 10 a^9 b + 45 a^8 b^2$$

---

example 4

Applying the Binomial Theorem

Use the binomial theorem to find the expansion of $(3x^2 - 5y)^4$.

Solution:

Write $(3x^2 - 5y)^4$ as $[(3x^2) + (-5y)]^4$. In this case, the expressions $3x^2$ and $-5y$ may be substituted for a and b in the expansion of $(a + b)^4$.

$$(a + b)^4 = \frac{4!}{4! \cdot 0!} a^4 + \frac{4!}{3! \cdot 1!} a^3 b + \frac{4!}{2! \cdot 2!} a^2 b^2 + \frac{4!}{1! \cdot 3!} ab^3 + \frac{4!}{0! \cdot 4!} b^4$$

$$= \frac{4!}{4! \cdot 0!} (3x^2)^4 + \frac{4!}{3! \cdot 1!} (3x^2)^3 (-5y) + \frac{4!}{2! \cdot 2!} (3x^2)^2 (-5y)^2$$

$$+ \frac{4!}{1! \cdot 3!} (3x^2)(-5y)^3 + \frac{4!}{0! \cdot 4!} (-5y)^4$$

$$= 1 \cdot (81x^8) + 4 \cdot (27x^6)(-5y) + 6 \cdot (9x^4)(25y^2) + 4 \cdot (3x^2)(-125y^3)$$
$$+ 1 \cdot (625y^4)$$

$$= 81x^8 - 540x^6 y + 1350x^4 y^2 - 1500x^2 y^3 + 625y^4$$

---

5. Finding a Specific Term of a Binomial Expansion

The binomial theorem may also be used to find a specific term in a binomial expansion.

---

example 5

Finding a Specific Term in a Binomial Expansion

Find the fourth term of the expansion $(a + b)^{13}$.

Solution:

There are 14 terms in the expansion of $(a + b)^{13}$. The first term will have variable factors $a^{13} b^0$. The second term will have variable factors $a^{12} b^1$. The third term will have $a^{11} b^2$, and the fourth term will have $a^{10} b^3$. Hence the fourth term is

$$\frac{13!}{10! \cdot 3!} a^{10} b^3 = 286 a^{10} b^3$$

From Example 5, we see that for the kth-term in the expansion $(a + b)^n$, where k is an integer greater than zero, the variable factors are $a^{n-(k-1)}$ and b^{k-1}. Therefore, to find the kth-term of $(a + b)^n$ we can make the following generalization.

Finding a Specific Term in a Binomial Expansion

Let n and k be positive integers such that $k \le n$. Then the kth-term in the expansion of $(a + b)^n$ is given by

$$\frac{n!}{[n - (k - 1)]! \cdot (k - 1)!} \cdot a^{n-(k-1)} \cdot b^{k-1}$$

example 6   **Finding a Specific Term in a Binomial Expansion**

Find the sixth term of $(p^3 + 2w)^8$.

Solution:

Apply the formula

$$\frac{n!}{[n - (k - 1)]! \cdot (k - 1)!} \cdot a^{n-(k-1)} \cdot b^{k-1} \quad \text{with } n = 8, k = 6, a = p^3, \text{ and } b = 2w$$

$$\frac{8!}{[8 - (6 - 1)]! \cdot (6 - 1)!} \cdot (p^3)^{8-(6-1)} \cdot (2w)^{6-1}$$

$$= \frac{8!}{[8 - (5)]! \cdot (5)!} \cdot (p^3)^{8-(5)} \cdot (2w)^5$$

$$= \frac{8!}{(3)! \cdot (5)!} \cdot (p^3)^3 \cdot (2w)^5$$

$$= 56 \cdot (p^9) \cdot (32w^5)$$

$$= 1792 p^9 w^5$$

section 13.3   PRACTICE EXERCISES

For Exercises 1–6, expand the binomials. Use Pascal's triangle to find the coefficients.

1. $(x + y)^4$

2. $(a + b)^3$

3. $(4 + p)^3$

4. $(1 + g)^4$

5. $(a^2 + b)^6$

6. $(p + q^2)^7$

For Exercises 7–12, rewrite each binomial of the form $(a - b)^n$ as $[a + (-b)]^n$. Then expand the binomials. Use Pascal's triangle to find the coefficients.

7. $(y - z)^5$

8. $(r - s)^6$

9. $(w - 2)^4$

10. $(t - 3)^5$

11. $(p^2 - w)^3$

12. $(5 - u^3)^4$

13. For $a > 0$ and $b > 0$, what happens to the signs of the terms when expanding the binomial $(a - b)^n$ compared with $(a + b)^n$?

For Exercises 14–19, evaluate the expression.

14. $5!$

15. $3!$

16. $4!$

17. $6!$

18. $0!$

19. $1!$

20. True or False: $0! \neq 1!$

21. True or False: $n!$ is defined for negative integers.

22. True or False: $n! = n$ for $n = 1$ and 2.

23. Show that $9! = 9 \cdot 8!$

24. Show that $6! = 6 \cdot 5!$

25. Show that $11! = 11 \cdot 10 \cdot 9!$

26. Show that $8! = 8 \cdot 7 \cdot 6!$

For Exercises 27–42, evaluate the expression.

27. $\dfrac{5!}{3!}$

28. $\dfrac{6!}{3!}$

29. $\dfrac{8!}{4!}$

30. $\dfrac{7!}{5!}$

31. $\dfrac{3!}{0!}$

32. $\dfrac{4!}{0!}$

33. $\dfrac{9!}{8!}$

34. $\dfrac{11!}{10!}$

35. $\dfrac{8!}{3!\,5!}$

36. $\dfrac{6!}{2!\,4!}$

37. $\dfrac{7!}{2!\,5!}$

38. $\dfrac{10!}{3!\,7!}$

39. $\dfrac{4!}{0!\,4!}$

40. $\dfrac{6!}{0!\,6!}$

41. $\dfrac{7!}{1!\,6!}$

42. $\dfrac{9!}{8!\,1!}$

43. When expanding $(a + b)^n$, how do you determine the coefficient of each term?

44. When expanding $(a + b)^n$, how do you determine the exponents on a and b?

For Exercises 45–56, use the binomial theorem to expand the binomials.

45. $(s + t)^6$

46. $(h + k)^4$

47. $(b - 3)^3$

48. $(c - 2)^5$

49. $(2x + y)^4$

50. $(p + 3q)^3$

51. $(c^2 - d)^7$

52. $(u - v^3)^6$

53. $(x + 1)^8$

54. $(x - 1)^8$

55. $\left(\dfrac{a}{2} - b\right)^5$

56. $\left(\dfrac{s}{3} + t\right)^5$

For Exercises 57–62, find the first three terms of the expansion.

57. $(m - n)^{11}$

58. $(p - q)^9$

59. $(2x + y)^{10}$

60. $(a + 3b)^{13}$

61. $(u^2 - v)^{12}$

62. $(r - s^2)^8$

63. How many terms are in the expansion of $(a + b)^8$?

64. How many terms are in the expansion of $(x + y)^{13}$?

For Exercises 65–76, find the indicated term of the binomial expansion.

65. $(m - n)^{11}$; sixth term

66. $(p - q)^9$; fourth term

67. $(2x + y)^{10}$; fourth term

68. $(a + 3b)^{13}$; fifth term

69. $(u^2 - v)^{12}$; fifth term

70. $(r - s^2)^8$; sixth term

71. $(5f + g)^9$; 10th term

72. $(4m + n)^{10}$; 11th term

73. $(p + 3q)^7$; p^3q^4 term

74. $(a + 2b)^5$; a^3b^2 term

75. $(x^2 - 3)^4$; x^4 term

76. $(4 - y^3)^6$; y^9 term

EXPANDING YOUR SKILLS

77. a. Expand $(a + b)^2$.

   b. Expand $[(x + y) + z]^2$ by substituting $a = (x + y)$ and $b = z$.

78. Explain how you could use the binomial theorem to expand $[(x + y) + z]^3$.

The binomial theorem can be used to approximate the value of a decimal number raised to an integer power. For example, to approximate $(1.04)^5$, we can expand $(1 + 0.04)^5$.

$$(1 + 0.04)^5 = (1)^5 + 5(1)^4(0.04)^1 + 10(1)^3(0.04)^2$$
$$+ 10(1)^2(0.04)^3 + 5(1)^1(0.04)^4 + (0.04)^5$$

$$= 1 + 0.2 + 0.016 + 0.00064$$
$$+ 0.0000128 + 0.0000001024$$

The sum of the first two terms is 1.2.

The sum of the first three terms is 1.216.

The sum of the first four terms is 1.21664.

The sum of the first five terms is 1.2166528.

The sum of the first six terms is 1.2166529024.

Notice that in this case, the contribution from the last several terms becomes smaller and smaller. Therefore, depending on the level of accuracy desired, we can approximate $(1.04)^5$ by adding the first several terms of the expansion.

In this example, we can estimate $(1.04)^5$ to the nearest hundredth by adding the first three terms and rounding to the nearest hundredth (1.22). We can estimate $(1.04)^5$ to the nearest thousandth by adding the first four terms and rounding to the nearest thousandth (1.217). Use this procedure to approximate the values given in Exercises 79–82.

79. Estimate $(1.01)^6$ to the nearest 0.001.

80. Estimate $(1.05)^6$ to the nearest 0.01.

81. Estimate $(0.97)^5$ to the nearest 0.01. *Hint*: Write $(0.97)^5$ as $(1 - 0.03)^5$.

82. Estimate $(0.96)^5$ to the nearest 0.01.

---

section

13.4   FUNDAMENTALS OF COUNTING

Concepts

1. Fundamental Principle of Counting

2. Permutations

3. Combinations

4. Comparing Permutations and Combinations

1. Fundamental Principle of Counting

Suppose a child makes an ice cream sundae with one scoop of ice cream plus a syrup. Suppose there are three choices of ice cream (vanilla, chocolate, and strawberry) and two choices of syrup (fudge and caramel). For each of the three ice cream choices there are two possible syrups, yielding $3 \cdot 2 = 6$ possible sundae combinations (Figure 13-1).

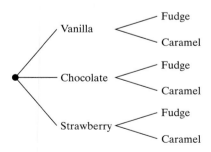

Figure 13-1

This example illustrates the **fundamental principle of counting**.

Fundamental Principle of Counting

If one event can occur in m different ways and a second event can occur in n different ways, then the sequence of both events can occur in $m \cdot n$ different ways.

The fundamental principle of counting can be extended to more than two events as demonstrated in the next example.

---

example 1

Applying the Fundamental Principle of Counting

Suppose Denisha visits Jimmy G's, a Cajun restaurant in Houston, Texas. She opts for a combo-meal in which she may choose from 12 different entrées, 4 different soups, and 3 different desserts. How many different dinners can she choose if she selects one item from each category?

Solution:

Applying the fundamental principle of counting, we have 144 different dinners.

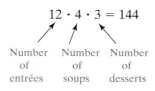

$$12 \cdot 4 \cdot 3 = 144$$

Number of entrées Number of soups Number of desserts

---

example 2

Applying the Fundamental Principle of Counting

A home security alarm consists of a code with four digits (allowing repetition of digits) that must be entered in a specific order.

a. How many different codes are possible?
b. If a burglar enters a house and has 45 seconds to turn off the alarm, do you think it's probable that he will guess the correct code in time?

Solution:

a. We can visualize the code as a sequence of four blanks that must each contain a digit.

_____ _____ _____ _____

Each digit in the code can be chosen from the numbers 0 to 9. Therefore, each blank has 10 different possibilities.

$$\underline{\ 10\ } \cdot \underline{\ 10\ } \cdot \underline{\ 10\ } \cdot \underline{\ 10\ } = 10{,}000 \text{ possible alarm codes}$$

b. Realistically, the burglar would probably only be able to enter a code every 1 to 2 seconds. If we assume that he entered 1 code per second, he would only be able to guess 45 different codes out of a possible 10,000. Therefore, it is highly improbable that he would guess the correct code in 45 seconds.

Sometimes the events in a sequence depend on a preceding event as shown in the next example.

example 3 **Applying the Fundamental Principle of Counting**

Maximus has five baby photos that he wants to arrange on a shelf. In how many different ways can he arrange the five photos?

Solution:

Think of the photo arrangement as five different slots on the shelf (Figure 13-2).

Figure 13-2

The first slot can have any of the five pictures. However, once the first picture is in place, there are only four available for the second slot. Similarly, once the first two pictures are in place, there are only three remaining, and so on. The total number of photo arrangements is

$$\underline{\quad5\quad} \cdot \underline{\quad4\quad} \cdot \underline{\quad3\quad} \cdot \underline{\quad2\quad} \cdot \underline{\quad1\quad} = 120.$$

The solution to Example 3 could have been written using factorial notation.

$$5 \cdot 4 \cdot 3 \cdot 2 \cdot 1 = 5!$$

Let n be a positive integer. Recall from Section 13.3, that $n!$ (read as "n factorial") is defined as the product of integers from 1 to n. That is,

$$n! = n(n - 1)(n - 2) \cdots (1) \text{ and by definition, } 0! = 1.$$

Graphing Calculator Box

Most scientific and graphing calculators have a factorial feature.

```
5!
              120
0!
                1
12!
        479001600
```

example 4   **Applying the Fundamental Principle of Counting**

Suppose eight horses run in a race. How many first-, second-, third-place arrangements are possible assuming no ties?

Solution:

Any of the eight horses can come in first place. That leaves seven possibilities for second place, and six possibilities for third. Therefore, there are $8 \cdot 7 \cdot 6 = 336$ possible first-, second-, third-place arrangements.

2. Permutations

The scenario presented in Example 4 has three different horses selected in a specified order from a group of eight horses. Each of the 336 arrangements is called a permutation of eight horses taken three at a time. In general, an ordered arrangement of r different items selected from n different items is called a **permutation** of n items taken r at a time. The number of all such arrangements is given by the following formula.

Permutation Rule

If $_nP_r$ represents the number of permutations of n items taken r at a time, then

$$_nP_r = \frac{n!}{(n-r)!}$$

Other commonly used notations for the number of permutations of n items taken r at a time are $P(n, r)$ and P_r^n.

From Example 4, we found the number of ways three different horses could be selected from eight horses in a race in a specified order. This value is equivalent to $_8P_3$.

$$_8P_3 = \frac{8!}{(8-3)!} = \frac{8!}{5!} = \frac{8 \cdot 7 \cdot 6 \cdot 5 \cdot 4 \cdot 3 \cdot 2 \cdot 1}{5 \cdot 4 \cdot 3 \cdot 2 \cdot 1} = 8 \cdot 7 \cdot 6 = 336$$

This is consistent with the result of Example 4.

example 5   **Computing Permutations**

Compute: a. $_{12}P_4$ b. $_7P_7$

Solution:

a. $_{12}P_4 = \frac{12!}{(12-4)!} = \frac{12!}{8!} = \frac{12 \cdot 11 \cdot 10 \cdot 9 \cdot 8 \cdot 7 \cdot 6 \cdot 5 \cdot 4 \cdot 3 \cdot 2 \cdot 1}{8 \cdot 7 \cdot 6 \cdot 5 \cdot 4 \cdot 3 \cdot 2 \cdot 1}$

$= 12 \cdot 11 \cdot 10 \cdot 9$

$= 11,880$

This result implies that there are 11,880 ways to select 4 items from a group of 12 items where the 4 items are selected in a specified order.

◆ **Avoiding Mistakes**

Remember that by definition, $0! = 1$.

b. $_7P_7 = \dfrac{7!}{(7-7)!} = \dfrac{7!}{0!} = \dfrac{7!}{1} = 7! = 5040$

This result implies that there are 5040 ways to select seven out of seven items in a specific order.

■

The next example will apply the permutation formula to solve a counting problem.

example 6

Applying Permutations to a Counting Problem

From a group of nine students, four are to be selected to receive cash prizes of $100, $50, $25, and $10, respectively. In how many ways can the four students be selected?

Tip: The order of selection is important in Example 6, because the four prizes are different. For example, suppose person A is awarded the $100 prize and B is awarded the $50 prize. It would be a different outcome if B got the $100 and A received the $50 prize.

Solution:

Because four different students are to be selected from a group of nine in a specified order, we have $_9P_4$.

$$_9P_4 = \frac{9!}{(9-4)!} = \frac{9!}{5!} = \frac{9 \cdot 8 \cdot 7 \cdot 6 \cdot 5 \cdot 4 \cdot 3 \cdot 2 \cdot 1}{5 \cdot 4 \cdot 3 \cdot 2 \cdot 1} = 9 \cdot 8 \cdot 7 \cdot 6 = 3024$$

There are 3024 ways to pick four different students from a group of nine in a specific order.

■

3. Combinations

In Example 6, we saw that a permutation defines a selection of four distinct items in a specified order from nine items. Now we will compare an event in which the order of selection is important to an event in which the order is not important.

Suppose that from a group of four members of student government we want to select two to serve as president and vice-president. If we label the students as A, B, C, and D, we can list all possible selections. The first student listed is designated as president and the second student listed is designated as vice-president. There are 12 possible outcomes shown here.

$$
\left.
\begin{array}{cccccc}
AB & AC & AD & BC & BD & CD \\
BA & CA & DA & CB & DB & DC
\end{array}
\right\} \text{ 12 permutations}
$$

These outcomes represent the set of all permutations of four students taken two at a time. Therefore, the number of president/vice-president selections can also be found by computing

$$_4P_2 = \frac{4!}{(4-2)!} = \frac{4!}{2!} = \frac{4 \cdot 3 \cdot 2 \cdot 1}{2 \cdot 1} = 12$$

Now suppose that we want to choose two students from the group of four to form a safety committee. In this case, there is no specific label assigned to the two students selected (in other words, we are not assigning roles to the students such as president or vice-president). In some sense, the two people selected are "equals." They are not holding distinguishable positions. In such a case, we can see that the order of selection is not important. Hence, selecting A first followed by B forms the same committee as selecting B first followed by A. We do not want to count the outcomes AB and BA twice. Therefore, there are only six possible groups as shown here.

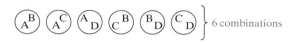

In this situation, the order of selection is not important. In general, an *unordered* selection of *r* different items taken from *n* different items is called a **combination** of *n* items taken *r* at a time. The number of all such arrangements is given by the following formula.

Combination Rule

If $_nC_r$ represents the number of combinations of *n* items taken *r* at a time, then

$$_nC_r = \frac{n!}{(n - r)! \cdot r!}$$

To count the number of ways two students can be selected from a group of four without regard to order, we compute $_4C_2$.

$$_4C_2 = \frac{4!}{(4 - 2)! \cdot 2!} = \frac{4!}{2! \cdot 2!} = \frac{4 \cdot 3 \cdot 2 \cdot 1}{(2 \cdot 1) \cdot (2 \cdot 1)} = 6$$

Notice that the combination formula differs from the permutation formula by a factor of *r*! in the denominator. In this example, there is an additional factor of 2! in the denominator. This factor divides out the repeated arrangements within the groups of two that result from order. In other words, the factor of 2! divides the total list of permutations by 2 to divide out the repeated arrangements such as AB and BA, AC and CA, and so on.

Tip: The number of combinations of *n* items taken *r* at a time can also be found by computing the number of permutations and dividing the result by *r*!. The factor of *r*! divides out repeated combinations that result from order within the permutations. Therefore, the combination formula

$$_nC_r = \frac{n!}{(n - r)! \cdot r!} \quad \text{can also be written as} \quad _nC_r = \frac{_nP_r}{r!}$$

example 7

Computing Combinations

Compute:

a. $_{10}C_2$

b. $_{12}C_{12}$

Solution:

a. $_{10}C_2 = \dfrac{10!}{(10-2)! \cdot 2!} = \dfrac{10!}{8! \cdot 2!} = \dfrac{10 \cdot 9 \cdot 8!}{8! \cdot 2 \cdot 1} = 45$

This result implies that there are 45 ways to select 2 items from a group of 10 when the order of selection is not considered.

b. $_{12}C_{12} = \dfrac{12!}{(12-12)! \cdot 12!} = \dfrac{12!}{0! \cdot 12!} = \dfrac{12!}{1 \cdot 12!} = 1$

This result implies that there is one way to select 12 items from a group of 12 without regard to order.

Tip: You might have noticed that the formula to compute $_nC_r$ follows the same format as the formula used to compute the coefficients of a binomial expansion (see Section 13.3).

Graphing Calculator Box

Most scientific and graphing calculators have a permutation function and a combination function.

```
4 nPr 2
                12
4 nCr 2
                 6
12 nCr 12
                 1
```

---

example 8

Applying Combinations to a Counting Problem

Sara picked out 15 different CDs that she likes equally well. However, she only has enough money to purchase four. In how many ways can she select 4 CDs from the group of 15?

Solution:

In this example, there is no implied order. Therefore, the number of ways she can select 4 CDs from 15 CDs is given by $_{15}C_4$.

$$_{15}C_4 = \dfrac{15!}{(15-4)! \cdot 4!} = \dfrac{15!}{11! \cdot 4!} = \dfrac{15 \cdot 14 \cdot 13 \cdot 12 \cdot 11!}{11! \cdot 4 \cdot 3 \cdot 2 \cdot 1} = 1365$$

4.   Comparing Permutations and Combinations

In this section three different rules for counting have been presented: the fundamental principle of counting, the permutation rule, and the combination rule. Perhaps the most difficult part of solving a counting problem is to select the most appropriate rule to apply.

- The fundamental principle of counting can always be applied, but it is not always the most convenient method.
- The permutation rule can be applied when r different items are selected from a group of n different items in a specified order.
- The combination rule can be applied when r different items are selected from a group of n different items in no specific order.

---

example 9

Applying Combinations and Permutations to a Counting Problem

Three raffle tickets are to be drawn from a group of 30 tickets.

a. Suppose the first ticket selected is for a weekend getaway. The second ticket selected is for a day at a health spa, and the third is for a free dinner. In how many different ways can the 3 tickets be selected from the 30?

b. Now suppose that the three tickets selected each warrant the same prize of a $100 gift certificate. In how many different ways can the 3 tickets be selected from the 30?

Solution:

a. Because the three tickets represent different prizes, the order in which the tickets are selected is important. We have $_{30}P_3$.

$$_{30}P_3 = \frac{30!}{(30-3)!} = \frac{30!}{27!} = \frac{30 \cdot 29 \cdot 28 \cdot \cancel{27!}}{\cancel{27!}} = 30 \cdot 29 \cdot 28 = 24{,}360$$

b. Because the prizes are equal and indistinguishable, the order in which the tickets are selected is *not* important. We have $_{30}C_3$.

$$_{30}C_3 = \frac{_{30}P_3}{3!} = \frac{30!}{(30-3)! \cdot 3!} = \frac{24{,}360}{6} = 4060$$

---

example 10

Applying the Rules of Counting

Suppose a license plate in Florida consists of three letters followed by three digits.

a. How many different license plates can be created using this scheme?

b. If no letter or digit may be repeated, how many different license plates can be created?

Solution:

For both parts (a) and (b), the order of the letters and digits is important. For instance, the license plate ABC-123 is different from BCA-321.

a. In this scenario, the permutation rule does not apply because two of the same letter or two of the same digit may be selected (remember that with both permutations and combination, different items must be selected). Therefore, we must apply the fundamental principle of counting.

$$26 \cdot 26 \cdot 26 \cdot 10 \cdot 10 \cdot 10 = 17{,}576{,}000 \text{ possible license plates}$$

There are 26 choices for each letter.   There are 10 choices for each digit.

b. The solution to part (a) can be modified so that no letter or digit is repeated. After each letter is used, the number of available letters is decreased by 1. After each digit is used, the number of available digits is decreased by 1.

$$26 \cdot 25 \cdot 24 \cdot 10 \cdot 9 \cdot 8 = 11{,}232{,}000 \text{ possible license plates}$$

Alternative Solution:

In part (b), the order of the letters and digits is important. Also notice that we may not reselect a letter or digit. Therefore, the number of license plates could also be found using the permutation rule along with the fundamental principle of counting.

$$\begin{pmatrix} \text{Number of ways to} \\ \text{select 3 letters from} \\ \text{26 letters in order} \end{pmatrix} \begin{pmatrix} \text{Number of ways to} \\ \text{select 3 digits from} \\ \text{10 digits in order} \end{pmatrix} = {}_{26}P_3 \cdot {}_{10}P_3$$

$$= (15{,}600)(720)$$

$$= 11{,}232{,}000$$

section 13.4   PRACTICE EXERCISES

For Exercises 1–4, evaluate the factorial expressions.

1. 6!

2. 8!

3. 0!

4. 1!

5. Evaluate $_{10}P_3$ and interpret its meaning.

6. Evaluate $_7P_2$ and interpret its meaning.

7. Evaluate $_{10}C_3$ and interpret its meaning.

8. Evaluate $_7C_2$ and interpret its meaning.

For Exercises 9–20, compute the permutation or combination.

9. $_{12}P_9$

10. $_6P_4$

11. $_{12}C_9$

12. $_6C_4$

13. $_7P_1$

14. $_5P_1$

15. $_7C_1$

16. $_5C_1$

17. $_8P_8$

18. $_4P_4$

19. $_8C_8$

20. $_4C_4$

21. Given the set of elements {A, B, C},

    a. List all permutations of two elements.

    b. List all combinations of two elements.

22. Three people must be selected from a group of 10 people.

    a. Explain the difference between permutations of three people versus combinations of three people.

    b. How many permutations of three can be found from the group of 10?

    c. How many combinations of three can be found from the group of 10?

For Exercises 23–28, apply the fundamental principle of counting.

23. How many different ways can six people be seated in a row?

24. In how many ways can 10 children line up to leave the classroom?

25. A computer password consists of six digits. How many six-digit passwords are possible?

26. A computer filename can consist of eight characters, where a character is any one of the 26 letters of the alphabet or any of the 10 digits. How many computer filenames are possible?

27. At a certain hospital, the dinner menu consists of four choices of entrée, three choices of salad, eight choices of beverage, and six choices of dessert. How many different meals can be formed if a patient chooses one item from each category?

28. Mr. Dehili must dress for an important business meeting. He can choose his outfit from three different suits, six different shirts, and 12 different ties. Assuming that Mr. Dehili has no regard for color combinations, how many different outfits can he form, given that he picks one item from each category?

For Exercises 29–36, use the permutation or combination rule.

29. How many first-, second-, and third-place finishes are possible in a dog race containing 10 dogs?

30. In how many ways can a judge award blue, red, and yellow ribbons to 3 films at a film festival if there are 12 films entered in the contest?

31. Heather wants to invite 11 girls from her fifth-grade class to a slumber party. However, her mother will only allow her to invite six people. In how many ways can she invite 6 girls out of the 11 to her party?

32. How many different five-member committees can be formed from the 100 U.S. senators?

33. A book club offers five books for $9.99 as an introductory offer. If you can choose from a list of 10 books, in how many ways can you make your selection of 5?

34. A basketball coach must pick 5 players from a roster of 12 to start a game. In how many ways can he choose his starting five players assuming that all players have equal ability?

35. Suppose there are eight employees who work at a chain coffee shop in Chicago. The manager wants to select two employees to work at two new shops (shop A and shop B) to help train new employees. If one of the selected employees is to work in shop A and the other is to work in shop B, how many possible selections can the manager make?

36. A disc jockey has five songs that he must play in a half-hour period. How many different ways can he arrange the five songs?

For Exercises 37–54, use an appropriate rule of counting.

37. Most radio stations that were licensed after 1927 have four call letters starting with K or W such as WROD. Assuming no repetitions of letters, how many four-letter sets are possible?

38. A lock on a school locker consists of three different numbers taken from 1 to 39 in a specific order. How many three-number codes are possible?

39. In how many ways can a book buyer select 4 books from a list of 10 different books?

40. How many samples of size 6 can be selected from a population of 30 members?

41. Three men and three women have reserved six seats in a row at a concert. In how many ways can they arrange themselves if the men and women are to alternate seats and a man must sit in the first seat?

42. Three men and three women have reserved six seats in a row for a play. In how many ways can they arrange themselves if the men must all sit together and the women must all sit together?

43. A musician plans to perform nine selections. In how many ways can she arrange the musical selections?

44. From a pool of 12 candidates, the offices of president, vice-president, treasurer, and secretary must be filled. In how many different ways can the offices be filled?

45. A committee is to be formed from a collection of 10 men and eight women. How many committees can be made consisting of exactly three men and one woman?

46. A committee is to be formed from a collection of 10 men and eight women. How many committees of four can be made consisting of two men and two women?

47. If a fair coin is flipped three times, how many different sequences of heads and tails can be formed?

48. If a couple plans to have four children, how many different gender sequences can be formed?

49. From a jury pool of 40 people, 12 are to be selected. In how many different ways can a jury of 12 be selected?

50. To play the Georgia lottery, a person must choose 6 numbers (in any order) from a list of 49 numbers. How many different combinations of six numbers are possible?

51. There are six Republicans and four Democrats sitting in a room.

    a. In how many different ways can a committee of two be selected?

    b. In how many different ways can a committee of two be selected if both people must be Republican?

    c. In how many different ways can a committee of two be selected if both people must be Democrat?

    d. In how many different ways can a committee of two be selected if one person from each party is selected?

52. In how many ways can a 10-question true or false test be answered assuming that a student answers all questions.

53. At a pizza place a customer can order a pizza with or without any of the following options: pepperoni, sausage, mushrooms, peppers, onions, olives, or anchovies. How many different pizzas can be formed?

54. Jeff wants to give his five most valuable baseball cards to his three brothers. In how many ways can he make the distribution?

■ EXPANDING YOUR SKILLS

55. In how many ways can the batting order be determined for a co-ed softball team with five women and four men if

   a. There are no restrictions.

   b. The first and last batters must be women.

   c. The women must all bat before the men.

   d. The men must all bat consecutively.

56. In how many ways can a group of six men and five women be lined up for a photograph if

   a. There are no restrictions.

   b. The men and women must alternate.

   c. The men must stand to the left of the women.

   d. There must be a man on each end.

57. a. List all the different sequences of letters that can be made from the word *pot*.

   b. List all the different sequences of letters that can be made from the word *tot*.

58. a. List all the different sequences that can be made from the letters in the word *desk*.

   b. List all of the different sequences that can be made from the letters in the word *door*.

59. Given the set of numbers {2, 3, 4, 5, 6, 7, 8}

   a. How many different three-digit numbers can be formed?

   b. How many different three-digit numbers can be formed if the number cannot have any repeated digits?

   c. How many different three-digit numbers can be formed if the number is to be even and repetition of digits is allowed?

60. Given the set of numbers {1, 2, 3, 4, 5, 6, 7}

   a. How many different four-digit numbers can be formed?

   b. How many different four-digit numbers can be formed if the number cannot have any repeated digits?

   c. How many different four-digit numbers can be formed if the number is to be divisible by 5 and repetition of digits is allowed?

For Exercises 61–64, use the following description of a standard deck of 52 cards. A standard deck of cards has four suits (clubs, diamonds, hearts, and spades). Each suit has 13 cards. The hearts and diamonds are red cards, and the clubs and spades are black cards. Assume that five cards are selected from a standard deck. In how many ways can the following occur?

61. All five cards are black.

62. All five cards are hearts.

63. There are three diamonds and two clubs.

64. There are more red cards than black cards.

section

13.5   INTRODUCTION TO PROBABILITY

1. Basic Definitions

The study of probability provides a mathematical means to measure the likelihood of an event occurring. It is of particular interest because of its application to everyday events.

- The National Cancer Institute estimates that a woman has a 1 in 8 chance of developing breast cancer in her lifetime.
- The probability of winning the California Fantasy Five lottery grand prize is

$$\frac{1}{575,757}$$

- Genetic DNA analysis can be used to determine the risk that a child will be born with cystic fibrosis. If both parents test positive, the probability is 25% that a child will be born with the disease.

To begin our discussion, we must first understand some basic definitions.

An activity with observable outcomes is called an **experiment**. Each repetition of an experiment is called a **trial**. The result of a trial is called an **outcome** of the experiment. The set of all possible outcomes of an experiment is called the **sample space**, S, of the experiment.

For example, if a single die is rolled, the sample space is $\{1, 2, 3, 4, 5, 6\}$. If a coin is tossed, the outcomes are heads (H) or tails (T). The sample space is $\{H, T\}$.

Any subset of a sample space is called an **event**. For example, if we define event, E_1, as the event that a number greater than 4 is rolled on a die, then, $E_1 = \{5, 6\}$. If event E_2 is the event that a coin lands as a head, then $E_2 = \{H\}$.

Tip: The word *die* is the singular of the word *dice*. Therefore, we may roll a pair of dice, but we roll a single die.

2. Probability of an Event

The number of elements in a sample space is denoted by $n(S)$. The number of elements in the sample space that are also in event E is denoted by $n(E)$. The notation $P(E)$ denotes the probability of event E, defined as follows.

Probability of Event, *E*

In a sample space, S, of equally likely outcomes, the **probability of E** is given by

$$P(E) = \frac{n(E)}{n(S)}$$

For the event, E_1, of rolling a number greater than 4 on a die, we have $E_1 = \{5, 6\}$ and $S = \{1, 2, 3, 4, 5, 6\}$. Then

$$P(E_1) = \frac{n(E_1)}{n(S)} = \frac{2}{6} = \frac{1}{3}$$

For the event, E_2, that a coin will land as a head, we have $E_2 = \{H\}$ and $S = \{H, T\}$. Then

$$P(E_2) = \frac{n(E_2)}{n(S)} = \frac{1}{2}$$

The value of a probability can be written as a fraction, as a decimal, or as a percent. Therefore, $P(E_2) = \frac{1}{2}$, or 0.5 or 50%. In words, this means that theoretically we expect half (50%) of the outcomes to land as a head. This does not necessarily mean that exactly one out of every two coin tosses will land as a head. Instead, it is a ratio that we expect experimental observations to approach after a large number of trials. For example, if we flip a coin 1000 times, we might get 493 heads for a ratio of $\frac{493}{1000}$, or 0.493. This value is close to the theoretical value of 0.500.

---

example 1

Computing Probabilities

A box contains two red, four white, and one blue marble. Suppose one marble is selected at random. Find the probability of selecting

a.   A red marble.
b.   A white marble.
c.   A green marble.

Solution:

Denote the sample space as $S = \{R_1, R_2, W_1, W_2, W_3, W_4, B_1\}$

a.   Let event R represent the event of selecting a red marble. Because there are two red marbles, then $R = \{R_1, R_2\}$. Then

$$P(R) = \frac{n(R)}{n(S)} = \frac{2}{7}$$

b.   Let W represent the event of selecting a white marble. Because there are four white marbles, then $W = \{W_1, W_2, W_3, W_4\}$. Then $P(W) = \frac{4}{7}$.
c.   Let G represent the event of selecting a green marble. Because there are no green marbles in the box, then G equals the empty set. $G = \{\ \}$. Then $P(G) = \frac{0}{7} = 0$.

From Example 1(c), the event of selecting a green marble is impossible. The probability of an **impossible event** is 0. An event that is certain to happen is called a **certain event**. Its probability is 1. For example, if a die is tossed, the probability that the die will land as a number between 0 and 7 is certain to happen. Any of the six outcomes 1, 2, 3, 4, 5, 6 will satisfy the event. Therefore, the probability of rolling a number between 0 and 7 is $\frac{6}{6} = 1$.

The counting rules learned in Section 13.4 can be helpful in determining the number of elements in an event and in a sample space. This is illustrated in the next example.

example 2

Applying the Counting Rules to Probability

Suppose a group of politicians consists of nine men and five women. If three people are selected at random to form a committee, what is the probability that all are women?

Solution:

Let W represent the event that a committee of three women is selected.

Let S represent the sample space consisting of all possible committees of three with no restrictions.

There are 14 people available to form a committee of 3. If no restrictions are imposed, the number of possible committees of three is given by $_{14}C_3 = 364$. The number of possible committees of three selected from the group of women is given by $_5C_3 = 10$. Therefore, the probability of selecting a committee that consists of all women is given by

$$P(W) = \frac{n(W)}{n(S)} = \frac{_5C_3}{_{14}C_3} = \frac{10}{364} = \frac{5}{182}$$

3. Estimating Probabilities from Observed Data

We were able to compute the probabilities in Examples 1 and 2 because the sample space was known. Sometimes we need to collect information from a series of repeated trials to help us estimate probabilities.

example 3

Estimating Probabilities from Observed Data

In a carnival game, Erin will win a prize if she can toss a ring around the neck of a bowling pin. After observing 200 players that had gone before her, she learns that 15 players won a prize. Based on this observation, what is the probability of winning a prize?

Solution:

In this situation, we may think of the outcomes of the 200 trials as the sample space. In this case, 15 trials came out as wins. Therefore, if W represents the event of a win, then

$$P(W) = \frac{15}{200} = \frac{3}{40}, \text{ or } 0.075$$

4. Complementary Events

Given an event, E, we define the **complement of E** (denoted E') as all elements in the sample space that are not in event E. The relationship between E and E' is shown in Figure 13-3. In particular note that the union of an event and its complement equals the sample space and the intersection of an event and its complement is the empty set.

$$E \cup E' = S \quad \text{and} \quad E \cap E' = \{ \ \}$$

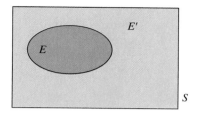

Figure 13-3

From Example 3, W represents the event that a person will win a prize in a carnival. Therefore, W' represents the probability that a person will not win (the person will lose). If there were 15 wins out of 200 trials, then there were 185 losses. Hence,

$$P(W') = \frac{185}{200} = \frac{37}{40}, \text{ or } 0.925$$

Notice that

$$P(W) + P(W') = \frac{15}{200} + \frac{185}{200} = 1$$

It is true in general that the sum of the probability of an event and its complement must equal 1 to account for 100% of all outcomes.

Probability of Complementary Events

If E' represents the complement of event E, then

$$P(E) + P(E') = 1$$

---

example 4

Finding the Probability of Complementary Events

Find $P(E)$ or $P(E')$ as indicated.

a. Given $P(E) = 0.309$, find $P(E')$.
b. Given $P(E') = \frac{7}{12}$, find $P(E)$.

Solution:

a. Because $P(E) + P(E') = 1$, we have $P(E') = 1 - P(E)$.

$$P(E') = 1 - 0.309$$
$$= 0.691$$

b. Because $P(E) + P(E') = 1$, we have $P(E) = 1 - P(E')$.

$$P(E) = 1 - \frac{7}{12}$$

$$= \frac{5}{12}$$

example 5   **Computing Probabilities Using the Complement of an Event**

An introductory psychology class at Michigan State University has 100 fresh-men, 80 sophomores, 37 juniors, and 6 seniors. If one student from the class is selected at random, find the probability that

> 100 freshmen
> 80 sophomores
> 37 juniors
> 6 seniors

a. The student is a freshman.
b. The student is not a freshman.

Total: 223 students

Solution:

a. Let F represent the event of selecting a freshman.

There are 100 freshmen out of 223 total students.

$$P(F) = \frac{100}{223}$$

b. F' represents the event of selecting a *non*freshman. $P(F') = 1 - P(F)$.

$$P(F') = 1 - \frac{100}{223} = \frac{123}{223}$$

---

5. Addition Rule

A compound event in probability involves two or more events. If two events are expressed as alternatives, they can be considered as a compound event often joined by the word *or*.

example 6   **Computing a Compound Event Involving Alternatives**

Suppose 10 Ping Pong balls numbered 0 through 9 are in a bag. If one ball is se-lected at random, what is the probability of selecting a number less than 3 or a number greater than 5?

Solution:

Let A represent the event of selecting a number less than 3. Then $A = \{0, 1, 2\}$.

Let B represent the event of selecting a number greater than 5. Then $B = \{6, 7, 8, 9\}$.

The compound event A or B equals the union of events A and B.

$$A \text{ or } B = A \cup B = \{0, 1, 2, 6, 7, 8, 9\}$$

Therefore

$$P(A \text{ or } B) = \frac{n(A \cup B)}{n(S)} = \frac{7}{10}$$

In Example 6, the events A and B have no elements in common (no number can be less than 3 and also greater than 5). Two events that have no common elements are said to be **mutually exclusive**. For two mutually exclusive events, $P(A \text{ or } B)$ can be found by adding the individual probabilities: $P(A \text{ or } B) = P(A) + P(B)$. In Example 6, we have

$$P(A \text{ or } B) = \frac{3}{10} + \frac{4}{10} = \frac{7}{10}$$

Two events that are *not* mutually exclusive share at least one common element. Therefore, we must be careful not to duplicate elements when we add probabilities. The next example demonstrates how the sum of the individual probabilities must be adjusted to accommodate elements that "overlap" in two events.

example 7

Computing a Compound Event Involving Alternatives

Suppose 10 Ping Pong balls numbered 0 through 9 are in a bag. If one ball is selected at random, what is the probability of selecting an even number or a number greater than 3?

Solution:

Let A represent the event of selecting an even number. Then $A = \{0, 2, 4, 6, 8\}$.

Let B represent the event of selecting a number greater than 3. Then $B = \{4, 5, 6, 7, 8, 9\}$.

The compound event A or B equals the union of events A and B. Note that the common elements $4, 6,$ and 8 are not listed twice.

$$A \text{ or } B = A \cup B = \{0, 2, 4, 5, 6, 7, 8, 9\}$$

Therefore,

$$P(A \text{ or } B) = \frac{n(A \cup B)}{n(S)} = \frac{8}{10}, \text{ or } \frac{4}{5}$$

 Avoiding Mistakes

In Example 7, if we had incorrectly added $P(A) + P(B)$ without subtracting $P(A$ and $B)$, we would have obtained a value greater than 1:

$$\frac{5}{10} + \frac{6}{10} = \frac{11}{10}$$

This is impossible for a probability.

In Example 7, the value of $P(A \text{ or } B)$ cannot be found by simply adding $P(A)$ and $P(B)$. An adjustment must be made because both $P(A)$ and $P(B)$ account for the common elements 4, 6, and 8. The sum $P(A) + P(B)$ would count these elements twice. To compensate for the duplication of elements, we subtract $P(A$ and $B)$, which denotes the probability that events A and B occur simultaneously.

Addition Rule for Probability

$$P(A \text{ or } B) = P(A) + P(B) - P(A \text{ and } B)$$

Note: If A and B are mutually exclusive events, then $P(A \text{ and } B) = 0$.

From Example 7, we conclude that three elements are included in both event A and in event B. Therefore, we have

$$P(A \text{ or } B) = \frac{5}{10} + \frac{6}{10} - \frac{3}{10} = \frac{8}{10}$$

example 8

Applying the Addition Rule

The safety and security department at a certain college asked a sample of 265 students to respond to the following question.

"Do you think that the College has adequate lighting on campus at night?"

The following table shows the results of the survey by gender and response.

	Yes	No	No Opinion	Total
Male	92	7	4	103
Female	36	102	24	162
Total	128	109	28	265

If one student is selected at random from the group, find the probability that

a.   The student answered yes or had no opinion.
b.   The student answered no or was female.

Solution:

a.   Let Y be the event that a student answered yes, and let Z represent the event that the student had no opinion. The events Y and Z are mutually exclusive. Hence,

$$P(Y \text{ or } Z) = P(Y) + P(Z)$$
$$= \frac{128}{265} + \frac{28}{265}$$
$$= \frac{156}{265}$$

b.   Let N be the event that a student answered no, and let F be the event that a student is female. The events N and F are *not* mutually exclusive. Hence,

$$P(N \text{ or } F) = P(N) + P(F) - P(N \text{ and } F)$$
$$= \frac{109}{265} + \frac{162}{265} - \frac{102}{265}$$
$$= \frac{169}{265}$$

There are 102 students who are both female and answered no.

Tip: From Example 8(b), the expression $P(N \text{ or } F)$ could have been found by adding all the elements in the "no" column and then adding the remaining females. In this way, we are careful not to duplicate the females who answered no.

$$P(N \text{ or } F) = \frac{7 + 102 + 36 + 24}{265} = \frac{169}{265}$$

6. Multiplication Rule for Independent Events

Two events in probability are said to be independent if one event does not affect the probability that the other will occur, and vice versa. For example, if a coin is flipped and a die is rolled, the outcome of the coin has no influence on the outcome of the die and vice versa.

Multiplication Rule for Independent Events

For two independent events A and B, the probability that A and B will occur is given by

$$P(A \text{ and } B) = P(A) \cdot P(B)$$

For example, if T is the event that a coin comes up tails and S is the event that a die lands on a 6, then the probability that a tail comes up on a coin followed by an outcome of 6 on a die is given by

$$P(T \text{ and } S) = P(T) \cdot P(S)$$

$$= \frac{1}{2} \cdot \frac{1}{6} = \frac{1}{12}$$

The multiplication rule can be extended to two or more events as shown in the next example.

example 9 **Applying the Multiplication Rule**

Clinical studies for a new pain medication indicate that approximately 6% of the people who take the drug experience nausea. If three patients take the drug, what is the probability that all three experience nausea?

Solution:

Let N represent the event that an individual patient experiences nausea.

Let E represent the event that all three patients experience nausea.

If all three patients experience nausea, then the first experiences nausea, and the second experiences nausea, and the third experiences nausea. The possibility of side effects is an independent event from patient to patient. Applying the multiplication rule, we have

$$P(E) = P(N) \cdot P(N) \cdot P(N)$$
$$= (0.06)(0.06)(0.06)$$
$$= 0.000216$$

If one event in a sequence of events influences the probability of another event, then the events are said to be **dependent**. The next example shows how the multiplication rule may be adapted for dependent events.

---

example 10

Applying the Multiplication Rule

Five $1 bills, two $5 bills, and three $10 bills are in a box.

a. If two bills are selected from the box with replacement, find the probability that both bills are $10 bills.
b. If two bills are selected from the box without replacement, find the probability that both are $10 bills.

Solution:

a. The probability of selecting the first $10 bill is $\frac{3}{10}$. Because the first bill is replaced before the second bill is selected, the probability of selecting the second $10 bill is also $\frac{3}{10}$. Therefore, the probability that two $10 bills are selected is

$$\frac{3}{10} \cdot \frac{3}{10} = \frac{9}{100}$$

5 $1
2 $5
3 $10

b. The probability of selecting the first $10 bill is $\frac{3}{10}$. However, because the first bill is *not* replaced before the second bill is selected, the probability of selecting the second $10 bill is $\frac{2}{9}$ (both the sample space and the number of $10 bills is decreased by 1). Therefore, the probability that two $10 bills are selected without replacement is

$$\frac{3}{10} \cdot \frac{2}{9} = \frac{6}{90}, \text{ or } \frac{1}{15}$$

In Example 10(b), the probability of selecting a second $10 bill, given that the first bill selected was also a $10 bill, is $\frac{2}{9}$ (rather than $\frac{3}{10}$). The given condition that a $10 bill was already removed from the sample space alters the probability of the second event. The events are dependent, and we say that the second probability is a **conditional probability**. The multiplication rule for probability may still be applied for dependent events as demonstrated in Example 10; however, care should be taken when computing conditional probabilities.

section 13.5 PRACTICE EXERCISES

1. In how many ways can 4 songs be selected from 10 different songs without regard to order?

2. Samira wants her father to buy her six different toys, but he only has enough money to buy two. In how many ways can Samira's father buy two toys from a group of six?

3. In how many different orders can the five musical notes A, B, C, D, and E be played?

4. In how many ways can Mr. Bishop rank three movies from a group of seven?

5. Which of the values can represent the probability of an event?

   a. 0.5   b. $\frac{2}{3}$ c. $-\frac{7}{5}$ d. 1.00

   e. 150%   f. 3.7   g. 3.7%   h. 0.92

6. Which of the values can represent the probability of an event?

   a. 1.62   b. $-\frac{2}{7}$ c. 0.00   d. 1.00

   e. 200%   f. 4.5   g. 4.5%   h. 0.87

For Exercises 7–10, find $P(E)$ or $P(E')$ as indicated.

7. Given $P(E) = 0.042$, find $P(E')$.

8. Given $P(E) = 0.871$, find $P(E')$.

9. Given $P(E') = \frac{7}{12}$, find $P(E)$.

10. Given $P(E') = \frac{3}{8}$, find $P(E)$.

11. If a single die is rolled, what is the probability that it will come up as a number less than 4?

12. If a single die is rolled, what is the probability that it will come up as a number greater than 5?

13. The final exam in a course in contemporary science resulted in the following distribution:

Grade	A	B	C	D	F
Number of students	8	15	21	10	5

a. What is the probability that a student selected at random received an "A" in the course?

b. What is the probability that a student did not pass the course if a passing grade is a "C" or better?

14. A sample of students is taken from a physical education class at a 4-year college. The distribution is given in the table. If one student is selected at random, find the probability that

a. The student is a sophomore.

b. The student is not a senior.

Class	Number of students
Freshman	15
Sophomore	11
Junior	6
Senior	3

15. A 1-year absentee record for a business is given in the table. If one employee is picked at random, find the probability that the employee missed

a. Exactly 3 days of work.

b. Between 1 and 5 days, inclusive.

c. At least 4 days.

d. More than 5 days or less than 2 days.

Number of days missed	Number of people
0	4
1	2
2	14
3	10
4	16
5	18
6	10
7	6

16. The data in the pie chart categorizes the method by which workers in a college town commute to work. If one working member of the community is selected at random, find the probability that the individual

    a. Commutes by bicycle.

    b. Does not use public transportation.

Method of Commuting to and from Work

Public transportation 17%

Carpool 14%

Drive alone 61%

Bicycle 8%

17. In a group of eight students, three are female and five are male. If a committee of two is to be selected, what is the probability that

    a. Both members are female?

    b. Both members are male?

    c. One member is male and one is female?

18. In a group of 10 students at a community college, 6 are freshmen and 4 are sophomores. If a committee of two is selected, what is the probability that

    a. Both members are sophomores?

    b. Both members are freshmen?

    c. One member is a sophomore and one is a freshman?

19. In the California Fantasy Five lottery a player wins the grand prize if the player picks the winning 5 numbers (in any order) out of 39 numbers.

    a. What is the probability that a player will win the grand prize?

    b. What is the probability that a player will not win the grand prize?

    c. Joanne thinks that the probability of winning the grand prize in the lottery is 0.50, because according to her "There's a 50–50 chance of winning, because you either win or you lose." What is wrong with Joanne's logic?

20. In the Florida lottery, a player wins the grand prize if the player picks the winning 6 numbers (in any order) out of 53 numbers.

    a. What is the probability that a player will win the grand prize?

    b. What is the probability that a player will not win the grand prize?

21. Five people enter their names in a hat for a drawing. If the names are drawn from the hat, what is the probability that they will be drawn in ascending alphabetical order?

22. Ten Ping Pong balls, numbered 0 through 9, are in a box. If the Ping Pong balls are selected one at a time, what is the probability that they will be removed in ascending order by number?

23. A couple plans to have four children. If the probability of having a boy or a girl on any given birth is equally likely, what is the probability that

    a. All the children will be boys?

    b. All the children will be girls?

24. If a student takes a five-question true/false test, what is the probability of getting all the questions right if the student guesses? What is the probability of getting all the questions wrong?

25. Suppose a student guesses on a four-question multiple-choice quiz. If each multiple-choice question has five possible responses (a, b, c, d, or e),

    a. What is the probability that the student will get all questions right?

    b. What is the probability that the student will get all questions wrong?

26. Suppose a student guesses on a 10-question multiple-choice test. If each multiple-choice question has four possible responses (a, b, c, or d),

    a. What is the probability that the student will get all questions right?

    b. What is the probability that the student will get all questions wrong?

27. The following table categorizes a sample of smokers and nonsmokers according to their blood pressure levels.

	Normal Blood Pressure	Elevated Blood Pressure	Total
Smokers	32	18	50
Nonsmokers	71	9	80
Total	103	27	130

If one person from the sample is selected at random, find the probability that

a. The person has elevated blood pressure.

b. The person is a nonsmoker.

c. The person does not have normal blood pressure.

d. The person is a smoker or has normal blood pressure.

e. The person is a nonsmoker or has normal blood pressure.

28. The following table categorizes a sample of alcoholics and nonalcoholics according to their cholesterol level.

	Normal Cholesterol	Elevated Cholesterol	Total
Alcoholic	20	80	100
Nonalcoholic	160	40	200
Total	180	120	300

If one person from the sample is selected at random, find the probability that

a. The person is a nonalcoholic.

b. The person has elevated cholesterol.

c. The person does not have elevated cholesterol.

d. The person is an alcoholic or has elevated cholesterol.

e. The person is a nonalcoholic or has normal cholesterol.

A standard deck of cards has 52 cards divided into four suits: clubs; diamonds; hearts; and spades. Each suit has 13 cards consisting of an ace, a king, a queen, a jack, and cards numbered from 2 to 10. Use this sample space to answer Exercises 29–32.

29. If one card is selected from a standard deck, what is the probability of selecting

a. A heart?

b. A face card (face cards are jacks, queens, and kings)?

c. A red card (hearts and diamonds are red)?

d. A red card or a jack?

e. A heart or a 6?

f. A spade or a heart?

30. If one card is selected from a standard deck, what is the probability of selecting

a. A club?

b. A 5 or a 10?

c. A black card (clubs and spades are black cards)?

d. A black card or an ace?

e. A diamond or a 2?

f. A club or a diamond?

31. If two cards are selected from a standard deck *with* replacement, what is the probability that

a. Both cards are hearts?

b. The first card is a jack, and the second card is a king?

c. How would the answers to parts (a) and (b) have changed if the cards had been selected without replacement?

32. If two cards are selected from a standard deck *with* replacement, what is the probability that

a. The first card is a heart and the second card is a diamond?

b. Both cards are 10s?

c. How would the answers to parts (a) and (b) have changed if the cards had been selected without replacement?

33. Approximately 7% of patients who take a particular drug experience side effects. If four patients take the drug, what is the probability that all four will experience side effects?

34. In a blood testing procedure, blood samples from four people are combined into one mixture. The mixture will test negative if all the individual samples are negative. The mixture will test positive if at least one individual sample within the mixture tests positive. Assume that the probability that an individual sample tests positive is 0.09. Find the probability that the mixture tests negative. (Round to four decimal places.)

35. In a certain town, 4% of people commute to work by bicycle. If two people are selected randomly from the town,

    a. What is the probability that they both commute to work by bicycle?

    b. What is the probability that neither commutes to work by bicycle?

36. A particular drug has a 90% cure rate. If six patients are randomly selected and given this treatment,

    a. What is the probability that they are all cured? (Round to four decimal places.)

    b. What is the probability that none of the patients is cured?

37. A bin contains 60 lightbulbs of which 8 are defective. If four different lightbulbs are randomly selected from the bin, what is the probability that none of the selected bulbs is defective? (Round to four decimal places.)

38. A box contains 100 batteries of which 12 are defective. If three different batteries are randomly selected from the box, what is the probability that all of the batteries are defective? (Round to four decimal places.)

39. In a box of a dozen eggs, four are cracked.

    a. If one egg is selected at random, what is the probability that a cracked egg is selected?

    b. If three different eggs are selected at random, what is the probability that all of the eggs selected are cracked?

    c. If three different eggs are selected at random, what is the probability that none of the cracked eggs is selected?

40. In a roll of film, 5 out of 24 pictures are blurry.

    a. If one picture is selected at random, what is the probability that it is one of the blurry pictures?

    b. If three different pictures are selected at random, what is the probability that they are all blurry?

    c. If three different pictures are selected at random, what is the probability that none of the selected pictures is blurry?

EXPANDING YOUR SKILLS

41. A metropolitan police force in the southeastern United States consists of 600 officers: 480 men and 120 women. Over the past 2 years, 160 officers on the police force have been promoted. The following table shows the breakdown of promotions for male and female officers.

	Promoted	Not Promoted	Total
Male	140	340	480
Female	20	100	120
	160	440	600

If a police officer is selected at random, what is the probability that

    a. The officer is a female?

    b. The officer was promoted?

    c. The officer is male or was not promoted?

    d. The officer was promoted, given that he is male?

    e. The officer was promoted, given that she is female?

    f. Write the probabilities in parts (d) and (e) in decimal form (round to three decimal places). What does the difference in probabilities mean in the context of this problem?

42. The following table depicts the grade distribution for a college algebra class based on age and grades.

	A	B	C	F	Total
17–26 years	150	220	370	180	920
27–36 years	140	200	220	90	650
37–46 years	150	120	60	40	370
Total	440	540	650	310	1940

If one student is selected at random from the group, find the probability that

a. The student received an "A" in the course.

b. The student was in the 27–36 age group.

c. The student was in the 37–46 age group or received a "B" in the course.

d. The student received an "A" in the course, given that the student is in the 37–46 age group.

e. The student received an "A" in the course, given that the student is in the 17–26 age group.

f. Write the probabilities in parts (d) and (e) in decimal form (round to three decimal places). What does the difference in probabilities mean in the context of this problem?

The probability of event, E, is defined as

$$P(E) = \frac{n(E)}{n(S)}$$

This is the ratio of the number of elements in the event to the total number of elements in the sample space. The odds of event, E, are defined as $n(E):n(E')$. The odds of an event represent the ratio of the number of elements in the event to the number of elements not in the event. For example, the probability of rolling a 2 on a die is $\frac{1}{6}$, whereas the *odds* of rolling a 2 are $1:5$. Use the definition of the odds of an event to answer Exercises 43–46.

43. a. What is the probability of rolling a number less than 3 on a die?

 b. What are the odds of rolling a number less than 3 on a die?

44. a. What is the probability of flipping a coin and getting a head?

 b. What are the odds of flipping a coin and getting a head?

45. A box of marbles has three yellow marbles, two green marbles, and five red marbles. Suppose one marble is selected at random.

 a. What is the probability of selecting a yellow marble?

 b. What are the odds of selecting a yellow marble?

 c. What is the probability of selecting a marble that is not green?

 d. What are the odds against selecting a green marble?

46. A box of 100 batteries has 5 defective ones. Suppose one battery is selected at random.

 a. What is the probability of selecting a defective battery?

 b. What are the odds of selecting a defective battery?

 c. What is the probability of selecting a battery that is not defective?

 d. What are the odds against selecting a defective battery?

SECTION 13.1—SEQUENCES AND SERIES

KEY CONCEPTS:

An infinite sequence is a function whose domain is the set of positive integers.

A finite sequence is a function whose domain is the set of the first n positive integers.

The expression a_n defines the nth term (or general term) of a sequence.

Sometimes the terms of a sequence may have alternating signs. Such a sequence is called an alternating sequence.

The indicated sum of the terms of a sequence is called a series. The Greek letter Σ (sigma) is used to indicate sums.

KEY TERMS:

a_n
alternating sequence
finite sequence
index of summation
infinite sequence
nth term of a sequence
series
sigma notation
terms of a sequence

EXAMPLES:

$1, 4, 9, 16, 25, \ldots$ is an infinite sequence.

$1, 4, 9, 16, 25$ is a finite sequence.

The nth term of the sequence
$1, 4, 9, 16, 25, \ldots$ is given by $a_n = n^2$.

Write the terms of the alternating sequence

$$a_n = (-1)^n(3n) \quad 1 \leq n \leq 6.$$

Solution: $-3, 6, -9, 12, -15, 18$

Evaluate the sum.

$$\sum_{i=1}^{4} 5i$$

Solution:

$$\sum_{i=1}^{4} 5i = 5 + 10 + 15 + 20 = 50.$$

SECTION 13.2—ARITHMETIC AND GEOMETRIC SEQUENCES AND SERIES

KEY CONCEPTS:

An arithmetic sequence is a sequence in which the difference between consecutive terms is constant.

The nth term of an arithmetic sequence is given by $a_n = a_1 + (n - 1)d$, where a_1 is the first term and d is the common difference between a term and its predecessor.

The indicated sum of an arithmetic sequence is called an arithmetic series. The sum, S_n, of the first n terms of an arithmetic series is given by

$$S_n = \frac{n}{2}(a_1 + a_n)$$

where a_1 is the first term and a_n is the nth term of the series.

EXAMPLES:

The following sequence is arithmetic:

$$-4, -2, 0, 2, 4, 6, 8, 10, \ldots$$

The nth term of the preceding sequence can be written as: $a_n = -4 + (n - 1)(2)$

Find the sum of the series.

$$\sum_{i=1}^{30} 5 + (i - 1)(2)$$

Solution: $a_1 = 5, n = 30, d = 2, a_{30} = 63$
Therefore,

$$S_{30} = \frac{30}{2}(5 + 63) = 1020.$$

A geometric sequence is a sequence in which each term after the first term is a constant multiple of the preceding term.

The nth term of a geometric sequence is given by $a_n = a_1 r^{n-1}$, where a_1 is the first term and r is the common ratio.

The indicated sum of a geometric sequence is called a geometric series. The sum, S_n, of the first n terms of a geometric series is given by:

$$S_n = \frac{a_1(1 - r^n)}{1 - r}$$

where a_1 is the first term of the series and r is the common ratio and $r \neq 1$.

Given an infinite geometric series

$$a_1 + a_1 r + a_1 r^2 + \cdots, \text{ with } |r| < 1$$

the sum S of all terms in the series is given by

$$S = \frac{a_1}{1 - r}$$

Note: If $|r| \geq 1$, then the sum does not exist.

KEY TERMS:

arithmetic sequence
arithmetic series
common difference

common ratio
geometric sequence
geometric series

The following sequence is geometric:

$$50, 30, 18, \frac{54}{5}, \frac{162}{25} \cdots$$

The nth term of the preceding sequence can be written as $a_n = 50\left(\frac{3}{5}\right)^{n-1}$.

Find the sum of the series.

$$\sum_{i=1}^{6} 48\left(\frac{1}{2}\right)^{i-1}$$

Solution: $a_1 = 48$, $r = \frac{1}{2}$, $n = 6$. Hence,

$$S_n = \frac{48[1 - (\frac{1}{2})^6]}{1 - \frac{1}{2}} = \frac{189}{2}$$

Find the sum of the infinite series.

$$4 - 2 + 1 - \frac{1}{2}, + \cdots$$

Solution: $a_1 = 4$, $r = -\frac{1}{2}$.
Hence

$$S = \frac{4}{1 - (-\frac{1}{2})} = \frac{8}{3}$$

SECTION 13.3—BINOMIAL EXPANSIONS

KEY CONCEPTS:

The expression $n!$ (read as "n factorial") is defined as the product of integers from 1 to n. That is,

$$n! = n(n - 1)(n - 2) \cdots (2)(1)$$

Note: $0! = 1$.

For a positive integer, n, the expression $(a + b)^n$ can be expanded using the binomial theorem.

$$(a + b)^n = \frac{n!}{n! \cdot 0!}a^n + \frac{n!}{(n - 1)! \cdot 1!}a^{(n-1)}b +$$

$$\frac{n!}{(n - 2)! \cdot 2!}a^{(n-2)}b^2 + \cdots + \frac{n!}{0! \cdot n!}b^n$$

The coefficients of the expansion may also be found using Pascal's triangle.

EXAMPLES:

$$6! = (6)(5)(4)(3)(2)(1) = 720$$

Expand: $(x + 2y)^4$

Solution:
Using the fifth row of Pascal's triangle for the coefficients, we have

$$(x + 2y)^4$$

$$= 1(x)^4 + 4(x)^3(2y)^1 + 6(x)^2(2y)^2 + 4(x)^1(2y)^3 + 1(2y)^4$$

$$= x^4 + 8x^3y + 24x^2y^2 + 32xy^3 + 16y^4$$

Pascal's triangle:

$$
\begin{array}{ccccccccc}
 & & & & 1 & & & & \\
 & & & 1 & & 1 & & & \\
 & & 1 & & 2 & & 1 & & \\
 & 1 & & 3 & & 3 & & 1 & \\
1 & & 4 & & 6 & & 4 & & 1
\end{array}
$$

(and so on . . .)

Let n and k be positive integers such that $k \le n$. Then the kth-term in the expansion of $(a + b)^n$ is given by

$$
\frac{n!}{[n - (k - 1)]! \cdot (k - 1)!} \cdot a^{n - (k - 1)} \cdot b^{k - 1}
$$

KEY TERMS:

binomial expansion
binomial theorem
factorial notation
Pascal's triangle

Find the third term of $(3s + t^2)^7$.

Solution: $n = 7$, $k = 3$, $a = 3s$, and $b = t^2$.
The third term is given by

$$
\frac{7!}{[7 - (3 - 1)]! \cdot (3 - 1)!} \cdot (3s)^{7 - (3 - 1)} \cdot (t^2)^{3 - 1}
$$

$$
= \frac{7!}{5! \cdot 2!} (3s)^5 (t^2)^2
$$

$$
= 21 (3s)^5 (t^2)^2
$$

$$
= 5103 s^5 t^4
$$

SECTION 13.4—FUNDAMENTALS OF COUNTING

KEY CONCEPTS:

Fundamental Principle of Counting
If one event can occur in m different ways and a second event can occur in n different ways, then the sequence of both events can occur in $m \cdot n$ different ways.

An ordered arrangement of r different items selected from n different items is called a permutation of n items taken r at a time. The number of such permutations is given by

$$
{}_nP_r = \frac{n!}{(n - r)!}
$$

An unordered selection of r different items taken from n different items is called a combination of n items taken r at a time. The number of such combinations is given by

$$
{}_nC_r = \frac{n!}{(n - r)! \cdot r!}
$$

KEY TERMS:

combination
fundamental principle of counting
permutation

EXAMPLES:

A menu has four choices for salad, six main dishes, and three desserts. How many different meals are available if one item is selected from each category?

Solution: $4 \cdot 6 \cdot 3 = 72$

Suppose there are 12 students in a class and 3 are to be selected to be president, vice-president, and treasurer of the class. How many different arrangements are possible?

Solution:

$$
{}_{12}P_3 = \frac{12!}{(12 - 3)!} = \frac{12!}{9!} = 1320
$$

Suppose there are 12 students in a class, and 3 are to be selected to represent the class at a fund raiser. How many different combinations are possible?

Solution:

$$
{}_{12}C_3 = \frac{12!}{(12 - 3)! \cdot 3!} = \frac{12!}{9! \cdot 3!}
$$

$$
= 220
$$

SECTION 13.5—INTRODUCTION TO PROBABILITY

KEY CONCEPTS:

The probability of an event, E, is given by

$$P(E) = \frac{n(E)}{n(S)}$$

where $n(E)$ is the number of elements in the event common to the sample space, and $n(S)$ is the number of elements in the sample space.

The complement of E (denoted E') is the set of elements in the sample space that are not in event E. Furthermore,

$$P(E) + P(E') = 1$$

The Addition Rule for Probability

$$P(A \text{ or } B) = P(A) + P(B) - P(A \text{ and } B)$$

If A and B are mutually exclusive events, then $P(A \text{ and } B) = 0$.

Multiplication Rule for Independent Events

For two independent events A and B, the probability that A and B will occur is given by $P(A \text{ and } B) = P(A) \cdot P(B)$.

KEY TERMS:

addition rule for probability
certain event
complement of E
conditional probability
dependent events
event
experiment
impossible event
multiplication rule for independent events
mutually exclusive events
outcome
probability of an event, E
sample space
trial

EXAMPLES:

A box contains one bill each in the denominations $1, $5, $10, $20, $50, and $100. If one bill is randomly selected from the box, the probability that the $100 bill is chosen is $\frac{1}{6}$.

$1 $5
$10 $20
$50 $100

The probability that a $100 bill is *not* chosen is $\frac{5}{6}$.

A survey of single men and single women are categorized in the following table according to whether they own a cat.

	Cat	No Cat	Total
Male	20	45	65
Female	35	15	50
Total	55	60	115

The probability that a person randomly selected from the group owns a cat or is a female is given by

$$P(C \text{ or } F) = P(C) + P(F) - P(C \text{ and } F)$$

$$= \frac{55}{115} + \frac{50}{115} - \frac{35}{115} = \frac{70}{115} = \frac{14}{23}$$

If a fair coin is flipped four times, the probability that all outcomes are heads is given by

$$\frac{1}{2} \cdot \frac{1}{2} \cdot \frac{1}{2} \cdot \frac{1}{2} = \frac{1}{16}$$

chapter 13   REVIEW EXERCISES

Section 13.1

1. List the terms of the sequence $a_n = \left(\frac{3}{4}\right)^n$ for $1 \le n \le 3$

2. Find a formula for the nth term of the sequence: $\frac{2}{3}, \frac{4}{9}, \frac{8}{27}, \frac{16}{81}, \ldots$

3. Find a formula for the nth term of the sequence: $1, 4, 7, 10, 13, \ldots$

4. Find the sum:
$$\sum_{i=1}^{5} 4i^2$$

5. Find the sum:
$$\sum_{k=0}^{4} (-1)^k (2k)$$

6. Write the series in summation notation: $2 - 4 + 6 - 8 + 10 - 12 + 14$

7. Write the series in summation notation: $x^3 + x^6 + x^9 + x^{12}$

8. A radioactive substance decays with a half-life of 1 week. This means that each week the substance will lose half of its mass from the week before. If there is 10 g of the substance initially, write a sequence that represents the amount present at the end of each week for the next 5 weeks.

9. In Miami, a speeding ticket costs $100 plus $10 for each mile per hour over the speed limit.

   a. Write the nth term of a sequence describing the cost of a speeding ticket for a car traveling n mph over the speed limit.

   b. Write out the first five terms of the sequence.

   c. Find the 27th term and interpret its meaning in the context of this problem.

Section 13.2

10. Find the common difference for the arithmetic sequence: $10, 6, 2, -2, -6, \ldots$

11. Find the common difference for the arithmetic sequence: $\frac{1}{2}, \frac{1}{6}, -\frac{1}{6}, -\frac{1}{2}, -\frac{5}{6}, \ldots$

12. Write the first five terms of the arithmetic sequence in which $a_1 = 3$ and $d = 4$.

13. Write the nth term of the sequence: $1, 6, 11, 16, \ldots$

14. Write the nth term of the sequence:
$$2, \frac{2}{3}, \frac{2}{9}, \frac{2}{27}, \ldots$$

15. Find the 10th term of the arithmetic sequence in which $a_1 = 7$ and $d = -4$.

16. Find the number of terms in the arithmetic sequence: $10, 12, 14, \ldots 94$.

17. Find the sum of the series:
$$\sum_{i=1}^{50} (i - 4)$$

18. Find the sum of the series: $-4 + (-7) + (-10) + \cdots + (-67)$.

19. Determine the common ratio for the geometric sequence: $24, -12, 6, -3, \ldots$

20. Write the first five terms of the geometric sequence in which $a_1 = 8$ and $r = \frac{1}{2}$.

21. Find the nth term of the geometric sequence: $4, 6, 9, \frac{27}{2}, \frac{81}{4}, \ldots$

22. Find a_8 for the sequence $a_n = -4\left(\frac{3}{2}\right)^{n-1}$.

23. Find the sum of the series:
$$\sum_{k=1}^{5} -4\left(\frac{3}{4}\right)^{k-1}$$

24. Find the sum of the series:
$$9 + 3 + 1 + \frac{1}{3} + \frac{1}{9} + \frac{1}{27} + \frac{1}{81} + \frac{1}{243}$$

25. Find the common ratio, r, then determine the sum of the infinite series, if it exists.

$$2 + \frac{1}{3} + \frac{1}{18} + \frac{1}{108} + \cdots$$

26. Suppose $1000 is invested at 8% interest compounded annually.

a. What will the value of the investment be at the end of the first year? At the end of the second year?

b. Write a formula for the nth term of the sequence describing the value of the investment after n years. Is this sequence arithmetic or geometric?

c. Find the value of the investment after 30 years. (Round to two decimal places.)

Section 13.3

27. Expand the binomial. Use Pascal's triangle to find the coefficients. $(x^2 + 4)^5$

28. Evaluate the expression.

$$\frac{8!}{6!}$$

29. Evaluate the expression.

$$\frac{7!}{3! \cdot 4!}$$

30. Use the binomial theorem to expand the binomial: $(c - 3d)^4$.

31. Find the first three terms of the binomial expansion: $(a + 2b)^{11}$

32. Find the eighth term of the binomial expansion: $(5x - y^2)^{10}$.

33. Find the middle term of the binomial expansion: $(a + 2b)^6$.

Section 13.4

34. A pasta bar allows customers to "build" their own dinner. They may choose from five different kinds of pasta, six different meats, 16 different vegetables, and eight sauces. If a customer chooses one item from each category, how many different dinners are possible?

35. If a couple plans to have five children, how many different gender sequences can be formed?

36. A company sells a certain automobile in eight different colors with either automatic or standard transmission. In addition, the car comes in a deluxe, standard, or economy model. How many automobiles would a dealer have to stock if the dealer wanted to have one car of every color, model, and transmission option?

37. In how many ways can a woman pick a computer password if the password must contain four letters and no letter can be repeated?

38. Jonas found five books at a bookstore that he thinks he would like to read. If he can only select two of the books, how many different choices of two books does he have?

39. A committee is to be formed from a collection of 10 men and eight women. How many committees of four can be made consisting of three women and one man?

40. Seven horses are in a race. How many different first- and second-place arrangements are possible?

Section 13.5

41. In 1997, Florida International University conducted a survey of 1200 randomly selected Cuban Americans to measure attitudes regarding Cuban and U.S. political issues. One question regarded the timeframe for a major political change in Cuba. The results of the survey are shown in the following table. If one survey respondent is selected at random, what is the probability that:

When do you think major political change will occur in Cuba?	Percentage response (%)
2–5 years	26.9
6–10 years	16.2
More than 10 years	12.7
Never	18.6
No opinion	25.6

a. The person thought that major political change will never occur in Cuba?

b. The person thought that major political change would occur in more than 5 years?

c. The person had no opinion.

42. The following table describes the smoking habits of a group of asthma sufferers.

	Non-smoker	Occasional smoker	Regular smoker	Heavy smoker	Total
Men	382	37	60	34	513
Women	403	31	74	37	545
Total	785	68	134	71	1058

If one of the 1058 people is randomly selected, find the probability that the person is

a. A heavy smoker.

b. A woman.

c. Not a heavy smoker.

d. An occasional smoker or a regular smoker.

e. A nonsmoker or a man.

f. A woman or a regular smoker.

g. A heavy smoker given that the person is a woman.

43. Refer to the table from Exercise 42. If two different people are selected at random, what is the probability that both are nonsmokers? (Round to four decimal places.)

44. A fair coin is tossed five times. What is the probability of getting all heads?

45. A red die and a green die are thrown, resulting in 36 possible outcomes for the pair of dice. Find the probability that

a. The sum of the numbers on the dice is 4.

b. The sum of the numbers on the dice is greater than 8.

46. In a certain town, it is estimated that only 15% of the adults watch the 6 o'clock news. If three adults are selected at random from the town, what is the probability that all watch the 6 o'clock news?

chapter 13   TEST

1. Write the terms of the sequence. Is the sequence arithmetic or geometric?

$$a_n = -3\left(\frac{2}{3}\right)^{n-1} \quad \text{for } 1 \le n \le 4.$$

2. Write the nth term of the sequence. Is the sequence arithmetic or geometric?

$$-6, -\frac{11}{2}, -5, -\frac{9}{2}, \dots$$

3. Find the sum:

$$\sum_{i=1}^{7} 5(-1)^{i-1}$$

4. Study the following figures and the corresponding expression for the area of each region. Write the nth term of a sequence representing the area of the region.

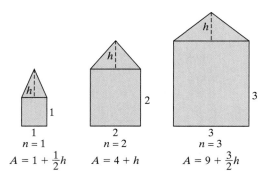

$n=1$	$n=2$	$n=3$
$A = 1 + \frac{1}{2}h$	$A = 4 + h$	$A = 9 + \frac{3}{2}h$

Figure for Exercise 4

5. Write the sum in summation notation.
$$\frac{4}{1} + \frac{5}{2} + \frac{6}{3} + \frac{7}{4} + \frac{8}{5} + \frac{9}{6} + \frac{10}{7}$$

6. Find the 33rd term of the arithmetic sequence in which $a_1 = -7$ and $d = -16$.

7. Find the sum of the series.
$$\sum_{i=1}^{45} [7 + (i-1)2]$$

8. a. Find the number of terms of the sequence: $6, 10, 14, 18, 22, \ldots, 210$

   b. Find the sum of the series: $6 + 10 + 14 + 18 + 22 + \cdots + 210$

9. Find the fifth term of the sequence defined by $a_n = \frac{1}{3}(2)^n$.

10. Find the first term of the geometric sequence in which $a_4 = \frac{5}{81}$ and $r = \frac{1}{3}$.

11. Find the sum: $4 + (-8) + 16 + (-32) + \cdots + (-2048)$

12. Find the sum.
$$\sum_{n=1}^{6} 5\left(\frac{3}{2}\right)^{n-1}$$

13. Suppose a student smokes one pack of cigarettes per day at a cost of $3.00 per pack.

   a. If the student quits smoking and puts the $3.00 saved per day in a jar, how much money will the student have saved at the end of 1 year? (Ignore leap years.)

   b. If the student takes the savings from part (a) and invests the money in a bond fund paying 6% annual interest, how much will this money be worth 1 year later?

   c. Suppose that the student reinvests the principal and interest each year so that effectively the money is compounded annually. The sequence defined by $a_n = 1095(1.06)^n$ represents the value of the investment after n years. Find the value of the investment after 29 years. (Round to two decimal places.)

   d. Now suppose the student saves $1095 per year, each year for 30 years, by not buying cigarettes. At the end of each year, the stu-

dent invests the year's savings at 6% interest compounded annually. The table shows the amount of money that the student has at the end of each year.

Year	Amount
End of first year	$1095
End of second year	$1095(1.06) + $1095
End of third year	$1095(1.06)^2 + $1095(1.06) + $1095
...	...
End of 30th year	$1095(1.06)^{29} + $1095(1.06)^{28} + \cdots + $1095

Notice that the first year's savings of $1095 will be compounded 29 times. The second year's savings will be compounded 28 times and so on. Evaluate the sum
$$\sum_{i=1}^{30} 1095(1.06)^{n-1}$$
to two decimal places and interpret this value in the context of the problem.

14. Find the infinite sum, if possible: $2 + \frac{2}{3} + \frac{2}{9} + \frac{2}{27} + \cdots$

15. Write the expansion of $(a + b)^4$. Use Pascal's triangle to determine the coefficients of the expansion.

16. Expand $(3y - 2x^2)^4$.

17. Find the third term of the expansion of $(w + 3z)^7$.

18. Three airlines fly from Atlanta to Philadelphia. If you can choose from any of the three airlines and can travel either first class or business class, how many different travel options do you have for a one-way trip between the two cities?

19. At an art show, 25 artists display their work. In how many ways can the judges choose the first-, second-, and third-place winners?

20. If a fair coin is flipped two times, how many different sequences of heads and tails can be formed?

21. To play the Colorado lottery game, Lotto, a person must choose 6 numbers in any order from a list of 42 numbers. How many different combinations of 6 numbers are possible?

22. A survey of 2225 people in a community revealed the following distribution by type of housing. If one of the survey respondents is randomly selected, find the probability of selecting someone who

    a. Lives in a mobile home.

    b. Does not live in a house, mobile home, or apartment.

Type of Housing	Number of People
House	690
Mobile home	387
Apartment	543
Other	605

23. The following table depicts a sample of 50 people organized by educational level and gender. If one person is selected at random from the group, find the probability that

    a. The person is a college graduate.

    b. The person is female.

    c. The person is male or a college graduate.

    d. The person is a college graduate, given that the person is a male.

	College Graduate	Not a College Graduate	Total
Male	8	16	24
Female	12	14	26
Total	20	30	50

24. In a certain town, 33% of households have at least one computer. If four households are randomly selected, what is the probability that all four have at least one computer? (Round to four decimal places.)

CUMULATIVE REVIEW EXERCISES, CHAPTERS 1–13

1. Simplify.

$$\frac{-2 - 3\sqrt{25 - 16}}{\sqrt{8^2 + 6^2}}$$

2. Simplify: $-3\{4 - 2[5 + 2(3 - x)] - 5x\}$

3. Solve: $-4(2x - 5) - 2(3x + 1) = -10 + 7x$

4. $10,000 is invested in two accounts, one earning 8% simple interest and one earning 5% simple interest. If the total interest at the end of 1 year is $566.75, find the amount invested in each account.

5. Two complementary angles are such that the measure of one is 6° more than three times the other. Find the measure of each angle.

6. Solve the inequality. Write the final answer in interval notation. $-3(x - 4) - x > -8$

7. Find the x- and y-intercept and graph the line: $y = 3x$

8. Find the slope and y-intercept of the line.

$$-\frac{x}{2} + \frac{y}{2} = 1$$

9. Find an equation of a line passing through $(2, 3)$ and $(-3, 1)$. Write the final answer in slope-intercept form.

10. Find an equation of a line passing through $(-2, 4)$ and perpendicular to the line $x + 3y = 4$.

11. Solve the system.

$$\begin{aligned} 2x + 3y - 4z &= 17 \\ x - 2y + z &= -5 \\ 3x + 4y - 3z &= 21 \end{aligned}$$

12. Solve the system.

$$y = \frac{1}{3}x + 4$$

$$-x + 3y = 6$$

13. Solve the system using Gauss-Jordan elimination.

$$2x - 4y = -10$$
$$-5x + y = 16$$

14. Evaluate the determinant.

$$\begin{vmatrix} -6 & 3 \\ -1 & -4 \end{vmatrix}$$

15. Solve for y using Cramer's rule.

$$2x - 3y = 12$$
$$-x + 4y + z = 2$$
$$y + 3z = 6$$

16. State the domain and range of the relation:
$\{(4, 2), (3, -6), (2, 2), (4, 5), (4, 1)\}$

17. Refer to the figure.

a. State the domain in interval notation.

b. State the range in interval notation.

c. Find $f(2)$.

d. Find all values of x for which $f(x) = 1$.

e. State the open interval(s) over which f is increasing.

f. State the open interval(s) over which f is decreasing.

g. State the open interval(s) over which f is constant.

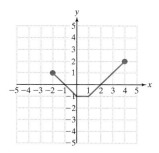

Figure for Exercise 17

18. Graph the piecewise-defined function.

$$f(x) = \begin{cases} |x| & \text{for } x \le 1 \\ 3 & \text{for } x > 1 \end{cases}$$

19. The wavelength, w, of a radio wave varies inversely as its frequency, f. A wave with a length of 300 m has a frequency of 1200 kHz (kilohertz). Find the frequency of a 450-m wave.

20. Simplify.

$$\left(\frac{3x^3 y^{-4}}{x^4 y^2}\right)^{-2}$$

21. Simplify. Write the answer in scientific notation.

$$\frac{(2.0 \times 10^3)(3.2 \times 10^{-7})}{1.6 \times 10^{-9}}$$

22. Add or subtract as indicated.

$(3x^3 - 2x - 4) - (4x^3 + 2x^2 + 5) + (-8x^2 - 5x - 3)$

23. Multiply and simplify: $[(x + 2y) - 3][(x + 2y) + 3]$

24. Divide: $(3x^4 - 2x^2 + 5x - 3) \div (x^2 + 2)$

25. Simplify. Assume that x can be any real number.
$\sqrt[4]{x^4}$

26. Find the domain: $g(x) = \sqrt{2x - 6}$

27. Simplify: $8^{-2/3}$

28. Simplify.

$$\left(\frac{x^{1/3} y^{5/6}}{x^{-1/3} y^{1/6}}\right)^{12}$$

29. Simplify: $\sqrt[3]{16x^5 y^{12}}$

30. Rationalize the denominator.

$$\frac{2}{\sqrt[3]{4x}}$$

31. Solve: $\sqrt[3]{4x + 2} + 5 = 3$

32. Simplify: $3i^4 - 2i^2 + 5i - 1$

33. Divide and write the answer in the form $a + bi$.

$$\frac{-6}{3 - 7i}$$

34. Factor completely: $6x^2 + 19x - 36$

35. Factor completely: $8x^6 + y^3$

36. Solve: $4x^2 - 9 = 0$

37. Solve by completing the square and applying the square root property: $2x^2 + 12x = 10$

38. Solve by using the quadratic formula:
$2x(x - 5) + 7x = -2$

39. Solve: $x^4 - x^2 - 12 = 0$

40. The number of diagonals, N, of a polygon having k sides (where k is an integer and $k \geq 3$) is given by

$$N = \frac{k^2 - 3k}{2}$$

   a. Find the number of diagonals for a four-sided polygon.

   b. Find the number of sides for a polygon having 209 diagonals.

41. Write the domain in interval notation.

$$f(x) = \frac{1}{x^2 - 49}$$

42. Divide.

$$\frac{2x^2 + 10x - 12}{x^2 - 16} \div \frac{5x + 30}{x^2 - 3x - 4}$$

43. Simplify.

$$\frac{\dfrac{1}{y} - \dfrac{y}{x^2}}{\dfrac{1}{x} + \dfrac{1}{y}}$$

44. Solve.

$$\frac{x + 5}{x - 2} = \frac{5}{x + 2} + \frac{28}{x^2 - 4}$$

45. Solve.

   a. $-3x + 2 \leq 4$ or $2x + 3 \leq -5$

   b. $-3x + 2 \leq 4$ and $2x + 3 \leq -5$

46. Solve: $|2x - 3| = |x + 5|$

47. Solve and write the solution in interval notation: $|x - 5| + 3 < 10$

48. Solve and write the solution in interval notation.

$$\frac{2}{x - 4} + 1 \leq 0$$

49. Graph the inequality: $2x + y \geq 3$

50. Find the inverse.

$$f(x) = \frac{3x - 1}{2}$$

For Exercises 51–52, state the domain and range and graph the function.

51. $f(x) = e^x$

52. $g(x) = \log_2 x$

53. Evaluate: $\log_2 8$

54. Evaluate: $\ln(e^5)$

55. Write as a single logarithm: $3 \ln x - \ln y + \frac{1}{2} \ln z$

56. Marc invests $5000 for his son's college education. At the end of 18 years, Marc hopes to have $20,000. At what interest rate (compounded continuously) must Marc average to reach his goal? (*Hint:* Use $A = Pe^{rt}$.) Round to the nearest tenth of a percent.

57. Solve: $\log(x + 2) + \log(x - 1) = 1$

58. Given $P(x) = -2x^4 - 3x^2 + x + 2$, use synthetic division to determine $P(6)$.

59. Determine whether $(x + 3)$ is a factor of $Q(x) = x^3 - 4x^2 + 2x + 6$.

60. Find the zeros of the polynomial, $P(x) = 2x^4 - 7x^3 + 11x^2 - 28x + 12$

61. Given $f(x) = 2x^4 - 3x^3 - 6x^2 + 13x - 6$,

   a. Determine the end behavior of the graph of the function.

   b. Find the x-intercepts.

   c. Find the y-intercept.

   d. Sketch the graph of the function.

62. Given

$$g(x) = \frac{x + 3}{2x - 5}$$

   a. Find the x-intercept(s) if any exist.

   b. Find the y-intercept.

   c. Find any horizontal asymptotes.

   d. Find any vertical asymptotes.

   e. Sketch the function.

For Exercises 63–64, state whether the sequence is arithmetic, geometric, or neither, and then find the nth term of the sequence.

63. $-16, -21, -26, -31, -36, \ldots$

64. $\dfrac{3}{4}, \dfrac{3}{2}, 3, 6, 12, \ldots$

65. Find the sum of the series: $\displaystyle\sum_{i=1}^{6} 3\left(\dfrac{1}{5}\right)^{i-1}$

66. Find the sum of the series: $-5 + (-2) + 1 + 4 + 7 + \cdots + 88$

67. Expand the binomial: $(3 - 2t^2)^4$

68. To play the Arizona lottery, a person must choose 6 numbers in any order from a list of 41 numbers. How many different combinations of 6 numbers are possible?

69. There are six front-row seats in a classroom. In how many ways can 6 students out of 15 students be arranged in the front-row seats?

70. The students in a psychology class are categorized by gender and year of study as shown in the table.

	Freshman	Sophomore	Junior	Senior	Total
Male	16	15	8	1	40
Female	12	15	3	4	34
Total	28	30	11	5	74

If one student is selected at random, find the probability that

a. The student is female.

b. The student is not a freshman.

c. The student is a sophomore or a male.

d. The student is a sophomore or a junior.

71. Given the parabola defined by $y = \frac{1}{4}(x - 2)^2 - 4$

a. Find the coordinates of the vertex.

b. Find the y-intercept.

c. Find the x-intercept(s) if any exist.

d. Write an equation for the directrix of the parabola.

e. Sketch the parabola and the features found in parts (a)–(d).

72. Identify the center and radius of the circle: $(x - 3)^2 + (y + 4)^2 = 35$

73. Graph the ellipse.

$$\dfrac{x^2}{9} + \dfrac{y^2}{4} = 1$$

74. Graph the hyperbola.

$$\dfrac{y^2}{16} - \dfrac{x^2}{9} = 1$$

75. Solve the system.

$$x^2 + y^2 = 100$$
$$3y = 4x$$

76. Add the matrices, if possible.

$$\begin{bmatrix} 2 & -3 & 4 \\ 1 & 0 & -2 \end{bmatrix} + \begin{bmatrix} 4 & 6 & 10 \\ -8 & 0 & 3 \end{bmatrix}$$

77. Multiply the matrices, if possible.

$$\begin{bmatrix} 3 & 5 & -1 \\ 2 & -6 & 0 \end{bmatrix} \cdot \begin{bmatrix} 2 & 1 \\ 6 & 3 \\ 7 & -5 \end{bmatrix}$$

STUDENT ANSWER APPENDIX

CHAPTER 1

Section 1.1 Practice Exercises, pp. 11–14

1.

$\{1.7, \pi, 4, -5, 4.\overline{2}\}$

3. Real Numbers: $5, -\sqrt{9}, -1.7, \frac{1}{2}, \sqrt{7}, \frac{0}{4}$
Irrational Numbers: $\sqrt{7}$
Rational Numbers: $5, -\sqrt{9}, -1.7, \frac{1}{2}, \frac{0}{4}$
Integers: $5, -\sqrt{9}, \frac{0}{4}$
Whole Numbers: $5, \frac{0}{4}$
Natural Numbers: 5

5. a. $t > 98.6$ **b.** [graph at 98.6] **7. a.** $0 \le a < 21$ **b.** [graph 0 to 21] $[0, 21)$

9. [graph at −3] $(-\infty, -3)$ **11.** [graph at $\frac{5}{2}$] $\left(\frac{5}{2}, \infty\right)$

13. [graph at 2] $[2, \infty)$ **15.** [graph at −8] $(-\infty, -8]$

17. [graph −4 to 4] $(-4, 4)$ **19.** [graph −3 to 0] $[-3, 0]$

21. [graph at 5] $(-\infty, 5]$ **23.** [graph at 7.1] $[7.1, \infty)$

25. [graph at 8.6] $(8.6, \infty)$ **27.** [graph −4 to 5] $(-4, 5]$

29. [graph at 5, 6.5]
$(-\infty, 5) \cup [6.5, \infty)$

31. All real numbers less than -4
33. All real numbers greater than -2 and less than or equal to 7
35. All real numbers between -180 and 90, inclusive
37. All real numbers greater than 3.2
39. a. $\{-3, -1\}$ **b.** $\{-4, -3, -2, -1, 0, 1, 3, 5\}$
41. $(-3, 0]$ **43.** $(-\infty, 4)$

[graph −3 to 0] [graph at 4]

$\{x \mid -3 < x \le 0\}$ $\{x \mid x < 4\}$
45. $[-1, 4)$ **47.** empty set

[graph −1 to 4] $\{\ \}$

$\{x \mid -1 \le x < 4\}$
49. $p < 130$ mm Hg **51.** 130 mm Hg $\le p \le 139$ mm Hg
53. $p < 85$ mm Hg **55.** $7.6 \le$ pH ≤ 8.0 alkaline
57. $6.6 \le$ pH ≤ 6.9 acidic **59.** rational **61.** rational **63.** rational
65. irrational

Section 1.2 Practice Exercises, pp. 25–27

1. {integers} **3.** {whole numbers}
5. Distance can never be negative **7. b.** negative

9. $-6, \frac{1}{6}, 6$; $\frac{1}{11}, 11, \frac{1}{11}$; $-8, 8, 8$; $-0.13, -\frac{100}{13}, 0.13$; $-1.1, \frac{10}{11}, 1.1$;
0, undefined, 0; $-3, 3, 3$
11. $-|6| < |-6|$ **13.** $|-4| = |4|$ **15.** $(-9) < |-9|$
17. $|2 + (-5)| < |2| + |-5|$ **19.** $81.7°F$ **21.** $-10.1°C$ **23.** -4
25. -19 **27.** 3 **29.** 14 **31.** -21 **33.** -8.1 **35.** $-\frac{5}{3}$ **37.** $-\frac{67}{45}$
39. -32 **41.** $\frac{8}{21}$ **43.** $\frac{7}{9}$ **45.** undefined **47.** 0 **49.** 3.72
51. 6.02 **53.** 17 **55.** -11 **57.** -603 **59.** $\frac{109}{150}$ **61.** 5.4375
63. $\frac{2}{3}$ **65.** 7 **67.** 6 **69.** $\frac{9}{10}$ **71. a.** $25°C$ **b.** $100°C$ **c.** $0°C$
d. $-40°C$ **73.** 132.73 in.^{2} **75.** $9\frac{3}{4}$ in.^{2} **77.** 8.06 cm^2 **79.** 14.1 ft^3
81. 26.8 ft^3 **83.** 141.4 in.^{3}
85. $12/(6-2)$ **87.** $\text{abs}(-9-7)$ **89.** 17

91. -603 **93.** $\frac{2}{3}$ or 0.6666667

Section 1.3 Practice Exercises, pp. 32–34

1. a. rational number, integer, real number **b.** $-\frac{1}{4}$ **c.** 4 **d.** 4
3. a. whole number, rational number, integer, real number
b. undefined **c.** 0 **d.** 0
5. $(3, \infty)$ **7.** $\left(-\infty, \frac{1}{3}\right]$ **9.** $[5, \infty)$
11. a. three terms **b.** 6 **c.** $2, -5, 6$
13. a. five terms **b.** -7 **c.** $1, -7, 1, -4, 1$ **15.** -36 **17.** $\frac{23}{2}$
19. $4b + 8$ **21.** $14y - 2$ **23.** $6p^2 + p - 6$ **25.** $8x - 23$
27. $-4c - 6$ **29.** $-9w + 10$ **31.** $4z - 16$ **33.** $7s - 26$
35. $4c + 2$ **37.** $1.4x + 10.2$ **39.** $-2a^2 + 3a + 38$
41. $2y^2 - 3y - 5$ **43.** true **45.** false **47.** true **49.** false **51.** a
53. e **55.** b **57.** d **59.** a **61.** d **63.** c
65. 1, for example: $2 \cdot 1 = 2$ **67.** opposite
69. no, for example: $8 \div 2 \ne 2 \div 8$
$\qquad\qquad\qquad 4 \ne \frac{1}{4}$

Section 1.4 Practice Exercises, pp. 43–44

1. 10 **3.** $-\frac{1}{6}$ **5.** $3x - 3y + 14xy$ **7.** $5z - 20$
9. linear $2x - 4 = 0$ **11.** nonlinear **13.** nonlinear
15. a. not a solution **b.** is a solution **c.** not a solution **d.** not a solution

17. $x = 12$ **19.** $x = -\dfrac{1}{32}$ **21.** $z = \dfrac{21}{20}$ **23.** $a = \dfrac{8}{5}$ **25.** $t = -1.1$

27. $p = 6.7$ **29.** $q = 11$ **31.** $y = 13$ **33.** $b = 16$ **35.** $x = 2$

37. $x = 5$ **39. a.** $y + 8$ **b.** $y = -8$ **c.** Simplifying an expression clears parentheses and combines *like* terms. Solving an equation isolates a variable to find a solution.

41. An equation that is true only under certain conditions.

43. all real numbers;   **45.** $x = 0$;
an identity   a conditional equation

47. $x = 0$;
a conditional equation

49. $c = 3$ **51.** $b = -1$ **53.** no solution   **55.** $c = \dfrac{8}{5}$ **57.** $x = -\dfrac{3}{2}$

59. all real numbers   **61.** $b = 6.6$ **63.** $x = -8$ **65.** $y = \dfrac{3}{4}$

67. $x = 60$ **69.** $x = 6$ **71.** $x = 3$ **73.** $q = -6$

Midchapter Review, p. 45

1. a. $\left\{-7.1, -2, -\dfrac{1}{8}, 0, 0.\overline{3}, \dfrac{7}{8}, 6, \dfrac{9}{2}\right\}$ **b.** $\{6\}$

c. $\left\{-7.1, -5\pi, -2, -\dfrac{1}{8}, 0, 0.\overline{3}, \sqrt{2}, \dfrac{7}{8}, 6, \dfrac{9}{2}\right\}$ **d.** $\{-5\pi, \sqrt{2}\}$

e. $\{0, 6\}$

2. a. vi **b.** i **c.** iv **d.** ii **e.** iii **f.** v

3. 8   **4.** 15   **5.** $-\dfrac{6}{5}$ **6.** $\dfrac{9}{10}$ **7.** 59   **8.** 29   **9.** -58 **10.** 2

11. 18   **12.** 64

13. equation;   **14.** expression;   **15.** expression;
$x = -34$ $0.17a + 4.495$ $-x - 4$

16. equation;   **17.** equation;   **18.** equation;
$b = 68$ $n = -\dfrac{3}{32}$ all real numbers

19. equation;   **20.** expression;   **21.** expression;
no solution $0.39q + 500$ $\dfrac{3}{5}c - \dfrac{1}{5}$

22. equation;
$y = 4$

23. $(-3, \infty)$ **24.** $[6, \infty)$

25. $\left(-\infty, 2\frac{1}{2}\right]$ **26.** $(-\infty, 4.8)$

27.   **28.**
$(-\infty, 0) \cup (4, \infty)$ $[1, 13]$

Section 1.5 Practice Exercises, pp. 54–56

1. $a = \dfrac{13}{7}$ **3.** $x = 6$ **5.** $b = -1$ **7.** $p = \dfrac{18}{5}$ **9.** $d = 10,000$

11. 5, 13   **13.** -3 **15.** $-20, -19, -18$ **17.** 10, 20   **19.** 0.0252 oz of impurities   **21.** 6%   **23.** $60,000   **25.** 4-year loan at 8.5% is better.
27. 13% increase   **29.** 3%   **31.** 3 L   **33.** 2 oz   **35.** 250 orchestra level seats; 125 balcony seats   **37.** 10 lb almonds; 6 lb cashews
39. $8500 at 8%; $4000 at 12%   **41.** $4500 at 5%; $9000 at 6%
43. 456 miles   **45.** $1\frac{1}{4}$ h   **47.** 65 mph, 75 mph

Section 1.6 Practice Exercises, pp. 61–64

1. $x = -\dfrac{14}{3}$ **3.** $z = 1$ **5.** -2 **7.** $18,000   **9.** 60: 34¢ stamps; 15:
20¢ stamps   **11.** 6 m, 8 m, 10 m   **13. a.** $11\frac{1}{2}$ yd by 8 yd   **b.** 39 yd
15. $4\frac{1}{2}$ ft on a side   **17.** 30°, 30°, 120°   **19.** 15°, 75°
21. $x = 20$; 139°, 41°   **23.** $x = 27.5$; 60°, 30°
25. $x = 18$; 36°, 91°, 53°   **27.** $x = 11$; 20°   **29.** a, b, c   **31.** a, b

33. $l = \dfrac{A}{w}$ **35.** $P = \dfrac{I}{rt}$ **37.** $K_1 = K_2 - W$ **39.** $C = \frac{5}{9}(F - 32)$

41. $v^2 = \dfrac{2K}{m}$ **43.** $a = \dfrac{v - v_0}{t}$ **45.** $v_2 = \dfrac{w}{p} + v_1$ **47. a.** $r = \dfrac{d}{t}$

b. 145.2 mph   **49. a.** $m = \dfrac{F}{a}$ **b.** 2.35 kg   **51. a.** $x = z\sigma + \mu$

b. $x = 130$ **53.** $y = -3x + 6$ **55.** $y = \dfrac{5}{4}x - 5$

57. $y = -3x + \dfrac{13}{2}$ **59.** $y = x - 2$ **61.** $y = -\dfrac{27}{4}x + \dfrac{15}{4}$

63. $y = \dfrac{3}{2}x$

Section 1.7 Practice Exercises, pp. 72–74

1. $v = \dfrac{d + 16t^2}{t}$ **3.** -11 **5.** $500 in the 7% account; $400 in the
8% account   **7.** $t = -3$

9. $[10, \infty)$ **11.** $\left(\frac{13}{6}, \infty\right)$

13. $(-\infty, -12)$ **15.** $\left(-\infty, \frac{13}{8}\right)$

17. $(-\infty, -21]$ **19.** $(-3, \infty)$

21. $\left[\frac{9}{10}, \infty\right)$ **23.** $(-\infty, 5)$

25. $\left[-\frac{5}{4}, \infty\right)$ **27.** $[1.5, \infty)$

29. $\left[-\frac{2}{3}, 5\right)$ **31.** $(2, 6)$

33. $[-55, 5]$ **35.** $\left[-\frac{9}{2}, \frac{3}{2}\right]$

37. $(-4, 5)$

39. a. She needs to sell in excess of $375,000.   **b.** She needs to sell in excess of $1,375,000.   **c.** The base salary is still the same, the increase comes solely from commission.   **41.** More than 73 jackets must be sold.   **43.** $32° \le F \le 42.08°$ **45. a.** 1960 to 1975   **b.** 1968 to 1983

47. $(-\infty, -3)$ **49.** $(-\infty, 12]$

51. $(-\infty, -0.5]$ **53.** $\left(\frac{13}{6}, 4\right]$

55. $\left(-\infty, -\frac{5}{11}\right]$ **57.** $(-\infty, -6)$

59. $\left[\frac{1}{2}, 6\right]$

61. $a + c > b + c$, for $c > 0$ **63.** $ac > bc$, for $c > 0$ **65.** $\dfrac{1}{a} < \dfrac{1}{b}$

Review Exercises, pp. 81–85

1. For example: 1, 2, 3, 4, 5 **3.** For example: $-\frac{1}{2}, -\frac{3}{4}, \frac{5}{2}$
5. For example: $-2, -1, 0, 1, 2$
7. All real numbers greater than 0 but less than or equal to 2.6
9. All real numbers between $\frac{3}{4}$ and $1\frac{1}{2}$, inclusive
11. All real numbers greater than 8
13. All real numbers less than or equal to 13
15. $C \cap D$ is the set of all elements in both sets, C and D. $C \cup D$ is the set of all elements in either set, C or D, or in both sets.

17. $[-3, \infty)$
19. $(-1, 5)$
21. $[0, 2)$
23. $[0, 5)$
25. $(-1, \infty)$
27. True

29. $0.03, -\dfrac{100}{3}, 0.03$ **31.** $-1, 1, 1$ **33.** $256, 4$ **35.** $81, 3$ **37.** -7
39. $-\dfrac{19}{24}$ **41.** -8.151 **43.** $\dfrac{4}{11}$ **45.** -40 **47.** -8 **49.** 16
51. -348.843 **53.** 37 **55.** negative **57.** positive **59.** 756 in.^{2}
61. For example: $2x, -5x$ **63.** For example: 6, 13
65. For example: $3x, 3y$ **67.** $3x + 15y$ **69.** $2a - 4b + \dfrac{14}{3}$
71. $4x - 10y + z$ **73.** $7q - 14$ **75.** $-6y - 5$ **77.** $5x - 6$
79. For example: $3 + x = x + 3$ **81.** For example: $5(2y) = (5 \cdot 2)y$
83. For example: $4(x + y) = 4x + 4y$ **85.** The empty set; no solution **87.** $x = -5$; a conditional equation **89.** $z = -0.67$; a conditional equation **91.** $w = \dfrac{4}{9}$; a conditional equation
93. $x = -18.075$; a conditional equation **95.** $m = \dfrac{31}{6}$; a conditional equation **97.** all real numbers; identity **99.** no solution; contradiction **101.** $y = \dfrac{21}{4}$; a conditional equation **103.** $x, x + 1, x + 2$
105. Distance equals rate times time. **107.** 2 ft and $\frac{2}{3}$ ft **109.** $4\frac{1}{8}$ mph
111. 2 L of 10% solution; 1 L of 25% solution **113.** 5.0 million men
115. a. 13% decrease **b.** 7% increase **117.** 29 in., 31 in., 33 in.
119. $x = 52; 27°$ **121.** $y = \dfrac{3}{2}x - 2$ **123.** $x = -\dfrac{5}{3}y + \dfrac{13}{3}$
125. $h = \dfrac{S - 2\pi r}{\pi r^2}$ **127. a.** $\pi = \dfrac{C}{2r}$ **b.** $\pi \approx 3.14$
129. $\left[-\dfrac{3}{2}, \infty\right)$ **131.** $\left(-\dfrac{1}{8}, \dfrac{5}{4}\right)$
133. $\left(-\infty, -\dfrac{25}{2}\right]$ **135.** $\left[\dfrac{46}{7}, \infty\right)$
137. $\left(-\infty, \dfrac{29}{2}\right]$ **139.** $[-5, \infty)$
141. $\left[-\dfrac{2}{5}, \dfrac{9}{5}\right)$ **143.** $(1980, \infty)$

Test, pp. 85–86

1. a. $-5, -4, -3, -2, -1, 0, 1, 2$ **b.** For example: $\dfrac{3}{2}, \dfrac{5}{4}, \dfrac{8}{5}$
2. $(-3, 4)$ does not include the endpoints. $[-3, 4]$ does include the endpoints.
3. a. $(-\infty, 6)$ **b.** $[-3, \infty)$
4. $[-5, -2)$
5. a. $\dfrac{1}{2}, -2, \dfrac{1}{2}$ **b.** $-4, \dfrac{1}{4}, 4$ **c.** 0, no reciprocal exists, 0 **6.** 6
7. $z = 1.1$ **8. a.** False **b.** True **c.** True **d.** True **9. a.** $-2b - 6$
b. $-2x + 1$ **10.** $x = 133$ **11.** $z = \dfrac{4}{5}$ **12.** $x = 142,500$ **13.** $a = 2$
14. a. identity **b.** contradiction **c.** a conditional equation
15. 18 and 90 **16. a.** $\frac{2}{5}$ h (24 min) **b.** 1.8 miles **17.** Shawnna invested $1000 in the CD. **18.** 27 in. on each side **19.** $y = -2x + 3$
20. $z = \dfrac{x - \mu}{\sigma}$
21. $(34, \infty)$ **22.** $\left(-\infty, \dfrac{18}{5}\right]$
23. $\left(-\dfrac{1}{3}, 2\right]$
24. It can carry at most seven more passengers.

CHAPTER 2

Section 2.1 Practice Exercises, pp. 97–100

1. For (x, y) if $x > 0, y > 0$ the point is in Quadrant I
if $x < 0, y > 0$ the point is in Quadrant II
if $x < 0, y < 0$ the point is in Quadrant III
if $x > 0, y < 0$ the point is in Quadrant IV

3.   **5.**

7.

9. An equation is linear if it can be written in the form $ax + by = c$, where a and b are not both 0. **11.** Linear; $5x - 3y = 11$
13. Linear; $-3x + y = 7$ **15.** Nonlinear **17.** Linear; $x = 3$
19. Nonlinear **21.** Linear; $y = -3$

23. $(0, -6), \left(\dfrac{11}{3}, -\dfrac{1}{2}\right), (-4, -12), (4, 0), (-5.1, -13.65)$

25. $(2, 5)$, $(2,$ any real number$)$, $(2,$ any real number$)$, $(2, -1)$

27.

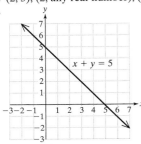

$x + y = 5$

29.

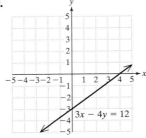

$3x - 4y = 12$

31.

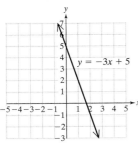

$y = -3x + 5$

33.

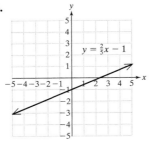

$y = \frac{2}{5}x - 1$

35.

$x - 2 = 3$

37.

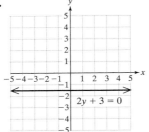

$2y + 3 = 0$

39. The x-intercept is a point where the graph intersects the x-axis. The y-intercept is a point where the graph intersects the y-axis.

41. a. $(9, 0)$ **b.** $(0, 6)$ **c.**

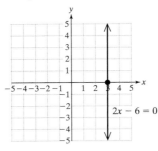

$2x + 3y = 18$

43. a. $(3, 0)$ **b.** None **c.**

$2x - 6 = 0$

45. a. $(4, 0)$ **b.** $(0, -2)$ **c.**

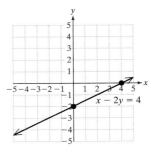

$x - 2y = 4$

47. a. $(0, 0)$ **b.** $(0, 0)$ **c.**

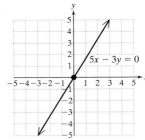

$5x - 3y = 0$

49. a. None **b.** $(0, 6)$ **c.**

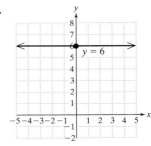

$y = 6$

51. #46, 47 Two distinct points are needed to graph a line.

53. #43, 50 These lines are parallel to the y-axis.

55. a. The charge is constant for less than 1 mile. **b.** For 0 miles, the cost is $2.00. **c.** After the first mile, the cost increases with increasing miles. **d.** $4.75

57. x-intercept $(2, 0)$ **59.** x-intercept $(a, 0)$
  y-intercept $(0, 3)$ y-intercept $(0, b)$

61. Linear   **63.** Nonlinear   **65.** Linear

67. $y = (2/3)x - (7/3)$ **69.** $y = 3$

71.

73. Linear

Section 2.2 Practice Exercises, pp. 109–113

1. a. $\left(-1, -\dfrac{8}{3}\right)$ **b.** $(0, -2)$ **c.** $(3, 0)$

3. $(-4, 0)$ No y-intercept   **5.** $(3, 0)(0, -3)$

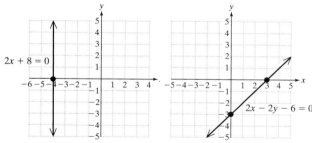

7. The slope of a line is the ratio of the change in y to the change in x between two points on a line.

9. No, since the lines cross at 90°, one line has a slope that is the opposite of the reciprocal of the slope of the other line.

11. $m = 1$ **13.** $m = 0$ **15.** $m = \dfrac{1}{10}$ **17.** $m = -1$

19. $m = \dfrac{1}{2}$ **21.** $m = -\dfrac{5}{3}$

          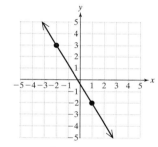

23. Undefined slope   **25.** $m = -\dfrac{1}{6}$

27. $m = 0$

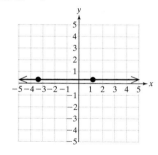

29. a. $(0, 4)(-4, 0)$ **b.** 1 **c.** -1 **d.** 1

31. a. $(0, 2)(1, 5)$ **b.** 3 **c.** $-\dfrac{1}{3}$ **d.** 3

33. a. $(0, 3)(5, 3)$ **b.** 0 **c.** Undefined **d.** 0

35. a. $(0, 0)(1, 2)$ **b.** 2 **c.** $-\dfrac{1}{2}$ **d.** 2

37. a. $(-4, 0)(-4, 3)$ **b.** Undefined **c.** 0 **d.** Undefined

39. $m = 2$; $m = -\dfrac{1}{2}$; perpendicular. One slope is the opposite of the reciprocal of the other slope.

41. Undefined; $m = 0$; perpendicular. One line is horizontal and one is vertical.

43. $m = 1$; $m = 1$; parallel. The slopes are the same.

45. $m = -4$; $m = -4$; parallel. The slopes are the same.

47. $m = \pm\dfrac{24}{7}$ **49. a.** Beef declines in consumption over the years.

b. Chicken and turkey; chicken is greatest; the rate of increase (decrease) equals the slope. **c.** Pork and fish appear to remain constant.

51. a. b. c.

Year Where $x=0$ Represents 1970

d. Male: $m = 0.067$. The average increase in the number of men attending college per year is 0.067 million.
Female: $m = 0.202$. The average increase in the number of women attending college per year is 0.202 million.

e. The rate of increase in the number of female college students
f. between 1981 and 1982

53. For example: $(1, 2)$ **55.** For example: $(2, 0)$

          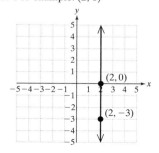

57. For example: $(-1, 2)$

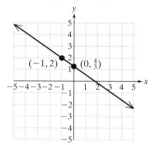

59. Positive slope: $(3, \infty)$
Negative slope: $(-\infty, 3)$
61. Positive slope: $(-\infty, -1)$
Negative slope: $(-1, \infty)$

Midchapter Review, p. 114

1. x-intercept is $(-3, 0)$; y-intercept is $(0, 2)$; slope is $\frac{2}{3}$

2. x-intercept is $(-1, 0)$; y-intercept is $(0, -4)$; slope is -4

3. Positive slope   **4.** Undefined slope

3x − y = −6

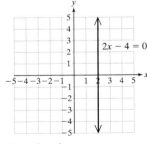

2x − 4 = 0

5. Slope is 0   **6.** Negative slope

−3y = 9

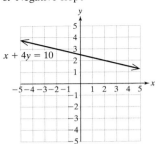

x + 4y = 10

7. a. $-\dfrac{1}{2}$ **b.**   **c.** 2

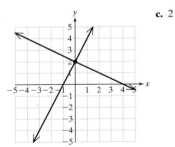

8. a. 1 **b.**   **c.** 1

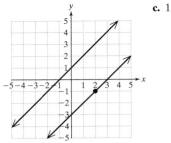

9. $m = \pm\dfrac{13}{3}$ **10.** $m = \pm\dfrac{50}{13}$

Section 2.3 Practice Exercises, pp. 123–126

1. yes

3. a. $\left(\dfrac{1}{3}, 0\right)$ **b.** $\left(0, \dfrac{1}{2}\right)$ **c.**

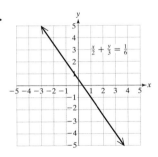

$\frac{x}{2} + \frac{y}{3} = \frac{1}{6}$

5. Two lines with the same slope are parallel.   **7.** Slope is the ratio between the change in the y-coordinates to the change in the x-coordinates of two points.   **9. a.** 2 **b.** 2 **c.** $-\dfrac{1}{2}$

11.   **13.**

(2, 1)

(0, 2)

15.   **17.** d   **19.** f   **21.** b

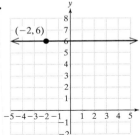

(−2, 6)

23. $x = -2$ is not in slope-intercept form. No y-intercept, undefined slope.   **25.** $y = 3$ is in slope-intercept form. Slope is 0 and y-intercept is $(0, 3)$.

27. $y = 4x + 2$ **29.** $y = -\dfrac{3}{2}x + 3$

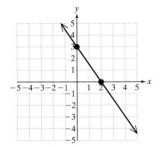

31. $y = \dfrac{5}{3}x - 2$

33. $y = -2$

35. Cannot be written in slope-intercept form, $x = 2$.

37. $y = \dfrac{2}{5}x$

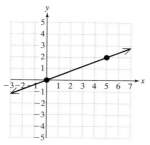

39. $y = 3x - 2$ **41.** $y = 2x + 3$ **43.** $y = -\dfrac{4}{5}x + \dfrac{9}{5}$

45. $y = -\dfrac{4}{3}x + 4$ **47.** $y = x + 6$ **49.** $y = -3$ **51.** $x = \dfrac{5}{2}$

53. $y = -\dfrac{3}{4}x + \dfrac{17}{4}$ **55.** $y = \dfrac{3}{2}x + 1$ **57.** $y = \dfrac{3}{4}x - 5$ **59.** $y = 5$

61. $y = 11$

63. For example: $x = -2$, $x = -4$, $y = 6$, $y = 4$.

65. For example: $y = x + 1$, $y = x - 1$, $y = -x + 1$, $y = -x - 1$.

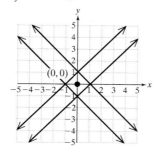

67. The lines have the same slope but different y-intercepts; they are parallel lines.

69. The lines have different slopes but the same y-intercept.

71. The lines are perpendicular.

73.

75.

Section 2.4 Practice Exercises, pp. 134–139

1. a. False, a horizontal line may not have an x-intercept. **b.** False, a vertical line may not have a y-intercept.

3. $y = x - 2$

5. Cannot be written in slope-intercept form, $x = 5$

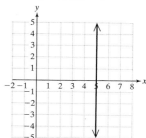

7. a. $m = -\dfrac{1}{3}$ **b.** $y = -\dfrac{1}{3}x - 5$

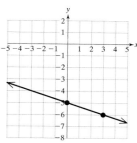

c. $y = -\dfrac{1}{3}x + c$ $(c \neq -5)$ **d.** $y = 3x + c$ $(c = \text{any real number})$

9. $x = -2$

11. a. $y = 0.2x + 19.95$ **b.**

c. $(0, 19.95)$; cost is $19.95 for 0 miles. **d.** 50 miles $29.95; 100 miles $39.95; 200 miles $59.95 **e.** $42.35 **f.** No, one cannot drive a negative number of miles.

13. a. $y = 52x + 2742$ **b.**

c. $m = 52$. Taxes increase $52 per year. **d.** $(0, 2742)$. Initial year $(x = 0)$ taxes were $2742. **e.** 10 years: $3262; 15 years: $3522

15. a. 11 seconds—2.2 miles; 4 seconds—0.8 miles; 15 seconds—3 miles **b.** 21 seconds   **17. a.** $132.3 thousand, or $132,300

b. $105,800 **c.** $m = 5.3$. $5300 increase in median housing cost per year. **d.** $(0, 63.4)$. In 1980 $(x = 0)$ the cost was $63,400.

19. a.

b. $y = -350x + 1000$

c. 405 hot dogs

21. a. $y = 0.027x + 3.3$ **b.** 3.84 m **c.** 5.352 m **d.** The linear model can only be used to approximate the winning heights. **e.** $m = 0.027$. Winning heights increase by 0.027 m per year.   **23.** $(1, 2)$

25. $(-1, 0)$ **27.** $(-1, 6)$ **29.** $(0, 3)$ **31.** $\left(-\frac{1}{2}, \frac{3}{2}\right)$ **33.** $(-0.4, -1)$

35. $(40, 7\frac{1}{2})$ they should meet 40 miles east, $7\frac{1}{2}$ miles north of the warehouse.

37. a. Yes, there is a linear trend.

b. $y = \frac{1}{2}x + 39$ **c.** 102 minutes gives 90%. This model is not appropriate for other students because it is based on Loraine's scores.

d. 54%

39. Collinear   **41.** Collinear

43. a.

b.

45. a.

b.

Review Exercises, pp. 144–146

1.

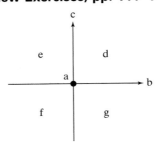

3.

x	y
0	3
-2	0
1	$\frac{9}{2}$
$-\frac{7}{3}$	-0.5
$\frac{2}{3}$	4

5.

x	y
4	0
4	$\frac{1}{8}$
4	1
4	-2

7. x- and y-intercept $(0, 0)$

$\left(1, \frac{5}{2}\right)\left(\frac{8}{5}, 4\right)$

9. x-intercept $(-2, 0)$

$(-2, 1) \; (-2, -2)$

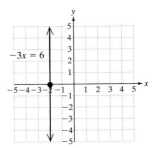

11. For example: $y = 2x$ **13.** $m = 2$ **15.** $m = 0$

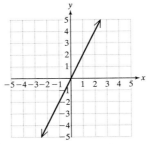

17. Bunny-slope would be a small number; double-diamond slope would be a larger number.   **19.** Neither   **21.** Neither   **23. a.** $y = k$ **b.** $y - y_1 = m(x - x_1)$ **c.** $ax + by = c$ **d.** $x = k$ **e.** $y = mx + b$

25. $y = -\frac{2}{3}x + 2$ **27.** $y = 3x - 20$ **29. a.** $y = -2$ **b.** $x = -3$

c. $x = -3$ **d.** $y = -2$

31. a. $y = 0.25x + 20$ **b.**

c. Cost totals $20 if no ice cream is sold **d.** $132.50 **e.** 0.25 **f.** Cost is $0.25 per ice cream product

33. $\left(-\dfrac{9}{2}, -3\right)$

Test, pp. 146–147

1. $(0, -9)$ $(6, 0)$ $(8, 3)$

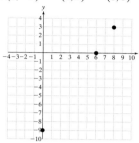

2. a. False, product is positive in Quadrant III also. **b.** False, quotient is negative in Quadrant II also. **c.** True **d.** True **3.** To find the x-intercept, let $y = 0$ and solve for x. To find the y-intercept, let $x = 0$ and solve for y.

4. x-intercept $(4, 0)$
   y-intercept $(0, -3)$

5. x-intercept $(-4, 0)$
   no y-intercept

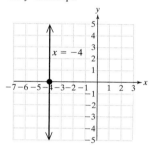 $x = -4$

$6x - 8y = 24$

6. x- and y-intercept $(0, 0)$

7. no x-intercept
   y-intercept $(0, -3)$

 $3x = 5y$
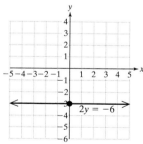 $2y = -6$

8. a. $m = \dfrac{5}{8}$ **b.** $m = \dfrac{6}{5}$ **9. a.** The slopes are the same. **b.** The slope of one line is the opposite of the reciprocal of the other.
10. a. For example: $y = 3x + 2$ **b.** For example: $x = 2$ **c.** For example: $y = 3$; $m = 0$ **d.** For example: $y = -2x$ **11.** $y = -2x + \dfrac{31}{2}$
12. $y = \dfrac{1}{3}x + \dfrac{1}{3}$

13. a. $y = 300x + 800$ **b.**

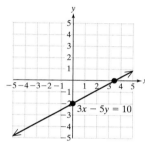

c. Jack earns a base salary of $800. **d.** $5900
14. a. $(0, 66)$. For a woman born in 1940 life expectancy was about 66 years. **b.** $m = \dfrac{3}{10}$. Life expectancy rises 3 years every 10 years.
c. $y = \dfrac{3}{10}x + 66$ **d.** 82.2 years old **15.** $\left(13, \dfrac{17}{2}\right)$

Cumulative Review Exercises, Chapters 1–2, p. 148

1. -1 **2.** 4 **3.** $z = -7$ **4. a.** $h = \dfrac{V}{\pi r^2}$ **b.** 10.4 cm
5. a. $[-2, \infty)$ **b.** $(-\infty, 3)$
6. a. $\left(\dfrac{10}{3}, 0\right)(0, -2)$ **b.** $m = \dfrac{3}{5}$ **c.**

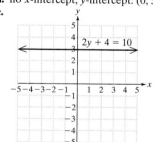 $3x - 5y = 10$

7. a. no x-intercept, y-intercept: $(0, 3)$ **b.** $m = 0$
c.

 $2y + 4 = 10$

8. $y = -2x - 2$ **9.** $y = -4x$ **10. a.** $\{5, 10, 15, 20, 25, 30, 40, 50\}$
b. $\{10, 20, 30\}$ **11.** $ab + 9a + 3b$ **12.** No solution
13. a. Quadrant IV **b.** Quadrant III **c.** Quadrant II
14. $y = -\dfrac{3}{8}x - \dfrac{1}{8}$

CHAPTER 3

Section 3.1 Practice Exercises, pp. 160–162

1. a. $y = 4x - 3$ **b.** $m = 4$ **c.** $(0, -3)$ **d.** Intersecting lines
   $y = 2x + 1$ $m = 2$ $(0, 1)$
3. a. $y = -\dfrac{1}{5}x + \dfrac{3}{5}$ **b.** $m = -\dfrac{1}{5}$ **c.** $\left(0, \dfrac{3}{5}\right)$ **d.** Coinciding lines
   $y = -\dfrac{1}{5}x + \dfrac{3}{5}$ $m = -\dfrac{1}{5}$ $\left(0, \dfrac{3}{5}\right)$

5. a. $y = \frac{7}{3}x - \frac{14}{3}$ **b.** $m = \frac{7}{3}$ **c.** $\left(0, -\frac{14}{3}\right)$ **d.** Parallel lines

$y = \frac{7}{3}x - \frac{11}{3}$ $m = \frac{7}{3}$ $\left(0, -\frac{11}{3}\right)$

7. False **9.** True **11.** $(2, -4)$ is a solution.
13. 1. Isolate a variable in one equation.
2. Substitute this variable into the other equation and solve.
3. Substitute the answer from #2 into the equation in #1.

15. $(-2, 1)$ **17.** $\left(-3, \frac{1}{3}\right)$ **19.** $(2\frac{2}{3}, 1\frac{2}{3})$ **21.** Dependent;

$\{(x, y) \mid x = 3y - 1\}$ **23.** No solution **25.** $\left(\frac{1}{2}, \frac{3}{4}\right)$

27. 1. Write both equations in standard form.
2. Multiply each equation by an appropriate constant to get opposite coefficients for one of the variable terms.
3. Add equations and solve.
4. Substitute the answer from #3 into one of the original equations to solve for the second variable.

29. $(-2, -3)$ **31.** $\left(-\frac{1}{2}, 2\right)$ **33.** $(9, 9)$ **35.** No solution

37. $(12, 30)$ **39.** Dependent; $\{(x, y) \mid 3x - 2y = 1\}$ **41.** Use the substitution method if one equation has x or y already isolated.

43. $(5, 2)$ **45.** $(4, -1)$ **47.** $\left(2, -\frac{3}{2}\right)$ **49.** Dependent;

$\{(x, y) \mid \frac{3}{5}x - y = 0\}$ **51.** $(-3, -3)$ **53.** Dependent;

$\{(x, y) \mid x = y + 4\}$ **55.** No solution **57.** $\left(2, -\frac{3}{4}\right)$

59. **61.** **63.**

Section 3.2 Practice Exercises, pp. 169–172

1. If the system reduces to an identity, the system is dependent.
3. a. Substitution **b.** $(5, -1)$ **5.** $(12, -27)$ **7.** Parallel lines
9. Intersecting lines **11.** 4 dimes, 11 quarters **13.** Eleven 50¢ pieces, ten $1 coins **15.** 102 nonstudent tickets, 84 student tickets
17. Hamburger $1.39; fish sandwich $1.59 **19.** $12,500 in the 10% account; $14,500 in the 12% account **21.** $2800 in CD's; $2600 in savings **23.** $5\frac{1}{3}$ L of the 18% solution; $10\frac{2}{3}$ L of the 45% solution
25. 1 oz of bleach; 11 oz of 4% solution **27. a.** Plane: 180 mph; train: 90 mph **b.** 120 miles **29.** Juan: 6 mph; Jeannie: 4 mph **31.** 69°; 21°
33. 134.5°; 45.5° **35.** 29°; 61° **37.** 200 miles **39.** $30

41. **43.**

Section 3.3 Practice Exercises, pp. 181–184

1. $(1, 1)$ **3.** $\left\{(x, y) \mid x - \frac{2}{3}y = 2\right\}$ **5.** 65 mph, 58 mph
7. $(4, 0, 2)$ is a solution. **9.** None **11.** $(1, 2, 3)$ **13.** $(-2, -1, -3)$

15. $(-1, 3, 4)$ **17.** $(-6, 1, 7)$ **19.** $\left(\frac{1}{2}, \frac{2}{3}, -\frac{5}{6}\right)$ **21.** $67°, 82°, 31°$
23. 9 cm, 18 cm, 27 cm **25.** 148 adult tickets, 51 children's tickets, 23 senior tickets **27.** 24 oz peanuts, 8 oz pecans, 16 oz cashews
29. $(-9, 5, 5)$ **31.** No solution; inconsistent **33.** $(1, 3, 1)$
35. Dependent **37.** $(1, 0, 1)$ **39.** $(0, 0, 0)$ **41.** Dependent
43. $(0, 0, 0)$

45. $\left\{(x, y, z) \middle| x \text{ is arbitrary}, y = \frac{1}{3}x, z = 4 - \frac{5}{3}x\right\}$

or $\{(x, y, z) \mid x = 3y, y \text{ is arbitrary}, z = 4 - 5y\}$

or $\left\{(x, y, z) \middle| x = \frac{12 - 3z}{5}, y = \frac{4 - z}{5}, z \text{ is arbitrary}\right\}$

47. $\left\{(x, y, z) \middle| x \text{ is arbitrary}, y = -2x - 3, z = \frac{1}{4}x - \frac{3}{4}\right\}$

$\left\{(x, y, z) \middle| x = \frac{-y - 3}{2}, y \text{ is arbitrary}, z = \frac{-y - 9}{8}\right\}$

$\{(x, y, z) \mid x = 4z + 3, y = -8z - 9, z \text{ is arbitrary}\}$

Midchapter Review, pp. 184–185

1. $(1, 0)$ **2.** No solution **3.** $\{(x, y) \mid y = 3x + 1\}$ **4.** $(2, -1)$
5. $\{(x, y) \mid y = 2x - 8\}$ **6.** No solution
7. $\{(x, y) \mid -x + 5y = -12\}$ **8.** $(8, 3)$ **9.** No solution
10. $(1, -1, 2)$ **11.** $(-2, 4, 6)$ **12.** No solution **13.** Coffee is $1.50 and a doughnut is $0.80. **14.** The angles are 48°, 12°, and 120°.

Section 3.4 Practice Exercises, pp. 191–194

1. $(1, 1)$ **3.** $(6, 1, -1)$ **5.** An augmented matrix is one constructed from the coefficients of the variable terms and the constants. **7.** The order is the number of rows by the number of columns. **9.** 4×1, column matrix **11.** 3×3, square matrix **13.** 1×2, row matrix
15. 2×4, none of these **17.** $\left[\begin{array}{cc|c} 1 & -2 & -1 \\ 2 & 1 & -7 \end{array}\right]$ **19.** $\left[\begin{array}{cc|c} -9 & 13 & -5 \\ 7 & 5 & 19 \end{array}\right]$

21. $\left[\begin{array}{ccc|c} 1 & 1 & 1 & 6 \\ 1 & -1 & 1 & 2 \\ 1 & 1 & -1 & 0 \end{array}\right]$ **23.** $\left[\begin{array}{ccc|c} 1 & -2 & 1 & 5 \\ 2 & 6 & 3 & -2 \\ 3 & -1 & -2 & 1 \end{array}\right]$ **25. a.** 7 **b.** -2

27. a. 0 **b.** 4 **29.** $\left[\begin{array}{cc} 1 & \frac{1}{2} & \frac{11}{2} \\ 2 & -1 & 1 \end{array}\right]$ **31.** $\left[\begin{array}{cc} 1 & -4 & 3 \\ 5 & 2 & 1 \end{array}\right]$

33. $\left[\begin{array}{cc} 1 & 5 & 2 \\ 0 & 11 & 5 \end{array}\right]$ **35.** $\left[\begin{array}{cc} 1 & 0 & -22 \\ 0 & 1 & 3 \end{array}\right]$

37. a. $\left[\begin{array}{ccc|c} 1 & 3 & 0 & -1 \\ 0 & -11 & -5 & 10 \\ -2 & 0 & -3 & 10 \end{array}\right]$ **b.** $\left[\begin{array}{ccc|c} 1 & 3 & 0 & -1 \\ 0 & -11 & -5 & 10 \\ 0 & 6 & -3 & 8 \end{array}\right]$

39. a. $\left[\begin{array}{ccc|c} 1 & 0 & 13 & -4 \\ 0 & 1 & 3 & -3 \\ 0 & 5 & 9 & 8 \end{array}\right]$ **b.** $\left[\begin{array}{ccc|c} 1 & 0 & 13 & -4 \\ 0 & 1 & 3 & -3 \\ 0 & 0 & -6 & 23 \end{array}\right]$

41. a. $\left[\begin{array}{ccc|c} 1 & 0 & 0 & -5 \\ 0 & 1 & -8 & -11 \\ 0 & 0 & 1 & 4 \end{array}\right]$ **b.** $\left[\begin{array}{ccc|c} 1 & 0 & 0 & -5 \\ 0 & 1 & 0 & 21 \\ 0 & 0 & 1 & 4 \end{array}\right]$ **43.** False

45. False **47.** $x = -1, y = -7$ **49.** $x = 8, y = 0, z = -1$
51. Interchange rows 1 and 2. **53.** Multiply row 1 by -3 and add to row 2. Replace row 2 with the result. **55.** $(-3, -1)$ **57.** $(-21, 9)$
59. Dependent **61.** $(3, -1)$ **63.** $(-10, 3)$ **65.** No solution
67. $(1, 2, 3)$ **69.** $(1, -2, 0)$ **71.** $(1, 2, 1)$ **73.** No solution

75. $\begin{bmatrix} 1 & 0 & | & -3 \\ 0 & 1 & | & -1 \end{bmatrix}$ **77.** $\begin{bmatrix} 1 & 0 & | & -21 \\ 0 & 1 & | & 9 \end{bmatrix}$ **79.** $\begin{bmatrix} 1 & 3 & | & 3 \\ 0 & 0 & | & 0 \end{bmatrix}$; Dependent

81. $\begin{bmatrix} 1 & 0 & 0 & | & 1 \\ 0 & 1 & 0 & | & 2 \\ 0 & 0 & 1 & | & 3 \end{bmatrix}$ **83.** $\begin{bmatrix} 1 & 0 & 0 & | & 1 \\ 0 & 1 & 0 & | & -2 \\ 0 & 0 & 1 & | & 0 \end{bmatrix}$ **85.** $\begin{bmatrix} 1 & 0 & 0 & | & 1 \\ 0 & 1 & 0 & | & 2 \\ 0 & 0 & 1 & | & 1 \end{bmatrix}$

Section 3.5 Practice Exercises, pp. 205–209

1. 7 **3.** 5 **5.** 8 **7.** 0 **9.** −2 **11.** Two matrices are equal if their corresponding elements are equal. **13.** $x = 0, y = -6$

15. $x = 5, y = \dfrac{3}{4}, z = -1$ **17.** $\begin{bmatrix} 4 & 9 \\ 8 & 1 \end{bmatrix}$ **19.** $\begin{bmatrix} 5 & 12 & 10 \\ 17 & 3 & -3 \end{bmatrix}$

21. $\begin{bmatrix} 4 & -5 & -9 \\ -8 & 2 & -6 \\ \frac{3}{8} & -3 & 0 \end{bmatrix}$ **23.** $\begin{bmatrix} 4 & 9 \\ -5 & -10 \end{bmatrix}$ **25.** $\begin{bmatrix} -15 & 1 \\ 3 & -3 \\ 9 & 3 \\ 6 & 7 \end{bmatrix}$

27. $\begin{bmatrix} 24 & -16 \\ 32 & -8 \end{bmatrix}$ **29.** $\begin{bmatrix} 0 & -12 & 20 \\ -12 & 8 & -40 \end{bmatrix}$ **31.** $10 \cdot \begin{bmatrix} 3 & 4 \\ -1 & 10 \end{bmatrix}$

33. $-4 \cdot \begin{bmatrix} -3 & -7 \\ 1 & -4 \\ -2 & -5 \end{bmatrix}$ **35.**

	Fri.	Sat.	Sun.
Driver 1	$7\frac{1}{2}$	6	$6\frac{1}{2}$
Driver 2	$5\frac{1}{2}$	5	8
Driver 3	8	6	$6\frac{1}{2}$
Driver 4	$7\frac{1}{2}$	$4\frac{1}{2}$	7

37. $\begin{bmatrix} 9 & -5 & 5 \\ 4 & -2 & 1 \end{bmatrix}$ **39.** Not possible **41.** $\begin{bmatrix} 6 & -7 & 10 \\ -4 & -2 & -12 \end{bmatrix}$

43. $\begin{bmatrix} 14 & -9 & 5 \\ 10 & -10 & 2 \end{bmatrix}$ **45.** Not possible **47.** $\begin{bmatrix} -21 & 19 & -10 \\ -14 & 26 & 9 \end{bmatrix}$

49. [57.14], or $57.14 **51.** $\begin{bmatrix} -22 & -6 & 37 \\ 8 & 30 & -29 \end{bmatrix}$ **53.** $\begin{bmatrix} 42 & -6 \\ 1 & -4 \\ 12 & -12 \end{bmatrix}$

55. Not possible **57.** $\begin{bmatrix} 27 & -18 \\ -9 & 18 \end{bmatrix}$ **59.** Not possible

61. a. $\mathbf{C} = \begin{bmatrix} 79.00 \\ 56.50 \\ 67.40 \end{bmatrix}$ represents the cost to the vendor for each game.

b. $\mathbf{R} = \begin{bmatrix} 230.00 \\ 165.00 \\ 196.00 \end{bmatrix}$ represents the revenue to the vendor for each game.

c. $\mathbf{P} = \begin{bmatrix} 151.00 \\ 108.50 \\ 128.60 \end{bmatrix}$ represents the profit for each game.

63. $6x + 5y = 1$
$x - 3y = 4$

65. $x - 2y + z = 7$
$2x + y - z = 0$
$3x + 2y - 2z = -2$

67. a.

b. $\begin{bmatrix} -1 & -1 & 1 & 1 \\ 6 & -6 & 6 & -6 \end{bmatrix}$

c.

d. The length in the x-direction is $\frac{1}{4}$ of the original size. The width in the y-direction is three times the original size.

69. a. $\begin{bmatrix} 4 & 0 \\ 0 & 4 \end{bmatrix} \cdot \begin{bmatrix} -1 & -1 & 1 & 1 \\ 1 & -1 & 1 & -1 \end{bmatrix} = \begin{bmatrix} -4 & -4 & 4 & 4 \\ 4 & -4 & 4 & -4 \end{bmatrix}$

b.

Section 3.6 Practice Exercises, pp. 215–217

1. −11 **3.** 16 **5.** 8 **7.** 0 **9.** $-\dfrac{13}{6}$ **11.** 18 **13.** 52 **15.** 68

17. −48 **19.** 26 **21.** The sign array determines the sign for each minor when evaluating a determinant. **23. a.** 3 **b.** 3 **25. a.** 25 **b.** 25 **27.** 20 **29.** −26 **31.** −26 **33.** 0 **35.** −3 **37.** $-2x - 3y$ **39.** $-n$ **41.** $-12a - 23b - 3c$ **43.** 0 **45.** $-7x - 5y + 18$ **47.** $\frac{31}{2}$ **49.** $\frac{9}{2}$ **51.** 1 **53.** Collinear **55.** Collinear **57.** Collinear

59. Not collinear **61.** $y = 5x - 4$ **63.** $y = -\dfrac{6}{5}x - \dfrac{2}{5}$ **65.** $y = 5$ **67.** $x = 4$ **69.** $4x^2 - 16$ **71.** $7t + 5$ **73.** $x = -19$ **75.** $w = 1$ **77.** 36

Section 3.7 Practice Exercises, pp. 223–224

1. $\mathbf{D} = 16; \mathbf{D}_x = -63; \mathbf{D}_y = 66$ **3.** $\mathbf{D} = \dfrac{4}{3}; \mathbf{D}_x = -77; \mathbf{D}_y = -35$

5. $\mathbf{D} = -4; \mathbf{D}_x = 1; \mathbf{D}_y = 41$ **7.** $(2, -1)$ **9.** $(4, -1)$

11. $\left(\dfrac{23}{13}, \dfrac{9}{13}\right)$ **13.** $(0, 0)$ **15.** Cramer's rule does not apply when the determinant, $\mathbf{D} = 0$. **17.** No solution (inconsistent) **19.** $(0, 0)$ **21.** $\{(x, y) \mid x + 5y = 3\}$ (dependent) **23.** Katia has eight dimes and five quarters. **25.** $x = 1$ **27.** $z = \dfrac{1}{2}$ **29.** $x = \dfrac{49}{24}$ **31.** $y = \dfrac{16}{41}$ **33.** $(3, 2, 1)$ **35.** Cramer's rule does not apply. **37.** Cramer's rule does not apply. **39.** The angles are $21°, 51°$, and $108°$. **41. a.** 2 **b.** −2 **c.** $x = -1$

Review Exercises, pp. 231–233

1. $(4, -1)$ **3.** Dependent; $\{(x, y) \mid 4x + y = 7\}$ **5.** $(1, 1)$ **7.** $(2, -1)$ **9.** $4500 invested at 5% **11.** Plane 150 mph, wind 10 mph **13. a.** $y = 0.1x + 9.95$ **b.** $y = 0.08x + 12.95$ **c.** 150 min

15. No solution **17.** 5 ft, 12 ft, 13 ft **19.** 3×3 **21.** 1×4

23. $\begin{bmatrix} 1 & 1 & 3 \\ 1 & -1 & -1 \end{bmatrix}$ **25.** $x = 9, y = -3$ **27. a.** 1

b. $\begin{bmatrix} 1 & 3 & | & -11 \\ 2 & 0 & | & 5 \end{bmatrix}$ **29. a.** 4 **b.** $\begin{bmatrix} 1 & 3 & | & 1 \\ 0 & -13 & | & 2 \end{bmatrix}$ **31.** $(1, 2)$

33. $x = 1, y = 5$ **35.** $\begin{bmatrix} 4 & 11 \\ 1 & 4 \end{bmatrix}$ **37.** Not possible **39.** $\begin{bmatrix} 48 & 12 \\ -10 & 16 \\ 4 & 14 \end{bmatrix}$

41. $\begin{bmatrix} 12 & 1 \\ -5 & 16 \end{bmatrix}$ **43.** $\begin{bmatrix} 3 & 17 \\ 66 & 46 \end{bmatrix}$ **45.** $[125 \quad 173.75 \quad 142.50]$ The profits from shipping fruit to markets 1, 2, and 3 are $125.00, $173.75, and
$142.50, respectively. **47.** -60 **49.** 12 **51.** 0 **53.** 48 **55.** 0

57. 4 **59.** 18 **61.** $D = -5$ $x = -\dfrac{14}{5}$ **63.** $(1, 4)$ **65.** $(5, -2, 0)$

$D_x = 14$

$D_y = 18$ $y = -\dfrac{18}{5}$

67. No solution

Test, p. 234

1. $(4, 15)$ **2.** Dependent; $\{(x, y) \mid 3x - 5y = -7\}$ **3.** $(16, -37, 9)$
4. No solution **5.** 80 L of 20%, 120 L of 60% solution **6.** The
length is 21 cm and the width is 15 cm. **7.** Joanne: 142 orders; Kent:

162 orders; Geoff: 200 orders **8.** For example: $\begin{bmatrix} 2 & 1 \\ 0 & -4 \\ 2.6 & 7 \end{bmatrix}$

9. a. $\begin{bmatrix} 1 & 2 & 1 & | & -3 \\ 0 & -8 & -3 & | & 10 \\ -5 & -6 & 3 & | & 0 \end{bmatrix}$ **b.** $\begin{bmatrix} 1 & 2 & 1 & | & -3 \\ 0 & -8 & -3 & | & 10 \\ 0 & 4 & 8 & | & -15 \end{bmatrix}$

10. $(6, -1)$ **11.** $(4, 3, 2)$ **12.** $\begin{bmatrix} 0 & 7 \\ 6 & 7 \end{bmatrix}$ **13.** $\begin{bmatrix} 17 & 56 \\ 3 & -8 \end{bmatrix}$ **14.** The

product of $\mathbf{AB}$ is not possible because the number of columns in $\mathbf{A}$
does not equal the number of rows in $\mathbf{B}$. **15.** In general, $\mathbf{AB} \neq \mathbf{BA}$.
Sometimes the commuted product may not be possible or may result
in a different size matrix. Even if the matrices are square matrices the
product $\mathbf{AB}$ and $\mathbf{BA}$ may not be the same. For example,

$\begin{bmatrix} -2 & 7 \\ 3 & -1 \end{bmatrix} \cdot \begin{bmatrix} 2 & 0 \\ 3 & 8 \end{bmatrix} \neq \begin{bmatrix} 2 & 0 \\ 3 & 8 \end{bmatrix} \cdot \begin{bmatrix} -2 & 7 \\ 3 & -1 \end{bmatrix}$ **16.** 7 **17.** -6

18. 20 **19.** No. The matrix must be square. **20.** $y = -\dfrac{40}{11}$

21. $y = 8$ **22.** $\{(x, y) \mid y = 3x\}$

Cumulative Review Exercises, Chapters 1–3, p. 235

1. 0 **2.** $4x^2 - x + 14$ **3.** $x = -2$ **4.** $x = -4y - 6$ **5.** The
length is 22.5 ft. **6.** $\left(-3, -\frac{1}{4}\right]$
7. Slope is $-\frac{2}{3}$; y-intercept is $(0, 0)$ **8.** $y = \frac{1}{3}x - \frac{2}{3}$ **9.** No solution

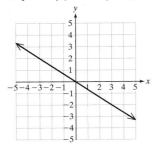

10. $(1, 2)$ **11.** 4 nickels, 6 dimes, 9 quarters **12. a.** $y = 2.50x + 25$
b. $y = 3x + 10$ **c.** 30 tapes **13.** $(2, 0, -1)$ **14.** 2×3 **15.** For

example: $\begin{bmatrix} 2 & 3 & 1 & 7 \\ -1 & 4 & 2 & 6 \end{bmatrix}$ **16.** Interchange two rows. Multiply a

row by a nonzero constant. Add a multiple of one row to another
row. **17.** $(1, 1)$

CHAPTER 4

Section 4.1 Practice Exercises, pp. 244–248

1. $\{(A, 1)(A, 2)(B, 2)(C, 3)(D, 5)(E, 4)\}$ **3.** $\{$(Pregnant women, 60)
(Nursing mothers, 65)(Infants under 1 year, 14)(Children 1–4 years, 16)
(Adults, 50)$\}$ **5.** Domain $\{A, B, C, D, E\}$; range $\{1, 2, 3, 4, 5\}$
7. Domain $\{$Pregnant women, nursing mothers, infants under 1 year,
children 1–4 years, adults$\}$; range $\{60, 65, 14, 16, 50\}$ **9. a.** For
example: $\{$(Julie, New York)(Peggy, Florida)(Stephen, Kansas)(Pat,
New York)$\}$ **b.** Domain $\{$Julie, Peggy, Stephen, Pat$\}$; range $\{$New York,
Florida, Kansas$\}$ **11. a.** $y = 2x - 1$ **b.**

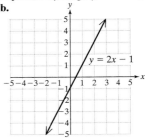

c. Domain $(-\infty, \infty)$; range $(-\infty, \infty)$ **13.** Domain $[-5, 3]$; range
$[-2.1, 2.8]$ **15.** Domain $[0, 4.2]$; range $[-2.1, 2.1]$ **17.** Domain
$(-\infty, 0]$; range $(-\infty, \infty)$ **19.** Domain $[-4, \infty)$; range
$[-4, -2] \cup (2, \infty)$ **21.** Domain $[-4, \infty)$; range $[0, \infty)$ **23.** Domain
$\{-3, -1, 1, 3\}$; range $\{0, 1, 2, 3\}$ **25.** Domain $[-4, 5)$; range $\{-2, 1, 3\}$
27. a. 2.85 **b.** 9.33 **c.** Dec **d.** Nov **e.** 7.63 **f.** $\{$Jan, Feb, Mar, Apr,
May, June, July, Aug, Sept, Oct, Nov, Dec$\}$ **29. a.** 81.46%, 68.82%,
56.18%, 43.54% **b.** No, 7 is not in the domain. **31.** Domain
$(-\infty, \infty)$; range $[0, \infty)$ **33.** Domain $(-\infty, \infty)$; range $[0, \infty)$
35. Domain $(-\infty, \infty)$; range $[-2, \infty)$ **37.** The domain $(-\infty, \infty)$ and
the range $[c, \infty)$ will be the same for all values of c.
39. a. **b.**

Section 4.2 Practice Exercises, pp. 260–264

1. a. $\{$(Doris, Mike)(Richard, Nora)(Doris, Molly)(Richard, Mike)$\}$
b. $\{$Doris, Richard$\}$ **c.** $\{$Mike, Nora, Molly$\}$ **d.** Not a function
3. a. $\{(3, 10)(4, 12)(5, 12)(6, 12)\}$ **b.** $\{3, 4, 5, 6\}$ **c.** $\{10, 12\}$ **d.** Is a
function **5.** Domain $[0, 4]$; range $[1, 4]$ **7.** Domain $\{-4\}$; range
$(-\infty, \infty)$ **9.** Not a function **11.** Function **13.** Not a function
15. 10 **17.** 7 **19.** 0 **21.** $6t - 2$ **23.** 7 **25.** $x^2 + 2xk + k^2$
27. $6a + 4$ **29.** 7 **31.** 400 **33.** 40 **35.** 4 **37.** 3 **39.** 16 **41.** 63

43. 0 **45.** 1 **47.** $-3x - 5$ **49.** $x^2 - \dfrac{11}{3}$ **51.** $\dfrac{2}{3}x - 4$

53. $\dfrac{-4x + 1}{x^2 - 3}$ **55.** $-4x - 5$ **57.** $-\dfrac{16}{3}$ **59.** $x^2 - 9$ **61.** -7

63. 2π **65.** -5 **67.** 15 **69.** -5 **71.** 4 **73.** -63 **75.** 0
77. a. 2 **b.** 1 **c.** 1 **d.** $x = -3$ **e.** $x = 1$ **79.** The domain is all real
numbers that do not make the denominator zero. Domain: $\{x \mid x \neq 2\}$
or $(-\infty, 2) \cup (2, \infty)$ **81.** $(-\infty, 4) \cup (4, \infty)$ **83.** $(-\infty, 0) \cup (0, \infty)$
85. $(-\infty, \infty)$ **87.** $[-7, \infty)$ **89.** $[3, \infty)$ **91.** $\left[-\dfrac{1}{2}, \infty\right)$ **93.** The domain of a polynomial is all real numbers. **95.** $(-\infty, \infty)$ **97.** $(-\infty, \infty)$
99. a. 45.1, 38.975 **b.** After 1 s, the height of the ball is 45.1 m. After
1.5 s, the height of the ball is 38.975 m. **101. a.** 5.9, 11.8 **b.** After
1 h, the distance is 5.9 km. After 2 h, the distance is 11.8 km.
103. a. [15000, 45000] **b.** $P(20,000) = 76$. 76% of people with an annual income of \$20,000 read the paper; $P(30,000) = 81$. 81% of peo-
ple with an annual income of \$30,000 read the paper; $P(40,000) = 82$.
82% of people with an annual income of \$40,000 read the paper.
105. a. $N(1) = 2.6$. A person of age 1 averages 2.6 visits per year to
a doctor. $N(20) = 1.9$. A person of age 20 averages 1.9 visits per year
to a doctor. $N(40) = 2.3$. A person of age 40 averages 2.3 visits per
year to a doctor. $N(75) = 5.6$. A person of age 75 averages 5.6 visits per
year to a doctor. **c.** About 24 years old **107.** $\left(-\infty, \dfrac{1}{3}\right) \cup \left(\dfrac{1}{3}, \infty\right)$
109. $(4, \infty)$
111.   **113.**   **115. a.**

b. $h(1) = 45.1$;
$h(1.5) = 38.975$

Section 4.3 Practice Exercises, pp. 273–277

1. a. Yes **b.** $\{6, 5, 4, 3, 2, 1\}$ **c.** $\{1, 2, 3, 4, 5, 6\}$ **3.** -2 **5.** $a^2 - 2$
7. 2 **9.** $b^2 - 2$ **11.** $(-\infty, \infty)$ **13.** $[6, \infty)$ **15. a.** $f(3) = 9$; It takes
9 lb to stretch the spring 3 in. **b.** $f(0) = 0$; It takes 0 lb to stretch the
spring 0 in.
17.   **19.**

21.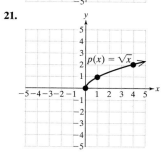

23. a. $[-4, \infty)$ **b.** $f(0) = 2, f(2) = \sqrt{6}, f(-2) = \sqrt{2}$
25. a. $(-\infty, \infty)$ **b.** $h(1) = 1, h(-1) = 1, h(0) = 2$

27. a. $(-\infty, 3) \cup (3, \infty)$ **b.** $p(0) = -\dfrac{2}{3}, p(1) = -1, p(2) = -2,$
$p(4) = 2, p(5) = 1, p(6) = \dfrac{2}{3}$ **29.** x-intercept $(-1, 0)$; y-intercept
$(0, 1)$ **31.** x-intercepts $(-2, 0), (2, 0)$; y-intercept $(0, -2)$
33. x-intercept–none; y-intercept $(0, 2)$
35. a.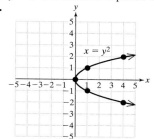

b. $y = x^2$ is a function. It passes the vertical line test.
c.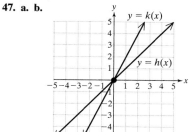

d. $x = y^2$ is not a function. The graph does not pass the vertical line
test. **37. a.** $(-\infty, \infty)$ **b.** $(0, 0)$ **c.** vi **39. a.** $(-\infty, \infty)$ **b.** $(0, 1)$ **c.** viii
41. a. $[-1, \infty)$ **b.** $(0, 1)$ **c.** vii **43. a.** $(-\infty, 3) \cup (3, \infty)$
b. $\left(0, -\dfrac{1}{3}\right)$ **c.** ii **45. a.** $(-\infty, \infty)$ **b.** $(0, 2)$ **c.** iv
47. a. b.

49. a. b.

51. a. b.

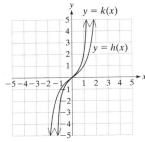

53. The graphs of $2h(x)$ are "steeper" than the graphs of $h(x)$ with generally the same shape.

55.   **57.**   **59.**

Midchapter Review, pp. 277–278

1. Domain {Colorado, Rhode Island, Kentucky, Alabama}; Range {16, −1.3, 5.3, 5.8}; Function   **2.** Domain {2, 4, 6, 8}; Range {10}; Function   **3.** Domain {1, −1, 2, −2, 0}; Range {1, −1, 8, −8, 0}; Function   **4.** Domain {A, B, C, D}; Range {1, 2, 3, 4}; Not a function   **5.** Domain {13, 8, −6, $\sqrt{2}$}; Range {6, 2, 4π, 1}; Not a function   **6.** Domain {0.1}; Range {−6.4, 9.0, −2.7, 3.0}; Not a function   **7.** Function   **8.** Not a function   **9.** Not a function   **10.** Function

11. a. $g(3) = -17, g(0) = 1, g\left(\dfrac{1}{2}\right) = -2, g\left(-\dfrac{1}{3}\right) = 3, g(-2) = 13$

b. $(-\infty, \infty)$ **12. a.** $f(0) = -\dfrac{1}{5}, f(2) = -\dfrac{1}{3}, f(4) = -1, f\left(4\dfrac{1}{2}\right) = -2,$

$f\left(5\dfrac{1}{2}\right) = 2, f(6) = 1, f(8) = \dfrac{1}{3}$ **b.** $(-\infty, 5) \cup (5, \infty)$

13. a. $p(-1) = 0, p(0) = 1, p(3) = 2, p(5) = \sqrt{6}$ **b.** $[-1, \infty)$
14. a. $k(0) = 4, k(1) = 3, k(2) = 2, k(3) = 1, k(4) = 2, k(5) = 3$
b. $(-\infty, \infty)$

15.

16.

17.

18.

19.

20.

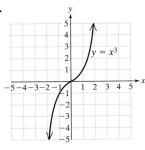

Section 4.4 Practice Exercises, pp. 284–289

1. $(-\infty, -5) \cup (-5, \infty)$ **3.** $(-\infty, \infty)$ **5.** 10   **7.** −3   **9.** 2   **11.** 13
13. 6   **15.** 4
17. increasing $(0, \infty)$; decreasing $(-\infty, 0)$

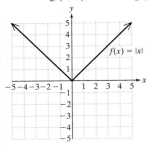

19. increasing $(-\infty, \infty)$; decreasing: none

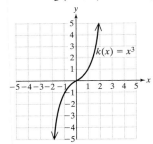

21. increasing: none; decreasing $(-\infty, 0) \cup (0, \infty)$

23. a. $N(1978) = 28,000$ $N(1984) = 22,000$
b. $(1984, 1986) \cup (1988, 1992)$
c. $(1976, 1984) \cup (1986, 1988) \cup (1992, 1996)$
25. a. $(1981, 1997)$ **b.** $(1977, 1997)$ **c.** none **d.** $(1993, 1997)$
e. $(1977, 1980) \cup (1983, 1987) \cup (1992, 1994)$
27. $f(-2) = 4, f(0) = 0, f(6) = 6$
29. $h(-4) = -2, h(-3) = 4, h(0) = 4, h(3) = 4, h(4) = 64$

31. a.

b.

c.
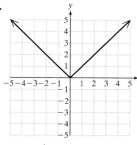

d. $h(-3) = -3, h(0) = 0, h(4) = 2$

33.

35.

37. $f(x) = \begin{cases} -2 \text{ for } x < -1 \\ 3 \text{ for } x \geq -1 \end{cases}$

39. $f(x) = \begin{cases} x^2 \text{ for } x \leq 1 \\ 2 \text{ for } x > 1 \end{cases}$

41. a. $S(30) = 16, S(35) = 16, S(60) = 10, S(65) = 20$ **b.** 24 mph

c.
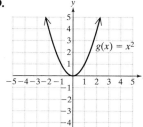

43. b. Constant speed is a constant function whose graph is a horizontal line.   **45. a.** $[-4, \infty)$ **b.** $(-\infty, 3]$ **c.** -1 **d.** 0 **e.** $x = -3, -1, 3$ **f.** $x = 0$ **g.** $(-4, -2) \cup (-1, 0)$ **h.** $(-2, -1) \cup (0, \infty)$ **i.** None **j.** False **k.** False   **47. a.** $(1900, 1950)$ **b.** $(1950, 1970)$ **c.** $(1900, 1940)$ **d.** $(1900, 1970)$

49.

51.

53.
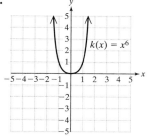

55. If n is even, the graph has the general shape of $y = x^2$. If n is odd, the graph has the general shape of $y = x^3$:

57. a. $(-\infty, \infty)$ **b.** $[-2, \infty)$ **c.** $(-4, \infty)$ **d.** $(-\infty, -4)$

59. a. $(-\infty, 3]$ **b.** $(-\infty, 0]$ **c.** $(-\infty, 3)$ **d.** Not decreasing

61.

Section 4.5 Practice Exercises, pp. 295–297

1. 4   **3.** 3   **5.** 3   **7.** Not a function   **9.** Function   **11.** Not a function   **13.** Not a function   **15. a.** Increase **b.** Decrease

17. $T = kq$ **19.** $W = \dfrac{k}{p^2}$ **21.** $Q = \dfrac{kx}{y^3}$ **23.** $L = kw\sqrt{v}$

25. $k = \dfrac{9}{2}$ **27.** $k = 512$ **29.** $k = 1.75$ **31.** $Z = 56$ **33.** $L = 9$

35. $B = \dfrac{15}{2}$ **37.** 355,000 tons   **39.** 42.6 ft   **41.** 18.5 A   **43.** 1.25 Ω

45. 20 lb   **47.** 2224 lb   **49. a.** $A = kl^2$ **b.** 4 times **c.** 9 times **d.** In doubling the length of the sides, the area of a square increases by a factor of 4. Therefore, the figure makes it appear that 1980 dollars are worth 4 times as much as 1998 dollars rather than 2 times as much.

Review Exercises, pp. 302–305

1. For example: {(Peggy, Kent)(Charlie, Laura)(Tom, Matt)(Tom, Chris)}   **3.** Domain $[-3, 9]$; range $[0, 60]$ **5.** Domain $\{-3, -1, 0, 2, 3\}$; range $\left\{-2, 1, 0, \dfrac{5}{2}\right\}$

7.
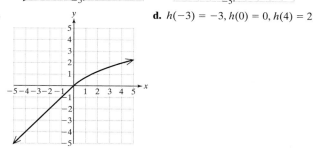

9. a. Function **b.** $(-\infty, \infty)$ **c.** $(-\infty, 0.35)$ **11. a.** Not a function
b. $\{0, 4\}$ **c.** $\{2, 3, 4, 5\}$ **13. a.** Function **b.** $\{6, 7, 8, 9\}$
c. $\{9, 10, 11, 12\}$ **15.** 2 **17.** $6t^2 - 4$ **19.** $6\pi^2 - 4$
21. $6x^2 + 12xh + 6h^2 - 4$ **23.** $(-\infty, 11) \cup (11, \infty)$ **25.** $[-2, \infty)$
27.

29.

c.

41. a. $[0, 70]$ **b.** $(9, 23)$ **c.** $(0, 9) \cup (23, 70)$ **d.** 18 years and 29 years
e. 16 years and 45 years
43. $k(-2) = 4, k(-1) = 1, k(0) = 7, k(3) = 0, k(5) = \sqrt{2}$
45. **47.** $y = 256$ **49.** 54.1 km

31.

33.

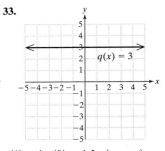

35. a. $s(4) = 4, s(3) = 1, s(2) = 0, s(1) = 1, s(0) = 4$ **b.** $(-\infty, \infty)$
c.

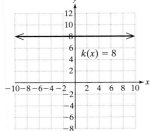

Test, pp. 305–307

1. a. Not a function **b.** $\{-3, -1, 1, 3\}$ **c.** $\{3, -2, -1, 1\}$
2. a. Function **b.** $(-\infty, \infty)$ **c.** $(-\infty, 0]$ **3. a.** Function **b.** $\{1975, 1985, 1997\}$ **c.** $\{47.4\%, 62.2\%, 72.1\%\}$ **4. a.** 5 **b.** 3 **c.** 12 **d.** 9 **e.** 3
f. 7 **5. a.** $k(0) = 8, k(-2) = 8, k(15) = 8$ **b.** $(-\infty, \infty)$
c. **d.** $\{8\}$

37. a. $h(-3) = -\frac{1}{2}, h(-1) = -\frac{3}{4}, h(0) = -1, h(2) = -3, h(4) = 3,$
$h(5) = \frac{3}{2}, h(7) = \frac{3}{4}$ **b.** $(-\infty, 3) \cup (3, \infty)$
c.

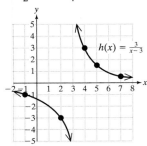

6. a. $r(-2) = -27, r(-1) = -8, r(0) = -1, r(1) = 0, r(2) = 1,$
$r(3) = 8$ **b.** $(-\infty, \infty)$ **c.**

39. a. $b(0) = 4.5$. In 1985 consumption was 4.5 gal of bottled water per capita. $b(7) = 9.4$. In 1992 consumption was 9.4 gal of bottled water per capita. **b.** $m = 0.7$. Consumption increased by 0.7 gal/year.

7. a. $s(0) = 36$. In 1985 the per capita consumption was 36 gal. $s(7) = 47.2$. In 1992 the per capita consumption was 47.2 gal.
b. $m = 1.6$. Increase of 1.6 gal/year **c.**

8.

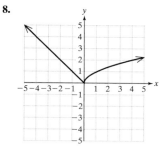

9. a. $(-1, 1) \cup (4, 7)$ **b.** $(3, 4)$ **c.** $(1, 3)$ **d.** $f(1) = 1, f(4) = 2,$ $f(7) = -1$ **e.** $x = 6$ **10. a.** ii **b.** iii **c.** v **d.** iv **e.** i **11. a.** 1985 **b.** (1985, 1996) **c.** (1980, 1985) **d.** G represents the total per capita consumption of refined sugar and corn sweetener. **12.** 2.37 s

Cumulative Review Exercises, Chapters 1–4, pp. 307–308

1. $t = -\dfrac{12}{7}$ **2.** 14 **3. a.** $[6, \infty)$ **b.** $(-\infty, 17)$ **c.** $[-2, 3]$

4. $\left(-\infty, \dfrac{1}{6}\right)$ **5.** 1474.45 in.^{3} **6.** $y = -\dfrac{4}{3}x$ **7.** $m = \pm\dfrac{2}{5}$ **8. a.** To find x-intercepts, let $f(x) = 0$. To find the y-intercept, find $f(0)$. **b.** $(0, 2)$ **c.** $\left(-\dfrac{2}{3}, 0\right)$ **9.** $(2, 1, 0)$ is not a solution because it is not a solution to all three equations. **10.** \$9.70/h tutoring; \$8.00/h taking notes

11. $\begin{bmatrix} 8 & -9 & | & 3 \\ 3 & 2 & | & -4 \end{bmatrix}$ **12.** 6 **13. a.** 8620 students **b.** The year 2011

14. Domain {12, 15, 18, 21}; range {a, c, e}; yes **15. a.** 1 **b.** 33 **c.** 18 **d.** 5 **16. a.** $-x - 2$ **b.** $7x - 2$ **c.** $-12x - 2$

17. a. $(-\infty, 15) \cup (15, \infty)$ **b.** $[6, \infty)$ **18.** \$3500 **19. a.** 29 **b.** 0

20. $y = -\dfrac{40}{63}$

CHAPTER 5

Section 5.1 Practice Exercises, pp. 316–318

1. $b^4 \cdot b^3 = (b \cdot b \cdot b \cdot b) \cdot (b \cdot b \cdot b) = b^7$
$(b^4)^3 = b^4 \cdot b^4 \cdot b^4 = (b \cdot b \cdot b \cdot b) \cdot (b \cdot b \cdot b \cdot b) \cdot (b \cdot b \cdot b \cdot b) = b^{12}$
3. For example: $3^2 \cdot 3^4 = 3^6$; $x^8 \cdot x^2 = x^{10}$
5. For example: $(x^2)^4 = x^8$; $(2^3)^5 = 2^{15}$
7. For example: $\left(\dfrac{x}{y}\right)^3 = \dfrac{x^3}{y^3}$; $\left(\dfrac{2}{7}\right)^2 = \dfrac{2^2}{7^2}$ **9.** 6^8 **11.** 13^6 **13.** y^8

15. $81x^8$ **17.** $\dfrac{1}{p^3}$ **19.** $\dfrac{1}{7^3}$ **21.** $\dfrac{1}{w^2}$ **23.** 1 **25.** 3 **27.** $\dfrac{q^2}{p^3}$

29. $-\dfrac{3b^7}{2a^3}$ **31.** $\dfrac{x^{16}}{8^4 y^{20} z^8}$ **33.** $-\dfrac{4m^4}{n^2}$ **35.** $\dfrac{4q^{11}}{p^4}$ **37.** $\dfrac{5x^8}{y^2}$ **39.** $\dfrac{16a^2}{b^6}$

41. $\dfrac{27y^{27}}{8x^{24}}$ **43. a.** 4.2×10^{-3} **b.** 6.022×10^{23} **c.** 4.6×10^{-4}

45. a. 1,881,600,000 **b.** 0.000018 **c.** 5,981,000,000 **47.** 3.38×10^{-4}
49. 1.608×10^4 **51.** 3.4×10^{13} **53.** 2.5×10^3 **55.** 3.5×10^5
57. Proper **59.** Proper **61.** 6.02×10^{23} oxygen atoms and 1.204×10^{24} hydrogen atoms **63.** Anyone over 32 years old. **65.** b
67. c **69.** x^{2a+6} **71.** y^{a+2} **73.** $x^{b-3}y^{-b-1}$ **75.** $\dfrac{4x^{18}}{y^{10}}$ **77.** $27x^3y^9$

Section 5.2 Practice Exercises, pp. 322–326

1. p^8 **3.** p^{15} **5.** p^2 **7.** $\dfrac{1}{p^2}$ **9.** 1 **11.** $-6a^3 + a^2 - a$; leading coefficient -6; degree 3 **13.** $3x^4 + 6x^2 - x - 1$; leading coefficient 3; degree 4 **15.** $-t^2 + 100$; leading coefficient -1; degree 2 **17.** For example: $3x^5$ **19.** For example: $x^2 + 2x + 1$ **21.** For example: $6x^4 - x^2$ **23.** For example: 8 **25.** For example: $-3x^2 + 2x - 1$ **27.** For example: $y^4 + y^2$ **29. a.** 7 **b.** 2 **c.** -1 **d.** -1 **31. a.** -9 **b.** -6 **c.** -5 **d.** -61 **33. a.** $\dfrac{1}{4}$ **b.** $2\dfrac{1}{4}$ **c.** $-1\dfrac{3}{4}$ **d.** $\dfrac{3}{4}$ **35. a.** 7.08 **b.** 5.12 **c.** 6.1 **d.** 7.88 **37. a.** $D(0) = 1741$; In 1985, the yearly dormitory charge was \$1741. **b.** $D(2) = 2015$; In 1987, the yearly dormitory charge was \$2015. **c.** $D(4) = 2321$; In 1989, the yearly dormitory charge was \$2321. **d.** $D(6) = 2659$; In 1991, the yearly dormitory charge was \$2659. **39. a.** $W(0) = 4435$ $W(1) = 4578$ $W(2) = 4721$ **b.** $W(0) = 4435$ means 4435 thousand women were owed child support in 1985. $W(1) = 4578$ means 4578 thousand women were owed child support in 1986. $W(2) = 4721$ means 4721 thousand women were owed child support in 1987. **41.** 1980 24.1% 1994 24.3% **43. a.** $(0, 0)$; At $t = 0$ s the position of the rocket is at the origin. **b.** $(25, 27.3)$; At 1 s the position of the rocket is $(25, 27.3)$. **c.** $(50, 22.6)$

45. a. **b.**

Section 5.3 Practice Exercises, pp. 332–335

1. $\dfrac{16a^8c^4}{b^4}$ **3.** $27x^9y^{12}$ **5.** $\dfrac{s^4}{r}$ **7.** A binomial is a two-term polynomial of degree ≥ 1. A second-degree polynomial has a leading term of degree 2. **9.** For example: $x^7 + 8x$ **11.** $m^2 + 10m$
13. $6z^5 - 6z^2$ **15.** $4y^3 + 5y^2$ **17.** $-7r^4 - 11r$
19. $3x^4 + 2x^3 - 8x^2 + 2x$ **21.** $-4x^3 + 3x^2 + 5$
23. $\dfrac{1}{2}a^2 - \dfrac{9}{10}ab + \dfrac{3}{5}b^2 + 8$ **25.** $2w^3 + \dfrac{1}{9}w^2 + 0.9w$ **27.** $3p - 9$
29. $17x^2 - 4x - 14$ **31.** $-x^2 + 6x - 16$ **33.** $3x^5 - x^4 - 4x^3 + 11$
35. $(f + g)(x) = 17x^2 + 5x - 5; (f - g)(x) = 9x^2 + 5x + 11$
37. $(f + g)(x) = 18x - 42; (f - g)(x) = 4x - 4$ **39.** $P(x) = 4x + 6$
41. a. $P(x) = 3.78x - 1$ **b.** \$188 **43. a.** $F(t) = 0.2t + 4.4$. F represents the outstanding child support due. **b.** $F(0) = 4.4$ means in 1985, 4.4 billion dollars of child support was not paid. $F(2) = 4.8$ means in 1987, 4.8 billion dollars of child support was not paid. $F(4) = 5.2$ means in 1989, 5.2 billion dollars of child support was not paid.
45. $(-2x + 217)°$ **47.** $(-x + 105)°$ **49.** $(-2x + 93)°$
51. $(-3x + 175)°$ **53.** $-x^2 - 2x + 8$ **55.** $4y^2 + 4y + 2$
57. $9.37x^3 - 10.33x^2 + 5.53$
59. The expressions appear to be equal.

Midchapter Review, pp. 335–336

1. x^9 **2.** y^4 **3.** 6^9 **4.** 16 **5.** x^{10} **6.** y^7 **7.** b^5 **8.** c^5 **9.** $\dfrac{1}{a^{24}}$
10. $\dfrac{1}{x}$ **11.** $32m^9n^2$ **12.** $\dfrac{25b^8}{a^{18}}$ **13.** a^6b^{18} **14.** $\dfrac{1}{x^4y^6}$ **15.** $\dfrac{x^{16}}{y^{15}}$
16. \$2.90525 × 10^{11} **17.** \$6.0639 × 10^{12} **18. a.** 5.84 × 10^8 miles **b.** 8.76 × 10^3 h **c.** 6.67 × 10^4 mph **19. a.** \$40,000 **b.** \$60,000

20. a. $m = 11.828$; the income is increasing $11.828 thousand/year.
b. $m = 1.3996$; malpractice insurance is increasing $1.3996 thousand/year. **c.** $P(x) = 10.4284x + 110.438$; P represents the net income of physicians after paying malpractice insurance. **d.** $I(10) = 253.6$. The average annual income in 1995 was $253,600. $M(10) = 38.878$. The average cost of malpractice insurance was $38,878 in 1995. $P(10) = 214.722$. The average net income in 1995 was $214,722.

Section 5.4 Practice Exercises, pp. 343–346

1. $\dfrac{z^{16}}{81}$ **3.** $\dfrac{a^5}{b^5}$ **5. a.** 103 **b.** -5 **c.** -37 **7. a.** $2x^2 - 4x - 7$
b. $4x^2 - 10x + 3$ **c.** $-4x^2 + 10x - 3$ **9.** They cannot be added because they are not *like* terms. They can be multiplied: $(2x^3)(3x^2) = 6x^5$
11. $3a^2b + 3ab^2$ **13.** $\dfrac{2}{5}a - \dfrac{3}{5}$ **15.** $2m^5n^5 - 6m^4n^4 + 8m^3n^3$
17. $x^2 - xy - 2y^2$ **19.** $3.25a^2 - 0.9ab - 28b^2$
21. $6x^3 + 7x^2y + 4xy^2 + y^3$ **23.** $x^3 - 343$
25. $4a^4 - 17a^3b + 8a^2b^2 - 5ab^3 + b^4$
27. $\dfrac{1}{2}a^2 + ab + \dfrac{1}{2}ac - 12b^2 + 8bc - c^2$ **29.** $-3x^3 + 11x^2 - 7x - 5$
31. $a^2 - 64$ **33.** $9p^2 - 1$ **35.** $x^2 - \dfrac{1}{9}$ **37.** $9h^2 - k^2$
39. $9h^2 - 6hk + k^2$ **41.** $t^2 - 14t + 49$ **43.** $u^2 + 6uv + 9v^2$
45. $h^2 + \dfrac{1}{3}hk + \dfrac{1}{36}k^2$ **47. a.** $A^2 - B^2$ **b.** $x^2 + 2xy + y^2 - B^2$ Both are examples of multiplying conjugates to get a difference of squares.
49. $w^2 + 2wv + v^2 - 4$ **51.** $4 - x^2 - 2xy - y^2$
53. $9a^2 - 24a + 16 - b^2$ **55.** Write $(x + y)^3$ as $(x + y)^2(x + y)$. Square the binomial and then use the distributive property to multiply the resulting trinomial by the remaining factor of $x + y$.
57. $8x^3 + 12x^2y + 6xy^2 + y^3$ **59.** $64a^3 - 48a^2b + 12ab^2 - b^3$
61. Multiply and simplify the first two binomials. Then multiply the resulting trinomial to the third binomial using the distributive property. **63.** $-8x^2 + 40x - 18$ **65.** $9x^5 - 3x^3 + 10x^2$
67. $f(x) = 4x^2 + 70x + 300$ **69.** $x^2 - 4x + 4$ **71.** $x^2 - 4$
73. $x^2 - 9$ **75.** $x - 6$ **77.** $9x^3 + 30x^2$ **79.** $x^3 + 12x^2 + 48x + 64$
81. Multiply $(x + 2)^2(x + 2)^2$ by squaring the binomials. Then multiply the resulting trinomials using the distributive property.
83. $(5x - 6)$ **85.** $(2y - 1)$
87.   The expressions appear to be equal.

89.   The expressions appear to be equal.

Section 5.5 Practice Exercises, pp. 351–352

1. a. $5x - 4$ **b.** $6x^2 - 13x - 5$
3. a. $y^2 + 5y$ **b.** $2y^4 - 10y^3 + 3y^2 - 5y + 1$
5. For example: $3x(x + 1) = 3x^2 + 3x$
7. For example: $(4x^2 + x - 1) + (8x^2 - x + 3) = 12x^2 + 2$
9. For example: $(5y + 1)^2 = 25y^2 + 10y + 1$ **11.** $12 + 8y + 2y^2$
13. $x^2 + 3xy - y^2$ **15.** $2y^2 + 3y - 8$ **17.** $-\dfrac{1}{2}p^3 + p^2 - \dfrac{1}{3}p + \dfrac{1}{6}$
19. $a^2 + 5a + 1 - \dfrac{5}{a}$ **21.** $-3s^2t + 4s - \dfrac{5}{t^2}$

23. $8p^2q^6 - 9p^3q^5 - 11p - \dfrac{4}{p^2q}$
25. a. Divisor $(x - 2)$; quotient $(2x^2 - 3x - 1)$; remainder (-3).
b. Multiply the quotient and the divisor, then add the remainder.
27. $x + 7 - \dfrac{9}{x + 4}$ **29.** $3y^2 + 2y + 2 + \dfrac{9}{y - 3}$ **31.** $-4a + 11$
33. $6y - 5$ **35.** $4a^2 - 2a + 1$ **37.** $x^2 - 2x + 2$
39. $x^2 - 1 + \dfrac{8}{x^2 - 2}$ **41.** $n^3 + 2n^2 + 4n + 8$
43. $-x^2 - 4x + 13 - \dfrac{54}{x + 4}$ **45.** $2x - 1 + \dfrac{3}{x}$
47. $4y - 3 + \dfrac{4y + 5}{3y^2 - 2y + 5}$ **49.** $2x^2 + 3x - 1$
51. $2k^3 - 4k^2 + 1 - \dfrac{5}{k^4}$ **53.** $x + \dfrac{9}{5} + \dfrac{2}{x}$ **55.** $\left(\dfrac{f}{g}\right)(x) = x^2 - 4x + 5$

Section 5.6 Practice Exercises, pp. 356–358

1. $3x^2 - 13x - 10$ **3.** $2x^3y^2 + x - 3x^4y$
5. $-6p^3q - 12p^3q^2 + 15p^2q^3$ **7.** $3y^2 + 5y + 11$ **9.** No, the divisor must be of the form $x - r$. **11. a.** $x - 5$ **b.** $x^2 + 3x + 11$ **c.** 58
13. a. $x + 3$ **b.** $2x^3 + 3x^2 - 2x + 5$ **c.** 0 **15.** $x + 6$ **17.** $t - 4$
19. $5y + 10 + \dfrac{11}{y - 1}$ **21.** $x + 7$ **23.** $3y^2 - 2y + 2 + \dfrac{-3}{y + 3}$
25. $x^2 - x - 2$ **27.** $m^2 - 3m + 9$ **29.** $a^3 - 2a^2 + 2a - 4$
31. $3p^3 + p^2 + 4p + 2 + \dfrac{-2}{p - 4}$ **33.** $x^3 + x^2 + 2x - 1 + \dfrac{3}{x + 9}$
35. $4w^3 + 2w^2 + 6$ **37.** $8x^2 - 4x + 1 + \dfrac{\frac{3}{4}}{x + \frac{1}{4}}$
39. a. 61 **b.** $2x^2 + 6x + 22$; remainder 61 **41. a.** -84
b. $4x^2 - 6x + 16$; remainder -84 **43.** $P(r)$ equals the remainder of $P(x) \div (x - r)$. **45. a.** $10x + 2$ **b.** Yes **47. a.** $8x + 5$ **b.** Yes

Review Exercises, pp. 362–365

1. $243x^5$ **3.** m^5 **5.** $-3xy^2$ **7.** $-\dfrac{b^{15}}{8a^6}$ **9.** $\dfrac{5^4y^{24}}{4^4x^{20}}$ **11.** $\dfrac{x}{y}$ **13.** x^{6ab}
15. a. 3.362994×10^9 **b.** 4.247079×10^9 **17. a.** 0.001
b. 0.000000001 **19.** 3.125×10^5 **21.** 2.16×10^{-3} **23.** Trinomial; degree 4 **25.** Monomial; degree 5 **27. a.** -7 **b.** -23 **c.** 5
29. a. White high school seniors **b.** 25.6% **c.** 7.2% **d.** 18.4%
31. $20xy - 18xz - 3yz$ **33.** $-2a^2 + 6a$ **35.** $-5a^2 + 6b + 5$
37. $x^4 + \dfrac{3}{4}x^2$ **39.** $0.6a^4 + 3.1a^3 - 5.3a^2 + 23.9$ **41.** $-5x + 9y$
43. $4x^2 - 11x$ **45.** $-3x$ **47.** $3x$ **49.** $(-x + 185)°$
51. $-18x^3 + 15x^2 - 12x$ **53.** $40y^4z^2 - 10y^3z^3 + 5y^2z^4$
55. $x^2 - 11x + 18$ **57.** $2y^2 + \dfrac{1}{5}y - \dfrac{1}{25}$ **59.** $x^3 - y^3$
61. $-4a^5 - 6a^3 + 5a^2 + 4a + 10$
63. $4a^2 - 4ab - 2ac + b^2 + bc - 6c^2$
65. $4x^2 - 20x + 25$ **67.** $\dfrac{1}{9}x^2 - \dfrac{10}{3}x + 25$ **69.** $-12x$
71. $36w^2 - 1$ **73.** $z^2 - \dfrac{1}{16}$ **75.** $c^2 - w^2 - 6w - 9$
77. $y^6 - 9y^4 + 27y^2 - 27$ **79. a.** $P(x) = 8x + 4$
b. $A(x) = 3x^2 + 2x$ **81.** $2x^2 + 4x - 3$ **83.** $-\dfrac{3x}{2} + \dfrac{5}{3x} - \dfrac{2}{x^3}$
85. $-x^3y - 2x^2y + 3xy$ **87. b.** quotient: $3y^3 - 2y^2 + 6y - 4$; no remainder **c.** Multiply the quotient and the divisor.

89. $x + 4 + \dfrac{-32}{x + 4}$ **91.** $3y - 2$

93. $2x^3 - 2x^2 + 5x - 4 + \dfrac{4x - 4}{x^2 + x}$

95. $2y^3 + 6y^2 + 5y + 9 + \dfrac{20y - 12}{y^2 - 3y + 1}$

97. a. $x - 3$ **b.** $2x^3 + 11x^2 + 31x + 99$ **c.** 298 **99.** $t^2 - t + 6$

101. $x + 4 + \dfrac{4}{x + 4}$ **103.** $3y^3 - 3y^2 + 3y - 4$

105. $p^3 + 2p^2 + 4p + 8$

Test, pp. 365–366

1. $5a^{13}$ **2.** x^{11} **3.** $\dfrac{9x^{12}}{25y^{14}}$ **4.** $\dfrac{8y^{12}}{x^7}$ **5.** 5.68 **6.** 2.3×10^9

7. 3.4164×10^7 **8.** $F(-1) = 1$ $F(2) = 40$ $F(0) = 8$

9. a. $R(0) = 8.683$, $R(2) = 10.133$, $R(4) = 11.583$ **b.** $R(0) = 8.683$ means in 1985 the amount of child support paid was 8.683 billion dollars. $R(2) = 10.133$ means in 1987 the amount of child support paid was 10.133 billion dollars. $R(4) = 11.583$ means in 1989 the amount of child support paid was 11.583 billion dollars.

10. $8x^2 - 8x + 8$ **11.** $2a^3 - 13a^2 + 2a + 45$ **12.** $2x^2 - \dfrac{23}{3}x - 6$

13. $25x^2 - 16y^4$ **14.** The expression $25x^2 + 49$ does not account for the middle term, $70x$. **15.** $49x^2 - 56x + 16$

16. $x^2y^3 + \dfrac{5}{2}xy - 3y^2 - \dfrac{1}{2}$ **17.** $5p^2 - p + 1$

18. $y^3 + 2y^2 + 4y + 6 + \dfrac{17}{y - 2}$

Cumulative Review Exercises, Chapters 1–5, pp. 366–367

1. [5, 12] **2.** $-x^2 - 5x - 10$

3. a.

b.

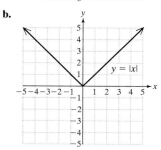

4. $8\dfrac{7}{8}$ **5.** 1.97×10^8 people **6.** Notre Dame scored 26 points; Florida State scored 31 points. **7.** $37°, 74°, 69°$ **8.** $x^2 - 4x + 16$

9. $m = \dfrac{4}{3}$; y-intercept $(0, 3)$;

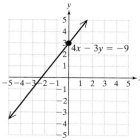

10. $\dfrac{1}{4}$ **11.** $\dfrac{a^6}{8b^{30}}$ **12.** $(0, 3, 2)$ **13. a.** Function **b.** Not a function

14. $m = 7$ **15.** 7 **16.** $x = 8$ **17.** $y = \dfrac{3}{2}x - \dfrac{5}{2}$ **18. a.** The fourth test would have to be 107%; therefore, it is not possible. **b.** Student can get between 67% and 100%, inclusive. **19.** 15 L of 40% solution; 10 L of 15% solution **20.** $8b^3 - 6b^2 + 4b - 3$

21. $3a^3 + 5a^2 - 2a + 5$ **22.** $3w - \dfrac{5}{2} - \dfrac{1}{w}$ **23.** Not possible

24. $\begin{bmatrix} 20 \\ 0 \end{bmatrix}$ **25.** $\begin{bmatrix} 11 & -8 & -3 \\ 9 & 4 & -5 \end{bmatrix}$

CHAPTER 6

Section 6.1 Practice Exercises, pp. 379–382

1. a. $8, -8$ **b.** 8 **c.** There are two square roots for every positive number. $\sqrt{64}$ identifies the positive square root. **3. a.** 9 **b.** -9 **5.** There is no real number b such that $b^2 = -36$. **7.** 5

9. -3 **11.** 2 **13.** $\dfrac{1}{2}$ **15.** 2 **17.** 4 **19.** Not a real number

21. 10 **23.** -0.2 **25.** -0.12 **27.** 8.3066 **29.** 3.7100 **31.** 2.0305 **33.** -0.1235 **35. a.** Not a real number **b.** Not a real number **c.** Not a real number **d.** 0 **e.** 1 **f.** 1.41 **g.** 1.73 **h.** 2; Domain: $[2, \infty)$ **37. a.** -1.44 **b.** -1.26 **c.** -1 **d.** 0 **e.** 1 **f.** 1.26 **g.** 1.44 **h.** 1.59; Domain: $(-\infty, \infty)$ **39.** $[1, \infty)$ **41.** $(-\infty, \infty)$ **43.** b **45.** d **47.** $|a|$ **49.** a **51.** $|a|$ **53.** x^2 **55.** $|xz^5| y^2$ **57.** $-\dfrac{x}{y}$ **59.** $\dfrac{2}{|x|}$ **61.** -9 **63.** -2 **65.** xy^2 **67.** $\dfrac{a^3}{b}$ **69.** $-\dfrac{5}{q}$ **71.** $3xy^2z$ **73.** $\dfrac{hk^2}{4}$ **75.** $-\dfrac{t}{3}$ **77.** $2y^2$ **79.** $2p^2q^3$ **81.** $q + p^2$ **83.** $\dfrac{6}{\sqrt[4]{x}}$ **85.** The sum of the square of a and the square root of b. **87.** The quotient of 1 and the square of the quantity c plus d. **89.** 8 in. **91.** 9.8 in. **93.** 9 cm **95.** 13 ft

97. a. It appears to be constant. **b.** $\dfrac{D}{L}$ should be approximately $\sqrt{2}$. **99.**

101.

Section 6.2 Practice Exercises, pp. 387–388

1. a. 3 **b.** 27 **3.** 5 **5.** 3 **7.** Not a real number **9.** $a + 1$ **11.** $a^{m|n} = \sqrt[n]{a^m}$; The numerator of the exponent represents the power of the base. The denominator of the exponent represents the index of the radical.

13. 5   **15.** 2   **17.** 3   **19.** -2 **21.** -2 **23.** $\dfrac{1}{2}$ **25.** $\dfrac{1}{9}$ **27.** 6

29. 10   **31.** $\dfrac{3}{4}$ **33.** -5 **35.** $\dfrac{9}{2}$ **37.** x **39.** p **41.** y^2 **43.** 6

45. $4t$ **47.** a^7 **49.** $\dfrac{25a^4d}{c}$ **51.** $\dfrac{y^9}{x^8}$ **53.** $\dfrac{2z^3}{w}$ **55.** $5xy^2z^3$ **57.** $\dfrac{x^{16}}{y^7z^4}$

59. $\dfrac{x^3y^2}{z^5}$ **61.** $\sqrt[3]{2x^2y}$ **63.** $\sqrt{\dfrac{2}{y}}$ **65.** $x^{1/3}$ **67.** $5x^{1/2}$ **69.** 3

71. 0.3761   **73.** 2.9240   **75.** 31.6228   **77. a.** 10 in. **b.** 8.5 in.
79. a. 10.9% **b.** 8.8% **c.** The account in part (a).   **81.** $\sqrt[6]{x}$
83. $\sqrt[8]{y}$ **85.** $\sqrt[15]{w}$

Section 6.3 Practice Exercises, pp. 393–395

1. a^2b **3.** $\dfrac{s^6}{r^2}$ **5.** $\sqrt[4]{x^4}$ **7.** $y^{9/2}$ **9. a.** 0.07 **b.** -0.06 **11.** $10x$

13. $2x$ **15.** $x+2$ **17.** $2y$ **19.** 3   **21.** $2b$ **23.** $3x+1$ **25.** $\dfrac{1}{a+b}$

27. $2\sqrt{7}$ **29.** $4\sqrt{5}$ **31.** $15\sqrt{2}$ **33.** $3\sqrt[3]{2}$ **35.** $5x^2y\sqrt{y}$

37. $3yz\sqrt[3]{x^2z}$ **39.** $\dfrac{2}{b}$ **41.** $\dfrac{2\sqrt[5]{x}}{y^2}$ **43.** $\dfrac{5x\sqrt{2xy}}{3y^2}$ **45.** $2a^7b^4c^{15}d^{11}\sqrt{2c}$

47. $\dfrac{1}{\sqrt[3]{w^6}} = \dfrac{1}{w^2}$ **49.** $\sqrt{k^3} = k\sqrt{k}$ **51.** $2\sqrt{41}$ ft   **53.** $6\sqrt{5}$ m

55. 127.3 ft   **57.** The path from A to B and B to C is faster.

Midchapter Review, p. 395

1. 4   **2.** 9   **3.** $\dfrac{1}{2}$ **4.** $\dfrac{3}{5}$ **5.** $3w\sqrt[3]{2x^2w}$ **6.** $2tuv^3\sqrt{5uv}$

7. $5xy^2\sqrt{2y}$ **8.** $2wz^3\sqrt[3]{z}$ **9.** $4r-3$ **10.** $\dfrac{ab}{a+b}$ **11.** Write x^{51}
as $x^{50} \cdot x^1$. Then apply the multiplication property of radicals.
$\sqrt{x^{51}} = \sqrt{x^{50} \cdot x^1} = \sqrt{x^{50}} \cdot \sqrt{x} = x^{25}\sqrt{x}$ **12.** 4   **13.** 8   **14.** 5
15. $\dfrac{5}{2}$ **16.** $\dfrac{t^2}{sr^3}$ **17.** $\dfrac{pr^{5/2}}{q^{3/2}}$ **18.** $u^{2/3}v^{3/2}$ **19.** $xy^{7/12}$ **20.** First take the
cube root of 125, then square the result. $125^{2/3} = (\sqrt[3]{125})^2 = (5)^2 = 25$
21. a. $2x^2$ **b.** $5b^2$ **22. a.** $\sqrt[4]{x^2}$ **b.** $(\sqrt[4]{c})^3$

Section 6.4 Practice Exercises, pp. 399–400

1. $-2st^3\sqrt[3]{2s}$ **3.** $6p^3$ **5.** $\sqrt{(4x^2)^3} = 8x^3$ **7.** $y^{11/12}$ **9.** 1.95
11. a. Both expressions can be simplified using the distributive
property. $7\sqrt{5} + 4\sqrt{5} = (7+4)\sqrt{5} = 11\sqrt{5}$; $7x + 4x =$
$(7+4)x = 11x$ **b.** Neither expression can be simplified because
they do not contain *like* terms or *like* radicals.   **13.** $9\sqrt{5}$ **15.** $\sqrt[3]{t}$
17. $5\sqrt{10}$ **19.** $8\sqrt[4]{3} - \sqrt[4]{14}$ **21.** $2\sqrt{x} + 2\sqrt{y}$ **23.** Cannot be
simplified further   **25.** Cannot be simplified further   **27.** $\dfrac{29}{18}z\sqrt[3]{6}$
29. $0.70x\sqrt{y}$ **31.** Simplify each radical: $3\sqrt{2} + 35\sqrt{2}$. Then add
like radicals: $38\sqrt{2}$ **33.** 15   **35.** $8\sqrt{3}$ **37.** $3\sqrt{7}$ **39.** $-5\sqrt{2a}$
41. $8s^2t^2\sqrt[3]{s^2}$ **43.** $6x\sqrt[3]{x}$ **45.** $14p^2\sqrt{5}$ **47.** $2a^2b\sqrt{6a}$
49. $5x\sqrt[3]{2} - 6\sqrt[3]{x}$ **51.** False. For example: $\sqrt{9} + \sqrt{16} \neq \sqrt{9+16}$
$7 \neq 5$ **53.** True.   **55.** False. $\sqrt{y} + \sqrt{y} = 2\sqrt{y} \neq \sqrt{2y}$
57. $\sqrt{48} + \sqrt{12} = 6\sqrt{3}$ **59.** $5\sqrt[3]{x^6} - x^2 = 4x^2$
61. The difference of the square root of 18 and the square of 5
63. The sum of the fourth root of x and the cube of y
65. a. $10\sqrt{5}$ yards **b.** 22.36 yards **c.** \$105.95

Section 6.5 Practice Exercises, pp. 406–408

1. a. 2 **b.** 4   **3.** $x-y$ **5.** $-2xy^2z^2\sqrt[3]{2x^2z}$ **7.** 3   **9.** $x^{1/6}y^{7/12}$
11. $a^{1/6}$ **13.** $2\sqrt[3]{7}$ **15.** $2\sqrt{5}$ **17.** $4\sqrt[4]{4}$ **19.** $6\sqrt[3]{35}$
21. $-24ab\sqrt{a}$ **23.** $12 - 6\sqrt{3}$ **25.** $2\sqrt{3} - \sqrt{6}$
27. $-3x - 21\sqrt{x}$ **29.** $-8 + 7\sqrt{30}$ **31.** $x - 5\sqrt{x} - 36$
33. $\sqrt[3]{y^2} - \sqrt[3]{y} - 6$ **35.** $9a - 28\sqrt{ab} + 3b$
37. $-8 + \sqrt{14} - 2\sqrt{7} + 3\sqrt{2}$
39. $8\sqrt{p} + 3p + 5\sqrt{pq} + 16\sqrt{q} - 2q$ **41.** $\sqrt[4]{x^3}$ **43.** $\sqrt[15]{(2z)^8}$
45. $p^2\sqrt[6]{p}$ **47.** $u\sqrt[6]{u}$ **49.** $\sqrt[6]{(a+b)}$ **51. a.** $x^2 - y^2$ **b.** $x^2 - 25$
53. $3 - x^2$ **55.** 4   **57.** $64x - 4y$ **59.** $29 + 8\sqrt{13}$
61. $p - 2\sqrt{7p} + 7$ **63.** $2a - 6\sqrt{2ab} + 9b$ **65.** True   **67.** False;
$(x - \sqrt{5})^2 = x^2 - 2x\sqrt{5} + 5$ **69.** False; 5 is multiplied only to the 3.
71. True   **73.** $12\sqrt{5}$ ft^2 **75.** $18\sqrt{15}$ in.^{2} **77.** 40 m^2 **79.** $\dfrac{a+b}{}$
81. $\sqrt[6]{x^2y}$ **83.** $\sqrt[4]{2^3 \cdot 3^2}$ or $\sqrt[4]{72}$ **85.** $\sqrt[3]{3 \cdot 2^3}$ or $\sqrt[3]{24}$ **87.** $\sqrt[15]{p^3q^5}$

Section 6.6 Practice Exercises, pp. 414–416

1. $12y\sqrt{5}$ **3.** $-18y + 3\sqrt{y} + 3$ **5.** $9\sqrt{3}$ **7.** $64 - 16\sqrt{t} + t$
9. -5 **11.** $\dfrac{\sqrt{5}}{\sqrt{5}}; \dfrac{x\sqrt{5}}{5}$ **13.** $\dfrac{\sqrt[3]{x^2}}{\sqrt[3]{x^2}}; \dfrac{7\sqrt[3]{x^2}}{x}$ **15.** $\dfrac{\sqrt{3z}}{\sqrt{3z}}; \dfrac{8\sqrt{3z}}{3z}$
17. $\dfrac{\sqrt[4]{2^3a^2}}{\sqrt[4]{2^3a^2}}; \dfrac{\sqrt[4]{8a^2}}{2a}$ **19.** $\dfrac{\sqrt{3}}{3}$ **21.** $2\sqrt{5}$ **23.** $\dfrac{\sqrt{x}}{x}$ **25.** $\dfrac{3\sqrt{2y}}{y}$
27. $-2\sqrt{a}$ **29.** $\dfrac{7\sqrt[3]{2}}{2}$ **31.** $\dfrac{4\sqrt[3]{w}}{w}$ **33.** $\dfrac{2\sqrt[4]{27}}{3}$ **35.** $\dfrac{\sqrt[10]{x^3}}{x}$
37. $\dfrac{\sqrt[3]{2x}}{x}$ **39.** $\dfrac{2x\sqrt[3]{2y^2}}{y}$ **41.** $\dfrac{xy^2\sqrt{10xy}}{10}$ **43.** $\sqrt{2} + \sqrt{6}$
45. $\sqrt{x} - 23$ **47.** -7 **49.** 3   **51.** $\dfrac{4\sqrt{2} - 12}{-7}$ or $\dfrac{-4\sqrt{2} + 12}{7}$
53. $\dfrac{\sqrt{5} + \sqrt{2}}{3}$ **55.** $-\sqrt{21} + 2\sqrt{7}$ **57.** $\dfrac{-\sqrt{p} + \sqrt{q}}{p - q}$
59. $\dfrac{5 + \sqrt{21}}{4}$ **61.** $-6\sqrt{5} - 13$ **63.** $\dfrac{16}{\sqrt[3]{4}} = 8\sqrt[3]{2}$
65. $\dfrac{4}{x - \sqrt{2}} = \dfrac{4x + 4\sqrt{2}}{x^2 - 2}$ **67. a.** 1.57 s **b.** 1.11 s **c.** 0.79 s
69. $\dfrac{2\sqrt{6}}{3}$ **71.** $\dfrac{17\sqrt{15}}{15}$ **73.** $\dfrac{8\sqrt[3]{25}}{5}$ **75.** $\dfrac{-33}{2\sqrt{3} - 12}$
77. $\dfrac{a - b}{a + 2\sqrt{ab} + b}$
79. a. b.   **c.** The expressions appear to be equal.

Section 6.7 Practice Exercises, pp. 424–427

1. $4\sqrt{3}$ **3.** $\dfrac{3w\sqrt{w}}{4}$ **5.** Not a real number   **7.** $\dfrac{p\sqrt[3]{p^2q}}{q}$
9. $\dfrac{7\sqrt{5t}}{5t^2}$ **11.** $\dfrac{\sqrt[4]{2mn^2}}{2n}$ **13.** $4x - 6$ **15.** $9p + 7$
17. $w^2 + 2w - 17$ **19.** $7r$ **21.** $x = 9$ **23.** $y = 3$ **25.** $z = 42$
27. $x = 29$ **29.** $w = 140$ **31.** No solution   **33.** $h = 9$
35. $a = -4$ **37.** No solution   **39.** $V = \dfrac{4\pi r^3}{3}$ **41.** $h^2 = \dfrac{r^2 - \pi^2 r^2}{\pi^2}$
43. $a^2 + 10a + 25$ **45.** $25w^2 - 40w + 16$ **47.** $5a - 6\sqrt{5a} + 9$
49. $a = -3$ **51.** No solution   **53.** No solution   **55.** $a = \dfrac{9}{5}$
57. $h = 2$ **59.** No solution   **61.** $x = -\dfrac{11}{4}$ **63.** No solution

65. No solution **67. a.** 305 m **b.** 460 m **69. a.** \$2 million **b.** \$1.2 million **c.** 50,000 passengers **71. a.** $\sqrt{13}$ versus 5 **b.** Not equal **73. a.** 12 lb **b.** $t(18) = 5.1$. An 18-lb turkey will take about 5.1 h to cook. **75.** $c = \sqrt{k^2 + 81}$ **77.** $b = \sqrt{25 - h^2}$ **79.** $a = \sqrt{k^2 - 196}$

81.

83.

85.

87.

89.

Section 6.8 Practice Exercises, pp. 435–436

1. $3\sqrt{5} - 15\sqrt{2}$ **3.** $9 - x$ **5.** $y = 8$ **7.** $p = -8$ **9.** $c = \dfrac{49}{36}$

11. $i = \sqrt{-1}$ **13.** $a - bi$ **15.** $12i$ **17.** $i\sqrt{3}$ **19.** $2i\sqrt{5}$ **21.** $29i\sqrt{2}$ **23.** $13i\sqrt{7}$ **25.** -7 **27.** -12 **29.** $-3\sqrt{10}$ **31.** $\sqrt{2}$

33. $3i$ **35.** $7 + 6i$ **37.** $\dfrac{3}{10} + \dfrac{3}{2}i$ **39.** $5 + 0i$ **41.** $-1 + 10i$

43. $-i$ **45.** 1 **47.** i **49.** 1 **51.** $-i$ **53.** -1 **55.** -24 **57.** $18 + 6i$ **59.** $26 - 26i$ **61.** $-29 + 0i$ **63.** $-9 + 40i$

65. $35 + 20i$ **67.** $1 - 3i; 10$ **69.** $4 + 3i; 25$ **71.** $\dfrac{1}{5} - \dfrac{3}{5}i$

73. $\dfrac{3}{25} - \dfrac{4}{25}i$ **75.** $\dfrac{21}{29} + \dfrac{20}{29}i$ **77.** $0 - \dfrac{3}{2}i$ **79.** $0 + 3i$

81. $0 - 7i$ **83.** $12 + 0i$ **85.** $-1 + 0i$

87.

89.

91.

93.

95.

97.

99.

101.

103.

Review Exercises, pp. 440–443

1. a. False; $\sqrt{0} = 0$ is not positive. **b.** False; $\sqrt[3]{-8} = -2$
3. a. False **b.** True **5.** 5 **7. a.** 3 **b.** 0 **c.** $\sqrt{7}$ **d.** $[1, \infty)$

9. $\dfrac{\sqrt[3]{2x}}{\sqrt[4]{2x}} + 4$ **11.** 8 cm **13.** Yes, provided the expressions are well defined. For example: $x^5 \cdot x^3 = x^8$ and $x^{1/5} \cdot x^{1/3} = x^{8/15}$ **15.** Take the reciprocal of the base and change the exponent to positive. **17.** $\dfrac{1}{2}$

19. b^{10} **21.** $x^{3/4}$ **23.** 2.1544 **25.** 54.1819 **27.** 1. Factors of the radicand must have powers less than the index 2. No fractions in the radicand 3. No radical in the denominator of a fraction **29.** $xz\sqrt[4]{xy}$

31. $\dfrac{-2x^2y^2\sqrt[3]{2x}}{z^3}$ **33.** 31 ft **35.** Cannot be combined; The indices are different. **37.** Can be combined: $3\sqrt[4]{3xy}$ **39.** $5\sqrt{7}$ **41.** $10\sqrt{2}$

43. False; 5 and $3\sqrt{x}$ are not *like* radicals. **45.** $a + b$ and $a - b$ are conjugates. **47.** 6 **49.** 12 **51.** $\sqrt[3]{4x^2} - 4\sqrt[3]{x^2} + 2\sqrt[3]{2x^2}$

53. $u^2\sqrt[6]{u^5}$ **55.** $(a + b)\sqrt[6]{(a + b)}$ **57.** $\dfrac{2x\sqrt{5} + 5\sqrt{x}}{5x}$

59. $\dfrac{6b - \sqrt{b} - 1}{9b - 1}$ **61.** $y = \dfrac{49}{2}$ **63.** $w = -12$ **65.** $t = 9$

67. a. 25.3 ft/s; When the water depth is 20 ft, a wave travels about 25.3 ft/s. **b.** 8 ft **69.** $a + bi$, where a and b are real numbers and $i = \sqrt{-1}$. **71.** In each case we simplify the expression by multiplying the numerator and denominator by the conjugate of the denominator. **73.** $-i\sqrt{5}$ **75.** -1 **77.** $-i$ **79.** $-2 + 5i$ **81.** $-20 + 0i$ **83.** $24 - 10i$ **85.** $-2 - i$; Real part: -2; Imaginary part: -1 **87.** $1 - 2i$

Test, pp. 443–444

1. a. 6 **b.** -6 **2. a.** Real **b.** Not real **c.** Real **d.** Real

3. a. y **b.** $|y|$ **4.** 3 **5.** $\dfrac{4}{3}$ **6.** $2\sqrt[3]{4}$ **7.** $a^2bc^2\sqrt{bc}$ **8.** $3x^2\sqrt{2}$

9. $\dfrac{4w^2\sqrt{6w}}{3}$ **10.** $\sqrt[10]{(7y)^7}$ **11.** $\sqrt[12]{10}$ **12. a.** $f(-8) = 2\sqrt{3}$; $f(-6) = 2\sqrt{2}$; $f(-4) = 2$; $f(-2) = 0$ **b.** $(-\infty, -2]$ **13.** -0.3080

14. -3 **15.** $\dfrac{1}{t^{3/4}}$ **16.** $3\sqrt{5}$ **17. a.** $3\sqrt{2x} - 3\sqrt{5x}$

b. $2x - 6\sqrt{2x} + 9$ **18. a.** $\dfrac{-2\sqrt[3]{x^2}}{x}$ **b.** $\dfrac{x + 6 + 5\sqrt{x}}{9 - x}$ **19. a.** $2i\sqrt{2}$

b. $8i$ **20.** $36 - 11i$ **21. a.** $1 + 4i$ **b.** $\dfrac{17}{25} + \dfrac{6}{25}i$ **22.** $r(10) = 1.34$; the radius of a sphere of volume 10 cubic units is 1.34 units.

23. 21 ft **24.** $x = -16$ **25.** $x = \dfrac{17}{5}$

Cumulative Review Exercises, Chapters 1–6, pp. 444–446

1. 54 **2.** $15x - 5y - 5$ **3.** $y = -3$ **4.** $(-\infty, -5)$
5. $y = -2x + 5$ **6.**

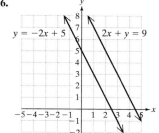

7. $\left(\dfrac{1}{2},\dfrac{1}{3}\right)$ **8.** $\left(2,-2,\dfrac{1}{2}\right)$ is not a solution.   **9.** $x = 6, y = 3, z = 8$

10. a. $f(-2) = -10; f(0) = -2; f(4) = 14; f\left(\dfrac{1}{2}\right) = 0$

b. $(-2, -10)\ (0, -2)\ (4, 14)\ \left(\dfrac{1}{2}, 0\right)$

c.

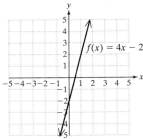

11. Not a function   **12.** $a^4b^8c^2$ **13.** $a^6b^{12}c^4$ **14.** 111,831 m/s
15. $2x^2 - x - 15$; Second degree   **16.** $\sqrt{15} + 3\sqrt{2} + 3$

17. $x - 4$; yes, $(x + 3)$ is a factor of $x^2 - x - 12$.   **18.** $-\dfrac{1}{6}$

19. $\dfrac{3c\sqrt[3]{2}}{d}$ **20.** $32b\sqrt{5b}$ **21.** $2 + 3i$ **22.** **E** and **F** cannot be added
because they have different dimensions. The product **EF** is possible
because the number of columns in **E** equals the number of rows in **F**.
However, **FE** is not possible because the number of columns in **F** does
not equal the number of rows in **E**.

CHAPTER 7

Section 7.1 Practice Exercises, pp. 453–455

1. A common factor is an expression that divides evenly into each
term of a polynomial. The greatest common factor is the *greatest* factor that divides evenly into each term.   **3.** $3(x + 4)$ **5.** $2z(3z + 2)$
7. $4p(p^5 - 1)$ **9.** $12x^2(x^2 - 3)$ **11.** $-9t(st - 3)$ or $9t(-st + 3)$
13. $9(a^2 + 3a + 2)$ **15.** $5xy(2x + 3y - 7)$ **17.** $b(13b - 11a^2 - 12a)$
19. $(3z - 2b)(2a - 5)$ **21.** $(2x - 3)(2x^2 + 1)$ **23.** $(2x + 1)^2(y - 3)$
25. $3(x - 2)^2(y + 2)$ **27.** $A = \dfrac{U}{v + cw}$ **29.** $y = \dfrac{bx}{c - a}$ or $y = \dfrac{-bx}{a - c}$
31. For example: $3x^3 + 6x^2 + 12x^4$ **33.** For example:
$6(c + d) + y(c + d)$ **35. a.** $(2x - y)(a + 3b)$ **b.** $(2w - 1)(5w - 3b)$
c. In part (b), $-3b$ was removed so that the signs in the last two terms
were changed. The resulting binomial factor matches the binomial factor in the first two terms.   **37.** $(y + 4)(y^2 + 3)$ **39.** $(p - 7)(6 + q)$
41. $(m + n)(2x + 3y)$ **43.** $(2x - 3y)(5a - 4b)$
45. $6p(p + 3)(q - 5)$ **47.** $100(x - 3)(x^2 + 2)$
49. $(3a + b)(2x - y)$ **51.** Cannot be factored   **53.** It is not possible
to get a common binomial factor regardless of the order of terms.

55. Length $= 2w + 1$ **57. a.** $P = \dfrac{A}{1 + rt}$ **b.** \$10,500

59. $(a + 3)^4(6a + 19)$ **61.** $18(3x + 5)^2(4x + 5)$

63. $(t + 4)(t + 3)$ **65.** $5w^2(2w - 1)^2(7w - 3)$

67.   **69.**

Section 7.2 Practice Exercises, pp. 467–468

1. $6c^2d^4e^7(6d^3e^4 + 2cde^8 - 1)$ **3.** $(3a - b)(2x - 1)$
5. $(z + 2)(wz - 33a)$ **7.** $(b - 8)(b - 4)$ **9.** $(y + 12)(y - 2)$
11. $(2x + 3)(x - 5)$ **13.** $(6a - 5)(a + 1)$ **15.** $(s + 3t)(s - 2t)$
17. $3(x - 18)(x - 2)$ **19.** $2(c - 4)(c + 3)$ **21.** $2(x - y)(x + 5y)$
23. Prime   **25.** $(3x + 5y)(x + 3y)$ **27.** $5uv(u - 3v)^2$
29. a. $x^2 + 10x + 25$ **b.** $(x + 5)^2$ **31. a.** $9x^2 - 12xy + 4y^2$
b. $(3x - 2y)^2$ **33.** $30x$ **35.** 36 **37.** 64 **39.** $(y - 4)^2$ **41.** Not a
perfect square trinomial   **43.** $(3a - 5b)^2$ **45.** $4(4t^2 - 20tv + 5v^2)$
Not a perfect square trinomial   **47.** $(x - 3)(3x^2 + 5)$ **49.** $(a + 6)^2$
51. $(9w + 5)^2$ **53.** $3(a + b)(x - 2)$ **55.** $(x^2 + 12)(x^2 + 3)$
57. $2abc^2(6a + 2b - 3c)$ **59.** $f(x) = (2x - 1)(x + 7)$
61. $m(t) = (t - 11)^2$ **63.** $P(x) = x(x + 1)(x + 3)$
65. $h(a) = (a + 5)(a^2 - 6)$ **67.** $(3x - 4)(3x + 1)$
69. $(2x - 9)(x - 1)$ **71.**   **73.**

Section 7.3 Practice Exercises, pp. 476–478

1. The trinomial must be of the form $a^2 + 2ab + b^2$ or
$a^2 - 2ab + b^2$.   **3.** $(2x - 5)^2$ **5.** $(5 + 3y)(2x + 1)$
7. $4(8p + 1)(p - 1)$ **9.** $9a(5a - c)$ **11.** Look for a binomial
of the form $a^2 - b^2$; $a^2 - b^2 = (a + b)(a - b)$.   **13.** Look for a
binomial of the form $a^3 - b^3$; $a^3 - b^3 = (a - b)(a^2 + ab + b^2)$.

15. $(x - 3)(x + 3)$ **17.** $(4 - w)(4 + w)$ **19.** $\left(6y - \dfrac{1}{5}\right)\left(6y + \dfrac{1}{5}\right)$

21. $2(2a - 9b)(2a + 9b)$ **23.** $2(3d^6 - 4)(3d^6 + 4)$ **25.** Prime
27. $2(121v^2 + 16)$ **29.** $(2m - 11)(2m + 1)$
31. $(2x - 1)(4x^2 + 2x + 1)$ **33.** $(5c - 3)(25c^2 + 15c + 9)$
35. $\left(3a + \dfrac{1}{2}\right)\left(9a^2 - \dfrac{3}{2}a + \dfrac{1}{4}\right)$ **37.** $2(m + 2)(m^2 - 2m + 4)$
39. $(x + y)(x^2 - xy + y^2)(x - y)(x^2 + xy + y^2)$
41. $(h^2 + k^2)(h^4 - h^2k^2 + k^4)$ **43.** $(x - y)(x + y)(x^2 + y^2)$
45. $(a + b)(a^2 - ab + b^2)(a^6 - a^3b^3 + b^6)$
47. $(p - 7)(p^2 - 2p + 13)$ **49.** $(x + 6 - a)(x + 6 + a)$
51. $(p - y + 3)(p + y - 3)$ **53.** $4x^2 - 9$ **55.** $8a^3 - 27$
57. $64x^6 + y^3$ **59. a.** $x^2 - y^2$ **b.** $(x + y)(x - y)$ **c.** 20 in.^{2}
61. $(x + y)(x - y + 1)$ **63.** $(x + y)(x^2 - xy + y^2)(5w - 2z)$
65. a.   **b.** $Y_1 = (x - 2)(x + 1)$

67. a.   **b.** $Y_1 = (x - 4)(x - 1)$

Midchapter Review: A Factoring Strategy, p. 478

1. An expression whose only factors are one and itself.   **2.** Factor
out the GCF.   **3.** Difference of squares $a^2 - b^2$, difference of cubes
$a^3 - b^3$, or sum of cubes $a^3 + b^3$ **4.** Look for a perfect square trinomial, $a^2 + 2ab + b^2$ or $a^2 - 2ab + b^2$.   **5.** Look for a trinomial
of the form $a^2 + 2ab + b^2$ or $a^2 - 2ab + b^2$.   **6.** Try factoring by
grouping (2 terms by 2 terms) or grouping 3 terms by 1 term.
7. a. Trinomial; **b.** $3(2x + 3)(x - 5)$ **8. a.** Trinomial;
b. $m(4m + 1)(2m - 3)$ **9. a.** Difference of squares;

b. $2(2a - 5)(2a + 5)$ **10. a.** Grouping; **b.** $(b + y)(a - b)$
11. a. Trinomial; **b.** $(2u - v)(7u - 2v)$ **12. a.** Perfect square
trinomial; **b.** $(3p - 2q)^2$ **13. a.** Difference of cubes;
b. $2(2x - 1)(4x^2 + 2x + 1)$ **14.** Prime   **15. a.** Sum of cubes;
b. $(3y + 5)(9y^2 - 15y + 25)$ **16.** Prime   **17. a.** Sum of cubes;
b. $2(4p^2 + 3q)(16p^4 - 12p^2q + 9q^2)$ **18. a.** Perfect square
trinomial; **b.** $5(b - 3)^2$ **19. a.** Difference of squares;
b. $(2a - 1)(2a + 1)(4a^2 + 1)$ **20. a.** Perfect square trinomial;
b. $(9u - 5v)^2$ **21. a.** Grouping; **b.** $(p - 6 - c)(p - 6 + c)$
22. a. None of these; **b.** $4(x^2 + 4)$ **23. a.** Grouping;
b. $2(2x - y)(3a + b)$ **24. a.** Difference of cubes;
b. $(5y - 2)(25y^2 + 10y + 4)$ **25. a.** Trinomial; **b.** $(5y - 1)(y + 3)$
26. a. Difference of squares; **b.** $2(m^2 - 8)(m^2 + 8)$

Section 7.4 Practice Exercises, pp. 489–492

1. a. The equation must be set equal to 0. **b.** The expression must
be factored.   **3.** Correct form   **5.** Incorrect form. Equation is not set
equal to 0.   **7.** Incorrect form. Equation is not set equal to 0.
9. $x = -3, x = -5$ **11.** $w = -\dfrac{9}{2}, w = \dfrac{1}{5}$

13. $x = 0, x = -4, x = \dfrac{3}{10}$ **15.** $y = 0.4, y = -2.1$

17. $x = -9, x = 3$ **19.** $x = -3, x = \dfrac{1}{2}$ **21.** $x = 0, x = \dfrac{3}{2}$

23. $y = -3$ **25.** $x = -1, x = \dfrac{1}{2}, x = 3$ **27.** $y = -5, y = 4$

29. $p = -12, p = 5$ **31. a.** $x = 0, x = 3$ **b.** $f(0) = 0$ **33. a.** $x = 7$
b. $f(0) = -35$ **35. a.** $x = 2, x = -1, x = 0$ **b.** $f(0) = 0$
37. a. $x = 1$ **b.** $f(0) = 1$
39. $\left(-\dfrac{1}{2}, 0\right)(5, 0)(0, -5)$; opens up

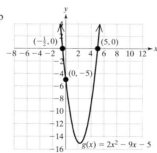

41. $(-3, 0)(1, 0)(0, 3)$; opens down

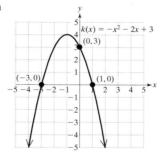

43. $(2, 0)(-2, 0)(0, -4)$; opens up

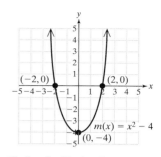

45. $(3, 0)(-3, 0)$; d   **47.** $(-1, 0)$; a   **49.** $5, -5$ **51.** $4, -3$
53. $-7, -6$ or $6, 7$ **55.** $10, 12$ or $-12, -10$ **57. a.** Base 5 in.;
height 6 in. **b.** 15 in.^2 **59.** $4, 5$ **61. a.** Quadratic **b.** 0 or 500
c. The x-intercepts $(0, 0)$ and $(500, 0)$ **d.** 100 or 400 systems
63. 7 ft by 5 ft   **65. a.** 14 miles **b.** The alternative route using
superhighways   **67.** $f(x) = (x - 5)(x - 2)$; $x = 5$ and $x = 2$
represent x-intercepts.   **69.** $f(x) = (2x - 5)(x + 2)$; $x = \dfrac{5}{2}$ and
$x = -2$ represent x-intercepts.   **71.** $f(x) = (x + 2)^2$; $x = -2$
represents the x-intercept.   **73.** $(x + 3)(x - 1) = 0$ or
$x^2 + 2x - 3 = 0$ **75.** $\left(x - \dfrac{2}{3}\right)\left(x + \dfrac{1}{2}\right) = 0$ or $x^2 - \dfrac{1}{6}x - \dfrac{1}{3} = 0$
77. $(x - 0)(x + 5) = 0$ or $x^2 + 5x = 0$
79. $(2, 0)(-1, 0)$

81. $\left(\dfrac{3}{2}, 0\right)(-1, 0)$

83. $(3, 0)$

Section 7.5 Practice Exercises, pp. 502–504

1. e   **3.** b   **5.** f   **7.** The trinomial must be in the form
$a^2 + 2ab + b^2$ or $a^2 - 2ab + b^2$.   **9.** $a^2 - b^2 = (a + b)(a - b)$
11. $x = \pm 10$ **13.** $a = \pm\sqrt{5}$ **15.** $v = \pm i\sqrt{11}$ **17.** $p = 8, p = 2$

19. $x = 2 \pm \sqrt{5}$ **21.** $h = 4 \pm 2i\sqrt{2}$ **23.** $a = \dfrac{1}{2} \pm \dfrac{\sqrt{3}}{2}$

25. $x = \dfrac{3}{2} \pm \dfrac{i\sqrt{7}}{2}$ **27.** 1. Factoring and applying the zero product rule.
2. Completing the square and applying the square root property. $x = \pm 9$
29. 4.2 ft   **31. a.** 8% **b.** 11% **c.** 14.02%   **33.** $k = 9; (x - 3)^2$
35. $k = \dfrac{25}{4}; \left(y + \dfrac{5}{2}\right)^2$ **37.** $k = \dfrac{1}{25}; \left(b + \dfrac{1}{5}\right)^2$ **39.** 1. Write equation
in the form $ax^2 + bx + c = 0$. 2. Divide each term by a. 3. Isolate
the variable terms. 4. Complete the square and factor. 5. Apply the
square root property.   **41.** $t = -3, t = -5$
43. $x = 2, x = -8$ **45.** $p = -2 \pm i\sqrt{2}$ **47.** $y = 5, y = -2$

49. $a = -1 \pm \dfrac{i\sqrt{6}}{2}$ **51.** $x = 2 \pm \dfrac{2}{3}i$ **53.** $p = \dfrac{1}{5} \pm \dfrac{\sqrt{3}}{5}$

55. $w = -\dfrac{3}{4} \pm \dfrac{\sqrt{65}}{4}$ **57.** $n = 2 \pm \sqrt{11}$

59. $r = \sqrt{\dfrac{A}{\pi}}$ or $r = \dfrac{\sqrt{A\pi}}{\pi}$ **61.** $a = \sqrt{d^2 - b^2 - c^2}$

63. $r = \sqrt{\dfrac{3V}{\pi h}}$ or $r = \dfrac{\sqrt{3V\pi h}}{\pi h}$ **65.** $x = \dfrac{s^2}{4}$ **67. a.** 4.5 thousand

textbooks or 35.5 thousand textbooks **b.** Profit increases to a point as more books are produced. Beyond that point, the market is "flooded," and profit decreases. Hence there are 2 points at which the profit is $20,000. Producing 4.5 thousand books makes the same profit using fewer resources than producing 35.5 thousand books.

69. a.

b. $x = 0.7090, x = 3.2910$
c. They are the same.

71. a.
b. $x = -5.6056, x = 1.6056$
c. They are the same.

73. a.
b. $x = -\dfrac{1}{2} \pm \dfrac{i\sqrt{23}}{2}$
c. There are no x-intercepts.

75. a.
b. $x = 1$
c. They are the same.

Section 7.6 Practice Exercises, pp. 513–517

1. $x = 2, x = -12$ **3.** $(x - 1)(x^2 + x + 1)$
5. $x = 2, x = -3, x = 3$ **7.** $(4v - 3)(2u + 3)$ **9.** $4 - 2\sqrt{10}$
11. $2 - i\sqrt{3}$ **13.** $x^2 + 2x + 1 = 0; a = 1, b = 2, c = 1$
15. $19m^2 - 8m + 0 = 0; a = 19, b = -8, c = 0$
17. $5p^2 + 0p - 21 = 0; a = 5, b = 0, c = -21$
19. $n^2 + 3n + 4 = 0; a = 1, b = 3, c = 4$ **21.** One rational solution
23. Two rational solutions   **25.** Two irrational solutions
27. Two imaginary solutions   **29.** If the equation is factorable
31. Any quadratic equation written in the form $ax^2 + bx + c = 0$
33. $a = -12, a = 1$ **35.** $y = \dfrac{1 \pm 2i\sqrt{11}}{9}$ **37.** $p = \dfrac{1 \pm i\sqrt{14}}{6}$
39. $z = 7, z = -5$ **41.** $a = \dfrac{-3 \pm \sqrt{41}}{2}$ **43.** $x = \dfrac{2}{5}$
45. $w = 3 \pm i\sqrt{5}$ **47.** $x = \dfrac{1 \pm \sqrt{29}}{2}$ **49.** $y = \dfrac{-2 \pm 2i\sqrt{2}}{3}$
51. $h = \dfrac{-5 \pm \sqrt{13}}{2}$ **53.** $x = -2, x = -4$ **55.** $t = \dfrac{-7 \pm \sqrt{109}}{6}$
57. a. $(x - 3)(x^2 + 3x + 9)$ **b.** $x = 3, x = \dfrac{-3 \pm 3i\sqrt{3}}{2}$
59. a. $3x(x^2 - 2x + 2)$ **b.** $x = 0, x = 1 \pm i$ **61.** 3 ft
63. $a = \dfrac{-3 \pm i\sqrt{7}}{2}$ **65.** $x = \pm\sqrt{2}$ **67.** $y = -\dfrac{5}{2}, y = \dfrac{1}{2}$
69. $x = -\dfrac{1}{2} \pm 2i$ **71. a.** 46 mph **b.** 36 mph   **73.** 8.2 m and 6.1 m

75. a. 6319 thousand farms **b.** $N(t)$ gives approximate values.
c. 1892, 1954   **77.**

79.

81. a. 7964 thousand **b.** 15,507 thousand **c.** 1989
d.

Section 7.7 Practice Exercises, pp. 521–522

1. $x = \dfrac{7}{2}, x = -\dfrac{1}{2}$ **3.** $\left(a - \dfrac{1}{2}\right)\left(a + \dfrac{1}{2}\right)\left(a^2 + \dfrac{1}{4}\right)$ **5.** $\left(\dfrac{4}{3}, 0\right), \left(\dfrac{1}{2}, 0\right)$
7. $n = 3 \pm 2i$ **9.** $3(2x - 1)^2$ **11.** $(\sqrt{10}, 0), (-\sqrt{10}, 0)$
13. $k = \dfrac{-7 \pm \sqrt{193}}{12}$ **15.** $y = 4$ **17.** $x = \dfrac{1}{4}$ **19.** $b = 6, b = 2$
21. $w = 7$ **23.** $x = \pm2, x = \pm2i$ **25.** $m = \pm3, m = \pm3i$
27. $a = -2, a = 1 \pm i\sqrt{3}$ **29.** $p = 1, p = \dfrac{-1 \pm i\sqrt{3}}{2}$
31. a. $u = -4, u = -6$ **b.** $y = -4, y = -1, y = -2, y = -3$
33. a. $u = 6, u = -4$ **b.** $x = 6, x = -1, x = 4, x = 1$
35. $x = -\dfrac{7}{4}, x = -\dfrac{3}{2}$ **37.** $x = -7$ **39.** $x = 1 \pm i\sqrt{2}, x = 1 \pm \sqrt{2}$
41. $x = 3, x = -3, x = 2, x = -2$
43. $x = 2, x = 1, x = -1 \pm i\sqrt{3}, x = \dfrac{-1 \pm i\sqrt{3}}{2}$
45. $m = 27, m = -8$ **47.** $t = -\dfrac{1}{32}, t = -243$ **49.** $x = \pm2$
51. $a = \pm4i, a = 1$ **53.** $x = 4, x = \pm i\sqrt{5}$
55. a. $x = \pm i\sqrt{2}$ **b.** Two imaginary solutions; zero real solutions
c. No x-intercepts **d.**

57. a. $x = 0, x = 3, x = -2$ **b.** Three real solutions; zero imaginary solutions **c.** Three x-intercepts **d.**

Review Exercises, pp. 528–531

1. $4y^2(2 + y^2)$ **3.** $4(4m^2 - 3n + 6)$ **5.** $(x - 7)(5x - 2)$
7. $2x(x - 13)$ **9.** $(m - 8)(m^2 + 1)$ **11.** $x(2a + b)(2x - 3)$
13. $(3p - 2)(4q + 5)$ **15.** The trinomial must be of the form $a^2 + 2ab + b^2$ or $a^2 - 2ab + b^2$.   **17.** $(2 + 3k)(1 + 2k)$ or $(3k + 2)(2k + 1)$ **19.** $2(2b - 5)^2$ **21.** $(k - 4)^2$ **23.** $(x + 5)(x - 3)$
25. $(-m + 6)(m + 3)$ or $-(m - 6)(m + 3)$ **27.** $(5q + 3)^2$
29. $\left(x - \dfrac{1}{3}\right)\left(x^2 + \dfrac{1}{3}x + \dfrac{1}{9}\right)$ **31.** $(a + 4)(a^2 - 4a + 16)$
33. $h(h^2 + 9)$ **35.** $(k - 2)(k + 2)(k^2 + 4)$ **37.** $y(3y - 2)(3y + 2)$
39. $(u - 10v)(u + 10v + 1)$ **41.** $(a + 6 - b)(a + 6 + b)$ **43.** It is a parabola.   **45.** Quadratic   **47.** Quadratic   **49.** $x = -3, x = 5$
51. $x = \dfrac{3}{2}, x = -\sqrt{7}$ **53.** $(1, 0)(-1, 0)(0, 4)$; b
55. $(2, 0)(-2, 0)(0, 40)$; c   **57.** Length 15 ft; width 8 ft; height 10 ft

59. $x = \pm\sqrt{5}$ **61.** $a = \pm 9$ **63.** $x = 2 \pm 6\sqrt{2}$ **65.** $y = \dfrac{1 \pm \sqrt{3}}{3}$

67. 8.7 in. **69.** 12.2 in. **71.** $k = \dfrac{81}{4}; \left(x - \dfrac{9}{2}\right)^2$

73. $k = \dfrac{1}{25}; \left(z - \dfrac{1}{5}\right)^2$ **75.** $y = \dfrac{3}{2} \pm i$ **77.** $b = \dfrac{1}{2}, b = -4$

79. $t = 4 \pm 3i$ **81.** Two rational solutions **83.** Two irrational solutions **85.** One rational solution **87.** $y = 2 \pm \sqrt{3}$

89. $a = 2, a = -\dfrac{5}{6}$ **91.** $b = \dfrac{4}{5}, b = -\dfrac{1}{5}$ **93.** $x = 8, x = -4$

95. $x = 2, x = -2$ **97. a.** 1822 ft **b.** 115 ft/s **c.** 78 mph

99. $x = 49$ **101.** $y = \pm 3, y = \pm\sqrt{2}$ **103.** $t = -243, t = 32$

105. $a = 3, a = 1$

Test, pp. 531–532

1. 1. Take out the GCF. 2. If a binomial, look for a difference of squares, a difference of cubes, or a sum of cubes. 3. If a trinomial, look for a perfect square trinomial. Otherwise use the grouping or trial-and-error method. 4. If more than three terms try grouping.
2. 1. Set equation equal to 0. 2. Factor the expression. 3. Set each factor equal to 0 and solve. **3.** $x = 0, x = \dfrac{1}{4}, x = -\dfrac{1}{4}$

4. $(3y - 1)(y + 8)$ **5.** $x = \sqrt{7}, x = -\dfrac{1}{10}$ **6.** $y = 3 \pm \sqrt{6}$

7. $(a - 6)(a + 1)(a - 1)$ **8.** $x = -\dfrac{1}{4}$ **9.** $a = \dfrac{5 \pm i\sqrt{7}}{3}$

10. $3(x + 2)(x^2 - 2x + 4)$ **11. a.** $x^2 - 3x + 12 = 0$
b. $a = 1, b = -3, c = 12$ **c.** -39 **d.** Two imaginary solutions
12. a. $y^2 - 2y + 1 = 0$ **b.** $a = 1, b = -2, c = 1$ **c.** 0

d. One rational solution **13.** $k = \dfrac{49}{4}; \left(d + \dfrac{7}{2}\right)^2$

14. $x = \dfrac{3 \pm i\sqrt{47}}{4}$ **15.** Height 4.6 ft; base 6.2 ft **16.** Radius 12.0 ft

17. $(4, 0)(2, 0)(0, 8)$; c **18.** $(-4, 0)(3, 0)(-3, 0)(0, -36)$; b
19. $(-3, 0)(-1, 0)(0, -6)$; d **20.** $(4, 0)(-3, 0)(0, 0)$; a **21.** 256 ft
22. a. 660 million **b.** 1238 million **c.** 1981 **d.** 1999

Cumulative Review Exercises, Chapters 1–7, pp. 533–534

1. a. $\{2, 4, 6, 8, 10, 12, 16\}$ **b.** $\{2, 8\}$ **2.** $-3x^2 - 13x + 1$ **3.** -16
4. 7.2×10^{13} **5. a.** $(x + 2)(x + 3)(x - 3)$

b. Quotient: $x^2 + 5x + 6$; No remainder **6.** $x + 2$ **7.** $\dfrac{2\sqrt{2x}}{x}$

8. $8000 in the 12% account; $2000 in the 3% account **9.** $(8, 7)$
10. a. 720 ft **b.** 720 ft **c.** 12 s **11.** $x = 3 \pm 4i$

12. $x = \dfrac{-5 \pm \sqrt{33}}{4}$ **13.** 25 **14.** $2(x + 5)(x^2 - 5x + 25)$

15.

16. a. $\left(\dfrac{5}{2}, 0\right)(2, 0)$ **b.** $(0, 10)$

17. a.

b. $y = 345x + 3022$ **c.** $9922

18. 1-pt. shots: 565 2-pt. shots: 851 3-pt. shots: 30 **19.** The domain element 3 has more than one corresponding range element.
20.

21. 39 **22. a.** Linear **b.** $(0, 300000)$. If there are no passengers, the airport runs 300,000 flights per year. **c.** $m = 0.008$ or $m = \dfrac{8}{1000}$. There are eight additional flights per 1000 passengers. **23. a.** 3 **b.** $\sqrt{2}$
c. Not a real number **24. a.** $\sqrt{x^2 + 6}; x \geq -4$ **b.** $x + 6; x \geq -4$
25. a. $(-\infty, 2]$ **b.** $(-\infty, 1) \cup \{2\} \cup [3, 4]$ **c.** $(-\infty, -2) \cup (1, 2)$
d. None **e.** $(-2, 1)$ **f.** 2 **g.** 3 **h.** 2 **i.** $x = -3$ **j.** $(-\infty, -3)$

CHAPTER 8

Section 8.1 Practice Exercises, pp. 545–547

1. $h(0) = 3, h(1)$ undefined, $h(-3) = \dfrac{3}{4}, h(-1) = \dfrac{3}{2}, h\left(\dfrac{1}{2}\right) = 6$

3. $k(0) = 2, k(1) = 1, k(-3) = -1, k(-1)$ undefined, $k(\tfrac{1}{2}) = \dfrac{4}{3}$

5. b; $\{x \,|\, x \neq -4\}$ **7.** d; $\{x \,|\, x \neq 4\}$ **9.** $\left(-\infty, \dfrac{1}{3}\right) \cup \left(\dfrac{1}{3}, \infty\right)$

11. $(-\infty, 1) \cup (1, \infty)$ **13.** $(-\infty, 3) \cup (3, 9) \cup (9, \infty)$

15. $\left(-\infty, -\dfrac{5}{2}\right) \cup \left(-\dfrac{5}{2}, 3\right) \cup (3, \infty)$ **17.** $\left(-\infty, -\dfrac{5}{6}\right) \cup \left(-\dfrac{5}{6}, 2\right) \cup (2, \infty)$

19. $\left(-\infty, -\dfrac{5}{3}\right) \cup \left(-\dfrac{5}{3}, \dfrac{5}{3}\right) \cup \left(\dfrac{5}{3}, \infty\right)$

21. $\left(-\infty, -\dfrac{3}{2}\right) \cup \left(-\dfrac{3}{2}, 0\right) \cup \left(0, \dfrac{5}{3}\right) \cup \left(\dfrac{5}{3}, \infty\right)$

23. a. $\dfrac{(x + 4)(x + 2)}{(x + 4)(x - 1)}$ **b.** $\{x \,|\, x \neq -4, x \neq 1\}$ **c.** $\dfrac{x + 2}{x - 1}, x \neq -4, x \neq 1$

25. a. $\dfrac{(x - 9)(x - 9)}{(x - 9)(x + 9)}$ **b.** $\{x \,|\, x \neq 9, x \neq -9\}$ **c.** $\dfrac{x - 9}{x + 9}, x \neq 9, x \neq -9$

27. $\dfrac{25x^2}{9y^3}$ **29.** $\dfrac{w^8 z^3}{2}$ **31.** $\dfrac{2b^7}{a}$ **33.** $\dfrac{2}{3}$ **35.** $\dfrac{b + 3}{b + 2}$ **37.** $-3c + 5$

39. 1 **41.** -1 **43.** -1 **45.** -2 **47.** $\dfrac{c + 4}{c - 4}$; cannot reduce

49. $-\dfrac{t + 4}{t + 3}$ **51.** $\dfrac{b + 5}{3b + 2}$ **53.** $\dfrac{3 - z}{2z - 5}$ **55.** $-\dfrac{2x}{5}$ **57.** $\dfrac{2(z^2 - 2z + 4)}{5 - z}$

59. $\dfrac{2x - 5}{-2}$

61. d

63. f

65. e

65. $\dfrac{2(x^2 + 5x + 3)}{(x + 2)(x + 1)}$ ft

Midchapter Review, p. 565

1. Factor the numerator and denominator. Then reduce common factors whose ratio is 1 or -1. **2.** Factor the numerator and denominator. Multiply straight across and reduce. **3.** Factor the numerator and denominator. Then multiply the first expression by the reciprocal of the second expression. **4.** Factor the denominator to find the LCD. Change all rational expressions to have the common denominator then add or subtract the numerators and reduce.

5. $\dfrac{4y^2 - 8y + 9}{2y(2y - 3)}$ **6.** $\dfrac{x^2 + x - 13}{x - 4}$ **7.** $\dfrac{5x - 1}{4x - 3}$ **8.** $\dfrac{a - 5}{3a}$

9. $\dfrac{2y - 5}{(y - 1)(y + 1)}$ **10.** $\dfrac{4}{w + 4}$ **11.** $\dfrac{a + 4}{2}$ **12.** $\dfrac{(t - 3)(t + 2)}{t}$

13. $\dfrac{-x^2 + 4xy - y^2}{(x - y)(x + y)}$ or $\dfrac{x^2 - 4xy + y^2}{(y - x)(y + x)}$ **14.** $3(x - 4)$

15. $-\dfrac{x - 3}{x + 3}$ **16.** $-(m + n)$ **17.** $\dfrac{3t^2 + 4t - 17}{3t - 5}$ **18.** $\dfrac{5}{x - 5}$

19. $\dfrac{5x - 6}{(x - 3)(x - 2)}$

Section 8.2 Practice Exercises, pp. 552–554

1. For example: $\dfrac{1}{x - 4}$ **3.** For example: $\dfrac{1}{x + 5}$ **5.** $\dfrac{xz^2}{4}$

7. $\dfrac{x + 5}{x - 5}$ **9.** $\dfrac{4}{3w^2}$ **11.** $\dfrac{p^3}{8q}$ **13.** $\dfrac{2}{3}$ **15.** $\dfrac{2(y - 1)}{y + 1}$

17. $-\dfrac{y - x}{2x}$ or $\dfrac{x - y}{2x}$ **19.** $\dfrac{2x(x + 5)}{x - 5}$ **21.** $2x(x - 2)$ **23.** $\dfrac{t}{t + 1}$

25. $\dfrac{1}{a - 4}$ **27.** $\dfrac{x + y}{x - y}$ **29.** $\dfrac{x(x - 1)}{x + 1}$ **31.** -1 **33.** $\dfrac{1}{4}$

35. $(a + b)(a - b)$ **37.** $\dfrac{2y}{x + 2y}$ **39.** $\dfrac{4x(x - 1)}{3}$ **41.** $\dfrac{1}{2}$

43. $\dfrac{2ab}{5}$ in.^{2} **45.** $\dfrac{2x}{x - 2}$ m^2

47. The graphs appear to be the same; however, $Y_1 \neq Y_2$ at $x = 7$.

49. The graphs appear to be the same; however, $Y_1 \neq Y_2$ at $x = 0$ or $x = 2$.

Section 8.3 Practice Exercises, pp. 563–565

1. $\dfrac{3(3 + a)}{9 + 3a + a^2}$ **3.** $-\dfrac{1}{x}$ **5.** $\dfrac{5a + 1}{2}$ **7.** $\dfrac{5(y - 5)}{4}$

9. a. $\dfrac{4(x + 1)}{(x + 1)(x - 1)}$ **b.** $\{x \mid x \neq 1, x \neq -1\}$ **11.** $\dfrac{2}{x}$ **13.** $\dfrac{1}{x + 1}$

15. $\dfrac{2x + 5}{(2x + 9)(x - 6)}$ **17.** $\dfrac{3}{x - 5}$ or $\dfrac{-3}{5 - x}$ **19.** $\dfrac{2x}{x - 6}$ or $\dfrac{-2x}{6 - x}$

21. 40 **23.** $600x^2$ **25.** $(x - 4)(x + 2)(x - 6)$ **27.** $x^2(x - 1)(x + 7)^2$

29. $(x - 6)(x - 2)$ **31.** $15xy$ **33.** $2x^2(x + 2)$ **35.** $y(y - 1)$

37. $\dfrac{(x + 6)(x + 1)}{2x^2}$ **39.** $\dfrac{-t - s}{st}$ or $\dfrac{-(t + s)}{st}$ **41.** $\dfrac{1}{3}$ **43.** $\dfrac{3}{w - 2}$

45. $\dfrac{w^2 - 3}{w - 2}$ **47.** $\dfrac{6b^2 + 5b + 4}{(b - 4)(b + 1)}$ **49.** $\dfrac{t^2 + 30}{(t - 5)(t + 5)}$

51. $\dfrac{11x + 6}{(x - 6)(x + 6)(x + 3)}$ **53.** $\dfrac{10 - x}{3(x - 5)(x + 5)}$ or $\dfrac{x - 10}{3(5 - x)(5 + x)}$

55. $\dfrac{5k^2 + 27k - 2}{(k + 7)(k - 1)}$ **57.** $\dfrac{-2y}{(x - y)(x + y)}$ or $\dfrac{2y}{(y - x)(y + x)}$ **59.** 0

61. a. $\dfrac{-(x - 1)}{x + 1}$ or $\dfrac{1 - x}{x + 1}$ **b.** $\dfrac{3x^2 + x + 4}{3x(x + 1)}$ **63.** $\dfrac{3x^2 + 5x + 18}{3x^2}$ cm

Section 8.4 Practice Exercises, pp. 573–575

1. a. $\dfrac{(x - 1)^2}{x + 3}$ **b.** $\dfrac{(x + 2)^2}{x + 3}$ **3. a.** $\dfrac{6x + 1}{(x + 1)(x - 1)(x - 4)}$

b. $\dfrac{-x + 4}{(x + 1)(x - 1)(x + 2)}$ **c.** $\dfrac{(6x + 1)(x + 2)}{-(x - 4)^2}$ or $\dfrac{(6x + 1)(x + 2)}{(x - 4)(-x + 4)}$

5. $\dfrac{5x^2}{27}$ **7.** $\dfrac{1}{x}$ **9.** $28y$ **11.** -8 **13.** $\dfrac{10}{3}$ **15.** $\dfrac{2y - 1}{4y + 1}$ **17.** $\dfrac{3 - p}{p - 1}$

19. $\dfrac{2a + 3}{4 - 9a}$ **21.** $\dfrac{-4(w - 1)}{w + 2}$ **23.** $\dfrac{1}{y + 4}$ **25.** $\dfrac{x + 2}{x - 1}$

27. $\dfrac{t^2}{(t + 1)^2}$ **29.** $\dfrac{-a + 2}{-a - 3}$ **31.** $-\dfrac{y + 1}{y - 5}$ **33.** $\dfrac{x^2 + 1}{2x}$

35. $(x + x^{-1})^{-1} = \dfrac{1}{x + x^{-1}} = \dfrac{1}{x + (1/x)}$ simplifies to $\dfrac{x}{x^2 + 1}$

37. $\dfrac{1}{x(x^2 + 3)}$ **39.** $\dfrac{2b^2 + 3a}{b(b - a)}$ **41.** $x(x + 1)$ **43.** $\left(\dfrac{x_1 + x_2}{2}, \dfrac{y_1 + y_2}{2}\right)$

45. $\left(-\dfrac{1}{4}, \dfrac{1}{20}\right)$ **47.** $\left(-\dfrac{1}{18}, -\dfrac{4}{21}\right)$ **49.** $\left(\dfrac{11}{16}, -\dfrac{25}{16}\right)$ **51.** $\dfrac{48}{25}$

53. $\dfrac{8}{5}$ **55.** $\dfrac{119}{30}$ **57. a.** **b.** 1 **c.** Yes

Section 8.5 Practice Exercises, pp. 581–582

1. $\dfrac{2x}{(x + 4)^2(x - 4)}$ **3.** $\dfrac{1}{m(m - 4)}$ **5.** $\dfrac{x}{x - 1}$ **7.** $\dfrac{2y + 5}{(y + 4)(y + 1)}$

9. a. Multiply by LCD, 12. **b.** $x = -14$ **11. a.** Multiply by LCD, $12(x - 1)$. **b.** $x = -3$ **13. a.** Multiply by LCD, $5(x - 5)$. **b.** $x = 5$

c. $x = 5$ does not check; there is no solution. **15.** 3 **17.** $\dfrac{2}{5}$

19. $y = 12$ **21.** $x = 6$ **23.** $x = 5$ **25.** $w = 6$ **27.** $x = -25$

29. $a = 4, a = -4$ **31.** $a = 3, a = 1$ **33.** $t = -\dfrac{5}{2}$ **35.** $x = \dfrac{31}{5}$

37. $k = 4$ **39.** No solution **41.** $r^2 = \dfrac{Gm_1m_2}{F}$

43. $a = \dfrac{fb}{b - f}$ or $a = \dfrac{-fb}{f - b}$ **45.** $\dfrac{1}{a + 1}$ **47.** $y = 1$

49. $\dfrac{x^2 - 12}{x(x - 1)}$ **51.** $w = -1$ **53.** $\dfrac{8p - 11}{4(2p - 3)}$

55. 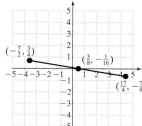 **57.**

Section 8.6 Practice Exercises, pp. 588–590

1. $x = -2, x = -3$ **3.** $\dfrac{11}{12(x - 2)}$ **5.** $y = -\dfrac{3}{5}, y = 3$

7. $\dfrac{8x - 3y}{x(x - y)(x + y)}$ **9.** $t = 3$ **11.** $y = 8$ **13.** $m = 6$

15. $p = -15$ **17.** $x = \dfrac{1}{3}$ **19.** $x = \dfrac{20}{9}$ **21.** $p = 2$ **23.** Six adults

25. 84 g of fat **27.** 1000 swordfish **29.** $a = 8$ ft $b = 8.4$ ft

31. $x = 11.69$ in., $y = 12.71$ in., $z = 4.09$ in. **33.** 224 bikes

35. 11 mph **37.** 12 mph **39.** 8 days **41.** Gus would take 6 h; Sid would take 12 h. **43.** $y = 5$ **45.** $x = 5$

Review Exercises, pp. 595–597

1. a. $g(2) = \dfrac{7}{8}, g(0) = \dfrac{1}{2}, g\!\left(-\dfrac{3}{2}\right) = 0, g(1)$ undefined,

$g(-6)$ undefined **b.** $(-\infty, -6) \cup (-6, 1) \cup (1, \infty)$

3. a. $k(2) = \dfrac{2}{3}, k(0) = 0, k(1)$ undefined, $k(-1)$ undefined,

$k\!\left(\dfrac{1}{2}\right) = -\dfrac{2}{3}$ **b.** $(-\infty, -1) \cup (-1, 1) \cup (1, \infty)$ **5.** $2a$ **7.** $x - 1$

9. $-\dfrac{x^2 + 3x + 9}{3 + x}$ **11.** $-\dfrac{2t + 5}{7 + t}$ **13.** c; $(-\infty, 3) \cup (3, \infty)$

15. b; $(-\infty, 0) \cup (0, 3) \cup (3, \infty)$ **17.** $\dfrac{a}{2}$ **19.** $-\dfrac{x - y}{5x}$ or $\dfrac{y - x}{5x}$

21. $\dfrac{7(k - 4)}{2(k - 2)}$ **23.** $\dfrac{x - 5}{x - 4}$ **25.** $\dfrac{8}{9w^2}$ **27.** $\dfrac{5}{2}$ **29.** $\dfrac{x^2 + x - 1}{x^3}$

31. $\dfrac{y - 3}{2y - 1}$ or $\dfrac{3 - y}{1 - 2y}$ **33.** $\dfrac{4k^2 - k + 3}{(k + 1)^2(k - 1)}$ **35.** $\dfrac{2(a^2 - 5)}{(a - 5)(a + 3)}$

37. $\dfrac{6(7 - 4x)}{3x - 5}$ or $\dfrac{-6(4x - 7)}{3x - 5}$ **39.** $\dfrac{9a^2 + a + 4}{(3a - 1)(a - 2)}$ **41.** $-y$

43. $\dfrac{x(2y + 1)}{4y}$ **45.** $\dfrac{1 + a}{1 - a}$ or $-\dfrac{a + 1}{a - 1}$ **47.** $\dfrac{y - 4}{y - 8}$ **49.** $\dfrac{y}{x - y}$

51. a. $\left(\dfrac{3}{8}, -\dfrac{7}{16}\right)$ **b.** $-\dfrac{9}{14}$ **53. a.** $\left(\dfrac{1}{3}, 2\right)$ **b.** undefined **55.** $x = 3$

57. $x = 0, x = 17$ **59.** $y = 5, y = 1$ **61.** $t_2 = \dfrac{d_2 - d_1 + Vt_1}{V}$

63. $x = \dfrac{15}{2}$ **65.** $x = -\dfrac{7}{11}$ **67.** \$18.75 **69.** 80 units

71. larger pipe, 9 h; smaller pipe, 18 h

Test, pp. 597–598

1. a. $f(0) = 2, f(1) = 1, f(7)$ undefined
b. $(-\infty, -1) \cup (-1, 7) \cup (7, \infty)$

c. $f(x) = \dfrac{2}{x + 1}$ provided $x \neq 7, x \neq -1$

2. $\dfrac{9(x - 1)}{x + 3}$ **3.** $\dfrac{2 - a}{a^2 - 2a + 4}$ **4.** $\dfrac{5}{(x + 3)^3}$

5. $\dfrac{(x - 3)^2}{5(x + 3)}$ **6.** $\dfrac{x^2 - x + 24}{(x + 3)^2(x - 3)}$ **7.** $\dfrac{x^2 - 11x - 6}{(x + 3)^2(x - 3)}$

8. a.

$\left(-\dfrac{7}{2}, \dfrac{3}{4}\right)$ $\left(\dfrac{3}{8}, -\dfrac{1}{16}\right)$ $\left(\dfrac{17}{4}, -\dfrac{7}{8}\right)$

b. $\left(\dfrac{3}{8}, -\dfrac{1}{16}\right)$ **c.** $-\dfrac{13}{62}$

9. $\dfrac{69}{25}$ **10.** $\dfrac{x^2 + 5x + 2}{x + 1}$ **11.** $\dfrac{3}{4}$ **12.** $\dfrac{u^2v^2}{2(v^2 - uv + u^2)}$ **13.** a

14. $\dfrac{1}{(x + 5)(x + 3)}$ **15.** $z = 3$ **16.** $y = 0, y = 4$ **17.** $T = \dfrac{PVt}{pv}$

18. $m_1 = \dfrac{Fr^2}{Gm_2}$ **19.** $\dfrac{1}{6}$ or 2 **20.** $a = 12$ m, $b = 15$ m, $c = 18$ m

21. 1960 miles **22.** 1000 units **23.** 16 mph and 20 mph **24.** $2\frac{6}{7}$ h

Cumulative Review Exercises, Chapters 1–8, pp. 599–600

1. Imaginary Numbers: $3 - 4i$;
Real Numbers: $-22, \pi, 6, -\sqrt{2}$;
Irrational Numbers: $\pi, -\sqrt{2}$;
Rational Numbers: $-22, 6$;
Integers: $-22, 6$;
Whole Numbers: 6;
Natural Numbers: 6

2. a. \$21,839,777 **b.** \$1,284,693 **3.** $x^2 - x - 13$ **4.** -6

5. $\dfrac{47}{36} - \dfrac{1}{3}i$ **6. a.** $6\sqrt{3}$ in. **b.** 6 in.²

7. $2(\sqrt{5} + \sqrt{3})$ or $2\sqrt{5} + 2\sqrt{3}$ **8.** $\dfrac{\sqrt[3]{x}}{x}$ **9.** $\dfrac{5b^2\sqrt{a}}{a}$

10. a. $b_1 = \dfrac{2A - hb_2}{h}$ or $\dfrac{2A}{h} - b_2$ **b.** 10 cm

11. 50 m by 30 m **12.** No solution; inconsistent system

13. $y = -\dfrac{1}{3}x + 4$ **14. a.** Linear **b.**

c. $(0, 15000)$. When the car is new (0 years old) the value is \$15,000.
d. $(12, 0)$. When the car is 12 years old the value is \$0. **e.** $m = -1250$.
The car is depreciating at a rate of \$1250 per year. **f.** $V(5) = 8750$.
After 5 years the value of the car is \$8750. **g.** $7\frac{1}{2}$ years **15.** 75 mph

16. a. $x = 3 \pm \sqrt{19}$ **17.** $(0, 0), \left(\dfrac{3}{4}, 0\right), \left(\dfrac{2}{3}, 0\right)$

18. $8(2y - z^2)(4y^2 + 2yz^2 + z^4)$

19. $-\mathbf{A} = \begin{bmatrix} -3 & 4 & -2 \\ -4 & -1 & 0 \\ -11 & -3 & -18 \end{bmatrix}$ **20.** Evaluate $D = \begin{vmatrix} 1 & 2 & -6 \\ 0 & 1 & -5 \\ 3 & -1 & 2 \end{vmatrix}$

and $D_z = \begin{vmatrix} 1 & 2 & 9 \\ 0 & 1 & 0 \\ 3 & -1 & -7 \end{vmatrix}$. Then $z = \dfrac{D_z}{D} = \dfrac{34}{15}$

21. a. $\left(-\infty, \frac{3}{2}\right) \cup \left(\frac{3}{2}, \infty\right)$ **b.** $(-\infty, -3) \cup (-3, 4) \cup (4, \infty)$

22. $\frac{x + a}{4(x - 7)}$ **23.** $\frac{-(x - 2)}{5}$ or $\frac{2 - x}{5}$ **24.** $\frac{x + 3}{(x + 10)(x - 2)}$

25. $\frac{c - 7}{c}$ **26.** $y = 3, y = -1$ **27.** 278 miles **28.** $x = 1, y = 3$

29. 184% **30. a.** $-x^2 + 5x - 5$ **b.** -19

CHAPTER 9

Section 9.1 Practice Exercises, pp. 606–609

1. $\left(-\frac{1}{2}, \infty\right)$ **3.** $[-16, \infty)$ **5.** $(66, \infty)$ **7. a.** $\{10, 20, 30\}$

b. $\{5, 10, 15, 20, 25, 30, 35, 40, 50\}$

9. a. $x > 2$ ⟶ (2 ⟶ **b.** $x < 4$ ⟵ 4)

c. $2 < x < 4$ ⟶ (2 4) ⟶

11. a. $x \geq -\frac{1}{3}$ ⟶ [$-\frac{1}{3}$ ⟶ **b.** $x \leq 4$ ⟵ 4]

c. $-\frac{1}{3} \leq x \leq 4$ ⟶ [$-\frac{1}{3}$ 4]

13. a. $x < 2$ ⟵ 2) **b.** $x < 5$ ⟵ 5)

c. $x < 2$ ⟵ 2)

15. $[-2, 3]$ ⟶ [-2 3] ⟶ **17.** $(3, 6)$ ⟶ (3 6) ⟶

19. $\left[\frac{5}{2}, 7\right)$ ⟶ [$\frac{5}{2}$ 7) **21.** $(-\infty, 2]$ ⟵ 2]

23. $(-6, 6]$ ⟶ (-6 6] ⟶ **25.** $(2, 8)$ ⟶ (2 8) ⟶

27. $[8, \infty)$ ⟶ [8 ⟶

29. a. $x < -1$ ⟵ -1) **b.** $x < -5$ ⟵ -5)

c. $x < -1$ ⟵ -1

31. a. $x \leq 3$ ⟵ 3] **b.** $x \geq 8$ [8 ⟶

c. $x \leq 3$ or $x \geq 8$ ⟵ 3] [8 ⟶

33. a. $x \geq 2$ [2 ⟶ **b.** $x \leq -1$ ⟵ -1]

c. $x \geq 2$ or $x \leq -1$ ⟵ -1] [2 ⟶

35. $(-\infty, -4) \cup (-2, \infty)$ ⟵ -4) (-2 ⟶

37. $(-\infty, -2) \cup [2, \infty)$ ⟵ -2) [2 ⟶

39. $(-\infty, -7) \cup [3, \infty)$ ⟵ -7) [3 ⟶

41. $[-6, \infty)$ [-6 ⟶

43. $\left(-\infty, -\frac{4}{3}\right) \cup (2, \infty)$ ⟵ $-\frac{4}{3}$) (2 ⟶

45. $(-\infty, -4] \cup \left(\frac{9}{2}, \infty\right)$ ⟵ -4] ($\frac{9}{2}$ ⟶

47. a. $-10 < x < 8$ ⟶ (-10 8) ⟶

b. All real numbers ⟵⟶

49. a. $x \geq 1.3$ or $x \leq -8$ ⟵ -8] [1.3 ⟶ **b.** No solution

51. a. $4800 \leq x \leq 10,800$ **b.** $x < 4800$ or $x > 10,800$

53. a. $13 \leq x \leq 16$ **b.** $x < 13$ or $x > 16$ **55.** All real numbers between $-\frac{3}{2}$ and 6 **57.** All real numbers greater than 2 or less than -1

Section 9.2 Practice Exercises, pp. 620–622

1. $\left(-\infty, \frac{3}{8}\right) \cup (3, \infty)$ **3.** $(-3, 0)$ **5.** $(5, \infty)$ **7.** All real numbers

9. a. $(-2, 0) \cup (3, \infty)$ **b.** $(-\infty, -2) \cup (0, 3)$ **c.** $(-\infty, -2] \cup [0, 3]$

d. $[-2, 0] \cup [3, \infty)$ **11. a.** $(-1, 1]$ **b.** $(-\infty, -1) \cup [1, \infty)$

c. $(-\infty, -1) \cup (1, \infty)$ **d.** $(-1, 1)$ **13. a.** $b = \frac{17}{6}$ **b.** $\left(-\infty, \frac{17}{6}\right)$

c. $\left(\frac{17}{6}, \infty\right)$ **15. a.** $y = 18$ **b.** $[18, \infty)$ **c.** $(-\infty, 18]$

17. a. $w = \frac{2}{3}, w = -5$ **b.** $\left(-5, \frac{2}{3}\right)$ **c.** $(-\infty, -5) \cup \left(\frac{2}{3}, \infty\right)$

19. a. $q = 5, q = -1$ **b.** $[-1, 5]$ **c.** $(-\infty, -1] \cup [5, \infty)$ **21.** $(-1, 7)$

23. $\left(-\infty, \frac{3}{5}\right) \cup (8, \infty)$ **25.** $[4, 8]$ **27.** $(-11, 11)$

29. $\left(-\infty, -\frac{1}{3}\right] \cup [3, \infty)$ **31.** $\left(-\frac{1}{3}, 0\right) \cup (4, \infty)$

33. $(-\infty, -3] \cup [0, 4]$ **35.** $(-2, -1) \cup (2, \infty)$ **37. a.** $x = \frac{26}{5}$

b. $(-\infty, 5) \cup \left(\frac{26}{5}, \infty\right)$ **c.** $\left(5, \frac{26}{5}\right)$ **39. a.** $z = 4$ **b.** $[4, 6)$

c. $(-\infty, 4] \cup (6, \infty)$ **41.** $(1, \infty)$ **43.** $(-1, 3)$ **45.** $\left(2, \frac{7}{2}\right)$ **47.** $(5, 7]$

49. $(-\infty, 0) \cup \left[\frac{1}{2}, \infty\right)$ **51.** $(0, \infty)$ **53.** All real numbers **55.** No solution **57.** No solution **59.** $\{0\}$ **61.** $[-2 - 2\sqrt{3}, -2 + 2\sqrt{3}]$

63. $(-3 - \sqrt{31}, -3 + \sqrt{31})$

65. $(-\infty, 0) \cup (2, \infty)$ **67.** $(-1, 1)$ **69.** $\{-5\}$

71. No solution

Midchapter Review, p. 623

1. $(-\infty, -9) \cup [10, \infty)$ **2.** $(-\infty, -1) \cup \left(\frac{7}{3}, \infty\right)$ **3.** $\left(\frac{4}{3}, 5\right]$

4. $(-\infty, 0) \cup (0, \infty)$ **5.** $(-3, 4)$ **6.** No solution

7. $[-2, -1] \cup [1, \infty)$ **8.** $[-1, 2)$ **9.** $\left(-\infty, -\dfrac{5}{4}\right) \cup (5, \infty)$

10. $(6.1, \infty)$ **11.** $(-\infty, -1) \cup (-1, \infty)$ **12.** $\left(-3, -\dfrac{3}{2}\right)$

13. No solution **14.** $(1, 9)$ **15.** No solution **16.** $(-\infty, -10)$
17. $(-\infty, -2] \cup (5, \infty)$ **18.** $(-\infty, 1]$

Section 9.3 Practice Exercises, pp. 629–630

1. $\left(\dfrac{2}{3}, \dfrac{23}{2}\right)$ **3.** $\left(4, \dfrac{16}{3}\right]$ **5.** All real numbers between -7 and 7

7. $(-\infty, -4) \cup \left(\dfrac{1}{2}, 2\right)$ **9.** $p = 7, p = -7$ **11.** $x = 6, x = -6$

13. $y = \sqrt{2}, y = -\sqrt{2}$ **15.** No solution **17.** $q = 0$

19. $x = \dfrac{1}{3}, x = 0$ **21.** $x = \dfrac{5}{2}, x = -\dfrac{3}{2}$ **23.** $z = \dfrac{10}{7}, z = -\dfrac{8}{7}$

25. $y = 2, y = -\dfrac{14}{5}$ **27.** No solution **29.** $w = -4, w = \dfrac{1}{3}$

31. $y = \dfrac{1}{2}$ **33.** $w = -12, w = 28$ **35.** $y = \dfrac{5}{2}, y = -\dfrac{7}{2}$ **37.** $b = \dfrac{7}{3}$

39. $w = 2, w = -\dfrac{1}{3}$ **41.** No solution **43.** $x = \dfrac{3}{2}$ **45.** $h = \dfrac{1}{4}$

47. $k = -4, k = \dfrac{16}{5}$ **49.** $m = -1.44, m = -0.4$ **51.** $|x| = 6$

53. $|x| = \dfrac{4}{3}$ **55.** $y = \dfrac{4}{5}, y = \dfrac{2}{5}$ **57.** $x = 7 - \sqrt{3}, x = -7 - \sqrt{3}$

59. $w = -\sqrt{6}, w = 0$

61. $x = 2, x = -\dfrac{1}{2}$

63. No solution **65.** $x = \dfrac{1}{2}$

67. $x = \dfrac{4}{3}, x = -2$

Section 9.4 Practice Exercises, pp. 639–641

1. $x = \dfrac{1}{10}$ **3.** No solution **5.** $x = -\dfrac{5}{3}, x = -\dfrac{1}{3}$

7. $(-\infty, 1.9)$

9. $(-3, -1]$

11. All real numbers

13. a. $x = -5, x = 5$ **b.** $(-\infty, -5) \cup (5, \infty)$
c. $(-5, 5)$

15. a. No solution **b.** $(-\infty, \infty)$ **c.** No solution

17. a. $x = 10, x = -4$ **b.** $(-\infty, -4) \cup (10, \infty)$
c. $(-4, 10)$

19. a. No solution **b.** $(-\infty, \infty)$ **c.** No solution
21. b **23.** a
25. $(-\infty, -6) \cup (6, \infty)$ **27.** $[-3, 3]$

29. $(-\infty, \infty)$
31. $(-\infty, -2] \cup [3, \infty)$ **33.** No solution

35. $[-10, 14]$

37. $\left(-\infty, -\dfrac{5}{4}\right) \cup \left[\dfrac{23}{4}, \infty\right)$

39. $\left(-\dfrac{21}{2}, \dfrac{19}{2}\right)$ **41.** $(-\infty, \infty)$

43. No solution **45.** $\{-5\}$

47. $(-\infty, \infty)$ **49.** $|x| > 7$ **51.** $|x - 2| \le 13$

53. $|x - 32| \le 0.05$ **55.** $\left|x - 6\dfrac{3}{4}\right| \le \dfrac{1}{8}$

57. $(-\infty, -6) \cup (2, \infty)$

59. $(-7, 5)$

61. No solution **63.** $(-\infty, \infty)$ **65.** $x = -\dfrac{1}{6}$

Section 9.5 Practice Exercises, pp. 649–651

1. Solve the inequality: $x + 3 < -4$ or $x + 3 > 4$ or use the test
point method. **3.** $(1, 4)$ **5.** $\left[-\dfrac{5}{6}, \dfrac{7}{6}\right]$ **7.** $(-\infty, -2] \cup [1, \infty)$

9. a. Yes **b.** No **c.** Yes **d.** No **11. a.** Yes **b.** Yes **c.** No **d.** No
13. $x - y > 2$ **15.** $y \ge -4$ **17.** $x \le 0$ and $y \ge 0$
19.   **21.**

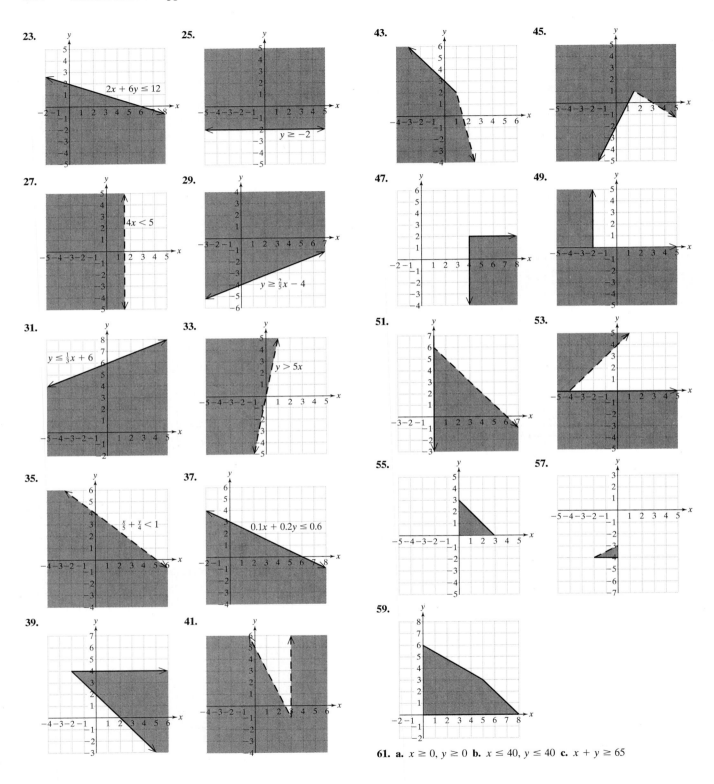

23. $2x + 6y \le 12$

25. $y \ge -2$

27. $4x < 5$

29. $y \ge \frac{2}{5}x - 4$

31. $y \le \frac{1}{3}x + 6$

33. $y > 5x$

35. $\frac{x}{5} + \frac{y}{4} < 1$

37. $0.1x + 0.2y \le 0.6$

39.

41.

43.

45.

47.

49.

51.

53.

55.

57.

59.

61. a. $x \ge 0$, $y \ge 0$ **b.** $x \le 40$, $y \le 40$ **c.** $x + y \ge 65$

d.

63. $y < -\frac{2}{3}x + 4$ **65.** $y > \frac{1}{2}x + 2$ **67.** $y > \frac{4}{3}x$

Review Exercises, pp. 656–659

1. $\left(-\frac{11}{4}, 4\right]$ **3.** $[-10, -3]$ **5.** $(-\infty, 6] \cup (12, \infty)$ **7.** $\left(-\infty, \frac{1}{2}\right)$

9. $\left[0, \frac{4}{3}\right]$ **11.** All real numbers between -6 and 12

13. a. $125 \le x \le 200$ **b.** $x < 125$ or $x > 200$ **15. a.** The solution is the intersection of the two inequalities. Answer: $-2 \le x \le 5$. **b.** The solution is the union of the two inequalities. Answer: All real numbers. **17. a.** $x = -2, x = 2$; $(-2, 0)(2, 0)$ are the x-intercepts. **b.** $-2 < x < 2$; On the interval $(-2, 2)$ the graph is below the x-axis. **c.** $x < -2$ or $x > 2$; On the interval $(-\infty, -2)$ and $(2, \infty)$ the graph is above the x-axis. **19.** $(-2, 6)$ **21.** $(-2, 0]$ **23.** $(-2, 0) \cup (5, \infty)$ **25.** $\{-2\}$ **27.** $(3, \infty)$ **29.** $\{-5\}$

31. $x = 10, x = -10$ **33.** $y = -\frac{11}{2}, y = -\frac{13}{2}$ **35.** $x = 1.3, x = 7.4$

37. $x = 5, x = -9$ **39.** No solution **41.** $x = \frac{3}{7}$ **43.** $x = 6, x = \frac{4}{5}$

45. Both expressions give the distance between 3 and -2.
47. $|x| < 4$
49. $(-\infty, -14] \cup [2, \infty)$

51. $\left(-\infty, \frac{1}{7}\right) \cup \left(\frac{1}{7}, \infty\right)$

53. $\left[-2, -\frac{2}{3}\right]$ **55.** $(2, 22)$

57. $(-\infty, -1) \cup (5, \infty)$

59. $(-1, 4)$ **61.** No solution

63. If an absolute value is less than a negative number there will be no solution.
65.   **67.**

69.   **71.**

73.   **75.**

77.   **79.**

Test, p. 660

1. a. $-\frac{1}{3} \le x \le 2$ **b.** $x \ge -15$ or $x \le -24$ **2. a.** $9 \le x \le 33$

b. $x < 9$ or $x > 33$ **c.** $x > 40$ **3.** $\left[\frac{1}{2}, 6\right)$ **4.** $(-5, 5)$

5. $(-\infty, -3) \cup (-2, 2)$ **6.** $\left(-3, -\frac{3}{2}\right)$ **7.** No solution **8.** $\{-11\}$

9. a. $x = 10, x = -22$ **b.** $x = -8, x = 2$ **10. a.** $x = 7, x = -1$; $(7, 0)(-1, 0)$ are the x-intercepts. **b.** $-1 < x < 7$; On the interval $(-1, 7)$ the graph is below the x-axis. **c.** $x < -1$ or $x > 7$; On the intervals $(-\infty, -1)$ and $(7, \infty)$ the graph is above the x-axis. **11.** No solution **12.** $\left(-\infty, -\frac{1}{3}\right) \cup \left(\frac{17}{3}, \infty\right)$ **13.** $(-18.75, 17.25)$

14. $(-\infty, \infty)$ **15.** $|x - 15.41| \le 0.01$
16.

17. a. $x \geq 0$, $y \geq 0$ **b.** $300x + 400y \geq 1000$
c.

Cumulative Review Exercises, Chapters 1–9, pp. 661–662

1. $x = \dfrac{5 + 3\sqrt{7}}{5}$ **2.** $m = \dfrac{2 \pm i\sqrt{2}}{2}$ **3. a.** $p = 0, p = 6$ **b.** $(0, 6)$
c. $(-\infty, 0) \cup (6, \infty)$ **4. a.** $y = 14, y = -10$ **b.** $(-10, 14)$
c. $(-\infty, -10) \cup (14, \infty)$
5.

6. a. $t(1) = 9$. After one trial the rat requires 9 min to complete the maze. $t(50) = 3.24$. After 50 trials the rat requires 3.24 min to complete the maze. $t(500) = 3.02$. After 500 trials the rat requires 3.02 min to complete the maze. **b.** The limiting time is 3 min **c.** Over 5 trials **7. a.** $\left(-\infty, -\dfrac{5}{2}\right] \cup [2, \infty)$ **b.** On these intervals, the graph is above the x-axis (greater than or equal to 0).
8.

9. a. ix **b.** vii **c.** vi **d.** v **e.** ii **f.** i **g.** iv **h.** viii **i.** iii
10. $\$1.5 \times 10^6$ per restaurant **11. a.** Quotient: $2x^2 - 5x + 12$; remainder: $-24x + 5$ **c.** No **12.** $5a\sqrt{2ab}$ **13.** $x - y$ **14.** $57°, 123°$
15. $\$8000$ in the 6.5% account; $\$5000$ in the 5% account **16.** Neither

17. a. x-intercept $(1, 0)$; no y-intercept; undefined slope **b.** x-intercept $(8, 0)$; y-intercept $(0, 4)$; slope $-\dfrac{1}{2}$

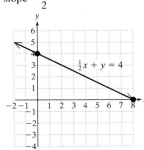

18. $y = -\dfrac{2}{3}x - \dfrac{13}{3}$ **19.** $(-1, 3, -2)$ **20. a.** 4×3 **b.** 3×3
21. Plane: 500 mph Wind: 20 mph **22. a.** Quadratic **b.** $P(0) = -2600$; The company will lose $2600 if no desks are produced.
c. $P(x) = 0$ for $x = 20$ and $x = 650$; The company will break even ($\$0$ profit) when 20 desks or 650 desks are produced. **d.** $(335, 19845)$; Producing 335 desks yields a profit of $\$19,845$. **23. a.** $\{x \mid x \leq 50\}$
b. $4\sqrt{3}$
24. a.

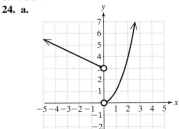

b. $(-\infty, 0) \cup (0, \infty)$ **c.** $(0, \infty)$ **d.** $(0, \infty)$ **e.** $(-\infty, 0)$ **f.** $k(3) = 9$
25. $\dfrac{xy}{x + y}$ **26.** $-\dfrac{a + 1}{a}$ **27.** -82

CHAPTER 10

Section 10.1 Practice Exercises, pp. 671–675

1. Yes **3.** No **5.** Yes **7.** Yes **9.** No **11.** Yes
13. $g^{-1} = \{(5, 3), (1, 8), (9, -3), (2, 0)\}$
15. $r^{-1} = \{(3, a), (6, b), (9, c)\}$ **17.** The function is not one-to-one.
19. Yes; $\{(240, \text{John Hancock Tower}), (236, \text{IDS Center}), (234, \text{Opera City Tower}), (290, \text{Society Tower})\}$ **21.** $h^{-1}(x) = x - 4$
23. $m^{-1}(x) = 3(x + 2)$ **25.** $p^{-1}(x) = -x + 10$ **27.** $f^{-1}(x) = \sqrt[3]{x}$
29. a. 1.2192 m, 15.24 m **b.** $f^{-1}(x) = \dfrac{1}{0.3048}x$ **c.** 4921.3 ft **31.** False
33. False **35.** False **37.** True **39.** $(b, 0)$ **41.** For example: $f(x) = x$ **43. a.** Domain $\{x \mid x \leq 0\}$, range $\{y \mid y \geq -4\}$ **b.** Domain $\{x \mid x \geq -4\}$, range $\{y \mid y \leq 0\}$ **45. a.** $\{x \mid -2 \leq x \leq 0\}$
b. $\{y \mid 0 \leq y \leq 2\}$ **c.** $\{x \mid 0 \leq x \leq 2\}$ **d.** $\{y \mid -2 \leq y \leq 0\}$

e.

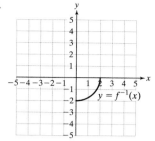

47. a. $\{x \mid 2 \le x \le 5\}$ **b.** $\{y \mid 0 \le y \le 3\}$ **c.** $\{x \mid 0 \le x \le 3\}$
d. $\{y \mid 2 \le y \le 5\}$ **e.**

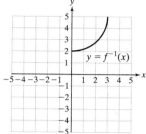

49. $p^{-1}(x) = \dfrac{3 - 3x}{x + 1}, \quad x \ne -1$ **51.** $w^{-1}(x) = \dfrac{4 - 2x}{x}, \quad x \ne 0$
53. $m^{-1}(x) = \sqrt{x + 1}$ **55.** $g^{-1}(x) = -\sqrt{x + 1}$
57. $v^{-1}(x) = x^2 - 16, \quad x \ge 0$ **59.** $u^{-1}(x) = x^2 - 16, \quad x \le 0$
61. **63.**

Section 10.2 Practice Exercises, pp. 683–685

1. 25 **3.** $\dfrac{1}{1000}$ **5.** 6 **7.** 8 **9.** 5.8731 **11.** 1385.4557

13. 0.0063 **15.** 0.8950 **17. a.** 2 **b.** 3 **c.** Between 2 and 3, closer to 2 **19. a.** 4 **b.** 5 **c.** Between 4 and 5, closer to 5 **21.** $f(0) = 1$,
$f(1) = \dfrac{1}{5}, f(2) = \dfrac{1}{25}, f(-1) = 5, f(-2) = 25$ **23.** $h(0) = 1$,
$h(1) = \pi \approx 3.14, h(-1) = 0.32, h(\sqrt{2}) = 5.05, h(\pi) = 36.46$

25. $r(0) = 9, r(1) = 27, r(2) = 81, r(-1) = 3, r(-2) = 1, r(-3) = \dfrac{1}{3}$

27. If $b > 1$, the graph is increasing. If $0 < b < 1$, the graph is decreasing.
29. **31.**

33.

35.

37. a. \$1640.67 **b.** \$2691.80 **c.** $A(0) = 1000$. The initial amount of the investment is \$1000. $A(7) = 2000$. The amount of the investment doubles in 7 years. **39. a.** $I(t) = 3,600,000(1.0036)^t$
b. $S(t) = 3,500,000(1.012)^t$
c. $I(20) = 3,900,000$ $S(20) = 4,400,000$
$I(40) = 4,200,000$ $S(40) = 5,600,000$
$I(60) = 4,500,000$ $S(60) = 7,200,000$ **d.** Because Singapore has a higher growth rate, the population of Singapore will eventually overtake the population of Ireland. **e.** The population density (number of people per square mile) is more than 100 times as large for Singapore as for Ireland.
41. **43.**

45. **47.**

49. a. **b.** 7, 14, 21

Section 10.3 Practice Exercises, pp. 694–696

1. ii **3. a.** $g(-2) = \dfrac{1}{9}, g(-1) = \dfrac{1}{3}, g(0) = 1, g(1) = 3, g(2) = 9$
b.

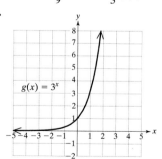

5. a. $s(-2) = \dfrac{25}{4}, s(-1) = \dfrac{5}{2}, s(0) = 1, s(1) = \dfrac{2}{5}, s(2) = \dfrac{4}{25}$

b.

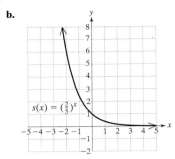
$s(x) = (\frac{2}{5})^x$

7. $b^y = x$ **9.** $\log_{10}(1000) = 3$ **11.** $\log_8(2) = \frac{1}{3}$

13. $\log_8\left(\frac{1}{64}\right) = -2$ **15.** $\log_b(x) = y$ **17.** $\log_e(x) = y$

19. $\log_H(q) = m$ **21.** $125^{2/3} = 25$ **23.** $25^{-1/2} = \frac{1}{5}$ **25.** $2^7 = 128$

27. $b^y = 82$ **29.** $2^x = 7$ **31.** $\left(\frac{1}{2}\right)^6 = x$ **33.** 3 **35.** -4 **37.** $\frac{1}{3}$

39. 1 **41.** 3 **43.** 0 **45.** 2 **47.** 4 **49.** -1 **51.** -3 **53.** 0.7782
55. 0.4971 **57.** -1.5051 **59.** -2.2676 **61.** 5.5315 **63.** -7.4202
65. a. Slightly less than 2 **b.** Slightly more than 1
c. $\log 93 = 1.9685$, $\log 12 = 1.0792$

67. a. $f\left(\frac{1}{64}\right) = -3, f\left(\frac{1}{16}\right) = -2, f\left(\frac{1}{4}\right) = -1, f(1) = 0,$
$f(4) = 1, f(16) = 2, f(64) = 3$

b.

$f(x) = \log_4 x$

69. $3^y = x$

x	y
$\frac{1}{9}$	-2
$\frac{1}{3}$	-1
1	0
3	1
9	2

$y = \log_3 x$

71. $\left(\frac{1}{2}\right)^y = x$

x	y
4	-2
2	-1
1	0
$\frac{1}{2}$	1
$\frac{1}{4}$	2

$y = \log_{1/2} x$

73. $\{x \mid x > 0\}$ **75.** $\{x \mid x > 0\}$ **77.** $(5, \infty)$ **79.** $(-1.2, \infty)$
81. $(-\infty, 0) \cup (0, \infty)$
83. a.

t **(months)**	0	1	2	6	12	24
$S_1(t)$	91	82.0	76.7	65.6	57.6	49.1
$S_2(t)$	88	83.5	80.8	75.3	71.3	67.0

b. Group 1: 91; Group 2: 88 **c.** Method II
85. Domain: $(-6, \infty)$; asymptote: $x = -6$

87. Domain: $(2, \infty)$; asymptote: $x = 2$

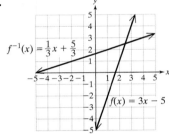

89. Domain: $(-\infty, 2)$; asymptote: $x = 2$

Midchapter Review, p. 697

1. a, b, c **2. a.** $f^{-1}(x) = \frac{1}{3}x + \frac{5}{3}$

b.

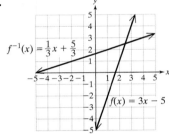
$f^{-1}(x) = \frac{1}{3}x + \frac{5}{3}$
$f(x) = 3x - 5$

c. $(f \circ f^{-1})(x) = 3\left(\frac{1}{3}x + \frac{5}{3}\right) - 5 = x + 5 - 5 = x$

$(f^{-1} \circ f)(x) = \frac{1}{3}(3x - 5) + \frac{5}{3} = x - \frac{5}{3} + \frac{5}{3} = x$

3. a.

$g(x) = 7^x$
$g^{-1}(x) = \log_7 x$

b. $7^{\log_7 x} = x$ **c.** $\log_7 7^x = x$

4. a.

b. $\log 10^x = x$ **c.** $10^{\log x} = x$

c.

d. Domain: $(0, \infty)$; range: $(-\infty, \infty)$

Section 10.4 Practice Exercises, pp. 704–706

1. $\dfrac{1}{64}$ **3.** 5 **5.** 2.9707 **7.** 1.4314 **9.** d **11.** b **13.** For example:
$\log_{10} 1 = 0$ **15.** For example: $\log_4 4^2 = 2$ **17.** 1 **19.** 4 **21.** 11
23. 3 **25.** 0 **27.** 9 **29.** Expressions a and c are equivalent.
31. Expressions a and c are equivalent. **33.** $\log_3 x - \log_3 5$
35. $\log 2 + \log x$ **37.** $4 \log_{10} x$ **39.** $\log_4 a + \log_4 b - \log_4 c$
41. $\dfrac{1}{2} \log_b x + \log_b y - 3 \log_b z - \log_b w$ **43.** $\log(CABIN)$
45. $\log_3\left(\dfrac{x^2 z}{y^3}\right)$ **47.** $\log_b(x^2)$ **49.** $\log_8(8a^5)$ or $\log_8 a^5 + 1$
51. a. $B = 10 \log I - 10 \log I_0$ **b.** $10 \log I + 160$
53. a. Domain: $(-\infty, 1) \cup (1, \infty)$ **b.** Domain: $(1, \infty)$

c. They are equivalent for all x in the intersection of their domains, $(1, \infty)$.

Section 10.5 Practice Exercises, pp. 714–718

1.

3.

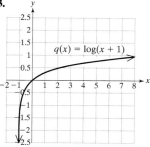

5. $4 \ln a + \dfrac{1}{2} \ln b - \ln c$ **7.** $\dfrac{1}{5} \ln a + \dfrac{1}{5} \ln b - \dfrac{2}{5} \ln c$ **9.** $\ln\left(\dfrac{a^2}{b\sqrt[3]{c}}\right)$
11. $\ln\left(\dfrac{x^4}{y^3 z}\right)$
13. a.

b. Domain: $(-\infty, \infty)$; range: $(0, \infty)$

15. Domain: $(-\infty, \infty)$; range: $(0, \infty)$

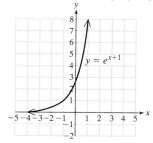

17. Domain: $(2, \infty)$; range: $(-\infty, \infty)$

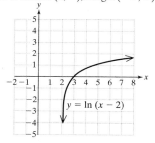

19. a. 2.9570 **b.** 2.9570 **c.** They are the same. **21.** 2.8074
23. 1.5283 **25.** -2.1269 **27.** 0 **29.** -3.3219 **31.** -3.8124
33. a. Between 2 and 3 **b.** Slightly less than 3 **c.** $\log_3 15 = 2.4650$,
$\log_3 25 = 2.9299$ **35. a.** Slightly more than 1 **b.** Slightly less than 2
c. $\log_6 10 = 1.2851$, $\log_6 30 = 1.8982$ **37. a.** 15.4 years **b.** 6.9 years
c. 13.8 years **39. a.** $(0, 72)$ **b.** $(72, \infty)$ **c.** 2.12 μmol/L
d. 3.59 μmol/L **e.** 0.06 μmol/L **f.** 300 min **41. a.** \$12,209.97
b. \$13,488.50 **c.** \$14,898.46 **d.** \$16,050.09; An investment grows
more rapidly at higher interest rates. **43. a.** \$12,423.76
b. \$12,515.01 **c.** \$12,535.94 **d.** \$12,546.15 **e.** \$12,546.50; More
money is earned at a greater number of compound periods per year.
45. a. \$6920.15 **b.** \$9577.70 **c.** \$13,255.84 **d.** \$18,346.48
e. \$35,143.44; More money is earned over a longer period of time.
47. a. b.

c. They appear to be the same.

49. a. b.

c. They appear to be the same.

51. **53.** **55.**

Section 10.6 Practice Exercises, pp. 730–732

1. a.

b. Domain: $(-\infty, \infty)$; range: $(0, \infty)$

3. a.

b. $x = 0$
c. Domain: $(0, \infty)$; range: $(-\infty, \infty)$

5. $\log_b[(x - 1)(x + 2)]$ **7.** $\log_b\left(\dfrac{x}{1 - x}\right)$ **9.** $x = 5$; domain: $(5, \infty)$

11. $x = -2$; domain: $(-2, \infty)$ **13.** $x = -\dfrac{1}{2}$; domain: $\left(-\dfrac{1}{2}, \infty\right)$

15. $x = 4$ **17.** $x = -6$ **19.** $x = \dfrac{1}{2}$ **21.** $x = 2$ **23.** $x = \dfrac{11}{12}$

25. $a = \dfrac{\ln 21}{\ln 8} \approx 1.464$ **27.** $x = \ln 8.1254 \approx 2.095$

29. $t = \log 0.0138 \approx -1.860$ **31.** $h = \dfrac{\ln 15}{0.07} \approx 38.686$

33. $m = \dfrac{\ln 4}{0.04} \approx 34.657$ **35.** $x = \dfrac{\ln 3}{\ln 5 - \ln 3} \approx 2.151$ **37.** 9.9 years

39. a. 7.8 g **b.** 18.5 days **41.** 38.4 years **43.** $x = 9$ **45.** $p = 10^{42}$
47. $x = e^{0.08} \approx 1.083$ **49.** $x = 5$ **51.** $b = 10$ **53.** $y = 25$

55. $c = 59$ **57.** $y = 1$ **59.** $k = \dfrac{3}{2}$ **61.** $x = 4$ **63.** $t = 2$ **65.** No

solution **67.** $x = 16, x = 256$ **69. a.** 1.42 kg **b.** No
71. a. i. \$660,348 **ii.** \$730,555 **iii.** \$772,840

b.
As the amount of money used for advertising increases, the amount in sales increases but at a slower rate.

c. $x \approx 251$ or \$251,000 for advertising

73.   **75.**

Review Exercises, pp. 738–741

1. Yes **3.** No **5.** $\{(5, 3), (9, 2), (-1, 0), (1, 4)\}$

7. $p^{-1}(x) = -\dfrac{1}{4}x + \dfrac{3}{4}$ **9.** $g^{-1}(x) = (x - 3)^5$

11. $m^{-1}(x) = \dfrac{-2x - 2}{x - 1}$

13. $(f \circ g)(x) = 5\left(\dfrac{1}{5}x + \dfrac{2}{5}\right) - 2 = x + 2 - 2 = x$

$(g \circ f)(x) = \dfrac{1}{5}(5x - 2) + \dfrac{2}{5} = x - \dfrac{2}{5} + \dfrac{2}{5} = x$

15. a. Domain: $\{x \mid x \geq -1\}$; range: $\{y \mid y \geq 0\}$
b. Domain: $\{x \mid x \geq 0\}$; range: $\{y \mid y \geq -1\}$ **17.** 1024 **19.** 2
21. 8.825 **23.** 1.627

25.   **27.**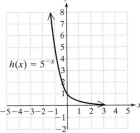

29. a. Horizontal **b.** $y = 0$ **31.** -3 **33.** 1 **35.** 4 **37.** 5
39.

41. a. Vertical asymptote **b.** $x = 0$ **43.** 1 **45.** 0

47. a. $\log_b x + \log_b y$ **b.** $\log_b\left(\dfrac{x}{y}\right)$ **c.** $p \log_b x$ **49.** 1.386 **51.** 3.218

53. 3.401 **55.** 2.119 **57.** 8.316 **59.** $\log_3\left(\dfrac{\sqrt{ab}}{c^2d^4}\right)$ **61.** 0

63. 14.0940 **65.** 57.2795 **67.** -2.1972 **69.** -4.1227 **71.** -2.2366
73. 1.3029 **75.** 1.9943 **77.** -4.1918 **79.** -3.6668
81. a. $S(0) = 95$; the student's score is 95 at the end of the course.
b. $S(6) \approx 23.7$; the student's score is 23.7 after 6 months.
c. $S(12) \approx 20.2$; the student's score is 20.2 after 1 year. **d.** The limiting value is 20. **83.** $(-\infty, \infty)$ **85.** $(-\infty, \infty)$ **87.** $(-5, \infty)$

89. $\left(\dfrac{4}{3}, \infty\right)$ **91.** $x = 125$ **93.** $y = 216$ **95.** $w = \dfrac{1001}{2} = 500.5$

97. $p = 5$ **99.** $x = -1$ **101.** $a = \dfrac{\ln 21}{\ln 4} \approx 2.1962$

103. $x = -\ln 0.1 \approx 2.3026$ **105.** $n = \dfrac{\log 1512}{2} \approx 1.5898$

107. a. 1.09 μg **b.** 0.15 μg **c.** 16.08 days

Test, pp. 742–743

1. A function is one to one if it passes the horizontal line test.
2. b **3.** $f^{-1}(x) = 4x - 12$ **4.** $g^{-1}(x) = \sqrt{x} + 1$, $x \geq 0$
5.

6. a. 4.6416 **b.** 32.2693 **c.** 687.2913
7.

8. a. $\log_{16} 8 = \dfrac{3}{4}$ **b.** $x^5 = 31$
9.

10. $\dfrac{\log_a n}{\log_a b}$ **11. a.** 1.3222 **b.** 1.8502 **c.** −2.5850 **12. a.** $1 + \log_3 x$

b. −5 **13. a.** $\log_b(\sqrt{x}\, y^3)$ **b.** $\log \dfrac{1}{a^3}$ or $-\log a^3$ **14. a.** 1.6487

b. 0.0498 **c.** −1.0986 **d.** 1 **15. a.** $y = \ln x$ **b.** $y = e^x$
16. a. $p(4) \approx 59.8$; 59.8% of the material is retained after 4 months.
b. $p(12) \approx 40.7$; 40.7% of the material is retained after 1 year.
c. $p(0) = 92$; 92% of the material is retained at the end of the course.
17. a. $P(0) = 300$; there are 300 bacteria initially. **b.** 35,588 bacteria
c. 1,120,537 bacteria **d.** 1,495,831 bacteria **e.** The limiting amount
appears to be 1,500,000 **18.** $x = 25$ **19.** $x = 32$ **20.** $x = 4.023$
21. $x = -7$ **22.** $x = 2.822$ **23.** $x = 2.301$
24. a. $P(2500) = 560.2$; At 2500 m the atmospheric pressure is
560.2 mm Hg. **b.** 760 mm Hg **c.** 1498.8 m **25. a.** $2909.98 **b.** 9.24
years to double

Cumulative Review Exercises, Chapters 1–10, pp. 743–746

1. $-\dfrac{5}{4}$ **2.** $-1 + \dfrac{p}{2} + \dfrac{3p^3}{4}$ **3.** Quotient: $t^3 + 2t^2 - 9t - 18$; remain-

der: 0; $(t - 2)$ is a factor of $t^4 - 13t^2 + 36$. **4.** $|x - 3|$ **5.** $\dfrac{2\sqrt[3]{25}}{5}$

6. $2\sqrt{7}$ in. **7.** $\dfrac{4d^{1/10}}{c}$ **8.** $(\sqrt{15} - \sqrt{6} + \sqrt{30} - 2\sqrt{3})$ m²

9. $-\dfrac{7}{29} - \dfrac{26}{29}i$ **10.** 42°, 48° **11.** $m = \dfrac{2}{3}$ **12.** $x = 6, x = \dfrac{3}{2}$

13. 4.8 L **14.** 24 min **15.** $(7, -1)$ **16.** $w = -\dfrac{23}{11}$ **17.** $x = \dfrac{c + d}{a - b}$

18. $t = \dfrac{\sqrt{2sg}}{g}$ **19.** $T = \dfrac{1 - \left(\dfrac{V_0}{V}\right)^2}{k}$ or $\dfrac{V^2 - V_0^2}{kV^2}$

20. $(7, 0), (3, 0)$ **21. a.** $-30t$ **b.** $-10t^2$ **c.** $2t^2 + 5t$ **22.** $q = 0$
23. a. $x = 2$ **b.** $y = 6$ **c.** $y = \dfrac{1}{2}x + 5$

24. a.

b. $y = 82{,}500x + 1{,}148{,}000$
c. $m = 82{,}500$; There is
an increase of 82,500
inmates per year.
d. 1,973,000 inmates

25. 40°, 80°, 60° **26.** $\{(x, y)\,|\,-2x + y = -4\}$ **27. a.** vi **b.** i **c.** v
d. x **e.** ii **f.** ix **g.** iv **h.** viii **i.** vii **j.** iii **28. a.** $\begin{bmatrix} 1 & 10 \\ 9 & 0 \end{bmatrix}$

b. $\begin{bmatrix} -6 & 30 \\ -15 & 59 \end{bmatrix}$ **29.** $f^{-1}(x) = \dfrac{1}{5}x + \dfrac{2}{15}$ **30.** 40 m³

31. $\dfrac{-x^2 + 5x - 25}{(2x + 1)(x - 2)}$ **32.** $1 + x$ **33. a.** Yes; $x \neq 4, x \neq -2$

b. $x = 8$ **c.** $(-\infty, -2) \cup (4, 8]$ **34.** The numbers are $-\dfrac{3}{4}, 4$

35. $x = -4$ **36.** $(-\infty, \infty)$
37. a. $P(6) = 2{,}000{,}000$, $P(12) = 1{,}000{,}000$, $P(18) = 500{,}000$,
$P(24) = 250{,}000$, $P(30) = 125{,}000$

b.

c. 48 h

38. a. 2 **b.** −3 **c.** 6 **d.** 3 **39. a.** 217.0723 **b.** 23.1407 **c.** 0.1768

d. 3.7293 **e.** −0.4005 **f.** 2.6047 **40.** $x = \dfrac{2}{3}$ **41.** $x = 4.6052$

42. $x = 3$ **43.** $\log\left(\dfrac{\sqrt{z}}{x^2 y^3}\right)$ **44.** $\dfrac{2}{3}\ln x - \dfrac{1}{3}\ln y$

CHAPTER 11

Section 11.1 Practice Exercises, pp. 755–757

1. The value of k shifts the graph of $y = x^2$ vertically.

3.

$f(x) = x^2 + 2$

5.
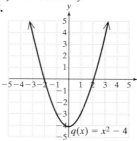
$q(x) = x^2 - 4$

7.
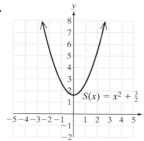
$S(x) = x^2 + \frac{3}{2}$

9.

$n(x) = x^2 - \frac{1}{3}$

11.
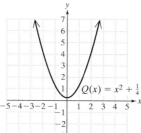
$Q(x) = x^2 + \frac{1}{4}$

13.
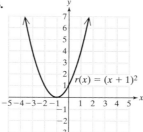
$r(x) = (x + 1)^2$

15.
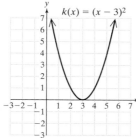
$k(x) = (x - 3)^2$

17.
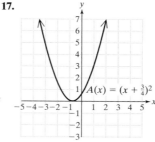
$A(x) = (x + \frac{3}{4})^2$

19.
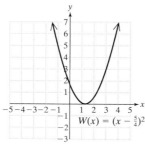
$W(x) = (x - \frac{5}{4})^2$

21.
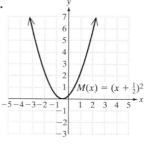
$M(x) = (x + \frac{1}{2})^2$

23. The value of a vertically stretches or shrinks the graph of $y = x^2$.
25. d **27.** g **29.** a **31.** b

33.
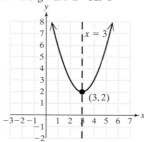
$x = 3$ $(3, 2)$

35.

$x = -1$ $(-1, -3)$

37.
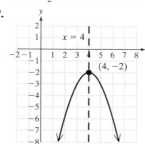
$x = 4$ $(4, -2)$

39.
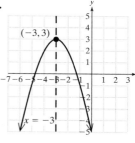
$(-3, 3)$ $x = -3$

41.

$(-1, 1)$ $x = -1$

43. Vertex $(6, -9)$; minimum point; minimum value: -9 **45.** Vertex $(2, 5)$; maximum point; maximum value: 5 **47.** Vertex $(-8, -3)$; minimum point; minimum value: -3 **49.** Vertex $\left(-\frac{3}{4}, \frac{21}{4}\right)$; maximum point; maximum value: $\frac{21}{4}$ **51.** Vertex $\left(7, -\frac{3}{2}\right)$; minimum point; minimum value: $-\frac{3}{2}$ **53.** True **55.** False **57. a.** $(60, 30)$ **b.** 30 ft **c.** 70 ft

59.

Minimum X=6.000001B Y=-9

61.

Maximum X=1.9999988 Y=5

63.

Minimum X=-8.000001 Y=-3

65.
Maximum X=-.7500016 Y=5.25

Section 11.2 Practice Exercises, pp. 766–768

1. $f(x)$ is like the graph of $y = x^2$ but opening downward and stretched vertically by a factor of 2. **3.** $Q(x)$ is the graph of $y = x^2$ shifted down $\frac{8}{3}$ units. **5.** $s(x)$ is the graph of $y = x^2$ shifted to the right 4 units. **7.** 16 **9.** $\frac{49}{4}$ **11.** $\frac{1}{81}$ **13.** $\frac{1}{36}$

15. $g(x) = (x - 4)^2 - 11; (4, -11)$ **17.** $n(x) = 2(x + 3)^2 - 5; (-3, -5)$
19. $p(x) = -3(x - 1)^2 - 2; (1, -2)$
21. $k(x) = \left(x + \frac{7}{2}\right)^2 - \frac{89}{4}; \left(-\frac{7}{2}, -\frac{89}{4}\right)$
23. $f(x) = (x + 4)^2 - 15; (-4, -15)$ **25.** $(2, 3)$ **27.** $(-1, -2)$
29. $(-4, -15)$ **31.** $(-1, 2)$ **33.** $(1, 3)$ **35. a.** $\left(-\frac{9}{2}, -\frac{49}{4}\right)$ **b.** $(0, 8)$
c. $(-8, 0)(-1, 0)$ **d.**

37. a. $\left(\frac{1}{2}, \frac{7}{2}\right)$ **b.** $(0, 4)$ **c.** no x-intercepts
d.

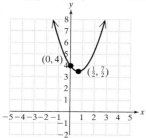

39. a. $\left(\frac{3}{2}, 0\right)$ **b.** $\left(0, -\frac{9}{4}\right)$ **c.** $\left(\frac{3}{2}, 0\right)$ **d.**

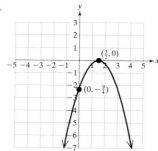

41. a. 18.9 thousand miles (18,900) **b.** 32.7 psi
43. a. \$450 **b.** \$800 **c.** 50 books or 550 books **d.** $(300, 1250)$
e.

f. 300 books produced will yield a maximum profit of \$1250.
45. a. The sum of the three sides must equal the total amount of
fencing. **b.** $A = x(200 - 2x)$ **c.** 50 ft by 100 ft
47. **49.** **51.**

Section 11.3 Practice Exercises, pp. 776–778

1. For a parabola whose equation is written in the form
$y = a(x - h)^2 + k$, if $a > 0$ the parabola opens upward, if $a < 0$ the
parabola opens downward. For a parabola written in the form
$x = a(y - k)^2 + h$, if $a > 0$ the parabola opens right, if $a < 0$ the
parabola opens left. **3.** Vertical axis of symmetry; opens upward
5. Vertical axis of symmetry; opens downward **7.** Horizontal axis of
symmetry; opens right **9.** Horizontal axis of symmetry; opens left
11. Vertical axis of symmetry; opens downward **13.** The focus is
$(h, k + p)$, where $p = \frac{1}{4a}$. **15.** The directrix is the line $x = h - p$,
where $p = \frac{1}{4a}$. **17.** True **19.** False **21.** True
23. **25.**

27. **29.**

31. **33.**

35.

37. 4 **39.** 1 **41.** $\frac{1}{4}$ **43.** $\frac{25}{4}$ **45.** $y = (x - 2)^2 - 1$; vertex $(2, -1)$;
focus $\left(2, -\frac{3}{4}\right)$; directrix $y = -\frac{5}{4}$ **47.** $x = (y + 1)^2 + 5$; vertex $(5, -1)$;
focus $\left(\frac{21}{4}, -1\right)$; directrix $x = \frac{19}{4}$ **49.** $y = -2(x - 2)^2 + 8$; vertex $(2, 8)$;
focus $\left(2, \frac{63}{8}\right)$; directrix $y = \frac{65}{8}$ **51.** $y = \left(x - \frac{3}{2}\right)^2 - \frac{1}{4}$; vertex $\left(\frac{3}{2}, -\frac{1}{4}\right)$; focus $\left(\frac{3}{2}, 0\right)$; directrix $y = -\frac{1}{2}$ **53.** $x = -2(y - 4)^2 + 33$; vertex $(33, 4)$;

focus $(\frac{263}{8}, 4)$; directrix $x = \frac{265}{8}$ **55.** Focus $(0, \frac{25}{2})$ **57.** Opens downward   **59.** Opens right   **61.** Opens downward   **63.** Opens left   **65.** Opens right   **67.** Opens upward

Midchapter Review, p. 778

1. Yes, if the x-intercept is the vertex.   **2.** No, because it would not be a function.   **3.** Completing the square and the vertex formula.
4. Find the real solutions to the equation $f(x) = 0$.   **5.** Evaluate $f(0)$.
6. The maximum or minimum value is the y-coordinate of the vertex.   **7. a.** Up **b.** $(\frac{5}{6}, \frac{23}{12})$ **c.** Minimum point **d.** Minimum value $\frac{23}{12}$
e. $x = \frac{5}{6}$ **f.** No x-intercept **g.** $(0, 4)$ **8. a.** Up **b.** $(0.9, -14.4)$
c. Minimum point **d.** Minimum value -14.4 **e.** $x = 0.9$
f. $(2.1, 0)(-0.3, 0)$ **g.** $(0, -6.3)$ **9. a.** Down **b.** $(-\frac{1}{4}, -\frac{1}{2})$
c. Maximum point **d.** Maximum value $-\frac{1}{2}$ **e.** $x = -\frac{1}{4}$ **f.** No
x-intercept **g.** $(0, -\frac{9}{16})$ **10.** Vertex: $(2, 3)$; focus $(\frac{7}{4}, 3)$; directrix $x = \frac{9}{4}$
11. Vertex: $(-1, -2)$; focus $(-\frac{3}{4}, -2)$; directrix $x = -\frac{5}{4}$ **12.** Vertex:
$(5, 0)$; focus $(5, \frac{1}{8})$; directrix $y = -\frac{1}{8}$

Section 11.4 Practice Exercises, pp. 784–786

1.

3.

5.

7.

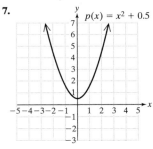

9. $\sqrt{281}$ **11.** $3\sqrt{2}$ **13.** $\dfrac{\sqrt{226}}{10}$ **15.** 19   **17.** 10   **19.** $\sqrt{255}$

21. Subtract 5 and -7: $5 - (-7) = 12$.   **23.** $y = 13$ or $y = 1$
25. $x = 0$ or $x = 8$ **27.** Yes   **29.** No
31. Center $(4, -2)$; $r = 3$;

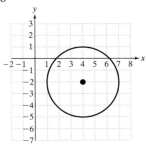

33. Center $(-1, -1)$; $r = 1$;

35. Center $(0, 5)$; $r = 5$;

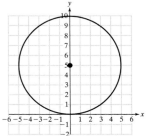

37. Center $(3, 0)$; $r = 2\sqrt{2}$;

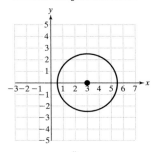

39. Center $(0, 0)$; $r = \sqrt{6}$;

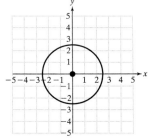

41. Center $\left(-\dfrac{4}{5}, 0\right)$; $r = \dfrac{8}{5}$;

43. Center $(1, 3)$; $r = 6$;

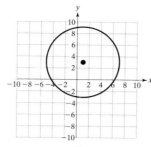

45. Center $(0, -3)$; $r = \dfrac{4}{3}$;

47. $x^2 + y^2 = 4$ **49.** $x^2 + (y - 2)^2 = 4$ **51.** $(x + 2)^2 + (y - 2)^2 = 9$
53. $x^2 + y^2 = 49$ **55.** $(x + 3)^2 + (y + 4)^2 = 36$
57. $(x - 4)^2 + (y - 4)^2 = 16$

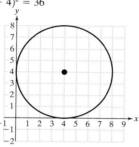

59. $(x - 1)^2 + (y - 1)^2 = 29$

61. 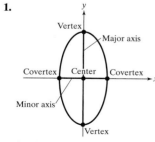 **63.** **65.**

Section 11.5 Practice Exercises, pp. 795–798

1.

3. $(0, 0)$; vertical **5.** $(2, 5)$; horizontal **7.** $(-2, -4)$; vertical
9. $(-4, 1)$; horizontal

11.

13.

15.

17.

19.

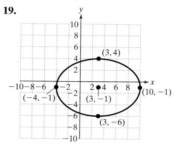

21. The length of the string is constant and the two tacks are fixed points. The sum of the distances from each tack to a point on the curve is constant, therefore an elliptical curve is traced. **23.** 97 ft

25.

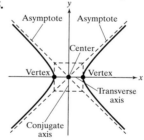

27. $(0, 0)$; horizontal **29.** $(0, 0)$; vertical **31.** $(-1, -8)$; horizontal
33. $(-1, -4)$; vertical

35.

37.

39.

41.

43.

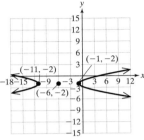

45. $y = x, y = -x$ **47.** $y = \frac{1}{2}x - 5, y = -\frac{1}{2}x - 3$

49. An ellipse can be written in the form

$$\frac{(x-h)^2}{a^2} + \frac{(y-k)^2}{b^2} = 1 \quad \text{or} \quad \frac{(x-h)^2}{b^2} + \frac{(y-k)^2}{a^2} = 1$$

whereas a hyperbola can be written in the form

$$\frac{(x-h)^2}{a^2} - \frac{(y-k)^2}{b^2} = 1 \quad \text{or} \quad \frac{(y-k)^2}{a^2} - \frac{(x-h)^2}{b^2} = 1$$

51. Ellipse   **53.** Hyperbola   **55.** Ellipse   **57.** Hyperbola
59. $(0, 4), (0, -4)$ **61.** $(8, 0), (-8, 0)$ **63.** $(5, 0), (-5, 0)$
65. $(0, 13), (0, -13)$
67.

69.

Section 11.6 Practice Exercises, pp. 803–806

1. $d = \sqrt{(x_2 - x_1)^2 + (y_2 - y_1)^2}$ **3.** 4.2   **5.** $(x + 1)^2 + (y - 1)^2 = 4$
7. $(x - 8)^2 + (y + 2)^2 = 11$ **9.** Circle   **11.** Parabola
13. Hyperbola   **15.** Ellipse   **17.** g   **19.** j   **21.** e   **23.** i   **25.** f
27. Zero, one, or two   **29.** Zero, one, or two   **31.** Zero, one, two,
three, or four   **33.** Zero, one, two, three, or four   **35.** $(-3, 0)(2, 5)$
37. $(0, 1)(-1, 0)$ **39.** $(\sqrt{2}, 2)(-\sqrt{2}, 2)$ **41.** $(4, 2)$ **43.** $(0, 0)$
45. $\left(\frac{3}{2}, \frac{9}{4}\right)$ **47.** $(3, 2)(3, -2)(-3, 2)(-3, -2)$ **49.** $(0, 3)(0, -3)$
51. $(2, 1)(-2, 1)(2, -1)(-2, -1)$ **53.** $(\sqrt{2}, 0)(-\sqrt{2}, 0)$
55. $(2, 0)(-2, 0)$ **57.** 3 and 4   **59.** 5 and $\sqrt{7}$, -5 and $\sqrt{7}$,
5 and $-\sqrt{7}$, or -5 and $-\sqrt{7}$
61.

63.

65.

No solution

Review Exercises, pp. 813–816

1.

3.

5.

7.

9. $\left(4, \frac{5}{3}\right)$ is the minimum point. The minimum value is $\frac{5}{3}$.

11. $x = -\frac{2}{11}$ **13.** $z(x) = (x - 3)^2 - 2; (3, -2)$

15. $p(x) = -5(x + 1)^2 - 8; (-1, -8)$ **17.** $(1, -15)$ **19.** $\left(\frac{1}{2}, \frac{41}{4}\right)$

21. a. 1097.8 thousand tourists   **b.** 1140 thousand tourists
23. a. \$499.2 million   **b.** \$579.5 million   **25.** Vertical axis of symmetry; parabola opens downward   **27.** Horizontal axis of symmetry; parabola opens left
29. Vertex: $(0, 1)$; focus: $(2, 1)$; Directrix: $x = -2$

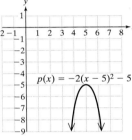

31. Vertex: $(0, 0)$; focus: $(0, -1)$; Directrix: $y = 1$

33. $y = (x - 3)^2 - 4$; vertex: $(3, -4)$; Focus: $(3, -\frac{15}{4})$; directrix: $y = -\frac{17}{4}$ **35.** $x = -4(y - \frac{1}{2})^2 + 1$; vertex: $(1, \frac{1}{2})$; Focus: $(\frac{15}{16}, \frac{1}{2})$; directrix: $x = \frac{17}{16}$ **37.** $2\sqrt{10}$ **39.** $x = 5$ or $x = -1$ **41.** Collinear
43. Center $(12, 3)$; $r = 4$ **45.** Center $(-3, -8)$; $r = 2\sqrt{5}$
47. a. $x^2 + y^2 = 64$ **b.** $(x - 8)^2 + (y - 8)^2 = 64$
49. $(x + 2)^2 + (y + 8)^2 = 8$ **51.** $(x - 3)^2 + \left(y - \dfrac{1}{3}\right)^2 = 9$
53. $x^2 + (y - 2)^2 = 9$ **55.** Center: $(0, 0)$; major axis is vertical
57. Center: $(1, 0)$; major axis is horizontal
59.

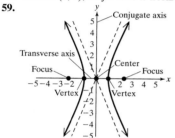

61. Center: $(0, 0)$; transverse axis is vertical. **63.** Center: $(-1, 0)$; transverse axis is horizontal.
65. Ellipse **67.** Hyperbola

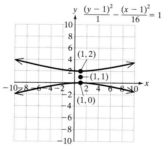

69. a. Line and parabola
c. $(-5, 15)(3, -1)$ **b.**

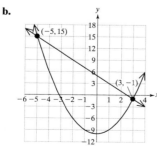

71. a. Circle and line **b.**
c. $(0, -4)\left(\dfrac{16}{5}, -\dfrac{12}{5}\right)$

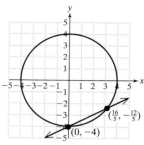

73. $\left(-\dfrac{7}{5}, \dfrac{13}{5}\right)(-5, -1)$ **75.** $(\sqrt{2}, 2)(-\sqrt{2}, 2)(2, 4)(-2, 4)$
77. $(6, 5)(-6, 5)(6, -5)(-6, -5)$

Test, pp. 817–818

1. $y = x^2 - 2$ is the graph of $y = x^2$ shifted down 2 units.
2. $y = (x + 3)^2$ is the graph of $y = x^2$ shifted 3 units to the left.
3. $y = -4x^2$ is the graph of $y = 4x^2$ opening downward instead of upward. **4. a.** $(4, 2)$ **b.** Down **c.** Maximum point **d.** 2 **e.** $x = 4$
5. a. $2(x - 5)^2 + 1$; $(5, 1)$ **b.** $(5, 1)$ **6. a.** 1.20 **b.** \$60 Canadian
c. \$83.33 U.S. **d.** 1.15 **7.** Vertex: $(3, -6)$; focus: $(\frac{11}{4}, -6)$ Directrix:
$x = \frac{13}{4}$
8. $y = (x - 2)^2 + 1$

9. $\sqrt{85}$ **10.** Yes, they form a right triangle. **11.** $\left(\dfrac{5}{6}, -\dfrac{1}{3}\right)$; $r = \dfrac{5}{7}$
12. $(0, 2)$; $r = 3$ **13. a.** $\sqrt{5}$ **b.** $x^2 + (y - 4)^2 = 5$ **14.** Center: $(3, 0)$; major axis is vertical.
15. Center: $(0, 0)$; vertices: $(0, 1)$, $(0, -1)$

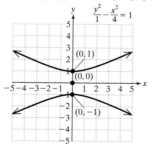

16. a. $(-3, 0)(0, 4)$; i **b.** No solution; ii **17.** Addition method can be used if the equations have corresponding *like* terms.
18. $(2, 0)(-2, 0)$

Cumulative Review Exercises, Chapters 1–11, pp. 818–819

1. All real numbers 2. $\left(\dfrac{10}{3}, \infty\right)$ ← → $\dfrac{10}{3}$ 3. 10, 15

4. a. $(-5, 0)(0, 3)$ b. $m = \dfrac{3}{5}$ c.

5. a. $m = 10$ b. $y = 10x + 30$ c. \$80 million 6. 12 dimes,
5 quarters 7. $(2, -3, 1)$ 8. a. $\begin{bmatrix} 1 & -2 & | & -8 \\ 0 & 1 & | & 2 \end{bmatrix}$ b. $\begin{bmatrix} 1 & 0 & | & -4 \\ 0 & 1 & | & 2 \end{bmatrix}$

9. $\left(\dfrac{5}{2}, \dfrac{3}{2}\right)$ 10. $f(0) = -12; f(-1) = -16; f(2) = -10; f(4) = -16$
11. $g(2) = 5; g(8) = -1; g(3) = 0; g(-5) = 5$ 12. 32 13. a. -5
b. $(x + 1)(x^2 + 1); -5$ c. They are the same. 14. a. No solution
b. $x = -11$ 15. a. $-30 + 24i$ b. $\dfrac{12}{41} + \dfrac{15}{41}i$ 16. a. 17.6 ft; 39.6 ft;

70.4 ft b. 8 s 17. $w = -\dfrac{1}{5}; w = \dfrac{1}{10} \pm \dfrac{i\sqrt{3}}{10}$ 18. $x = 2 \pm \sqrt{11}$

19. $(-1, 19)$ 20. $\log_8 32 = \dfrac{5}{3}$ 21. $(-5, -36)$
22. a. $(-3, 0)(1, 0)$
b. $(0, 3)$
c. $(-1, 4)$

23. $x^2 + (y - 5)^2 = 16$ 24. Yes, the circle can be tangent to the
parabola. 25. $(0, -4)$

CHAPTER 12

Section 12.1 Practice Exercises, pp. 827–829

1. $x = -\dfrac{3}{2}, x = 4$ 3. $x = 2i, x = -2i$ 5. $x = 0, x = -2, x = -\dfrac{5}{4}$

7. $x = -\dfrac{7}{2}, x = 6$ 9. $x = -3, x = 3$ 11. $x = 0, x = -21$

13. $P(x) = (x - 2)(x^2 - 5x + 3) + 9$
15. $P(x) = (x + 1)(2x^3 - 2x^2 + 5x - 10) + 17$
17. $P(x) = (x + 2)(x^3 - 2x^2 - 4x + 8) - 1$ 19. $f(3) = -16$
21. $k(-3) = -62$ 23. a. 11 b. -24 c. -184 d. -193 25. a. 166
b. -158 c. $\dfrac{3}{2}$ d. 11 27. Yes 29. Yes 31. Yes 33. No

35. Yes 37. Yes 39. Yes 41. Yes 43. Yes 45. No 47. Yes

49. No 51. $x^2 - 3x - 4$ 53. $x^3 - 4x^2 + 3x$ 55. $x^3 - 5x^2 + x - 5$
57. Both 59. For example: $x^2(x - 1)^3(x - 3)$ 61. 0

Section 12.2 Practice Exercises, pp. 839–841

1. -60 3. -10 5. Yes 7. No 9. Yes 11. Yes
13. $x = 3$, multiplicity of 1 15. $x = 9$, multiplicity of 4
  $x = -5$, multiplicity of 1 $x = -12$, multiplicity of 2
  $x = \dfrac{3}{2}$, multiplicity of 3

17. $x^3 - x^2 - 4x + 4$ 19. $x^3 + 6x^2 + x + 6$ 21. $x^3 - 6x^2 + 13x$
23. $F(x) = -3x^3 + 6x^2 + 60x + 72$
25. $F(x) = -x^3 + 2x^2 + 16x - 32$
27. $F(x) = 3x^3 - 3x^2 + 75x - 75$
29. $F(x) = x^4 - 2x^3 + 6x^2 - 8x + 8$
31. $\dfrac{c}{d} = \left\{\pm 1, \pm 5, \pm\dfrac{1}{2}, \pm\dfrac{5}{2}, \pm\dfrac{1}{4}, \pm\dfrac{5}{4}\right\}$
33. $\dfrac{c}{d} = \left\{\pm 1, \pm 2, \pm 4, \pm 8, \pm\dfrac{1}{2}\right\}$
35. $\dfrac{c}{d} = \left\{\pm 1, \pm 2, \pm 4, \pm\dfrac{1}{2}, \pm\dfrac{1}{3}, \pm\dfrac{2}{3}, \pm\dfrac{4}{3}, \pm\dfrac{1}{4}, \pm\dfrac{1}{6}, \pm\dfrac{1}{12}\right\}$
37. $\dfrac{c}{d} = \left\{\pm 1, \pm\dfrac{1}{2}, \pm\dfrac{1}{5}, \pm\dfrac{1}{10}\right\}$ 39. The coefficients are not integers.
41. Positive zeros: 2 or 0; Negative zeros: 1 43. Positive zeros: 1;
Negative zeros: 2 or 0 45. Positive zeros: 0; Negative zeros: 0
47. Positive zeros: 0; Negative zeros: 1 49. Positive zeros: 3 or 1;
Negative zeros: 0 51. There are no sign changes between consecutive terms in $f(x)$. 53. Upper bound 55. Lower bound 57. Upper
bound 59. Lower bound 61. $x = -1, x = 2, x = 5$ 63. $x = -2,$
$x = -\dfrac{3}{2}, x = \dfrac{1}{3}$ 65. $x = -5, x = 1, x = 2, x = 3$ 67. $x = -2,$
$x = -\dfrac{1}{2}, x = \dfrac{3}{2}, x = 2$ 69. $x = -1, x = \sqrt{7}, x = -\sqrt{7}$ 71. $x = \dfrac{1}{2},$
$x = 1 - i, x = 1 + i$ 73. $x = -2$, multiplicity of 3; $x = 3$, multi-
plicity of 2 75. $x = -3, x = 2 - 4i$ 77. $x = 3 + 2i, x = 1 + \sqrt{2},$
$x = 1 - \sqrt{2}$ 79. The polynomial $P(x) = x^n - 1$ has one sign change,
which implies that there is exactly one positive real zero. Furthermore,
because n is even, $P(-x) = x^n - 1$. Therefore, $P(-x)$ has one sign
change, which implies that there is exactly one negative real zero.
Hence, $P(x)$ has one positive and one negative real zero for a total of
two real zeros.

Midchapter Review, pp. 841–842

1. Quotient: $2x^2 + x + 2$; remainder: 12 2. Quotient:
$2x^2 - 3x - 4$; remainder: 2 3. 126 4. -600 5. Yes 6. Yes
7. Yes 8. Yes 9. Quotient: $3x^2 - 5x - 5$; remainder: -7
10. Quotient: $3x^2 - 14x + 19$; remainder: -16 11. 39 12. -672
13. Yes 14. No 15. No 16. Yes

Section 12.3 Practice Exercises, pp. 853–857

1. Zeros: $-10, 3$; x-intercepts: $(-10, 0)$, $(3, 0)$
3. Zeros: $0, -\dfrac{5}{2}, \pm i\sqrt{3}$; x-intercepts: $(0, 0)$, $\left(-\dfrac{5}{2}, 0\right)$
5. Zeros: $-7, -2$; x-intercepts: $(-7, 0)$, $(-2, 0)$
7. Zeros: $-8, 1, 8$; x-intercepts: $(-8, 0)$, $(1, 0)$, $(8, 0)$
9. Zeros: $\dfrac{7 \pm \sqrt{41}}{2}$; x-intercepts: $\left(\dfrac{7 + \sqrt{41}}{2}, 0\right)$, $\left(\dfrac{7 - \sqrt{41}}{2}, 0\right)$

11.

13.

c. $f(x) = \frac{1}{60}(x-4)(x+3)^3(x-2)^2$

15.

17.

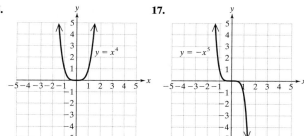

19. a **21.** b **23.** $6x^3$; down to left and up to right **25.** $-7x^4$; down to left and down to right **27.** $\frac{1}{3}x^2$; up to left and up to right **29.** $2x^3$; down to left and up to right **31.** $-3x^3$; up to left and down to right **33.** Continuous **35.** Discontinuous **37.** Discontinuous **39.** Continuous **41.** Evaluate $f(0)$.

43. a. Down to the left and down to the right **b.** x-intercepts: $(0, 0)$, $(3, 0)$ y-intercept: $(0, 0)$ **c.**

45. a. Up to the left and down to the right
b. x-intercepts: $(0, 0)$, $(1, 0)$, $(-3, 0)$ y-intercept: $(0, 0)$
c.

47. a. Up to the left and up to the right
b. x-intercepts: $(4, 0)$, $(-3, 0)$, $(2, 0)$ y-intercept: $\left(0, -\frac{36}{5}\right)$

49. a. Up to the left and up to the right
b. x-intercepts: $\left(\frac{3}{2}, 0\right)$, $\left(-\frac{10}{3}, 0\right)$ y-intercept: $(0, 6)$
c. $h(x) = \frac{1}{150}(2x-3)^2(3x+10)^2$

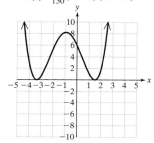

51. a. Up to the left and up to the right
b. x-intercepts: $(2, 0)$, $(-2, 0)$, $(-1, 0)$, $(1, 0)$ y-intercept: $(0, 4)$
c.

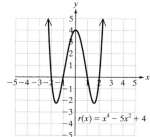

53. a. Up to the left and down to the right
b. x-intercepts: $(0, 0)$, $(1, 0)$, $\left(-\frac{3}{2}, 0\right)$ y-intercept: $(0, 0)$
c.

55. a. Up to the left and up to the right **b.** x-intercepts:
$\left(\frac{1}{2}, 0\right), \left(-\frac{1}{2}, 0\right), (\sqrt{2}, 0), (-\sqrt{2}, 0)$ y-intercept: $(0, 2)$
c.

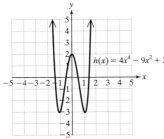

$h(x) = 4x^4 - 9x^2 + 2$

57. a. Down to the left and up to the right
b. x-intercepts: $(-4, 0), (-1, 0), (2, 0)$ y-intercept: $(0, -8)$
c. $P(x) = x^3 + 3x^2 - 6x - 8$

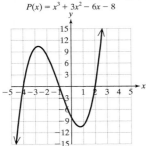

59. a. Down to the left and down to the right
b. x-intercepts: $\left(-\frac{3}{2}, 0\right)$ y-intercept: $(0, -9)$
c.

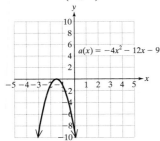

$a(x) = -4x^2 - 12x - 9$

61. True **63.** False **65.** b **67.** a, c **69.** a **71. a.** The zeros represent the number of months after January 1 that the average temperature is 0°C. **b.** The turning points represent the number of months after the first of the year that the trend in temperature changes from either decreasing to increasing or from increasing to decreasing. **73. a.** The zeros represent the number of units produced that will result in a profit of $0. **b.** The turning point represents the point at which the profit changes from increasing to decreasing.
75.

$g(x) = (x - 2)^4$

$f(x) = (x - 2)^2$

77.

$g(x) = -(x + 3)^5 + 1$

$f(x) = -(x + 3)^2 + 1$

79. a. $f(-2) = -1$ and $f(-1) = 1.875$. Therefore, f has a zero on $[-2, -1]$. **b.** $x \approx -1.6954$ **81. a.** $h(1) = -2$ and $h(2) = 4$. Therefore, h has a zero on $[1, 2]$. $h(2) = 4$ and $h(3) = -4$. Therefore, h has a zero on $[2, 3]$. **b.** $x \approx 1.3409$ and $x \approx 2.8220$ **83.** $[-1, 0], [2, 3]$
85. $[-5, -4], [-2, -1], [0, 1]$

Section 12.4 Practice Exercises, pp. 867–870

1. x-intercepts: $(-3, 0), (\sqrt{2}, 0), (-\sqrt{2}, 0)$; y-intercept: $(0, -6)$
3. x-intercepts: $(-1, 0), \left(\frac{1}{3}, 0\right)$; y-intercept: $(0, -2)$
5. x-intercepts: none; y-intercept: $(0, 10)$
7. x-intercept: $(3, 0)$; y-intercept: $(0, -2)$
9. x-intercept: $(0, 0)$; y-intercept: $(0, 0)$
11. x-intercepts: none; y-intercept: $\left(0, -\frac{1}{7}\right)$
13. $g(x)$ approaches 0 as x approaches infinity. Horizontal asymptote
15. $h(x)$ approaches infinity as x approaches 3 from the right. Vertical asymptote **17.** $y = 1$; c **19.** $y = -2$; b **21.** $y = 3x$; b
23. $y = -x + 1$; a **25.** Horizontal asymptote: $y = 0$ **27.** Horizontal asymptote: $y = -3$ **29.** Horizontal asymptote: $y = -\frac{1}{2}$
31. Slant asymptote: $y = x$ **33.** Horizontal asymptote: $y = \frac{3}{4}$
35. $x = -1$; c **37.** $x = 2$; $x = -2$; d **39.** $x = -4$ **41.** $x = 1$, $x = -5$ **43.** $x = 2$ **45.** No vertical asymptote **47.** $x = 3$
49. 1. Find any vertical asymptotes. 2. Find any horizontal or slant asymptotes. 3. Find any x-intercepts. 4. Find the y-intercept. 5. Determine if the function intersects its horizontal asymptote, $y = a$, by solving the equation $f(x) = a$. 6. Sketch the features found in steps 1–5. Draw the asymptotes as dashed lines. 7. Evaluate the function at test points to the left and right of the vertical asymptotes, x-intercepts, and points where the function intersects the horizontal asymptote. 8. Complete the sketch.
51.   **53.**

$f(x) = \frac{1}{x + 2}$

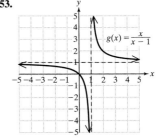

$g(x) = \frac{x}{x - 1}$

55.

$p(x) = \frac{3}{x}$

57.

$b(x) = \frac{2}{x^2 - 9}$

59.

$m(x) = \frac{x + 3}{2x - 2}$

61.

$f(x) = \frac{x^3 - 1}{x^2}$

63.

$k(x) = \frac{x^2 - 2x - 3}{x^2 - 2x + 1}$

65.

$P(x) = \frac{-1}{x^2 + x - 6}$

67.

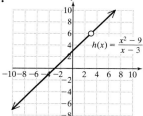

$h(x) = \frac{x^2 - 9}{x - 3}$

69.

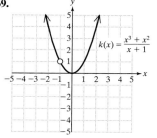

$k(x) = \frac{x^3 + x^2}{x + 1}$

Review Exercises, pp. 876–879

1. $x = 9, x = -2$ **3.** $x = 7, x = -5$ **5.** $x = 4 + i, x = 4 - i$
7. If the polynomial $P(x)$ is divided by $(x - c)$, then the remainder is $P(c)$.   **9. a.** 126   **b.** 96   **c.** 0   **d.** -42 **11.** Synthetic division and the remainder theorem can be used to evaluate $P(c)$. Furthermore, if $P(c) = 0$, then c is a zero of $P(x)$.   **13.** Yes   **15.** No   **17.** Yes
19. No   **21.** $x^2 - 12x + 27$ **23.** $x^3 + 25x$
25. $x = 8$, multiplicity of 3; $x = -\frac{5}{2}$, multiplicity of 2
27. $F(x) = -6x^3 - 24x^2 + 18x + 108$
29. $F(x) = -\frac{16}{3}x^3 + 16x^2 - \frac{16}{3}x + 16$ **31.** First list the possible rational zeros of the function. Then use synthetic division to test each

value to determine whether the value is a zero of the function. If a rational zero is found, repeat the process to find a rational zero of the quotient. Continue this process until all zeros are found or until all potential rational zeros have been tested.

33. $\frac{c}{d} = \left\{ \pm 1, \pm 5, \pm\frac{1}{3}, \pm\frac{5}{3}, \pm\frac{1}{5}, \pm\frac{1}{15} \right\}$ **35.** Positive zeros: 3 or 1
Negative zeros: 2 or 0   **37.** Upper bound   **39.** Lower bound
41. Cannot be determined   **43.** $x = -2, x = -\frac{3}{2}, x = \frac{1}{3}$
45. $x = -2$, multiplicity of 2; $x = 3$, multiplicity of 2   **47.** $x = 2$, multiplicity of 2, $x = -2 + \sqrt{3}, x = -2 - \sqrt{3}$ **49.** Down to left, up to right   **51.** Down to left, down to right   **53.** Up to left, up to right
55. Up to left, down to right   **57.** Discontinuous   **59.** Continuous
61. Down to the left and up to the right
x-intercepts: $(-3, 0), (0, 0), (2, 0)$
y-intercept: $(0, 0)$

$k(x) = \frac{1}{2} x(x + 3)(x - 2)$

63. Up to the left and up to the right
x-intercepts: none
y-intercept: $(0, 2)$

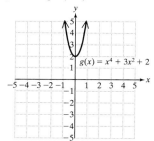

$g(x) = x^4 + 3x^2 + 2$

65. Down to the left and up to the right
x-intercepts: $(-4, 0), (-1, 0)$
y-intercept: $(0, 16)$

$p(x) = x^3 + 9x^2 + 24x + 16$

67. $f(0) = 8, f(1) = -10$. Therefore, f has at least one zero on $[0, 1]$.
69. $q(2) = -16, q(3) = 1$. Therefore, q has at least one zero on $[2, 3]$.

71. a. The zeros represent the number of months after January 1 that the average temperature is 0°C. **b.** The turning points represent the number of months after the first of the year that the trend in temperature changes from either decreasing to increasing or from increasing to decreasing. **73.** $y = 0$ **75.** $y = \dfrac{1}{2}$ **77.** $y = -1$

79. The function will have a horizontal asymptote if the degree of the numerator is less than or equal to the degree of the denominator. The function will have a slant asymptote if the degree of the numerator is 1 greater than the degree of the denominator. **81.** $y = x$
83. $y = 2x + 13$ **85.** $x = 4, x = -4$ **87.** $x = -3$ **89.** $x = 1$
91.

93.

95.

Test, p. 880

1. $x = 0, x = -6, x = 3$ **2.** $P(x) = (x - 2)(x^2 + 4x - 5) + 4$
3. a. -4 **b.** 80 **c.** 80 **4.** Yes **5.** If $P(c) = 0$, then c is a zero of $P(x)$ and $(x - c)$ is a factor of $P(x)$. **6.** Yes **7.** True **8.** False
9. $x = 0$, multiplicity of 3; $x = -1$, multiplicity of 1; $x = 9$, multiplicity of 3 **10.** $p(x) = x^4 + 4x^3 - 12x^2 - 32x + 64$

11. a. $\dfrac{c}{d} = \left\{ \pm 1, \pm 2, \pm 3, \pm 6, \pm 9, \pm 18, \pm \dfrac{1}{2}, \pm \dfrac{3}{2}, \pm \dfrac{9}{2}, \pm \dfrac{1}{3}, \pm \dfrac{2}{3}, \pm \dfrac{1}{6} \right\}$

b. Positive zeros: 2 or 0; Negative zeros: 2 or 0 **c.** $x = -2$, multiplicity of 1; $x = -\dfrac{1}{6}$, multiplicity of 1; $x = 3$, multiplicity of 2 **12. a.** $3x^6$

b. Up to left, up to right
13. a.

b.

14. a. Up to left, down to right **b.** x-intercepts: $\left(-\dfrac{1}{2}, 0 \right)$, $(1, 0)$, $(3, 0)$
y-intercept: $(0, -3)$ **c.**

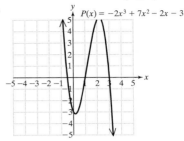

15. $g(-1) = -5, g(2) = 70$. Therefore, g has one at least zero on $[-1, 2]$. **16. a.** Vertical asymptote: $x = 1$; Horizontal asymptote: $y = 2$ **b.** x-intercept: $(0, 0)$; y-intercept: $(0, 0)$ **c.** At the point $\left(\dfrac{1}{2}, 2 \right)$
d.

Cumulative Review Exercises, Chapters 1–12, pp. 880–881

1. -7 **2.** $\dfrac{3}{10}x - 13$ **3.** $t = 6$ **4. a.** True **b.** False **c.** True

5. a. Not possible **b.** Not possible **c.** $\begin{bmatrix} -62 & 9 \\ -5 & 66 \\ 3 & 6 \end{bmatrix}$ **6.** $(-3, 2)$

7. $p(0) = 5, p(2) = 3, p(3) = 2, p(-3) = 8$ **8. a.** $x^2 - 10x + 25$
b. $x^2 - 25$ **c.** $x^3 - 15x^2 + 75x - 125$ **9.** 7.5×10^8 **10.** 9
11. $-xy^2 \sqrt[3]{3x^2y}$ **12.** The length of a side is $(2 + 2\sqrt{2})$ ft.
13. Vertex: $(-3, -7)$ **14.**
Opens upward

15. $(0, -1), \left(\dfrac{\sqrt{17}}{3}, \dfrac{8}{9} \right), \left(-\dfrac{\sqrt{17}}{3}, \dfrac{8}{9} \right)$ **16.** $x = 0, x = \dfrac{7}{5}$ **17.** $\dfrac{13}{6x}$

18. $(-1, 4)$ **19.** $2^y = x$ **20.** $\ln \left(\dfrac{x^2 - 4}{x^3} \right)$ **21.** True **22.** $x = -2$,
$x = 2, x = 4$ **23.** Vertical asymptotes: $x = -2$ and $x = 1$
Horizontal asymptote: $y = 1$

CHAPTER 13

Section 13.1 Practice Exercises, pp. 891–893

1. 4, 7, 10, 13   **3.** $\sqrt{3}, 2, \sqrt{5}, \sqrt{6}$ **5.** $3, \frac{3}{2}, 1, \frac{3}{4}, \frac{3}{5}$

7. $-\frac{2}{3}, \frac{3}{4}, -\frac{4}{5}, \frac{5}{6}$ **9.** $0, -3, 8, -15$ **11.** $\frac{5}{2}, \frac{8}{3}, \frac{11}{4}, \frac{14}{5}$ **13.** 0, 2, 6, 12

15. $-3, 9, -27, 81$ **17.** When n is odd, the term is negative. When n is even, the term is positive.   **19.** \$60, \$58.80, \$57.62, \$56.47, \$55.34, \$54.24   **21.** 25,000; 50,000; 100,000; 200,000; 400,000; 800,000; 1,600,000   **23.** $a_n = 2n$ **25.** $a_n = 2n - 1$ **27.** $a_n = \dfrac{1}{n^2}$

29. $a_n = (-1)^{n+1}$ **31.** $a_n = (-1)^n 2^n$ **33.** $a_n = \dfrac{3}{5^n}$ **35.** A sequence is an ordered list of terms. A series is the sum of the terms of a sequence.   **37.** 90   **39.** $\dfrac{31}{16}$ **41.** 30   **43.** 10   **45.** $\dfrac{73}{12}$ **47.** 38

49. -1 **51.** 55   **53.** $\displaystyle\sum_{n=1}^{6} n$ **55.** $\displaystyle\sum_{i=1}^{5} 4$ **57.** $\displaystyle\sum_{j=1}^{5} 4j$

59. $\displaystyle\sum_{k=1}^{4} (-1)^{k+1}\frac{1}{3^k}$ **61.** $\displaystyle\sum_{n=1}^{5} x^n$

63. $1 + 1\frac{1}{2} + 1\frac{1}{2} + 1\frac{1}{2} + 1\frac{1}{2} + 1\frac{1}{2} + 1\frac{1}{2} + 1\frac{1}{2}; 1 + \displaystyle\sum_{i=1}^{7} 1\frac{1}{2}; 11\frac{1}{2}$ in.

65. 15.4 g   **67.** 4.8 g   **69.** $-3, 2, 7, 12, 17$ **71.** 5, 21, 85, 341, 1365   **73.** 1, 1, 2, 3, 5, 8, 13, 21, 34, 55

75.

77.

79.   **81.**

Section 13.2 Practice Exercises, pp. 903–907

1. A sequence is arithmetic if the difference between any term and the preceding term is constant.   **3.** 6   **5.** -5 **7.** 4

9. $-3, -1, 1, 3, 5$ **11.** $0, \frac{1}{3}, \frac{2}{3}, 1, \frac{4}{3}$ **13.** $10, 4, -2, -8, -14$

15. $a_n = 2 + 5n$ **17.** $a_n = 5 - 4n$ **19.** $a_n = \frac{2}{3} + \frac{1}{3}n$

21. $a_n = 12 - 3n$ **23.** $a_n = -17 + 8n$ **25.** 17   **27.** 47   **29.** 46   **31.** -48 **33.** 19   **35.** 22   **37.** 23   **39.** 11   **41.** $a_1 = -2, a_2 = -5$ **43.** 670   **45.** 290   **47.** -15 **49.** 95   **51.** 924   **53.** 300   **55.** -210 **57.** 5050   **59.** 2500   **61.** 980 seats; \$14,700   **63.** A sequence is geometric if the ratio between a term and the preceding term is constant.

65. $\dfrac{1}{2}$ **67.** -3 **69.** 4   **71.** $-4, 4, -4, 4, -4$ **73.** $8, 2, \frac{1}{2}, \frac{1}{8}, \frac{1}{32}$

75. $2, -6, 18, -54, 162$ **77.** $a_n = 2(3)^{n-1}$ **79.** $a_n = -6(-2)^{n-1}$

81. $a_n = \dfrac{16}{3}\left(\dfrac{3}{4}\right)^{n-1}$ **83.** $-\dfrac{3}{128}$ **85.** $-\dfrac{2}{81}$ **87.** 135   **89.** -10 **91.** $\dfrac{1}{9}$

93. 1   **95.** $\dfrac{1562}{125}$ **97.** $-\dfrac{11}{8}$ **99.** $\dfrac{3124}{27}$ **101.** $\dfrac{2059}{729}$ **103.** -172

105. a. \$1050.00, \$1102.50, \$1157.63, \$1215.51   **b.** $a_{10} = \$1628.89$; $a_{20} = \$2653.30$; $a_{40} = \$7039.99$ **107.** $r = \dfrac{1}{6}; \dfrac{6}{5}$ **109.** $r = -\dfrac{1}{3}; -\dfrac{9}{4}$

111. $r = -\dfrac{3}{2}$; sum does not exist   **113.** \$800 million   **115.** 28 ft

117. a. $\dfrac{7}{10}$ **b.** $\dfrac{1}{10}$ **c.** $\dfrac{7}{9}$ **119.** c   **121.** a   **123.** Geometric, $r = -\dfrac{3}{2}$

125. Arithmetic, $d = \dfrac{2}{3}$ **127.** Geometric, $r = 3$ **129.** Arithmetic, $d = 4$ **131.** Neither   **133.** Neither   **135.** Geometric, $r = -1$ **137. a.** \$1,191,123   **b.** \$1,254,857   **c.** \$63,734

139.

seq(125000*1.04^
n,n,1,4,1)
(130000 135200 …

141.

sum(seq(n,n,1,15
,1))
120

143. 8;

sum(seq(4*(1/2)^
(n-1),n,1,10,1)
7.9921875
sum(seq(4*(1/2)^
(n-1),n,1,20,1)
7.999992371

Midchapter Review, p. 908

1. a. Geometric   **b.** $a_n = \dfrac{3}{4}\left(\dfrac{2}{3}\right)^{n-1}$ **2. a.** Neither   **b.** $a_n = \dfrac{n^2}{n+1}$

3. a. Arithmetic   **b.** $a_n = -\dfrac{3}{4} + (n-1)\left(\dfrac{1}{2}\right)$ **4. a.** Arithmetic

b. -465 **5. a.** Geometric   **b.** $\dfrac{3093}{125}$ or 24.744   **6. a.** Neither   **b.** 40

7. a. Geometric   **b.** 1   **8.** -34 **9.** -60 **10.** 20   **11.** 6

12. -600 **13.** $\dfrac{22{,}344}{625}$ or 35.7504   **14.** $A_n = n^2 + \dfrac{n^2\sqrt{3}}{4}$ **15.** 45

Section 13.3 Practice Exercises, pp. 914–916

1. $x^4 + 4x^3y + 6x^2y^2 + 4xy^3 + y^4$ **3.** $64 + 48p + 12p^2 + p^3$
5. $a^{12} + 6a^{10}b + 15a^8b^2 + 20a^6b^3 + 15a^4b^4 + 6a^2b^5 + b^6$
7. $y^5 - 5y^4z + 10y^3z^2 - 10y^2z^3 + 5yz^4 - z^5$
9. $w^4 - 8w^3 + 24w^2 - 32w + 16$ **11.** $p^6 - 3p^4w + 3p^2w^2 - w^3$
13. The signs alternate on the terms of the expression $(a - b)^n$. The signs for the expression $(a + b)^n$ are all positive.   **15.** 6   **17.** 720
19. 1   **21.** False   **23.** $9! = 9 \cdot (8 \cdot 7 \cdot 6 \cdot 5 \cdot 4 \cdot 3 \cdot 2 \cdot 1) = 9 \cdot 8!$
25. $11! = 11 \cdot 10 \cdot (9 \cdot 8 \cdot 7 \cdot 6 \cdot 5 \cdot 4 \cdot 3 \cdot 2 \cdot 1)$
$\quad = 11 \cdot 10 \cdot 9!$
27. 20   **29.** 1680   **31.** 6   **33.** 9   **35.** 56   **37.** 21   **39.** 1   **41.** 7
43. By using Pascal's triangle or $\dfrac{n!}{r!(n-r)!}$
45. $s^6 + 6s^5t + 15s^4t^2 + 20s^3t^3 + 15s^2t^4 + 6st^5 + t^6$
47. $b^3 - 9b^2 + 27b - 27$ **49.** $16x^4 + 32x^3y + 24x^2y^2 + 8xy^3 + y^4$
51. $c^{14} - 7c^{12}d + 21c^{10}d^2 - 35c^8d^3 + 35c^6d^4 - 21c^4d^5 + 7c^2d^6 - d^7$
53. $x^8 + 8x^7 + 28x^6 + 56x^5 + 70x^4 + 56x^3 + 28x^2 + 8x + 1$
55. $\dfrac{1}{32}a^5 - \dfrac{5}{16}a^4b + \dfrac{5}{4}a^3b^2 - \dfrac{5}{2}a^2b^3 + \dfrac{5}{2}ab^4 - b^5$
57. $m^{11} - 11m^{10}n + 55m^9n^2$ **59.** $1024x^{10} + 5120x^9y + 11{,}520x^8y^2$
61. $u^{24} - 12u^{22}v + 66u^{20}v^2$ **63.** Nine terms   **65.** $-462m^6n^5$
67. $15{,}360x^7y^3$ **69.** $495u^{16}v^4$ **71.** g^9 **73.** $2835p^3q^4$ **75.** $54x^4$
77. a. $a^2 + 2ab + b^2$ **b.** $x^2 + 2xy + y^2 + 2xz + 2yz + z^2$
79. 1.062   **81.** 0.86

Section 13.4 Practice Exercises, pp. 924–927

1. 720   **3.** 1   **5.** 720; There are 720 ways in which 3 items can be selected from 10 in a specified order.   **7.** 120; There are 120 ways in which 3 items can be selected from 10 in *no* specific order.

9. 79,833,600 **11.** 220 **13.** 7 **15.** 7 **17.** 40,320 **19.** 1
21. a. AB, BA, AC, CA, BC, CB **b.** AB, AC, BC **23.** 6! = 720
25. 10^6 = 1,000,000 **27.** 4 · 3 · 8 · 6 = 576 **29.** $_{10}P_3$ = 720
31. $_{11}C_6$ = 462 **33.** $_{10}C_5$ = 252 **35.** $_8P_2$ = 56
37. 2 · 25 · 24 · 23 = 27,600 **39.** $_{10}C_4$ = 210
41. 3 · 3 · 2 · 2 · 1 · 1 = 36 **43.** $_9P_9$ = 362,880
45. $_{10}C_3 \cdot _8C_1$ = 960 **47.** 2^3 = 8 **49.** $_{40}C_{12}$ or 5,586,853,480
51. a. $_{10}C_2$ = 45 **b.** $_6C_2$ = 15 **c.** $_4C_2$ = 6 **d.** $_6C_1 \cdot _4C_1$ = 24
53. 2^7 = 128 **55. a.** 9! = 362,880 **b.** 5 · 4 · 7! = 100,800
c. 5! · 4! = 2880 **d.** 6 · 5! · 4! = 17,280 **57. a.** pot, pto, opt, otp,
top, tpo **b.** tot, tto, ott **59. a.** 7^3 = 343 **b.** 7 · 6 · 5 = 210
c. 7 · 7 · 4 = 196 **61.** $_{26}C_5$ = 65,780 **63.** $_{13}C_3 \cdot _{13}C_2$ = 22,308

Section 13.5 Practice Exercises, pp. 937–941

1. $_{10}C_4$ = 210 **3.** 5! = 120 **5.** a, b, d, g, h **7.** 0.958 **9.** $\dfrac{5}{12}$
11. $\dfrac{3}{6} = \dfrac{1}{2}$ **13. a.** $\dfrac{8}{59}$ **b.** $\dfrac{15}{59}$ **15. a.** $\dfrac{10}{80} = \dfrac{1}{8}$ **b.** $\dfrac{60}{80} = \dfrac{3}{4}$ **c.** $\dfrac{50}{80} = \dfrac{5}{8}$
d. $\dfrac{22}{80} = \dfrac{11}{40}$ **17. a.** $\dfrac{_3C_2}{_8C_2} = \dfrac{3}{28}$ **b.** $\dfrac{_5C_2}{_8C_2} = \dfrac{5}{14}$ **c.** $\dfrac{15}{28}$
19. a. $\dfrac{1}{_{39}C_5} = \dfrac{1}{575,757}$ **b.** $\dfrac{575,756}{575,757}$ **c.** The events of winning the
grand prize and losing are not equally likely events. **21.** $\dfrac{1}{5!} = \dfrac{1}{120}$
23. a. $\left(\dfrac{1}{2}\right)^4 = \dfrac{1}{16}$ **b.** $\left(\dfrac{1}{2}\right)^4 = \dfrac{1}{16}$ **25. a.** $\left(\dfrac{1}{5}\right)^4 = \dfrac{1}{625}$ **b.** $\left(\dfrac{4}{5}\right)^4 = \dfrac{256}{625}$
27. a. $\dfrac{27}{130}$ **b.** $\dfrac{80}{130} = \dfrac{8}{13}$ **c.** $\dfrac{27}{130}$ **d.** $\dfrac{121}{130}$ **e.** $\dfrac{112}{130} = \dfrac{56}{65}$
29. a. $\dfrac{13}{52} = \dfrac{1}{4}$ **b.** $\dfrac{12}{52} = \dfrac{3}{13}$ **c.** $\dfrac{26}{52} = \dfrac{1}{2}$ **d.** $\dfrac{28}{52} = \dfrac{7}{13}$ **e.** $\dfrac{16}{52} = \dfrac{4}{13}$
f. $\dfrac{26}{52} = \dfrac{1}{2}$ **31. a.** $\dfrac{13}{52} \cdot \dfrac{13}{52} = \dfrac{1}{16}$ **b.** $\dfrac{4}{52} \cdot \dfrac{4}{52} = \dfrac{1}{169}$ **c.** After removing the first card, the sample space changes, making the second event
dependent on the first event. For part (a), the probability would be
$\frac{13}{52} \cdot \frac{12}{51} = \frac{1}{17}$. For part (b), the probability would be $\frac{4}{52} \cdot \frac{4}{51} = \frac{4}{663}$.
33. $(0.07)^4$ = 0.00002401 **35. a.** $(0.04)^2$ = 0.0016
b. $(0.96)^2$ = 0.9216 **37.** $\dfrac{52}{60} \cdot \dfrac{51}{59} \cdot \dfrac{50}{58} \cdot \dfrac{49}{57} \approx 0.5552$ **39. a.** $\dfrac{4}{12} = \dfrac{1}{3}$
b. $\dfrac{4}{12} \cdot \dfrac{3}{11} \cdot \dfrac{2}{10} = \dfrac{1}{55}$ **c.** $\dfrac{8}{12} \cdot \dfrac{7}{11} \cdot \dfrac{6}{10} = \dfrac{14}{55}$ **41. a.** $\dfrac{120}{600} = \dfrac{1}{5}$
b. $\dfrac{160}{600} = \dfrac{4}{15}$ **c.** $\dfrac{580}{600} = \dfrac{29}{30}$ **d.** $\dfrac{140}{480} = \dfrac{7}{24}$ **e.** $\dfrac{20}{120} = \dfrac{1}{6}$ **f.** $\frac{7}{24} \approx 0.292$;
$\frac{1}{6} \approx 0.167$; male officers are more likely to be promoted.
43. a. $\dfrac{2}{6}$ or $\dfrac{1}{3}$ **b.** 2:4 or 1:2 **45. a.** $\dfrac{3}{10}$ **b.** 3:7 **c.** $\dfrac{8}{10} = \dfrac{4}{5}$
d. 8:2 or 4:1

Review Exercises, pp. 946–948

1. $\dfrac{3}{4}, \dfrac{9}{16}, \dfrac{27}{64}$ **3.** $a_n = 1 + (n-1)(3)$ **5.** 4 **7.** $\sum\limits_{k=1}^{4} x^{3k}$
9. a. a_n = 100 + 10n **b.** 110, 120, 130, 140, 150 **c.** a_{27} = 370; The
cost of a speeding ticket is $370 for a driver traveling 27 mph over
the speed limit. **11.** $-\dfrac{1}{3}$ **13.** $a_n = 1 + (n-1)(5)$ **15.** a_{10} = −29
17. 1075 **19.** $-\dfrac{1}{2}$ **21.** $a_n = 4\left(\dfrac{3}{2}\right)^{n-1}$ **23.** $-\dfrac{781}{64}$ **25.** r = $\dfrac{1}{6}$;
$S = \dfrac{12}{5}$ **27.** $x^{10} + 20x^8 + 160x^6 + 640x^4 + 1280x^2 + 1024$ **29.** 35

31. $a^{11} + 22a^{10}b + 220a^9b^2$ **33.** $160a^3b^3$ **35.** 2^5 = 32
37. $_{26}P_4$ = 358,800 **39.** $_8C_3 \cdot _{10}C_1$ = 560 **41. a.** 0.186 **b.** 0.289
c. 0.256 **43.** $\dfrac{785}{1058} \cdot \dfrac{784}{1057} \approx 0.5503$ **45. a.** $\dfrac{3}{36} = \dfrac{1}{12}$ **b.** $\dfrac{10}{36} = \dfrac{5}{18}$

Test, pp. 948–950

1. $-3, -2, -\dfrac{4}{3}, -\dfrac{8}{9}$; geometric **2.** $a_n = -6 + (n-1)\left(\dfrac{1}{2}\right)$;
arithmetic **3.** 5 **4.** $a_n = n^2 + \left(\dfrac{n}{2}\right)h$ **5.** $\sum\limits_{i=1}^{7} \dfrac{3+i}{i}$ **6.** a_{33} = −519
7. 2295 **8. a.** 52 **b.** 5616 **9.** $a_5 = \dfrac{32}{3}$ **10.** $a_1 = \dfrac{5}{3}$ **11.** −1364
12. $\dfrac{3325}{32}$ **13. a.** $1095 **b.** $1160.70 **c.** $5933.13 **d.** 86,568.71. By
saving money instead of buying cigarettes, the total savings plus
interest amounts to $86,568.71 **14.** 3
15. $a^4 + 4a^3b + 6a^2b^2 + 4ab^3 + b^4$
16. $81y^4 - 216y^3x^2 + 216y^2x^4 - 96yx^6 + 16x^8$ **17.** $189w^5z^2$
18. 3 · 2 = 6 **19.** $_{25}P_3$ = 13,800 **20.** 2 · 2 = 4
21. $_{42}C_6$ = 5,245,786 **22. a.** $\dfrac{387}{2225}$ **b.** $\dfrac{605}{2225} = \dfrac{121}{445}$ **23. a.** $\dfrac{20}{50} = \dfrac{2}{5}$
b. $\dfrac{26}{50} = \dfrac{13}{25}$ **c.** $\dfrac{36}{50} = \dfrac{18}{25}$ **d.** $\dfrac{8}{24} = \dfrac{1}{3}$ **24.** $(0.33)^4$ = 0.0119

Cumulative Review Exercises, Chapters 1–13, pp. 950–953

1. $-\dfrac{11}{10}$ **2.** 3x + 54 **3.** x = $\dfrac{4}{3}$ **4.** $2225 is invested at 8% and
$7775 is invested at 5%. **5.** The angles are 69° and 21°. **6.** $(-\infty, 5)$
7. x-intercept: (0, 0); y-intercept: (0, 0);

8. Slope: 1; y-intercept: (0, 2) **9.** $y = \dfrac{2}{5}x + \dfrac{11}{5}$ **10.** y = 3x + 10
11. (2, 3, −1) **12.** No solution **13.** (−3, 1) **14.** 27 **15.** $y = \dfrac{36}{13}$
16. Domain: {4, 3, 2}; range: {2, −6, 5, 1} **17. a.** [−2, 4] **b.** [−1, 2]
c. 0 **d.** x = −2, x = 3 **e.** (1, 4) **f.** (−2, 0) **g.** (0, 1)
18.

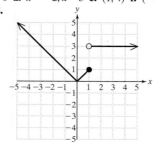

19. 800 kHz **20.** $\dfrac{x^2y^{12}}{9}$ **21.** 4.0×10^5 **22.** $-x^3 - 10x^2 - 7x - 12$

23. $x^2 + 4xy + 4y^2 - 9$ **24.** $3x^2 - 8 + \dfrac{5x + 13}{x^2 + 2}$ **25.** $|x|$

26. $\{x \mid x \geq 3\}$ **27.** $\dfrac{1}{4}$ **28.** x^8y^8 **29.** $2xy^4\sqrt[3]{2x^2}$ **30.** $\dfrac{\sqrt[3]{2x^2}}{x}$

31. $x = -\dfrac{5}{2}$ **32.** $4 + 5i$ **33.** $-\dfrac{9}{29} - \dfrac{21}{29}i$ **34.** $(2x + 9)(3x - 4)$

35. $(2x^2 + y)(4x^4 - 2x^2y + y^2)$ **36.** $x = \pm\dfrac{3}{2}$ **37.** $x = -3 \pm \sqrt{14}$

38. $x = \dfrac{3 \pm i\sqrt{7}}{4}$ **39.** $x = \pm 2, x = \pm i\sqrt{3}$ **40. a.** 2 **b.** 22 sides

41. $(-\infty, -7) \cup (-7, 7) \cup (7, \infty)$ **42.** $\dfrac{2(x - 1)(x + 1)}{5(x + 4)}$ **43.** $\dfrac{x - y}{x}$

44. $x = -4$ ($x = 2$ does not check) **45. a.** $(-\infty, -4] \cup [-\frac{2}{3}, \infty)$

b. No solution **46.** $x = 8, x = -\dfrac{2}{3}$ **47.** $(-2, 12)$ **48.** $[2, 4)$

49.

$2x + y \geq 3$

50. $f^{-1}(x) = \dfrac{2x + 1}{3}$

51. Domain: $(-\infty, \infty)$; range: $(0, \infty)$

52. Domain: $(0, \infty)$; range: $(-\infty, \infty)$

$f(x) = e^x$

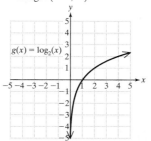

$g(x) = \log_2(x)$

53. 3 **54.** 5 **55.** $\ln\left(\dfrac{x^3\sqrt{z}}{y}\right)$ **56.** 7.7%

57. $x = 3$ ($x = -4$ does not check) **58.** -2692 **59.** No.

60. $3, \dfrac{1}{2}, \pm 2i$ **61. a.** Up to the left and up to the right

b. $(-2, 0), (\frac{3}{2}, 0), (1, 0)$ **c.** $(0, -6)$ **d.** $f(x) = 2x^4 - 3x^3 - 6x^2 + 13x - 6$

62. a. $(-3, 0)$ **b.** $\left(0, -\dfrac{3}{5}\right)$ **c.** $y = \dfrac{1}{2}$ **d.** $x = \dfrac{5}{2}$

e.

$g(x) = \dfrac{x + 3}{2x - 5}$

63. Arithmetic; $a_n = -16 + (n - 1)(-5)$ **64.** Geometric;

$a_n = \dfrac{3}{4}(2)^{n-1}$ **65.** $\dfrac{11,718}{3125} = 3.74976$ **66.** 1328

67. $81 - 216t^2 + 216t^4 - 96t^6 + 16t^8$ **68.** $_{41}C_6 = 4,496,388$

69. $_{15}P_6 = 3,603,600$ **70. a.** $\dfrac{34}{74} = \dfrac{17}{37}$ **b.** $\dfrac{46}{74} = \dfrac{23}{37}$ **c.** $\dfrac{55}{74}$ **d.** $\dfrac{41}{74}$

71. a. $(2, -4)$ **b.** $(0, -3)$ **c.** $(-2, 0)$ and $(6, 0)$ **d.** $y = -5$

e.

$y = \dfrac{1}{4}(x - 2)^2 - 4$

72. Center: $(3, -4)$; radius: $\sqrt{35}$

73.

$\dfrac{x^2}{9} + \dfrac{y^2}{4} = 1$

74.

$\dfrac{y^2}{16} - \dfrac{x^2}{9} = 1$

75. $(6, 8)$ and $(-6, -8)$ **76.** $\begin{bmatrix} 6 & 3 & 14 \\ -7 & 0 & 1 \end{bmatrix}$ **77.** $\begin{bmatrix} 29 & 23 \\ -32 & -16 \end{bmatrix}$

INDEX

Properties of Real Numbers

Commutative Property of Addition	$a + b = b + a$
Commutative Property of Multiplication	$ab = ba$
Associative Property of Addition	$(a + b) + c = a + (b + c)$
Associative Property of Multiplication	$(ab)c = a(bc)$
Distributive Property of Multiplication over Addition	$a(b + c) = ab + ac$
Identity Property of Addition	0 is the **identity element for addition** because $a + 0 = 0 + a = a$
Identity Property of Multiplication	1 is the **identity element for multiplication** because $a \cdot 1 = 1 \cdot a = a$
Inverse Property of Addition	a and $(-a)$ are **additive inverses** because $a + (-a) = 0$ and $(-a) + a = 0$
Inverse Property of Multiplication	a and $\frac{1}{a}$ are **multiplicative inverses** because $a \cdot \frac{1}{a} = 1$ and $\frac{1}{a} \cdot a = 1$ (provided $a \neq 0$)

Sets of Real Numbers

Natural numbers: $\{1, 2, 3, \dots\}$

Whole numbers: $\{0, 1, 2, 3, \dots\}$

Integers: $\{\dots -3, -2, -1, 0, 1, 2, 3, \dots\}$

Rational numbers: $\{\frac{p}{q} | p$ and q are integers and q does not equal $0\}$

Irrational numbers: $\{x | x$ is a real number that is not rational$\}$

Application Formulas

Sales tax = (cost of merchandise)(tax rate)

Commission = (dollars in sales)(commission rate)

Simple interest = (principal)(rate)(time): $I = Prt$

Distance = (rate)(time): $d = rt$

Compound interest: $A(t) = P\left(1 + \dfrac{r}{n}\right)^{nt}$

Continuous compound interest: $A(t) = Pe^{rt}$,

where $A(t) =$ balance of account after t years,
$P =$ principal, $r =$ annual interest rate, $t =$ time in years,
$n =$ number of compound periods per year

Proportions

An equation that equates two ratios is called a proportion:

$$\frac{a}{b} = \frac{c}{d} \quad (b \neq 0, d \neq 0)$$

The cross products are equal: $ad = bc$.

Exponential Functions

A function defined by $y = b^x$ $(b > 0, b \neq 1)$ is an exponential function.

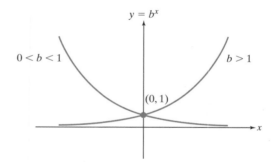

Logarithmic Functions

A function defined by $y = \log_b(x)$ is a logarithmic function.

$y = \log_b(x) \Leftrightarrow b^y = x \quad (x > 0, b > 0, b \neq 1)$

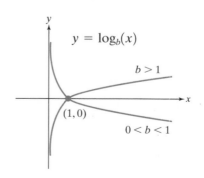